Addison Wesley

Mathematics Makes Sense

Program Overview

Making sense of your needs...

Addison Wesley
Mathematics
Makes Sense

Student understanding
in a manageable and
easy-to-use program

Addison Wesley Mathematics Makes Sense

Program Overview

Kindergarten to Grade 3 Authors

Pat Dickinson
Michelle Jackson
Maggie Martin Connell
Heather Spencer
Susan Gordon
Linden Gray
Nirmala Nutakki
Ken Harper
Lynn Bryan
Peggy Morrow
Ralph Connelly
Don Jones
Michael Davis
Trevor Brown
Brenda Lightburn
Cathy Anderson
Angie Harding
Jennifer Travis
Sharon Jeroski
Carole Saundry
Maureen Dockendorf
Steve Thomas
Jeananne Thomas
Michelle Skene
Sandra Ball
Donna Beaumont

Grade 4 to 8 Authors

Peggy Morrow
Bryn Keyes
Jason Johnston
Ken Harper
Margaret Sinclair
Angela D'Alessandro
Manuel Salvati
Ralph Connelly
Trevor Brown
Michael Davis
Don Jones
Cathy Heideman
Antonietta Lenjosek
Linden Gray
Sharon Jeroski
Maggie Martin Connell
Jeananne Thomas
Steve Thomas
Mary Doucette
Linda Edwards
Sue Gordon

PEARSON
Addison Wesley

Elementary Mathematics Publishing Team

Enid Haley
Lesley Haynes
Mei Lin Cheung
Lynne Gulliver
Tricia Carmichael
Susan Lishman
Ingrid D'Silva
Lynn Pereira
Keltie Thomas
Ellen Davidson
Rosalyn Steiner
Kirsten Vanstone
Susan Ginsberg
Alison Rieger
Kathleen ffolliott
Marg Bukta
Judy Wilson
Nicole Argyropoulos

Elementary Mathematics Production Coordinators

Stephanie Cox
Denise Wake

Product Manager

Anne-Marie Scullion

Mathematics Publishers

Claire Burnett
Susan Green

Program Overview Design

Ezio Lisi

Pages 10, 14-15: From John A. Van de Walle *Elementary and Middle School Mathematics: Teaching Developmentally,* 5e. Published by Allyn and Bacon, Boston, MA. Copyright (c) 2004 by Pearson Education. Reprinted by permission of the publisher.

Page 10: *Principles and Standards for School Mathematics.* Published by The National Council of Teachers of Mathematics, Inc. Reston, VA. Copyright (c) 2000.

Program Overview Publication 0-321-11825-1

This book contains recycled product and is acid free. Printed and bound in Canada

12 18

PEARSON
Addison Wesley

Table of Contents

Welcome to

Addison Wesley Mathematics Makes Sense

Addison Wesley Mathematics Makes Sense Kindergarten

Core:
- Teacher Guide – binder with 8 modules
- Big Math Book

- *Addison Wesley Little Books*
- Audio
- Website www.pearsoned.ca/mathmakessense
- e tools

Addison Wesley Mathematics Makes Sense Grades 1 and 2

Core:
- Teacher Guide with CD – binder with 15 modules
- Student Book i.e. consumable or BLM
- Big Math Book

- *Addison Wesley Little Books*
- *Together Resource:* Support for Combined Grades
- Audio
- Website www.pearsoned.ca/mathmakessense
- e tools

Addison Wesley Mathematics Makes Sense Grades 3 to 8

Core

- Teacher Guide with CD – binder with 14 modules
- Student Book – hard cover text

- Practice and Homework Book
- *Together Resource:* Support for Combined Grades
- *Addison Wesley Little Books*
- Website www.pearsoned.ca/mathmakessense
- e-tools

French Editions

Addison Wesley Mathematics recognizes the importance of developing a parallel French Edition of *Addison Wesley Mathematics Makes Sense* for French-speaking students.

- Les Editions de la Chenelière is translating all grade levels of *Addison Wesley Mathematics Makes Sense* K-8, therefore ensuring consistency in their translation, Chenelière Mathématiques Un choix logique. Les Editions de la Chenelière is Canada's leading publisher of resources for the French-speaking community outside of Quebec. We look forward to servicing the needs of your French and English students.

Chenelière Mathématiques

Program Principles

Part 2

- ➤ What patterns can you find in the table?
- ➤ What do you notice about the numbers of pieces that have icing on three faces?
- ➤ One cake has 16 pieces with icing on two faces. How many pieces are there in the whole cake?
- ➤ Suppose you made a 10 by 10 cake. How many of each kind of piece would there be?

Display Your Work

Make a poster display to show all the patterns you found.

Take It Further

Model rectangular cakes with 24 Snap cubes.

- ➤ How many different cakes can you model using all 24 cubes?
- ➤ How many cakes have pieces with icing on four faces?
- ➤ Which cake has the greatest number of pieces with icing on one face? Two faces? Three faces?
- ➤ Write about what you found out.

117

- All students need opportunities to learn mathematics in ways that are meaningful to them. A responsible mathematics program recognizes many learning styles and offers guidance to teachers as they plan for individual student differences.
- Teacher understanding of mathematics is a critical factor in their students' success. Teacher understanding can and must be supported in program methodology and pedagogy.
- Students best develop conceptual mathematical understanding when they have opportunities to "do" math, to engage in hands-on experiences in which they explore concepts in a rich mathematical context.
- Students demonstrate conceptual understanding by communicating and modelling their reasoning, and connecting a new concept or strategy to other contexts they have seen before.
- Problem solving is an integral part of learning mathematics. Students best learn new mathematical concepts when they pose and solve problems.
- Mathematics understanding is deepened and enhanced when students have opportunities to make connections between mathematical concepts and other mathematics strands, other disciplines, and the real world.

- Procedural fluency with number is an essential skill for life. Both mental and written computational strategies must be accurate, efficient, flexible, and adaptable.

- Parents have a significant role to play in student learning, in supporting and reinforcing what is learned in the classroom each day, and promoting a positive attitude toward mathematics in the home.

- The purposeful use of technology in the mathematics classroom can enrich learning experiences for students, allowing them to explore and develop concepts, and extend critical thinking and problem-solving skills.

- A mathematics program should support curriculum implementation and assessment with 100% curriculum fit and practical teacher support – pacing guidelines; combined grades strategies; models for independent and group learning; performance-based assessment suggestions.

- Teachers need a balance of diagnostic, formative, and summative assessment opportunities, with practical assessment tools to track student achievement and meet reporting requirements.

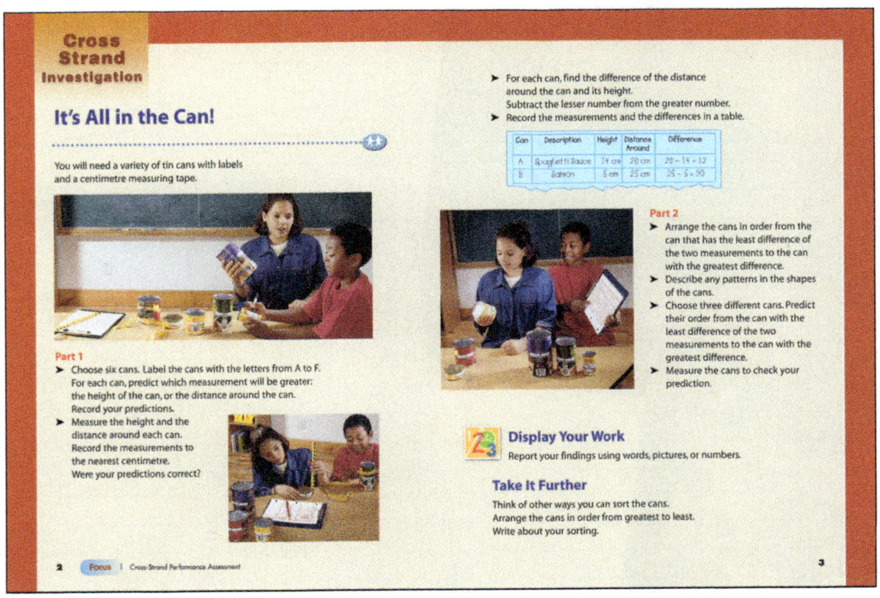

Cross Strand Investigation

It's All in the Can!

You will need a variety of tin cans with labels and a centimetre measuring tape.

Part 1

- Choose six cans. Label the cans with the letters from A to F. For each can, predict which measurement will be greater: the height of the can, or the distance around the can. Record your predictions.
- Measure the height and the distance around each can. Record the measurements to the nearest centimetre. Were your predictions correct?
- For each can, find the difference of the distance around the can and its height. Subtract the lesser number from the greater number.
- Record the measurements and the differences in a table.

Can	Description	Height	Distance Around	Difference
A	Spaghetti Sauce	14 cm	26 cm	26 – 14 = 12
B	Salmon	5 cm	25 cm	25 – 5 = 20

Part 2

- Arrange the cans in order from the can that has the least difference of the two measurements to the can with the greatest difference.
- Describe any patterns in the shapes of the cans.
- Choose three different cans. Predict their order from the can with the least difference of the two measurements to the can with the greatest difference.
- Measure the cans to check your prediction.

Display Your Work

Report your findings using words, pictures, or numbers.

Take It Further

Think of other ways you can sort the cans. Arrange the cans in order from greatest to least. Write about your sorting.

2 Focus | Cross-Strand Performance Assessment

3

From Research to Classroom Practice

Addison Wesley Mathematics Makes Sense is based on the most current research about how students learn. The Addison Wesley development team examined published academic research and professional development resources, while we learned about ongoing research into the impact of current issues on classroom practice.

This research was shared with educators across Canada, as the development team assessed its implications for the creation of new mathematics resources for the classroom.

The Addison Wesley development team also met with experienced and new teachers, with principals, parents, and consultants, in a series of symposia, focus groups, and one-on-one interviews. Our purpose was to define the resources that would best suit the needs of student learning and teacher instruction.

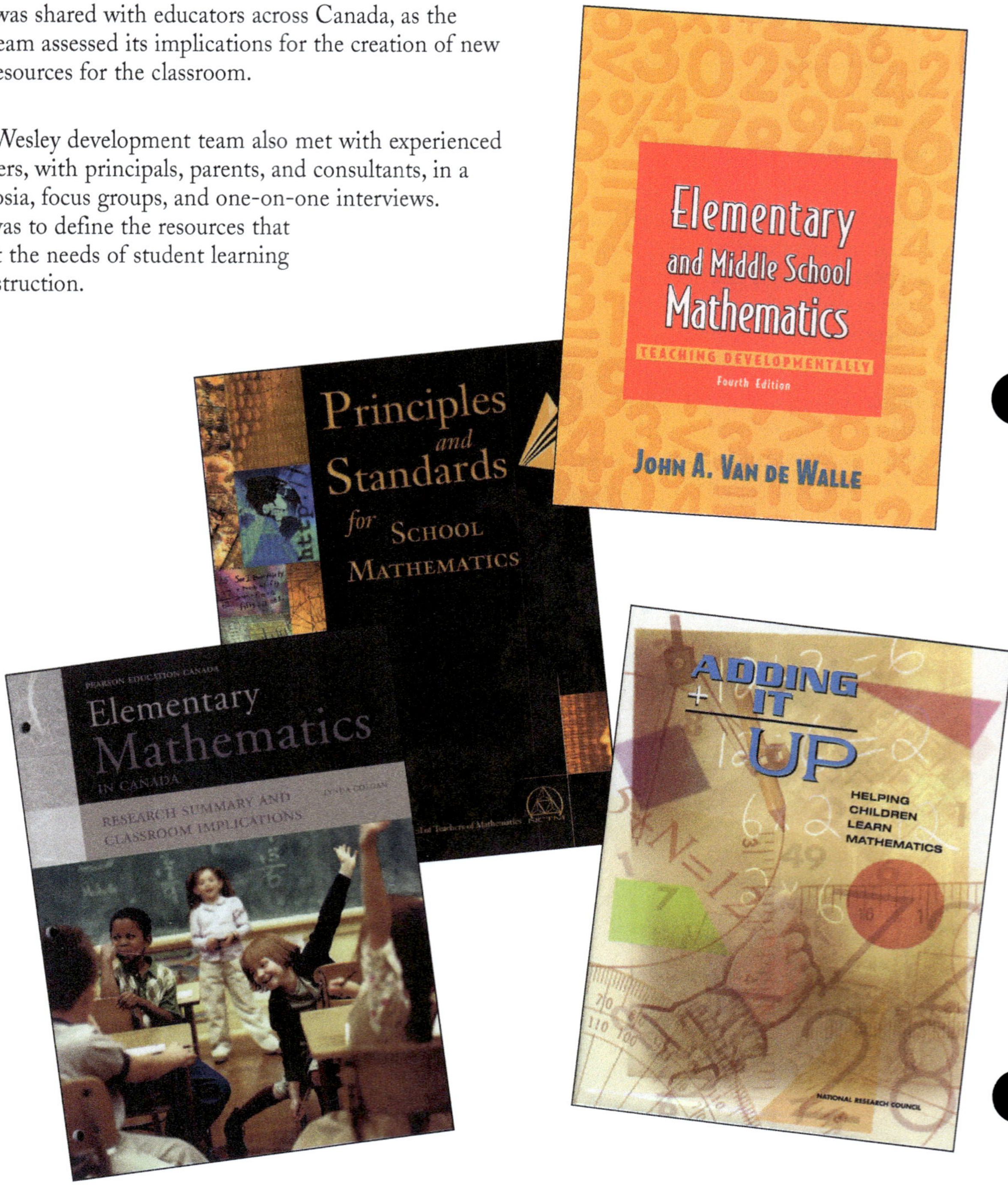

> Current research has profound implications for new classroom resources.
>
> – Lynda Colgan, Program Adviser

Program development included field tests at each grade level. In the first year of field testing, 200 classrooms across Canada participated, involving 10,000 students and their teachers to validate program content and organization.

The Addison Wesley development team incorporated field-test teacher input as we refined program design at all levels.

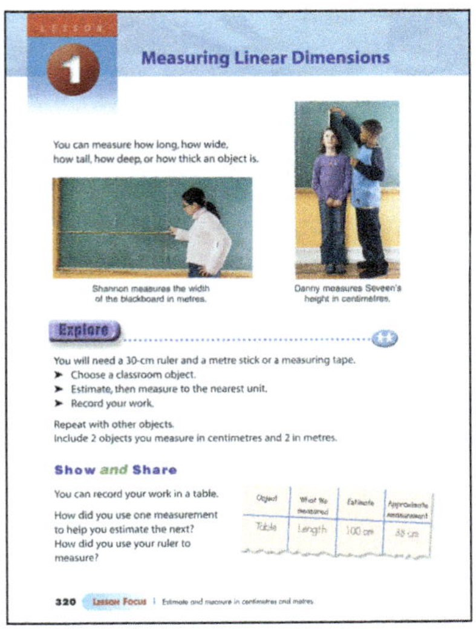
LESSON 1

Measuring Linear Dimensions

You can measure how long, how wide, how tall, how deep, or how thick an object is.

Shannon measures the width of the blackboard in metres.

Danny measures Seveen's height in centimetres.

Explore

You will need a 30-cm ruler and a metre stick or a measuring tape.

- Choose a classroom object.
- Estimate, then measure to the nearest unit.
- Record your work.

Repeat with other objects.
Include 2 objects you measure in centimetres and 2 in metres.

Show and Share

You can record your work in a table.

How did you use one measurement to help you estimate the next?
How did you use your ruler to measure?

Object	What We measured	Estimate	Approximate measurement
Table	Length	100 cm	88 cm

320 Lesson Focus | Estimate and measure in centimetres and metres

Unit Problem

Design a Backyard

Design a backyard for the Rizvi family.

360

Addison Wesley Mathematics Makes Sense is:

- Built from an understanding of current educational research
- Shaped against the backdrop of extensive market research into resource needs
- Field tested in hundreds of schools across Canada

Balanced Instruction

For real understanding, students need a combination of open-ended problem-solving opportunities, meaningful dialogue, and purposeful practice that reinforces, and extends, new learning.

Balanced instruction recognizes four key components that build mathematical literacy, as illustrated here.

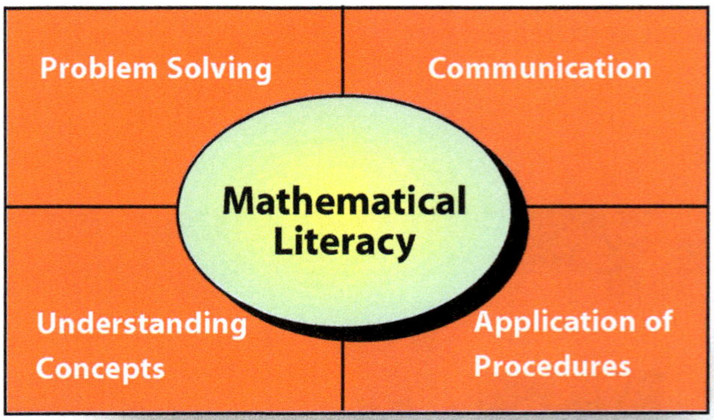

Addison Wesley Mathematics Makes Sense supports each key component in the following ways.

Problem Solving

- Introduces new concepts by presenting a problem to solve.
- Includes whole group, partner, and independent problem-solving activities.

Understanding Concepts

- A variety of activities allows students to bring their own experiences to new concepts.
- Question prompts guide the student dialogue that follows each new learning experience.
- Consolidates key concepts before moving to independent work.

Application of Procedures

- Gives purposeful practice for students to apply, clarify, and extend the learning.
- Provides regular opportunities for calculator or computer applications, or the introduction of new problem-solving strategies.

Communication

- Guides students to represent their thinking in pictures, numbers, or words.
- Provides a balance of oral and written communication opportunities.

It's time for a program that simplifies teacher planning so teachers have more time with their students.
– Peggy Morrow, Program Author

Balanced instruction is delivered in a consistent three-part lesson structure that supports the way students learn, and the way teachers teach.

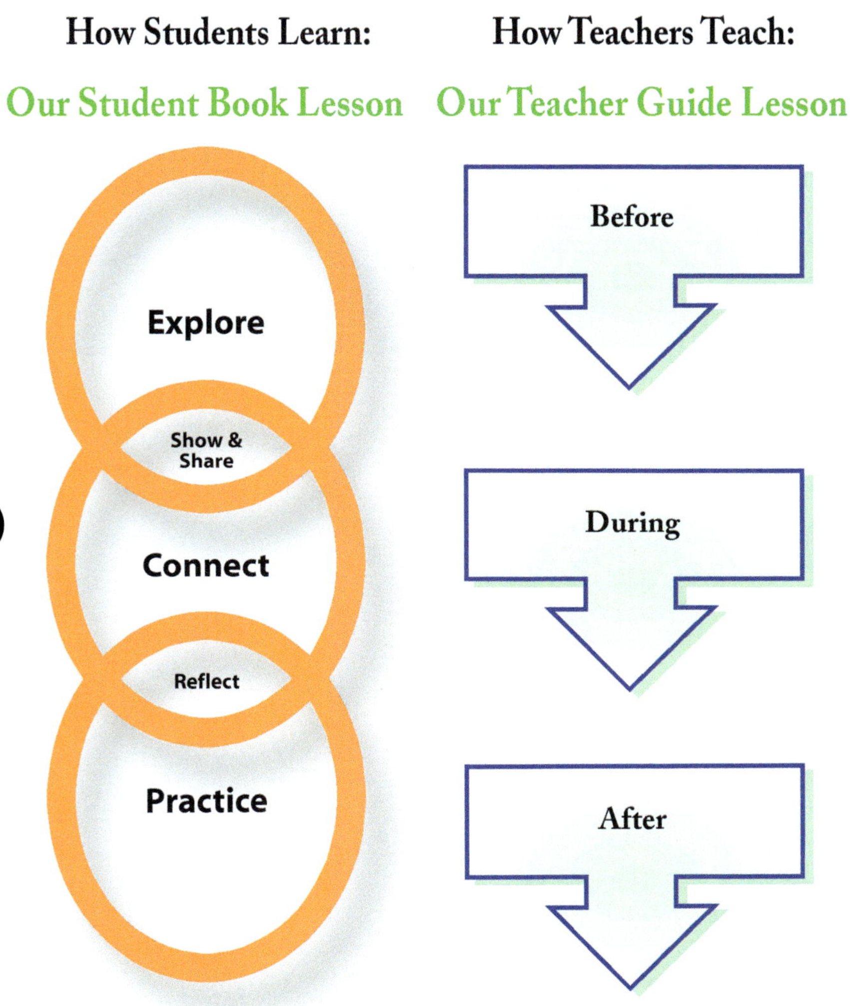

Manageable and Easy-to-Use

The problem-solving approach in *Addison Wesley Mathematics Makes Sense* is balanced with purposeful practice of skills and reinforcement of concepts. *Addison Wesley Mathematics Makes Sense* gives you quick access to ideas for instruction, while your students get clean, clear content appropriately paced.

- An "all-in-one-place" Teacher Guide
- Predictable, consistent format
- Open, readable design

Teaching and Learning for Understanding

Addison Wesley Mathematics Makes Sense has been built on the belief that mathematics is more than a list of isolated facts, that mathematics as a whole can make sense for students, teachers, and parents. Fundamental to this belief is our understanding of the importance of mathematical connections: Math makes sense for students when they see how mathematical ideas are connected to the real world, to other mathematical ideas, and to what they are learning in other subject areas.

Children come to us with experiences and understandings they have already developed into personal networks of understanding. As they work with new ideas, their active engagement leads them to fit new learning within their established understanding. The more ideas students connect, the more solid their understanding.

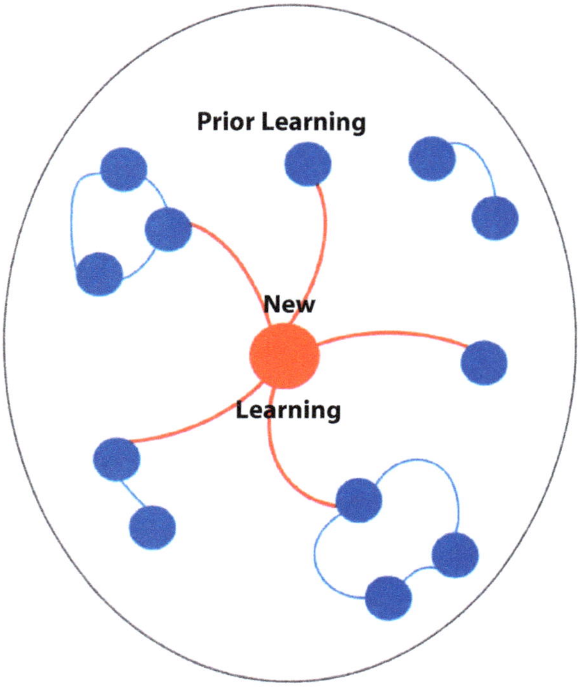

Teaching for understanding reaps many benefits for students:

- When students understand mathematical procedures, they can recall them easily and apply them in a variety of settings.
- When students understand the main concepts and connections of mathematical topics, they rely on reasoning more, and on memory less.
- Conceptual understanding provides the basis for acquiring new knowledge and solving unfamiliar problems.
- Conceptual understanding helps students spot and correct errors in their problem solutions.

The tools that we use to build understanding are our existing ideas, the knowledge that we already possess.
– John A. Van de Walle, Elementary Mathematics Consultant

In *Addison Wesley Mathematics Makes Sense*, the lesson framework delivers instruction in the way in which students learn most effectively.

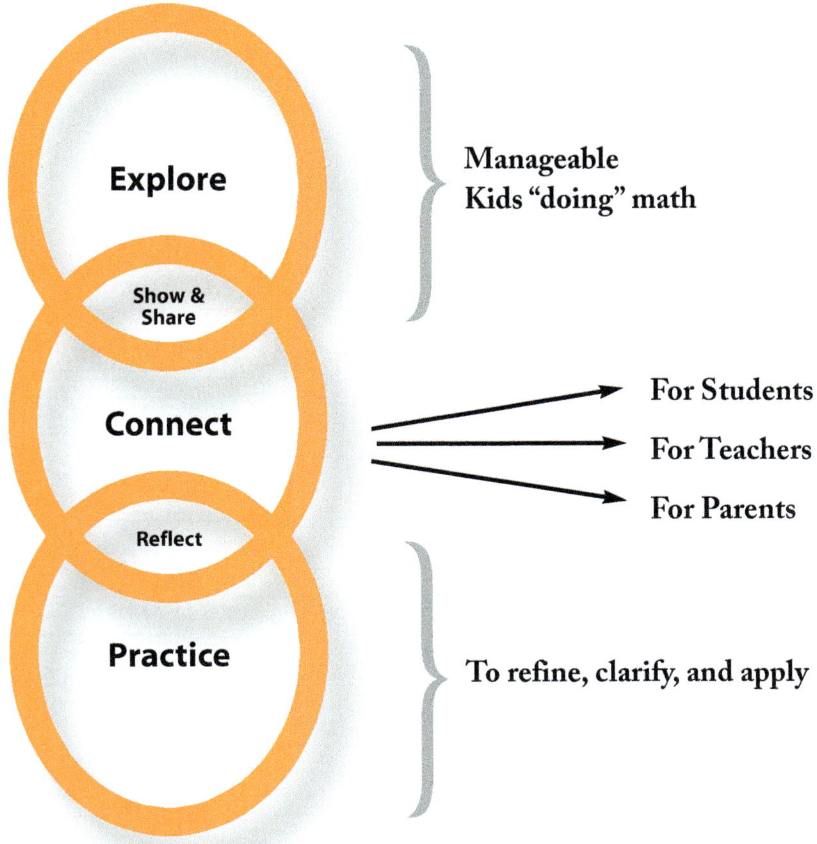

Supporting the lesson framework of *Addison Wesley Mathematics Makes Sense* is an over-arching understanding of how students' mathematical understanding, skills, and strategies develop from the early years (pre-school) through elementary school.

Developmental Continuum — A Useful Tool

- Based on current research on key developmental stages
- Enables teachers to view each student's achievements and challenges within a broader perspective
- Provides a tool for teachers to use with parents and supports teachers when discussing student progress

Purposeful Practice

Educators recognize the important role practice plays within a balanced program. Purposeful practice allows students to clarify, refine, consolidate, and apply new learning through a variety of experiences. In *Addison Wesley Mathematics Makes Sense*, purposeful practice is offered in every lesson to suit a range of learner needs.

At K to 2

Teacher Guide **Practice** suggestions for each core lesson include

- **Reinforcement** for all students
- **Extra Support** for students who may face ESL challenges, or need more experiences with early concepts, problem solving, or applying procedures
- *Extension* for students who are ready to take concepts further

Lessons also regularly include **Numbers Every Day,** and **Activity Banks.** These additional ideas for activities provide hands-on practice.

At grades 1 and 2, the Student Book provides a mechanism for students to record a selection of their mathematics practice.

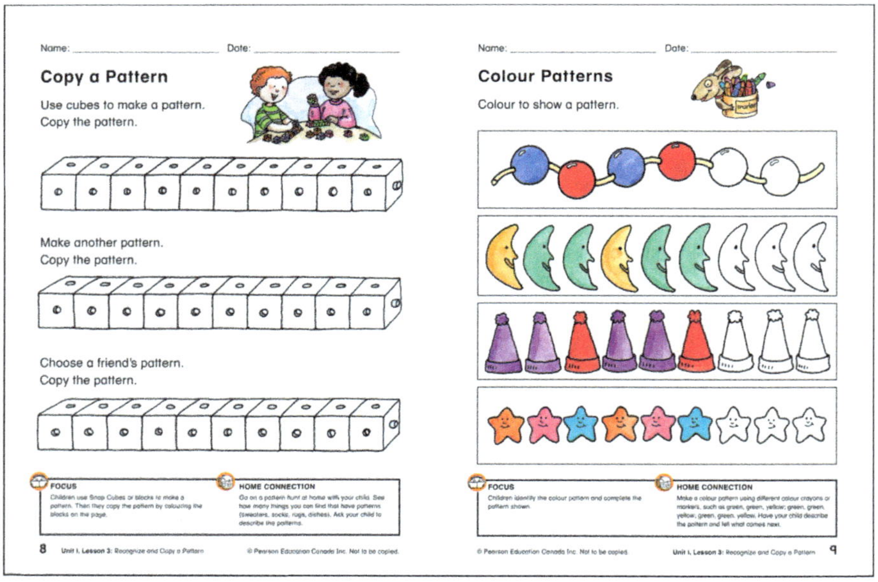
Name: Date:

Copy a Pattern

Use cubes to make a pattern.
Copy the pattern.

Make another pattern.
Copy the pattern.

Choose a friend's pattern.
Copy the pattern.

FOCUS
Children use Snap Cubes or blocks to make a pattern. Then they copy the pattern by colouring the blocks on the page.

HOME CONNECTION
Go on a pattern hunt at home with your child. See how many things you can find that have patterns (sweaters, socks, rugs, dishes). Ask your child to describe the patterns.

8 Unit 1, Lesson 3: Recognize and Copy a Pattern © Pearson Education Canada Inc. Not to be copied.

Name: Date:

Colour Patterns

Colour to show a pattern.

FOCUS
Children identify the colour pattern and complete the pattern shown.

HOME CONNECTION
Make a colour pattern using different colour crayons or markers, such as green, green, yellow; green, green, yellow; green, green, yellow. Have your child describe the pattern and tell what comes next.

© Pearson Education Canada Inc. Not to be copied. Unit 1, Lesson 3: Recognize and Copy a Pattern 9

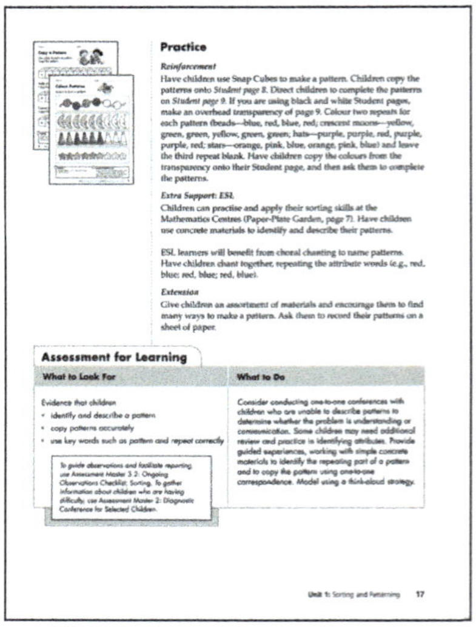
Practice

Reinforcement
Have children use Snap Cubes to make a pattern. Children copy the patterns onto *Student page 8*. Direct children to complete the patterns on *Student page 9*. If you are using black and white Student pages, make an overhead transparency of page 9. Colour two repeats for each pattern (beads—blue, red, blue, red; crescent moons—yellow, green, green, yellow, green, green; hats—purple, purple, red, purple, purple, red; stars—orange, pink, blue, orange, pink, blue) and leave the third repeat blank. Have children copy the colours from the transparency onto their Student page, and then ask them to complete the patterns.

Extra Support: ESL
Children can practise and apply their sorting skills at the Mathematics Centres (Paper-Plate Garden, page 7). Have children use concrete materials to identify and describe their patterns.

ESL learners will benefit from choral chanting to name patterns. Have children chant together, repeating the attribute words (e.g., red, blue; red, blue; red, blue).

Extension
Give children an assortment of materials and encourage them to find many ways to make a pattern. Ask them to record their patterns on a sheet of paper.

Assessment for Learning

What to Look For	What to Do
Evidence that children • identify and describe a pattern • copy patterns accurately • use key words such as *pattern* and *repeat* correctly	Consider conducting one-to-one conferences with children who are unable to describe patterns to determine whether the problem is understanding or communication. Some children may need additional review and practice in identifying attributes. Provide guided experiences, working with simple concrete materials to identify the repeating part of a pattern and to copy the pattern using one-to-one correspondence. Model using a think-aloud strategy.

To guide observations and facilitate reporting, use Assessment Master 3 2: Ongoing Observations Checklist: Sorting. To gather information about children who are having difficulty, use Assessment Master 2: Diagnostic Conference for Selected Children.

Unit 1: Sorting and Patterning 17

Students naturally solve mathematical problems daily.
Purposeful practice authenticates our classroom instruction.
– Jeananne Thomas, Program Author

At Grades 3 and up

Each lesson in the Student Book provides one to two pages of **Practice**.

This exercise set includes patterning and visual estimation, as well as reinforcement and problem-solving opportunities.

One question in each Practice is identified as an **Assessment Focus:** it provides a good barometer of students' level of conceptual understanding.

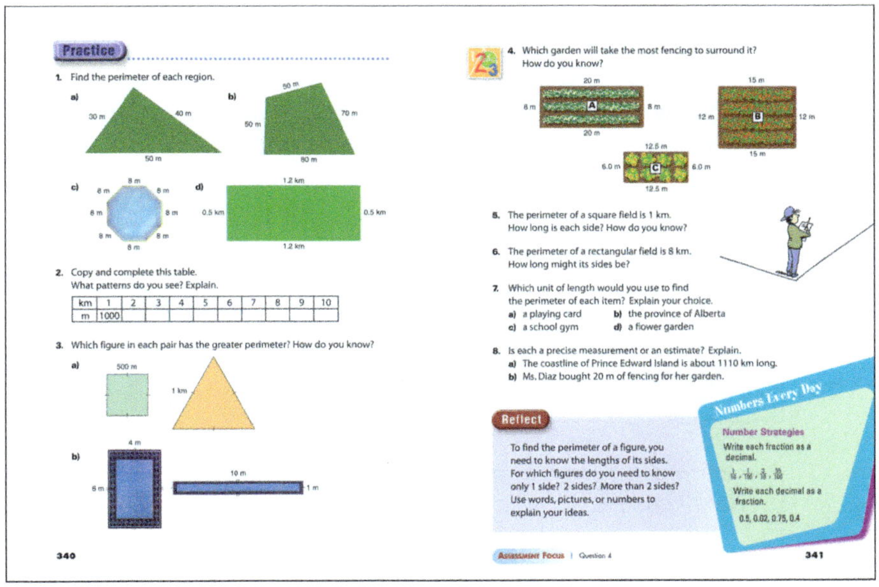

In each lesson, **Numbers Every Day** reinforces students'

- Number Sense
- Calculator Skills
- Mental Math

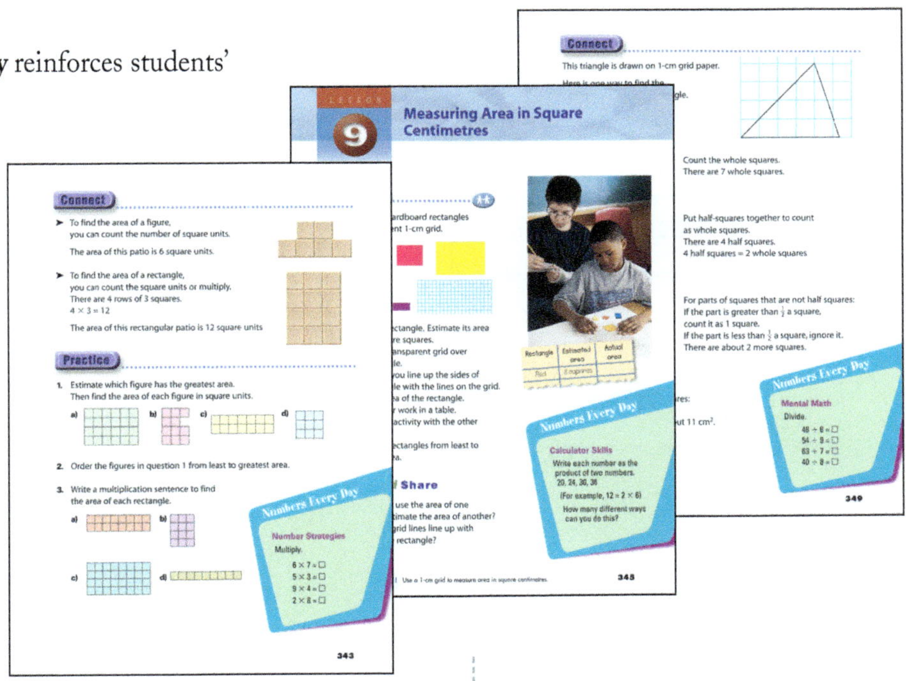

The **Teacher Guide** provides

- Answers and sample responses to **Practice** questions
- Answers and strategy suggestions for **Numbers Every Day**
- **Extra Practice** masters to support specific student needs

Also available at grade 3 and beyond: A **Practice and Homework Book** with two pages of additional support for each lesson in the Student Book

Making Sense of...

Assessment for Learning

Assessment that informs instruction, with direct links to the curriculum and teacher reporting, is *purposeful, practical,* and *powerful* — a major contributor to how well students learn. In *Addison Wesley Mathematics Makes Sense,* assessment opportunities are woven right into the main flow of instruction, across every unit.

Unit Structure

Component	Assessment
Unit Launch	Diagnostic
Core Lessons	Diagnostic, Formative
Strategies Toolkit	Formative
Show What You Know	Formative, Summative
Unit Problem (Grade 3 and up)	Summative

Term Structure

Component	Assessment
Cross-Strand Investigation	Summative

Comprehensive Assessment Support

Your Teacher Guide provides detailed assessment support in each unit, with **Planning for Assessment** charts at the start of each unit, **Assessment for Learning** notes in each lesson, and a selection of **Assessment** masters specific to the unit content.

The **Assessment Module** in your Teacher Guide provides additional background support as well as generic assessment tools for use throughout the school year.

Assessment is not an event, but a continuous process embedded in instruction.

– Sharon Jeroski, Program Author

Diagnostic Assessment

- ☑ To identify students who are at risk in terms of acquiring concepts, procedures, and strategies required in the unit
- ☑ To develop insights into particular needs so that instruction can be adjusted to ensure students have the best possibility to succeed

At Grades 1 and 2

- The **Diagnostic Checklist** lets you record your observations during the **Unit Launch.**
- Mid-unit, use the **Diagnostic Conference** outline with students who appear to be at risk. This form includes scaffolding and observation cues.

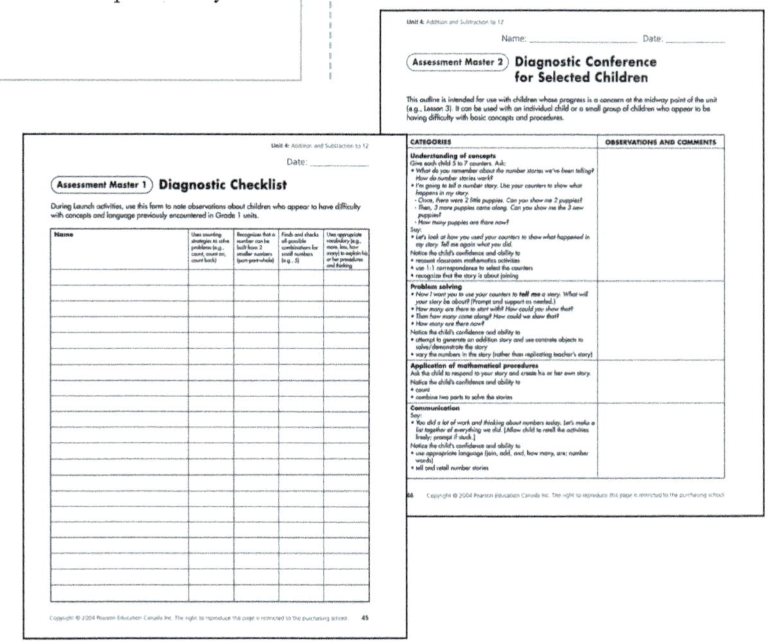

Unit 4: Addition and Subtraction to 12

Name: ____________ Date: ____________

Assessment Master 2 **Diagnostic Conference for Selected Children**

This outline is intended for use with children whose progress is a concern at the midway point of the unit (e.g., Lesson 3). It can be used with an individual child or a small group of children who appear to be having difficulty with basic concepts and procedures.

CATEGORIES	OBSERVATIONS AND COMMENTS
Understanding of concepts Give each child 5 to 7 counters. Ask: • *What do you remember about the number stories we've been telling? How do number stories work?* • *I'm going to tell a number story. Use your counters to show what happens in my story.* - *Once, there were 2 little puppies. Can you show me 2 puppies?* - *Then, 3 more puppies came along. Can you show me the 3 new puppies?* - *How many puppies are there now?* Say: • *Let's look at how you used your counters to show what happened in my story. Tell me again what you did.* Notice the child's confidence and ability to • recount classroom mathematics activities • use 1:1 correspondence to select the counters • recognize that the story is about joining	
Problem solving • *Now I want you to use your counters to **tell me** a story. What will your story be about?* (Prompt and support as needed.) • *How many are there to start with? How could you show that?* • *Then how many come along? How could we show that?* • *How many are there now?* Notice the child's confidence and ability to • attempt to generate an addition story and use concrete objects to solve/demonstrate the story • vary the numbers in the story (rather than replicating teacher's story)	
Application of mathematical procedures Ask the child to respond to your story and create his or her own story. Notice the child's confidence and ability to • count • combine two parts to solve the stories	
Communication Say: • *You did a lot of work and thinking about numbers today. Let's make a list together of everything we did.* (Allow child to retell the activities freely; prompt if stuck.) Notice the child's confidence and ability to • use appropriate language (join, add, and, how many, are; number words) • tell and retell number stories	

46 Copyright © 2004 Pearson Education Canada Inc. The right to reproduce this page is restricted to the purchasing school.

Unit 4: Addition and Subtraction to 12

Date: ____________

Assessment Master 1 **Diagnostic Checklist**

During Launch activities, use this form to note observations about children who appear to have difficulty with concepts and language previously encountered in Grade 1 units.

Name	Uses counting strategies to solve problems (e.g., count, count on, count back)	Recognizes that a number can be built from 2 smaller numbers (part-part-whole)	Finds and checks all possible combinations for small numbers (e.g., 5)	Uses appropriate vocabulary (e.g., more, less, how many) to explain his or her procedures and thinking

Copyright © 2004 Pearson Education Canada Inc. The right to reproduce this page is restricted to the purchasing school. 45

At Grades 3 to 8

- Each **Unit Launch** in the Student Book is designed to probe children's prior knowledge and skills. The Teacher Guide provides additional diagnostic questions and support.
- The first **Cross-Strand Investigation** in the text lets you start the year with a meaningful context in which students re-visit key concepts from the previous year.
- Use the **Diagnostic Assessment** form; it cues you regarding what to watch for and how to help.

Formative Assessment

- ☑ To gather ongoing information in a variety of ways
- ☑ To provide feedback to students about how they are doing, and how they might improve
- ☑ To adjust instruction
- ☑ To provide additional scaffolding to students who need it
- ☑ To engage students in their own learning and in self-assessment

- At all grades, during all parts of the lesson, the Teacher Guide offers specific questions to probe student understanding.
- Because each lesson engages students directly in **actively exploring** the key concept, teachers have opportunities to observe what students are able to do.

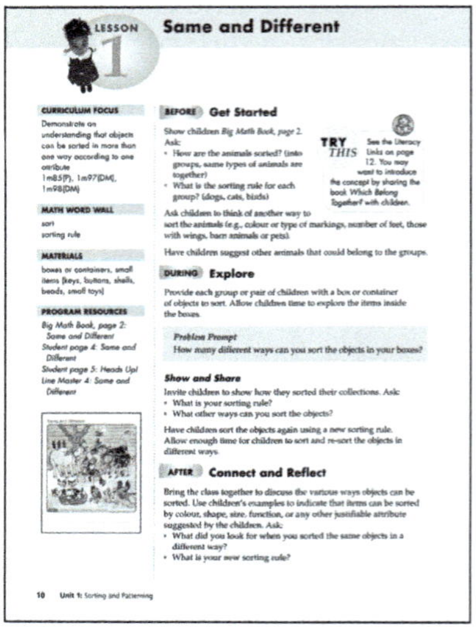

LESSON 1

Same and Different

CURRICULUM FOCUS

Demonstrate an understanding that objects can be sorted in more than one way according to one attribute
1m85(P), 1m97(DM), 1m98(DM)

MATH WORD WALL

sort
sorting rule

MATERIALS

boxes or containers, small items (keys, buttons, shells, beads, small toys)

PROGRAM RESOURCES

Big Math Book, page 2: Same and Different
Student page 4: Same and Different
Student page 5: Heads Up!
Line Master 4: Same and Different

BEFORE **Get Started**

Show children *Big Math Book, page 2.*
Ask:
- How are the animals sorted? (into groups, same types of animals are together)
- What is the sorting rule for each group? (dogs, cats, birds)

Ask children to think of another way to sort the animals (e.g., colour or type of markings, number of feet, those with wings, barn animals or pets).

Have children suggest other animals that could belong to the groups.

TRY THIS See the Literacy Links on page 12. You may want to introduce the concept by sharing the book *Which Belong Together?* with children.

DURING **Explore**

Provide each group or pair of children with a box or container of objects to sort. Allow children time to explore the items inside the boxes.

Problem Prompt
How many different ways can you sort the objects in your boxes?

Show and Share

Invite children to show how they sorted their collections. Ask:
- What is your sorting rule?
- What other ways can you sort the objects?

Have children sort the objects again using a new sorting rule. Allow enough time for children to sort and re-sort the objects in different ways.

AFTER **Connect and Reflect**

Bring the class together to discuss the various ways objects can be sorted. Use children's examples to indicate that items can be sorted by colour, shape, size, function, or any other justifiable attribute suggested by the children. Ask:
- What did you look for when you sorted the same objects in a different way?
- What is your new sorting rule?

10 **Unit 1:** Sorting and Patterning

- At all grades, **Show and Share** provides a key opportunity for eliciting students' understanding through communication.

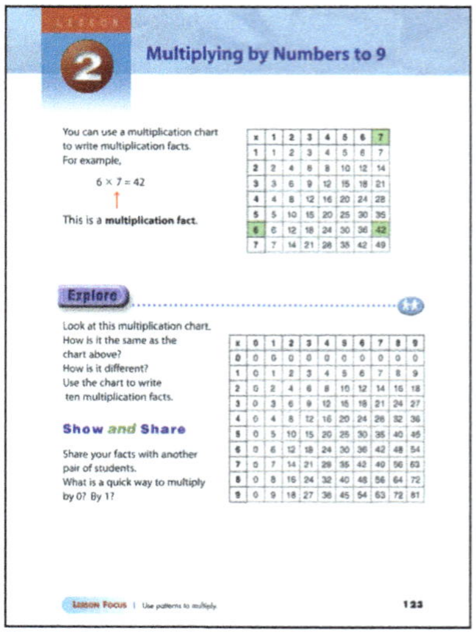

LESSON 2

Multiplying by Numbers to 9

You can use a multiplication chart to write multiplication facts.
For example,

6 × 7 = 42

This is a **multiplication fact**.

×	1	2	3	4	5	6	7
1	1	2	3	4	5	6	7
2	2	4	6	8	10	12	14
3	3	6	9	12	15	18	21
4	4	8	12	16	20	24	28
5	5	10	15	20	25	30	35
6	6	12	18	24	30	36	42
7	7	14	21	28	35	42	49

Explore

Look at this multiplication chart.
How is it the same as the chart above?
How is it different?
Use the chart to write ten multiplication facts.

×	0	1	2	3	4	5	6	7	8	9
0	0	0	0	0	0	0	0	0	0	0
1	0	1	2	3	4	5	6	7	8	9
2	0	2	4	6	8	10	12	14	16	18
3	0	3	6	9	12	15	18	21	24	27
4	0	4	8	12	16	20	24	28	32	36
5	0	5	10	15	20	25	30	35	40	45
6	0	6	12	18	24	30	36	42	48	54
7	0	7	14	21	28	35	42	49	56	63
8	0	8	16	24	32	40	48	56	64	72
9	0	9	18	27	36	45	54	63	72	81

Show and Share

Share your facts with another pair of students.
What is a quick way to multiply by 0? By 1?

LESSON FOCUS | Use patterns to multiply. 123

Assessment has taken on new importance in its impact on instructional decisions.

– Ralph Connelly, Program Author

- In the Teacher Guide, **Assessment for Learning** directs your attention to specific behaviours you may see in students' work, and provides practical instructions about what to do to help students who may be struggling.
- **Practice** questions provide more opportunities for you to observe, probe, and provide feedback about student development.

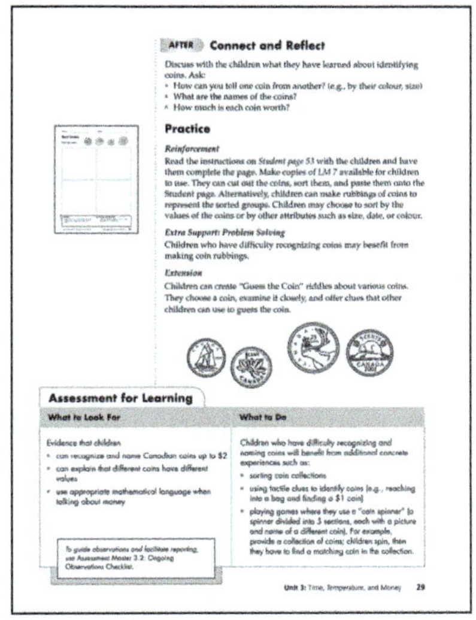

AFTER Connect and Reflect

Discuss with the children what they have learned about identifying coins. Ask:

- How can you tell one coin from another? (e.g., by their colour, size)
- What are the names of the coins?
- How much is each coin worth?

Practice

Reinforcement

Read the instructions on *Student page 53* with the children and have them complete the page. Make copies of LM 7 available for children to use. They can cut out the coins, sort them, and paste them onto the Student page. Alternatively, children can make rubbings of coins to represent the sorted groups. Children may choose to sort by the values of the coins or by other attributes such as size, date, or colour.

Extra Support: Problem Solving

Children who have difficulty recognizing coins may benefit from making coin rubbings.

Extension

Children can create "Guess the Coin" riddles about various coins. They choose a coin, examine it closely, and offer clues that other children can use to guess the coin.

Assessment for Learning

What to Look For	What to Do
Evidence that children • can recognize and name Canadian coins up to $2 • can explain that different coins have different values • use appropriate mathematical language when talking about money	Children who have difficulty recognizing and naming coins will benefit from additional concrete experiences such as: • sorting coin collections • using tactile clues to identify coins (e.g., reaching into a bag and finding a $1 coin) • playing games where they use a "coin spinner" (a spinner divided into 3 sections, each with a picture and name of a different coin). For example, provide a collection of coins; children spin, then they have to find a matching coin in the collection.

To guide observations and facilitate reporting, use Assessment Master 3.3: Ongoing Observations Checklist.

Unit 3: Time, Temperature, and Money 29

- At grades 3 to 8, Practice sets always include one exercise highlighted as an **Assessment Focus** question: this open-ended problem allows for a range of performance levels, and provides a quick touchstone for you as you circulate to observe students at work.

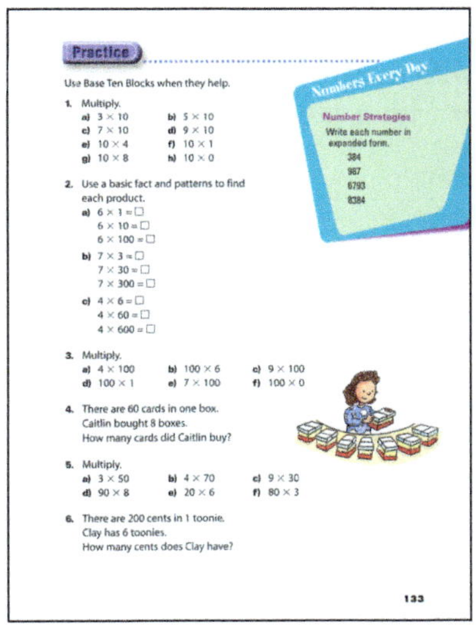

Practice

Use Base Ten Blocks when they help.

1. Multiply.
   a) 3 × 10 b) 5 × 10
   c) 7 × 10 d) 9 × 10
   e) 10 × 4 f) 10 × 1
   g) 10 × 8 h) 10 × 0
2. Use a basic fact and patterns to find each product.
   a) 6 × 1 = ☐
   6 × 10 = ☐
   6 × 100 = ☐
   b) 7 × 3 = ☐
   7 × 30 = ☐
   7 × 300 = ☐
   c) 4 × 6 = ☐
   4 × 60 = ☐
   4 × 600 = ☐
3. Multiply.
   a) 4 × 100 b) 100 × 6 c) 9 × 100
   d) 100 × 1 e) 7 × 100 f) 100 × 0
4. There are 60 cards in one box. Caitlin bought 8 boxes. How many cards did Caitlin buy?
5. Multiply.
   a) 3 × 50 b) 4 × 70 c) 9 × 30
   d) 90 × 8 e) 20 × 6 f) 80 × 3
6. There are 200 cents in 1 toonie. Clay has 6 toonies. How many cents does Clay have?

Numbers Every Day

Number Strategies

Write each number in expanded form.

384

987

6793

8384

133

7. Multiply.
   a) 2 × 300 b) 7 × 600 c) 5 × 200
   d) 1000 × 6 e) 2000 × 3 f) 4 × 1000
8. There are 1000 mL in 1 L. Jan has 6 L of juice. How many millilitres is that?
9. Make up some examples to show how you can multiply by:
   a) multiples of 10
   b) multiples of 100
   c) multiples of 1000

   Explain how you know your strategies work.
10. There are 50¢ in 1 roll of pennies. How many cents are in 9 rolls of pennies?
11. One tower is made with 100 red blocks, 200 yellow blocks, and 200 white blocks.
    a) How many blocks of each colour would you need to make 4 towers?
    b) How many blocks would you need altogether?

Reflect

Which patterns do you use when you multiply by 10, by 100, or by 1000? Use words, pictures, or numbers to explain.

134 Assessment Focus | Question 9

- At grades 3 to 8, the Teacher Guide support for the Practice includes notes on **common misconceptions** and **opportunities for reteaching.**

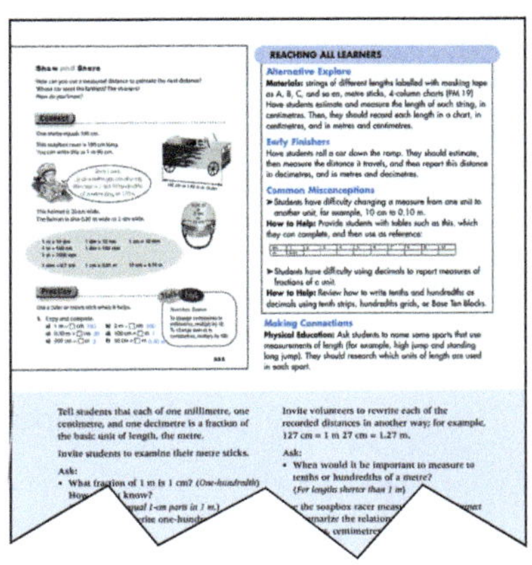

REACHING ALL LEARNERS

Alternative Explore

Early Finishers

Common Misconceptions

Making Connections

Tell students that each of one millimetre, one centimetre, and one decimetre is a fraction of the basic unit of length, the metre.

Invite students to examine their metre sticks.

Invite volunteers to rewrite each of the recorded distances in another way; for example, 127 cm = 1 m 27 cm = 1.27 m.

Summative Assessment

- ☑ To make a judgment about a student's achievement of the learning goals for the unit
- ☑ To facilitate reporting

Addison Wesley Mathematics Makes Sense provides a variety of options to meet your summative assessment needs.

At Grades 1 and 2

Show What You Know features performance tasks that enable students to work with concepts from the unit with new materials, or with a new context.

My Journal, in the Student Book, invites students to use pictures, words, or numbers to show their learning.

Cross-Strand Investigations appear once each term. These rich problems have a strong story element. They present an engaging context to students, and allow you to assess the extent to which students are able to synthesize and apply their learning in an integrated way.

The Teacher Guide provides a rubric and supporting notes for each Cross-Strand Investigation, in the **Additional Assessment Support** module that accompanies the Teacher Guide.

At Grades 3 and up

Show What You Know includes a combination of short answer and open-ended questions, all cross-referenced to relevant lessons of the unit.

A **Unit Problem** involves students in the context used to introduce the unit. A **Check List** in the Student Book tells students how their work will be assessed.

Reflect on the Unit presents a journal opportunity that asks students to consolidate their understanding of the big idea for the unit.

Cross-Strand Investigations appear once each term in the Student Book. These rich problems present an engaging context to students, and allow you to assess the extent to which students are able to synthesize and apply their learning in an integrated way.

The Teacher Guide provides a rubric and supporting notes for each Cross-Strand Investigation, in the **Additional Assessment Support** module that accompanies the Teacher Guide.

A three-part **Unit Test** in the Teacher Guide includes a short-answer section, conceptual items, and a problem to be solved.

Teachers are facing increased pressures around accountability. They need some practical support to meet new reporting requirements.
– Jason Johnston, Program Author

Reporting Opportunities

Managing your assessment strategies is a first step in your effective communication regarding student performance, whether informally through parent interviews, or through your preparation of student reports. *Addison Wesley Mathematics Makes Sense* supports your reporting requirements in a number of ways.

- By offering a **Scope and Sequence** that allows you to cover several strands in each term, with each strand appearing at least once in each grade
- With a **Learning Skills Checklist** that lets you summarize observations for possible use in report card comments
- With an **Ongoing Observations Checklist** for each unit that lets you track student performance lesson by lesson, with each lesson tied to your specific curriculum expectations/outcomes
- With specific **rubrics** that match your provincial reporting protocols
- With a **Unit Summary** tracking sheet that lets you record a student's most consistent achievement level in each block of lessons from the unit, with space for anecdotal comments

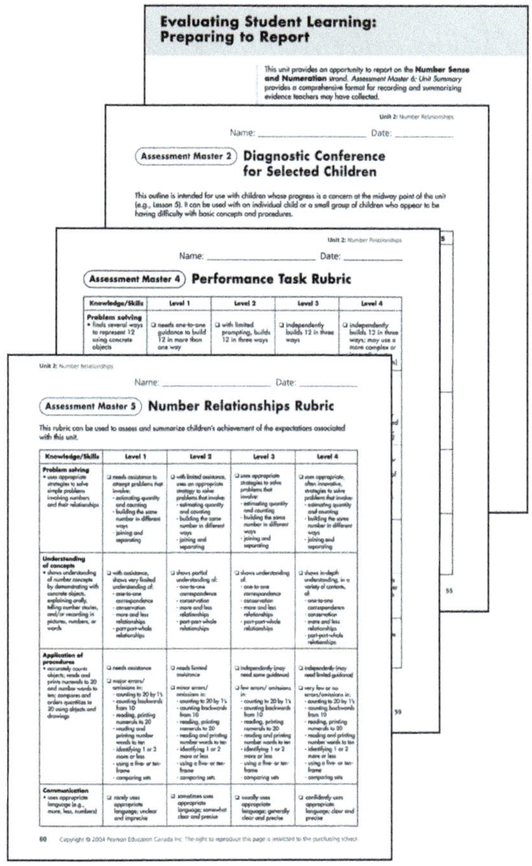
Evaluating Student Learning: Preparing to Report

Assessment Master 2 Diagnostic Conference for Selected Children

Assessment Master 4 Performance Task Rubric

Assessment Master 5 Number Relationships Rubric

At the close of the unit, look for reporting guidelines and sample report card comments in **Evaluating Student Learning: Preparing to Report.**

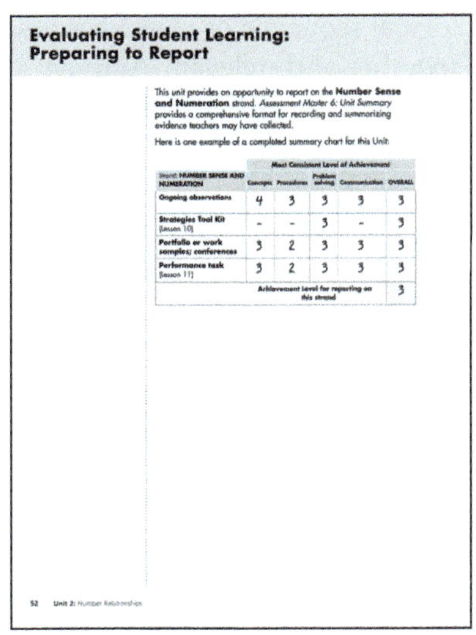
Evaluating Student Learning: Preparing to Report

Your Curriculum Requirements

Addison Wesley Mathematics Makes Sense organizes your curriculum into clusters of expectations/outcomes across and within grades to create a logical, conceptual, and developmental progression of curriculum presentation.

The authors and development team have analyzed your curriculum document carefully, against the backdrop of sound conceptual development. The result is a carefully structured program that makes sense across the grades and, within each grade, designed to enhance student understanding and to recognize students' developmental stages.

Our scope and sequence is designed to meet the demands of your school year calendar. At each grade level, *Addison Wesley Mathematics Makes Sense* has 11 units to keep formal reporting needs to a minimum, while ensuring complete curriculum coverage.

At each grade level, unit by unit, the program filters your curriculum requirements into a selection of "curriculum clusters." Each curriculum cluster represents a "big idea," a building block to creating a deep understanding of mathematics concepts.

- The **Curriculum Overview** in each Teacher Guide unit reveals the "big ideas" of the unit at a glance.

At Grades 1 and 2

For each curriculum cluster at grades 1 and 2, we've organized a logical sequence of core **Lessons**, together with relevant **Activity Banks** to provide additional teaching options.

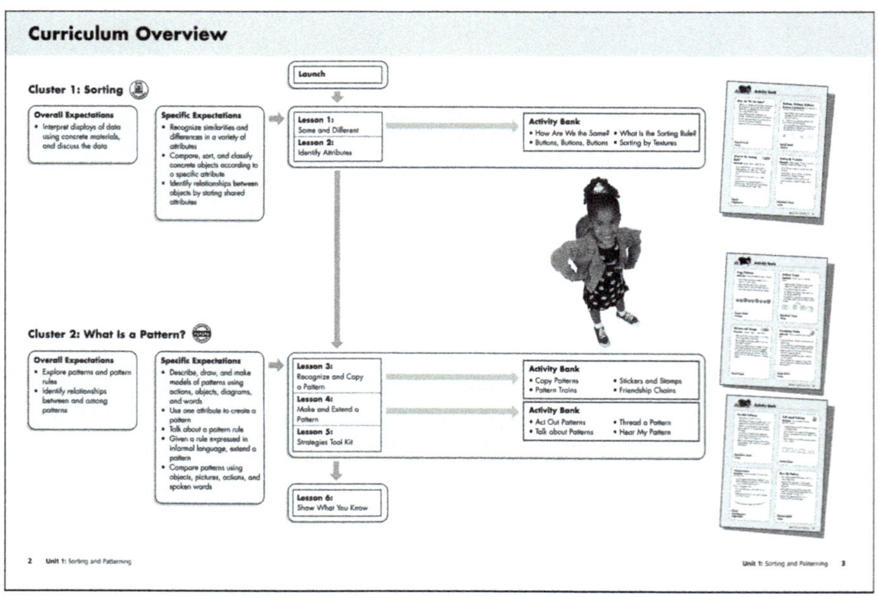
Curriculum Overview

Cluster 1: Sorting

Overall Expectations
- Interpret displays of data using concrete materials, and discuss the data

Specific Expectations
- Recognize similarities and differences in a variety of attributes
- Compare, sort, and classify concrete objects according to a specific attribute
- Identify relationships between objects by stating shared attributes

Launch

Lesson 1: Same and Different
Lesson 2: Identify Attributes

Activity Bank
- How Are We the Same?
- What Is the Sorting Rule?
- Buttons, Buttons, Buttons
- Sorting by Textures

Cluster 2: What Is a Pattern?

Overall Expectations
- Explore patterns and pattern rules
- Identify relationships between and among patterns

Specific Expectations
- Describe, draw, and make models of patterns using actions, objects, diagrams, and words
- Use one attribute to create a pattern
- Talk about a pattern rule
- Given a rule expressed in informal language, extend a pattern
- Compare patterns using objects, pictures, actions, and spoken words

Lesson 3: Recognize and Copy a Pattern
Lesson 4: Make and Extend a Pattern
Lesson 5: Strategies Tool Kit

Activity Bank
- Copy Patterns
- Stickers and Stamps
- Pattern Trains
- Friendship Chains

Activity Bank
- Act Out Patterns
- Thread a Pattern
- Talk about Patterns
- Hear My Pattern

Lesson 6: Show What You Know

2 Unit 1: Sorting and Patterning

Unit 1: Sorting and Patterning 3

> A curriculum document sets out overall content goals. It is our responsibility to make that content unfold in the classroom on a daily basis.
> – Bryn Keyes, Program Author

At Grades 3 and up

The Curriculum Overview in grades 3 and up shows how the lessons develop across the unit.

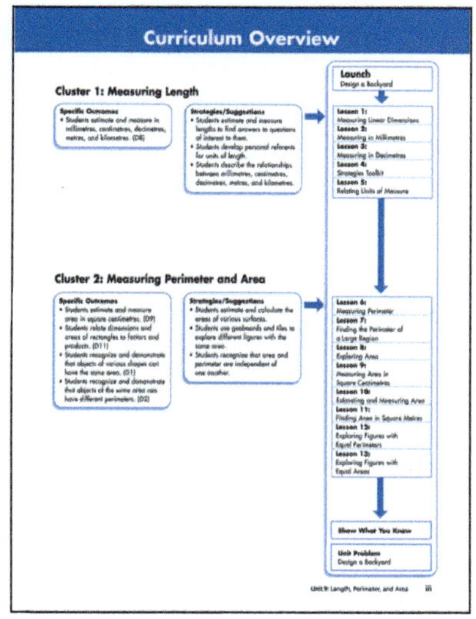

- The **Curriculum Focus** is summarized for each lesson and lists specific outcomes/expectations that relate to the lesson.

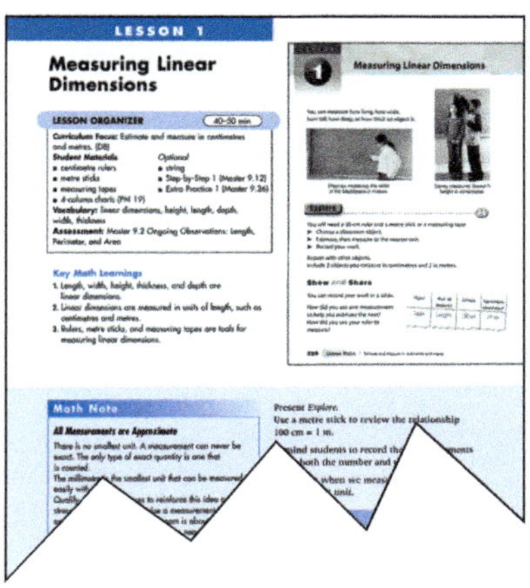

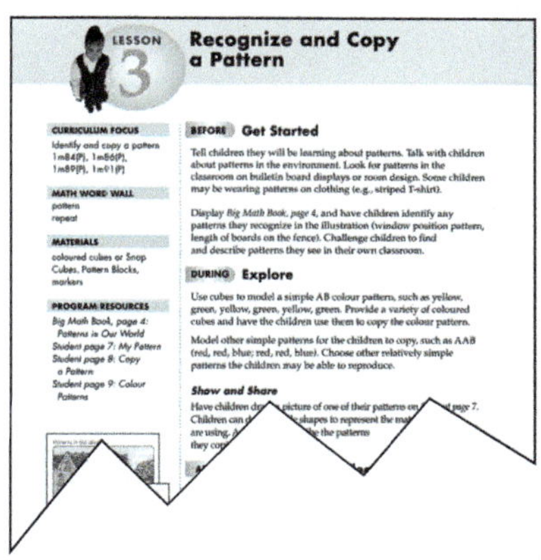

Your regional **Teacher Guide** highlights specific curriculum requirements and

- Year-long planning suggestions
- A **Curriculum Overview** in each unit that clusters and correlates your curriculum to specific lessons
- Specific lesson notes and suggestions
- The CD-ROM that accompanies your Teacher Guide

Making Sense of...

Solutions for Combined Grades

Teachers of combined grades have a special challenge in their task of providing full curriculum coverage for different grade levels, in the same classroom and during the same class period, while addressing the learning needs of all their students. *Addison Wesley Mathematics Makes Sense* offers planning tools for day-to-day support of combined grades classrooms.

Available as a supplement to your Teacher Guide, our **Together Resources** provide practical suggestions for planning and teaching combined grades.

- Background notes outline 3 general lesson approaches, depending on the nature of the content at hand and students' prior knowledge
- Specific unit suggestions identify a day-to-day unit plan with recommended lesson approaches, notes for specific activities, and homework assignments from the unit

In our earliest planning, combined grades have been considered in the creation of the **K to 8 Scope and Sequence.** Wherever the mathematical content allowed, and the curriculum requirements indicated, our development team strove to ensure that unit content aligned across the grades.

Benchmarks for Developing Measurement

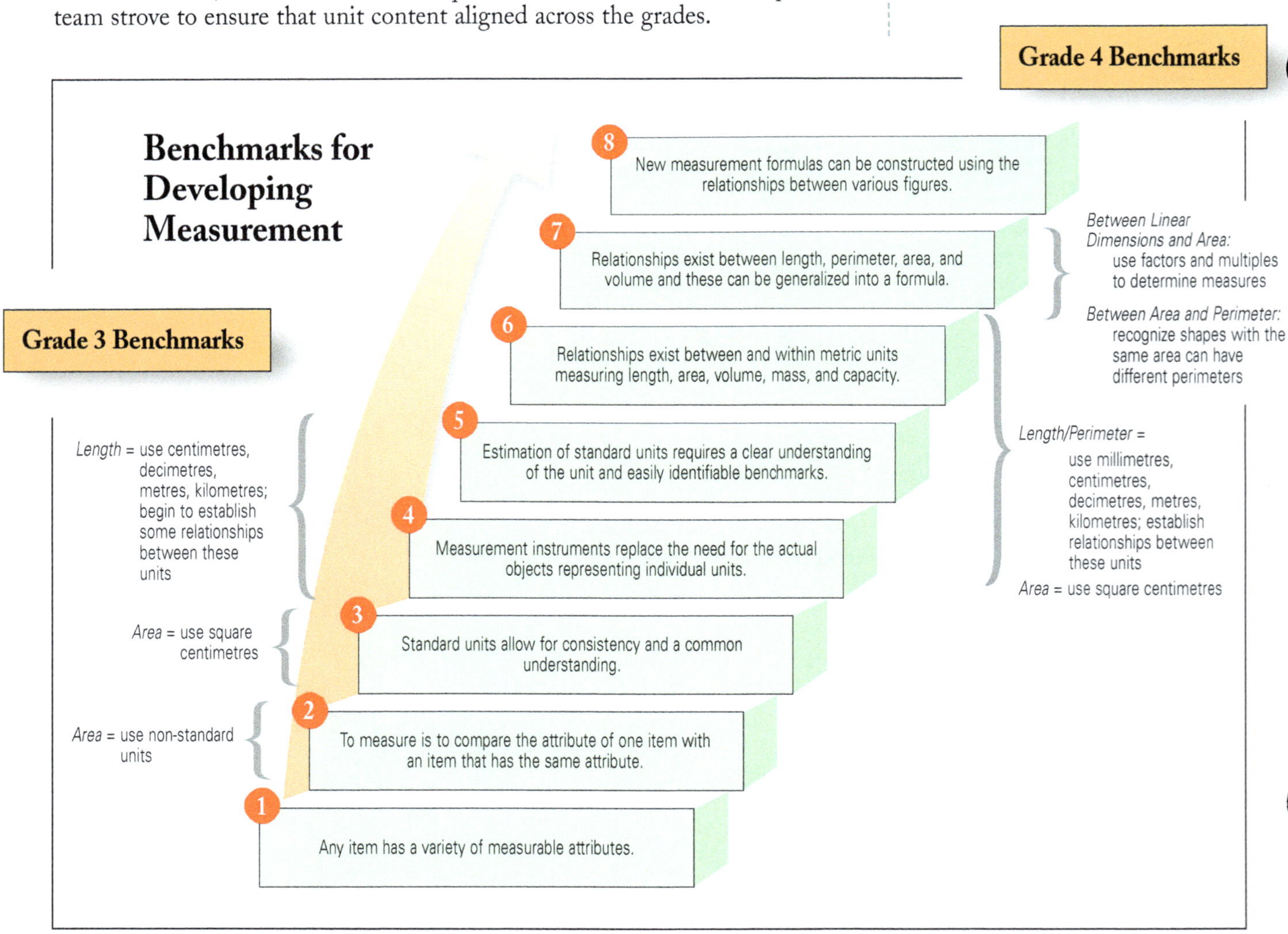

Understanding developmental stages provides a framework for planning effective mathematics lessons to meet the needs of all students.
– Craig Featherstone, Program Consultant

K to 2 Scope and Sequence: Supporting Combined Grades

Although headings may change, they accurately reflect content plans.

Kindergarten	Unit	Grade 1	Grade 2
Number Sense and Numeration	1	**Sorting and Patterning**	**Sorting and Patterning**
Measurement	2	**Number Development:** Number Relationships	**Number Development:** Counting and Patterns
Geometry	3	**Measurement:** Time, Temperature, and Money	**Measurement:** Time, Temperature, and Money
		Cross-Strand Investigation	Cross-Strand Investigation
Patterning and Algebra	4	**Number Operations:** Addition and Subtraction to 12	**Number Operations:** Exploring Addition and Subtraction
Data Management	5	**Data Management and Probability**	**Data Management and Probability**
	6	**3-Dimensional Geometry**	**3-Dimensional Geometry**
	7	**Number Operations:** Addition and Subtraction	**Number Operations:** Addition and Subtraction
		Cross-Strand Investigation	Cross-Strand Investigation
	8	**Measurement:** Linear Measurement and Area	**Measurement:** Linear Measurement and Area
	9	**2-Dimensional Geometry**	**2-Dimensional Geometry**
	10	**Number Operations:** Number and Applications	**Number Operations:** Number and Number Patterns
	11	**Measurement:** Mass and Capacity	**Measurement:** Mass and Capacity
		Cross-Strand Investigation	Cross-Strand Investigation

Grades 3 to 6 Scope and Sequence: Supporting Combined Grades

Although headings may change, they accurately reflect content plans.

Unit	Grade 3	Grade 4	Grade 5	Grade 6
1	**Patterns in Number:** Patterns and Place Value	**Patterns in Number**	**Patterns in Number**	**Patterns in Number:** Patterns and Algebra
2	**Number Operations:** Patterns in Addition and Subtraction	**Number Operations:** Whole Numbers and Operations	**Number Operations:** Whole Numbers and Operations	**Number Operations:** Whole Numbers and Operations
3	**Geometry**	**Geometry**	**Geometry**	**Geometry**
	Cross-Strand Investigation	Cross-Strand Investigation	Cross-Strand Investigation	Cross-Strand Investigation
4	**Number Operations:** Multiplication and Division	**Number Operations:** Multiplication and Division	**Number Development:** Decimals	**Number Development:** Fractions and Decimals
5	**Data Management**	**Data Management**	**Data Management**	**Data Management**
6	**Measurement:** Time, Money, and Mass	**Measurement:** Time, Money, and Mass	**Measurement:** Time, Money, and Mass	**Measurement:** Time, Money, and Mass
7	**Geometry:** Transformational Geometry	**Geometry:** Transformational Geometry	**Geometry:** 3-D Geometry and Measurement	**Geometry:** 3-D Geometry and Measurement
	Cross-Strand Investigation	Cross-Strand Investigation	Cross-Strand Investigation	Cross-Strand Investigation
8	**Fractions**	**Fractions and Decimals**	**Fractions and Decimals**	**Fractions:** Ratio, Rate, and Percent
9	**Measurement:** Length, Perimeter, and Area	**Measurement:** Length, Perimeter, and Area	**Measurement:** Length, Perimeter, and Area	**Measurement:** Length, Perimeter, and Area
10	**Patterns and Relationships:** Patterns in Geometry	**Patterns and Relationships:** Patterns in Number and Geometry	**Patterns and Relationships:** Patterns in Number and Geometry	**Patterns and Relationships:** Patterning and Algebra
11	**Probability**	**Probability**	**Probability**	**Probability**
	Cross-Strand Investigation	Cross-Strand Investigation	Cross-Strand Investigation	Cross-Strand Investigation

Grades 7 to 8 Scope and Sequence: Supporting Combined Grades

Although headings may change, they accurately reflect content plans.

Unit	Grade 7	Grade 8
1	**Whole Numbers and Patterns**	**Number and Patterns**
2	**Number Development:** Fractions and Decimals	**Number Development:** Fractions and Decimals
3	**Geometry**	**Geometry**
	Cross-Strand Investigation	Cross-Strand Investigation
4	**Number Development:** Working with Percent	**Number Development:** Working with Percent
5	**Data Management:** Collect, Analyse, and Display	**Data Management:** Collect, Analyse, Display, Infer from Data
6	**Measurement:** Perimeter and Area	**Measurement:** Circle and Triangle Measurement
7	**Geometry and Measurement**	**Geometry and Measurement**
	Cross-Strand Investigation	Cross-Strand Investigation
8	**Ratio and Proportion**	**Ratio and Proportion**
9	**Integers**	**Integers**
10	**Patterning and Algebra:** Linear Equations	**Patterning and Algebra:** Linear Equations
11	**Data Analysis and Probability**	**Data Analysis and Probability**
	Cross-Strand Investigation	Cross-Strand Investigation

Making Sense of...

Reaching All Learners

Addison Wesley Mathematics Makes Sense meets diverse needs in both the Student Book and Teacher Guide. Through the Teacher Guide, the program also provides strategies for creating an inclusive learning environment while supporting individual student needs.

From the ground up . . . the Lesson Model

A consistent lesson model simplifies the instructional design while offering a balanced approach to learning new concepts.

- **Explore** activities use a variety of groupings and types of materials; their exploratory nature allows for varying background knowledge
  - **Show and Share** highlights opportunities for students to support each other in developing new concepts
- **Connect** consolidates key concepts for all learners
- **Practice** questions cover a range of difficulty levels and learning styles

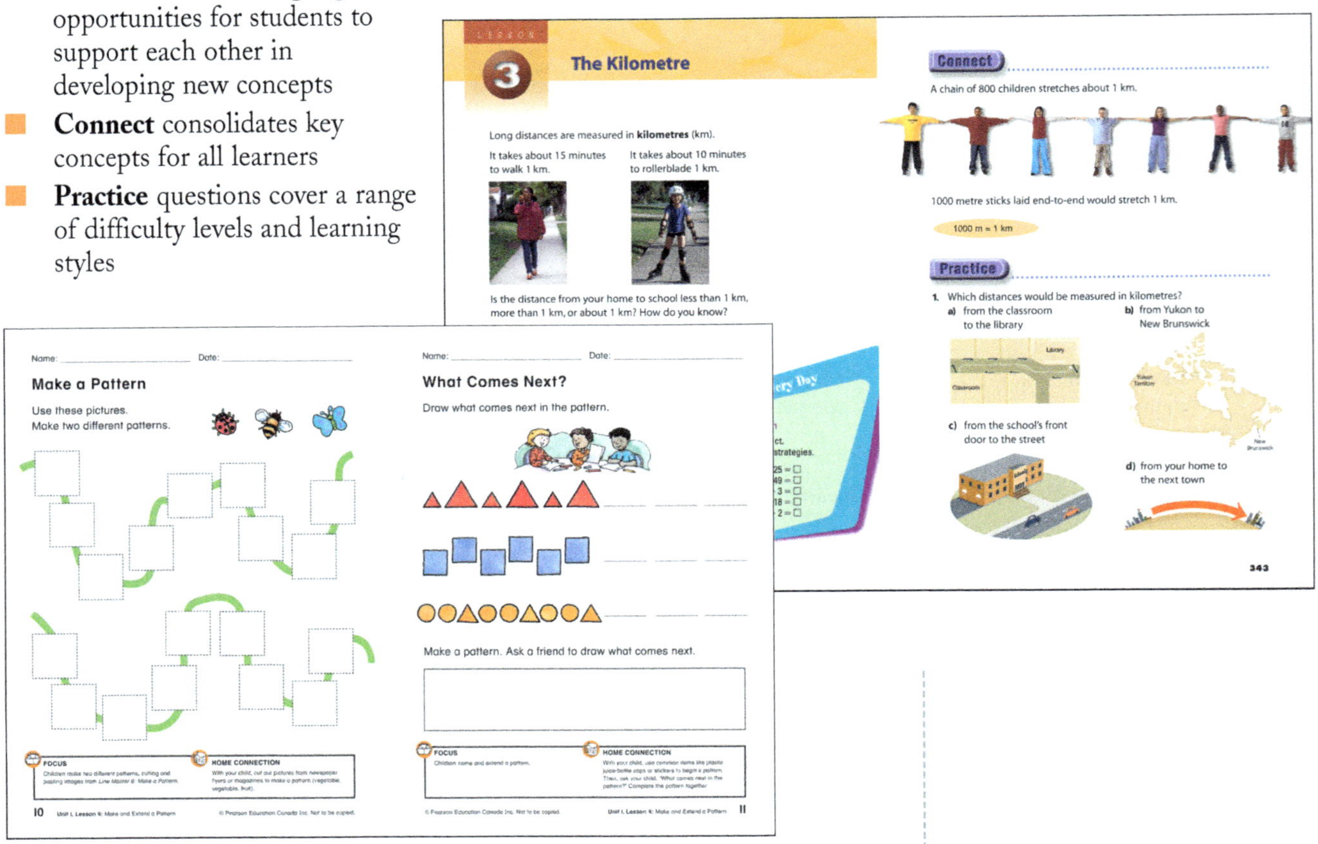

Understanding the elementary-level student:

- An open, inviting design with language at an appropriate reading level
- Content pacing that fits the developmental stage of the learner
- Contexts that are meaningful across cultures — from First Nations people to our multicultural mosaic
- Opportunities to communicate responses in a variety of ways — through words, numbers, pictures, or models

All students need opportunities to apply mathematics skills and concepts in ways that are meaningful to them.
– Sue Gordon, Author

Reaching all learners . . . through support in the Teacher Guide

In the Teacher Guide, additional activities address multiple intelligences, while teaching notes offer suggestions for supporting specific student needs.

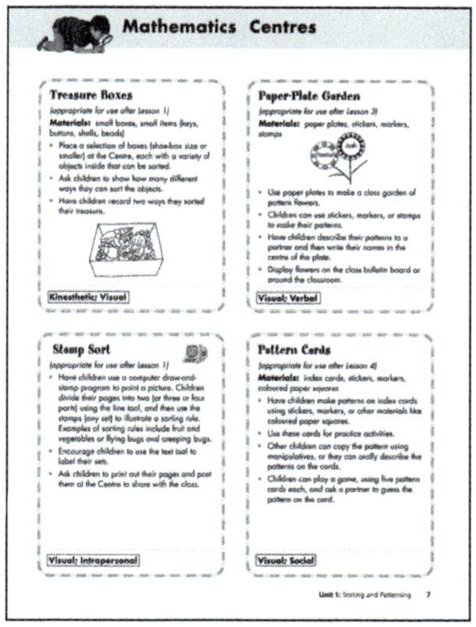

Mathematics Centres

Treasure Boxes
(appropriate for use after Lesson 1)
Materials: small boxes, small items (keys, buttons, shells, beads)
- Place a selection of boxes (shoe-box size or smaller) at the Centre, each with a variety of objects inside that can be sorted.
- Ask children to show how many different ways they can sort the objects.
- Have children record two ways they sorted their treasure.

Kinesthetic; Visual

Paper-Plate Garden
(appropriate for use after Lesson 3)
Materials: paper plates, stickers, markers, stamps
- Use paper plates to make a class garden of pattern flowers.
- Children can use stickers, markers, or stamps to make their patterns.
- Have children describe their patterns to a partner and then write their names in the centre of the plate.
- Display flowers on the class bulletin board or around the classroom.

Visual; Verbal

Stamp Sort
(appropriate for use after Lesson 1)
- Have children use a computer draw-and-stamp program to paint a picture. Children divide their pages into two (or three or four parts) using the line tool, and then use the stamps (any set) to illustrate a sorting rule. Examples of sorting rules include fruit and vegetables or flying bugs and creeping bugs.
- Encourage children to use the text tool to label their sets.
- Ask children to print out their pages and post them at the Centre to share with the class.

Visual; Intrapersonal

Pattern Cards
(appropriate for use after Lesson 4)
Materials: index cards, stickers, markers, coloured paper squares
- Have children make patterns on index cards using stickers, markers, or other materials like coloured paper squares.
- Use these cards for practice activities.
- Other children can copy the pattern using manipulatives, or they can orally describe the patterns on the cards.
- Children can play a game, using five pattern cards each, and ask a partner to guess the pattern on the card.

Visual; Social

Unit 1: Sorting and Patterning 7

Activity Bank

Copy Patterns
Materials: coloured beads (buttons, counters)
- Tell children to create a pattern using a material of their choice.
- Ask children in each pair to exchange patterns and to copy each other's pattern.
- Have them describe their partner's pattern.

Visual; Verbal
Partners

Pattern Trains
Materials: Snap Cubes or coloured blocks
- Model a simple AB pattern and create a pattern train using cubes or blocks.
- Have children copy the pattern.
- Ask children to describe the pattern and explain the pattern rule.
- Arrange for a volunteer to create a pattern train and for the rest of the class to copy its pattern.

Kinesthetic; Visual
Group

Stickers and Stamps
Materials: stickers, stamps, index cards
- Have each child make a pattern on an index card using stickers and stamps.
- Ask children to exchange patterns and copy their partner's pattern.
- Arrange for several pairs of children to copy each other's patterns. Put the cards together to make a set. Use the cards in a matching game where children pick out one card and have to find its match by looking for the same pattern.

Visual; Social

Friendship Chains
Materials: different-coloured paper strips, glue
- Provide children with two different colours of paper strips.
- Discuss different possibilities before deciding on a colour pattern for the friendship chain.
- Build one section of the chain following the children's suggested pattern.
- Have children identify the pattern and then copy the pattern.
- When sections are completed, connect the sections and display the friendship chain in the classroom.

Social; Visual
Group

Unit 1: Sorting and Patterning 19

At Grades 1 and 2

- **Mathematics Centres** provide ideas for extra support and reinforcement throughout the unit
- **Practice** suggestions for core lessons include ideas for **Extra Support** for ESL learners or students who require additional reinforcement
- **Activity Banks** for core lessons identify multiple intelligences and grouping options
- **Assessment for Learning** provides suggestions for identifying and addressing specific student needs

At Grades 3 and up

- **Additional Activities** at the start of each unit provide ideas for extra support
- Notes in each lesson provide suggestions for **ESL Strategies; Alternative Explore; Common Misconceptions,** and **How to Help**
- **Assessment for Learning** provides suggestions for identifying and addressing specific student needs
- **Step by Step** offers a scaffolded problem in worksheet form, featuring the Assessment Focus question from the Practice set, provided for every lesson

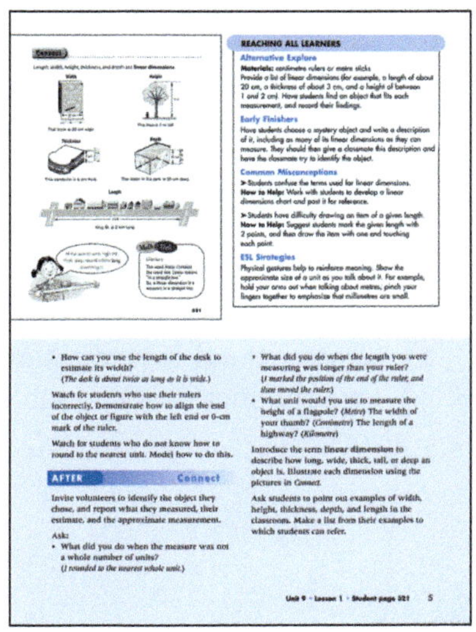

REACHING ALL LEARNERS

Alternative Explore
Materials: centimetre rulers or metre sticks
Provide a list of linear dimensions (for example, a length of about 20 cm, a thickness of about 3 cm, and a height of between 1 and 2 cm). Have students find an object that fits each measurement, and record their findings.

Early Finishers
Have students choose a mystery object and write a description of it, including as many of its linear dimensions as they can measure. They should then give a classmate this description and have the classmate try to identify the object.

Common Misconceptions
➤ Students confuse the terms used for linear dimensions.
How to Help: Work with students to develop a linear dimensions chart and post it for reference.

➤ Students have difficulty drawing an item of a given length.
How to Help: Suggest students mark the given length with 2 points, and then draw the item with one end touching each point.

ESL Strategies
Physical gestures help to reinforce meaning. Show the approximate size of a unit as you talk about it. For example, hold your arms out when talking about metres; pinch your fingers together to emphasize that millimetres are small.

- How can you use the length of the desk to estimate its width?
(The desk is about twice as long as it is wide.)

Watch for students who use their rulers incorrectly. Demonstrate how to align the end of the object or figure with the left end or 0-cm mark of the ruler.

Watch for students who do not know how to round to the nearest unit. Model how to do this.

AFTER Connect

Invite volunteers to identify the object they chose, and report what they measured, their estimate, and the approximate measurement.

Ask:
- What did you do when the measure was not a whole number of units?
(I rounded to the nearest whole unit.)
- What did you do when the length you were measuring was longer than your ruler?
(I marked the position of the end of the ruler, and then moved the ruler.)
- What unit would you use to measure the height of a flagpole? *(Metre)* The width of your thumb? *(Centimetre)* The length of a highway? *(Kilometre)*

Introduce the term **linear dimension** to describe how long, wide, thick, tall, or deep an object is. Illustrate each dimension using the pictures in *Connect.*

Ask students to point out examples of width, height, thickness, depth, and length in the classroom. Make a list from their examples to which students can refer.

Unit 9 • Lesson 1 • Student page 321 5

Building a Math Community

This section in the Grade 4 Planning and Program Masters module in your Teacher Guide gives you:

- Guidelines for creating a supportive environment for learning mathematics
- Suggestions for age-appropriate activities, games, and routines that help to create positive attitudes toward learning mathematics

Making Sense of...

Math Connections

Addison Wesley Mathematics Makes Sense recognizes that mathematical understanding is deepened and enhanced when students make connections between what they are learning and their own experience.

Real-World Contexts

- **Unit Launches** provide contexts to prompt mathematical conversation
- **Problem prompts** and activities in core lessons are relevant to the student's experience
- **Unit Problems** feature applied settings

Numbers Every Day

- Connects "number" to everyday class routines in Kindergarten to Grade 2, threading number concepts through all core learning in Grades 3-8

Cross-Curricular Connections

- At Kindergarten to grade 2, Teacher Guide notes in each lesson provide suggestions for relating mathematics to other subject areas – art, science, social studies, physical education, music
- At grades 3 and up, **Math Link** features in the student book highlight cross-curricular, mathematical, or real-world connections; the Teacher Guide details additional ideas

Across Strands

- Integration of strands occurs within units at the lesson level, and through the **Activity Banks** and **Mathematics Centres.**
- **Cross-Strand Investigations** appear each term, to provide opportunities for rich problem solving that draws on multiple strand concepts.

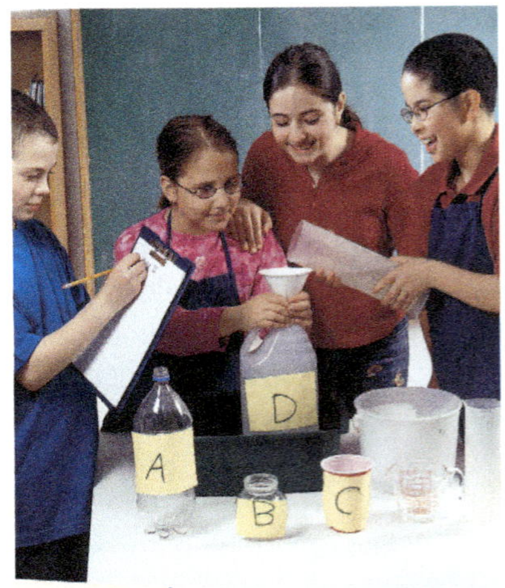

Container	Estimated Capacity	Actual Capacity
Paper Cup	200 mL	180 mL

Students better understand mathematical concepts when they make real-life connections and talk about personal experiences.
– Angela D'Alessandro, Program Author

The Literacy and Numeracy Connection

At K to 2

- **Addison Wesley Mathematics Little Books** and **Lap Books** provide an alternative for launching or extending lessons.
- The **Big Math Book** appeals to primary-level children, many of whom may not yet be comfortable reading print. It includes chants, poems and songs that connect the kinesthetic to the linguistic.
- A take-home book with each **Investigation** in the Student Book provides a shared reading opportunity with mathematical elements.
- The **Literacy Links** feature in the Teacher Guide suggests titles that can be integrated with each lesson or used as a cross-over point with the teaching of language arts.
- Teacher Guide suggestions include use of **cooperative journals**, **pocket charts**, and a **Math Word Wall.**

At Grades 3 to 8

- **Key Words** are listed in the Student Book at the start of each unit
- Students' vocabulary is supported with an illustrated **Glossary** in the Student Book
- **Literature Opportunities** are listed in the Teacher Guide with each Unit Launch; share these literature suggestions before starting the unit to help motivate learning

Home Connections

Parents have a significant role to play in student learning, in supporting and reinforcing what is learned in the classroom each day, and promoting a positive attitude toward mathematics in the home.

Addison Wesley Mathematics Makes Sense provides several tools for communicating with parents, with a changing emphasis as the learner matures from grade 2 to grade 3, and beyond.

At Grades 1 and 2 ...in the Student Book

- Each unit includes a **Dear Family** letter regarding the upcoming unit.
- Each page presents a **Focus** statement to communicate the key learning, and a **Home Connection** suggestion for further reinforcement.
- Between selected units, **Math at Home** – a tear-out, take-home booklet – provides a magazine-style family connection with mathematical information, Canadian trivia, and game suggestions.

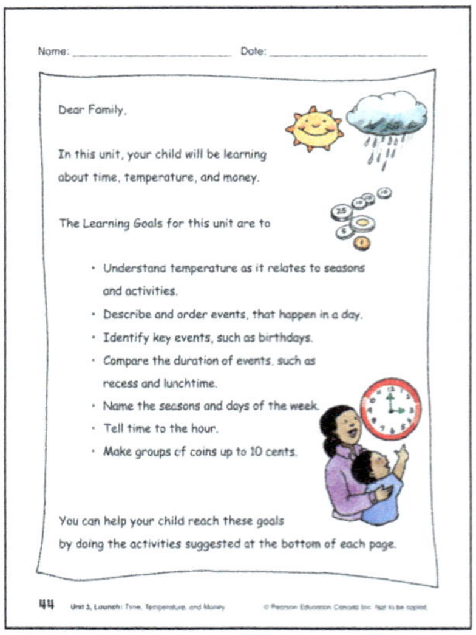
Name: ______ Date: ______

Dear Family,

In this unit, your child will be learning about time, temperature, and money.

The Learning Goals for this unit are to

- Understand temperature as it relates to seasons and activities.
- Describe and order events, that happen in a day.
- Identify key events, such as birthdays.
- Compare the duration of events, such as recess and lunchtime.
- Name the seasons and days of the week.
- Tell time to the hour.
- Make groups of coins up to 10 cents.

You can help your child reach these goals by doing the activities suggested at the bottom of each page.

44 Unit 3, Launch: Time, Temperature, and Money © Pearson Education Canada Inc. Not to be copied.

At K to 2 ...in the Teacher Guide

- Look for **At Home** line masters that provide a summary of the Big Ideas in the unit, with accompanying activities to reinforce key concepts at home.
- In each unit, content-specific **Assessment Tools** support the teacher when speaking with parents about children's progress.

> Students, teachers, and parents are all partners in the learning process.
>
> – Maggie Martin Connell, Program Author

At Grades 3 and up ...in the Student Book

- **Learning Goals** and **Key Words**, presented at the start of each unit, identify the content to be covered for parents as well as students.
- The **Lesson Focus** statement, on the first page of each lesson, identifies the key learning goal for the lesson.
- Parents can use the **Connect** section of each lesson to check the key concepts students have covered in class.
- Regular **At Home** features suggest activities for students to do with family members at home.

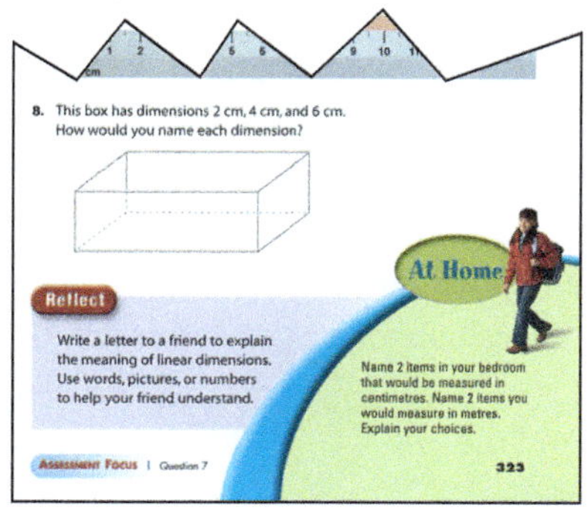
8. This box has dimensions 2 cm, 4 cm, and 6 cm. How would you name each dimension?

Reflect

Write a letter to a friend to explain the meaning of linear dimensions. Use words, pictures, or numbers to help your friend understand.

At Home

Name 2 items in your bedroom that would be measured in centimetres. Name 2 items you would measure in metres. Explain your choices.

Assessment Focus | Question 7

323

Practice and Homework Book for Grades 3 to 8

- For each lesson, a Quick Review of the key concepts
- For each lesson, graded practice questions that students can complete at home
- Games and activities used for practice when appropriate

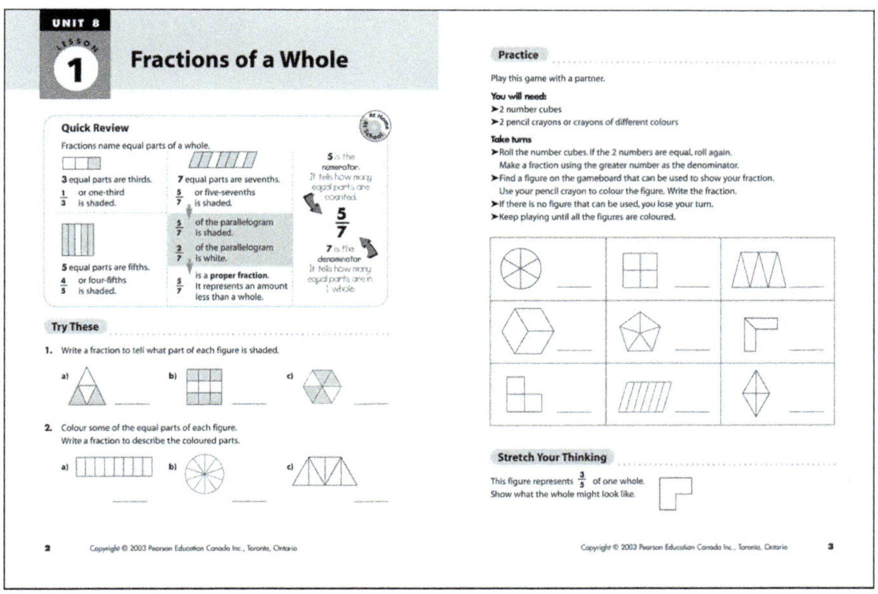
UNIT 8 LESSON 1

Fractions of a Whole

Quick Review

Fractions name equal parts of a whole.

3 equal parts are thirds. $\frac{1}{3}$ or one-third is shaded.

7 equal parts are sevenths. $\frac{5}{7}$ or five-sevenths is shaded.

$\frac{5}{7}$ of the parallelogram is shaded.

$\frac{2}{7}$ of the parallelogram is white.

5 equal parts are fifths. $\frac{4}{5}$ or four-fifths is shaded.

$\frac{5}{7}$ is a **proper fraction.** It represents an amount less than a whole.

5 is the numerator. It tells how many equal parts are counted.

$\frac{5}{7}$

7 is the denominator. It tells how many equal parts are in 1 whole.

Try These

1. Write a fraction to tell what part of each figure is shaded.

a) b) c)

2. Colour some of the equal parts of each figure. Write a fraction to describe the coloured parts.

a) b) c)

2 Copyright © 2003 Pearson Education Canada Inc., Toronto, Ontario

Practice

Play this game with a partner.

You will need:

- 2 number cubes
- 2 pencil crayons or crayons of different colours

Take turns

- Roll the number cubes. If the 2 numbers are equal, roll again. Make a fraction using the greater number as the denominator.
- Find a figure on the gameboard that can be used to show your fraction. Use your pencil crayon to colour the figure. Write the fraction.
- If there is no figure that can be used, you lose your turn.
- Keep playing until all the figures are coloured.

Stretch Your Thinking

This figure represents $\frac{3}{5}$ of one whole. Show what the whole might look like.

Copyright © 2003 Pearson Education Canada Inc., Toronto, Ontario 3

Across the Grades

The Pearson Education mathematics Website provides parent information and support.

Making Sense of...

Technology

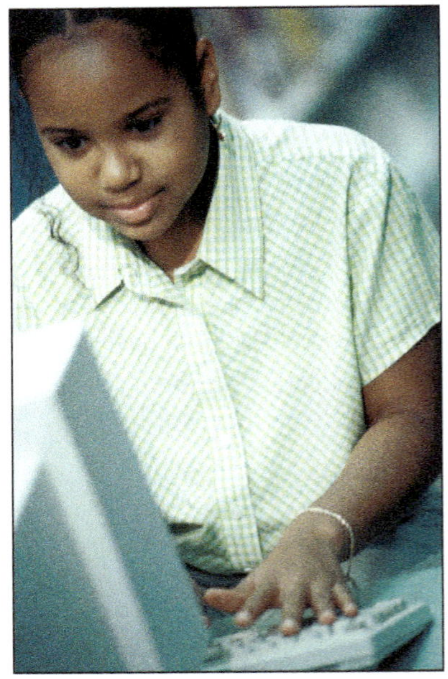

Addison Wesley Mathematics Makes Sense integrates technology in the following ways.

- **Technology Lessons** in the student book highlight opportunities for learning new mathematical concepts through the use of the calculator or the computer.

Grade 1

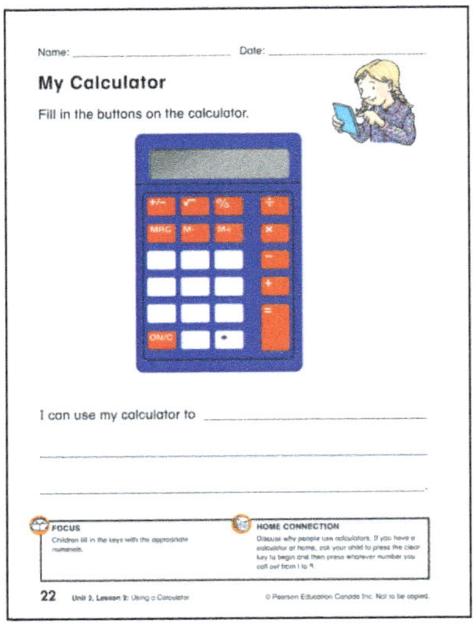

Name: ______________ Date: ______________

My Calculator

Fill in the buttons on the calculator.

I can use my calculator to ______________

FOCUS
Children fill in the keys with the appropriate numerals.

HOME CONNECTION
Discuss why people use calculators. If you have a calculator at home, ask your child to press the clear key to begin and then press whatever number you call out from 1 to 9.

22 Unit 2, Lesson 2: Using a Calculator © Pearson Education Canada Inc. Not to be copied.

Grade 4

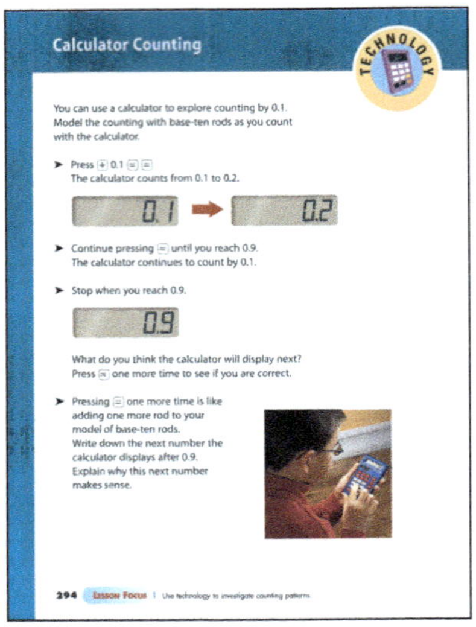

Calculator Counting

You can use a calculator to explore counting by 0.1. Model the counting with base-ten rods as you count with the calculator.

- Press + 0.1 = =
  The calculator counts from 0.1 to 0.2.

- Continue pressing = until you reach 0.9.
  The calculator continues to count by 0.1.
- Stop when you reach 0.9.

What do you think the calculator will display next?
Press = one more time to see if you are correct.

- Pressing = one more time is like adding one more rod to your model of base-ten rods.
  Write down the next number the calculator displays after 0.9.
  Explain why this next number makes sense.

294 LESSON FOCUS | Use technology to investigate counting patterns.

- When appropriate, individual activities within the student book suggest the use of a calculator or computer application to enrich and extend the mathematics.
- Suggestions for Numbers Every Day regularly include suggestions related to Calculator Skills.

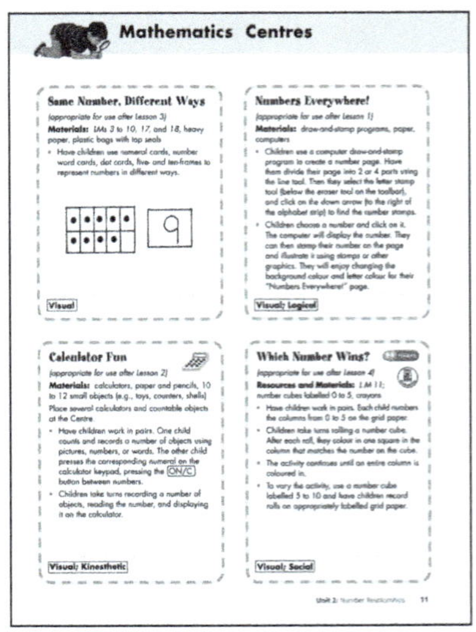

Mathematics Centres

Same Number, Different Ways
(appropriate for use after Lesson 3)
Materials: *LMs 3 to 10, 17, and 18,* heavy paper, plastic bags with top seals
- Have children use numeral cards, number word cards, dot cards, five- and ten-frames to represent numbers in different ways.

Visual

Numbers Everywhere!
(appropriate for use after Lesson 1)
Materials: draw-and-stamp programs, paper, computers
- Children use a computer draw-and-stamp program to create a number page. Have them divide their page into 2 or 4 parts using the line tool. Then they select the letter stamp tool (below the eraser tool on the toolbar), and click on the down arrow (to the right of the alphabet strip) to find the number stamps.
- Children choose a number and click on it. The computer will display the number. They can then stamp their number on the page and illustrate it using stamps or other graphics. They will enjoy changing the background colour and letter colour for their "Numbers Everywhere!" page.

Visual; Logical

Calculator Fun
(appropriate for use after Lesson 2)
Materials: calculators, paper and pencils, 10 to 12 small objects (e.g., toys, counters, shells)
Place several calculators and countable objects at the Centre.
- Have children work in pairs. One child counts and records a number of objects using pictures, numbers, or words. The other child presses the corresponding numeral on the calculator keypad, pressing the ON/C button between numbers.
- Children take turns recording a number of objects, reading the number, and displaying it on the calculator.

Visual; Kinesthetic

Which Number Wins?
(appropriate for use after Lesson 4)
Resources and Materials: *LM 11;* number cubes labelled 0 to 5, crayons
- Have children work in pairs. Each child numbers the columns from 0 to 5 on the grid paper.
- Children take turns rolling a number cube. After each roll, they colour in one square in the column that matches the number on the cube.
- The activity continues until an entire column is coloured in.
- To vary the activity, use a number cube labelled 5 to 10 and have children record rolls on appropriately labelled grid paper.

Visual; Social

Unit 2: Number Relationships 11

> The purposeful use of technology in the mathematics classroom can enrich student learning. It allows students to explore and develop concepts, to extend critical thinking and problem-solving skills. – Addison Wesley Mathematics Research Report

Addison Wesley Mathematics e-Tools (K-8) software helps students develop important math concepts using an electronic form of mathematics manipulatives.

- Use to guide class discussion
- Have students use e-Tools as an alternative to concrete materials
- Especially relevant for students who face motor challenges

- Place-Value Blocks
- Counters
- Money
- Time
- Fractions
- Probability
- Spreadsheet-data-grapher
- Geometry Shapes
- Geometry Drawing

Addison Wesley Mathematics Makes Sense **Website** provides a wealth of interactive online resources for teachers, students, and parents. Teachers can access their *Math Makes Sense* Teacher Guide making it easy to customize planning and assessment tools. On-line professional development opportunities, additional activities, samples of student work, sample report card comments, and parent letters in different languages are just a few of the resources teachers will find on this site. Support for students includes additional practice, activities, and web links correlated to their student book. Parents can download our *Math@Home* magazine filled with background information, Canadian math trivia, and fun games and activities the whole family can do together.

http://www.pearsoned.ca/mathmakessense/

Professional Development

Addison Wesley Mathematics Makes Sense integrates professional development for teachers throughout the program resources, and provides in-service and other tools to ensure success of program implementation.

Professional Development built right into the program. . .

Each unit in the Teacher Guide provides planning detail that includes

- A **Mathematics Background** section, with information for the teacher about the key mathematics concepts to be developed
- **Across the Grades** summary, to show how the topic develops over a three-year window, from the previous grade, to this grade, to the next grade
- Information about how the unit makes connections between various mathematics strands, in **Across the Strands**
- Expert quotes that point to further reading for interested teachers

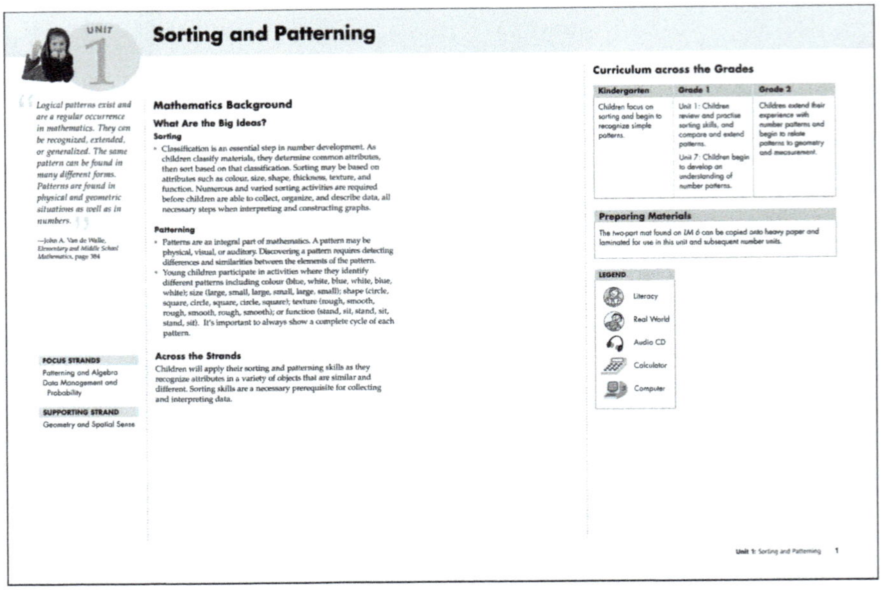

UNIT 1

Sorting and Patterning

"Logical patterns exist and are a regular occurrence in mathematics. They can be recognized, extended, or generalized. The same pattern can be found in many different forms. Patterns are found in physical and geometric situations as well as in numbers."

—John A. Van de Walle, *Elementary and Middle School Mathematics*, page 384

FOCUS STRANDS
Patterning and Algebra
Data Management and Probability

SUPPORTING STRAND
Geometry and Spatial Sense

Mathematics Background

What Are the Big Ideas?

Sorting

- Classification is an essential step in number development. As children classify materials, they determine common attributes, then sort based on that classification. Sorting may be based on attributes such as colour, size, shape, thickness, texture, and function. Numerous and varied sorting activities are required before children are able to collect, organize, and describe data, all necessary steps when interpreting and constructing graphs.

Patterning

- Patterns are an integral part of mathematics. A pattern may be physical, visual, or auditory. Discovering a pattern requires detecting differences and similarities between the elements of the pattern.
- Young children participate in activities where they identify different patterns including colour (blue, white, blue, white, blue, white); size (large, small, large, small, large, small); shape (circle, square, circle, square, circle, square); texture (rough, smooth, rough, smooth, rough, smooth); or function (stand, sit, stand, sit, stand, sit). It's important to always show a complete cycle of each pattern.

Across the Strands

Children will apply their sorting and patterning skills as they recognize attributes in a variety of objects that are similar and different. Sorting skills are a necessary prerequisite for collecting and interpreting data.

Curriculum across the Grades

Kindergarten	Grade 1	Grade 2
Children focus on sorting and begin to recognize simple patterns.	Unit 1: Children review and practise sorting skills, and compare and extend patterns. Unit 7: Children begin to develop an understanding of number patterns.	Children extend their experience with number patterns and begin to relate patterns to geometry and measurement.

Preparing Materials

The two-part mat found on *LM 6* can be copied onto heavy paper and laminated for use in this unit and subsequent number units.

LEGEND
Literacy
Real World
Audio CD
Calculator
Computer

Unit 1: Sorting and Patterning 1

Each lesson further supports professional development in a lesson model that offers

- Connect section to establish the key mathematical understanding of the lesson
- Focus statement to identify the key concepts of the lesson to teachers as well as parents and children
- A variety of instructional strategies detailed in the supporting Teacher Guide notes

Teachers' confidence and understanding of mathematics is an essential criterion for their students' success.
– Trevor Brown, Program Author

Professional Development in direct support of the program

Pearson Education offers flexibility and choice with a range of professional development options.

Customized In-Service and Partnerships

- Workshops, institutes, and on-line in-service led by leading local, national and international math educators such as:

John A. Van de Walle
Elementary Mathematics Advisor

Craig Featherstone
Pearson Education Consultant

Trevor Brown
Toronto, Ontario

Mignonne Wood
Vancouver, British Columbia

Maggie Martin Connell
Atlantic Canada

Jodi Mackie
Edmonton, Alberta

Administrator's Handbook

- Authored by Mignonne Wood, Steve Cairns
- Designed to assist principals in implementing a new mathematics program
- Shows how to foster a positive attitude toward teaching mathematics by building understanding within the school community, with teachers and parents

Van de Walle Facilitator's Guide

- Based on *Elementary and Middle School Mathematics: Teaching Developmentally* by John A. Van de Walle, a teaching methodology resource for the elementary teacher of mathematics
- Provides an organization for a Van de Walle Book Study group model

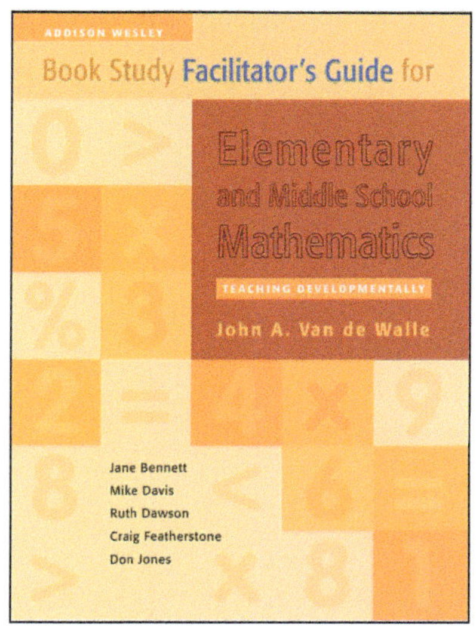

Pearson Professional Learning

- Quality, sustained, comprehensive teacher professional development at affordable prices

PEARSON Professional Learning

Using Your Teacher Guide...

Addison Wesley Mathematics Makes Sense recognizes that teachers need a program with quick access to ideas for instruction and teacher support features.

Your Teacher Guide has separate modules for each unit of instruction, with additional modules to support your year-long planning:

- **Program Overview** provides detailed information about the overall structure and features of the program.
- **Building a Math Community** (grades 1 and 2) provides a description of a positive environment, and practical suggestions for organizing your classroom and materials, as well as grade-specific ideas for routines and activities.
- The **Additional Assessment Support** module includes a selection of assessment tools that can be used throughout the program for your assessment and reporting needs.
- **Planning and Program Masters** (grades 3 to 8) provide year at a glance planning, materials list, literature connections, and generic program blackline masters. This module includes the feature "Building a Math Community."

The enclosed CD provides additional support and ensures ease of use, with

- A grade-level correlation showing our complete curriculum fit
- Editable versions of unit planning charts, rubrics, and other assessment tools
- Files for selected line masters

Planning a Unit

Each unit module in your Teacher Guide starts with several pages to support your planning for the unit. You'll see **Mathematics Background, Curriculum across the Grades,** and a **Curriculum Overview.**

Planning Charts provide overviews of lessons, materials requirements, assessment opportunities, and suggested times.

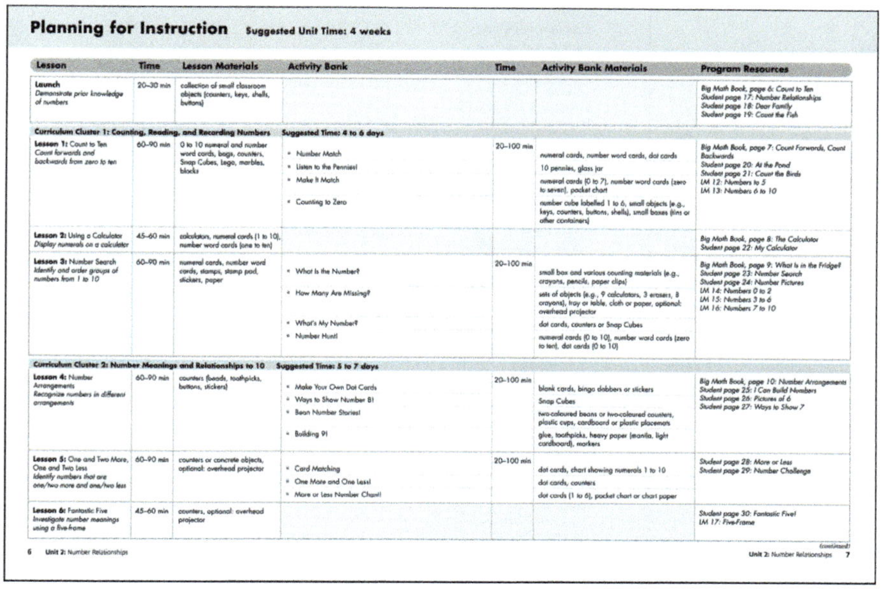

In grades 1 and 2, one of your planning pages describes **Mathematics Centres** that you can set up in advance for use at various points through the unit. Lesson notes reference centres for support in individualizing instruction.

Grade 1

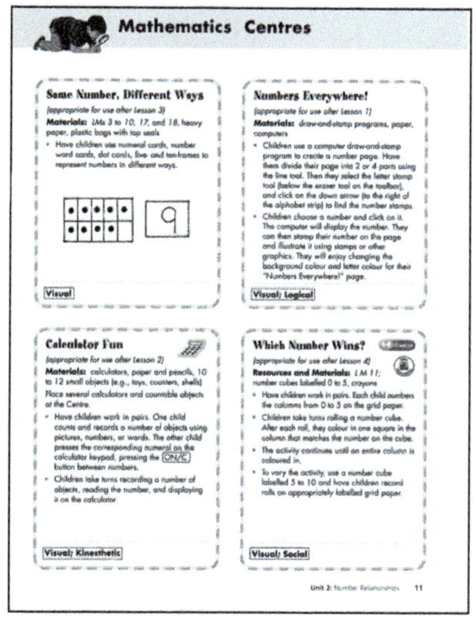

Grade 4

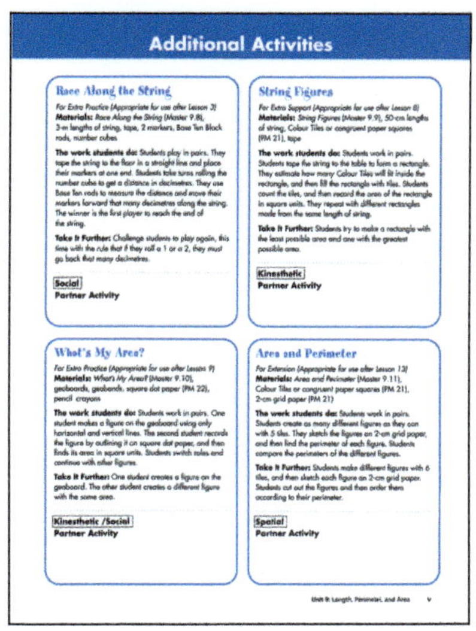

In grades 3 and up, one of your planning pages describes **Additional Activities** that you can organize for use at various points through the unit. Each **Additional Activity** comes with an accompanying activity **Master**, provided at the end of the module.

At Grades 1 and 2

When you're ready to start the unit, the Teacher Guide lessons provide professional choices within a consistent structure.

The suggested **Unit Launch** describes a 20-minute introduction to activate prior knowledge and engage the learner.

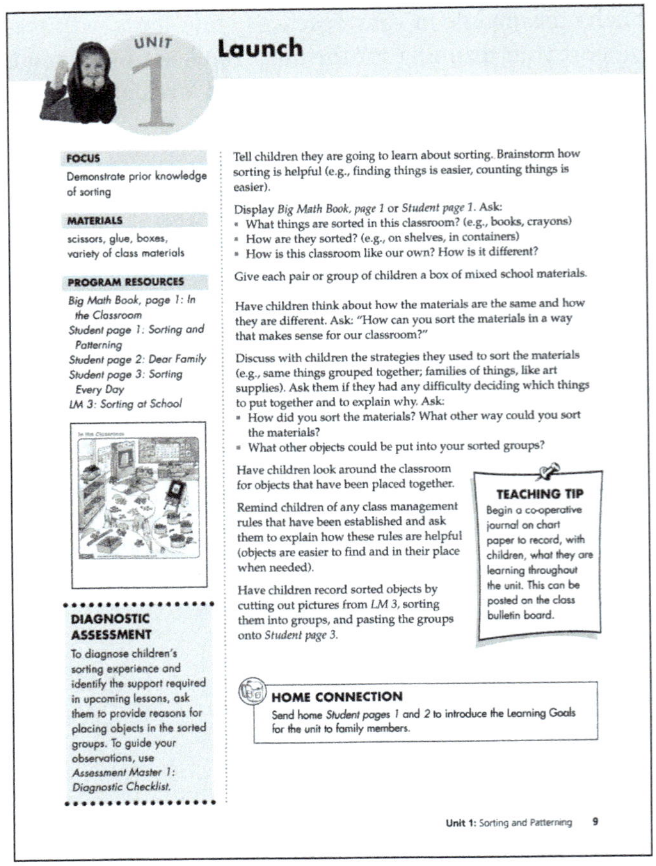

UNIT 1 **Launch**

FOCUS
Demonstrate prior knowledge of sorting

MATERIALS
scissors, glue, boxes, variety of class materials

PROGRAM RESOURCES
Big Math Book, page 1: In the Classroom
Student page 1: Sorting and Patterning
Student page 2: Dear Family
Student page 3: Sorting Every Day
LM 3: Sorting at School

DIAGNOSTIC ASSESSMENT
To diagnose children's sorting experience and identify the support required in upcoming lessons, ask them to provide reasons for placing objects in the sorted groups. To guide your observations, use *Assessment Master 1: Diagnostic Checklist.*

Tell children they are going to learn about sorting. Brainstorm how sorting is helpful (e.g., finding things is easier, counting things is easier).

Display *Big Math Book, page 1* or *Student page 1.* Ask:
- What things are sorted in this classroom? (e.g., books, crayons)
- How are they sorted? (e.g., on shelves, in containers)
- How is this classroom like our own? How is it different?

Give each pair or group of children a box of mixed school materials.

Have children think about how the materials are the same and how they are different. Ask: "How can you sort the materials in a way that makes sense for our classroom?"

Discuss with children the strategies they used to sort the materials (e.g., same things grouped together; families of things, like art supplies). Ask them if they had any difficulty deciding which things to put together and to explain why. Ask:
- How did you sort the materials? What other way could you sort the materials?
- What other objects could be put into your sorted groups?

Have children look around the classroom for objects that have been placed together.

Remind children of any class management rules that have been established and ask them to explain how these rules are helpful (objects are easier to find and in their place when needed).

Have children record sorted objects by cutting out pictures from *LM 3,* sorting them into groups, and pasting the groups onto *Student page 3.*

TEACHING TIP
Begin a co-operative journal on chart paper to record, with children, what they are learning throughout the unit. This can be posted on the class bulletin board.

HOME CONNECTION
Send home *Student pages 1* and *2* to introduce the Learning Goals for the unit to family members.

Unit 1: Sorting and Patterning 9

Notes on **Diagnostic Assessment** help you interpret students' responses, and provide support where needed. Use the supporting master available in the module.

Home Connection highlights opportunities for communication with the home that also appear in the Student Book.

Throughout the teaching notes for the unit, **Teaching Tip** highlights instructional strategies.

As a teacher, I'm looking for lessons I know I can deliver. As an author, I look for ways to embed professional development in the Teacher Guide, in student activities that are developmentally appropriate.
– Michelle Jackson, Program Author

Lessons

Each lesson provides a consistent framework for teaching new concepts and procedural skills: **Explore, Connect and Reflect,** and **Practice.**

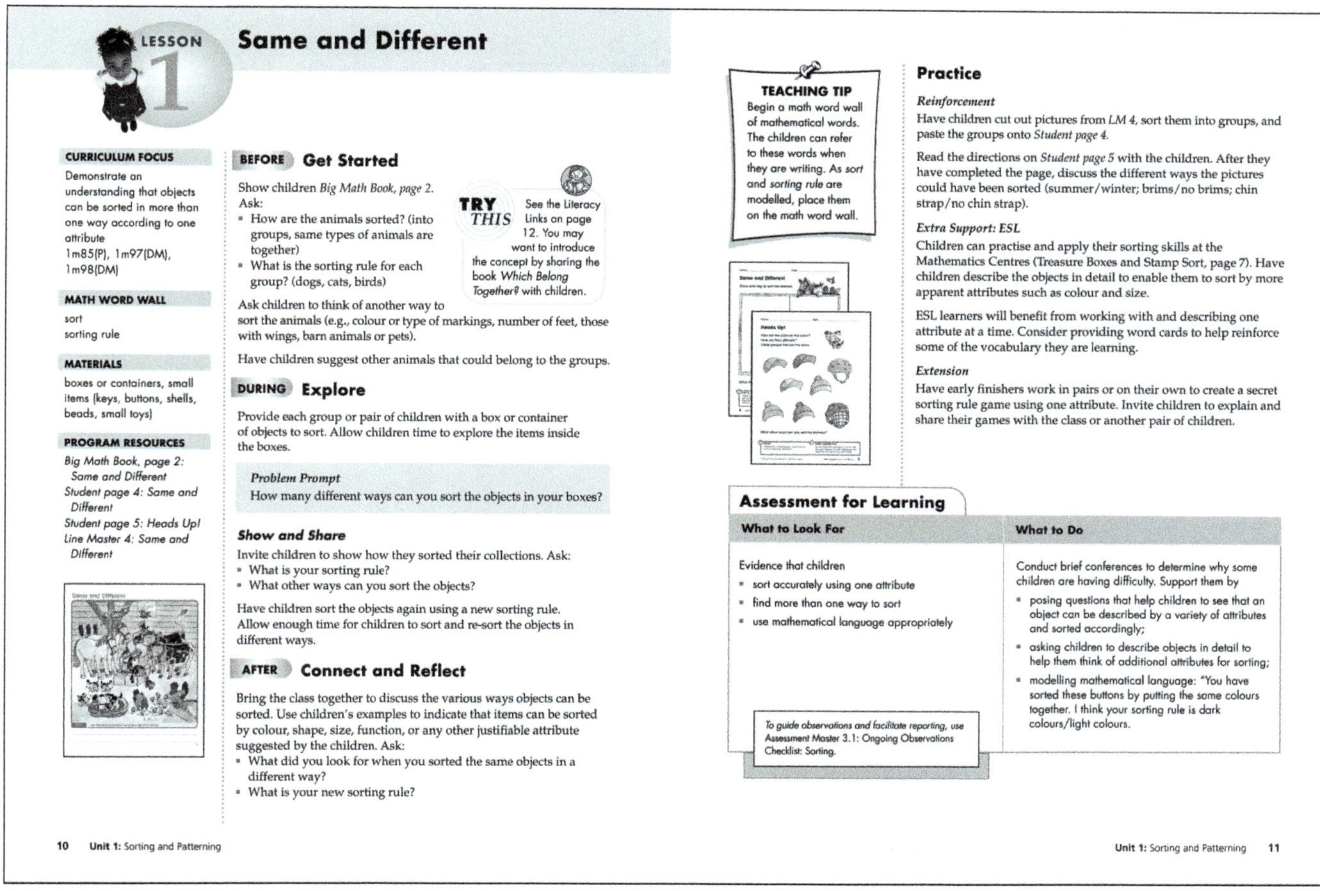

LESSON 1

Same and Different

CURRICULUM FOCUS

Demonstrate an understanding that objects can be sorted in more than one way according to one attribute
1m85(P), 1m97(DM), 1m98(DM)

MATH WORD WALL

sort
sorting rule

MATERIALS

boxes or containers, small items (keys, buttons, shells, beads, small toys)

PROGRAM RESOURCES

Big Math Book, page 2: Same and Different
Student page 4: Same and Different
Student page 5: Heads Up!
Line Master 4: Same and Different

BEFORE Get Started

Show children *Big Math Book, page 2.*
Ask:
- How are the animals sorted? (into groups, same types of animals are together)
- What is the sorting rule for each group? (dogs, cats, birds)

TRY THIS See the Literacy Links on page 12. You may want to introduce the concept by sharing the book *Which Belong Together?* with children.

Ask children to think of another way to sort the animals (e.g., colour or type of markings, number of feet, those with wings, barn animals or pets).

Have children suggest other animals that could belong to the groups.

DURING Explore

Provide each group or pair of children with a box or container of objects to sort. Allow children time to explore the items inside the boxes.

Problem Prompt
How many different ways can you sort the objects in your boxes?

Show and Share

Invite children to show how they sorted their collections. Ask:
- What is your sorting rule?
- What other ways can you sort the objects?

Have children sort the objects again using a new sorting rule. Allow enough time for children to sort and re-sort the objects in different ways.

AFTER Connect and Reflect

Bring the class together to discuss the various ways objects can be sorted. Use children's examples to indicate that items can be sorted by colour, shape, size, function, or any other justifiable attribute suggested by the children. Ask:
- What did you look for when you sorted the same objects in a different way?
- What is your new sorting rule?

10 **Unit 1:** Sorting and Patterning

TEACHING TIP
Begin a math word wall of mathematical words. The children can refer to these words when they are writing. As *sort* and *sorting rule* are modelled, place them on the math word wall.

Practice

Reinforcement
Have children cut out pictures from *LM 4,* sort them into groups, and paste the groups onto *Student page 4.*

Read the directions on *Student page 5* with the children. After they have completed the page, discuss the different ways the pictures could have been sorted (summer/winter; brims/no brims; chin strap/no chin strap).

Extra Support: ESL
Children can practise and apply their sorting skills at the Mathematics Centres (Treasure Boxes and Stamp Sort, page 7). Have children describe the objects in detail to enable them to sort by more apparent attributes such as colour and size.

ESL learners will benefit from working with and describing one attribute at a time. Consider providing word cards to help reinforce some of the vocabulary they are learning.

Extension
Have early finishers work in pairs or on their own to create a secret sorting rule game using one attribute. Invite children to explain and share their games with the class or another pair of children.

Assessment for Learning

What to Look For	What to Do
Evidence that children • sort accurately using one attribute • find more than one way to sort • use mathematical language appropriately	Conduct brief conferences to determine why some children are having difficulty. Support them by • posing questions that help children to see that an object can be described by a variety of attributes and sorted accordingly; • asking children to describe objects in detail to help them think of additional attributes for sorting; • modelling mathematical language: "You have sorted these buttons by putting the same colours together. I think your sorting rule is dark colours/light colours.

To guide observations and facilitate reporting, use Assessment Master 3.1: Ongoing Observations Checklist: Sorting.

Unit 1: Sorting and Patterning 11

Here, and in all lessons, check the margin if you need information on curriculum match, or specific materials needed.

- **Curriculum Focus**
- **Materials**
- **Program Resources**

Assessment for Learning appears in every lesson with the main teaching notes, to help shape your formative assessment.

Then, turn the page for additional features that let you deepen the content, or spend additional focused time when needed.

Literacy Links
Providing an alternative way to begin some lessons, using literature and literacy as an entry point for learning

Numbers Every Day
Creating an awareness of number in classroom routine and day-to-day activities

Cross-Curricular Connections
Connecting math to other subject areas

Activity Banks provide up to four additional activity ideas related to the core content of the lesson. Select Activity Banks based on your class needs, and those of individual students. Each activity is keyed to learning style, and grouping requirements.

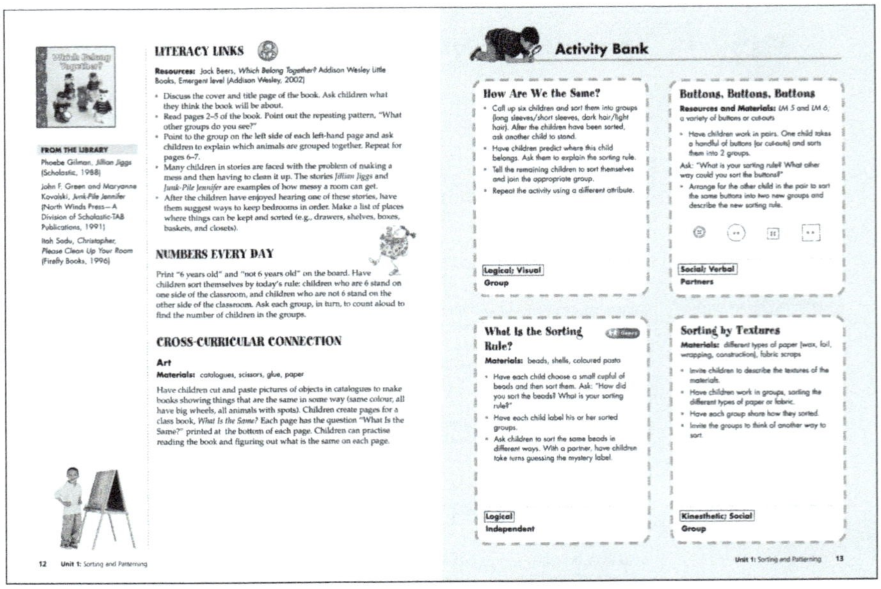

LITERACY LINKS

Resources: Jock Beers, *Which Belong Together?* Addison Wesley Little Books, Emergent level (Addison Wesley, 2002)

- Discuss the cover and title page of the book. Ask children what they think the book will be about.
- Read pages 2–5 of the book. Point out the repeating pattern, "What other groups do you see?"
- Point to the group on the left side of each left-hand page and ask children to explain which animals are grouped together. Repeat for pages 6–7.
- Many children in stories are faced with the problem of making a mess and then having to clean it up. The stories *Jillian Jiggs* and *Junk-Pile Jennifer* are examples of how messy a room can get.
- After the children have enjoyed hearing one of these stories, have them suggest ways to keep bedrooms in order. Make a list of places where things can be kept and sorted (e.g., drawers, shelves, boxes, baskets, and closets).

FROM THE LIBRARY

Phoebe Gilman, *Jillian Jiggs* (Scholastic, 1988)

John F. Green and Maryanne Kovalski, *Junk-Pile Jennifer* (North Winds Press—A Division of Scholastic-TAB Publications, 1991)

Itah Sadu, *Christopher, Please Clean Up Your Room* (Firefly Books, 1996)

NUMBERS EVERY DAY

Print "6 years old" and "not 6 years old" on the board. Have children sort themselves by today's rule: children who are 6 stand on one side of the classroom, and children who are not 6 stand on the other side of the classroom. Ask each group, in turn, to count aloud to find the number of children in the groups.

CROSS-CURRICULAR CONNECTION

Art

Materials: catalogues, scissors, glue, paper

Have children cut and paste pictures of objects in catalogues to make books showing things that are the same in some way (same colour, all have big wheels, all animals with spots). Children create pages for a class book, *What Is the Same?* Each page has the question "What Is the Same?" printed at the bottom of each page. Children can practise reading the book and figuring out what is the same on each page.

12 Unit 1: Sorting and Patterning

Activity Bank

How Are We the Same?

- Call up six children and sort them into groups (long sleeves/short sleeves, dark hair/light hair). After the children have been sorted, ask another child to stand.
- Have children predict where this child belongs. Ask them to explain the sorting rule.
- Tell the remaining children to sort themselves and join the appropriate group.
- Repeat the activity using a different attribute.

Logical; Visual
Group

Buttons, Buttons, Buttons

Resources and Materials: *LM 5* and *LM 6*; a variety of buttons or cut-outs

- Have children work in pairs. One child takes a handful of buttons (or cut-outs) and sorts them into 2 groups.

Ask: "What is your sorting rule? What other way could you sort the buttons?"

- Arrange for the other child in the pair to sort the same buttons into two new groups and describe the new sorting rule.

Social; Verbal
Partners

What Is the Sorting Rule?

Materials: beads, shells, coloured pasta

- Have each child choose a small cupful of beads and then sort them. Ask: "How did you sort the beads? What is your sorting rule?"
- Have each child label his or her sorted groups.
- Ask children to sort the same beads in different ways. With a partner, have children take turns guessing the mystery label.

Logical
Independent

Sorting by Textures

Materials: different types of paper (wax, foil, wrapping, construction), fabric scraps

- Invite children to describe the textures of the materials.
- Have children work in groups, sorting the different types of paper or fabric.
- Have each group share how they sorted.
- Invite the groups to think of another way to sort.

Kinesthetic; Social
Group

Unit 1: Sorting and Patterning 13

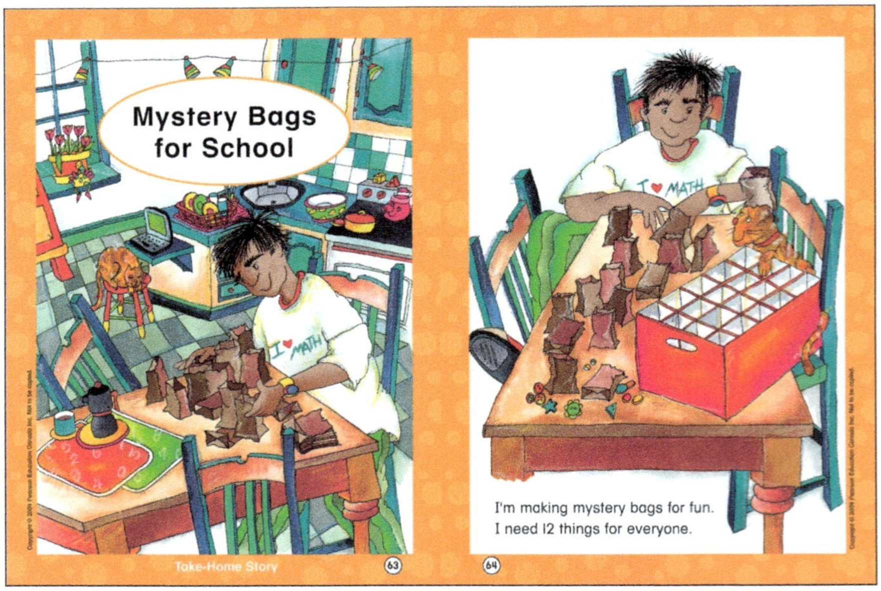

Each unit also provides ideas for teaching problem solving, and assessing student performance on the whole unit.

Strategies Tool Kit

Focusing on the strategies and processes children need to master to become effective problem solvers

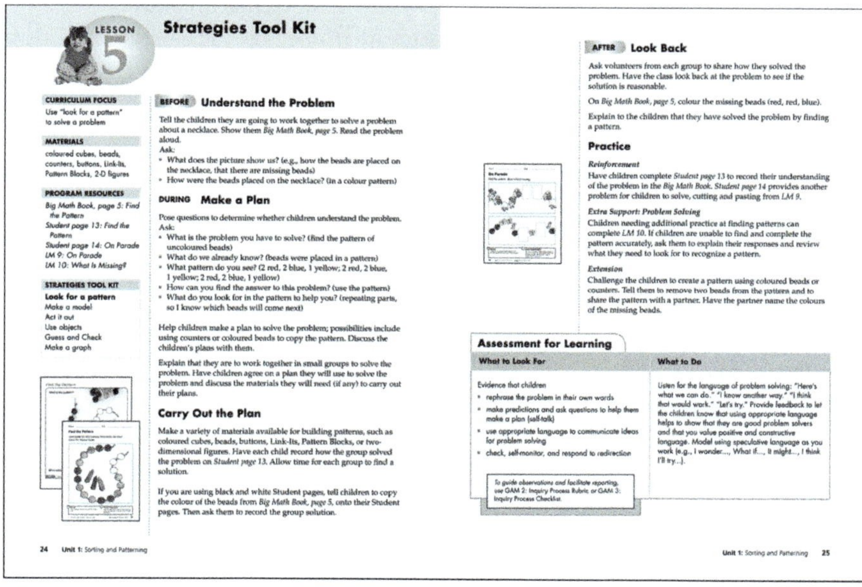

LESSON 5

Strategies Tool Kit

CURRICULUM FOCUS
Use "look for a pattern" to solve a problem

MATERIALS
coloured cubes, beads, counters, buttons, Link-Its, Pattern Blocks, 2-D figures

PROGRAM RESOURCES
Big Math Book, page 5: Find the Pattern
Student page 13: Find the Pattern
Student page 14: On Parade
LM 9: On Parade
LM 10: What Is Missing?

STRATEGIES TOOL KIT
Look for a pattern
Make a model
Act it out
Use objects
Guess and Check
Make a graph

BEFORE **Understand the Problem**

Tell the children they are going to work together to solve a problem about a necklace. Show them *Big Math Book, page 5*. Read the problem aloud.
Ask:
- What does the picture show us? (e.g., how the beads are placed on the necklace, that there are missing beads)
- How were the beads placed on the necklace? (in a colour pattern)

DURING **Make a Plan**

Pose questions to determine whether children understand the problem. Ask:
- What is the problem you have to solve? (find the pattern of uncoloured beads)
- What do we already know? (beads were placed in a pattern)
- What pattern do you see? (2 red, 2 blue, 1 yellow; 2 red, 2 blue, 1 yellow; 2 red, 2 blue, 1 yellow)
- How can you find the answer to this problem? (use the pattern)
- What do you look for in the pattern to help you? (repeating parts, so I know which beads will come next)

Help children make a plan to solve the problem; possibilities include using counters or coloured beads to copy the pattern. Discuss the children's plans with them.

Explain that they are to work together in small groups to solve the problem. Have children agree on a plan they will use to solve the problem and discuss the materials they will need (if any) to carry out their plans.

Carry Out the Plan

Make a variety of materials available for building patterns, such as coloured cubes, beads, buttons, Link-Its, Pattern Blocks, or two-dimensional figures. Have each child record how the group solved the problem on *Student page 13*. Allow time for each group to find a solution.

If you are using black and white Student pages, tell children to copy the colour of the beads from *Big Math Book, page 5*, onto their Student pages. Then ask them to record the group solution.

24 Unit 1: Sorting and Patterning

AFTER **Look Back**

Ask volunteers from each group to share how they solved the problem. Have the class look back at the problem to see if the solution is reasonable.

On *Big Math Book, page 5*, colour the missing beads (red, red, blue).

Explain to the children that they have solved the problem by finding a pattern.

Practice

Reinforcement
Have children complete *Student page 13* to record their understanding of the problem in the *Big Math Book*. *Student page 14* provides another problem for children to solve, cutting and pasting from *LM 9*.

Extra Support: Problem Solving
Children needing additional practice at finding patterns can complete *LM 10*. If children are unable to find and complete the pattern accurately, ask them to explain their responses and review what they need to look for to recognize a pattern.

Extension
Challenge the children to create a pattern using coloured beads or counters. Tell them to remove two beads from the pattern and to share the pattern with a partner. Have the partner name the colours of the missing beads.

Assessment for Learning

What to Look For	What to Do
Evidence that children • rephrase the problem in their own words • make predictions and ask questions to help them make a plan (self-talk) • use appropriate language to communicate ideas for problem solving • check, self-monitor, and respond to redirection	Listen for the language of problem solving: "Here's what we can do." "I know another way." "I think that would work." "Let's try." Provide feedback to let the children know that using appropriate language helps to show that they are good problem solvers and that you value positive and constructive language. Model using speculative language as you work (e.g., I wonder..., What if..., It might..., I think I'll try...).

To guide observations and facilitate reporting, use GAM 2: Inquiry Process Rubric or GAM 3: Inquiry Process Checklist.

Unit 1: Sorting and Patterning 25

Show What You Know

Your Teacher Guide pages detail a performance task that will allow for demonstration of the learning through the unit.

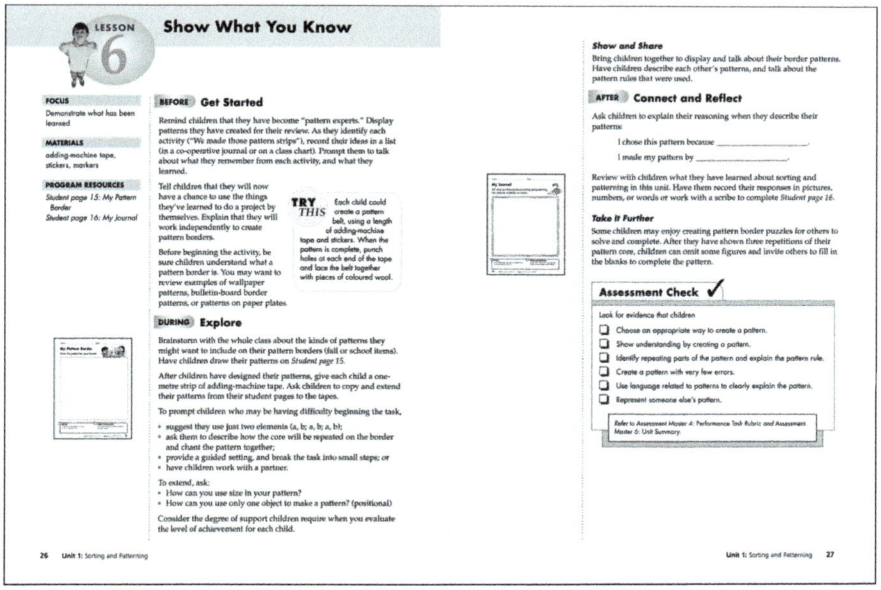

LESSON 6

Show What You Know

FOCUS
Demonstrate what has been learned

MATERIALS
adding-machine tape, stickers, markers

PROGRAM RESOURCES
Student page 15: My Pattern Border
Student page 16: My Journal

BEFORE **Get Started**

Remind children that they have become "pattern experts." Display patterns they have created for their review. As they identify each activity ("We made those pattern strips"), record their ideas in a list (in a co-operative journal or on a class chart). Prompt them to talk about what they remember from each activity, and what they learned.

Tell children that they will now have a chance to use the things they've learned to do a project by themselves. Explain that they will work independently to create pattern borders.

Before beginning the activity, be sure children understand what a pattern border is. You may want to review examples of wallpaper patterns, bulletin-board border patterns, or patterns on paper plates.

TRY THIS Each child could create a pattern belt, using a length of adding-machine tape and stickers. When the pattern is complete, punch holes at each end of the tape and lace the belt together with pieces of coloured wool.

DURING **Explore**

Brainstorm with the whole class about the kinds of patterns they might want to include on their pattern borders (fall or school items). Have children draw their patterns on *Student page 15*.

After children have designed their patterns, give each child a one-metre strip of adding-machine tape. Ask children to copy and extend their patterns from their student pages to the tapes.

To prompt children who may be having difficulty beginning the task,
- suggest they use just two elements (a, b; a, b; a, b);
- ask them to describe how the core will be repeated on the border and chant the pattern together;
- provide a guided setting, and break the task into small steps; or
- have children work with a partner.

To extend, ask:
- How can you use size in your pattern?
- How can you use only one object to make a pattern? (positional)

Consider the degree of support children require when you evaluate the level of achievement for each child.

26 Unit 1: Sorting and Patterning

Show and Share
Bring children together to display and talk about their border patterns. Have children describe each other's patterns, and talk about the pattern rules that were used.

AFTER **Connect and Reflect**

Ask children to explain their reasoning when they describe their patterns:

I chose this pattern because ____________.
I made my pattern by ____________.

Review with children what they have learned about sorting and patterning in this unit. Have them record their responses in pictures, numbers, or words or work with a scribe to complete *Student page 16*.

Take It Further
Some children may enjoy creating pattern border puzzles for others to solve and complete. After they have shown three repetitions of their pattern core, children can omit some figures and invite others to fill in the blanks to complete the pattern.

Assessment Check ✓

Look for evidence that children
- ❑ Choose an appropriate way to create a pattern.
- ❑ Show understanding by creating a pattern.
- ❑ Identify repeating parts of the pattern and explain the pattern rule.
- ❑ Create a pattern with very few errors.
- ❑ Use language related to patterns to clearly explain the pattern.
- ❑ Represent someone else's pattern.

Refer to Assessment Master 4: Performance Task Rubric and Assessment Master 6: Unit Summary.

Unit 1: Sorting and Patterning 27

Use the **Assessment Check** checklist to guide your assessment of students' performance. For a more detailed assessment, use the corresponding Assessment Master, which provides a specific rubric.

At Grades 3 and up

Addison Wesley Mathematics Makes Sense moves to a more mature student book format at grade 3. The hard-cover **Student Book** provides a resource for use in the classroom, and at home. For day-to-day planning, the **Teacher Guide** gives reduced pages of the Student Book with accompanying teaching notes.

REACHING ALL LEARNERS

Alternative Explore

Materials: cardboard strips just longer than 1 m, metre sticks, markers

Have students use a metre stick to measure and mark the cardboard at 0, 10 cm, 20 cm, ... to 100 cm. They should then label the marks 0, 1 dm, 2 dm, ... to 10 dm. Students use their homemade rulers to measure objects to the nearest decimetre.

Early Finishers

Have students find objects with a dimension close to each of these measurements:
1 dm, 4 dm, 8 dm, and 10 dm.

Common Misconceptions

➤ Students have difficulty using a ruler to measure in decimetres.
How to Help: Have students line Base Ten rods (or orange Cuisenaire Rods) end to end along the length of the object they are measuring, and then count the number of rods used.

➤ Students choose inappropriate objects to measure in decimetres or to match to a given number of decimetres.
How to Help: Suggest students look for objects that are longer than a Base Ten rod and shorter than a metre stick.

Numbers Every Day

When multiplying by 10 or 100, count the total number of zeros. For example, 3 times 10 is 3 tens, or 30.

Connect

You can read the height of this seedling in 3 ways.

The seedling is 3 dm tall.
The seedling is 30 cm tall.
The seedling is 300 mm tall.

1 dm = 10 cm
1 dm = 100 mm

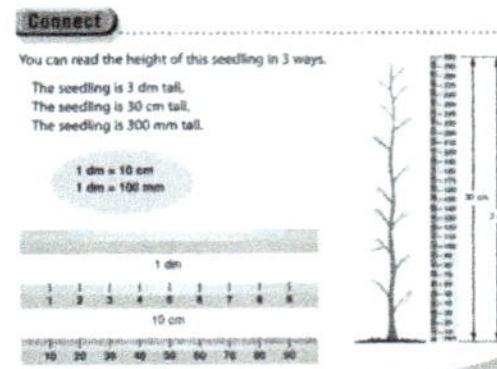

Practice

Use a ruler or metre stick to help you.

1. Copy and complete this table.
What patterns do you see? Explain.

dm	1	2	3	4	5	6	7	8	9	10
cm	10	20	30	40	50	60	70	80	90	100
mm	100	200	300	400	500	600	700	800	900	1000

Numbers Every Day

Mental Math

Multiply.
Explain your strategies.

3 × 10 = □ 30
30 × 10 = □ 300
4 × 100 = □ 400
40 × 100 = □ 4000

2. Copy and complete.
a) 8 dm = □ cm 80 b) 9 dm = □ cm 90 c) 70 dm = □ cm 700

3. Copy and complete.
a) 40 cm = □ dm 4 b) 70 cm = □ dm 7 c) 100 cm = □ dm 10

328

4. Which is shorter? How do you know?
a) 5 dm or 45 cm b) 200 mm or 8 dm c) 26 cm or 200 mm

5. Match each item below with an estimate of its measure:
2 mm, 19 cm, 7 dm, 1 dm
a) the width of your hand 1 dm b) the length of a new pencil 19 cm
c) the thickness of a loonie 2 mm d) the height of a dog house 7 dm

6. Name 2 objects that are about 1 dm long.

7. How could you measure something in decimetres if your ruler was marked in centimetres?
Use words, pictures, or numbers to explain.

8. Oscar found an interesting plant in the woods.
When he measured it, he said it was 3 dm tall.
a) What is this height in centimetres? In millimetres?
b) Which unit is best for measuring this plant? Explain.

9. Which unit would you use to measure each item?
Explain your choice.
a) the height of a flagpole
b) the height of a bookcase
c) the width of your fingernail
d) your height
e) the distance between Earth and the moon

Reflect

You have estimated and measured in 4 units.
When do you think a precise measurement would be needed?
When would an estimate be good enough?
Write about your ideas.

At Home

Measure the height of a relative.
Draw a picture.
Write the height using as many different units as you can.
Round when you need to.

Assessment Focus | Question 9

329

Sample Answers

4. Convert each length in decimetres to centimetres or millimetres, and then compare.
6. A French fry and a wax crayon are about 1 dm long.
7. First, I would measure the object in centimetres. Then I would round the measurement to the nearest 10 cm. For example, I would round 26 cm to 30 cm. I would then use my ruler to count how many decimetres are in 30 cm. (Students might also suggest using a calculator to divide the centimetre measure by 10.)
8. a) 30 cm, 300 mm
b) Centimetres give a good approximate measurement. Decimetres are too big to give a precise measurement. When something measures 30 cm, we do not need to know its measure to the nearest millimetre. It is enough to know that it is between 29 cm and 31 cm.
9. a) Metres (or decimetres); a flagpole is taller than a person, so I would use metres.
b) Centimetres; a bookcase is about as tall as a person, so I would use centimetres.
c) Millimetres; my fingernail is less than 1 cm wide, so I would use millimetres.
d) Centimetres; I am about 1 m tall, so I would use centimetres.
e) Kilometres; the moon is very far from Earth, so I would use kilometres.

REFLECT: An exact measurement is needed to measure wood for building a house. If the measurements are not exact, the house might not fit together properly.

An estimated measurement is good enough when reporting how far someone walks to school every day. This measurement is only needed to give an idea of the distance.

Discuss what strategies students used to round to the nearest decimetre.

Ask:

- When might you use decimetres to measure? *(For objects larger than 10 cm and smaller than 1 m, and when I do not need a precise measurement.)*
- When you measure an object in decimetres, will the number of units be greater than or less than when you measure the same object in centimetres? Explain. *(There will be fewer units because decimetres are larger units and you will need fewer of them.)*

Elicit from students 3 ways to report the length of a Base Ten rod or orange Cuisenaire Rod. Record the 3 ways in a column on the board:
1 dm
10 cm
100 mm

Use the height of the seedling in *Connect* to relate decimetres to both centimetres and millimetres. Encourage students to refer to these relationships as they complete *Practice* questions.

Practice

Assessment Focus: Question 9

Students think about the units they know: millimetre, centimetre, decimetre, metre, and kilometre. Students should compare the object with the length of the unit chosen. They might compare the object with another object they have already measured, using appropriate units. For example, a student's height is measured in centimetres or metres. Anything much taller than a student, such as a flagpole, would be measured in metres. The decimetre is not a common unit and might not be chosen.

ASSESSMENT FOR LEARNING

What to Look For	What to Do
Understanding concepts ✔ Students understand that the decimetre is a unit of length equal to 10 cm and 100 mm.	***Extra Support:*** Have students make trains of 15 or more interlocking cubes. They should estimate, measure, and record the length of each train in millimetres, to the nearest whole centimetre, and to the nearest whole decimetre. Students can use Step-by-Step 3 (Master 9.14) to complete question 9.
Applying procedures ✔ Students can measure the linear dimensions of objects to the nearest decimetre.	***Extra Practice:*** Students who need extra practice measuring in decimetres can use the Additional Activity, *Race Along the String* (Master 9.8). Students can complete Extra Practice 2 (Master 9.27).
	Extension: Have students make up a unit based on a certain number of tens of centimetres. They should then measure objects in the classroom using their new unit. For example, if one kevinmetre is 30 cm, this book is about 1 kevinmetre long.

Recording and Reporting
Master 9.2 Ongoing Observations: Length, Perimeter, and Area

12 Unit 9 • Lesson 3 • Student page 328

Unit 9 • Lesson 3 • Student page 329 13

In the Teacher Guide, each **Unit Launch** provides suggestions to support your **Diagnostic Assessment** of students.

Look for **Literature Connections** that relate to the topics at hand.

In a Teacher Guide I look for daily support for content presentation, classroom management, assessment, and ideas for supporting all learners.
– Mary Doucette, Program Author

In core lessons, beside the reduced student pages you will find

- **Lesson Organizer** with curriculum information, materials, and vocabulary
- **Key Learnings** for the lesson
- **Reaching All Learners** with suggestions for an **Alternative Explore,** suggested **ESL Strategies,** and **Common Misconceptions/How to Help**
- **Sample Answers** to questions that require a written or diagrammatic response

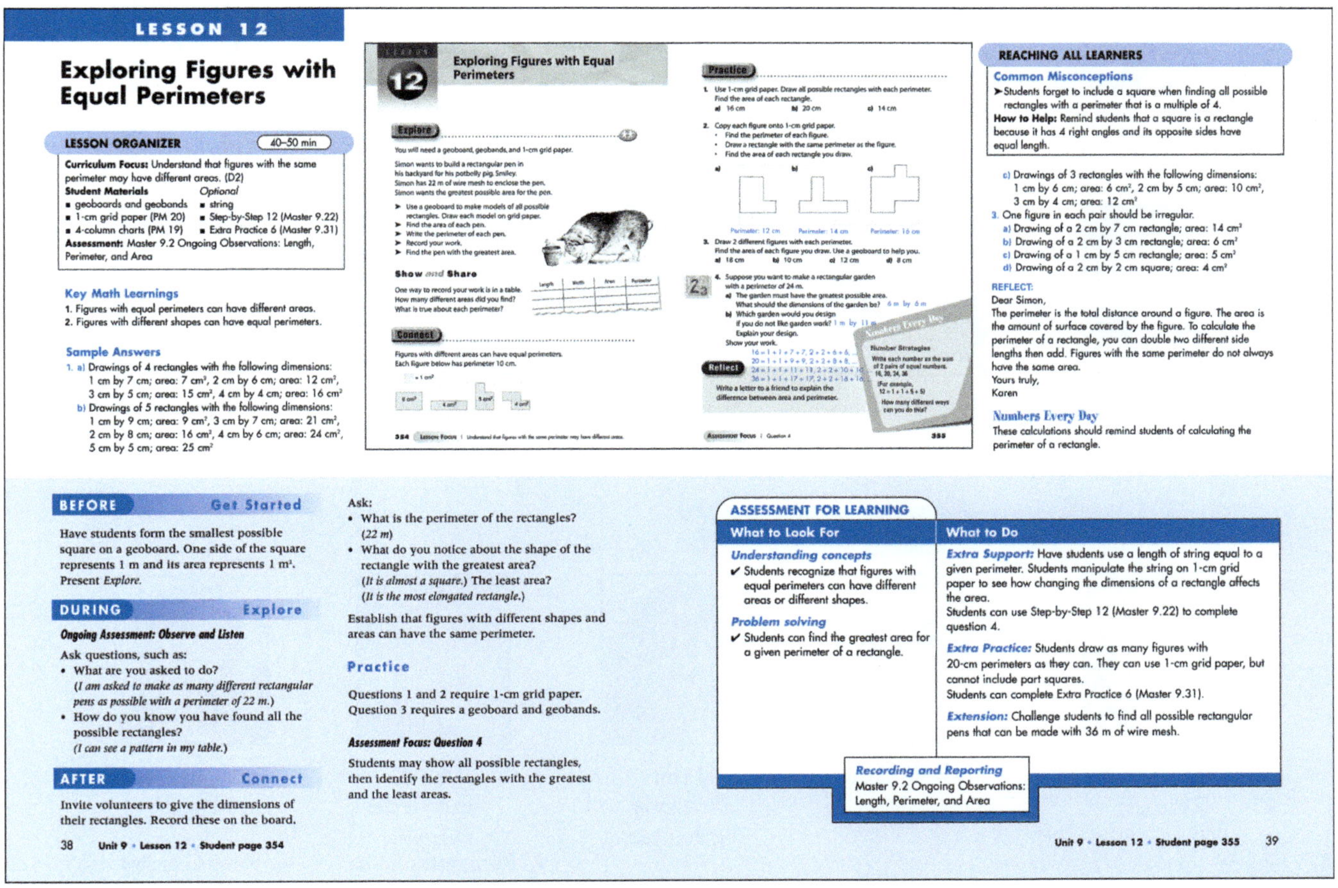

Your lesson plan appears across the bottom half of your lesson pages, with teaching suggestions to support the lesson structure established in the Student Book: **Explore, Connect,** and **Practice.**

Assessment for Learning appears in every lesson with the main teaching notes, to help shape your formative assessment.

Meet our *Addison Wesley Mathematics Makes Sense* In-Service and Professional Development Faculty

Trevor Brown
Toronto, Ontario

Steve Cairns
Burnaby, British Columbia

Lynda Colgan
Kingston, Ontario

Maggie Martin Connell
Atlantic Canada

Marg Craig
Southwestern Ontario

Craig Featherstone
Pearson Education Consultant

Angie Harding
Regina, Saskatchewan

Sharon Jeroski
Assessment Consultant

Jodi Mackie
Edmonton, Alberta

Bill Nimigon
Toronto, Ontario

Carole Saundry
Richmond, British Columbia

Michelle Skene
Ottawa, Ontario

Lynn Strangway
Toronto, Ontario

John A. Van de Walle
Elementary Mathematics Advisor

Mignonne Wood
Vancouver, British Columbia

ADDISON WESLEY

Ontario

Math Makes Sense

5

Ontario

Teacher Guide

Grade 5 Planning and Program Masters

ISBN 0-321-12044-2

9 780321 120441

Teacher Guide Modules

ISBN 0-321-11822-7

9 780321 118226

Complete Teacher Guide package

PEARSON Addison Wesley

Building a Math Community

Contents

Creating a Math Community in the Classroom

> *"Because young children's experiences fundamentally shape their attitude toward mathematics, an engaging and encouraging climate for children's early encounters with mathematics is important."*
>
> (NAEYC and NCTM 2002, 5)

Each new school year provides fresh opportunities to create a community of learners in the classroom. The goal is to facilitate the development of an inclusive classroom where all students feel safe, valued, and supported in their learning.

As members of a classroom community, teacher and students:

- Demonstrate mutual respect.
- Take risks.
- Seek, evaluate, and apply information to solve problems.
- Make decisions.
- Learn successfully together.

> *"Community building is an ongoing process. Students who feel they are part of a cohesive group take more responsibility for what happens in the classroom and may perform better because of encouragement from their peers."*
>
> (Barnes 2002, 84)

Helping children acquire "mathematical power" means helping them develop the capacity to apply mathematical knowledge to new or familiar tasks. (Baroody and Coslick 1998, 1 and 2) Mathematics in the classroom must promote a positive disposition to learn and use mathematics.

> *"For students to be comfortable with the processes of mathematical inquiry, they need to explore, reason, solve problems, and communicate about mathematics—and they need regular feedback. When students have these learning opportunities, they begin to develop a deeper understanding of mathematics, enabling them to see connections between mathematical ideas, between mathematics and other subject areas, and between mathematics and everyday life situations."*
>
> (Baroody and Coslick, 1998)

As facilitators of learning, teachers are responsible for creating a classroom environment that allows each student to experience success. The reward is in knowing that students will view math as fun, exciting, engaging, and something they are capable of doing.

Setting the Stage for Community Building

Central to the life of any community is a group meeting time—when the whole class meets to learn what it means to belong to a community. The group meeting should facilitate effective communication—each person has the opportunity to speak, to share successes and challenges, and to listen to and value the ideas of others. Group meetings also reinforce communication skills, such as listening with respect, and speaking clearly and in turn.

Regular meeting times demonstrate to students they have a voice in the classroom. You might consider creating a T-chart with students that describes what an effective meeting should "look like and sound like." Refer to this chart during meeting times through the day as you observe behaviours you identified together as important.

Using the Meeting Time

- Discuss difficulties that occur in the classroom or on the playground. As a community, discuss tools and strategies that may help resolve difficulties or conflicts.
- Share ideas, strategies, or completed work.
- Celebrate successes or provide encouragement.
- Share information about upcoming events in the class or school.
- Trade information about what happened outside the classroom after school hours.

OUR MEETING TIME

LOOKS LIKE	SOUNDS LIKE
• Everyone arranges his/her chair in a circle, and demonstrates a positive attitude. • Students are attentive. • The atmosphere is one of respect. • Students come prepared with notebooks. • Each student raises a hand to be heard.	• Everyone takes turns to talk. • The student/teacher talks clearly. • Offer compliments: "I like your idea." • Suggest questions: "Can you share how you solved the problem?"

A math meeting can be held any time. Your needs will direct the activity and discussion. Some possibilities are to:

- Introduce a new math concept.
- Brainstorm students' prior knowledge about a math topic.
- Share a new manipulative and explore possible uses.
- Revisit a math concept to reinforce a specific skill.
- Introduce new math activities/games/etc.
- Discuss any difficulties arising from the previous math period.
- Share and celebrate student work.

Classroom Seating

Arrange students' desks in groups. Students will then have a sense of belonging. In each group, include students with varied strengths and abilities. This encourages peer modelling and role definition within the group. These groups should not be static; however, they should stay together for at least four weeks so that students can become familiar with one another and comfortable in their group.

Regularly reinforce the classroom principles students have agreed to. These principles will be integral to the development of group cohesiveness and classroom norms.

> *"An effective mathematics learning environment is an environment that encourages the establishment of a community of mathematics learners."*
>
> (Ontario Ministry of Education 2003, 12)

Developing Common Principles

To create a successful classroom community, develop common principles. These principles should reflect the beliefs students and you have about an exemplary learning environment. All students should be encouraged to contribute; and all contributions should be respected.

Characteristics of a Community

- security
- open communication
- mutual liking
- shared goals or objectives
- connectedness
- trust

(Sapon-Shevin 1999, 16 and 17)

Establishing Community Principles

You and your students arrange your seats (chairs) in a circle in the classroom.

- Make sure that everyone is together and can see one another. Explain that you are sitting in a circle so that everyone will have a chance to speak and to hear what the others are saying.
- Explain that the meeting you are having now is to decide what will help you learn together and get along in the classroom.
- Tell students that you are excited about beginning a new school year together. You want to make sure that it is a successful year for everyone. To make the class a fun and happy place to be, there will be some expectations for all students. These will be your common principles.

Give an example of a class principle, such as, "It is important to help one another."

- Ask for a student volunteer to begin by suggesting a principle.
- Ensure all have a chance to contribute. Some students may feel reluctant to share; have them "pass" when it is their turn to speak. Return to these students later to invite them to contribute.

Discuss the principles that were suggested.

- Note principles that were mentioned multiple times, and encourage additional suggestions.
- As the discussion progresses, note all principles mentioned on chart paper or on the blackboard. Summarize the ideas in three to six statements.

Divide students into groups, so that each group can discuss one principle.

- Print each principle on a strip of paper.
- Instruct each group to choose one principle and find a quiet spot in the room to discuss the importance of that principle. (You may need to reread each group's principle as it is selected.)
- Ask each group to decide if it feels that principle should or should not become part of the class rules. The group must provide justification for its decision.

Note

Circulate among the groups to ensure students understand the task and the principle. They may need some discussion prompts:

- Why do you think we should have that principle?
- What may happen if we don't have that principle?

This process allows students to take ownership of the class principles. Students are more likely to remember and apply these ideas when they are part of the decision-making process. Throughout the year, revisit these principles with students and discuss their effectiveness. Students may suggest which principles are working well, and which principles could be changed. Encourage students to give reasons.

Bring the groups back.

- Ask each group to put its principle on the chart or write it on the blackboard. Time should be provided for others to comment.
- As a class, decide if any of the groups' decisions should be changed (only after all ideas about the principles have been heard).
- Create the final list of principles based on student decisions. Record the list on chart paper and post it in the classroom.

An Inclusive Math Community

Support Different Learning Styles

Try to get to know your students so you can plan effectively. Students should leave a math class feeling their needs have been addressed and they are successful.

Students have a range of learning styles. To effectively teach all students, it is essential to provide a multitude of classroom experiences. *Addison Wesley Mathematics Makes Sense* uses a variety of approaches to reach all learners.

Different Learning Styles

LEARNING STYLE	STRENGTHS AND PREFERENCES	*MATH MAKES SENSE*
Linguistic	Reading, writing, telling stories, remembering, talking, interacting, hearing, seeing words	Provides learning opportunities to talk, discuss, explain, write, read, and see words
Logical/Mathematical	Experimenting, working with numbers, asking questions, exploring patterns and relationships, math reasoning, applying logic, problem solving, classifying	Provides learning opportunities to experiment, work with numbers, ask questions, explore patterns and relationships, reason mathematically, work with logic, solve problems, classify items
Visual/Spatial	Drawing, building, designing, creating, visualizing, imagining, working with pictures/colours, doing mazes and puzzles, reading maps and charts	Provides learning opportunities to draw, build, design, create, visualize, imagine, work with pictures/colours, do puzzles, read maps and charts
Musical	Singing, humming tunes, listening and responding to music, playing instruments, picking up sounds/rhythms/melodies, noticing pitches	Provides learning opportunities to work with patterns and make music connections
Kinesthetic	Moving and doing, touching and talking, feeling objects, using body language, physical activities, sports/dance, acting, making crafts, interacting with space	Provides learning opportunities to move and do, touch and talk, feel objects, use body language, work with manipulatives, make models, interact with space
Social (Interpersonal)	Having many friends, talking to people, joining groups, understanding/leading others, organizing, communicating, mediating, sharing, comparing, relating, cooperating, interviewing,	Provides learning opportunities to talk to people, work in groups, understand/lead others, organize, communicate, mediate, share, compare, relate, cooperate, interview
Individual (Intrapersonal)	Working alone, pursuing own interests, understanding self, focusing inward, following instincts, pursuing goals, being original, having own space, doing individual projects	Provides learning opportunities to work individually, build thinking skills, think critically, follow instincts, solve problems, find original solutions, pursue individual projects

Adapted from *Instructor*, Scholastic Inc., 1990.

Preparing Students for Success

When students experience success at math and perceive themselves as doers of math, they can encourage their peers to participate actively in math as well.

Creating Positive Attitudes

Children are more likely to develop a positive attitude toward mathematics when the teacher models the same attitudes.

Activating Prior Knowledge

Students come to the classroom with different experiences and knowledge of math. By determining where students are starting out, you are in a better position to provide appropriate math experiences and to assess ongoing learning.

How to Activate Prior Knowledge

- Pose a question to initiate discussion. For example, "When have you seen decimals before?" "How would you measure the length of your desk?"
- Brainstorm a class chart when introducing a new topic. For example, draw a clock on chart paper and have the students share words that could be connected to the clock (hour, minute, estimated time, actual time, rotation (turn), and so on).
- Use a manipulative to investigate a new type of problem. For example, observe how students may use a geoboard to create different fractions.

Reaching All Learners

Since there is no single way to reach all students, we are challenged to provide a wide variety of instructional strategies and learning experiences. Through observation, you can determine the strengths of each student. This information, combined with what is known about a student's prior knowledge, can help you address learning needs.

The following classroom practices are recommended as appropriate for students' cognitive development:

- New learning must be connected to existing knowledge.
- Examples should be concrete.
- Experiences must be hands-on.
- Lessons need to be active.
- Students must be engaged.
- It is essential to use manipulatives.
- There must be time for active exploration.

Tools for Learning

Working with manipulatives can facilitate math exploration and understanding among a range of learners, especially ESL students.

Supporting ESL Students

To comprehend meaning and instruction, ESL students often require other resources in addition to words, such as manipulatives, drawings, and models. You can use these strategies to help ESL learners understand math concepts and language.

- Use facial expressions, gestures, and pantomime to help convey meaning. Repeat key language and concepts, rephrasing concepts in simple words.
- Use manipulatives, drawings, and real-world objects to demonstrate concepts, clarify instructions, and develop language.
- Use charts, graphs, and graphic organizers to introduce and explore concepts. Present additional examples and demonstrations.
- Provide a variety of ways for students to respond and/or show their findings.
- Provide brief previews and reviews of materials to reinforce language and concepts.
- Set a classroom tone that encourages and rewards students who interact, take risks, and use language to express their ideas.

Making Learning Meaningful

When learning is meaningful, students see the connections between themselves and the learning experience. Students do best with activities they find interesting and can actively engage in, including problem scenarios.

To engage learners in meaningful math:

- Use interesting materials.
- Provide students with a choice of manipulatives.
- Connect new activities to what students already know.
- Pose problems that relate to students, and include student names in problems.

> *"Children's confidence, competence, and interest in mathematics flourish when new experiences are meaningful and connected with their prior knowledge and experience."*
>
> (NAEYC and NCTM 2002, 6)

Promoting Classroom Communication

It is important to encourage all students to participate in class discussions. As the year progresses, students tend to take more risks at these meetings, especially if they perceive that all ideas are accepted.

To create effective and inclusive small groups or pairs:

- Group heterogeneously to promote modelling and diverse thinking. (Include boys and girls.)
- Keep work groups to five students or fewer to encourage interaction.
- Group students in a way that will encourage positive social behaviours.
- Remind the groups of the class principles.
- Change group members regularly to promote a variety of interactions.

Fostering Collaborative Learning

It is always important to impress upon students that they are in the classroom together to help each other learn.

It is beneficial for students to experience a variety of groupings. When students work in pairs or small groups, they are provided with more opportunities for interaction and discussion than when they work in larger groups. Providing opportunities to experience math concepts in pairs or small groups enables students to:

- Observe one another.
- Build on one another's ideas by hearing and trying out different strategies.
- Discuss their findings and pose questions.
- Give explanations and demonstrations, using math vocabulary.
- Search for connections and commonalities.

As students work collaboratively, you can glean valuable information by observing their interactions, discussions, explanations, and active involvement. Question students to encourage deeper understanding and reflection. In this way, students identify their own misconceptions and adjust their activity/thinking to reflect their new knowledge.

Questions to Prompt Discussion and Reflection

- What are you thinking?
- What are you doing right now?
- Why do you think that will work?
- What strategy did you use to solve that problem? How did you solve the problem?
- Is there another way you could solve that problem? Why did you try it that way?
- What are you stuck on?
- How did you figure that out?
- How did you make that happen?
- What are you going to do next?
- What would happen if ...?
- What gave you that idea?

The NCTM standards state that mathematics programs should enable all children to:

- Organize and consolidate their math thinking through communication.
- Communicate their math thinking coherently and clearly to peers/teachers.
- Analyse and evaluate the math thinking and strategies of others.
- Use the language of math to express math ideas precisely.

> *"Although organizing instructions for heterogeneous groups definitely involves a different kind of planning and preparation, many teachers report increased enthusiasm in their students, as well as greater learning and deeper involvement when curricula and instruction are organized around diverse learners working together."*
>
> (Sapon-Shevin 1999, 68)

Sharing and Reflecting

Encourage classroom communication to give all students an opportunity to share their thinking and understanding. This also gives you an opportunity to gain an insight into what students are thinking and learning. By providing students with a sharing and reflecting time at the end of a math activity, you offer the opportunity for metacognition. *Show and Share* in each lesson in the Student Book encourages such sharing.

Students are encouraged to:

- Check their own thinking.
- Highlight their own ideas, and see that their solutions are valued.
- Validate their problem-solving strategies and share those ideas.
- Consolidate their learning by explaining it to their peers.
- Ask further questions and learn from their peers as they share their insights.

The Math Journal Entry

Students provide a written or visual reflection of their math experience for the day. You may provide a journal sentence starter to guide their thoughts. Encourage students to write about their thinking using the math vocabulary, pictures, diagrams, symbols, or charts. You may wish to have students respond to *Reflect* at the end of each lesson in the Student Book. Students may share their entries with a peer or their work group.

Math Routines

Students benefit from a classroom structure that is predictable, follows certain routines, and allows concepts to be revisited regularly. Incorporating math throughout the day gives students the chance to experience more success with math, since they gain more practice with concepts and develop an awareness that math is connected to everyday experiences.

> ***Numbers Every Day***
> Have students do *Numbers Every Day,* a five- to ten-minute activity in each lesson of the Student Book. Use these activities any time during the day to help students build number sense and develop mental math, number strategies, and calculator skills.

Games

Incorporate games into your routine once a week to reinforce concepts and give students the opportunity to realize that math can be fun, and to develop strategies. The Student Book contains math games, such as *What's My Rule?* and *Less Is More*. You may also wish to have students play with jigsaw puzzles to develop spatial sense.

> ***Math in the Picture***
> Select an appropriate photograph or picture from a magazine and have students work together to identify math concepts in the picture. Glue the picture onto chart paper and record students' ideas about where they can find math in the picture.

Some ideas for Math in the Picture are:

- Sports
- Fashion
- Music
- Seasons
- Time of day
- Shapes
- Measuring tools/ devices
- Temperature
- Patterns
- Money

Creating the Learning Environment

A Problem-Solving Approach

Problem solving is a key instructional strategy that enables students to take risks, secure in the knowledge that their thoughts, queries, and ideas are valued. In time, students become well versed in the language of cooperation and collaboration.

As students share their solutions and findings, you have the opportunity to provide direct instruction on problem-solving strategies.

For example, several students may draw a picture as a strategy to understand and solve a problem, while others may use objects to model the problem. After students share their solutions and justifications, you can elaborate on their methods and encourage students to comment or ask questions of their peers. Using student findings and solution methods as a means to guide instruction also allows students to see the value in their work, and encourages peers to share their strategies. While some strategies may be more efficient than others, you can note that several strategies may work and often a combination of strategies is required to solve a problem. Students must use strategies that are meaningful to them and make sense to them.

Problem-Solving Strategies

Supporting students to become problem solvers is a key element of *Addison Wesley Math Makes Sense 5*. The *Strategies Toolkit* lesson in every unit provides opportunities for students to explore and outline a particular problem-solving strategy to add to their repertoire. In Grade 5, the lessons highlight these problem-solving strategies:

- Make a table.
- Use a model.
- Draw a diagram.
- Solve a simpler problem.
- Work backward.
- Guess and check.
- Make an organized list.
- Use a pattern.
- Draw a graph.

Here are some suggestions to empower students to become problem solvers.

Before

Before students begin:

- Prepare meaningful problem scenarios for students. These should be sufficiently challenging, but easy to solve.
- Ensure the problem is understood by all.
- Begin with a simpler version of the task. Brainstorm possible strategies to use.
- Estimate what the answer might be.
- Explain the expectations for the process and the product.

During

As students work through the problem:

- Let students approach the problem in a way that makes sense to them.
- Listen to conversations to observe student thinking.
- Provide hints or suggestions if students are on the wrong path.
- Encourage students to test their ideas.
- Ask questions to stimulate ideas.
- Assess student understanding of her/his solution.

After

After students have solved their problem:

- Gather for a group meeting to reflect and share.
- Provide ample time for all to discuss the solution.
- Highlight the variety of answers and methods.
- Encourage students to justify their solutions.
- Encourage students to comment positively or ask questions regarding their peers' solutions.

Note

For more detail on using a problem-solving approach to teach mathematics, see John A. Van de Walle, *Elementary and Middle School Mathematics: Teaching Developmentally.* Boston: Allyn and Bacon, 2004, from which these ideas are drawn.

"Problem solving should be a primary goal of all mathematics instruction and an integral part of all mathematical activity."

(NCTM 1989, 23)

Creating the Physical Environment

Building a community of learners can begin with the physical arrangement of the classroom. Students should know where all necessary materials are so they can access them easily. They should also know they are responsible for collecting and returning any materials they have used, and that they are expected to cooperate with other members of the classroom. The classroom set-up should:

- Promote independence for students.
- Provide choices within a structured setting.
- Be organized to encourage sharing.

To set up the physical space:

- Arrange student desks or tables in groups (about four students per group) to facilitate working together.
- Create a variety of work areas so students have a selection (group areas, individual areas, floor spaces, table spaces, and so on).
- Set up a special area for you to conference with students individually.

Maximizing Classroom Space

Here are some suggestions for maximizing space.

- Establish a bulletin board as a Math Corner where students can display their work. Place a shelf underneath the bulletin board for work that cannot be posted. Include an area where students can write "I wonder about" questions.
- Post Bristol board or a white board to use as a message centre.
- Store math portfolios and games in stackable plastic crates or tubs. Or, turn desks upside down and tape Bristol board around the legs to create a filing cabinet for portfolios and games.
- Create an instant math centre by placing game(s) at a table or meeting space for students to play.
- Store manipulatives in stackable shoeboxes. Tape a manipulative outside each shoebox so students—especially ESL students—can easily find what they seek.

Storage of Materials

Provide a variety of manipulative materials in labelled bins in an accessible area of the classroom. This ensures students know where to find and return what they need. Label the bins clearly.

Organize the mathematics tools. For example, you might want to have math toolkits for each group. These toolkits could contain rulers, measuring tapes, protractors, calculators, various counters stored in small plastic bags, string, elastic bands, math vocabulary words, journal sentence starters, and so on. Be sure there are enough items in the kits for the group to work together.

You could also create a materials centre containing pencils, scissors, tape, glue, erasers, crayons, markers, different sizes and types of paper (lined, unlined, grid paper, dot paper, centimetre grid paper), and so on.

You will need a variety of manipulatives to address different math concepts throughout the year. Students should have access to these materials. Open access allows students to explore manipulatives in greater depth; for example, to further their understanding of a concept, to revisit an activity that was previously provided, or to experiment with their own math problem.

To recognize the importance of personal space while promoting the sharing of materials:
- Provide a personal place in the classroom for each student—for example, the inside of a desk.
- Use labelled bins or shelves to hold math books, workbooks, and journals.

Recommended Math Materials

- Snap Cubes
- Cuisenaire Rods
- A variety of counters
- Decks of cards
- Pattern Blocks
- Base Ten Blocks
- Geoboards and geobands
- Plastic figures and solids
- Calculators
- Number cubes
- Square tiles
- Miras
- Rulers and measuring tapes
- Protractors

Math Tubs

Math Tubs are a great way to extend and reinforce student learning daily. A Math Tub can be put together following any manipulative activity, game, or problem-solving scenario. Math Tubs should change as the year progresses, to reflect current math topics. You may also want to use these to revisit a particular concept over the course of the year.

Why Use Math Tubs?

- To provide an opportunity to revisit a math concept
- To increase student success by drawing on previously built knowledge
- To provide opportunities to attempt new strategies
- To provide extensions for students who have completed their daily activities
- To reuse materials you have already put together

Each Math Tub should be in its own bin or plastic bag with a zipper-type closure for easy organization and storage. Each tub/bag should be labelled on the outside with the name of the activity and the number of students that can use that tub at one time. The tub should include:

- instructions for the activity
- any required manipulatives
- a list of common materials required that are not in the tub; for example, glue, scissors
- expectations for the completed activity (whether it is a game or a created piece of work)

Math Vocabulary

Students should be exposed to math vocabulary regularly. This will build their confidence in using math terms. You could create a math vocabulary bulletin board that continues throughout the year. As new vocabulary is introduced during a lesson, identify the word and add it to the bulletin board. A picture or symbol can accompany the word, if appropriate.

This provides a visual connection for students and helps them identify the word. Students can use the bulletin board as a resource when discussing math events and activities; they will soon see the value in using special math words to communicate their thoughts.

Key Words are listed on the opening page of each unit of the Student Book. These words can be added to language lessons and spelling lists when a particular math concept is being developed.

At times through the year, you can choose a math word and ask students to "Tell what you know about _____" as a math journal entry. This checks prior knowledge or assesses knowledge (as students are using an open-ended forum to share what they know about a math word in pictures, numbers, or words).

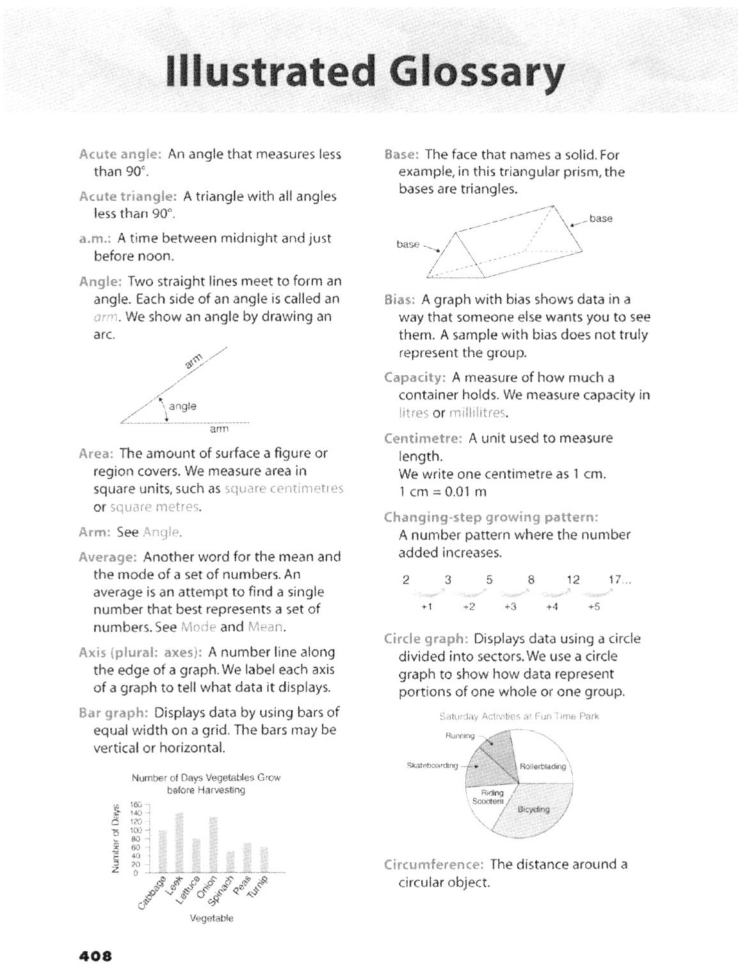

Illustrated Glossary

Acute angle: An angle that measures less than 90°.

Acute triangle: A triangle with all angles less than 90°.

a.m.: A time between midnight and just before noon.

Angle: Two straight lines meet to form an angle. Each side of an angle is called an arm. We show an angle by drawing an arc.

Area: The amount of surface a figure or region covers. We measure area in square units, such as square centimetres or square metres.

Arm: See Angle.

Average: Another word for the mean and the mode of a set of numbers. An average is an attempt to find a single number that best represents a set of numbers. See Mode and Mean.

Axis (plural: axes): A number line along the edge of a graph. We label each axis of a graph to tell what data it displays.

Bar graph: Displays data by using bars of equal width on a grid. The bars may be vertical or horizontal.

Base: The face that names a solid. For example, in this triangular prism, the bases are triangles.

Bias: A graph with bias shows data in a way that someone else wants you to see them. A sample with bias does not truly represent the group.

Capacity: A measure of how much a container holds. We measure capacity in litres or millilitres.

Centimetre: A unit used to measure length.
We write one centimetre as 1 cm.
1 cm = 0.01 m

Changing-step growing pattern: A number pattern where the number added increases.

2 3 5 8 12 17...
+1 +2 +3 +4 +5

Circle graph: Displays data using a circle divided into sectors. We use a circle graph to show how data represent portions of one whole or one group.

Circumference: The distance around a circular object.

408

Community-Building Activities

The following ideas provide opportunities for students to work together to develop relationships built on co-operation and mutual respect. These activities also provide opportunities to model classroom principles while using math concepts.

Co-Operative Math Posters

Have students work co-operatively to create a math poster when you introduce new concepts/topics. Students can work in groups to develop a poster that shows what they know about the new concepts/topic. The group may wish to select pictures from magazines, draw pictures, print words, label diagrams, or use a combination of the above to create the poster.

Create a Math Bulletin Board

Devote a bulletin board to math. As students work through a concept, all students can contribute work to be displayed. Or, students can work together to create a bulletin board demonstrating a concept they have learned. For example, they could make a mural of a city or town and label the different figures and/or solids represented throughout the mural.

Math Meetings

Use math meetings to gather first-hand information about student attitudes and feelings about math. This is the time to pose a question about a particular math activity, centre, or group work time. All student responses should be valued and considered for future planning. Students may also have suggestions that could be explored for future learning experiences.

Problem of the Week

At the beginning of the week, pose a math problem to the class and have small groups work on it. Toward the end of the week, invite groups to share their solutions and encourage the class to discuss and compare the different problem-solving strategies presented. You may also wish to have students create similar problems and trade with classmates to solve.

Mathematics and Other Subject Areas

Students have individual learning styles and strengths in different areas. When math is meaningfully integrated into other subject areas, it can provide significant learning connections for students. Students who demonstrate strengths in other areas of the curriculum can use these strengths to show what they know about mathematics. *Math Link* features in the Student Book highlight connections between the math students are learning and other subject areas as well as the real world.

MUSIC

- Recite songs/poems/chants that describe math concepts.
- Use poetry to demonstrate rhythm patterns.
- Use musical instruments or clapping to rehearse basic facts (for example, shake maracas to the number sentence $8 \times 7 = 56$).
- Clap to the beat of a pattern, or create a clapping pattern.
- Write a song or poem to describe a math concept.
- Collect and graph data on syllables in a name, words in a song title, and so on.

PHYSICAL EDUCATION

- Estimate, then measure the time it takes to walk around the gym or schoolyard.
- Estimate, then measure the size of a soccer field, basketball court, or baseball diamond.
- Estimate, then measure the mass of a baseball, basketball, soccer ball, and/or hockey puck.

SCIENCE

- Collect data in the school to graph; for example, the forms of energy (mechanical, electrical) used in the school.
- Measure and record response times; for example, have someone catch a ruler after it is dropped by another person.
- Create plans to build a garden outside; include measurements.
- Use elements of geometry to build a bridge or structure.
- Identify patterns in the weather; for example, the water cycle.

SOCIAL STUDIES

- Go on a walk in the neighbourhood, create a chart to classify items as municipal, federal, or provincial responsibilities.
- Draw and construct nets for pyramids to make a model of Ancient Egypt.

LANGUAGE

- Use a math journal to record problem-solving strategies and students' thinking/reflecting on their processes and solutions.
- Read literature related to math concepts.
- Create word or letter patterns.
- Use poems or rhymes during shared reading that include math concepts.
- Create riddles involving math concepts.
- Use math vocabulary in spelling lists and lessons.

COMPUTERS

- Draw a picture onscreen using congruent figures.
- Transfer survey data onto a pictograph using stamps or picture icons.
- Draw and shade regions of figures and grids to illustrate fractions.
- Create triangles, given specific measures of angles and sides, with *The Geometer's Sketchpad* or with appropriate geometry software.

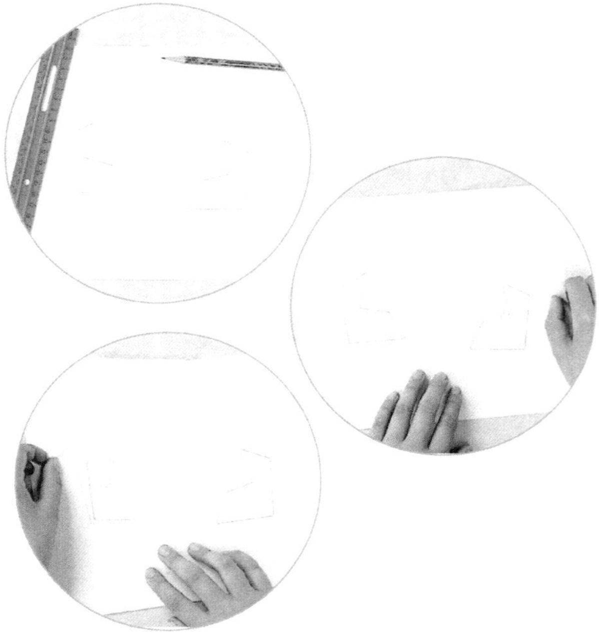

VISUAL ARTS

- Use paint to create visual patterns.
- Create a 3-D model of a house, apartment building, or sports stadium.
- Create a mural to illustrate figures in our city or in nature.
- Use moulding clay to create solids.
- Fold paper in half and cut out symmetrical pictures.
- Create border patterns using geometric figures and colour.

Math through the Day

The math curriculum is extensive; thus, some concepts may be taught early in the year and not revisited in a formal way for some time. By providing students with many opportunities to revisit concepts, you can enhance learning and encourage students to strengthen their understanding. Incorporating math into daily routines provides students with ongoing support and ways to connect math learning to real-life experiences.

NUMBER SENSE AND NUMERATION

- Practise estimation whenever possible: How many pages do you think are in this book?
- Practise mental math addition and subtraction strategies. Play games where students have to mentally add and subtract to determine what numbers have been called.
- Use *Numbers Every Day* in the Student Book to promote number sense while you take attendance.

MEASUREMENT

- Regularly give students a time reference. For example: "We have half an hour for additional math activities."
- Estimate the number of steps to the library.
- Discuss things that are closer to or farther from certain places.
- Discuss the capacity of drink containers.
- Create and post around the classroom number lines using various standard measurements of the unit.

PATTERNING AND ALGEBRA

- Line up in a pattern on the way to another class or recess; for example, boy/girl, short sleeves/long sleeves.
- Line up to show a growing pattern; for example, 1 boy, 1 girl; 2 boys, 2 girls; 3 boys, 3 girls.
- Move in a pattern in gym (hop, hop, skip, jump).
- Play *I Spy* for:
  - colour patterns
  - geometric patterns
- Discuss art from ancient civilizations.

DATA MANAGEMENT AND PROBABILITY

- Use probability language in everyday discussion. (It probably will rain tonight. We are unlikely to go to school on Saturday.)
- Pose probability questions and have students respond with justification. (Is it going to snow tonight? No, it is possible but unlikely, because it doesn't snow here in June.)
- Ask questions about data collected informally. (I wonder why so many people brought umbrellas today.)

GEOMETRY AND SPATIAL SENSE

- Use positional language when instructing students where to find something in the room, or letting students know where their group will be working; for example, in front of the chart stand, behind the computers.
- Discuss directions to another place in the school (turn left/right, go straight, go up/down).
- Play *I Spy* for:
  - polygons
  - solids that have 6 or 8 faces
- Discuss number and letter grids on road maps.

Extending the Math Community

Parents and other adults at home need to understand the purpose of a math community in the classroom. Some family members feel uncomfortable with the "new way of doing math" and are unfamiliar with the principles that underlie it.

Here are some ways to open the lines of communication, while providing important information about your math program and each student's progress.

- Keep families informed of current math topics through a biweekly newsletter. Include what, why, and how you are teaching to ensure others understand your instructional strategies.
- Use newsletters to share classroom happenings, procedures, expectations, and celebrations. In each newsletter, publish one problem students have worked through and a few student solutions demonstrating different strategies.
- Include in each newsletter an idea or two that families could try at home, to extend the classroom math experiences.
- Once a game or activity has been used in the classroom, put the necessary materials and instructions into a Zip Lock bag for students to take home on a rotating basis for a few nights, so they can share them with their families. Include information on the expectations of the activity.
- Send home a math journal with the game or activity, with suggestions for sentence starters and an explanation of use, for adults and students to write in together after they have tried the Math Bag activity.
- Use a student *Practice and Homework* book as a follow-up to a class experience so that students can re-create a similar experience at home with their families. This should involve interaction and activity, and not be a worksheet students would complete on their own.
- Send home celebratory notes comprising one or two sentences, sharing a student's mathematical success.
- Take photographs of students involved in a variety of math activities and create a photo album with captions. Send this home with students on a rotating basis, providing space for parents to comment, or with a comment sheet that would provide a focus for writing.
- Encourage families to play number games when travelling. You may include in your newsletter suggestions for simple games. The *Letter Home* in the *Addison Wesley Math Makes Sense 5* Teacher Guide suggests such games for each unit.
- If students have agendas or day planners, use them to share celebratory notes, as well as other "items."

It is important for families to develop a comfort level with the "what, how, and why" of their children's math learning. Encourage families to become involved in a way that makes sense for them. Family attitudes will have a significant impact on student attitudes regarding math, and you are instrumental in helping others see this "new math" positively.

When you provide support and offer simple ideas about making math real for students at home, you will have succeeded in extending the classroom math community to the homes of students.

REFERENCES

Barnes, Peter. 2002. A Community of Support. *Teaching PreK-8*, August/September, 33, 1, page 84.

Baroody, Arthur J., and Ronald Coslick. 1998. *Fostering Children's Mathematical Power: An Investigative Approach to K–8 Mathematics Instruction.* Mahwah, NJ: Lawrence Erlbaum Associates, pages 1, 2.

National Association for the Education of Young Children (NAEYC) and National Council of Teachers of Mathematics (NCTM). 2002. *Early Childhood Mathematics: Promoting Good Beginnings.* A joint position statement. Adopted April 2002, pages 5, 6.

National Council of Teachers of Mathematics (NCTM). 1989. *Curriculum and Evaluation Standards for School Mathematics.* Reston, VA: NCTM, page 23.

Ontario Ministry of Education. 2003. *Early Math Strategy, The Report of the Expert Panel on Early Math in Ontario; 2003*. Toronto: Queen's Printer for Ontario, page 12.

Sapon-Shevin, Mara. 1999. *Because We Can Change The World; A Practical Guide to Building Cooperative, Inclusive Classroom Communities.* Boston: Allyn and Bacon, pages 16, 17, 68.

Van de Walle, John A. 2004. *Elementary and Middle School Mathematics: Teaching Developmentally.* 5th ed. Boston: Allyn and Bacon.

Addison Wesley Math Makes Sense 5 accommodates these planning needs:

- Each strand is addressed with a major emphasis at least twice through the school year, to provide a rich variety of math experiences for students and to accommodate provincial reporting requirements.
- All units can be completed in about 30 weeks —depending on the needs of the class—to accommodate the normal interruptions that occur during a regular 36-week school year.
- The grade 5 program aligns, unit by unit, with both the grade 4 and grade 6 programs, to support teaching of combined grades.

Some teachers prefer to plan their own sequence of topics through the school year. *Addison Wesley Math Makes Sense 5* accommodates this, as well, within the larger framework of the mathematics to be developed across the grade 5 program. Some units need to remain in the sequence in which they're placed: for example, it is not wise to change the order of the number units. Other units are independent, and can be shifted if desired: for example, the units on patterning and probability can be shifted, although the teacher needs to bear in mind that the Probability unit does assume prior knowledge of fractions.

If you're teaching *Addison Wesley Math Makes Sense 5* for the first time, you may prefer to follow the order in the text. This will ensure that the grade-level prerequisites for each unit have been covered previously within the school year. Once you have taught the units in sequence, and become familiar with the content detail in each unit, you will be able to determine whether you prefer a different order.

Here is a suggested timing chart for *Addison Wesley Math Makes Sense 5*:

MONTH	SEPTEMBER		OCTOBER	NOVEMBER	DECEMBER		JANUARY
Text Unit	1 Number Patterns	2 Whole Numbers	3 Geometry	4 Decimals	5 Data Management	Vacation	6 Measurement
Suggested Timing (weeks)	1–2	3–4	3–4	3–4	2–3		2–3

This timing chart shows one possible alternative unit sequence:

MONTH	SEPTEMBER		OCTOBER	NOVEMBER	DECEMBER		JANUARY
Text Unit	2 Whole Numbers	1 Number Patterns	3 Geometry	4 Decimals	6 Measurement	Vacation	5 Data Management
Suggested Timing (weeks)	3–4	1–2	3–4	3–4	2–3		2–3

Cross Strand Investigations

The *Cross Strand Investigations* are designed for flexible use:

- at the end of each term, as they occur in the text
- to assign during periods of the school year that are prone to interruption of regular class schedules, such as the weeks leading up to holidays
- in a cluster as a closing project—with choice for students—at the end of the school year.

Each *Investigation* provides an opportunity for students to use the math they have learned in the preceding units, or in earlier years, to solve a problem in context or to investigate an intriguing question or pattern. They can be used to gather assessment information to enable you to fulfill reporting requirements.

Teaching notes, sample responses, and accompanying check lists for the *Cross Strand Investigations* are in the Additional Assessment Support module.

FEBRUARY	MARCH	APRIL	MAY	JUNE	MONTH

7 Transformational Geometry	8 Fractions and Decimals	Vacation	9 Length, Perimeter, and Area	10 Patterns in Number and Geometry	11 Probability		**Text Unit**
2	3–4		3–4	2–3	1–2		**Suggested Timing (weeks)**

FEBRUARY	MARCH	APRIL	MAY	JUNE	MONTH

8 Fractions and Decimals	7 Transformational Geometry	Vacation	9 Length, Perimeter, and Area	11 Probability	10 Patterns in Number and Geometry		**Text Unit**
3–4	2		3–4	1–2	2–3		**Suggested Timing (weeks)**

Materials List for *Math Makes Sense 5*

Recommended quantities of materials other than program resources provided on Black Line Masters.

For classroom use	For each group of 3 or 4 students	For each pair of students	For each student
• Overhead projector • Overhead pattern blocks • Overhead geoboard • Clock • Metric bathroom scale • Overhead markers • Overhead Base Ten Blocks • Overhead place-value mat • Pictures of quilts, wallpaper, flags, tiles, rugs (variety of tiling patterns) — in books or magazines • Overhead calculator **Software** • *Appleworks* • *The Geometer's Sketchpad* • *Excel*	• Newspapers • Magazines • 50 pennies • Stopwatches • Play money (bills and coins) • Balance scales • Standard masses • Masking tape • Marbles • Assorted graduated cylinders • Different-sized containers • Measuring spoons • Bucket • Dimes • Blank transparency • Hole punch or compass • Paper fasteners • Decahedron • Circular objects (e.g., tin cans, spools, jar lids) • Paper towels • Dominoes • Playing cards • Cuisenaire rods • Seed catalogues	• Pattern Blocks • Bristol board • Coloured paper • Colour Tiles • Counters • Measuring tape • Metre stick • Small medicine measuring cup (cough medicine) • Envelopes • Ping-pong ball • Unit cubes • Modelling clay • 2-m lengths of fabric • Index cards • Brown paper bags • Triangles from a geometry set • Pyramids • Cubes • Tape • Labels • String • 2-colour counters • Dental floss • Number cubes	• Miras • Tracing paper • Geoboards • Geobands • Scissors • Tangrams • Calculators • Protractors • Millimetre rulers • Drinking straws (straight and flexible) • Pipe cleaners • Paper clips • Place-value mats

Literature Connections — Grade 5 Math

Anno and Anno. 1999. *Anno's Magic Seeds*. New York: Putnam Publishing Group. ISBN: 0698116186.

———. 2002. *Anno's Mysterious Multiplying Jar.* New York: PaperStar. ISBN: 0698117530.

Burns, Marilyn. 1997. *Spaghetti and Meatballs for All.* New York: Scholastic Press. ISBN: 0590944392.

Enzenberger, Hans Magnus. 1997. *The Number Devil: A Mathematical Adventure*. New York: Henry Holt and Company. ISBN: 0805062998.

Fowler, Allan. 1997. *The Dewey Decimal System*. Children's Press. ISBN: 0516261304.

Garland, Trudi Hammel. 1997. *Fibonacci Fun: Fascinating Activities with Intriguing Numbers.* Dale Seymour Publications. ISBN: 1572322659.

Holub, Joan. 2003. *Riddle-Iculous Math*. Albert Whitman Publications. ISBN: 0807549967.

Juster, Norton. 1961. *The Phantom Tollbooth*. Random House Books for Young Readers. ISBN: 0394815009.

Kaner, Etta. 1994. *Bridges*. Kids Can Press. ISBN: 1550741462.

Kenda, Margaret Elizabeth, Tim Robinson (Illustrator), and Phyllis S. Williams. 1995. *Math Wizardry for Kids*. Barron's Educational Series Incorporated. ISBN: 0812018095.

Nagda, Ann. 2002. *Tiger Math: Learning to Graph from a Baby Tiger*. Henry Holt & Company Inc. ISBN: 080507161X.

Pappas, Theoni. 2004. *Further Adventures of Penrose the Mathematical Cat*. Wide World Publishing/Tetra. ISBN: 1884550320.

Paterson, Katherine. 2003. *Bridge to Terabithia*. Trophy. ISBN: 00644001847.

Pluckrose. 2002. *Pattern*. New York: Children's Press. ISBN: 0516454552.

Salvadori, Mario, and Joseph P. Wright. 1998. *Math Games for Middle School: Challenges & Skill-Builders for Students at Every Level*. Chicago Review Press, Incorporated. ISBN: 1556522886.

Schwartz, David. 1999. *G is for Googol: A Math Alphabet Book*. Tricycle Press. ISBN: 1883672589.

Schwartz, David M., and Steven Kellogg. 2003. *Millions to Measure*. HarperCollins Publishers. ISBN: 0688129161.

Tang, Greg. 2003. *Math-Terpieces: The Art of Problem-Solving*. Scholastic, Inc. ISBN: 0439443881.

Program Masters

Contents **Page**

Name ____________________ Date ________________

Program Master 1

Inquiry Process Check List

	Understands Problem		Makes a Plan		Carries out Plan		Looks Back		
Name	Restates problem in own words.	Identifies information given.	Asks questions; makes predictions.	Chooses a strategy.	Applies procedures accurately.	Knows when plan is/is not working.	Explains solution.	Evaluates reasona-bleness of solution.	Describes processes.

Name ____________________ Date ________________

Program Master 2

Self-Assessment

Students can use this format to guide reflection and self-assessment at the end of an activity, lesson, or unit. They can record their ideas on the form or in a journal.

1. Tell the main mathematical topic or idea you learned about.

   We learned about ____.

2. Show how it works. You can use numbers, words, or pictures.

   Here is an example that shows how it works.

3. Tell why it is important.
   You can give an example of how someone might use it.

   One reason that this is important is:

4. Circle the word(s) that best tells how you understand it.

   very well   well   partly   not very well

5. Tell one way you can help yourself or someone else understand and remember what you learned.

Name ____________________ Date ______________

Program Master 3

Self-Assessment: Problem Solving

Step 1. Understand.

Here is the information I know.

Here is what I am asked to do.

I understand the problem: not very well ☐ a little ☐ very well ☐

Step 2. Plan.

Here is a strategy I can use to solve this problem.

I can explain how it will work.

I think my plan will work: not very well ☐ a little ☐ very well ☐

Step 3. Solve.

Here is how I solved the problem.
(Use the back of this page to show your work.)

Here is my answer.

Step 4. Look Back.

I think my solution is:

not very good ☐ partly good ☐ very good ☐

Here is another way I could have solved the problem.

Which way do you think is better? Tell why.

Name ____________________ Date ________________

Program Master 4

Learning Skills Check List

Record ongoing observations of students' learning skills. Use check marks or dates to indicate when behaviours are observed, or use the following key:

Level 1 – very limited; Level 2 – somewhat or limited; Level 3 – satisfactory; Level 4 – thorough

Name	Works independ-ently	Shows initiative	Completes tasks (work habits)	Asks questions (uses in-formation)	Co-operates with others	Resolves conflicts appropri-ately	Participates in class and group activities	Assesses own work (sets goals)

Name ____________________ Date ______________

Program Master 5

Mathematical Dispositions and Learning Skills

Teachers can record observations about students' dispositions and learning skills once or twice during each unit by noting a rating (for example, 1 to 4) along with brief comments.

Learning Skill	Observation 1		Observation 2	
	Rating*	Date/Evidence	Rating*	Date/Evidence
Independent work • shows self-responsibility • completes work on time and with care				
Initiative • takes risks in performing mathematical tasks • exhibits curiosity • shows enjoyment of mathematical experiences • approaches new tasks confidently				
Work habits • puts forward consistent effort • perseveres in mathematical tasks and projects • shows flexibility				
Class participation • contributes to mathematical discussions • contributes to co-operative problem solving • shares responsibility				
Problem solving • mathematically represents and organizes information • devises plans • carries out plans • self-checks to verify solutions • makes connections among different problems and solutions				
Goal setting • assesses own work; evaluates success • identifies goals • identifies specific steps or actions needed to improve • uses criteria				

*Level 1 – very limited; Level 2 – somewhat or limited; Level 3 – satisfactory; Level 4 – thorough

Name ____________________ Date _______________

Program Master 6

Observation Record 1

This form can be used to observe three students who are working together or who are in close proximity.

Unit _____ Lesson _____ Activity _______________

	Observation Notes
Name ____________ ***Focus: PS, UC, AP, CM** **Observed strengths:** **Observed needs:**	
Name ____________ ***Focus: PS, UC, AP, CM** **Observed strengths:** **Observed needs:**	
Name ____________ ***Focus: PS, UC, AP, CM** **Observed strengths:** **Observed needs:**	

*Circle one or more to indicate the focus of your observations and notes:

PS – Problem solving
UC – Understanding of concepts
AP – Application of procedures
CM – Communication

Name ____________________ Date _______________

Program Master 7

Observation Record 2

Use this form to record ongoing observations over a period of time. You can record more than one date/observation in each category.

Observation period from __________ to __________

Observation Notes
Problem solving
Understanding of concepts
Application of procedures
Communication
Summary ***Strengths:*** ***Needs:*** ***Next steps:***

Name ____________________ Date ________________

Program Master 8

Conference Prompts

Teachers can select and develop questions and prompts to use during both formal and informal conferences and interviews with students.
Answers will often provide evidence of more than one category.
Note: The questions are not intended to provide an overall sequence/conference outline. They are examples.

Problem solving	**Understanding of concepts**
• Explain the problem to me. • What have you tried? • How did you decide where to start/what to do? • Were there any places where you got stuck? How did you get going again? • Why did you choose . . . ? • How did you solve . . . ? • Show/tell me about your thinking. • Show me another way . . . • What other ways could someone solve this problem? • Have you found all possible solutions/answers? How do you know? • What advice would you give someone else who had to solve a problem like this? • Can you make up another problem like this for me to solve? • Here's what I saw you do . . .	• Tell me what you know/learned about . . . • Tell me about your thinking . . . • How do you know . . .? • Why does . . . ? • Tell me how you could . . . • Show me … • What do you predict/think will happen if …? Why? • Does that make sense to you? Tell me why/why not. • How could you explain this to someone who has not learned it yet? • Explain what you need to do . . . • About how much/how many . . .? Tell me about your thinking—how did you decide on your estimate? • What is the same/different . . .? What questions do you have about . . . ?
Application of procedures	**Communication**
• How many . . . ? • Show me how to . . . • What answer/solution do you have? • Does that make sense to you? • How could you check? • How did you get that answer/solution? • Have you answered all the parts? • Why is this important? How could you use . . . outside of school? • How is . . . connected to . . . ? • Have you done work like this before? Tell me about it.	Can be observed as children respond, through speech, writing, and drawing, to questions such as those listed above. Also: • Is there another way to say/show that? • What do you call that? Does it have another name? • How could you tell/show someone else what you learned/found out? • Tell me what you did.

Name ____________________ Date ______________

Program Master 9

Work Sample Records

Teachers can use this form to record key information about a portfolio or collection of work samples they select to keep as evidence of learning.

Unit ______

	Strand circle one or more	**Category** circle one or more*	**What this sample shows about student learning**
Date:________ **Work Sample:**	• Number Sense and Numeration • Measurement • Geometry and Spatial Sense • Patterning and Algebra • Data Management and Probability	PS UC AP CM	
Date:_____ **Work Sample:**	• Number Sense and Numeration • Measurement • Geometry and Spatial Sense • Patterning and Algebra • Data Management and Probability	PS UC AP CM	
Date:_____ **Work Sample:**	• Number Sense and Numeration • Measurement • Geometry and Spatial Sense • Patterning and Algebra • Data Management and Probability	PS UC AP CM	

* **PS** – Problem solving
UC – Understanding of concepts
AP – Application of procedures
CM – Communication

Name ____________________ Date ______________

Program Master 10

Summary Class Records: Strands

Achievement Levels
R – not demonstrated
1 – very limited; simple strategies; major errors; unclear
2 – somewhat or limited; somewhat appropriate strategies; several minor errors; some clear
3 – satisfactory; appropriate strategies; few minor errors; clear
4 – thorough; rarely makes errors; innovative strategies; clear and precise

Unit ______

	Strand ____________________				**Strand** ____________________			
	Most consistent achievement level				**Most consistent achievement level**			
Name	Observations	Work samples	Performance assessment	**Overall**	Observations	Work samples	Performance assessment	**Overall**

Name ____________________ Date ______________

Program Master 11

Summary Class Records: Achievement Categories

Teachers can use this form to keep a class record of the levels achieved on various tasks and activities. Levels can be assigned based on observations, conferences, work samples, and/or performance assessment.

Achievement Levels
R – not demonstrated
1 – very limited; simple strategies; major errors; unclear
2 – somewhat or limited; somewhat appropriate strategies; several minor errors; some clarity
3 – satisfactory; appropriate strategies; few minor errors; clear
4 – thorough; rarely makes errors; innovative strategies; clear and precise

Unit ____ Focus Strand ______________________________

	Level Achieved												Overall
	Problem solving			Understanding of concepts			Application of procedures			Communication			
Name													

Name ____________________ Date ________________

Program Master 12

Summary Record: Individual

Teachers can use this form to maintain an ongoing record of student achievement. For each strand, use records of ongoing observations and conferences, work samples, and performance assessments to determine the level achieved for each category. Record category levels in the boxes, and comments in the space provided.

Achievement Levels
R – not demonstrated
1 – very limited; simple strategies; major errors; unclear
2 – somewhat or limited; somewhat appropriate strategies; several minor errors; some clarity
3 – satisfactory; appropriate strategies; few minor errors; clear
4 – thorough; rarely makes errors; innovative strategies; clear and precise

	Most Consistent Level Achieved				
Category	**Problem solving**	**Understanding of concepts**	**Application of procedures**	**Communication**	**Overall**
NUMBER SENSE AND NUMERATION	level ☐	level ☐	level ☐	level ☐	level ☐
MEASUREMENT	level ☐	level ☐	level ☐	level ☐	level ☐
GEOMETRY AND SPATIAL SENSE	level ☐	level ☐	level ☐	level ☐	level ☐
PATTERNING AND ALGEBRA	level ☐	level ☐	level ☐	level ☐	level ☐
DATA MANAGEMENT AND PROBABILITY	level ☐	level ☐	level ☐	level ☐	level ☐
OVERALL	level ☐	level ☐	level ☐	level ☐	level ☐

Name ____________________ Date ________________

Program Master 13

Hundred Chart

1	2	3	4	5	6	7	8	9	10
11	12	13	14	15	16	17	18	19	20
21	22	23	24	25	26	27	28	29	30
31	32	33	34	35	36	37	38	39	40
41	42	43	44	45	46	47	48	49	50
51	52	53	54	55	56	57	58	59	60
61	62	63	64	65	66	67	68	69	70
71	72	73	74	75	76	77	78	79	80
81	82	83	84	85	86	87	88	89	90
91	92	93	94	95	96	97	98	99	100

Name ____________________ Date ________________

Program Master 14

Multiplication Chart

×	**0**	**1**	**2**	**3**	**4**	**5**	**6**	**7**	**8**	**9**	**10**	**11**	**12**
0	0	0	0	0	0	0	0	0	0	0	0	0	0
1	0	1	2	3	4	5	6	7	8	9	10	11	12
2	0	2	4	6	8	10	12	14	16	18	20	22	24
3	0	3	6	9	12	15	18	21	24	27	30	33	36
4	0	4	8	12	16	20	24	28	32	36	40	44	48
5	0	5	10	15	20	25	30	35	40	45	50	55	60
6	0	6	12	18	24	30	36	42	48	54	60	66	72
7	0	7	14	21	28	35	42	49	56	63	70	77	84
8	0	8	16	24	32	40	48	56	64	72	80	88	96
9	0	9	18	27	36	45	54	63	72	81	90	99	108
10	0	10	20	30	40	50	60	70	80	90	100	110	120
11	0	11	22	33	44	55	66	77	88	99	110	121	132
12	0	12	24	36	48	60	72	84	96	108	120	132	144

Name ____________________ Date ______________

Program Master 15

Hundredths Grids

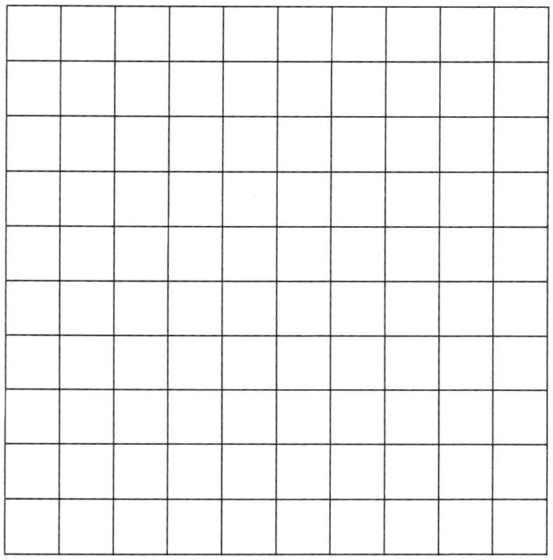

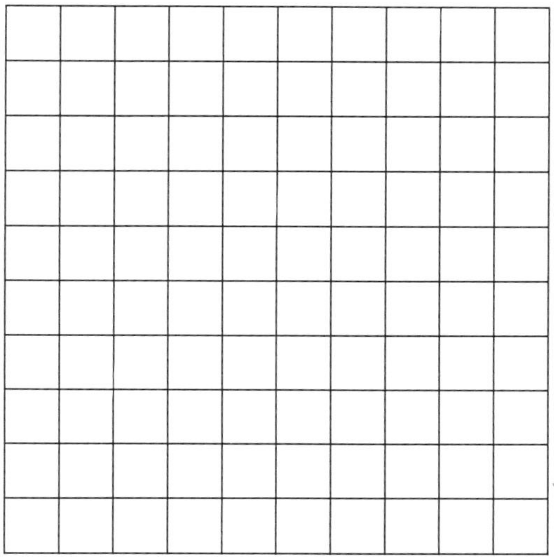

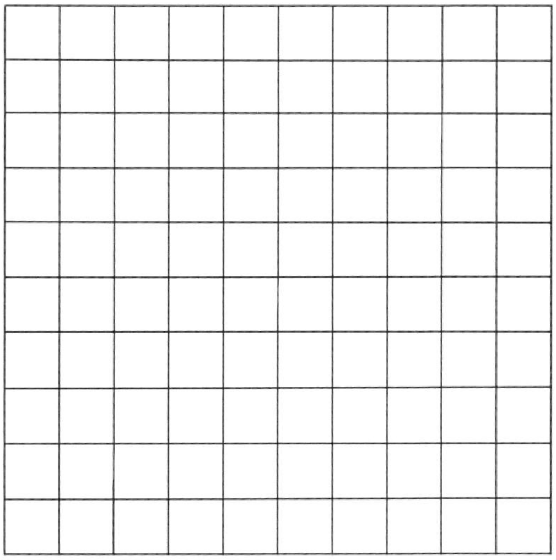

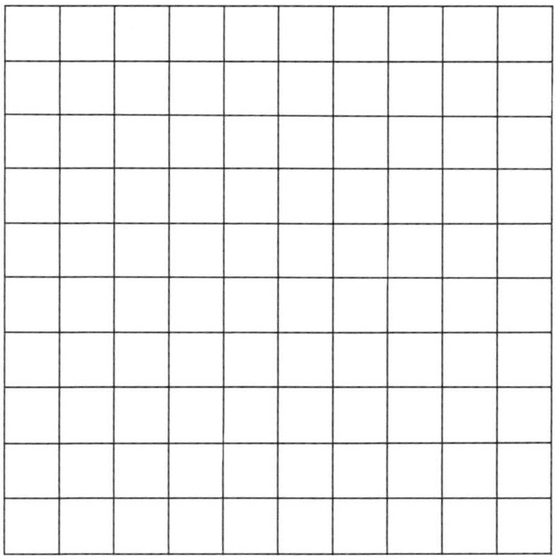

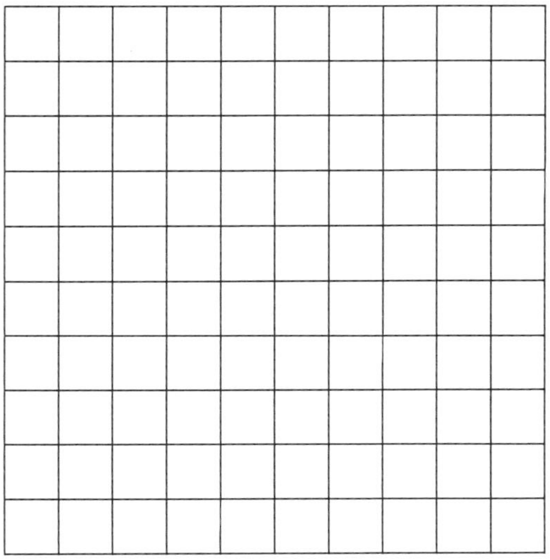

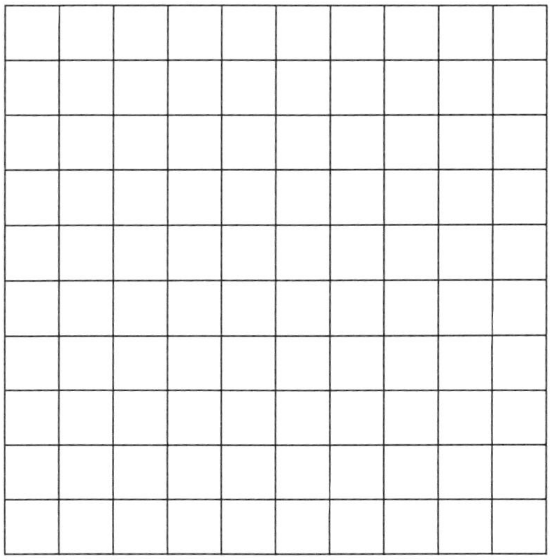

Name ____________________ Date ________________

Program Master 16

Number Lines

Name ____________________ Date ________________

Program Master 17

2-Column Chart

Name ____________________ Date ________________

Program Master 18

3-Column Chart

Name ____________________ Date ______________

Program Master 19

4-Column Chart

Name ____________________ Date ________________

Program Master 20

5-Column Chart

Name ____________________ Date ______________

Program Master 21

6-Column Chart

Name ____________________ Date ________________

Program Master 22

0.5-cm Grid Paper

Name ____________________ Date ________________

Program Master 23

1-cm Grid Paper

Name ____________________ Date ________________

Program Master 24

2-cm Grid Paper

Name ____________________ Date ______________

Program Master 25

Square Dot Paper

Name ____________________ Date ________________

Program Master 26

Triangular Dot Paper

Name ____________________ Date _______________

Program Master 27

Triangular Grid Paper

Name ____________________ Date ________________

Program Master 28

Pattern Blocks

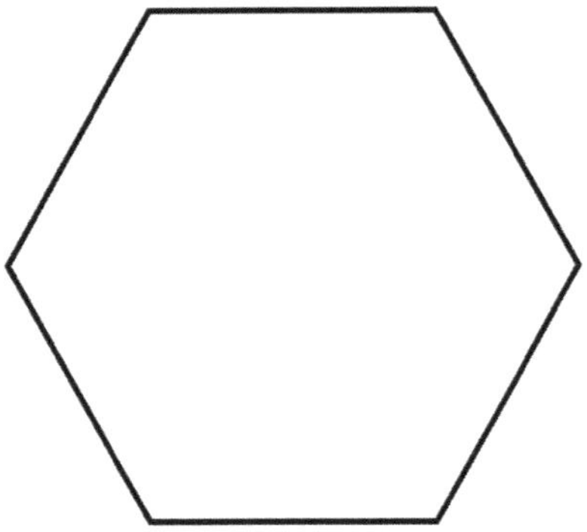

Yellow Hexagon

Orange Square

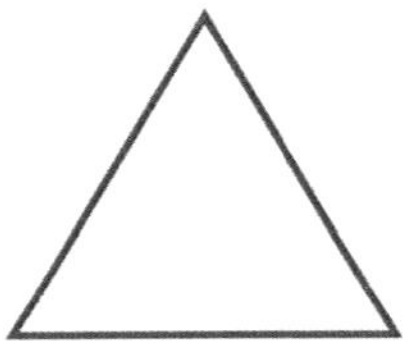

Green Triangle

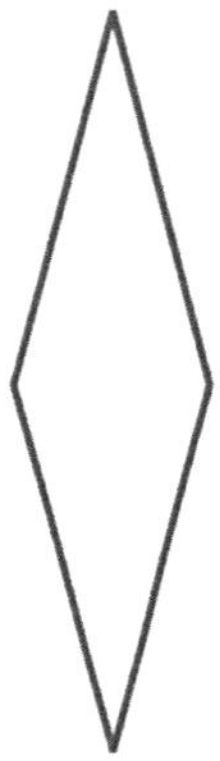

Tan Rhombus

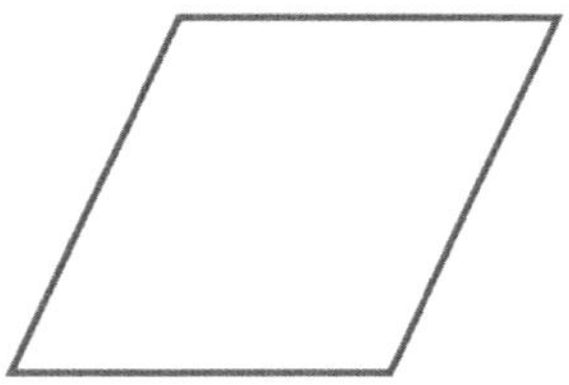

Blue Rhombus

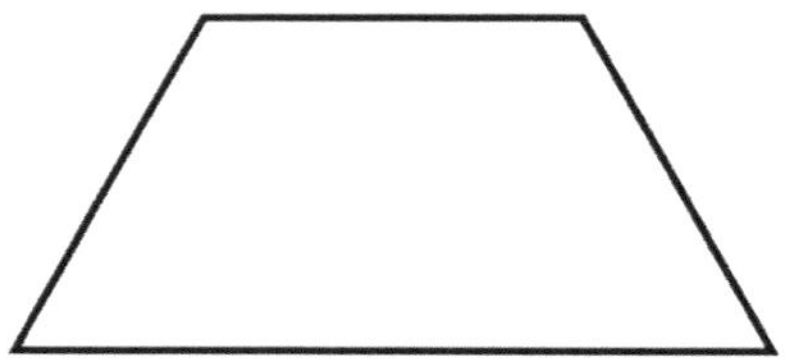

Red Trapezoid

Name ____________________ Date ______________

Program Master 29

Tangram

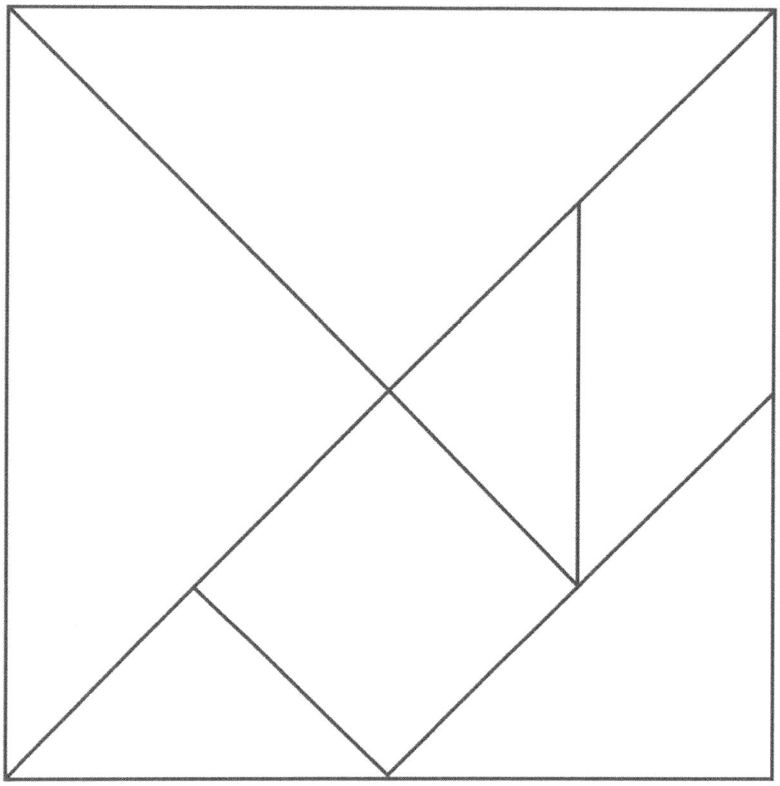

Name ____________________ Date ______________

Program Master 30

Play Money

Reproduced with permission from the Royal Canadian Mint and the Bank of Canada.

Addison Wesley **Mathematics** *Makes Sense*

Program Authors

Peggy Morrow
Ralph Connelly
Bryn Keyes
Jason Johnston
Steve Thomas
Jeananne Thomas
Angela D'Alessandro
Maggie Martin Connell
Don Jones
Michael Davis
Sharon Jeroski
Trevor Brown
Nora Alexander
Cynthia Pratt Nicolson

Printed and bound in Canada

8 9 MP 18 17

PEARSON Education Canada

Addison Wesley

Ontario

Math Makes Sense 5

Ontario

Teacher Guide

Additional Assessment Support

Pearson
Addison Wesley

ASSESSMENT BACKGROUND

1 An Introduction to Assessment

> *"A problem ... must begin where the students are ... Good* [assessment] *tasks should permit every student in the class ... to demonstrate some knowledge, skill, or understanding."*
>
> (Van de Walle 2004, 62)

Assessment and evaluation in *Addison Wesley Mathematics Makes Sense* are **purposeful** and **possible**—to ensure students are supported in reaching the highest possible levels of achievement, and teachers are supported with tools and strategies that enhance assessment and reporting. Assessment and evaluation reflect the exploratory, hands-on, problem-solving approach that is the foundation of *Addison Wesley Mathematics Makes Sense.*

Improving Student Learning

> *"Assessment should support the learning of important mathematics and furnish useful information to both teachers and children."*
>
> (NCTM: *Assessment Principles*)

The primary purpose of assessment and evaluation is to improve student learning. *Diagnostic assessment* helps teachers and students identify learning needs and plan for excellence. *Formative assessment* provides descriptive feedback for teachers and children to monitor their efforts, make adjustments that lead to enhanced learning, and work toward successful achievement. *Summative assessment* allows students to demonstrate and document their achievements, and share them with families, to ensure future effective learning. Student reflection and self-assessment help students become self-directed learners—able to set, work toward, and monitor their own goals.

Assessment strategies and materials in *Addison Wesley Mathematics Makes Sense* reflect the NCTM assessment standards.

Problem Solving

The active, exploratory, problem-solving approach to learning mathematics central to *Addison Wesley Mathematics Makes Sense* is reflected in assessment strategies and techniques. Students demonstrate their knowledge and skills by *doing* mathematics. Many assessment activities focus on performance assessment, where students are asked to demonstrate their knowledge and skills through problems and investigations that connect mathematics to open-ended problems and real-world contexts and issues.

NCTM ASSESSMENT STANDARDS	*ADDISON WESLEY MATHEMATICS MAKES SENSE*
Standard 1: Assessment should reflect the mathematics that all children need to know and be able to do.	Assessment is aligned with the provincial curriculum expectations and content standards that specify what students are to learn at each grade.
Standard 2: Assessment should enhance mathematics learning.	Assessment *for* Learning, a feature in every lesson in the Teacher Guide, focuses on teacher implementation of effective practices to support student learning and performance.
Standard 3: Assessment should promote equity.	At the beginning of every unit, open-ended *diagnostic assessment* helps teachers build on students' prior learning to support student success. *Formative assessment* is particularly helpful in supporting low-achieving students.
Standard 4: Assessment should be an open process.	From grade 1, expectations and criteria are made clear to students and their families. As students gain experience, they are increasingly involved in discussing and setting criteria for their work.
Standard 5: Assessment should promote valid inferences about mathematics learning.	Assessment is based on students *doing* mathematics. To ensure the full spectrum of mathematics achievement is addressed, attention is focused on all aspects of mathematics: understanding concepts and making connections; applying procedures, using problem-solving strategies; and communicating.
Standard 6: Assessment should be a coherent process.	All assessment techniques, tools, and activities are related to the content strands and curriculum expectations, and to student performance.

2 Effective Assessment Practices

> *"Researchers and policy-makers are finally recognizing what teachers have long known: assessment has a powerful effect on student learning."*
>
> (Jeroski 2002)

Goal-Setting, Shared Criteria, Effective Tasks

Learning is enhanced when goals are understood and shared by teachers and students. Recognizing goals and criteria for success is crucial to formative assessment.

Effective performance tasks include complex thinking, where students make choices and decisions. Effective tasks also focus on what children are supposed to **learn** or demonstrate, (not just what they are supposed to **do**).

Self-Assessment

Providing structured, focused opportunities for self-assessment helps students learn, and increases their sense of responsibility. Students engaged in self-assessment become more interested in learning goals, criteria, feedback, and self-improvement.

Provide Meaningful Feedback

Descriptive feedback improves student achievement—feedback that focuses on:

- what students have or have not achieved (rather than comparisons to others)
- timely explanations and corrections (what is incorrect and what is correct and why)
- specific ways in which work can be improved

Adjust Instruction

Teachers who use ongoing assessment results to adjust their teaching help students achieve better results. Thus, teachers are open to adapting their instructional plans to reflect student needs. Teachers should select and develop assessments with a clear sense of purpose—knowing what specific information they and the students need to work toward specific results or expectations.

Motivate Students

Student motivation is one of the keys to learning and improvement. Where assessment results are conveyed in a way that supports learning (rather than questioning ability and effort), teachers have found significant learning gains.

Assessment for learning (formative assessment) and *assessment of learning (summative assessment)* ought first and foremost to support learning. Research by Wynne Harlen and Ruth Deakin Crick found that the effects of summative assessment could support children's learning *when:*

- Assessments were consistent with teacher expectations and student capabilities.
- Students had opportunities to develop self-assessment skills and learning goals.
- The school took a constructive and supportive stance about testing.
- Learning goals were made explicit to low-achieving students, who were shown how to direct effort in learning.
- Assessment results were used to convey a sense of learning progress to children.

3 Diagnostic, Formative, and Summative Assessment

Diagnostic Assessment

Teachers use diagnostic information to make choices about the nature and extent of the learning experiences they provide. Teachers have to consider the varying mathematical knowledge and skills of the whole class as well as individual students.

Purpose

- Help teachers identify students who have difficulty acquiring the necessary concepts, procedures, and strategies.
- Develop insights into particular needs to adjust instruction to ensure at-risk children have the best possibility to succeed.

Diagnostic Opportunities in Addison Wesley Math Makes Sense 5

- The Student Book begins with a group *Cross Strand Investigation* designed to give teachers and students an opportunity to revisit some key concepts and procedures from prior knowledge, and document any gaps or misconceptions. Each unit in the Student Book begins with a *Unit Launch*, designed to activate and build upon students' prior knowledge.
- The notes for the *Unit Launch* in the Teacher Guide include diagnostic questions, and a Diagnostic Assessment feature that cues teachers about what to watch for and what to do. The lesson teaching notes include prompts and questions to help teachers activate prior knowledge to determine whether a student has the skills and understanding required to work on the lesson content.

Generic Tools

The generic tools are available in the *Grade 5 Planning and Program Masters* module.

Helping Teachers Plan

The Planning for Assessment chart at the beginning of each unit in the Teacher Guide includes a section on diagnostic assessment.

Planning for Assessment

Purpose	Tools and Process	Recording and Reporting
Diagnostic	*Unit Launch* Question; conference; scaffold problems throughout the unit	PM 8: Conference Prompts
Formative	*Explore* – Ongoing Assessment: Observe and Listen	Master 1.2 Ongoing Observations Number Patterns PM 1: Inquiry Process Check List PM 6: Observation Record 1 PM 7: Observation Record 2 PM 8: Conference Prompts
	Prompt student's self-assessment	PM 2: Self-Assessment PM 3: Self-Assessment: Problem Solving
	Practice – Assessment Focus Questions	PM 9: Work Sample Records
	Review student work; provide feedback, scaffold as needed, select key pieces	
Summative	*Show What You Know* *Unit Problem* – Performance Assessment Unit Test	Master 1.1 Unit Rubric: Number Patterns Master 1.3 Performance Assessment Rubric: Charity Fundraising Master 1.4 Unit Summary: Number Patterns
	Review assessment records, add unit results to ongoing records	PM 10: Summary Class Records: Strands PM 11: Summary Class Records Achievement Categories PM 12: Summary Record: Individual
Learning Skills/Mathematical Disposition	Observe and record throughout unit	PM 4: Learning Skills Check List PM 5: Mathematical Dispositions and Learning Skills

Program Masters (PM) are in the *Grade 5 Planning and Program Masters* module.
Extra Practice Masters are on the CD-ROM.

Formative Assessment (Assessment for Learning)

> *"Assessment for learning is the process of seeking and interpreting evidence for use by learners and their teachers to decide where the learners are in their learning, where they need to go and how best to get there."*
>
> (Assessment Reform Group, 2002)

Assessment *for* learning, at the heart of *Addison Wesley Mathematics Makes Sense,* is designed to help students learn. A comprehensive research summary concluded that *formative assessment* (assessment for learning) improves student achievement substantially, particularly for low achievers (Black and Wiliam, 1998). The research indicated that implementing effective formative assessment could be one of the most powerful intervention techniques ever identified, and estimated it could improve average student achievement between 1 to 2 levels.

Purpose

- Provide feedback to students so they know how they are doing, and how they might improve their learning.
- Gather information to adjust instruction for the group, and to provide additional scaffolding to students who need it.
- Engage students in their own learning, goal-setting, and self-assessment.
- Help teachers ensure students are provided with purposeful practice.

Formative Opportunities in Addison Wesley Math Makes Sense 5

Teachers can use the Planning for Assessment chart at the beginning of each unit to create a manageable and purposeful formative assessment plan.

- The Teacher Guide provides specific questions to probe student understanding at various stages of a lesson. Each lesson *(Explore/Show and Share)* engages students in *actively exploring* the key concept. This gives teachers opportunities to observe what students are able to do. The *Explore/Ongoing Assessment*: *Observe and Listen* sections of the Teacher Guide provide specific cues and questions.
- *Practice* in the Student Book provides opportunities for teachers to observe, probe, and provide feedback about student development. The *Assessment Focus* question in each lesson allows teachers to check various levels of achievement. Numerical and written answers in the Teacher Guide help teachers provide feedback. *Reflect* in the Student Book directs students to focus on what they have learned, and how well they understand the math. Teachers may choose to use these to prompt discussion, demonstration, or journal entries.
- In the Teacher Guide, *Assessment for Learning: What to Look For; What to Do* cues teachers' attention on specific behaviours in students' oral, concrete, or written work. It provides direct, practical instructions about what to do to provide extra support, extra practice, or extensions. *Reaching All Learners* helps teachers identify common misunderstandings and how to alleviate them.

Specific Tools in Each Unit

Name ____________ Date ____________

Master 1.3

Performance Assessment Rubric: Charity Fundraising

	Level 1	Level 2	Level 3	Level 4
Problem solving • chooses and carries out appropriate patterning and estimation strategies to relate costs and profits, and determine how much money will be raised	chooses and carries out a limited range of appropriate estimation and patterning strategies, resulting in an incomplete or seriously flawed solution	chooses and carries out some appropriate estimation and patterning strategies with partial success	chooses and carries out appropriate and effective estimation and pattern strategies resulting in a successful solution	chooses and carries out innovative appropriate and effective estimation and patterning strategies, resulting in a successful solution
Understanding of concepts • shows understanding of patterning concepts by explaining patterns in the table and predictions about the total amount of money to be raised	shows very limited understanding by giving inappropriate explanations	shows limited understanding by giving appropriate but incomplete explanations	shows understanding by giving appropriate explanations	shows thorough understanding by giving appropriate and complete explanations
Application of mathematical procedures • constructs table correctly	completes table with major errors or omissions	completes table with several minor errors or omissions	completes table with few minor errors or omissions	completes table with practically no minor errors or omissions
• calculates costs and profits accurately	limited accuracy; major errors or omissions in calculating costs and profits	somewhat accurate; several minor errors in calculating costs and profits	generally accurate; few errors or omissions in calculating costs and profits	accurate; very few or no errors in calculating costs and profits
Communication • uses mathematical terminology including units and symbols correctly (for example, relationship, variable, dollars and cents)	uses few appropriate mathematical terms and symbols	uses some appropriate mathematical terms and symbols	uses appropriate mathematical terms and symbols	uses a range of appropriate mathematical terminology and symbols clearly and precisely
• presents and explains results and procedures clearly	presents and explains results and procedures unclearly and imprecisely	presents and explains results and procedures with some clarity	presents and explains results and procedures clearly and precisely	presents and explains results and procedures clearly, precisely, and confidently

Copyright © 2005 Pearson Education Canada Inc. 27

- The *Ongoing Observations* master provides a recording form for teachers to record evidence of student key behaviours in relation to the unit content and the four categories of achievement. Teachers should accumulate observations under each category over the course of the unit.
- The *Unit Rubric* master can be used for both formative and summative assessment. It is based on specific expectations for the entire unit. As a formative assessment master, it can be used to monitor student development during the unit (for example, use a highlighter to indicate which behaviours are observed at different times). It can also be used to assess open-ended tasks or problems, such as the *Assessment Focus* questions in the Student Book, although only parts of the rubric will apply to a specific task.

Generic Tools

The generic tools, *Program Masters,* in the *Grade 5 Planning and Program Masters* module support formative assessment, but are optional. They are not part of the core assessment, but allow teachers to tailor the assessment programs that best suit them.

Name ____________ Date ____________

Program Master 8

Conference Prompts

Teachers can select and develop questions and prompts to use during both formal and informal conferences and interviews with students.
Answers will often provide evidence of more than one category.
Note: The questions are not intended to provide an overall sequence/conference outline. They are examples.

Problem solving	Understanding of concepts
• Explain the problem to me. • What have you tried? • How did you decide where to start/what to do? • Were there any places where you got stuck? How did you get going again? • Why did you choose ...? • How did you solve ...? • Show/tell me about your thinking. • Show me another way. • What other ways could someone solve this problem? • Have you found all possible solutions/answers? How do you know? • What advice would you give someone else who had to solve a problem like this? • Can you make up another problem like this for me to solve? • Here's what I saw you do.	• Tell me what you know/learned about ... • Tell me about your thinking. • How do you know ...? • Why does ...? • Tell me how you could ... • Show me ... • What do you predict/think will happen if ...? Why? • Does that make sense to you? Tell me why/why not. • How could you explain this to someone who has not learned it yet? • Explain what you need to do ... • About how much/how many ...? Tell me about your thinking—how did you decide on your estimate? • What is the same/different ...? What questions do you have about ...?
Application of procedures	**Communication**
• How many ...? • Show me how to ... • What answer/solution do you have? • Does that make sense to you? • How could you check? • How did you get that answer/solution? • Have you answered all the parts? • Why is this important? How could you use outside of school? • How is ... connected to ...? • Have you done work like this before? Tell me about it.	Can be observed as children respond, through speech, writing, and drawing, to questions such as those listed above. Also: • Is there another way to say/show that? • What do you call that? Does it have another name? • How could you tell/show someone else what you learned/found out? • Tell me what you did.

38 Copyright © 2005 Pearson Education Canada Inc.

- *Program Master 8: Conference Prompts* provides questions teachers can use to probe student understanding, and to help determine the strategies students are using.
- *Program Master 2: Self-Assessment,* and *Program Master 3: Self-Assessment: Problem-Solving* can be used to prompt reflection and self-assessment.
- *Program Master 1: Inquiry Process Check List* provides criteria and recording forms for teachers to document student development during *Strategies Toolkit* lessons, where students develop specific problem-solving strategies.
- *Program Masters 6 and 7: Observation Records 1 and 2* are recording formats for making observational notes. They are not specific to a particular unit or activity.
- *Program Master 9: Work Sample Records* provides a format for documenting work samples as part of portfolios.

Summative Assessment (Assessment of Learning)

> *"The goal of assessment is to provide a valid set of inferences related to particular expectations for children and schools."*
>
> (Linn and Baker 2002, 3)

Summative assessment involves both assessment (gathering and documenting evidence) and evaluation (judging student development and achievement). Effective summative assessment balances teacher observations and conferences, and student work samples or portfolios, with more structured performance tasks. Effective summative assessment includes assessments that are cumulative and integrated—it allows students to apply what they have learned over a period of time, and to integrate their mathematical understanding across strands.

In *Addison Wesley Mathematics Makes Sense:*

- Students are encouraged to demonstrate and recognize what they have achieved.
- Teachers document evidence and make decisions about student achievement.
- Family members/adults at home understand and have confidence in the reports they receive.

The achievement chart in each *Unit Summary* master in the Teacher Guide provides the framework for most assessments, so teachers can readily combine evidence from various tasks and observations. At the same time, all assessments are linked to the strands and "big ideas" of the math curriculum, supported by references to specific expectations.

Purpose

- Evaluate and judge student achievement of the expectations in the unit.
- Document student achievement to facilitate reporting to families.

Summative Assessment Opportunities in Addison Wesley Math Makes Sense 5

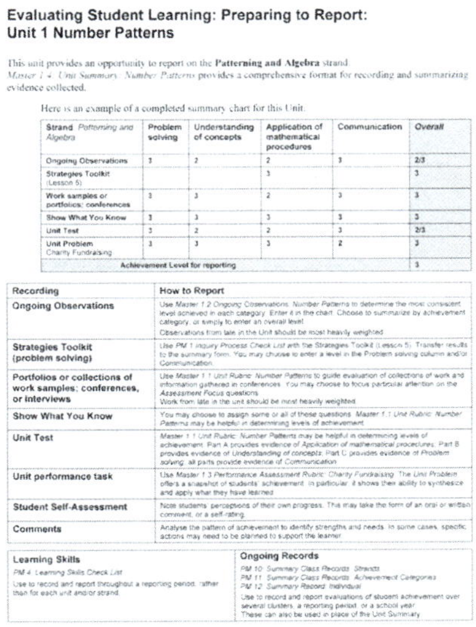

Evaluating Student Learning: Preparing to Report: Unit 1 Number Patterns

This unit provides an opportunity to report on the **Patterning and Algebra** strand.
Master 1.4: Unit Summary: Number Patterns provides a comprehensive format for recording and summarizing evidence collected.

Here is an example of a completed summary chart for this Unit.

Strand *Patterning and Algebra*	Problem solving	Understanding of concepts	Application of mathematical procedures	Communication	*Overall*
Ongoing Observations	3	2	2	3	2/3
Strategies Toolkit (Lesson 5)			3		3
Work samples or portfolios; conferences	3	3	2	3	3
Show What You Know	3	3	3	3	3
Unit Test	3	2	2	3	2/3
Unit Problem Charity Fundraising	3	3	3	2	3
Achievement Level for reporting					3

Recording	How to Report
Ongoing Observations	Use *Master 1.2 Ongoing Observations: Number Patterns* to determine the most consistent level achieved in each category. Enter it in the chart. Choose to summarize by achievement category, or simply to enter an overall level. Observations from late in the Unit should be most heavily weighted.
Strategies Toolkit (problem solving)	Use *PM 1 Inquiry Process Check List* with the Strategies Toolkit (Lesson 5). Transfer results to the summary form. You may choose to enter a level in the Problem solving column and/or Communication.
Portfolios or collections of work samples; conferences, or interviews	Use *Master 1.1 Unit Rubric: Number Patterns* to guide evaluation of collections of work and information gathered in conferences. You may choose to focus particular attention on the *Assessment Focus* questions. Work from late in the unit should be most heavily weighted.
Show What You Know	You may choose to assign some or all of these questions. *Master 1.1 Unit Rubric: Number Patterns* may be helpful in determining levels of achievement.
Unit Test	*Master 1.1 Unit Rubric: Number Patterns* may be helpful in determining levels of achievement. Part A provides evidence of *Application of mathematical procedures*; Part B provides evidence of *Understanding of concepts*; Part C provides evidence of *Problem solving*; all parts provide evidence of *Communication*.
Unit performance task	Use *Master 1.3 Performance Assessment Rubric: Charity Fundraising*. The *Unit Problem* offers a snapshot of students' achievement. In particular, it shows their ability to synthesize and apply what they have learned.
Student Self-Assessment	Note students' perceptions of their own progress. This may take the form of an oral or written comment, or a self-rating.
Comments	Analyse the pattern of achievement to identify strengths and needs. In some cases, specific actions may need to be planned to support the learner.

Learning Skills	Ongoing Records
PM 4: Learning Skills Check List Use to record and report throughout a reporting period, rather than for each unit and/or strand.	*PM 10: Summary Class Records: Strands* *PM 11: Summary Class Records: Achievement Categories* *PM 12: Summary Record: Individual* Use to record and report evaluations of student achievement over several clusters, a reporting period, or a school year. These can also be used in place of the Unit Summary.

The Planning for Assessment chart at the beginning of each unit helps teachers plan for summative assessment.

- In the Student Book, *Show What You Know* offers a set of short answer and open-ended questions, keyed to lessons in the unit. The *Unit Problem* in the Student Book presents a performance task that requires students to apply their learning to an engaging problem or problems. This task allows students to demonstrate various levels of achievement.
- In the Teacher Guide, the *Unit Test* is provided in line master form. The *Unit Test* assesses procedural skills, conceptual understanding, and responses to an open-ended problem.
- In each unit of the Teacher Guide, *Evaluating Student Learning: Preparing to Report* offers samples and suggestions on how teachers can summarize the evidence they collect, and make a summative judgment on student achievement. These are organized by strand.
- Each unit in the Student Book concludes with *Reflect,* which focuses student reflection on a key idea in the unit. Use *Reflect* to prompt demonstration, discussion, or journal entries.

- In the Student Book, there are four *Cross Strand Investigations,* one for the start of the school year, and one to close each term. These *Investigations* allow teachers to assess the extent to which students are able to synthesize and apply their learning in an integrated way.

Specific Tools in Each Unit

Name ______ Date ______

Master 1.1 Unit Rubric: Number Patterns

	Level 1	Level 2	Level 3	Level 4
Problem solving • chooses and carries out a range of patterning strategies to solve problems	with assistance, chooses and carries out a limited range of appropriate patterning strategies, rarely resulting in an accurate solution	with limited assistance, chooses and carries out appropriate patterning strategies that frequently result in an accurate solution	chooses and carries out appropriate patterning strategies to solve problems that usually result in an accurate solution	chooses and carries out appropriate patterning strategies to solve problems accurately; may offer an innovative approach
Understanding of concepts • shows understanding by appropriately demonstrating and explaining: – mathematical relationships in patterns – predictions based on patterns in a table of values – patterns in a variety of "real" contexts	may be unable to demonstrate or explain: – mathematical relationships in patterns – predictions based on patterns in a table of values – patterns in a variety of "real" contexts	partially able to demonstrate and explain: – mathematical relationships in patterns – predictions based on patterns in a table of values – patterns in a variety of "real" contexts	demonstrates and explains: – mathematical relationships in patterns – predictions based on patterns in a table of values – patterns in a variety of "real" contexts	in various contexts demonstrates and explains: – mathematical relationships in patterns – predictions based on patterns in a table of values – patterns in a variety of "real" contexts
Application of mathematical procedures • accurately: – identifies and extends patterns (two variables) – analyses pattern rules – creates tables to display patterns – makes models and charts to display patterns	limited accuracy; major errors in: – identifying and extending patterns (two variables) – analysing patterning rules – creating tables to display patterns – making models and charts to display patterns	somewhat accurate; makes several minor errors in: – identifying and extending patterns (two variables) – analysing patterning rules – creating tables to display patterns – making models and charts to display patterns	generally accurate; makes few minor errors in: – identifying and extending patterns (two variables) – analysing patterning rules – creating tables to display patterns – making models and charts to display patterns	accurate; makes very few or no errors in: – identifying and extending patterns (two variables) – analysing patterning rules – creating tables to display patterns – making models and charts to display patterns
Communication • offers analysis of patterns and explains reasoning clearly, including appropriate terminology	needs assistance to describe patterns and explain reasoning; often unclear and imprecise	describes patterns and explains reasoning with some clarity and precision	describes patterns and explains reasoning clearly and precisely	describes patterns and explains reasoning clearly, precisely, and confidently
• presents work clearly, including appropriate symbols	presents work with little clarity; rarely uses appropriate symbols	presents work with some clarity; uses some appropriate symbols	presents work clearly and precisely; uses appropriate symbols	presents work clearly and precisely; uses a range of appropriate symbols

Copyright © 2005 Pearson Education Canada Inc. 25

- The *Unit Rubric* master highlights strategies, concepts, procedures, and communication students are expected to develop over the course of the unit. It can be used to judge the level of achievement demonstrated in portfolios, conference notes, or other tasks. It describes four levels of performance, taking into account the specific expectations for the entire unit. It can also be used to assess performance tasks.
- The *Performance Assessment Rubric* master supports the assessment of the unit problem.
- In the *Unit Summary* master, teachers summarize results of various assessments, and write an overall evaluation of student achievement. In addition to recording and summarizing levels of achievement, teachers are encouraged to comment on the patterns they observe—strengths, needs, and next steps—and to seek student self-assessment.

Generic Tools

The *Grade 5 Planning and Program Masters* module includes several Program Masters teachers may use as part of their summative assessment. These include self-assessment forms and optional summary forms.

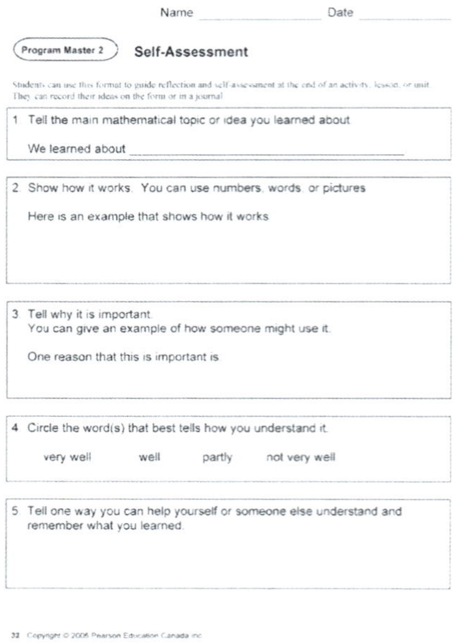
Name ______ Date ______

Program Master 2 Self-Assessment

Students can use this format to guide reflection and self-assessment at the end of an activity, lesson, or unit. They can record their ideas on the form or in a journal.

1. Tell the main mathematical topic or idea you learned about.
   We learned about ______
2. Show how it works. You can use numbers, words, or pictures.
   Here is an example that shows how it works.
3. Tell why it is important.
   You can give an example of how someone might use it.
   One reason that this is important is
4. Circle the word(s) that best tells how you understand it.
   very well   well   partly   not very well
5. Tell one way you can help yourself or someone else understand and remember what you learned.

32 Copyright © 2005 Pearson Education Canada Inc.

- *Program Master 2: Self-Assessment* prompts students to think about what they have learned and the progress they have made.
- *Program Master 10: Summary Class Records: Strands, Program Master 11: Summary Class Records: Achievement Categories,* and *Program Master 12: Summary Record: Individual,* offer options for record keeping. Teachers might choose one of these forms as an alternative to the *Unit Summary* master, or to create summary records over an extended time.

4 Assessing Student Progress

A. Observe and Listen

> *"Effective assessment involves ongoing, consistent, and focused observations. For a complete picture, we observe students at different times of the day, in different settings, doing different kinds of work."*
>
> (Stenmark and Bush 2001, 38)

Effective Observation

Skilful observation is one key to effective teaching. Teachers routinely adjust their lessons, offer support and feedback to children, modify tasks, ask probing questions, and make plans for future activities based on what they notice.

For many teachers, the most challenging part of observing is documenting what they see and hear. Experienced teachers have developed a variety of ways to observe and record.

Here are some suggestions for effective observation.

- Review provincial and professional documents that offer insights into the typical behaviour and development of students, including those younger and older than the ones you teach.
- Ensure students are actively engaged in exploring and problem solving. When students participate actively, they reveal their thinking and the strategies they use.
- Focus observations on a small number of behaviours or expectations that are central to the content of the lesson. Teachers who observe effectively plan their lessons at the same time as they observe. These lessons will focus on the strengths and weaknesses of students and help them develop the concepts and strategies they need.
- The top priority in observing is student understanding of concepts and use of strategies. Observation can be supplemented with assessment of student work samples and portfolios.
- For each lesson, choose 2 to 3 students to focus your observation. In this way, teachers ensure they have observed all students over each two- to three-week period.
  Use thoughtful prompts, such as:
  Tell me about your thinking.
  Show me what you have tried.
  How did you decide/know ...?
- Use a recording system compatible with the teaching style and other forms of record keeping.
  - Some teachers prefer to make anecdotal notes.
  - Often, teachers use a check list to identify specific behaviours associated with the lesson by entering a check mark, date, or code to indicate what they observed.
  - Rubrics can also be used to guide observation and document behaviours.
- Be flexible. Not all observations can be planned and focused. Often, students reveal their mathematical thinking and development during other subjects or outside of class. Some teachers write one sentence at the end of morning, and one sentence immediately after school, to capture these important events and insights. Over time, this can become a rich source of information.
- Frequently skim or reread past observations, especially just before focusing observations on a particular student or group of students. This helps to provide context and continuity.

Observation Features and Tools in Addison Wesley Math Makes Sense 5

Assessment for Learning and Ongoing Observations Check List

- Each lesson includes the feature, *Assessment for Learning,* which cues teachers about key student behaviours. Over the course of a unit, these behaviours should focus on most of the key expectations, and reflect all aspects of achievement—understanding concepts, applying procedures, using problem-solving strategies, and communicating.
- In each unit, the *Ongoing Observations* master provides a manageable form for recording the observations, such as those identified in *Assessment for Learning*. Each aspect of achievement is briefly described, in terms of what to look for within the particular unit. Teachers can make brief notes, enter dates, or use a coding system of their choice.

The tools are tailored to your provincial requirements. Summarize these observations in the *Unit Summary* master to ensure that reporting incorporates a range of evidence.

Other Observation Tools

- *Program Master 6: Observation Record 1* provides a format for teachers to make anecdotal notes about three students who are working together. Teachers can note which strand students are working on, which category of achievement they are observing (for example, concepts, procedures, problem solving, communication), and indicate specific strengths and needs they notice.
- *Program Master 7: Observation Record 2* is designed to help teachers accumulate anecdotal notes about an individual student over time—over an entire school term or reporting period. Four categories of achievements are identified: understanding concepts, applying procedures, problem-solving strategies, and communication. Teachers can use the final section of the form to summarize strengths, needs, and next steps.
- In each unit, the *Unit Rubric* master can be used to guide and record observations. It provides a comprehensive description of four levels of student achievement, and reflects the particular expectations associated with the unit. Some teachers copy a class set of rubrics, such as the *Unit Rubric* master, pre-code one copy with each student's name, then use a highlighter pen to record not only observations, but also evidence from conferences and work samples over the course of a unit. In some cases, teachers use a different colour highlighter pen for different occasions or sources of evidence.

B. Oral Questioning and Conferencing

Oral questioning plays a critical role in assessment:

- It prompts class and group discussion, where teachers are able to both stimulate student thinking and gain insights into their level of understanding.
- It is important in individual interviews or conferences, both formal and informal, where teachers prompt and support students as they explain and justify their thinking, the procedures they are using, and their results and conclusions.

Effective Questioning and Conferencing

- Keep a short list of key questions available for a conversation or short conference. Identify key questions for more formal interviews or conferences ahead of time.
- Respect the student. Focus carefully on what the student is saying.
- Accept the language students use without criticism or correction. Rephrase key ideas and model appropriate terminology so students become accustomed to hearing the language of mathematics.
- Ensure students understand that it is their *thinking* that is most interesting to you. Encourage through close attention, positive body language, and non-judgmental comments. However, clarify student language and misconceptions. Use student friendly language to establish comfort level so the student does not feel threatened. Consider prompts such as: *Tell me about ...* or *I wonder how we could ...* or *What if...?*
- Give students time to think. They need to reflect, self-correct, or confirm what they have said.
- Invite students to pose questions. These questions often reveal more of student understanding than do the responses. Consider the linguistic abilities of the ESL student who may be able to demonstrate mathematical thinking in ways other than talking about it.
- All students, regardless of their language competence, should have access to manipulatives during both informal questioning, and conferences or interviews.

Using the Questioning and Conferencing Features and Tools

Conference and Interview Prompts

Program Master 8: Conference Prompts offers a variety of prompts and questions teachers may choose to use in conferences, interviews, or informal conversations with students. The questions and prompts are organized under four categories: Problem Solving; Understanding of Concepts; Application of Mathematical Procedures; and Communication. They are intended to be samples only, and do not constitute a conference outline. Teachers can add to these from their own repertoire.

Ongoing Assessment: Observe and Listen

Each lesson includes prompts and questions designed to stimulate student thinking, provide scaffolding as needed, and offer insights into students' level of understanding. Under the heading, *Explore/Ongoing Assessment: Observe and Listen,* a short list of questions helps teachers determine how well students are developing lesson concepts. *Connect* often includes one or two key questions that help students formalize lesson concepts and allow teachers to gain insight into their understanding.

C. Performance Assessment

Addison Wesley Mathematics Makes Sense reflects the belief that students must *do* math to *learn* math, and focuses on exploration and problem solving. Performance assessment is a key component at all stages—students have opportunities to apply their learning and demonstrate their achievement through open-ended tasks and investigations.

Effective Performance Assessment

Effective performance assessment depends on effective tasks that help students, teachers, and parents focus on what is important in student learning, and gain insights into student development and achievement. Throughout the resource, a wide variety of open-ended problems, tasks, and investigations, along with rubrics and other scoring guides, have been designed to ensure that they meet the following criteria.

Using the Performance Assessment Features and Tools in Addison Wesley Math Makes Sense 5

Unit Rubric and Performance Assessment Rubric

- Each unit concludes with a performance assessment task linked to the *Unit Launch*.
- Teachers can choose to have students work independently, with a partner, or in a small group. Observing students working together often provides insights into their thinking—as students discuss and debate procedures, their thinking becomes "visible." On the other hand, it is also important to note individual student contributions. Teachers should clearly note on recording forms whether students worked independently, with the support of a peer, or with adult help. Where children work collaboratively, it is often best to have them record their solutions and justification independently.

EFFECTIVE PERFORMANCE ASSESSMENT CHECK LIST

Helps students, teachers, and families focus on learning goals and expectations

- ✓ Learning goals are specified.
- ✓ Expectations and criteria are clear, usually in the form of a rubric.
- ✓ Key mathematical concepts and skills for the grade level are emphasized.
- ✓ Tasks are meaningful to and valued by students and families.
- ✓ Rubrics and scoring guides are designed to provide meaningful feedback to help students see clearly what they are doing well and where they need to improve.

Engages students in applying what they have learned

- ✓ Students are engaged in realistic applications of their understanding and skill.
- ✓ Students are expected to think in complex ways, and to explain or justify their processes and results.

Allows for various levels of performance

- ✓ Tasks allow for a broad range of performance, and lead naturally to extensions—other problems, possibilities, and questions. They are complex and go beyond what could be assessed in a typical paper and pencil test.
- ✓ Students are required to make decisions about the strategies and procedures they use.
- ✓ Make the process open (multiple paths to a solution may be explored); thus the end product is open (multiple correct answers).

- In each unit, the *Performance Assessment Rubric* master can be used to assess students' level of achievement on the *Unit Problem*. The rubric incorporates all parts of the task, and considers concepts, procedures, strategies, and communication.
- The *Unit Summary* master includes space to record these results.

Investigations

- The Student Book has four *Cross Strand Investigations*, designed to take 2 to 4 days for students to complete. The teaching notes are in this *Assessment Module* (pp. 24–39). Each *Investigation* is accompanied by a sample response and check list.
- *Building Castles* appears at the beginning of the Student Book and is designed for diagnostic assessment at the beginning of the year. An *Investigation* follows each of Units 3, 7, and 11. These three *Investigations* are placed approximately at the end of each term. Each *Investigation* draws on concepts, skills, and strategies students have already developed.
- The Teacher Guide support for each *Investigation* includes a check list that describes the strand and the expectations addressed by the task. The check lists are cross strand.
- **Option:** Teachers who wish to focus on a specific strand can use the *Unit Rubric* master from previous units. This rubric focuses on generic observations that apply across tasks. For example, the *Unit Rubric* from Unit 1: Number Patterns could be used to assess the patterning aspects of *Cross Strand Investigation: Building Castles*.

Strategies Toolkit

- Each unit includes a *Strategies Toolkit* lesson, where students explore inquiry and problem-solving strategies, then solve one or more problems independently.
- The optional assessment tools *Program Master 1: Inquiry Process Check List* help teachers assess students' strategies for:
  - Understanding the problem
  - Making a plan
  - Carrying out the plan
  - Looking back
- The same problem-solving strategies may appear in several *Strategies Toolkit* lessons—they are not restricted to a particular unit. Using *Program Assessment Master 1: Inquiry Process Check List* across several units can help teachers look for patterns and document ways students' strategies are developing.

Other Opportunities for Performance Assessment

- One question in each *Practice* set is designated *Assessment Focus*. This question may be open-ended, and allows for various levels of achievement.
- Each *Unit Test* includes an open-ended problem. While this does not provide the scope of the *Unit Problem* or an *Investigation*, it does allow teachers to assess students' abilities to solve a problem. This item is particularly useful in assessing the problem-solving strategies students have developed.
- In each unit, the *Unit Rubric* master can be used to assess performance tasks based on unit content. This rubric provides an overall "standard" for the unit, outlining the concepts, procedures, strategies, and communication students are expected to develop. In some cases, teachers may wish to focus on only part of this rubric for a particular task.

D. Work Samples and Portfolios

Collections of student work over time provide both teachers and students with concrete evidence of progress. Portfolios and other collections are often best assessed in conjunction with an interview or conference. It is often difficult to make sense of a written sample without hearing the student's rationale. For ESL students and those who have not developed facility with written English, work samples may not accurately represent their learning.

Effective Portfolios and Work Samples

- Each item in a collection of work should illustrate something important about a student's development or progress, attitude, understanding of concepts, use of strategies, and application of procedures.
- Engage students in selecting work to collect. Schedule time for students to review, add, delete, and replace material from their portfolios regularly.
- Incorporate students' self-assessment because it is necessary to know the student's thought process. Self-assessment can address questions such as:
  - What does this work show about the math you learned?
  - What does it show about your learning skills or work habits—the way you approach and complete your work?
  - Which of these pieces was most challenging for you? How did you meet the challenge?
  - What are you most proud of in this collection?
  - What is one goal for improvement?
- Use the portfolios or collections as the basis for conferences with students and their parents.
- In assessing portfolios, look for patterns and trends, and try to make an overall or holistic assessment of the student's progress. The *Unit Rubric* master can help teachers make decisions. Some teachers work with students to develop criteria and a rubric for assessing portfolios.

Portfolio and Work Sample Features and Tools in Addison Wesley Math Makes Sense 5

Assessment Focus Questions

In each lesson, one *Practice* question is designated as *Assessment Focus*. These questions may be open ended, and allow students to show various levels of achievement. Responses to these questions can be an integral part of a collection of work samples over a unit.

Portfolio and Work Sample Records

- *Program Master 9: Work Sample Records* is a contents page for a collection of work. It provides space for recording information for up to four samples; teachers can add additional pages as needed. This form can help teachers keep track of the samples they collect, and summarize student achievement. For each unit, teachers record their insights and conclusions about student achievement in the *Unit Summary* master. Collectively, these insights will help teachers decide on a student's overall achievement.

Unit Rubric

- The *Unit Rubric* master guides teachers' decision making when they consider a portfolio or collection of work that reflects student learning over a unit. The *Unit Rubric* describes four levels of achievement, based on the unit expectations, and provides the basis for judging achievement on a collection of work, prior to completing the *Unit Summary*. Some teachers use one copy of the rubric for both observations and work samples.

E. Reflection and Self-Assessment

Opportunities to reflect, self-assess, and set goals improve student learning. Effective self-assessment is constructive and empowering. Students increase their sense of control and responsibility, and are able to focus on how they can improve. Through carefully structured reflection and self-assessment activities, students develop metacognition—they become increasingly aware of what is important in their learning and understand their own progress.

Writing is an important learning tool in mathematics. Students record their thinking, using a combination of pictures, words, or numbers.

Effective Reflection and Self-Assessment

- To become effective at reflection and self-assessment, students need frequent oral modelling and guided practice. Modelling helps students develop the language of self-assessment; they benefit from hearing and seeing examples from their peers, as well as from adults. A collaborative class journal is an excellent way of initiating self-assessment and reflection. In the Student Book, *Show and Share, Connect,* and *Reflect* highlight the importance of bringing students together to collaborate on their learning.
- Provide a variety of formats and media for self-assessment—oral, written, visual, kinesthetic—to ensure a comfort level for all students. It should not depend on a student's linguistic skills. *All* students should have opportunities to consider and assess their learning.
- When students are expected to provide written reflections, offer simple frames to help them get started, for example:
  - ➤ I want to get better at ...
  - ➤ I found out that ...
  - ➤ Look at these two pieces of work. What do you notice? What can you do now that you couldn't do before?
- Provide a concrete "anchor" for students as they self-assess and reflect. This may be a specific representation or piece of work, a portfolio, classroom charts, or a collaborative list of activities they have done. Students will find reflection and self-assessment easier and more natural if it is tied to the specific activities they have done. Provide opportunities for students to share their self-assessments with their families.
- If students are keeping math journals, ensure these are used only as places to share mathematical thinking and ideas. Students should be clear about their purpose and audience—what they are expected to share, to whom they are writing, and what result they can expect.

Reflection and Self-Assessment Features and Tools in Addison Wesley Math Makes Sense 5

Journals

There are questions and prompts for reflection at the end of each lesson, as well as at the end of every unit. Students can respond to these in their notebooks, or in special journals. Encourage students to record their ideas in any way they can. Emphasize that you are only interested in their *mathematical thinking.*

Self-assessment forms

- *Program Master 3: Self-Assessment: Problem Solving* provides a four-step outline for problem solving that includes: Understand, Plan, Solve, and Look Back. At each step, students are asked to assess their work. This form can be used with any problem-solving activity.
- *Program Master 2: Self-Assessment* guides reflection and self-assessment at the end of a lesson or activity. It prompts students to identify and

explain what they have learned, to tell why it is important, and to assess their understanding. It can be used after any activity.

Other reflection and self-assessment tools

Many conference prompts included in *Program Master 8: Conference Prompts* described in *Section 4B: Oral Questioning and Conferencing* (page 11) can be used to prompt reflection and self-assessment.

F. Learning Skills and Dispositions

Comprehensive assessment includes a focus on the learning skills and dispositions that enable student achievement and success. Students need to develop skills that support learning (for example, working independently, showing initiative, completing work, and participating in classroom activities). While these are important to mathematical achievement, they should be assessed and reported separately. It is also important for students to develop a positive attitude toward mathematics.

Effective Assessment of Learning Skills and Dispositions

- Document students' learning skills and dispositions separately from their mathematical development, and report on them separately, as outlined in provincial or local guidelines. Emphasize to students and their families the importance of assessing their skills and dispositions.
- Encourage students to assess their learning skills and set personal goals. Focus on one skill at a time, and focus on a short list of behaviours that a student can reflect on.
- Connect the learning skills students are focusing on in mathematics with those they are developing in other parts of their curriculum. Where possible, use the same recording or self-assessment formats and strategies, while ensuring that you include specific examples from mathematics. Students need to see the connections among various parts of their curriculum and their learning.

Using the Learning Skills and Dispositions Features and Tools in Addison Wesley Math Makes Sense 5

- Teachers can use *Program Master 5: Mathematical Dispositions and Learning Skills* to accumulate observations and notes about an individual student over time. As teachers notice specific behaviours, they can record the data and enter notes and/or a symbol (for example, E = excellent, G = good, S = satisfactory, N = needs improvement). Where teachers select specific students to observe each day (see *Section 4A: Observe and Listen,* page 9), they can record observations about learning skills as well as about mathematical development.
- *Program Master 4: Learning Skills Check List* focuses on information similar to that in *Program Master 5: Mathematical Dispositions and Learning Skills,* but in a more condensed form—a class check list. Teachers can use the check list to record assessments of an entire class, using a coding system such as the one described above.

G. Classroom Testing

Teachers recognize that tests have limited utility, and try to balance their assessments—collecting a range of evidence to ensure decisions about achievement are valid.

Effective Classroom Testing

- The development or selection of a test begins with a careful plan or set of specifications to ensure the test is a valid reflection of both the content (the topics and expectations) and the achievement categories (procedures, concepts, strategies) of interest.
- Make sure each question poses a clear task. For this reason, when designing multiple-choice items, a question is usually better than an incomplete statement. After reading the stem, the students should know *exactly* what is required.
- Word questions clearly; use simple straightforward language and short sentences. This is important for ESL children, or others who have difficulty reading.
- Create your own bank of items, organized by topic or expectation.
- Allow students sufficient time to complete the test. A test of mathematics should be a test of *power* (the extent to which the student has acquired the skills, concepts, and strategies required), not a test of the *speed* with which the student answers.
- Before you begin assessing, create a set of sample answers and decide how you will score each item. Apply your criteria and guidelines consistently.

Using the Unit Tests

The Teacher Guide includes a *Unit Test* for each unit. The tests reflect both the content of the unit and the aspects of achievement reflected in the achievement chart. They also present students with a variety of item types. Each test includes three sections:

- Part A: Requires application of procedures (short-answer or selection items)
- Part B: Assesses understanding of concepts (short-answer items)
- Part C: Presents a problem (open ended)

Sample answers are provided in the Teacher Guide. Teachers can use these to assess each item, then record a raw score, or use the *Unit Rubric* to determine the level of achievement for each section. Teachers can also consider the overall level of mathematical communication students demonstrated in responding to questions throughout the test. Results can be recorded on the *Unit Summary* master. Teachers then determine a student's level of achievement.

Assessing All Learners

Assessment needs to be fair and valid for *all* learners. Teachers also need to be sensitive to the impact assessment can have on students who are struggling.

- Ensure that assessment opportunities include a range of ways that students can represent their learning. Emphasize that you are most interested in students' thinking, rather than in their particular answer or solution.
- Provide opportunities for ESL children and others with limited language skills to demonstrate their learning pictorially and with concrete materials.
- Conduct frequent one-on-one conferences to clarify and extend student learning.
- Look for patterns in students' work that may help to identify those who are having trouble with an aspect that is unrelated to mathematics, such as fine motor control, attention, or language.
- Ensure students are not asked to perform assessment tasks they are incapable of attempting. Select tasks that all students can attempt; then provide adaptations and scaffolding to support them.

5 Summarizing and Reporting Progress

Addison Wesley Mathematics Makes Sense supports a balanced approach to summarizing and reporting. Teachers are encouraged to include observations and portfolios or work samples, as well as formal assessments, in making decisions about a student's progress. In considering evidence from various sources, it is important that teachers:

- establish a tentative plan for reporting at the beginning of each unit or term that includes identifying key evidence that will be collected
- make decisions based on a variety of evidence, collected at various times and in various ways
- ensure the evidence comprehensively addresses the learning expectations
- establish the most consistent level of achievement, rather than the mathematical average
- weight assessments from the end of a cluster, unit, or group of units most heavily
- look for patterns in the results—areas of consistent strength or concern; increasing/decreasing performance levels over time; characteristic differences from one type of assessment to another
- use a consistent rubric or definition of standards to guide decision making (for example, the *Unit Rubric*)
- invite students to offer their own assessments; conference with them to reconcile any discrepancies between their perceptions and the teacher's record
- base comments on the patterns of achievement noted through observation, conferences, work samples, and performance tasks; be as specific as possible about next steps

Record Keeping, Reporting Features, and Tools

Reporting by Strand

Assessment records and rubrics, as well as the *Unit Summary* master, are organized, first, by strand; then, within strand, by the categories of achievement (concepts, procedures, problem solving, and communication). Teachers are given the flexibility to record and report on each category for a particular strand, or to report on the overall level of achievement for the strand.

Features

- As part of *Planning for Assessment,* each unit begins with an outline of diagnostic and formative assessment opportunities and the available tools. This chart identifies both the core assessment tools that are included with the unit, and the optional *Program Masters* in the *Grade 5 Planning and Program Masters* module. The core set of assessment tools and features is consistent throughout.
- At the end of each unit, *Evaluating Student Learning: Preparing to Report* describes how teachers can summarize the evidence they have gathered to determine the most appropriate achievement level for each student. This description includes samples and is tied directly to the *Unit Summary* master. It offers suggestions about how teachers can summarize, record, and combine evidence from observations; problem-solving activities; conferences, portfolios or collections of student work; and performance tasks to complete the *Unit Summary* master.

Unit Rubric

Each unit includes a *Unit Rubric* that focuses on the content of the unit and can be used to assess a variety of student tasks. It can guide a teacher's decisions about the level each student has achieved and demonstrated. The *Unit Rubric* provides descriptions of four levels of achievement for each of the following categories: Problem Solving, Understanding Concepts, Application of Procedures, and Communication.

Unit Summary: The Chart

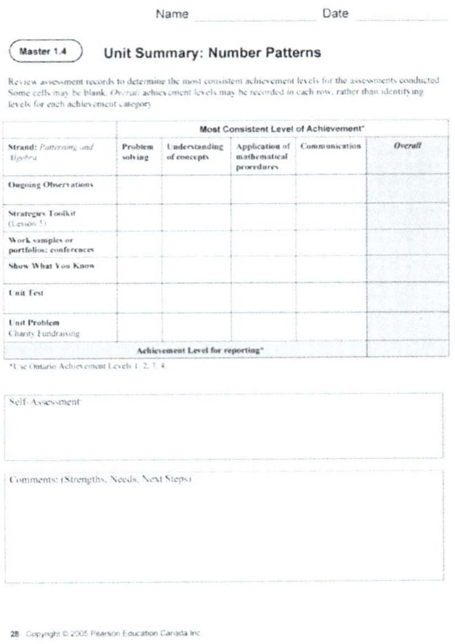

Name ______ Date ______

Master 1.4 Unit Summary: Number Patterns

Review assessment records to determine the most consistent achievement levels for the assessments conducted. Some cells may be blank. *Overall* achievement levels may be recorded in each row, rather than identifying levels for each achievement category.

	Most Consistent Level of Achievement*				
Strand: *Patterning and Algebra*	**Problem solving**	**Understanding of concepts**	**Application of mathematical procedures**	**Communication**	***Overall***
Ongoing Observations					
Strategies Toolkit (Lesson 5)					
Work samples or portfolios; conferences					
Show What You Know					
Unit Test					
Unit Problem Charity Fundraising					
Achievement Level for reporting*					

*Use Ontario Achievement Levels 1, 2, 3, 4.

Self-Assessment:

Comments: (Strengths, Needs, Next Steps)

28 Copyright © 2005 Pearson Education Canada Inc.

A *Unit Summary* master provides a chart to be completed for each student, summarizing the various types of summative evidence gathered. There is space to make notes about students' self-assessment, their strengths and needs, and the next steps needed to ensure their success. Teachers can choose to record information for each category of the achievement chart, or use the overall column.

Teachers use their assessment records to enter the following information:

Ongoing observations—Teachers should use the *Ongoing Observations* master to determine the most consistent level of achievement observed.

Problem solving (*Strategies Toolkit*)—Teachers who collected evidence of students' inquiry and problem-solving strategies using *Program Master 1: Inquiry Process Check List* during the *Strategies Toolkit* lesson can enter the student's level of achievement.

Conferences and interviews; portfolios or collections of work samples—Teachers can use the *Unit Rubric* master to assess a student's level of achievement.

Show What You Know—Teachers can use the *Unit Rubric* master to determine a student's achievement level. *Evaluating Student Learning: Preparing to Report* includes suggestions about which item reflects which category of achievement.

Unit performance task—The *Unit Problem* can be assessed using the *Performance Assessment Rubric* master. This master provides a snapshot of a student's achievement related to the expectations addressed in the unit.

Unit Test—Teachers can enter results of the *Unit Test* (see *Section 4G: Using the Unit Tests,* page 17). Teachers can enter the results as achievement levels, based on the *Unit Rubric,* or as raw scores.

Unit Summary

- Teachers can use the *Unit Summary* master to record brief comments about a student's strengths and needs, and next steps for supporting student progress. The *Unit Rubric* master can help to guide these comments, to ensure they deal with key learnings or big ideas in the strand or unit, as well as specific expectations. For example:

  Strengths: Travis shows understanding of most of the concepts related to measuring time, temperature, and money. He understands that measuring requires matching or making a comparison. This sound grasp of measurement concepts will provide a good foundation when we begin measuring length and width.

  Needs: Travis often makes minor errors, and needs help and reminding to complete all parts of the work required.

  Next steps: Travis may benefit from having a task broken into smaller parts, so that he can focus better on each procedure.

- A student's self-assessment can also be included in the *Unit Summary* master. It is preferable to quote a student's exact oral or written words. These may come from conferences, in-class discussions, journals, or other written reflections.

Report Card Comments

Teachers can synthesize their comments over 3 to 4 units when they are preparing to report. Comments should focus on the student's achievement of the curriculum, and describe areas of strength and growth throughout the term. The comments should also communicate areas needing further growth and suggest ways to promote this growth.

Learning Skills and Dispositions

- Evidence of learning skills should be ongoing throughout a reporting period, rather than broken down by units or strands. At reporting time, teachers can transfer decisions about the level of students' learning skills directly from *Program Master 5: Mathematical Dispositions and Learning Skills* or *Program Master 4: Learning Skills Check List,* to the report. (See *Section 4F: Learning Skills and Disposition*, page 16, for further information.)

6 District and Provincial Assessment Programs

In most regions, students at some grades participate in district and/or provincial assessments that are reported at the individual, school, and district level. Often, these are primarily designed to ensure accountability—that students are learning the required expectations or outcomes and achieving high standards.

In some cases—particularly at school and district levels—this may involve aggregating results from a standard performance assessment or test administered in all or a sample of classrooms at a particular grade. In other cases, the assessment is imposed by an external authority (for example, provincial assessments or examinations); the results are released to individual classrooms and students.

Impact of external testing

While these tests generally have little impact on classroom assessment and reporting for elementary students, research suggests that they can have a powerful effect and (sometimes) negative effect on students' motivation and self-esteem. However, where the following instructional practices are in place, students can respond positively:

- Tests and other assessments are consistent with teacher expectations and student capability.
- Students have opportunities to develop self-assessment skills and learning goals.
- The school takes a constructive and supportive stance about testing.
- Low-achieving students are supported when teachers make learning goals explicit and show students how to direct effort in learning.
- Assessment results are used to convey a sense of learning progress to students.

Enhancing Student Performance on Provincial Assessments

- In the Student Book, assessment and evaluation materials are organized around these four categories of achievement.
  - sound conceptual understanding
  - procedural fluency
  - effective and flexible problem-solving strategies
  - clear and precise mathematical communication
- Each lesson and unit include assessment items and tasks similar to the types of questions presented on provincial tests. For example:
  - short answer procedural questions
  - items that require students to explain their thinking in words, pictures, or numbers
  - problems to solve
  - timed tests (optional)
  - open-ended performance tasks that integrate the four Achievement Categories
- In each lesson, at least one question in *Practice* provides opportunities for students to display all four levels of performance, which also offers scope for students to demonstrate a Level 4 performance.
- Four *Cross Strand Investigations,* presented at intervals during the year, ensure students approach mathematics as an integrated study. These mirror some question types in the provincial tests.
- *SHOW YOUR BEST* in the Teacher Guide helps students prepare, achieve, and communicate their best work. It includes clear, direct information about specific topics including how to: read and understand a word problem; select the *best* answer for a multiple-choice item; manage time in a test situation; organize work to receive the maximum credit; and use words, pictures, or numbers to show a solution and the strategies.

References

Assessment Reform Group. 1999. *Assessment for Learning: Beyond the Black Box.* Cambridge, UK: University of Cambridge School of Education.

———. 2002. *News/Events: Current activities.* http://www.assessment-reform-group.org.uk

Black, Paul, and Dylan Wiliam. 1998. *Inside the Black Box: Raising Standards through Classroom Assessment.* London, UK: King's College London, School of Education.

———. 1998. Assessment and Classroom Learning. *Assessment in Education* 5 (1): 7–74.

BC Ministry of Education. 2000; 2002. BC Performance Standards: Numeracy. Victoria, BC: Ministry of Education. Available at www.gov.bc.ca/bced

Harlen, Wynne, and Ruth Deakin Crick. 2002. *Review: What is the evidence of the impact of summative assessment and tests on students' motivation for learning?* Presentation, Invitational Conference, Assessment Reform Group, March 5, 2002.

Marzano, Robert J., Debra J. Pickering, and Jane E. Pollock. 2001. *Classroom instruction that works: Research-based strategies for increasing student achievement.* Alexandria, VA: ASCD.

National Education Association in collaboration with Rick Stiggins and the Assessment Training Institute. 2003. *Balanced Assessment.* Washington, DC: National Education Association.

Stenmark, Jean Kerr, and William S. Bush, eds. 2001. *Mathematics Assessment: A Practical Handbook.* Reston, VA: NCTM.

Stiggins, Rick. 2001. *Making Classroom Assessment Instructionally Relevant.* Paper presented at the annual meeting of the American Educational Research Association, Seattle, 2001.

Van de Walle, John A. 2004. *Elementary and Middle School Mathematics: Teaching Developmentally.* 5th ed. Boston: Allyn and Bacon.

Cross Strand Investigation Notes

Building Castles

LESSON ORGANIZER (80–100 min)

Curriculum Focus: Cross Strand Performance Assessment: Patterning and Algebra, Measurement, Data Management and Probability

Student Materials
- Pattern Blocks
- 4-column tables (PM 19)

Vocabulary: frame, perimeter

Assessment: Cross Strand Performance Assessment Check List: Building Castles, PM 9 Work Sample Records

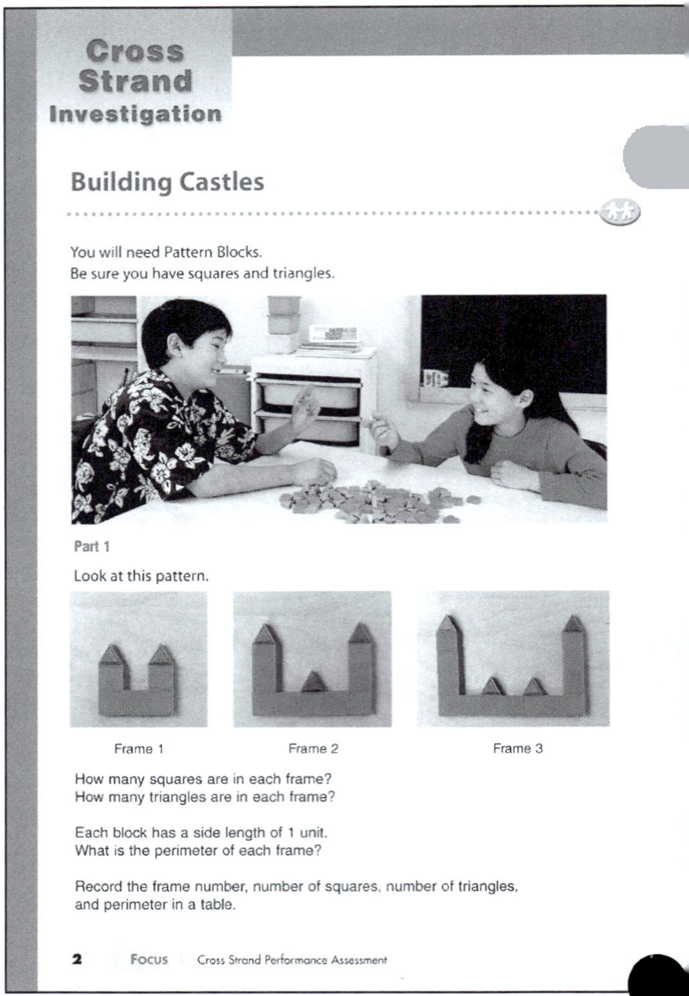

Cross Strand Investigation

Building Castles

You will need Pattern Blocks.
Be sure you have squares and triangles.

Part 1

Look at this pattern.

Frame 1 Frame 2 Frame 3

How many squares are in each frame?
How many triangles are in each frame?

Each block has a side length of 1 unit.
What is the perimeter of each frame?

Record the frame number, number of squares, number of triangles, and perimeter in a table.

2 FOCUS Cross Strand Performance Assessment

Key Math Learnings

1. Students apply patterning strategies to problem-solving situations.
2. Students solve problems related to the calculation of the perimeter of regular and irregular two-dimensional shapes.
3. Students interpret displays of data and present the information using mathematical terms.

BEFORE Get Started

To set the scene for building castles, tell students that Queen Perimeter wants to build 10 different castles throughout her kingdom. Each new one should be bigger than the last one, but they must be similar so that everyone who sees them will know that they are hers. So, they must follow a pattern.

Invite students to look at the photographs of castles built from Pattern Blocks on page 2 of the Student Book. Ask students questions such as

- What similarities can you see in the castles? (*They are made from square and triangle Pattern Blocks.*)

Make sure students can see the pattern in the blocks from one frame to the next. Ask:

- How are the castles increasing? (*A square is added to the towers at each end, 2 squares and a triangle are added in the centre part.*)

Present the *Investigation.* Remind students to record all their results in preparation for their report.

DURING Investigation

Ongoing Assessment: Observe and Listen

Ask questions, such as:

- How do you know your model is correct? (*It follows the pattern.*)
- How did you find the numbers in the table? (*I counted the squares and triangles in each frame. I counted the edges of the Pattern Blocks to find the perimeter.*)
- How do you know the numbers are correct? (*Each set of numbers follows a pattern.*)
- What patterns do you notice? (*The number of squares increases by 4 each frame, the number of triangles increases by 1 each frame, and the perimeter increases by 9 units each frame.*)

Part 2

- Build Frame 4.
  How many squares and triangles did you use?
  What is the perimeter?
  Record the data in your table.
- How many squares and triangles will you need to build Frame 5?
  How did you find out?
  Build Frame 5 to check your prediction.
- Predict the number of squares and triangles needed to build Frame 10.
  How did you make your prediction?
- Write each pattern rule:
  - the numbers of squares in the frames
  - the numbers of triangles in the frames
  - the perimeters of the frames

Display Your Work

Record your work.
Describe the patterns you discovered.

Take It Further

Choose three different Pattern Blocks.
Build your own pattern.
Sketch the first 4 frames.
What number patterns can you find?

3

REACHING ALL LEARNERS

Early Finishers

Challenge students to explain how high each tower will be. (*Frame number + 1 square and a triangle high.*) Invite them to create a line graph of their results and describe the graphs. (*The graphs are lines.*)

Common Misconceptions

- Students will often look for the visual pattern or the numerical pattern, but not see the relationship between them. Students should notice that they are related but are expressed in different ways. Each pattern form should be used to check the accuracy of the other.

How to Help: Ask students to compare the data in the table and describe where it appears on the model. For example, the squares increase by 4 each frame. Where are the 4 squares? Why is it 4? The triangles increase by 1 each frame. Why? On the model, show students how the perimeter increases by 9 each frame. Alternatively, as the students add blocks, fill in the table and ask them to explain where the numbers come from.

- How can you explain the patterns? (*Each tower increases in height by 1 square, the base increases by 2 squares. These increases, with the added triangle, mean that there are 9 extra exposed edges, so the perimeter increases by 9 units.*)

In *Take It Further*, ask students to explain the visuals patterns they see and the rule for building the next frame. Remind them to record their castles in a table so that they can look for patterns.

AFTER

Have volunteers share their findings.

Encourage students to explain their pattern in different ways (numbers, words, and pictures or models)

Invite pairs to share the results from Take It Further. Encourage discussion about different numerical and visual patterns they discover and how they are related.

Sample Response

Parts 1 and 2

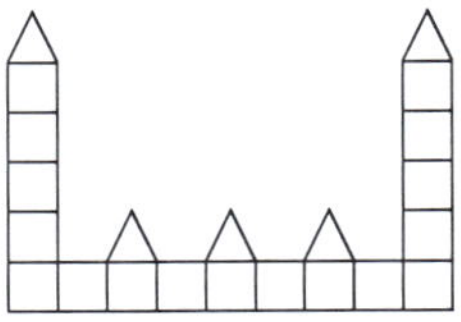

Frame 4

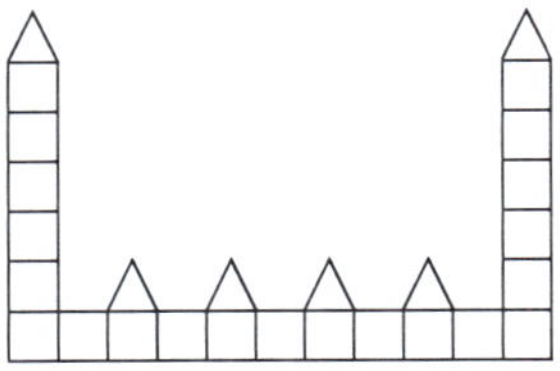

Frame 5

Frame	Squares	Triangles	Perimeter
1	5	2	14
2	9	3	23
3	13	4	32
4	17	5	41
5	21	6	50
6	25	7	59
7	29	8	68
8	33	9	77
9	37	10	86
10	41	11	95

➤ I think I will need 21 squares and 6 triangles to build Frame 5.

➤ From the patterns in the table, I will need 41 squares and 11 triangles to build Frame 10. I made my prediction by continuing the table down to Frame 10.

- The number of squares increases by 4 each frame.
- The number of triangles increases by 1 each frame.
- The perimeter increases by 9 each frame (7 new exposed edges are added from the squares and 2 additional edges from the new triangle. The triangle covers 1 edge of the square on which it sits).

Take It Further

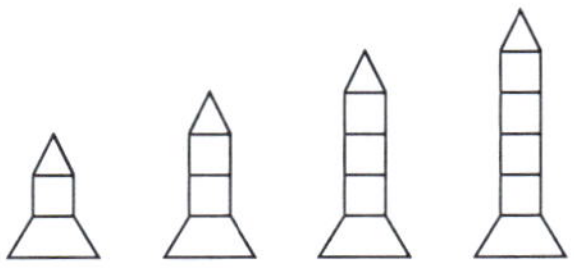

Each frame has 1 trapezoid, 1 square, and 1 triangle. I added 1 square each frame. There is a pattern in the perimeters. The first perimeter is 8 units, and each frame adds 2 units to the perimeter.

ASSESSMENT FOR LEARNING

What to Look For

Understanding concepts

✔ Students understand and explain the physical and numerical patterns and how the perimeter of each castle was determined.

Applying procedures

✔ Students can estimate, calculate, and record the perimeter of castles with accuracy and determine the pattern from one frame to another

Problem solving

✔ Students choose appropriate strategies for estimating, calculating, and recording data. They see patterns and apply what they have learned to new examples.

Communicating

✔ Students use mathematical terminology to analyse number patterns and state the rule for any relationships, and discuss and defend their choice of a patterning rule.

Recording and Reporting

PM 9 Work Sample Records

Cross Strand Performance Assessment Check List: Building Castles

Name	Measurement	Patterning and Algebra			Data Management
	Solves problems related to the calculation of the perimeter of regular and irregular two-dimensional shapes PS/UC/AP	Applies patterning strategies to problem-solving situations PS/AP	Recognizes and discusses the mathematical relationships between and among patterns PS/UC/AP/CM	Identifies, extends, and creates patterns in a variety of contexts PS/UC/AP	Interprets displays of data and presents the information using mathematical terms PS/UC/CM

PS – Problem Solving **UC** – Understanding of Concepts **AP** – Application of Procedures **CM** – Communication

Triangle, Triangle, Triangle

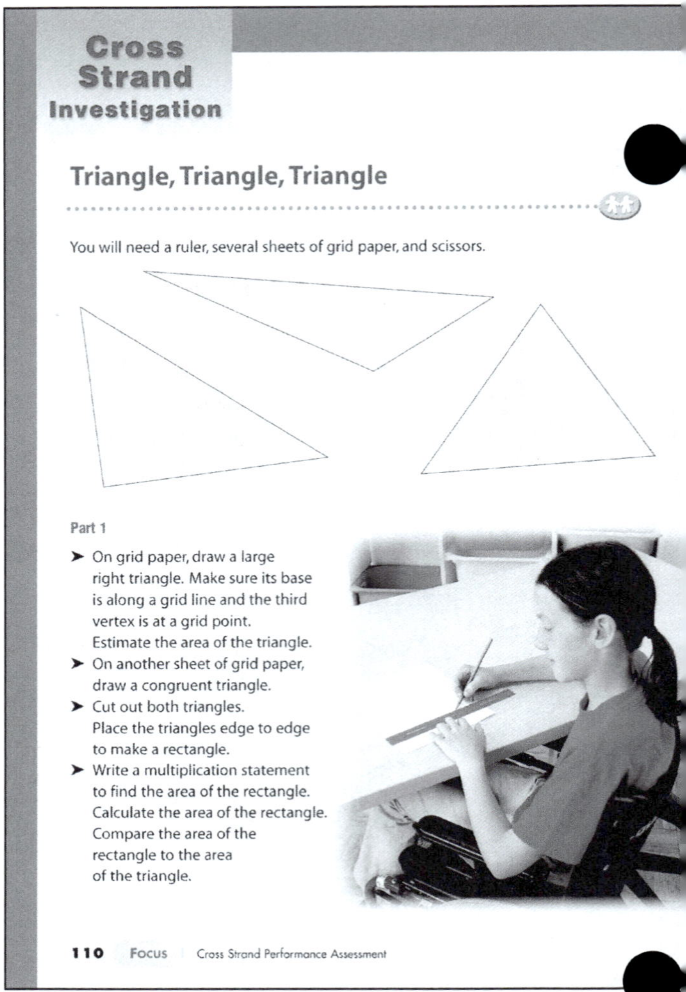
Cross Strand Investigation

Triangle, Triangle, Triangle

You will need a ruler, several sheets of grid paper, and scissors.

Part 1

- On grid paper, draw a large right triangle. Make sure its base is along a grid line and the third vertex is at a grid point. Estimate the area of the triangle.
- On another sheet of grid paper, draw a congruent triangle.
- Cut out both triangles. Place the triangles edge to edge to make a rectangle.
- Write a multiplication statement to find the area of the rectangle. Calculate the area of the rectangle. Compare the area of the rectangle to the area of the triangle.

110 Focus Cross Strand Performance Assessment

LESSON ORGANIZER (80–100 min)

Curriculum Focus: Cross Strand Performance Assessment: Measurement, Geometry and Spatial Sense, Patterning and Algebra

Teacher Materials
- transparency of 1-cm grid paper

Student Materials
- 1-cm grid paper (PM 23)
- rulers
- scissors

Vocabulary: right triangle, acute triangle, obtuse triangle, grid point, vertex

Assessment: Cross Strand Performance Assessment Check List: Triangle, Triangle, Triangle; PM 9 Work Sample Records

Key Math Learnings

1. Students solve problems related to the calculation of the area of regular and irregular figures.
2. Students explore the relationship between the area of a rectangle and the area of a triangle.
3. Students discuss geometric ideas using mathematical language.
4. Students recognize and discuss mathematical relationships between and among patterns.

TEACHING TIP

Students will find it easier to draw a triangle with vertices at grid points if they first mark each vertex with a small dot, then join the dots.

BEFORE Get Started

Ask students:
- What would you need to know if you were to paint the walls of your room? Why? (*The area of the walls; to determine how much paint is needed*)

Tell students they will investigate the area of a triangle by drawing on grid paper. Show students a sheet of grid paper and point out a grid line and grid point. Ask:
- What types of triangles do you know? (*right, acute, obtuse*)
- How can you identify each type of triangle? (*A right triangle has one angle that is a right angle, all the angles of an acute triangle are less than a right angle, one angle of an obtuse triangle is greater than a right angle.*)

Invite students to name the triangles drawn on page 110 of the Student Book.

DURING Investigation

Ongoing Assessment: Observe and Listen

Ask questions, such as:
- How did you estimate the area of your triangle? (*I counted whole squares first, then I tried to match partial squares to make full squares and added these.*)
- How do you know which edges to match? (*I look for sides with the same length.*)

Part 2

➤ Draw a large acute triangle with its base along a grid line and the third vertex at a grid point. Estimate the area of the triangle.
➤ Draw a congruent triangle.
➤ Cut out both triangles. Then, cut along a grid line on each triangle to make 2 triangles.
➤ Arrange the 4 triangles edge to edge to make a rectangle with no gaps or overlaps.
➤ Write a multiplication statement to find the area of the rectangle. Calculate the area of the original acute triangle.

Display Your Work

Create a summary of your work.
Show all your calculations. Explain your thinking.

Take It Further

➤ Draw an obtuse triangle on grid paper. Predict its area.
➤ How did you use what you learned about acute and right triangles to make your prediction?
➤ Find a way to check your prediction.

111

REACHING ALL LEARNERS

Early Finishers

Suggest that students keep the base the same and experiment with the position of the other vertex by placing it along its horizontal gridline (*The rectangle is the same each time. The area of each triangle remains the same.*)

If students have access to a computer, they can use *The Geometer's Sketchpad* to calculate the area of the triangles as the vertex moves along a line parallel to the base. They should notice that the area remains constant.

Common Misconceptions

➤ Students have difficulty, when working with an acute or obtuse triangle, deciding where to cut on a gridline to make a rectangle.
How to Help: Remind students that a rectangle needs right angles, so they need to cut their triangle along the grid line to make two right triangles. Ask them to use a ruler to show you the position of the line through the vertex that will create these.

ESL Strategies

Display a poster of a right triangle, an acute triangle, and an obtuse triangle, with the name of each written underneath.

- How did you move the small triangles? (*I had to flip both pieces of one triangle.*)
- What patterns can you see? (*The width of the rectangle is the length of the line from the vertex to the base. Its length is the length of the base of the original triangle.*)

As students work on *Take It Further*, ask questions such as:

- How can you use what you learned about acute and right triangles to make your prediction?
(*I draw the obtuse triangle with the longest side as the base. When I cut the triangle, I make 2 right triangles, and I know how to predict the area of a right triangle.*)

AFTER

Have volunteers share their findings.

Encourage discussion about the patterns they see. (*The area of a triangle is one-half the area of the rectangle that has length the same as the base of the triangle and width the height of the triangle.*)

Sample Response

Part 1

I estimate the area of the right triangle is about 5 cm^2.
The area of the rectangle is 5 cm × 2 cm = 10 cm^2.
The rectangle is twice the area of the right triangle. The area of the right triangle is one-half the area of the rectangle.

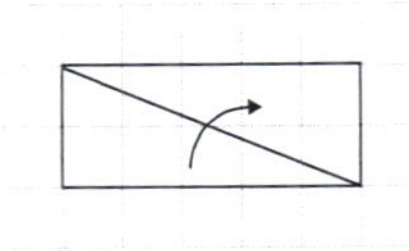

Part 2

I estimate the area of the acute triangle is about 9 cm^2
The area of the rectangle is 6 cm × 3 cm = 18 cm^2.
The rectangle is twice the area of the acute triangle. The area of the acute triangle is half the area of the rectangle, or 9 cm^2.

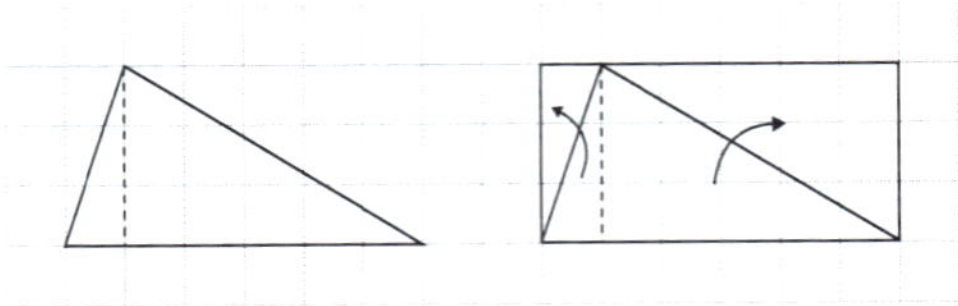

Take It Further

Suppose the vertices of triangles lie at grid points.
Place the longest side of the triangle along the base.
The area of the triangle is 6 cm^2.

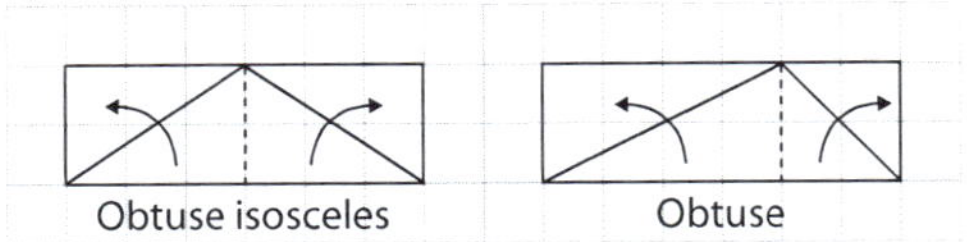

I used the same method as I used above to find the area of an acute triangle and a right triangle.
The area of each rectangle is 6 cm × 2 cm = 12 cm^2. The area of the triangle is always one-half the area of the rectangle.
I can check my prediction by calculating the area of each right triangle and adding the areas together.

ASSESSMENT FOR LEARNING

What to Look For

Understanding concepts

✔ Students understand and explain concepts of area and how the area of a triangle compares to the area of the bounding rectangle.

Applying procedures

✔ Students can estimate, calculate, and record the area of a triangle and rectangle with accuracy.

Problem solving

✔ Students choose appropriate strategies for estimating, calculating, and recording the area of a triangle. They see patterns and apply what they have learned to new examples.

Communicating

✔ Students use mathematical terminology to explain their estimation, measurement, and calculation strategies.

Recording and Reporting

PM 9 Work Sample Records

Cross Strand Performance Check List: Triangle, Triangle, Triangle

Name	Measurement			Geometry and Spatial Sense		Patterning and Algebra
	Solves problems related to the calculation of area of regular and irregular two-dimensional figures PS/AP	Explains the rules used in calculating the area of rectangles and squares UC/AP/CM	Estimates the area of irregular polygons and measures the area by dividing the polygons into parts using grid paper PS/AP	Uses mathematical language to describe geometric ideas (e.g., rectangle, acute triangle) CM/UC	Discusses ideas, makes conjectures, and articulates hypotheses about geometric properties and relationships SP/UC/CM	Recognizes and discusses mathematical relationships between and among patterns PS/UC/AP/CM

PS – Problem Solving **UC** – Understanding of Concepts **AP** – Application of Procedures **CM** – Communication

Rep-Tiles

LESSON ORGANIZER — 80–100 min

Curriculum Focus: Cross Strand Performance Assessment: Geometry and Spatial Sense, Patterning and Algebra, Data Management and Probability

Teacher Materials
- overhead Patterns Blocks or magnetic Pattern Blocks

Student Materials
- Pattern Blocks
- large sheets of paper and markers

Vocabulary: polygon, similar figure, area, perimeter

Assessment: Cross Strand Performance Assessment Check List: Rep-Tiles; PM 9 Work Sample Records

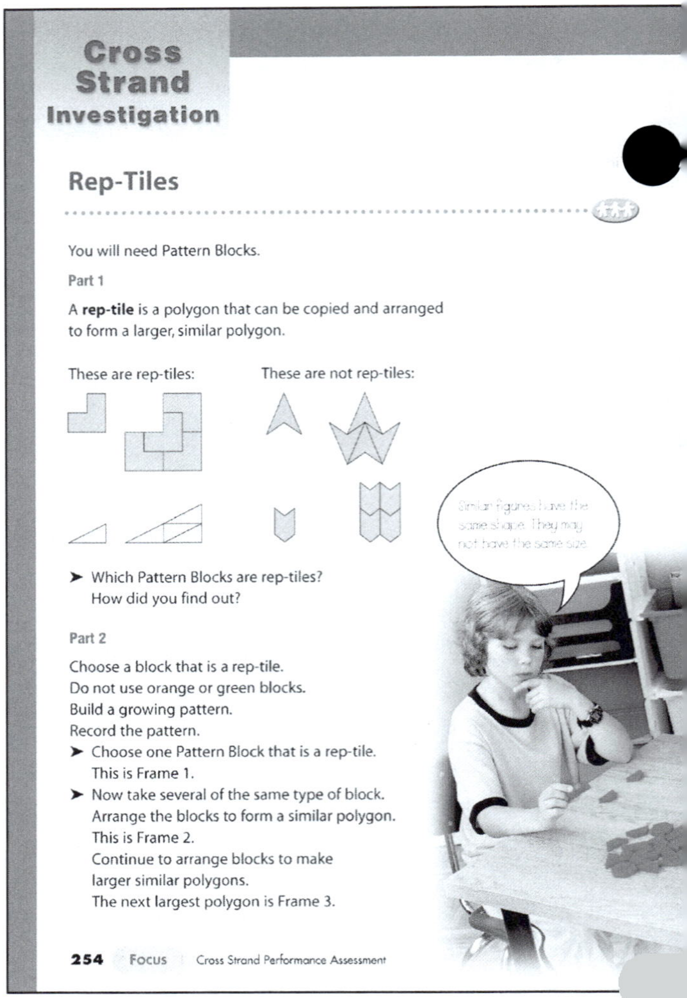
Cross Strand Investigation

Rep-Tiles

You will need Pattern Blocks.

Part 1

A **rep-tile** is a polygon that can be copied and arranged to form a larger, similar polygon.

These are rep-tiles: These are not rep-tiles:

➤ Which Pattern Blocks are rep-tiles? How did you find out?

Part 2

Choose a block that is a rep-tile.
Do not use orange or green blocks.
Build a growing pattern.
Record the pattern.

➤ Choose one Pattern Block that is a rep-tile. This is Frame 1.

➤ Now take several of the same type of block. Arrange the blocks to form a similar polygon. This is Frame 2. Continue to arrange blocks to make larger similar polygons. The next largest polygon is Frame 3.

254 Focus Cross Strand Performance Assessment

Key Math Learnings

1. Students identify similar figures.
2. Students use mathematical language effectively to describe their findings.
3. Students identify, extend, and create patterns.
4. Students create a table to display patterns
5. Students apply patterning strategies to problem solving situations.

Math Note

Only triangles and parallelograms of the well-known polygons are replicating tiles, or rep-tiles.

BEFORE — Get Started

Use an overhead projector to display an orange Pattern Block square, or draw a square on the board. Ask:

- If one edge of the orange Pattern Block is 1 unit in length, what is the perimeter? Area? (*4 units, 1 square unit*)
- How many more orange Pattern Blocks do I need to make another larger square with side length 2 units? (*3*)

Arrange 4 Pattern Blocks to make this next larger square, keeping the original single Pattern Block visible.

Explain that a "rep-tile" is a name for a polygon that can be copied and arranged to form a larger similar polygon. So, a square is a rep-tile. Ask:

- How many orange Pattern Blocks do I need to make the next larger square? (*9*)
- Can you see a pattern in the number of tiles we needed to make a similar figure? (*Yes, the numbers are the squares of the first 3 whole numbers.*)

Present the *Investigation* found on pages 254 and 255 in the Student Book.

DURING — Investigation

Ongoing Assessment: Observe and Listen

Ask questions such as:

- Why did you select this Pattern Block? (*You showed us the square so we thought the blue rhombus would be a rep-tile.*)
- How many blocks would Frame 4 need? (*16*)

➤ Suppose the side length of the green Pattern Block is 1 unit.
Find the perimeter of each figure.
Suppose the area of the green Pattern Block is 1 square unit.
Find the area of each frame.
Copy and complete the table.

Frame	Number of Blocks	Perimeter	Area
1	1		
2			

Part 3

➤ What patterns can you find in the table?
➤ How many blocks would you need to build Frame 7?
How do you know?
➤ Predict the area and the perimeter of Frame 9.
How did you make your prediction?

Display Your Work

Record your work.
Describe the patterns you found.

Take It Further

Draw a large polygon you think is a rep-tile.
Trace several copies.
Cut them out.
Try to arrange the copies to make a larger similar polygon.
If your polygon is a rep-tile, explain why it works.
If it is not, describe how you could change it to make it work.

255

REACHING ALL LEARNERS

Early Finishers

Ask students if they think all quadrilaterals are rep-tiles. Invite them to investigate all the quadrilaterals they know to determine which are rep-tiles.

Common Misconceptions

➤ Students confuse tiling rep-tiles with other polygons that tile a plane but do not replicate themselves.

How to Help: Remind students that a rep-tile has the same number of sides as the original tile. Show students a hexagon tiling of a plane. Invite students to identify, then count, the sides of one hexagon (*6*). Have them identify and count the sides of that polygon created by the chosen hexagon surrounded by 6 other hexagons (*18*).

ESL Strategies

Partner ESL students with a fluent reader to help follow the directions in the text.

- How did you figure out how many blocks you would need to build Frame 7?
  (*I looked at the pattern in the table. The number of blocks needed is the square of the frame number.*)
- What would be the perimeter of Frame 7? How do you know?
  (*28 units; the perimeter is 4 times the Frame number.*)

In Take It Further, ask questions such as:

- Why did you choose this polygon?
  (*I thought it had an interesting shape.*)
- How did you discover that this shape could be arranged to become a rep-tile?
  (*I made the side lengths multiples of the shortest side. I also made the angles either right angles, or made the angle measures multiples of 60°.*)

AFTER

Have volunteers share their findings.

Encourage students to explain the patterns they discovered in their table.

Invite pairs to share the results from Take It Further. Encourage discussion about their choice of polygon and why they thought it might be a rep-tile, and, if it was not, any changes they thought might be needed to make it a one. Elicit the information that the lengths of the sides of the polygon and the angles at the vertices are important if the figures are to fit together. For example, the trapezoid Pattern Block is a rep-tile because three sides have equal length, the fourth side has length twice that of the other sides, and the angles at the vertices measure either 60° or 120°.

Sample Response

Part 1

All the Pattern Blocks can be turned into rep-tiles except the hexagon.
I found out by creating a similar tile for each Pattern Block except the hexagon.

Part 2

For the blue Pattern Block:

Frame	Number of Blocks	Perimeter	Area
1	1	4	1
2	4	8	4
3	9	12	9

Part 3

➤The number of blocks is the same as the area; the area is equal to the square of the Frame Number; the perimeter is the Frame Number multiplied by 4.

➤49 blocks would be needed for Frame 7, $7 \times 7 = 49$. The number of blocks is equal to the Frame Number multiplied by itself.

➤The area of Frame 9 would be 81 square units and the perimeter 36 units. The area is equal to the Frame Number multiplied by itself, $9 \times 9 = 81$. The perimeter is the Frame Number multiplied by 4, $4 \times 9 = 36$.

Take It Further

This is a rep-tile because I can make a similar figure that is 4 times its size from 4 copies.

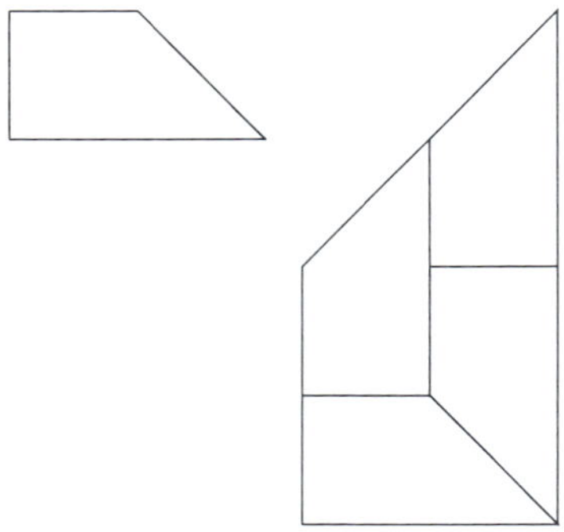

ASSESSMENT FOR LEARNING

What to Look For

Understanding concepts

✔ Students are able to find the perimeter and area of polygons.
✔ Students are able to recognize similar figures, using transformations.

Applying procedures

✔ Students can create a table displaying patterns.
✔ Students are able to identify and extend patterns.

Problem solving

✔ Students are able to identify which Pattern Blocks are rep-tiles.

Communicating

✔ Students are able to communicate their reasoning as to which Pattern Blocks are rep-tiles.
✔ Student are able ot use appropriate terminology to describe the patterns found in their tables.

Recording and Reporting

PM 9 Work Sample Records

Cross Strand Performance Check List: Rep-Tiles

Name	Data Management	Geometry and Spatial Sense	Patterning and Algebra	
	Creates a table to identify patterns AP	Identifies similar figures using transformations UC	Applies patterning strategies to problem-solving situations PS	Identifies, describes using appropriate terminology, and extends patterns found in a table CM

PS – Problem Solving **UC** – Understanding of Concepts **AP** – Application of Procedures **CM** – Communication

The Domino Effect

LESSON ORGANIZER 80–100 min

Curriculum Focus: Cross Strand Performance Assessment: Measurement, Patterning and Algebra, Data Management and Probability
Student Materials
- 70 dominoes per group
- metre stick
- stopwatch
- grid paper

Vocabulary: line graph
Assessment: Cross Strand Performance Assessment Check List: The Domino Effect; PM 9 Work Sample Records

Key Math Learnings

1. Students measure time to the nearest second.
2. Students collect and record data in a table.
3. Students describe patterns in data displayed in a table.
4. Students construct a labelled line graph.
5. Students interpret a line graph using mathematical terms.

Cross Strand Investigation

The Domino Effect

You will need dominoes, a metre stick, a stopwatch, and grid paper.

Part 1

- Begin with 20 dominoes.
  Stand them on end, 3 cm apart.
  Use a stopwatch.
  Push one domino at one end, so all the dominoes fall.
  Time how long it takes them to fall.
  Record the number of dominoes and the time in a table.
- Repeat with 30 dominoes, 40 dominoes, 50 dominoes, up to 80 dominoes.
- Describe any patterns you see in the table.
- Predict how long it would take 120 dominoes to fall.
  How did you make your prediction?

Part 2

Draw a line graph to display the data in your table.
Describe the graph.
About how long would it take 35 dominoes to topple?
How do you know?

402 Focus | Cross Strand Performance Assessment

TEACHING TIPS

This investigation requires the frequent setting up of dominoes in a line. A strip of masking tape with markings 3 cm apart will help space the dominoes correctly and reduce the likelihood of knocking over them with the metre stick. A stable flat surface at least 250 cm is required. Avoid setting the dominoes up on a carpet.

BEFORE Get Started

Tell the class that according to the *Guinness Book of World Records 2003*, the world record for the most dominoes toppled is 3 847 295. This took place on November 15, 2002, Domino Day in the Netherlands. There is no indication how long it took to topple the dominoes.

Ask:

- Have any of you set up a toppling domino display? If so, what happened?
  (Yes. I touched the first domino and it knocked over the domino next to it, all down the line.)

Explain to the students that this investigation will have them explore how long it takes for small numbers of dominoes to topple over. They will gather data for different numbers of dominoes and graph their results.

Present the *Investigation*. Have students work in small groups. One student could take the role of domino arranger, another could be the timer, while a third records the data. They could rotate roles as they conduct the experiments. You may wish to tell students that it may take several attempts to set up the dominoes, but that to achieve accurate results the dominoes must be aligned carefully.

Display Your Work

Report your findings using pictures, numbers, and words.

Take It Further

Investigate different arrangements of dominoes.
What effect does placing the dominoes closer together have on the time it takes them to topple? Explain.
Arrange the dominoes in a curve.
How long does it take them to topple?

403

REACHING ALL LEARNERS

Early Finishers

Early finishers can group together and continue investigating toppling times for increasing numbers of dominoes. If Internet access is available, students may investigate the many websites on domino toppling or the various games of dominoes.

Common Misconceptions

➤Students have difficulty interpreting their line graph.

How to Help: If the dominoes were not lined up in a line, the results will vary and the graph may show anomalies. Encourage students to repeat their experiment, setting up the dominoes very carefully.

ESL Strategies

To help ESL students understand how to conduct the experiment, direct their attention to the photograph on page 403 of the Student Book.

DURING Investigation

Ongoing Assessment: Observe and Listen

Ask questions, such as:

- Were you able to obtain an accurate timing on the first topple?
  (*No, we had to redo the 20 dominoes a couple of times. The stopwatch didn't start at the same time as the first domino was tipped over.*)
- Do you see any patterns with your data?
  (*No, we thought it would take twice as long for 40 dominos to topple over than 20, but it took longer!*)

As students complete Take it Further, ask questions, such as:

- What did you notice when the dominoes were closer together?
  (*They toppled much faster than when they were farther apart.*)
- How will you arrange the dominoes in a curve? (*The dominoes need to be closer together on the inside of the curve.*)

AFTER

Have volunteers share their findings.

Encourage students to describe the shape of their graphs. Have the class compare all the graphs obtained and describe similarities and differences. Brainstorm reasons why the graphs may differ. If groups placed their dominoes on different surfaces, have students to compare the resulting graphs and discuss the effect of the contact surface.

Ask groups who worked on Take It Further to share their results with the class. Encourage discussion about the various arrangements the teams explored and the results obtained.

Sample Response

Part 1

Number of Dominoes	Time (seconds)
20	1.5
30	2.2
40	3.0
50	4.0
60	4.9
70	5.9
80	7.0

➤As the number of dominoes increases by 10, the time taken to topple the dominoes increases by about 0.8 s.

➤For 120 dominoes it would take about 10 s. My table shows it takes 3 s to topple 40 dominoes and 7 s to topple 80. Since 80 + 40 is 120, I added the times, to get my estimate of 10s.

Part 2

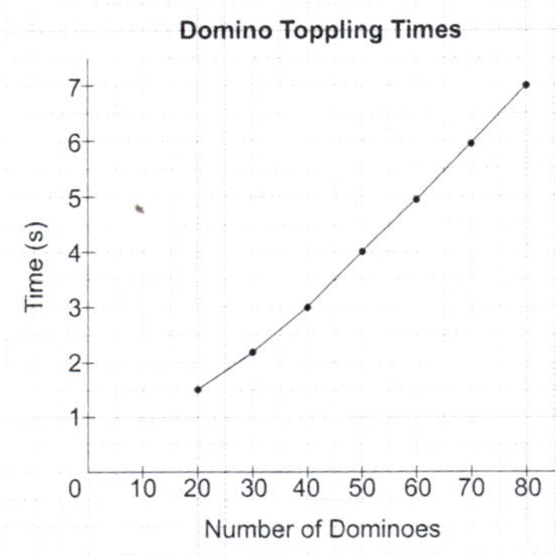

The graph slopes upward to the right.
From the graph, I think it would take about 2.6 s to topple 35 dominoes. It takes about 2.2 s to topple 30 dominoes and 3 s to knock over 40. Since 35 is halfway between 30 and 40, I estimate 2.6 s, which is halfway between 2.2 and 3 s.

Take It Further

The closer together the dominoes are, the faster they fall down. The shorter the distance is between tiles, the less time it takes for them to topple.
Thirty dominoes will take longer to topple if the dominoes are placed 3 cm apart along the inside of the curve than if placed in a straight line.

ASSESSMENT FOR LEARNING

What to Look For

Understanding concepts

✔ Students can collect and record data in a table, and construct a line graph of the data.

Applying procedures

✔ Student can measure time intervals to the nearest second.
✔ Students can create a graph from a set of data and interpret the data displayed.

Problem solving

✔ Students can use a graph to estimate and make predictions.

Communicating

✔ Students interpret a line graph using mathematical terms.

Recording and Reporting

PM 9 Work Sample Records

Cross Strand Performance Check List: The Domino Effect

Name	Data Management			Patterning and Algebra	Measurement
	Collects and records data in a table UC	Constructs a labelled line graph UC/AP	Interprets a line graph using mathematical terms PS/CM	Describes patterns in data recorded in a table. UC/CM	Measures time to the nearest second. AP

PS – Problem Solving **UC** – Understanding of Concepts **AP** – Application of Procedures **CM** – Communication

Addison Wesley
Mathematics
Makes Sense

Program Authors

Peggy Morrow
Ralph Connelly
Bryn Keyes
Jason Johnston
Steve Thomas
Jeananne Thomas
Angela D'Alessandro
Maggie Martin Connell
Don Jones
Michael Davis
Sharon Jeroski
Trevor Brown
Nora Alexander
Cynthia Pratt Nicolson

Printed and bound in Canada

8 9 MP 18 17

PEARSON
Education
Canada

Addison Wesley

Ontario

Math Makes Sense 5

Ontario

Teacher Guide

Unit 1: Number Patterns

PEARSON
Addison Wesley

UNIT 1

Number Patterns

"Mathematicians continue to search for and discover new patterns and relationships. Applications of mathematical patterns have lead to solutions of real-world problems that were once thought to be unsolvable. Patterns are powerful ideas."

—John A. Van de Walle

FOCUS STRAND
Patterning and Algebra

SUPPORTING STRAND
Number Sense and Numeration

Mathematics Background

What Are the Big Ideas?

- Patterns exist throughout mathematics.
- A number pattern provides an opportunity for students to articulate and express a generalization.
- A model provides an opportunity to organize patterns and examine different representations.
- A pattern can be used to represent a situation and to solve problems.

How Will the Concepts Develop?

Students investigate number patterns by writing rules for the patterns and extending the patterns.

Students are introduced to the concept of an Input/Output machine and its related table. Students determine the relationships in a table and consolidate their understanding by creating Input/Output machines.

Students model patterns with tables, then use the tables to extend the patterns and solve problems.

Why Are These Concepts Important?

Recognizing patterns and making generalizations are skills used throughout mathematics. These skills provide the foundation for algebraic reasoning and inquiry.

Working with an Input/Output table prepares students for more advanced algebra that involves functions.

Modelling patterns relates geometry patterns and number patterns.

Materials for This Unit

You may wish to collect materials such as Terry Fox Marathon of Hope pamphlets, pledge sheets, and data for the Unit Problem. These resources are available at www.terryfoxrun.org.

Curriculum Overview

Cluster 1: Understanding Number Patterns

Overall Expectations
- Recognize and discuss the mathematical relationships between and among patterns. (5m91)
- Identify, extend, and create patterns in a variety of contexts. (5m92)
- Analyse and discuss patterning rules. (5m93)
- Create tables to display patterns. (5m94)

Specific Expectations
- Recognize the relationship between the position of a number and its value. (5m96)
- Identify, extend, and create patterns that identify changes in terms of two variables. (5m97)
- Analyse number patterns and state the rule for any relationships. (5m102)
- Discuss and defend the choice of a pattern rule. (5m103)
- Given a rule expressed in informal mathematical language, extend a pattern. (5m104)

Cluster 2: Solving Problems

Overall Expectations
- Recognize and discuss the mathematical relationships between and among patterns. (5m91)
- Identify, extend, and create patterns in a variety of contexts. (5m92)
- Analyse and discuss patterning rules. (5m93)
- Create tables to display patterns. (5m94)
- Apply patterning strategies to problem-solving situations. (5m95)

Specific Expectations
- Describe patterns encountered in any context, make models of the patterns, and create charts to display the patterns. (5m98)
- Identify and extend patterns to solve problems in meaningful contexts. (5m99)
- Pose and solve problems by applying a patterning strategy. (5m101)
- Discuss and defend the choice of a pattern rule. (5m103)
- Use patterns in a table of values to make predictions. (5m105)

Launch
Charity Fundraising

Lesson 1:
Number Patterns and Pattern Rules

Lesson 2:
Creating Number Patterns

Lesson 3:
Modelling Patterns

Lesson 4:
Using Patterns to Solve Problems

Lesson 5:
Strategies Toolkit

Show What You Know

Unit Problem
Charity Fundraising

Curriculum across the Grades

Grade 4	Grade 5	Grade 6
Students count by 3s, 4s, 6s, 7s, 8s, 9s, and 10s to 100.	Students recognize the relationship between the position of a number and its value.	Students recognize relationships and use them to summarize and generalize patterns.
Students recognize mathematical relationships in patterns.	Students identify, extend, and create patterns that identify changes in terms of two variables.	Students identify, extend, and create patterns that identify changes in terms of two variables.
Students demonstrate equivalence in simple numerical equations using concrete materials, drawings, and symbols.	Students describe patterns encountered in any context, make models of the patterns, and create charts to display the patterns.	Students describe patterns encountered in any context, make models of the patterns, and create charts to display the patterns.
Students identify and extend patterns to solve problems in meaningful contexts.	Students identify and extend patterns to solve problems in meaningful contexts.	Students identify and extend patterns to solve problems in meaningful contexts.
Students describe patterns encountered in any context.	Students pose and solve problems by applying a patterning strategy.	Students use a calculator and computer applications to explore patterns.
Students identify and extend patterns to solve problems in meaningful contexts.	Students analyse number patterns and state the rule for any relationship.	Students pose and solve problems by recognizing a pattern.
Students analyse number patterns and state the rule for any relationship.	Students discuss and defend the choice of a pattern rule.	Students analyse number patterns and state the rule for any relationships.
Students pose and solve problems by applying a patterning strategy.	Given a rule expressed in informal mathematical language, students extend a pattern.	Students discuss and defend the choice of a pattern rule.
Students analyse number patterns and state the rule for any relationships.	Students use patterns in a table of values to make predictions.	Given a rule expressed in mathematical language, students extend a pattern.
Students discuss and defend the choice of a pattern rule.		

Additional Activities

What's Next?

For Extra Practice (Appropriate for use after Lesson 1)
Materials: *What's Next?* (Master 1.6)

The work students do: Students work individually to investigate number patterns. They find the missing terms and write each pattern rule.

Take It Further: Challenge students to describe two different patterns that begin with these 3 terms: 10, 20, 40, ...

Have them justify each pattern rule.

Logical/Mathematical
Individual Activity

Patterns with Eleven

For Extension (Appropriate for use after Lesson 1)
Materials: calculators, *Patterns with Eleven* (Master 1.7)

The work students do: Students work in pairs to find patterns in products when 11 is one factor. They use the patterns to write a rule for finding the product when a 2-digit number is multiplied by 11. They use their rule to predict products, then check their predictions using pencil and paper computations, or a calculator.

Take It Further: Challenge students to explain how their rule works for a factor with 2 digits that have a sum greater than 9.

Logical/Mathematical
Partner Activity

What's Missing?

For Extra Practice (Appropriate for use after Lesson 2)
Materials: *What's Missing?* (Master 1.8)

The work students do: Students work individually with Input/Output tables to determine the missing numbers. They look for patterns and describe the rule for each table.

Students should not assume that the numbers in the tables are in ascending or descending order. This challenges the students further.

Take It Further: Students create two different tables with missing numbers, then trade with a classmate to complete her or his tables. Students must ensure they give sufficient data for the patterns to be identified.

Logical/Mathematical
Individual Activity

Perimeter Patterns

For Extra Support (Appropriate for use after Lesson 3)
Materials: Colour Tiles, grid paper, *Perimeter Patterns* (Master 1.9)

The work students do: Students work in pairs. They use Colour Tiles to build the first 4 frames of a growing pattern. Students look for patterns in the perimeters of the figures.

Students predict the perimeters of the 5th and the 6th frames, then build the frames to check. Students make a table to organize their results.

Students write a pattern rule for the perimeters.

Take It Further: Challenge students to use Colour Tiles to create a growing pattern for a partner to use to repeat the activity.

Kinesthetic/Social
Partner Activity

Planning for Unit 1

Planning for Instruction

Suggested Unit time: 1–2 weeks

Lesson	Time	Materials	Program Support
Launch: Charity Fundraising, page 2	10–15 min		
Lesson 1: Number Patterns and Pattern Rules, page 4 Analyse a number pattern and state the pattern rule.	40–50 min	2-column charts calculators	Master 1.10: Step-by-Step 1 Master 1.16: Extra Practice 1 PM 17: 2-Column Chart
Lesson 2: Creating Number Patterns, page 7 Use an Input/Output machine to create number patterns.	40–50 min	2-column charts calculators	PM 17: 2-Column Chart Master 1.11: Step-by-Step 2 Master 1.16: Extra Practice 1
Lesson 3: Modelling Patterns, page 10 Model patterns and make predictions.	80–100 min	overhead geoboard geoboards geobands square dot paper 2-column charts 3-column charts 4-column charts Colour Tiles 0.5-cm grid paper 1-cm grid paper	PM 17: 2-Column Chart PM 18: 3-Column Chart PM 19: 4-Column Chart PM 22: 0.5-cm Grid Paper PM 23: 1-cm Grid Paper PM 25: Square Dot Paper Master 1.12: Step-by-Step 3 Master 1.17: Extra Practice 2 PM 13: Hundred Chart
Lesson 4: Using Patterns to Solve Problems, page 14 Pose and solve problems by applying a patterning strategy.	40–50 min	2-column charts calculators	PM 17: 2-Column Chart Master 1.13: Step-by-Step 4 Master 1.17: Extra Practice 2
Lesson 5: Strategies Toolkit, page 18 Interpret a problem and select an appropriate strategy.	40–50 min	calculators	
Show What You Know, page 20 Assessment	40–50 min	2-column charts calculators yellow Pattern Blocks	PM 17: 2-Column Chart
Unit Problem: Charity Fundraising, page 22 Assessment	40–50 min	poster paper coloured pencils 2-column charts	PM 17: 2-Column Chart

Planning for Assessment

Purpose	Tools and Process	Recording and Reporting
Diagnostic	*Unit Launch* Question; conference; scaffold problems throughout the unit	PM 8: Conference Prompts
Formative	*Explore* – Ongoing Assessment: Observe and Listen	Master: 1.2 Ongoing Observations: Number Patterns PM 1: Inquiry Process Check List PM 6: Observation Record 1 PM 7: Observation Record 2 PM 8: Conference Prompts
	Prompt student's self-assessment	PM 2: Self-Assessment PM 3: Self-Assessment: Problem Solving
	Practice – Assessment Focus Questions	PM 9: Work Sample Records
	Review student work; provide feedback; scaffold as needed; select key pieces	
Summative	*Show What You Know* *Unit Problem* – Performance Assessment Unit Test	Master 1.1 Unit Rubric: Number Patterns Master 1.3 Performance Assessment Rubric: Charity Fundraising Master 1.4 Unit Summary: Number Patterns
	Review assessment records; add unit results to ongoing records	PM 10: Summary Class Records: Strands PM 11: Summary Class Records: Achievement Categories PM 12: Summary Record: Individual
Learning Skills/Mathematical Disposition	Observe and record throughout unit	PM 4: Learning Skills Check List PM 5: Mathematical Dispositions and Learning Skills

Program Masters (PM) are in the *Grade 5 Planning and Program Masters* module.
Extra Practice Masters are on the CD-ROM.

Charity Fundraising

LESSON ORGANIZER 10–15 min

Curriculum Focus: Activate prior knowledge about number patterns and tables.

ASSUMED PRIOR KNOWLEDGE

- ✓ Students can extend a pattern from a pattern rule.
- ✓ Students can use a table to organize data.
- ✓ Students can describe a pattern.
- ✓ Students can add decimals.
- ✓ Students can convert metres to kilometres, and vice versa.

Teaching notes for Cross Strand Investigation *Building Castles* are in the *Additional Assessment Support* module.

ACTIVATE PRIOR LEARNING

Have students read the *Unit Launch.*

Ask questions, such as:

- What does each table show?
  (*The first table shows the amount of money Carl gets from different pledges. The second table shows how the number of laps relates to distance.*)
- Why would Carl use a table to record data?
  (*A table makes it easier to see patterns and predict results.*)

Discuss the first question, and record students' answers on the board.
(*Sample answers: Amount per Kilometre: start at 10¢; add 10¢ each time. Amount of Pledge: start at $1.00; add $1.00 each time.*)

Elicit that the pledge is 10 times the amount per kilometre. For the second question, a pledge of 60¢ per kilometre will be a pledge of $10 \times 60¢ = 600¢$ or $6.00.

Discuss the second table. Have students describe the relationship between number of laps and distance. Note that distance run in metres is converted to kilometres.

Have a volunteer extend the table on the board.

Ask:

- How does knowing the number of laps tell you the distance?
  (*Multiply the number of laps by 0.4 km.*)
- What pattern do you see in the distance?
  (*Start at 0.4 km. Add 0.4 km each time.*)

Discuss the third question.
(*Sample answer: I could extend the table until I get to 10.0 km in the distance column. That would be 25 laps.*)

Tell students that, in this unit, they will investigate number patterns. They will use number patterns to solve problems. At the end of this unit, students will plan a charity fundraiser.

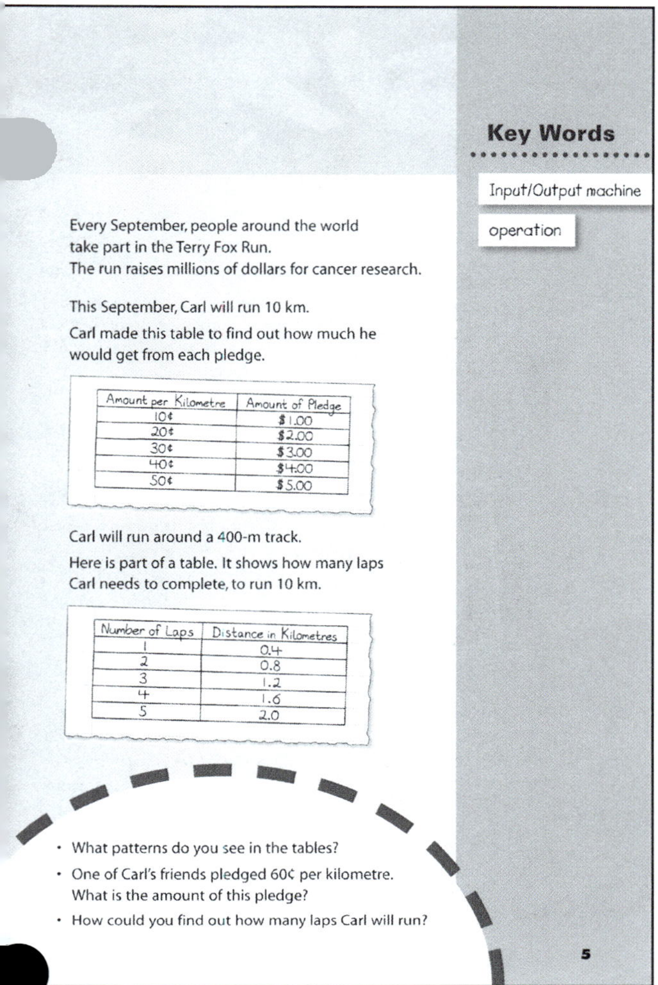
Key Words

Input/Output machine

operation

Every September, people around the world take part in the Terry Fox Run.
The run raises millions of dollars for cancer research.

This September, Carl will run 10 km.

Carl made this table to find out how much he would get from each pledge.

Amount per Kilometre	Amount of Pledge
10¢	$1.00
20¢	$2.00
30¢	$3.00
40¢	$4.00
50¢	$5.00

Carl will run around a 400-m track.

Here is part of a table. It shows how many laps Carl needs to complete, to run 10 km.

Number of Laps	Distance in Kilometres
1	0.4
2	0.8
3	1.2
4	1.6
5	2.0

- What patterns do you see in the tables?
- One of Carl's friends pledged 60¢ per kilometre. What is the amount of this pledge?
- How could you find out how many laps Carl will run?

5

LITERATURE CONNECTIONS FOR THE UNIT

Pattern by Pluckrose. New York: Children's Press, 2002.
ISBN: 0516454552
A picture book of brilliantly coloured photographs showing patterns.

Anno's Mysterious Multiplying Jar by Anno and Anno.
New York: PaperStar, 2002.
ISBN: 0698117530
This book uses colourful illustrations to introduce factorials. A jar contains a sea, the sea contains an island, this island contains 2 countries, each country contains 3 mountains, and so on. As well as the illustrations, there is a dot diagram to represent each step.

Anno's Magic Seeds by Anno and Anno. New York: Putnam Publishing Group, 1999.
ISBN 0698116186
A wizard gives Jack two magic seeds. He is to eat one and plant the other, which will grow into a plant bearing 2 new seeds. He repeats this for a few years, then tries planting both seeds to get 4 new seeds, then planting 3 of these to get 6 seeds, and so on.

DIAGNOSTIC ASSESSMENT

What to Look For	What to Do
✔ Students recognize that patterns result from repetition. ✔ Students can analyse a number pattern and state the pattern rule. ✔ Students can describe and extend patterns.	***Extra Support:*** Students who have difficulty finding patterns may benefit from more specific questions. For example, ask, "Do you see a pattern in the Amount per Kilometre column? How would you describe the pattern?" *Work on this skill during Lesson 1.* Students who have difficulty working with the decimal distances in kilometres may benefit from converting them to metres. Students who cannot describe a pattern may benefit from modelling the pattern with concrete materials or with drawings. For example, students could use Base Ten Blocks to model each additional lap Carl needs to run to complete the 10-km distance. *Work on this skill during Lessons 1 and 3.*

Number Patterns and Pattern Rules

LESSON ORGANIZER 40–50 min

Curriculum Focus: Analyse a number pattern and state the pattern rule. (5m96, 5m97, 5m102, 5m103, 5m104)

Student Materials
- 2-column charts (PM 17)

Optional
- Step-by-Step 1 (Master 1.10)
- Extra Practice 1 (Master 1.16)
- calculators

Vocabulary: pattern rule

Assessment: Master 1.2 Ongoing Observations: Number Patterns

Key Math Learning

A pattern rule can be identified by looking at how pairs of consecutive terms change.

LESSON 1

Number Patterns and Pattern Rules

Is each pattern a growing pattern, a shrinking pattern, or a repeating pattern?
- 9, 14, 19, 24, 29, ...
- 8, 5, 1, 8, 5, 1, ...
- 48, 46, 44, 42, 40, ...
- 4, 8, 16, 32, 64, ...

What is each pattern rule?

Explore

For each number pattern:
- 3, 4, 6, 9, 13, ... 18, 24, 31, 39, 48
- 3, 4, 6, 7, 9, ... 10, 12, 13, 15, 16
- 1, 4, 3, 6, 5, 8, ... 7, 10, 9, 12, 11
- 1, 2, 5, 10, 17, 26, ... 37, 50, 65, 82, 101

➤ Identify the pattern rule.
Write the next 5 terms.

➤ Make up a similar pattern.
Trade patterns with a classmate.
Write the rule for each of your classmate's patterns.

Show and Share

Share your patterns with other classmates.
How do you know each pattern rule is correct?
For any pattern, did you find more than one rule?
Explain.

6 LESSON FOCUS | Analyse a number pattern and state the pattern rule.

BEFORE Get Started

Discuss the patterns shown at the beginning of the lesson. For each pattern, ask a volunteer to read the numbers, identify the type of pattern, and state the pattern rule.
(*The first is a growing pattern. Start at 9. Add 5 each time. The second is a repeating pattern. Start at 8. Subtract 3, then subtract 4, then add 7. Repeat this process. The third is a shrinking pattern. Start at 48. Subtract 2 each time. The fourth is a growing pattern. Start at 4. Multiply by 2 each time.*)

Then ask:
- Why do we use pattern rules?
  (*We use them to describe, extend, and create patterns.*)

Present *Explore*. Students should record each pattern before they extend it.

DURING Explore

Ongoing Assessment: Observe and Listen

Ask questions, such as:
- How do the numbers grow in the first pattern?
  (*The number added increases by 1 each time.*)
- How did you extend the pattern?
  (*Each time, I added a number that was 1 greater than the previous number added.*)
- What is the pattern rule for the second pattern? (*Start at 3. Alternately add 1, then add 2.*)
- How are the first and second patterns alike? Different? (*They are both growing patterns; they both start with 3. In the first pattern, you add a different number each time. In the second pattern, you alternately add 1 then 2.*)
- How is the third pattern different from the others? (*In the other patterns, you always add; in the third pattern, you alternate between adding 3 and subtracting 1.*)

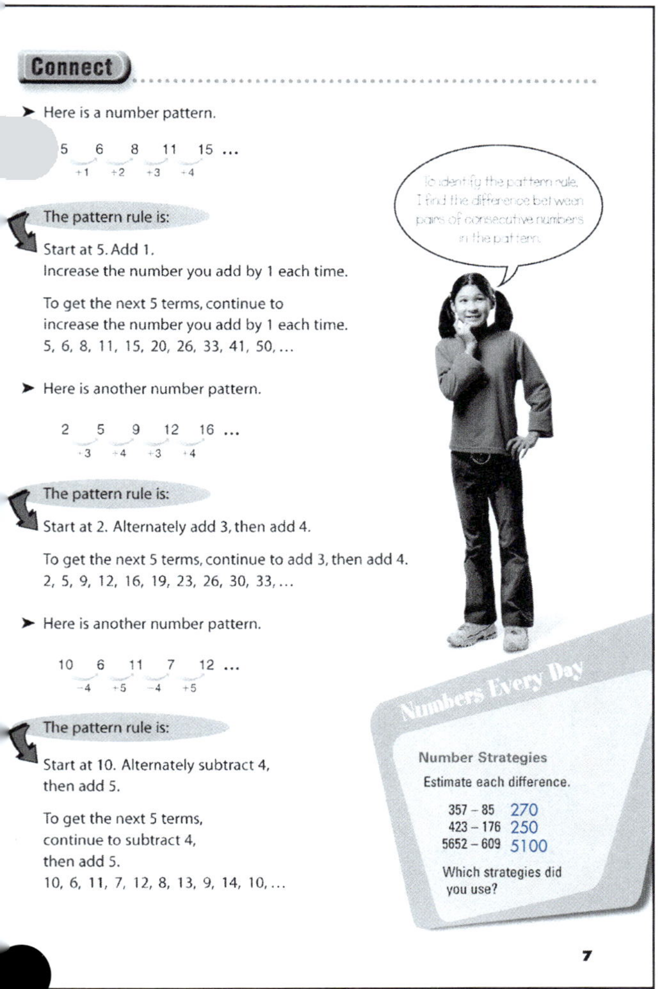
Connect

➤ Here is a number pattern.

5 6 8 11 15 …
+1 +2 +3 +4

The pattern rule is:

Start at 5. Add 1.
Increase the number you add by 1 each time.

To get the next 5 terms, continue to increase the number you add by 1 each time.
5, 6, 8, 11, 15, 20, 26, 33, 41, 50, …

➤ Here is another number pattern.

2 5 9 12 16 …
+3 +4 +3 +4

The pattern rule is:

Start at 2. Alternately add 3, then add 4.

To get the next 5 terms, continue to add 3, then add 4.
2, 5, 9, 12, 16, 19, 23, 26, 30, 33, …

➤ Here is another number pattern.

10 6 11 7 12 …
−4 +5 −4 +5

The pattern rule is:

Start at 10. Alternately subtract 4, then add 5.

To get the next 5 terms, continue to subtract 4, then add 5.
10, 6, 11, 7, 12, 8, 13, 9, 14, 10, …

Numbers Every Day

Number Strategies

Estimate each difference.

357 − 85 270
423 − 176 250
5652 − 609 5100

Which strategies did you use?

7

REACHING ALL LEARNERS

Early Finishers

Have students create several number patterns and erase one term from each of their patterns. They exchange patterns and try to find the missing terms in their classmates' patterns.

Common Misconceptions

➤ Students think that all number patterns involve adding (or subtracting) the same number each time.

How to Help: Have students work with examples of number patterns in which the number being added (or subtracted) changes each time, or alternates between 2 numbers, and examples of patterns involving multiplication. If the pattern cannot be extended by adding (or subtracting) the same number, students should examine consecutive terms to find the pattern in the differences.

ESL Strategies

ESL students can improve their language skills by working in groups with students for whom English is their first language. In groups of 3, one student is the interviewer, another student is the interviewee, and the third student takes notes. The interview could be based on a statement such as, "When (or where) are you likely to see multiples in a pattern?"

Numbers Every Day

Some students may round the numbers to the nearest ten. Others may prefer to use front-end estimation.

- What is the pattern rule for the fourth pattern? *(Start at 1. Add 1. Increase the number you add by 2 each time.)*

Watch for students who cannot identify a pattern rule. Encourage them to subtract consecutive numbers in the pattern, using a calculator if they need to, to find out which number is added or subtracted each time.

AFTER Connect

Invite students to share their number patterns. Discuss the strategies they used to find each pattern rule. If students found more than one pattern rule for a pattern, ask them how they know the pattern rules are both correct.

To review the use of the word *alternately* when describing a pattern, ask:

- What do we mean when we say *alternately* add one of two numbers? *(Add the first number, then add the second number, then add the first number, then add the second number, and so on.)*

Use *Connect* to review some different kinds of number patterns.

Practice

Have calculators available for all questions.

Assessment Focus: Question 7

Students should understand that the terms in a number pattern change in a predictable way. They understand that a pattern must have sufficient terms to be able to identify the pattern rule. Students should include several types of number patterns. For example, same-step growing patterns, changing-step growing patterns, patterns involving repeated multiplication, and patterns involving alternating operations.

Sample Answers

2. a) Start at 1. Alternately add 1, then add 2.
   b) Start at 2. Alternately add 2, then subtract 1.
   c) Start at 98. Alternately subtract 13, then add 2.
   d) Start at 1. Alternately multiply by 10, then subtract 3.
3. a) Start at 3. Alternately add 20, then subtract 10.
   b) Start at 99. Alternately subtract 1, then add 100.
   c) Start at 2. Alternately multiply by 11, then subtract 10.
4. To find the 7th term directly, subtract 48 because 6 × 8 = 48, and we need to subtract 8 six times to find the 7th term.
5. a) Start at 74. Add 74 each time.
   b) Start at 100. Add 98. Decrease the number you add by 1 each time.
   c) Start at 1122. Alternately subtract 10, then subtract 11.
7. There are many different patterns that begin 6, 12, …. Here are some examples:
   6, 12, 18, 24, 30, 36, …; Start at 6. Add 6 each time.
   6, 12, 13, 19, 20, 26, …; Start at 6. Alternately add 6, then add 1.
   6, 12, 24, 48, 96, 192, …; Start at 6. Multiply by 2 each time.
   6, 12, 10, 16, 14, 20, …; Start at 6. Alternately add 6, then subtract 2.
   6, 12, 19, 27, 36, 46, …; Start at 6. Add 6. Increase the number you add by 1 each time.

REFLECT: Example: 2, 6, 10, 14, 18, …
The first term is 2. The numbers increase. I look at how the number changes from the first term to the second. It increases by 4. Test to see if this works for the third term, fourth term, and fifth term. It does; therefore, the pattern rule is: Start at 2. Add 4 each time.

Practice

Use a calculator when it helps.

1. Write the first 5 terms of each pattern.
   a) Start at 3. Add 9 each time. 3, 12, 21, 30, 39
   b) Start at 5. Add 2. Increase the number you add by 2 each time. 5, 7, 11, 17,
   c) Start at 7. Alternately add 3, then subtract 1. 7, 10, 9, 12, 11
2. Write the next 4 terms in each pattern. Write each pattern rule.
   a) 1, 2, 4, 5, 7, 8, … 10, 11, 13, 14
   b) 2, 4, 3, 5, 4, 6, 5, … 7, 6, 8, 7
   c) 98, 85, 87, 74, 76, … 63, 65, 52, 54
   d) 1, 10, 7, 70, 67, 670, … 667, 6670, 6667,
3. Find each missing term. Write the pattern rule.
   a) 3, 23, 13, 33, □, 43, 33, … 23
   b) 99, 98, 198, 197, □, 296, 396, … 297
   c) 2, 22, 12, 132, 122, 1342, □, … 1332
4. What is the 7th term of this pattern?
   Start at 200. Subtract 8 each time. 152
   How could you find the 7th term without writing the first 6 terms?
5. Find each missing term. Write the pattern rule.
   a) 74, 148, 222, □, 370, … 296
   b) 100, 198, 295, 391, □, 580, … 486
   c) 1122, 1112, 1101, 1091, 1080, □, 1059, … 1070
6. What is the 10th term of this pattern?
   Start at 13. Alternately subtract 4, then add 5. 13
7. The first 2 terms of a pattern are 6, 12, ….
   How many different patterns can you write with these 2 terms?
   For each pattern, list the first 6 terms and write the pattern rule.
   Show your work.

Reflect

How do you find the pattern rule for a number pattern?
Use an example to explain.

8 ASSESSMENT FOCUS | Question 7

ASSESSMENT FOR LEARNING

What to Look For	What to Do
Understanding concepts ✔ Students understand that the terms in a number pattern change in a predictable way. ✔ Students understand that a number pattern can be described by a pattern rule. ***Applying procedures*** ✔ Students can identify, extend, and create patterns using pattern rules.	***Extra Support:*** Have students use Step-by-Step 1 (Master 1.10) to complete question 7. ***Extra Practice:*** Have students work independently to create and extend different types of number patterns. They can trade patterns, then try to identify the rules for their classmates' patterns. Students can do the Additional Activity, *What's Next?* (Master 1.6). Students can complete Extra Practice 1 (Master 1.16). ***Extension:*** Students can do the Additional Activity, *Patterns with Eleven* (Master 1.7).

Recording and Reporting
Master 1.2 Ongoing Observations: Number Patterns

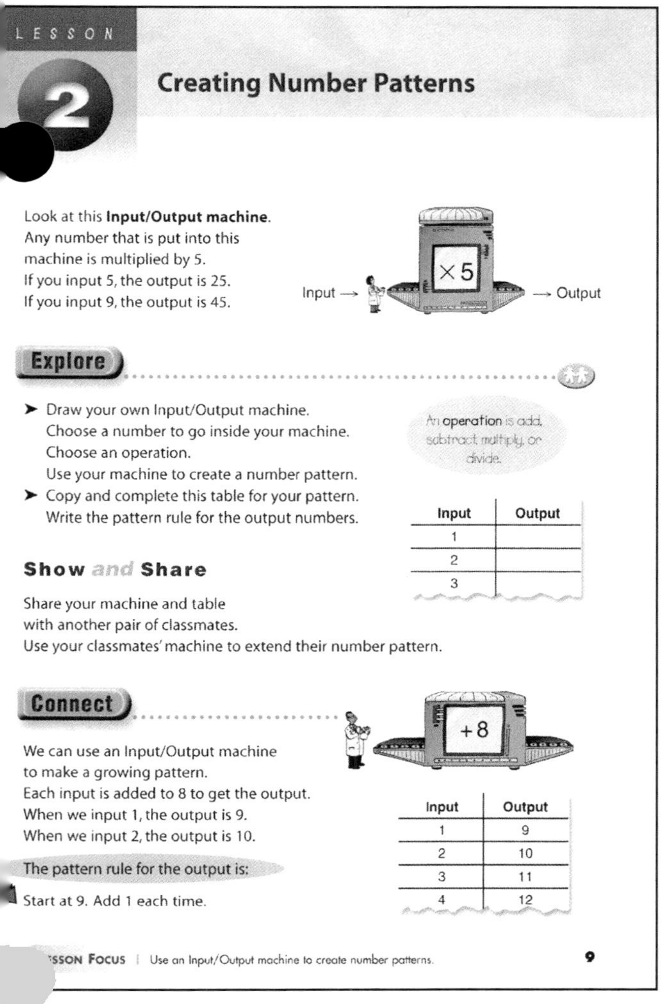

LESSON 2

Creating Number Patterns

Look at this **Input/Output machine**.
Any number that is put into this machine is multiplied by 5.
If you input 5, the output is 25.
If you input 9, the output is 45.

Explore

➤ Draw your own Input/Output machine.
Choose a number to go inside your machine.
Choose an operation.
Use your machine to create a number pattern.
➤ Copy and complete this table for your pattern.
Write the pattern rule for the output numbers.

An **operation** is add, subtract, multiply, or divide.

Input	Output
1	
2	
3	

Show and Share

Share your machine and table with another pair of classmates.
Use your classmates' machine to extend their number pattern.

Connect

We can use an Input/Output machine to make a growing pattern.
Each input is added to 8 to get the output.
When we input 1, the output is 9.
When we input 2, the output is 10.

Input	Output
1	9
2	10
3	11
4	12

The pattern rule for the output is:
Start at 9. Add 1 each time.

LESSON FOCUS | Use an Input/Output machine to create number patterns. 9

Creating Number Patterns

LESSON ORGANIZER — 40–50 min

Curriculum Focus: Use an Input/Output machine to create number patterns. (5m102, 5m104)

Student Materials
- 2-column charts (PM 17)

Optional
- Step-by-Step 2 (Master 1.11)
- Extra Practice 1 (Master 1.16)
- calculators

Vocabulary: input, output, operation

Assessment: Master 1.2 Ongoing Observations: Number Patterns

Key Math Learnings

1. Number patterns can be created using an Input/Output machine.
2. There is a relationship between corresponding input numbers and output numbers.
3. When there is a pattern in the input numbers, there is also a pattern in the output numbers.

Making Connections

Math Link: Ask students to describe how a multiplication table is like an Input/Output machine.

BEFORE — Get Started

Introduce the idea of an Input/Output machine. Describe how an operation (add, subtract, multiply, divide) is performed on the input number to get the output number.

Ask:

- How is a calculator like an Input/Output machine?
  (*A calculator can be used as an Input/Output machine. I can input a number, perform an operation, and the calculator gives me the output number.*)

Present *Explore*. Explain that students are to create their own Input/Output machine that models the one in the Student Book. Distribute copies of a 2-column chart. Have calculators available for students who want to use large numbers.

DURING — Explore

Ongoing Assessment: Observe and Listen

Ask questions, such as:

- Which numbers go in the Input?
  (*1, 2, 3, 4, 5, and so on*)
- Which operation and number did you choose? (*I chose +13.*)
- How did you write the pattern rule for the output numbers?
  (*For +13, the output numbers are 14, 15, 16, 17, 18, …. The pattern rule is: Start at 14. Add 1 each time.*)

Watch for students who do not start with the input numbers given. Encourage them to apply the same rule to each input number. Have them say the pattern rule for the output numbers, then write it.

Watch for students who want to use subtraction. They cannot subtract anything greater than 1 when the first input number is 1. If they do, they will get negative numbers.

REACHING ALL LEARNERS

Alternative Explore

Materials: calculator

Have students use large numbers for the input; perhaps in the hundreds. This will enable them to use subtraction as the operation, without reaching negative output numbers.

Early Finishers

Have students work in pairs with a calculator. They challenge each other to guess the operation and the number for an Input/Output machine. One student enters an Input number on the calculator. He chooses an operation, enters a second number, then presses [=]. He tells his partner the input number, and gives her the calculator. She looks at the answer, and guesses the rule. If she is incorrect, her partner chooses a different input number and follows the same rule. Once the rule is identified, students switch roles.

Common Misconceptions

➤Students apply a different rule to each input number in the same machine.

How to Help: Make sure students understand that the same rule applies for each input number in an Input/Output table.

➤Students cannot find a rule for the Input/Output machine.

How to Help: Have students choose one input number and apply different operations and numbers to get the output number. Make sure they record their attempts. If they find an operation and a number that work, have them check to see if they work for all pairs of input and output numbers.

Practice

Use a calculator when it helps.

1. For each Input/Output machine:
   - Choose 5 numbers to input.
   - Find each output number.
   - Copy and complete the table.

Input	Output

a) Input → [× 9] → Output   b) Input → [+ 12] → Output

2. Copy and complete the table for this Input/Output machine.

Input → [− 7] → Output

Input	Output
20	13
19	12
18	11
17	10
16	9

3. a) Copy and complete the table for this Input/Output machine.

Input → [÷ 6] → Output

Input	Output
36	6
42	7
48	8
54	9
60	10
66	11
72	12

b) What is the pattern rule for the input numbers? The output numbers?

Math Link

Number Sense

When an Input/Output machine uses multiplication, and the input numbers are whole numbers, the output numbers are multiples of the number in the machine.

10

AFTER Connect

Use the students' machines to discuss how an Input/Output machine creates patterns.

Ask:

- In the example on page 9, what do you do to the input number to get the output number? (*Add 8 to each input number.*)
- What is the pattern rule for the output numbers? (*Start at 9. Add 1 each time.*)
- What would you do to the output number to get the input number? (*Working backward, we would subtract 8 from each output number to get the input number.*)

Ensure students understand that when there is a pattern in the input numbers, there is also a pattern in the output numbers. Each input number and its corresponding output number are related in the same way.

Practice

Students will need 2-column charts for questions 1, 2, 3, and 6. Some students may benefit from using a calculator.

Assessment Focus: Question 6

Students should understand how to create an Input/Output machine. They use multiples of a number as input numbers. If there is a pattern in these multiples, then there will also be a pattern in the output numbers.

4. Each table shows the Input/Output from a machine.
- Identify the number and the operation in the machine.
- Continue the patterns.
- Write the next 4 input and output numbers for each table.

a)

Input	Output
2	20
4	40
6	60
8	80
10	100

b)

Input	Output
500	485
450	435
400	385
350	335
300	285

5. For each table:
- Write the pattern rules for the output numbers and the input numbers.
- The patterns continue. Write the next 4 input and output numbers.

a)

Input	Output
110	101
99	90
88	79
77	68
66	57

b)

Input	Output
84	12
91	13
98	14
105	15
112	16
119	17

6. Draw an Input/Output machine.
Choose a number and an operation.
Use multiples of any number as the input numbers.
Find the output numbers.
Make a table to show your results.
Write the pattern rules for the input numbers and the output numbers.

Numbers Every Day

Mental Math

Add.

156 + 302 458
411 + 298 709
2356 + 1009 3365

Which strategies did you use?

Reflect

When you see an Input/Output table, how can you tell what the operation is in the machine? Use words, pictures, or numbers to explain.

ASSESSMENT FOCUS | Question 6

11

Sample Answers

1. a)

Input	2	4	6	8	10
Output	18	36	54	72	90

b)

Input	1	3	5	7	9
Output	13	15	17	19	21

3. b) Input: Start at 36. Add 6 each time.
Output: Start at 6. Add 1 each time.

4. a) Multiply by 10.
Input: 12, 14, 16, 18;
Output: 120, 140, 160, 180

b) Subtract 15.
Input: 250, 200, 150, 100;
Output: 235, 185, 135, 85

5. a) Input: Start at 110. Subtract 11 each time. 55, 44, 33, 22
Output: Start at 101. Subtract 11 each time. 46, 35, 24, 13

b) Input: Start at 84. Add 7 each time. 126, 133, 140, 147
Output: Start at 12. Add 1 each time. 18, 19, 20, 21

6. I chose +8. I used multiples of 7 as the input numbers.

Input	7	14	21	28	35	42
Output	15	22	29	36	43	50

The pattern rule for the input numbers is: Start at 7. Add 7 each time.The pattern rule for the output numbers is: Start at 15. Add 7 each time.

REFLECT: For the Input/Output table from question 4a, I look at the first pair of input/output numbers: to go from 2 to 20, I could add 18 or multiply by 10. I look at the next pair to see which operation is correct. If I add 18 to 4, I get 22, not 40. But, if I multiply 4 by 10, I get 40. So, the operation in the machine is × 10. I check that the other pairs are related the same way: 6 × 10 is 60; 8 × 10 is 80; 10 × 10 is 100.

Numbers Every Day

Students can make a friendly number for all questions. 156 + 302 becomes 158 + 300; 411 + 298 becomes 409 + 300; and 2356 + 1009 becomes 2355 + 1010. Alternatively, students may prefer to add on.

ASSESSMENT FOR LEARNING

What to Look For

Understanding concepts

- ✔ Students understand that an Input/Output machine is used to create a pattern.
- ✔ Students understand that a pattern exists between the input and output numbers, and a pattern will exist in the output numbers if there is a pattern in the input numbers.

Applying procedures

- ✔ Students can identify, extend, and create patterns using Input/Output machines.

What to Do

Extra Support: Students can use Step-by-Step 2 (Master 1.11) to complete question 6.

Extra Practice: Write three Input/Output tables on the board. Write six pattern rules on a separate board. (The rules could be for the input numbers, the output numbers, or relating the input number to the output number.) Have students extend the tables and match the rules to the tables.
Students can complete Extra Practice 1 (Master 1.16).

Extension: Have students look at their completed tables from questions 2, 3, 4, and 5. Ask students which patterns will continue forever if they are extended, and which ones will end. Have them explain why.
Students can complete the Additional Activity, *What's Missing?* (Master 1.8).

Recording and Reporting

Master 1.2 Ongoing Observations: Number Patterns

Modelling Patterns

LESSON ORGANIZER

80–100 min

Curriculum Focus: Model patterns and make predictions. (5m98, 5m99, 5m101, 5m103, 5m105)

Teacher Materials
- overhead geoboard
- geobands
- square dot paper transparency (PM 25)

Student Materials
- geoboard
- geobands
- square dot paper (PM 25)
- 2-column charts (PM 17)
- 3-column charts (PM 18)
- 4-column charts (PM 19)
- Colour Tiles
- 1-cm grid paper (PM 23)

Optional
- Step-by-Step 3 (Master 1.12)
- Extra Practice 2 (Master 1.17)
- hundred charts (PM 13)
- 0.5-cm grid paper (PM 22)

Vocabulary: perimeter, similar

Assessment: Master 1.2 Ongoing Observations: Number Patterns

Key Math Learnings

1. Patterns can be represented numerically and geometrically.
2. Patterns can be modelled to make predictions.

LESSON 3

Modelling Patterns

Explore

You will need a geoboard, geobands, and dot paper.

➤ Use the geoboard to make a rectangle with length 2 units and width 1 unit. Count and record the number of pegs on the perimeter of the rectangle.

➤ Make a rectangle with length 3 units and width 2 units. Count and record the number of pegs on the perimeter.

➤ Continue to make rectangles with length 1 unit greater than the width. Record the length, the width, and the number of pegs each time.

Draw each rectangle on dot paper.

Rectangle	Length	Width	Number of Pegs on Perimeter
1	2	1	6
2	3	2	

- How many pegs will be on the perimeter of the 10th rectangle? 42
  The 20th rectangle? 82
- Will the perimeter of any rectangle have 42 pegs? Yes
  44 pegs? No 46 pegs? Yes How do you know?

Show and Share

Share your results with another pair of classmates.
What patterns do you see in the table?
How did you use these patterns to solve the problems?

12 LESSON FOCUS | Model patterns and make predictions.

BEFORE Get Started

Use an 11 by 11 transparent geoboard on the overhead projector. Model a square with side length 1 unit. Show how to count the pegs on the perimeter. Alternatively, draw a square with side length 1 unit on transparent dot paper, and count the dots on the perimeter.

Present *Explore*. You may wish to distribute copies of a 4-column chart. Suggest students take turns: one student uses the geoboard while the other student draws the rectangle on dot paper and completes the table.

DURING Explore

Ongoing Assessment: Observe and Listen

Encourage students to use patterns to answer the questions in *Explore*.
The geoboards are not large enough to make the 10th and 20th rectangles.

To check their predictions, students could draw each rectangle on 0.5-cm grid paper.

Ask questions, such as:
- How many pegs are on the perimeter of the 5th rectangle?
  (22 pegs)
- How many pegs are on the perimeter of the 9th rectangle?
  (38 pegs)
- What patterns do you see in the table?
  (I see a pattern in the width numbers. The pattern rule is: Start at 1. Add 1 each time. There is also a pattern in the length numbers. The pattern rule is: Start at 2. Add 1 each time. There is also a pattern in the number of pegs on the perimeter. This pattern rule is: Start at 6. Add 4 each time.)

Connect

…e is a pattern of similar triangles drawn on dot paper.
…triangle has 2 equal sides.

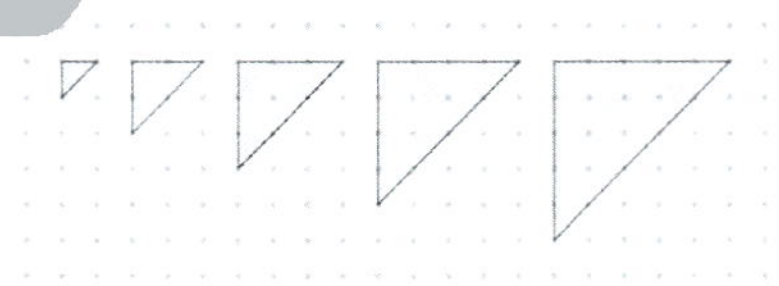

This pattern continues.

➤ Find the number of dots on the perimeter of the 10th triangle and the 20th triangle.

Make a table.

Triangle	Number of Dots on Perimeter
1	3
2	6
3	9
4	12
5	15

These numbers are multiples of 3.

One pattern rule for the number of dots on the perimeter is:

Start at 3. Add 3 each time.

Another pattern rule for the number of dots is:

The triangle number multiplied by 3

The 10th triangle will have 10 × 3, or 30 dots on its perimeter.
The 20th triangle will have 20 × 3, or 60 dots on its perimeter.

➤ Will any triangle have a perimeter of 50 dots? 51 dots?
Use the pattern to find out.

The number of dots on any perimeter is a multiple of 3.
50 is not a multiple of 3, so no triangle has 50 dots.
51 is a multiple of 3 because 17 × 3 = 51.
So, the 17th triangle has 51 dots.

13

REACHING ALL LEARNERS

Alternative Explore

Materials: square dot paper (PM 25)
Have students draw rectangles, as in *Explore*, but they count the number of dots inside each rectangle instead of the number of dots on the perimeter. The numbers of dots inside the rectangles are 0, 2, 6, 12, 20, and so on. Each number is a product 0 × 1, 1 × 2, 2 × 3, 3 × 4, 4 × 5, and so on. Students can answer problems such as: "How many dots are inside the 20th rectangle?" (*19 × 20 = 380*)

Early Finishers

Have students work in pairs. They find the area of each rectangle in *Explore*, record their findings in a table, describe any patterns, and write the pattern rules.

Common Misconceptions

➤ Students count the pegs on one side of a rectangle and use that number as a measure of its side length.

How to Help: Help students understand that the side length is a measure in units, and 1 unit is the distance between 2 pegs. So, the side length, in units, is 1 less than the number of pegs.

- Look at the numbers in the length and width columns. How is the number of pegs on the perimeter of a rectangle related to the length and width? What is another way to write the pattern rule?
  (*The number of pegs on the perimeter is double the sum of the length and width. Another way to write this pattern rule is: (width + length) × 2 = number of pegs.*)
- Will the perimeter of any rectangle have 42 pegs? 44 pegs? 46 pegs?
  (*I used the patterns in the table to answer this question. Each number in the Number of Pegs on Perimeter column is 2 more than a multiple of 4. So, only numbers that are 2 more than a multiple of 4 fit the pattern.*
  42 is 2 more than 40. 40 is a multiple of 4, so 42 pegs are possible.
  44 is a multiple of 4, so 44 pegs are not possible.
  46 is 2 more than 44, which is a multiple of 4.
  46 pegs are possible.)

AFTER — Connect

Discuss students' results. Have volunteers share the strategies they used to find the numbers of pegs on the perimeters. Students should use patterns to extend the table when the rectangles are too big to be made on the geoboard.

Review the problem in *Connect*. Have students suggest other problems they could solve using the similar triangles. For example, how many dots will be on the perimeter of the 100th triangle? (*3 × 100 = 300*) Or, will the perimeter of any triangle have 99 dots?
(*Yes, since 99 is a multiple of 3. 3 × 33 = 99, so the 33rd triangle will have 99 dots.*)

Ensure students understand they do not have to draw figures to find out about the number of dots on their perimeters; they can extend the patterns in tables.

Sample Answers

1. a)

Number of Pentagons	Perimeter (units)
1	5
2	8
3	11
4	14

2. a)

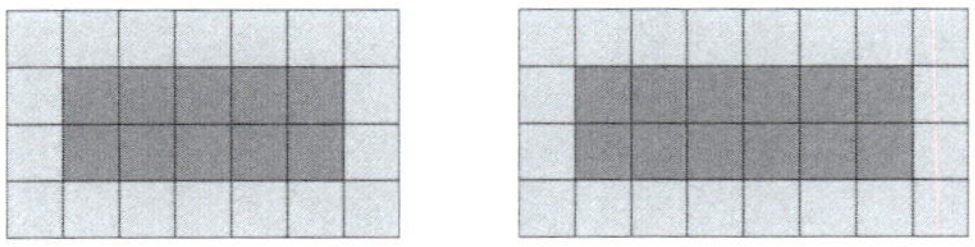

b)

Figure	Number of Green Tiles	Number of Yellow Tiles
1	2	10
2	4	12
3	6	14
4	8	16
5	10	18
6	12	20

f) Each tile pattern starts with an even number and increases by 2 each time, so odd numbers cannot be in the pattern.

3. b) Price with cheese: Start at 5. Add 5 each time.

c) Price with two toppings: Start at 7. Add 5 each time.

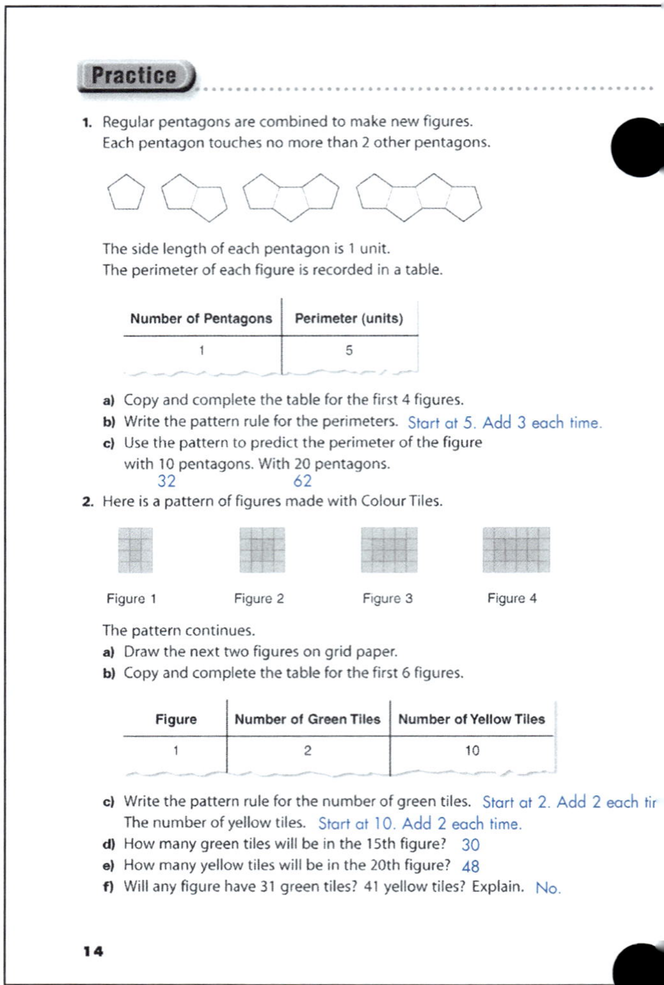

Practice

1. Regular pentagons are combined to make new figures.
Each pentagon touches no more than 2 other pentagons.

The side length of each pentagon is 1 unit.
The perimeter of each figure is recorded in a table.

Number of Pentagons	Perimeter (units)
1	5

a) Copy and complete the table for the first 4 figures.
b) Write the pattern rule for the perimeters. Start at 5. Add 3 each time.
c) Use the pattern to predict the perimeter of the figure with 10 pentagons. With 20 pentagons. 32 62

2. Here is a pattern of figures made with Colour Tiles.

Figure 1 Figure 2 Figure 3 Figure 4

The pattern continues.
a) Draw the next two figures on grid paper.
b) Copy and complete the table for the first 6 figures.

Figure	Number of Green Tiles	Number of Yellow Tiles
1	2	10

c) Write the pattern rule for the number of green tiles. Start at 2. Add 2 each tir
The number of yellow tiles. Start at 10. Add 2 each time.
d) How many green tiles will be in the 15th figure? 30
e) How many yellow tiles will be in the 20th figure? 48
f) Will any figure have 31 green tiles? 41 yellow tiles? Explain. No.

14

Practice

Question 1 requires a 2-column chart.

Question 2 requires grid paper and a 3-column chart.
Some students may benefit from using Colour Tiles.

Questions 3 and 4 require a 4-column chart.

Have hundred charts available for students to use to skip count.

Assessment Focus: Question 4

Students understand that there are two fixed costs. Each scoop costs $1.25 and extra topping costs 50¢. Students make a table based on the cost of the first 4 sundaes with extra topping. (The first four sundaes would be: 1 scoop, 2 scoops, 3 scoops, and 4 scoops.) Students write any pattern rules and use them to explain the cost of a 6-scoop sundae with extra topping.

3. Pizza Parlour has prices that follow a pattern.

Pizza Number	Pizza Size	Price with Cheese ($)	Price with Two Toppings ($)
1	4-slice	5	7
2	8-slice	10	12
3	12-slice	15	17
4	16-slice	20	22
5	20-slice	25	27

a) Copy and complete the table.
b) Write a pattern rule for the price with cheese.
c) Write a pattern rule for the price with two toppings.
d) The patterns continue.
What is the price of a 24-slice pizza with two toppings? $32
e) How is the price with two toppings related to the price with cheese? The price with two toppings is always $2 more.

4. Dreamy Ice-Cream Company sells a single-scoop sundae for $1.25.
Each additional scoop costs $1.25.
There is a fixed price of 50¢ for extra topping on all sundaes.
a) Make a table to show the prices of the first 4 sizes of sundaes with extra topping.
b) Write a pattern rule for any patterns you see.
c) What is the price of a 6-scoop sundae with extra topping? Explain. $8
Show your work.

Reflect

Use a question from this lesson.
How can patterns in a table help you solve a problem, without extending the table?
Use words, pictures, or numbers to explain.

Numbers Every Day

Number Strategies

Order the decimals in each set from least to greatest.

2.3, 1.3, 10.1 — 1.3, 2.3, 10.1
1.98, 2.01, 1.89 — 1.89, 1.98, 2.01
0.35, 0.23, 2.30 — 0.23, 0.35, 2.30

ASSESSMENT FOCUS | Question 4 — 15

4. a)

Sundae Number	Number of Scoops	Price ($)	Price with Extra Topping ($)
1	1	1.25	1.75
2	2	2.50	3.00
3	3	3.75	4.25
4	4	5.00	5.50
5	5	6.25	6.75
6	6	7.50	8.00

b) Price: Start at 1.25. Add 1.25 each time.
Price with extra topping: Start at 1.75. Add 1.25 each time.

c) I used patterns to extend the table to show 5 scoops, then 6 scoops.
(See the table in part a.)

REFLECT: In question 1, each time you add a pentagon to a figure, you add 3 sides to the figure.
From the table, the rule for the perimeters is: Start at 5. Add 3 each time.
So, to find the perimeter of a figure with 12 pentagons, I would start at 5, and skip count by 3 eleven times:
5 + 33 = 38. The figure with 12 pentagons has 38 sides.

Numbers Every Day

Students could arrange the numbers in a place-value chart to line up the decimal points and compare place value.

ASSESSMENT FOR LEARNING

What to Look For	What to Do
Understanding concepts ✔ Students understand that a geometry pattern can be modelled by a number pattern. ✔ Students understand that a table can be used to extend a pattern, and predict values of terms in the pattern. ***Applying procedures*** ✔ Students can identify, extend, and create patterns using models and tables.	***Extra Support:*** Students can complete the Additional Activity, *Perimeter Patterns* (Master 1.9). Students can use Step-by-Step 3 (Master 1.12) to complete question 4. ***Extra Practice:*** Students create a perimeter pattern with red Pattern Blocks. Students combine 2, then 3, then 4 red Blocks, and so on. They make a table for the first 4 figures and write a pattern rule for the perimeters. Students explain the similarities and differences between the perimeters of figures made with pentagons, and with trapezoids. Students can complete Extra Practice 2 (Master 1.17). ***Extension:*** Students use blue Pattern Blocks to repeat question 1. Students make the first 4 figures, complete a table, then predict the perimeters of the 10th and 20th figures.

Recording and Reporting
Master 1.2 Ongoing Observations: Number Patterns

Using Patterns to Solve Problems

LESSON ORGANIZER (40–50 min)

Curriculum Focus: Pose and solve problems by applying a patterning strategy. (5m98, 5m99, 5m101, 5m105)

Student Materials
- calculators
- 2-column charts (PM 17)

Optional
- Step-by-Step 4 (Master 1.13)
- Extra Practice 2 (Master 1.17)

Assessment: Master 1.2 Ongoing Observations: Number Patterns

Key Math Learning

Patterns can be used to make predictions and solve problems.

LESSON 4

Using Patterns to Solve Problems

Explore

Sam baby-sits to make money.
Sam charges $6 for each hour he works.

➤ How much does Sam earn when he works 2 hours? 3 hours? 4 hours? 5 hours?
Show your results in a table.

Time Worked (hours)	Money Earned ($)

➤ What patterns do you see in the table?
Write rules for these patterns.
Use the patterns to predict how much Sam will earn working 21 hours. $126

➤ Sam saves all the money he earns.
He needs $250 to buy a mountain bike.
How many hours does Sam need to work? 42 hours

➤ Make up your own problem you can solve using this table.
Trade problems with a classmate.
Solve your classmate's problem.

Show and Share

Share your answers with a classmate.
Did you solve the problems the same way? Explain.

16 LESSON FOCUS | Pose and solve problems by applying a patterning strategy

BEFORE — Get Started

Review the different patterns that can be found in tables. Write this table on the board:

Number of Pentagons	Perimeter (units)
1	5
2	8
3	11
4	14

Ask:
- What is the pattern rule for the perimeters? (*Start at 5. Add 3 each time.*)
- The perimeter is 20 units. How many pentagons are there? (*6*)
  How do you know?
  (*Each time I add a pentagon, I add 3 units to the perimeter. The figure with 4 pentagons has a perimeter of 14 units, so the figure with 5 pentagons has a perimeter of 17 units, and the figure with 6 pentagons has a perimeter of 20 units.*)

Present *Explore*. You may wish to distribute copies of a 2-column chart. Remind students that the entries in the first row in the table should be 1 hour and $6.

DURING — Explore

Ongoing Assessment: Observe and Listen

Ask questions, such as:
- How did you find out how much Sam earned for 2 hours of work?
  (*I multiplied $6 × 2 = $12.*)
- What patterns do you see in the table?
  (*For money earned: Start at 6. Add 6 each time. The entries in the Money Earned column are multiples of 6. Also, multiply the time worked by 6 to get the money earned.*)
- Which Input/Output machine would produce this table?
  (*A machine with × 6 in it*)

Connect

e puzzle book costs $17.
How much does it cost to buy 2 books? 3 books? 4 books?

Make a table.
When you add 1 to the number of books, you add $17 to the cost.

Number of Books	Cost ($)
1	17
2	34
3	51
4	68

These numbers are multiples of 17.

Two books cost $34.
Three books cost $51.
Four books cost $68.

➤ Use a pattern to predict the cost of 20 books.

One pattern rule for the cost is:
Start at 17. Add 17 each time.

Another pattern rule for the cost is:
The number of books multiplied by 17.

To predict the cost of 20 books, multiply: $20 \times 17 = 340$
Twenty books cost $340.

➤ Extend the pattern to find how many books you can buy with $200.
Use a calculator.
Press: 6 8 + 1 7 = = = = = = …
Record each number in the table.
Continue to press = until the number is greater than 200.

Number of Books	Cost ($)
1	17
2	34
3	51
4	68
5	85
6	102
7	119
8	136
9	153
10	170
11	187
12	204

Eleven books cost $187.
Twelve books cost $204.
So, you can buy 11 books with $200.

17

REACHING ALL LEARNERS

Alternative Explore

Write this table on the board.

Input	Output
1	12
2	24
3	36
4	48

Have students copy the table, then write the next four input numbers and output numbers. Have them describe the patterns in the table. Students then describe a situation that could produce the data in the table.

Early Finishers

Use *Practice* question 6 as a model. Have students create a workout schedule for push-ups. Students create a table and describe any patterns in it.

Common Misconceptions

➤Students misinterpret a problem or do not understand the problem.

How to Help: Have the student read the problem aloud to a partner. Have students discuss the problem and explain their understanding of it before they try to solve it.

ESL Strategies

ESL students may benefit from having the tables partially completed for each question. They should also have a partner read the problem aloud and paraphrase the problem.

- How did you find out how much Sam will earn working 21 hours?
  (*I multiplied $6 × 21 = $126.*)
- How did you find out how many hours Sam needs to work to earn $250?
  (*I know $6 × 40 = $240, so Sam earns $240 in 40 hours. That is close to $250. If Sam works 2 more hours, he will earn $12 more. In 42 hours, Sam earns $240 + $12 = $252. So, Sam needs to work 42 hours to buy a mountain bike.*)
- What problem did you make up?
  (*Sam needs $130 to buy his mother a DVD player for her birthday. How long does he need to work to get this money?*)
- How did you solve your partner's problem?
  (*I used a table.*)

AFTER Connect

Invite students to share some of the problems they created. Discuss how they used patterns to solve the problems.

Review the problem in *Connect.*

Ask:

- What does it mean by: "When you add 1 to the number of books, you add $17 to the cost."? (*It means if you buy 1 more book, then you have to pay $17 more.*)
- What patterns do you see in the table?
  (*For the number of books, start at 1. Add 1 each time. For the cost, start at 17. Add 17 each time. The numbers in the cost column are multiples of 17.*)
- How does knowing the number of books allow you to predict the cost of the books?
  (*Multiply the number of books by 17 to get the cost.*)

Ensure students understand that there is an Input/Output rule relating the number of books and the cost of the books.

Ask:

- Which Input/Output machine would produce this table?
  (*A machine with × 17 in it*)

Numbers Every Day

Students may use basic multiplication facts and place value to multiply. For example, 5 × 30 is
5 × 3 tens = 15 tens or 150.

Sample Answers

1. b) Start at 16. Add 16 each time. Or multiply the number by 16 to get the cost.
   c) The school wants to buy new volleyball shirts. Each shirt costs $16. How much would it cost to buy 12 shirts? (*Answer: $192*)

2. b)

Week	Total Money Collected ($)
1	31
2	62
3	93
4	124
5	155
6	186
7	217
8	248

   e) In which week had Jen collected close to $300 in total? (*Answer: Week 10*)

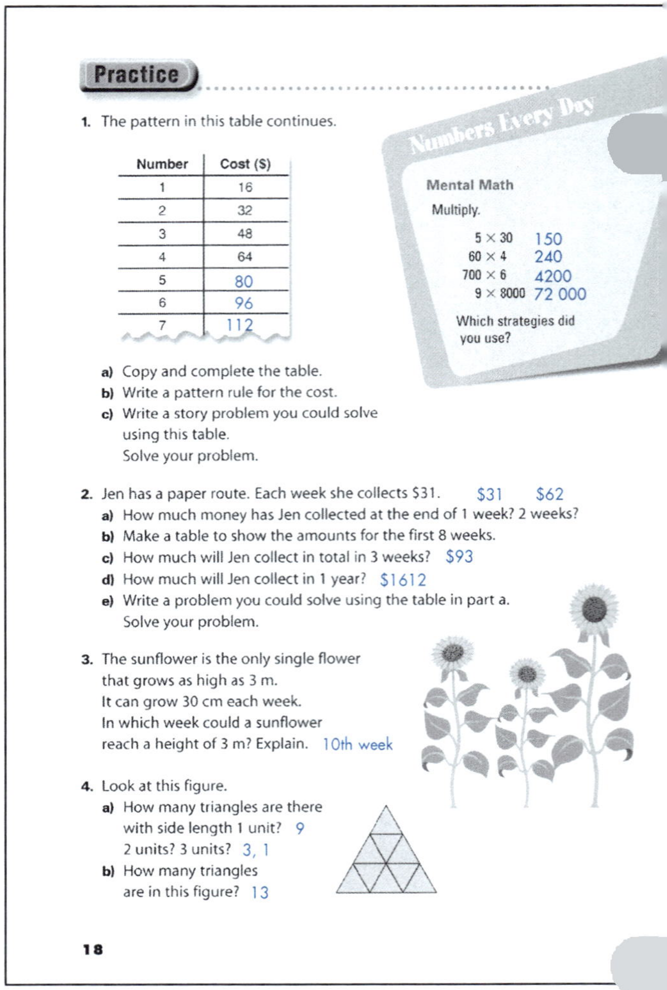

Practice

1. The pattern in this table continues.

Number	Cost ($)
1	16
2	32
3	48
4	64
5	80
6	96
7	112

a) Copy and complete the table.
b) Write a pattern rule for the cost.
c) Write a story problem you could solve using this table. Solve your problem.

Numbers Every Day

Mental Math

Multiply.

5 × 30 150
60 × 4 240
700 × 6 4200
9 × 8000 72 000

Which strategies did you use?

2. Jen has a paper route. Each week she collects $31.
a) How much money has Jen collected at the end of 1 week? 2 weeks? $31 $62
b) Make a table to show the amounts for the first 8 weeks.
c) How much will Jen collect in total in 3 weeks? $93
d) How much will Jen collect in 1 year? $1612
e) Write a problem you could solve using the table in part a. Solve your problem.

3. The sunflower is the only single flower that grows as high as 3 m. It can grow 30 cm each week. In which week could a sunflower reach a height of 3 m? Explain. 10th week

4. Look at this figure.
a) How many triangles are there with side length 1 unit? 9
2 units? 3 units? 3, 1
b) How many triangles are in this figure? 13

18

Practice

Have calculators and 2-column charts available for all questions.

Assessment Focus: Question 6

Students should understand this is a shrinking pattern. They should realize they can record the pattern in a table to predict the number of pages read. Students add the pages read to find the total number read after 7 days. Students may figure out how many days it took Dave to read the book, though this is not necessary to solve the problem. Students add 70 + 67 + 64 + ... + 34 + 31 to find the total number of pages in the book.

5. How many squares are in this figure? 30 squares

6. Dave read 70 pages on Monday, 67 pages on Tuesday, and 64 pages on Wednesday.
This pattern continued until Dave finished his book.
a) Make a table to show how many pages were read each day.
b) What was the total number of pages Dave read the first 7 days? 427 pages
c) Dave finished his book on the day he read 31 pages.
How many pages are in the book? 707 pages
Show your work.

7. Greenholme Elementary School has a car wash to raise money for the community.
The students charge $4 to wash a car.
a) Make a table to show how much money is collected when these numbers of cars are washed:
10, 20, 30, 40, 50
$40, $80, $120, $160, $200

The students spent $23 for soap and sponges.
This amount is subtracted from the amount collected.
b) How many cars have to be washed to raise $350? 94 cars
c) Write your own problem about this car wash.
Solve the problem you posed.

Reflect

How can using patterns help you solve problems?
Use an example from this lesson to explain.

At Home

What number patterns do you see at home?
Look through magazines and newspapers.
Write about the patterns you see.

ASSESSMENT FOCUS | Question 6 — 19

3.

Week	Height (cm)
1	30
2	60
3	90
4	120
5	150
6	180
7	210
8	240
9	270
10	300

First, I changed 3 m to 300 cm. Then I made a table. I wrote 30 cm for week 1 and added 30 cm each week until I reached a height of 300 cm. The sunflower could reach a height of 3 m in 10 weeks.

6. a)

Day	Number of Pages
1	70
2	67
3	64
4	61
5	58
6	55
7	52

7. c) How much money would you raise if you washed 35 cars? (*Answer: $117*)

REFLECT: Once you know the pattern rule, you can apply it to a problem. For example, in *Practice* question 3,
I used the rule: Start at 30 cm. Add 30 cm each time.
I found out that it took 10 weeks to reach 300 cm or 3 m.

ASSESSMENT FOR LEARNING

What to Look For

Problem solving

✔ Students use different strategies to solve problems.

Understanding concepts

✔ Students understand that patterns can be represented in tables and by rules.

Applying procedures

✔ Students can identify, extend, and create patterns using pattern rules or tables.

What to Do

Extra Support: As a class, review the students' solutions for the problems created by students in questions 1c, 2e, and 7c. Students can use Step-by-Step 4 (Master 1.13) to complete question 6.

Extra Practice: Students can complete Extra Practice 2 (Master 1.17).

Extension: Have students write a problem that can be solved using a pattern. Have them write to explain why their problem works.

Recording and Reporting

Master 1.2 Ongoing Observations: Number Patterns

Strategies Toolkit

LESSON ORGANIZER 40–50 min

Curriculum Focus: Interpret a problem and select an appropriate strategy. (5m101)

Student Materials

- calculators

Assessment: PM 3: Self-Assessment: Problem Solving
PM 1: Inquiry Process Check List

Key Math Learnings

1. Interpret a problem involving patterns.
2. Solve a problem by using a pattern.

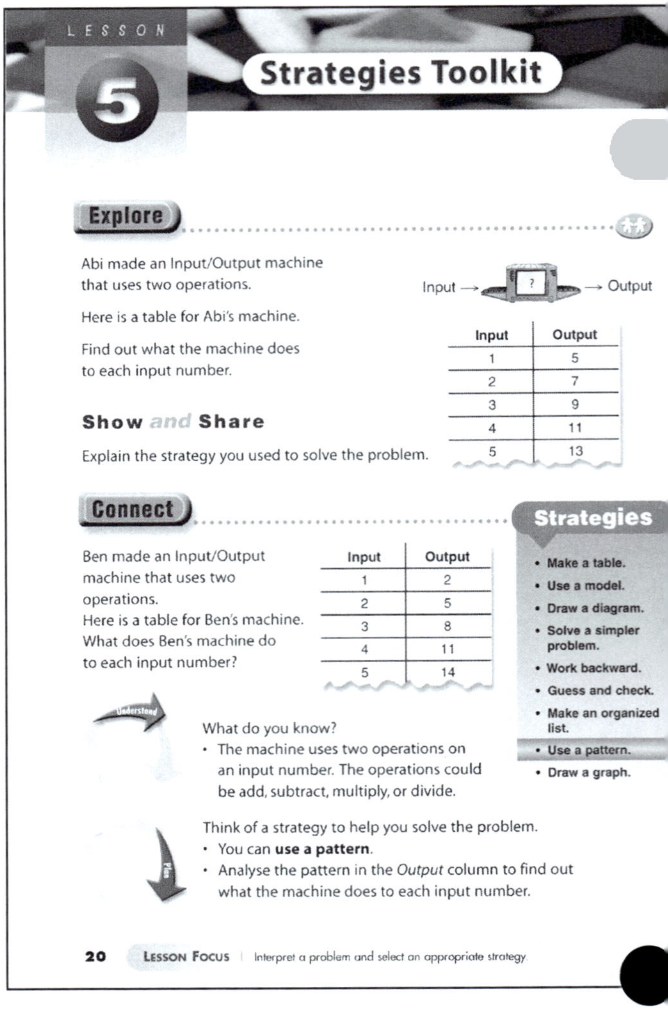

LESSON 5 Strategies Toolkit

Explore

Abi made an Input/Output machine that uses two operations.

Input → ? → Output

Here is a table for Abi's machine.

Find out what the machine does to each input number.

Input	Output
1	5
2	7
3	9
4	11
5	13

Show and Share

Explain the strategy you used to solve the problem.

Connect

Ben made an Input/Output machine that uses two operations.
Here is a table for Ben's machine.
What does Ben's machine do to each input number?

Input	Output
1	2
2	5
3	8
4	11
5	14

Understand

What do you know?
- The machine uses two operations on an input number. The operations could be add, subtract, multiply, or divide.

Plan

Think of a strategy to help you solve the problem.
- You can **use a pattern**.
- Analyse the pattern in the *Output* column to find out what the machine does to each input number.

Strategies
- Make a table.
- Use a model.
- Draw a diagram.
- Solve a simpler problem.
- Work backward.
- Guess and check.
- Make an organized list.
- Use a pattern.
- Draw a graph.

20 LESSON FOCUS | Interpret a problem and select an appropriate strategy.

BEFORE Get Started

Review the Input/Output machines from Lesson 2. Draw a table of input and output numbers for a machine such as × 6, and for a machine such as × 3 + 1. Explain that you multiply by 3, then add 1.

Present *Explore*. Review the key steps in problem solving: understand the problem, plan how to solve it, solve it, then check the solution.

DURING Explore

Ongoing Assessment: Observe and Listen

Make sure students understand there are two operations. Ask questions, such as:

- Which strategy will you use to solve the problem? (*Use a pattern.*)
- How did you use the table to solve the problem?(*The Output numbers increase by 2. I guessed each input number was multiplied by 2 first. I multiplied each input number by 2. I saw I needed to add 3 to get the output numbers.*)
- What does the Input/Output machine do to each number? (*It multiplies by 2, then adds 3.*)

Have students share their solutions with the class. They should explain any strategies used.

AFTER Connect

Work through the problem in *Connect*. Record each problem-solving step on the board and refer to it as you proceed. Tell the students that for the "plan" stage, they can pick one of several strategies to solve the problem.

Ask:

- Why do you think *use a pattern* is a good strategy?
  (*The pattern in the Output numbers helps you find what the machine does to the Input numbers.*)
- Which other strategy could you use?
  (*Guess and check.*)

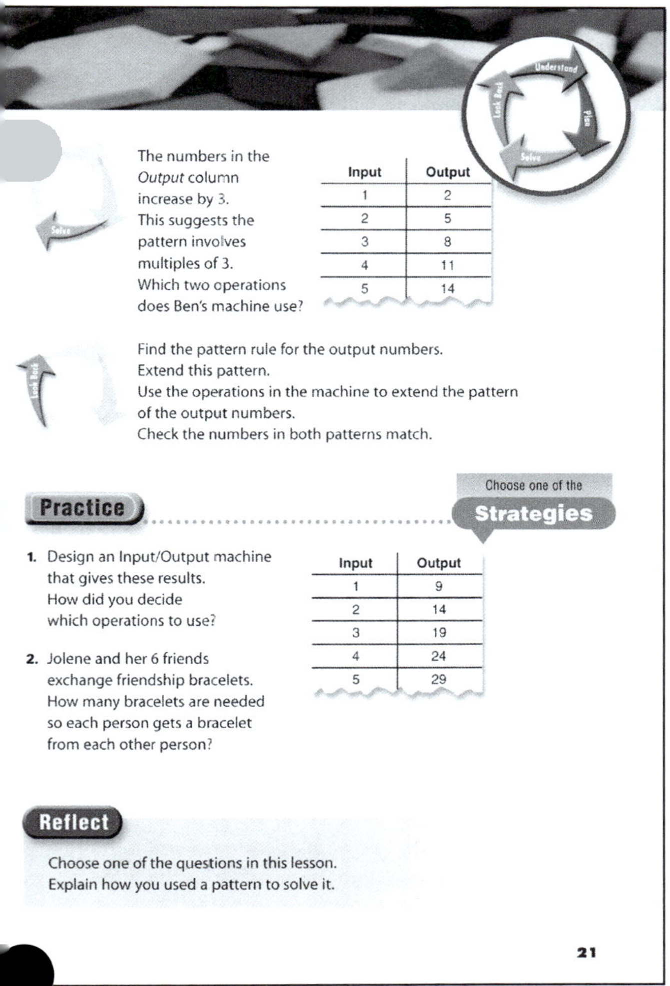

The numbers in the *Output* column increase by 3.
This suggests the pattern involves multiples of 3.
Which two operations does Ben's machine use?

Input	Output
1	2
2	5
3	8
4	11
5	14

Find the pattern rule for the output numbers.
Extend this pattern.
Use the operations in the machine to extend the pattern of the output numbers.
Check the numbers in both patterns match.

Practice

Choose one of the **Strategies**

1. Design an Input/Output machine that gives these results.
How did you decide which operations to use?

Input	Output
1	9
2	14
3	19
4	24
5	29

2. Jolene and her 6 friends exchange friendship bracelets.
How many bracelets are needed so each person gets a bracelet from each other person?

Reflect

Choose one of the questions in this lesson.
Explain how you used a pattern to solve it.

21

REACHING ALL LEARNERS

Common Misconceptions

➤ Students have difficulty using a pattern as a strategy.

How to Help: Students do not have to "use a pattern" for each question. For questions 1 and 2, students could "guess and check."

Sample Answers

1. Multiply by 5, then add 4.
2. The total number of bracelets for 7 people is 42.

REFLECT: I found a pattern in question 2. I figured out how many bracelets you would need for 2 people, 3 people, and 4 people.
I saw there was a pattern. The pattern was: Start at 2. Add 4. Increase the number added by 2 each time.
The numbers of bracelets for 2, 3, 4, 5, 6, 7 people are 2, 6, 12, 20, 30, 42. So, 42 bracelets are needed for 7 people.

- Why is it important to "look back"?
(*To check if the machine gives the correct Output numbers*)

Practice

Encourage students to refer to the Strategies list.

ASSESSMENT FOR LEARNING

What to Look For	What to Do
Problem solving ✔ Students can follow the "understand, plan, solve, and look back" steps to solve a problem. ✔ Students can use a pattern to solve problems.	***Extra Support:*** For question 1, suggest that students pick one pair of numbers (Input and Output) and come up with 5 ways of getting from the Input to the Output. Then have them check which of these ways might work for other pairs. For question 2, students may benefit from drawing a diagram. Encourage them to look for patterns by trying the question with 2 friends, 3 friends, and so on. ***Extension:*** Challenge students to use a different problem-solving strategy to solve each problem.

Recording and Reporting

PM 1 Inquiry Process Check List
PM 3 Self-Assessment: Problem Solving

LESSON ORGANIZER 40–50 min

Student Materials
- 2-column charts (PM 17)
- calculators
- yellow Pattern Blocks

Assessment: Master 1.1 Unit Rubric: Number Patterns
Master 1.4 Unit Summary: Number Patterns

Unit 1 Show What You Know

LESSON

1 **1.** Write the first 6 terms of each pattern.
- **a)** Start at 100. Subtract 9 each time. 100, 91, 82, 73, 64, 55
- **b)** Start at 10. Alternately add 5, then multiply by 2. 10, 15, 30, 35, 70, 75

2. Write the next 5 terms in each pattern.
Write the pattern rule.
- **a)** 5, 8, 12, 15, 19, … 22, 26, 29, 33, 36
- **b)** 50, 48, 47, 45, 44, … 42, 41, 39, 38, 36
- **c)** 10, 12, 16, 22, 30, … 40, 52, 66, 82, 100

2 **3.** For this Input/Output machine:

Input →  → Output

- **a)** Choose 6 numbers to input.
- **b)** Find each output number.
- **c)** Copy and complete the table.

Input	Output

4. For each table:

- Write the pattern rules for the input numbers and the output numbers.
- The patterns continue. Write the next 5 input and output numbers.
- What do you do to each input number to get the output number?

a)

Input	Output
240	20
216	18
192	16
168	14
144	12

b)

Input	Output
21	189
31	279
41	369
51	459
61	549

22

Sample Answers

2. a) Start at 5. Alternately add 3, then add 4.
b) Start at 50. Alternately subtract 2, then subtract 1.
c) Start at 10. Add 2. Increase the number added by 2 each time.

3.

Input	Output
1	12
2	13
3	14
4	15
5	16
6	17

4. a) Input numbers: Start at 240. Subtract 24 each time. Output numbers: Start at 20. Subtract 2 each time. Divide each input number by 12.

Input	Output
240	20
216	18
192	16
168	14
144	12
120	10
96	8
72	6
48	4
24	2

b) Input numbers: Start at 21. Add 10 each time. Output numbers: Start at 189. Add 90 each time. Multiply each input number by 9.

Input	Output
21	189
31	279
41	369
51	459
61	549
71	639
81	729
91	819
101	909
111	999

ongruent hexagons are combined to make new figures.
Each hexagon touches no more than 2 other hexagons.

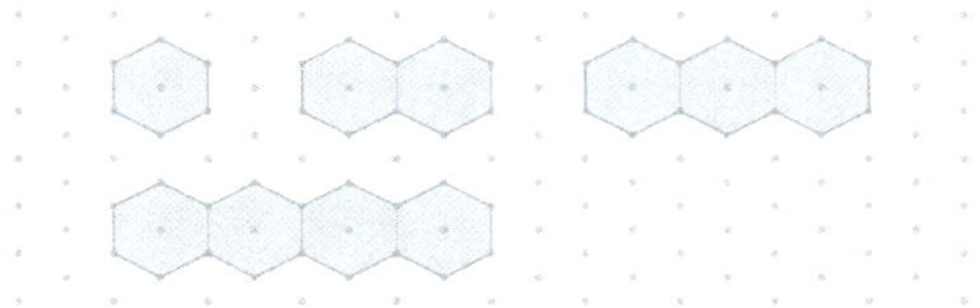

The side length of each hexagon is 1 unit.
The perimeter of each figure is recorded in a table.
The pattern continues.
Use Pattern Blocks when they help.

Number of Hexagons	Perimeter (units)
1	6
2	10
3	14
4	18
5	22

a) Copy and complete the table.
b) Write the pattern rule for the perimeters.
c) Use the pattern to predict the perimeter of the figure with 8 hexagons. 34 units
d) What is the perimeter of the figure with 15 hexagons? 62 units
e) Will a figure have a perimeter of 30 units? Yes 40 units? Explain. No

6. A magazine costs $3.50.
a) What is the cost of 2 magazines? 3 magazines? 4 magazines? 5 magazines? 6 magazines? Show your answers in a table.
b) How much would 98 magazines cost? $343
c) How many magazines can you buy with $100? 28 magazines
d) Write your own problem about these magazines. Solve the problem.

UNIT 1 **Learning Goals**

- ✓ find a pattern rule for a number pattern
- ✓ identify, extend, and create patterns
- ✓ describe and model patterns
- ✓ use patterns to pose and solve problems
- ✓ use patterns in a table to make predictions

23

5. b) Start at 6. Add 4 each time.

e) When we start at 6 and skip count by 4, we see the pattern 6, 10, 14, 18, 22, 26, 30, 34, 38, 42, ... Therefore, a figure can have a perimeter of 30 units, but not 40 units.

6. a)

Number of Magazines	Cost ($)
1	3.50
2	7.00
3	10.50
4	14.00
5	17.50
6	21.00

d) I want to buy 15 magazines for my friends. I have $50. Do I have enough money?
Answer: 15 magazines cost 15 × $3.50 = $52.50. I do not have enough money. I will be $2.50 short.

ASSESSMENT FOR LEARNING

What to Look For

Understanding of concepts

✔ **Questions 3 and 4:** Student understands that an Input/Output machine illustrates a relationship between pairs of numbers.

✔ **Question 5:** Student understands that a table can be used to model a geometry pattern.

Application of mathematical procedures

✔ **Question 1:** Student can write a number pattern, given a rule expressed in informal mathematical language.

✔ **Question 2:** Student can analyse a number pattern, state the pattern rule, and extend the pattern.

✔ **Question 3:** Student can use an Input/Output machine to create a number pattern.

✔ **Question 4:** Student can use Input/Output machines to analyse and extend number patterns.

Problem solving

✔ **Question 6:** Student can pose and solve problems by applying a patterning strategy.

Recording and Reporting

Master 1.1 Unit Rubric: Number Patterns
Master 1.4 Unit Summary: Number Patterns

Charity Fundraising

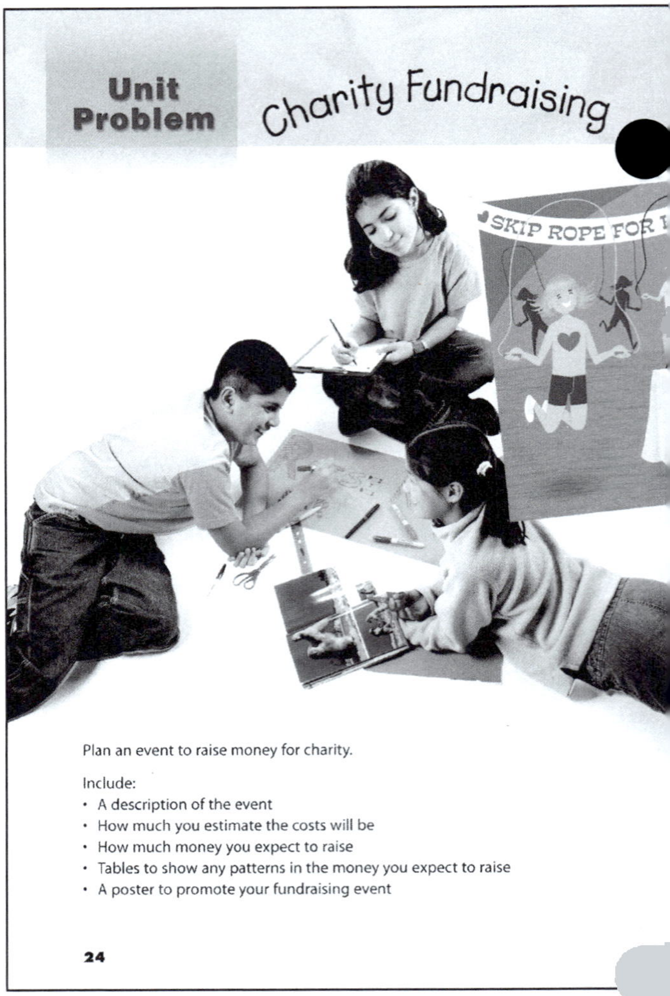
Unit Problem
Charity Fundraising

Plan an event to raise money for charity.

Include:
- A description of the event
- How much you estimate the costs will be
- How much money you expect to raise
- Tables to show any patterns in the money you expect to raise
- A poster to promote your fundraising event

24

LESSON ORGANIZER

40–50 min

Student Grouping: 2
Student Materials
- poster paper
- coloured pencils
- 2-column chart (PM 17)

Assessment: Master 1.3 Performance Assessment Rubric: Charity Fundraising
Master 1.4 Unit Summary: Number Patterns

Sample Response

Description

Our school wants to raise money for the hospital. We decided to have a 3-on-3 charity basketball tournament. Each team pays $12 to enter. The local grocery store donated refreshments that could be sold to raise money for the hospital. We will sell a can of pop for 75¢.

Costs

Referee: $50
Winners' plaques: $30

Goal

We expect to raise $500 for charity.

Remind students of the tables in the Unit Launch.

Present the *Unit Problem.* Invite a volunteer to read the instructions.
Clarify any points.

Have students review the *Check List.* Explain any points about which students may be unclear. Discuss possible ways in which students might complete the *Unit Problem.*

Show examples of completed pledge sheets and discuss patterns on the sheets. Include samples of posters that advertise charity events.

Reflect on the Unit

I made a pattern of Colour Tile figures that were getting bigger each time. I used the pattern to find out how many tiles would be in a really big figure and whether any figures would have a certain number of tiles.

I used a table to show how much a person who is paid by the hour earns when he works different numbers of hours. I used the patterns in the table to find out how long he would have to work to earn enough to buy a mountain bike.

Check List

Your work should show

- ✓ a detailed plan of the event
- ✓ how you calculate the amount you expect to raise
- ✓ any tables and patterns you used
- ✓ correct math language

Reflect on the Unit

Write about some of the different patterns in the unit, and how you used them to solve problems.

25

Number of Teams	Money Collected ($)
1	12
2	24
3	36
4	48
5	60
6	72
7	84
8	96
9	108
10	120

Cans of Pop Sold	Money Collected ($)
10	7.50
20	15.00
30	22.50
40	30.00
50	37.50
60	45.00
70	52.50
80	60.00
90	67.50
100	75.00

To reach our goal of $500, the money collected from teams and refreshments sold must be at least $580, since we need to pay $80 in costs.

We made tables to show how much we think we could make. With 10 teams entering and selling 100 cans of pop, we could make $120 + $75 = $195. We have to pay $80 in costs. So, we would make $195 – $80 = $115.

So, we have to increase the entry fee and the cost of a can of pop, or increase the number of teams in the tournament and the number of cans of pop sold, or reduce the amount we hope to raise.

ASSESSMENT FOR LEARNING

What to Look For

Understanding concepts

- ✓ Students understand they can use a table to show a pattern.
- ✓ Students understand there are costs associated with fundraising.

Applying procedures

- ✓ Students use tables to estimate the amount of money they expect to raise.

Problem solving

- ✓ Students provide a plan of the event, using their knowledge of patterns.

Communicating

- ✓ Students describe patterns clearly and use mathematical terminology.

What to Do

Extra Support: Break the task into manageable parts.

Some students may have difficulty planning the event. Provide examples of other fundraising events, such as the Terry Fox Run, Jump Rope For Heart, Run For the Cure, and so on.

Have students start by describing their event. Scaffold the task by asking:

- What costs will there be for your event?
- How much money do you expect to raise? Are your expectations reasonable?
- Have you seen any examples of tables you could use in your fundraiser?
- What do you think an effective poster would look like?

As students complete the task, have them review the instructions frequently.

Recording and Reporting

Master 1.3 Performance Assessment Rubric: Charity Fundraising
Master 1.4 Unit Summary: Number Patterns

Evaluating Student Learning: Preparing to Report: Unit 1 Number Patterns

This unit provides an opportunity to report on the **Patterning and Algebra** strand.
Master 1.4: Unit Summary: Number Patterns provides a comprehensive format for recording and summarizing evidence collected.

Here is an example of a completed summary chart for this Unit:

Strand: *Patterning and Algebra*	**Problem solving**	**Understanding of concepts**	**Application of mathematical procedures**	**Communication**	***Overall***
Ongoing Observations	3	2	2	3	**2/3**
Strategies Toolkit (Lesson 5)			3		**3**
Work samples or portfolios; conferences	3	3	2	3	**3**
Show What You Know	3	3	3	3	**3**
Unit Test	3	2	2	3	**2/3**
Unit Problem Charity Fundraising	3	3	3	2	**3**
Achievement Level for reporting					**3**

Recording	**How to Report**
Ongoing Observations	Use *Master 1.2 Ongoing Observations: Number Patterns* to determine the most consistent level achieved in each category. Enter it in the chart. Choose to summarize by achievement category, or simply to enter an overall level. Observations from late in the Unit should be most heavily weighted.
Strategies Toolkit (problem solving)	Use *PM 1 Inquiry Process Check List* with the Strategies Toolkit (Lesson 5). Transfer results to the summary form. You may choose to enter a level in the Problem solving column and/or Communication.
Portfolios or collections of work samples; conferences, or interviews	Use *Master 1.1 Unit Rubric: Number Patterns* to guide evaluation of collections of work and information gathered in conferences. You may choose to focus particular attention on the *Assessment Focus* questions. Work from late in the unit should be most heavily weighted.
Show What You Know	You may choose to assign some or all of these questions. *Master 1.1 Unit Rubric: Number Patterns* may be helpful in determining levels of achievement. #3–5 provide evidence of Understanding of concepts; #1–4 provide evidence of Application of mathematical procedures; #6 provides evidence of Problem solving; all questions provide evidence of Communication.
Unit Test	*Master 1.1 Unit Rubric: Number Patterns* may be helpful in determining levels of achievement. Part A provides evidence of *Application of mathematical procedures*; Part B provides evidence of *Understanding of concepts*; Part C provides evidence of *Problem solving*; all parts provide evidence of *Communication*.
Unit performance task	Use *Master 1.3 Performance Assessment Rubric: Charity Fundraising*. The *Unit Problem* offers a snapshot of students' achievement. In particular, it shows their ability to synthesize and apply what they have learned.
Student Self-Assessment	Note students' perceptions of their own progress. This may take the form of an oral or written comment, or a self-rating.
Comments	Analyse the pattern of achievement to identify strengths and needs. In some cases, specific actions may need to be planned to support the learner.

Learning Skills	**Ongoing Records**
PM 4: Learning Skills Check List Use to record and report throughout a reporting period, rather than for each unit and/or strand.	*PM 10: Summary Class Records: Strands* *PM 11: Summary Class Records: Achievement Categories* *PM 12: Summary Record: Individual* Use to record and report evaluations of student achievement over several clusters, a reporting period, or a school year. These can also be used in place of the Unit Summary.

Name ____________________ Date ______________

Master 1.1

Unit Rubric: Number Patterns

	Level 1	Level 2	Level 3	Level 4
Problem solving • chooses and carries out a range of patterning strategies to solve problems	with assistance, chooses and carries out a limited range of appropriate patterning strategies, rarely resulting in an accurate solution	with limited assistance, chooses and carries out appropriate patterning strategies that frequently result in an accurate solution	chooses and carries out appropriate patterning strategies to solve problems that usually result in an accurate solution	chooses and carries out appropriate patterning strategies to solve problems accurately; may offer an innovative approach
Understanding of concepts • shows understanding by appropriately demonstrating and explaining: – mathematical relationships in patterns – predictions based on patterns in a table of values – patterns in a variety of "real" contexts	may be unable to demonstrate or explain: – mathematical relationships in patterns – predictions based on patterns in a table of values – patterns in a variety of "real" contexts	partially able to demonstrate and explain: – mathematical relationships in patterns – predictions based on patterns in a table of values – patterns in a variety of "real" contexts	demonstrates and explains: – mathematical relationships in patterns – predictions based on patterns in a table of values – patterns in a variety of "real" contexts	in various contexts, demonstrates and explains: – mathematical relationships in patterns – predictions based on patterns in a table of values – patterns in a variety of "real" contexts
Application of mathematical procedures • accurately: – identifies and extends patterns (two variables) – analyses pattern rules – creates tables to display patterns – makes models and charts to display patterns	limited accuracy; major errors in: – identifying and extending patterns (two variables) – analysing patterning rules – creating tables to display patterns – making models and charts to display patterns	somewhat accurate; makes several minor errors in: – identifying and extending patterns (two variables) – analysing patterning rules – creating tables to display patterns – making models and charts to display patterns	generally accurate; makes few minor errors in: – identifying and extending patterns (two variables) – analysing patterning rules – creating tables to display patterns – making models and charts to display patterns	accurate; makes very few or no errors in: – identifying and extending patterns (two variables) – analysing patterning rules – creating tables to display patterns – making models and charts to display patterns
Communication • offers analysis of patterns and explains reasoning clearly, including appropriate terminology	needs assistance to describe patterns and explain reasoning; often unclear and imprecise	describes patterns and explains reasoning with some clarity and precision	describes patterns and explains reasoning clearly and precisely	describes patterns and explains reasoning clearly, precisely, and confidently
• presents work clearly, including appropriate symbols	presents work with little clarity; rarely uses appropriate symbols	presents work with some clarity; uses some appropriate symbols	presents work clearly and precisely; uses appropriate symbols	presents work clearly and precisely; uses a range of appropriate symbols

Name ____________________ Date ______________

Master 1.2

Ongoing Observations: Number Patterns

The behaviours described under each heading are examples; they are not intended to be an exhaustive list of all that might be observed. More detailed descriptions are provided in each lesson under *Assessment for Learning.*

STUDENT ACHIEVEMENT: Patterning and Place Value

Student	Problem solving	Understanding of concepts	Application of mathematical procedures	Communication
	▪ Uses appropriate patterning strategies to solve problems	▪ Demonstrates and explains mathematical relationships in patterns ▪ Makes and justifies predictions based on patterns	▪ Identifies, analyses, and extends patterns (2 variables) ▪ Creates models and charts to display patterns	▪ Describes patterns and explains reasoning clearly ▪ Presents work, procedures, and reasoning clearly

Level 1 – very limited; Level 2 – somewhat or limited; Level 3 – satisfactory; Level 4 – thorough

Name ______________________ Date ________________

Master 1.3

Performance Assessment Rubric: Charity Fundraising

	Level 1	Level 2	Level 3	Level 4
Problem solving • chooses and carries out appropriate patterning and estimation strategies to relate costs and profits, and determine how much money will be raised	chooses and carries out a limited range of appropriate estimation and patterning strategies, resulting in an incomplete or seriously flawed solution	chooses and carries out some appropriate estimation and patterning strategies, with partial success	chooses and carries out appropriate and effective estimation and pattern strategies, resulting in a successful solution	chooses and carries out innovative, appropriate, and effective estimation and patterning strategies, resulting in a successful solution
Understanding of concepts • shows understanding of patterning concepts by explaining patterns in the table and predictions about the total amount of money to be raised	shows very limited understanding by giving inappropriate explanations	shows limited understanding by giving appropriate but incomplete explanations	shows understanding by giving appropriate explanations	shows thorough understanding by giving appropriate and complete explanations
Application of mathematical procedures • constructs table correctly	completes table with major errors or omissions	completes table with several minor errors or omissions	completes table with few minor errors or omissions	completes table with practically no minor errors or omissions
• calculates costs and profits accurately	limited accuracy; major errors or omissions in calculating costs and profits	somewhat accurate; several minor errors in calculating costs and profits	generally accurate; few errors or omissions in calculating costs and profits	accurate; very few or no errors in calculating costs and profits
Communication • uses mathematical terminology, including units and symbols, correctly (for example, relationship; variable; dollars and cents)	uses few appropriate mathematical terms and symbols	uses some appropriate mathematical terms and symbols	uses appropriate mathematical terms and symbols	uses a range of appropriate mathematical terminology and symbols clearly and precisely
• presents and explains results and procedures clearly	presents and explains results and procedures unclearly and imprecisely	presents and explains results and procedures with some clarity	presents and explains results and procedures clearly and precisely	presents and explains results and procedures clearly, precisely, and confidently

Name ____________________ Date ______________

Master 1.4

Unit Summary: Number Patterns

Review assessment records to determine the most consistent achievement levels for the assessments conducted. Some cells may be blank. *Overall* achievement levels may be recorded in each row, rather than identifying levels for each achievement category.

	Most Consistent Level of Achievement*				
Strand: *Patterning and Algebra*	**Problem solving**	**Understanding of concepts**	**Application of mathematical procedures**	**Communication**	***Overall***
Ongoing Observations					
Strategies Toolkit (Lesson 5)					
Work samples or portfolios; conferences					
Show What You Know					
Unit Test					
Unit Problem Charity Fundraising					
Achievement Level for reporting*					

*Use Ontario Achievement Levels 1, 2, 3, 4.

Self-Assessment:

Comments: (Strengths, Needs, Next Steps)

Name ____________________ Date ______________

Master 1.5

To Parents and Adults at Home …

Your child's class is starting a mathematics unit on number patterns. Patterns surround us — they are in the games we play, the routes we take to school, and the routines we have each day. Patterns help us make sense of the world we live in and allow us to pose and solve problems.

Patterns occur regularly in mathematics and can be represented by numbers, words, pictures, and models. As children learn to identify, extend, and create patterns, they develop powerful skills that will help them make sense of mathematics and science.

In this unit, your child will:

- Find a pattern rule for a number pattern.
- Identify, extend, and create patterns.
- Describe and model patterns.
- Use patterns to pose and solve problems.
- Use patterns in a table to make predictions.

Patterns occur in many forms. Ask your child to describe some of the patterns she or he has learned. See if your child can give examples of them. Often, adults use tables and spreadsheets to organize data at work. Encourage your child to explain how she or he uses tables to organize and analyse patterns. As you look through the newspaper, discuss the patterns in the business, sports, or entertainment sections.

Name ____________________ Date ________________

Master 1.6

Additional Activity 1: What's Next?

Work on your own.

Write the next three terms in each pattern. Write each pattern rule.

- 4, 24, 14, 34, 24, ____, ____, ____

  Rule:

- 88, 77, 87, 76, 86, ____, ____, ____

  Rule:

- 4, 20, 10, 50, 40, ____, ____, ____

  Rule:

What is the 8th term in each pattern? Write each pattern rule.

- 144, 132, 120, 108, …

  Rule:

- 166, 177, 188, 199, …

  Rule:

Take It Further: Write two different patterns that begin: 10, 20, 40, …
For each pattern, list the next 3 terms and write the pattern rule.

Name ____________________ Date ______________

Master 1.7

Additional Activity 2: Patterns with Eleven

Work with a partner.

You will need a calculator.

Each product below has one factor of 11.

- Find each product.

  $14 \times 11 =$

  $26 \times 11 =$

  $45 \times 11 =$

  $53 \times 11 =$

What patterns do you see in the products?
Write a rule for finding the product of a two-digit number and 11.

- Use your rule to predict these products.

  $16 \times 11 =$

  $23 \times 11 =$

  $81 \times 11 =$

  $33 \times 11 =$

- Are there any 2-digit numbers for which your rule does not apply? Make up your own multiplication statements to find out.

Take It Further: Find these products.
How are these statements different from those above?

$56 \times 11 =$
$83 \times 11 =$

Does your rule for multiplying by 11 still work?

Name ____________________ Date ______________

Master 1.8

Additional Activity 3: What's Missing?

Work on your own. Find the missing numbers.

Write a rule for each table. Your rule must explain what you do to the input number to get the output number.

1.

Input	**Output**
2	6
	12
6	
8	24
10	

Rule:

2.

Input	**Output**
30	6
25	
	4
15	3
10	

Rule:

3.

Input	**Output**
35	
13	0
27	
	35
74	61

Rule:

Take It Further: Create two different Input/Output tables with missing numbers.
Trade tables with a classmate.
Complete your classmate's tables.

Name ____________________ Date _______________

Master 1.9

Additional Activity 4: Perimeter Patterns

Work with a partner.

Use Colour Tiles or grid paper.

Step 1

Build these 4 figures of a growing pattern.

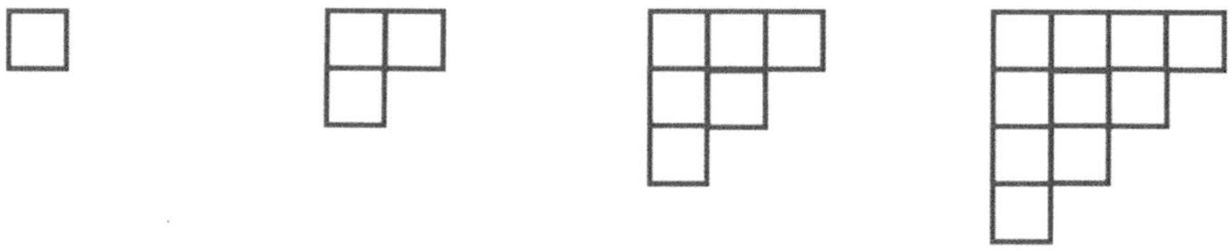

Figure 1 Figure 2 Figure 3 Figure 4

Step 2

Find the perimeter of each figure.

Record your results in the table.

Figure	Perimeter
1	
2	
3	
4	
5	
6	

Predict the perimeter of the 5th figure and the 6th figure.

Build the figures to check.

Write a pattern rule for the perimeters.

Take It Further:

Use Colour Tiles to create your own growing pattern.

Make the first 4 figures.

Trade patterns with your partner.

Repeat Step 2 above for your partner's pattern.

Name ____________________ Date ______________

Master 1.10

Step-by-Step 1

Lesson 1, Question 7

Here are the first two terms of a pattern: 6, 12, …

Step 1 How can you get 12 from 6?

Find the missing numbers:

6 + ____ = 12   6 × ____ = 12

Step 2 Start at 6. Add 6 each time. Write these terms.

6, 12, ____, ____, ____, ____

Write the pattern rule.

____

Step 3 Start at 6. Use a calculator. Multiply by 2 each time. Write these terms.

6, 12, ____, ____, ____, ____

Write the pattern rule.

____

Step 4 Think about alternately adding two numbers.

Create a different pattern that begins with 6, 12, ….

6, 12, ____, ____, ____, ____

Write the pattern rule.

____

Step 5 Think about alternately adding a number, then subtracting a smaller number. Create a different pattern that begins with 6, 12, ….

6, 12, ____, ____, ____, ____

Write the pattern rule.

____

Name ____________________ Date ______________

Master 1.11

Step-by-Step 2

Lesson 2, Question 6

Step 1 Draw an Input/Output machine in the space below.
Choose addition or multiplication.
Choose a number to go with your operation.
Write the operation and number in your machine.

Input	Output

Use the input numbers 3, 6, 9, and 12.
Find the output numbers.
Record your work in the table.

Step 2 What is the pattern rule for the input numbers?

____

Step 3 What is the pattern rule for the output numbers?

____

Name ____________________ Date ________________

Master 1.12

Step-by-Step 3

Lesson 3, Question 4

Step 1 Fill in the missing numbers.

Sundae	Number of Scoops	Price ($)	Price with Extra Topping ($)
1	1	1.25	1.75
2	2	2.50	3.00

Step 2 Complete the pattern rule for the price:

Start with $1.25. Add _____ each time.

Step 3 Complete the pattern rule for the price with extra topping:

Start with $1.75. Add _____ each time.

Step 4 Extend the pattern in the table. Show 5 scoops, then 6 scoops.
Fill in the missing numbers.

Sundae	Number of Scoops	Price ($)	Price with Extra Topping ($)
1	1	1.25	1.75
2	2	2.50	3.00
3	3		
4	4		
5			
6			

Step 5 The price of a 6-scoop sundae with extra topping is $ ____________.

Name ____________________ Date ______________

Master 1.13

Step-by-Step 4

Lesson 4, Question 6

Use a calculator when it helps.

Step 1 Continue this number pattern until you reach 31.

70, 67, 64, 61, 58, ____

Which day will Dave read 31 pages? ________________

Step 2 Complete the table.

Day	Number of Pages
1	70
2	67
3	64
4	
5	
6	
7	

Day	Number of Pages
8	

Step 3 Find the sum of the number of pages read from Day 1 to Day 7.

70 + 67 + 64 + _____ + _____ + _____ + _____ = _____

Step 4 What is the total number of pages in the book?

____

Name ________________ Date ______________

Master 1.14a

Unit Test: Unit 1 Number Patterns

Part A

1. Write the next 3 terms for each pattern. Write each pattern rule.

   a) 13, 36, 59, 82, ____, ____, ____

   Rule: ____

   b) 17, 117, 110, 210, 203, ____, ____, ____

   Rule: ____

   c) 142, 131, 121, 110, ____, ____, ____

   Rule: ____

2. This table shows the Input/Output from a machine.

   a) Identify the operation in the machine. ______________

   b) Write the pattern rule for the input numbers.

   ____

   c) Write the pattern rule for the output numbers.

   ____

   d) Complete the table. Which rule or rules did you use?

   ____

Input	Output
44	22
40	20
36	18
32	16

Name ____________________ Date ______________

Master 1.14b

Unit Test continued

Part B

3. Power Glen Elementary School has a plant sale to raise money for a local charity. Each plant costs $3. It is sold for $10.
   a) Make a table to show how much money is collected when these numbers of plants are sold: 10, 20, 30, 40, 50
   b) How many plants have to be sold to collect $500?

   c) How many plants have to be sold to be able to give the charity $500?

   d) Why are your answers to parts b and c different?

   ____

   ____

   e) Write your own problem about this plant sale. Solve the problem you posed.

   ____

   ____

   ____

Name ____________________ Date ______________

Master 1.14c

Unit Test continued

Part C

4. The table shows the output numbers from an Input/Output machine. What might the input numbers be?

Input	Output
	5
	6
	7
	8
	9
	10

____

How many different answers can you find?

____

Show your work.

Name ____________________ Date ______________

Master 1.15

Sample Answers

Unit Test – Unit 1 Number Patterns

Part A

1. a) 105, 128, 151; Start at 13. Add 23 each time.
   b) 303, 296, 396; Start at 17. Alternately add 100, then subtract 7.
   c) 100, 89, 79; Start at 142. Alternately subtract 11, then subtract 10.

2. a) ÷ 2
   b) Start at 44. Subtract 4 each time.
   c) Start at 22. Subtract 2 each time.
   d)

Input	Output
44	22
40	20
36	18
32	16
28	14
24	12
20	10

Part B

3.a)

Numbers of Plants Sold	Money Collected ($)
10	100
20	200
30	300
40	400
50	500

   b) 50
   c) 72
   d) The school has to subtract what it cost to buy the plants from the money collected.
   e) How much money is given to charity when 70 plants are sold? (*Answer: $490*)

Part C

4. Many answers are possible.
   For + 4, input would be 1, 2, 3, 4, 5, 6.
   For – 4, input would be 9, 10, 11, 12, 13, 14.
   For ÷ 4, input would be 20, 24, 28, 32, 36, 40.

Extra Practice Masters 1.16–1.18

Go to the CD-ROM to access editable versions of these Extra Practice Masters

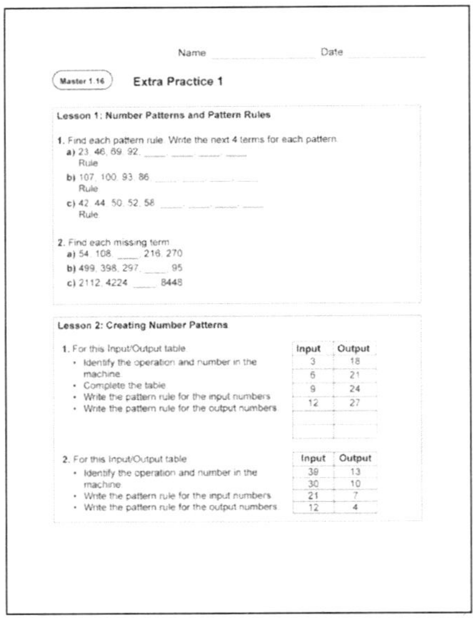

Name ______ Date ______

Master 1.16 **Extra Practice 1**

Lesson 1: Number Patterns and Pattern Rules

1. Find each pattern rule. Write the next 4 terms for each pattern.
   a) 23, 46, 69, 92, ____, ____, ____, ____
   Rule
   b) 107, 100, 93, 86, ____, ____, ____, ____
   Rule
   c) 42, 44, 50, 52, 58, ____, ____, ____, ____
   Rule

2. Find each missing term.
   a) 54, 108, ____, 216, 270
   b) 499, 398, 297, ____, 95
   c) 2112, 4224, ____, 8448

Lesson 2: Creating Number Patterns

1. For this Input/Output table:
   - Identify the operation and number in the machine.
   - Complete the table.
   - Write the pattern rule for the input numbers.
   - Write the pattern rule for the output numbers.

Input	Output
3	18
6	21
9	24
12	27

2. For this Input/Output table:
   - Identify the operation and number in the machine.
   - Write the pattern rule for the input numbers.
   - Write the pattern rule for the output numbers.

Input	Output
39	13
30	10
21	7
12	4

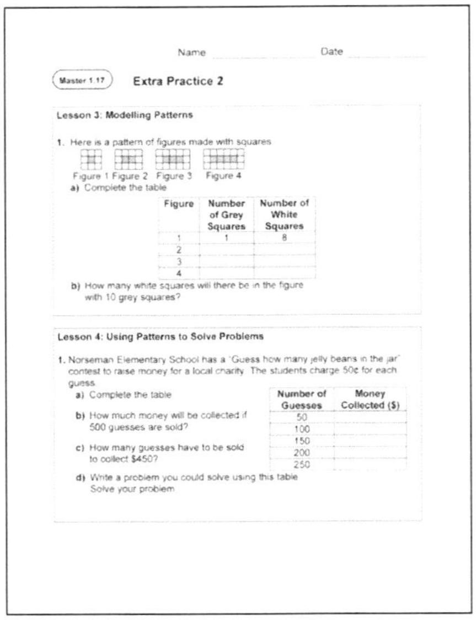

Name ______ Date ______

Master 1.17 **Extra Practice 2**

Lesson 3: Modelling Patterns

1. Here is a pattern of figures made with squares.
   Figure 1 Figure 2 Figure 3 Figure 4
   a) Complete the table.

Figure	Number of Grey Squares	Number of White Squares
1	1	8
2		
3		
4		

   b) How many white squares will there be in the figure with 10 grey squares?

Lesson 4: Using Patterns to Solve Problems

1. Norseman Elementary School has a "Guess how many jelly beans in the jar" contest to raise money for a local charity. The students charge 50¢ for each guess.
   a) Complete the table.
   b) How much money will be collected if 500 guesses are sold?
   c) How many guesses have to be sold to collect $450?
   d) Write a problem you could solve using this table. Solve your problem.

Number of Guesses	Money Collected ($)
50	
100	
150	
200	
250	

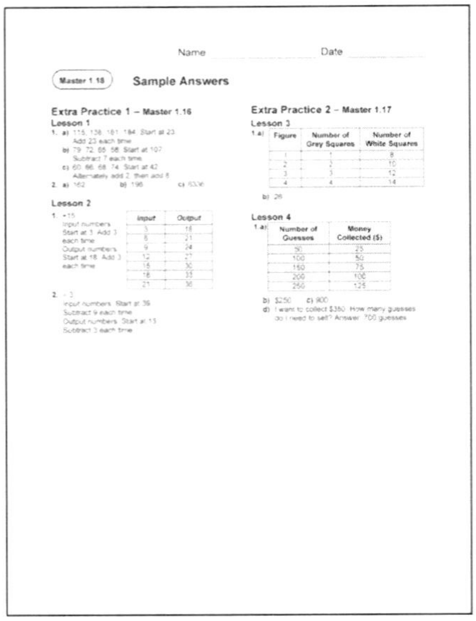

Name ______ Date ______

Master 1.18 **Sample Answers**

Extra Practice 1 – Master 1.16

Lesson 1

1. a) 115, 138, 161, 184. Start at 23. Add 23 each time.
   b) 79, 72, 65, 58. Start at 107. Subtract 7 each time.
   c) 60, 66, 68, 74. Start at 42. Alternately add 2, then add 6.
2. a) 162 b) 196 c) 6336

Lesson 2

1. +15
   Input numbers: Start at 3. Add 3 each time.
   Output numbers: Start at 18. Add 3 each time.

Input	Output
3	18
6	21
9	24
12	27
15	30
18	33
21	36

2. ÷ 3
   Input numbers: Start at 39. Subtract 9 each time.
   Output numbers: Start at 13. Subtract 3 each time.

Extra Practice 2 – Master 1.17

Lesson 3

1. a)

Figure	Number of Grey Squares	Number of White Squares
1	1	8
2	2	10
3	3	12
4	4	14

   b) 26

Lesson 4

1. a)

Number of Guesses	Money Collected ($)
50	25
100	50
150	75
200	100
250	125

   b) $250 c) 900
   d) I want to collect $350. How many guesses do I need to sell? Answer: 700 guesses

Addison Wesley
Mathematics
Makes Sense

Program Authors

Peggy Morrow
Ralph Connelly
Bryn Keyes
Jason Johnston
Steve Thomas
Jeananne Thomas
Angela D'Alessandro
Maggie Martin Connell
Don Jones
Michael Davis
Sharon Jeroski
Trevor Brown
Nora Alexander
Cynthia Pratt Nicolson

Printed and bound in Canada

8 9 MP 18 17

PEARSON
Education Canada

ADDISON WESLEY

Ontario

Math Makes Sense 5

Ontario

Teacher Guide

Unit 2: Whole Numbers

PEARSON
Addison Wesley

UNIT 2

Whole Numbers

"It is the mathematical activity of the learner that ultimately matters; thus strategies, big ideas, and models need to be understood as schematizing, structuring, and modelling."

Young Mathematicians at Work, Catherine Twomey Fosnot and Maarten Dolk

FOCUS STRAND
Number Sense and Numeration

SUPPORTING STRAND
Patterning and Algebra

Mathematics Background

What Are the Big Ideas?

- The position of a digit in a number determines what the digit represents (ones, tens, hundreds, thousands, ten thousands, hundred thousands).
- There are different strategies for adding and subtracting.
- Multiplication involves counting groups of equal size, then determining how many groups there are in all.
- Mathematical operations are related. For example, addition is related to subtraction and multiplication, subtraction is related to addition and division, and multiplication is related to division and addition.
- There are different strategies for multiplying and dividing.
- Number strategies are based on place-value concepts. These strategies can be applied to solve two-step problems.

How Will the Concepts Develop?

Students develop strategies for comparing and ordering numbers. They explore different mental math strategies to add and subtract whole numbers. They use Base Ten Blocks, place value, and expanded form to add 3- and 4-digit numbers, and to subtract with 4-digit numbers. These strategies are then applied to adding three numbers.

Students use patterns to multiply and divide, with particular focus on multiples of 10. They explore different strategies to multiply 2 numbers, including mental math. They estimate quotients, then investigate different strategies to divide a 4-digit number by a 1-digit number. Students use the number strategies they have developed to solve problems with more than one step.

Why Are These Concepts Important?

Students who understand the structure of numbers, the relationships among numbers, and the relationships among the basic operations will be able to work with whole numbers flexibly. These students will have computational fluency. This is an essential skill in the world since numbers are everywhere. It is important that students develop a sense of number to know when to estimate, when to perform a computation mentally, and which strategy to use to solve a problem.

Curriculum Overview

Cluster 1: Understanding, Adding, and Subtracting Whole Numbers

Overall Expectations

- Compare, order, and represent whole numbers, ... using concrete materials and drawings. (5m2)
- Understand the significance of numbers within the surrounding environment. (5m5)
- Select and perform computation techniques appropriate to specific problems involving whole numbers, ... and determine whether the results are reasonable. (5m7)
- Justify in oral and written expression the method chosen for calculations: estimation, mental computation, concrete materials, algorithms, or calculators. (5m9)

Specific Expectations

- Read and write whole numbers to 100 000 in standard, expanded, and written forms. (5m11)
- Compare, order, and represent the place value of whole numbers ... to 100 000 using concrete materials, drawings, and symbols. (5m14)
- Explain processes and solutions with whole numbers ... using mathematical language. (5m18)
- Use mental computation strategies to solve number problems. (5m30)
- Pose problems involving whole numbers ... and solve them using the appropriate calculation method: pencil and paper, or calculator or computer. (5m34)
- Explain their thinking when solving problems involving whole numbers .... (5m35)
- Use and explain estimation strategies. (5m36)

Launch
On the Dairy Farm

Lesson 1:
Representing, Comparing, and Ordering Numbers

Lesson 2:
Using Mental Math to Add

Lesson 3:
Adding 3- and 4-Digit Numbers

Lesson 4:
Lesson 4: Adding Three Numbers

Lesson 5:
Using Mental Math to Subtract

Lesson 6:
Subtracting with 4-Digit Numbers

Curriculum Overview

Cluster 2: Multiplying and Dividing Whole Numbers

Overall Expectations

- Understand the significance of numbers within the surrounding environment. (5m5)
- Select and perform computation techniques appropriate to specific problems involving whole numbers, … and determine whether the results are reasonable. (5m7)
- Justify in oral and written expression the method chosen for calculations: estimation, mental computation, concrete materials, algorithms, or calculators. (5m9)

Specific Expectations

- Count by 11's and 12's to 144. (5m12)
- Explain processes and solutions with whole numbers … using mathematical language. (5m18)
- Identify and investigate the use of number in various careers. (5m19)
- Multiply and divide numbers using concrete materials, drawings, and symbols. (5m28)
- Recall multiplication and division facts to 144. (5m29)
- Use mental computation strategies to solve number problems. (5m30)
- Select operations and solve two-step problems involving whole numbers … with and without a calculator. (5m33)
- Pose problems involving whole numbers … and solve them using the appropriate calculation method: pencil and paper, or calculator or computer. (5m34)
- Explain their thinking when solving problems involving whole numbers …. (5m35)
- Use and explain estimation strategies. (5m36)

Lesson 7: Multiplication and Division Facts to 144

Lesson 8: Multiplying with Multiples of 10

Lesson 9: Using Mental Math to Multiply

Lesson 10: Multiplying 2-Digit Numbers

Lesson 11: Estimating Quotients

Lesson 12: Dividing with Whole Numbers

Lesson 13: Solving Problems

Lesson 14: Strategies Toolkit

Show What You Know

Unit Problem
On the Dairy Farm

Curriculum across the Grades

Grade 4	Grade 5	Grade 6
Students read and write whole numbers to 10 000 in standard, expanded, and written forms. They count by 3's, 4's, 6's, 7's, 8's, 9's, and 10's to 100. They represent, compare, and order whole numbers to 10 000. Students multiply whole numbers by 10, 100, and 1000. They relate division to multiplication. Students multiply and divide numbers using concrete materials, drawings, and symbols. They multiply and divide a 3-digit number by a 1-digit number. Students recall multiplication and division facts to 81. Students add and subtract numbers mentally. Students pose and solve problems involving the addition, subtraction, multiplication, and division of whole numbers. They explain their thinking when solving problems and interpret the answers correctly.	Students read and write whole numbers to 100 000 in standard, expanded, and written forms. They count by 11's and 12's to 144. They represent, compare, and order whole numbers to 100 000. Students multiply and divide numbers using concrete materials, drawings, and symbols. They multiply a 2-digit number by a 2-digit number, and divide a 4-digit number by a 1-digit number. Students recall multiplication and division facts to 144. Students use mental computation strategies to solve number problems. Students select operations and solve two-step problems involving whole numbers. They pose and solve problems involving whole numbers, and explain their thinking. Students use and explain estimation strategies.	Students read and write whole numbers to 1 000 000 in standard and expanded forms. They multiply whole numbers by 0.1, 0.01, and 0.001. They represent, compare, and order whole numbers to 1 000 000. Students identify and describe the characteristics of multiples and factors, and composite and prime numbers, to 100. They use skip counting to assist in solving questions about factors and denominators. Students recall multiplication and division facts and use them to estimate and do mental computation. They multiply a 3-digit number by a 2-digit number, and divide a 4-digit number by a 2-digit number. Students use the correct order of operations when solving number sentences involving whole numbers. Students select operations and solve multi-step problems involving whole numbers. They pose and solve problems involving whole numbers, and explain their thinking.

Additional Activities

Go for the Greatest

For Extra Support (Appropriate for use after Lesson 1)
Materials: *Go for the Greatest* (Master 2.9), decahedron numbered 0 to 9

The work students do: Students play in a group. Each player draws a 5-digit number frame. Players take turns rolling the decahedron and record the number in any position in their number frame. Once a player has recorded a number, he or she cannot move it. Play continues until each player has filled her or his number frame. The player with the greatest number scores 2 points. The player with the least number scores 1 point. The first player to score 8 points wins.

Take It Further: Have players arrange all the numbers in order from greatest to least at the end of each round.

Logical/Mathematical/Social
Group Activity

What's the Difference?

For Extra Practice (Appropriate for use after Lesson 6)
Materials: *What's the Difference?* (Master 2.10), digit cards (0 to 9)

The work students do: Students work in pairs. The digit cards are shuffled and placed face down on the table. Player 1 selects 4 digit cards and makes the least number possible. Player 2 turns over 3 cards and makes the greatest number possible. Player 1 finds the difference between the 4-digit number and the 3-digit number. Then Player 1 and Player 2 switch roles. The player with the least difference scores 1 point. If there is a tie, both players score 1 point. The player with more points after 8 rounds of play is the winner.

Take It Further: Have pairs of students play the game using 4 sets of digit cards.

Logical/Mathematical
Partner Activity

Powerful Products

For Extra Practice (Appropriate for use after Lesson 9)
Materials: *Powerful Products* (Master 2.11), 2 sets of digit cards (0 to 9)

The work students do: Students play in pairs. Each player takes 3 cards. Players arrange their cards to make a 2-digit by 1-digit multiplication problem with the greatest product. Students record their multiplication problems, and compare answers. The player with the greater product scores 1 point. Play continues for 6 rounds. The player with the greater score wins.

Take It Further: Have students take 4 cards each. Players make 2-digit by 2-digit multiplication problems. The player with the greater product scores a point.

Logical/Mathematical
Partner Activity

The Range Game

For Extension (Appropriate for use after Lesson 11)
Materials: *The Range Game* (Master 2.12), Range Cards (Master 2.12b)

The work students do: Students play in pairs. Players take turns to select a range card. Player 1 chooses a factor and finds the product or quotient. If the result is in the range, Player 1 scores a point. If not, Player 2 chooses a factor and finds the product or quotient. Play continues until one player chooses a factor that gives a result in the range. That player scores 1 point. The first player to score 5 points wins.

Take It Further: Have students make their own set of range cards. They trade sets with another pair of students.

Social/Logical/Mathematical
Partner Activity

Planning for Unit 2

Planning for Instruction

Suggested Unit time: 3–4 weeks

Lesson	Time	Materials	Program Support
Launch: On the Dairy Farm, page 2	15–20 min		
Lesson 1: Representing, Comparing, and Ordering Numbers, page 4 Represent, compare, and order numbers to 999 999.	40–50 min	6-column charts	PM 21: 6-Column Chart Master 2.13: Step-by-Step 1 Master 2.28: Extra Practice 1
Lesson 2: Using Mental Math to Add, page 7 Use different mental math strategies to add whole numbers.	40–50 min		Master 2.14: Step-by-Step 2 Master 2.28: Extra Practice 1
Lesson 3: Adding 3- and 4-Digit Numbers, page 10 Use different strategies to add 3- and 4-digit numbers.	40–50 min	overhead Base Ten Blocks Base Ten Blocks	Master 2.15: Step-by-Step 3 Master 2.29: Extra Practice 2
Lesson 4: Adding Three Numbers, page 13 Use different strategies to add 3 or more numbers.	40–50 min	clear protractor blank transparency overhead markers	Master 2.16: Step-by-Step 4 Master 2.29: Extra Practice 2
Lesson 5: Using Mental Math to Subtract, page 17 Use different mental math strategies to subtract whole numbers.	40–50 min		Master 2.17: Step-by-Step 5 Master 2.30: Extra Practice 3
Lesson 6: Subtracting with 4-Digit Numbers, page 20 Use different strategies to subtract 4-digit numbers.	40–50 min	overhead Base Ten Blocks overhead place-value mat Base Ten Blocks	Master 2.18: Step-by-Step 6 Master 2.30: Extra Practice 3
Lesson 7: Multiplication and Division Facts to 144, page 23 Use patterns to multiply and to divide.	40–50 min	multiplication charts and transparency	Master 2.6: Multiplication Chart Master 2.19: Step-by-Step 7 Master 2.31: Extra Practice 4
Game: Multiplication Tic-Tac-Toe, page 27	20–35 min	counters in 2 different colours paper clips game boards	Master 2.7: Multiplication Tic-Tac-Toe Game Board
Lesson 8: Multiplying with Multiples of 10, page 28 Use patterns to multiply with multiples of 10.	40–50 min	5-column charts 6-column charts calculators	PM 20: 5-Column Chart PM 21: 6-Column Chart Master 2.20: Step-by-Step 8 Master 2.31: Extra Practice 4
Lesson 9: Using Mental Math to Multiply, page 31 Use different strategies to mentally multiply 2 numbers.	40–50 min		Master 2.21: Step-by-Step 9 Master 2.32: Extra Practice 5
Lesson 10: Multiplying 2-Digit Numbers, page 34 Use different strategies to multiply two 2-digit numbers.	40–50 min	overhead Base Ten Blocks transparency of 1-cm grid Base Ten Blocks 1-cm grid paper	PM 23: 1-cm Grid Paper Master 2.22: Step-by-Step 10 Master 2.32: Extra Practice 5

Lesson	Time	Materials	Program Support
Lesson 11: Estimating Quotients, page 37 Use different strategies to estimate quotients.	40–50 min		Master 2.23: Step-by-Step 11 Master 2.33: Extra Practice 6
Lesson 12: Dividing with Whole Numbers, page 40 Use different strategies to divide a 4-digit number by a 1-digit number.	40–50 min	6-sector spinners number cubes	Master 2.8: 6-Sector Spinner Master 2.24: Step-by-Step 12 Master 2.33: Extra Practice 6
Lesson 13: Solving Problems, page 44 Solve problems with more than one step.	40–50 min		Master 2.25: Step-by-Step 13 Master 2.34: Extra Practice 7
Game: Less Is More, page 47	20–35 min	decahedron numbered 0 to 9	
Lesson 14: Strategies Toolkit, page 48 Interpret a problem and select an appropriate strategy.	40–50 min		
Show What You Know, page 50 Assessment	40–50 min		
Unit Problem: On the Dairy Farm, page 52 Assessment	40–50 min		

Planning for Unit 2

Planning for Assessment

Purpose	Tools and Process	Recording and Reporting
Diagnostic	*Unit Launch* Question; conference; scaffold problems throughout the unit	 PM 8: Conference Prompts
Formative	*Explore* – Ongoing Assessment: Observe and Listen Prompt student's self-assessment *Practice* – Assessment Focus Questions Review student work; provide feedback; scaffold as needed; select key pieces	Master 2.2 Ongoing Observations: Whole Numbers PM 1: Inquiry Process Check List PM 6: Observation Record 1 PM 7: Observation Record 2 PM 8: Conference Prompts PM 2: Self-Assessment PM 3: Self-Assessment: Problem Solving PM 9: Work Sample Records
Summative	*Show What You Know* *Unit Problem* – Performance Assessment Unit Test Review assessment records; add unit results to ongoing records	Master 2.1 Unit Rubric: Whole Numbers Master 2.3 Performance Assessment Rubric: On the Dairy Farm Master 2.4 Unit Summary: Whole Numbers PM 10: Summary Class Records: Strands PM 11: Summary Class Records: Achievement Categories PM 12: Summary Record: Individual
Learning Skills/ Mathematical Disposition	Observe and record throughout the unit	PM 4: Learning Skills Check List PM 5: Mathematical Dispositions and Learning Skills

Program Masters (PM) are in the *Grade 5 Planning and Program Masters* module.
Extra Practice Masters are on the CD-ROM.

On the Dairy Farm

LESSON ORGANIZER

15–20 min

Curriculum Focus: Activate prior learning about operations and whole numbers.

ASSUMED PRIOR KNOWLEDGE

✓ Students can choose the appropriate operation (addition, subtraction, multiplication, or division) to solve a problem with whole numbers.

ACTIVATE PRIOR LEARNING

Discuss the first question on page 27 of the Student Book. Ask:

- What do we need to do to find out how much hay 2 cows would eat in 1 week?
  (*We need to divide 140 by 2. Two cows eat about 70 kg of hay each week.*)
- Do we need to find out exactly how much hay 2 cows would eat in 1 week? How do you know?
  (*No, the question asks us to find "about how much ...."*)

Record students' responses. Discuss any different strategies students used.

Discuss the second question. Ask:

- How would you find about how much hay 2 cows eat each day?
  (*Divide the weekly amount by 7; 70 ÷ 7 = 10. Two cows eat about 10 kg of hay each day.*)

Discuss the third question.

- How would you estimate the amount of milk produced by 30 cows?
  (*I know 1 cow produces 27 L each day. To estimate the amount produced by 30 cows, I estimated the product 27 × 30 as 30 × 30 = 900 L.*)

Tell students that, in this unit, they will represent, compare, and order whole numbers. They will also choose the appropriate operation and solve whole number problems that involve addition, subtraction, multiplication, and division.

At the end of the unit, students will create and solve problems related to a dairy farm.

Key Words

- compensation
- dividend
- divisor
- quotient
- compatible numbers

- Hay is one part of a dairy cow's diet.
  140 kg of hay feeds 2 cows for 2 weeks.
  About how much hay do 2 cows eat each week? 70 kg
  Each day? 10 kg
- The Colyns have 30 dairy cows on their farm.
  Each day, they collect 27 L of milk from 1 cow.
  Estimate the amount of milk produced by 30 cows.
  $30 \text{ L} \times 30 = 900 \text{ L}$

27

LITERATURE CONNECTIONS FOR THE UNIT

Math-Terpieces: The Art of Problem-Solving by Greg Tang. Scholastic, Inc., 2003.
ISBN: 0439443881
Math wizard Greg Tang presents an artfully awesome method for learning addition in this combination of math and art history. Tang combines classic pieces of fine art with arithmetic to teach kids that grouping objects together means adding faster and easier.

Riddle-Iculous Math by Joan Holub. Albert Whitman Publications, 2003.
ISBN: 0807549967
What is a math teacher's favourite game? Divide and seek. This silly book will delight young math whizzes and make math practice a bit more tolerable for the less-than-whizzes. Every page is filled with riddles that enable children to practise adding, subtracting, counting money, skip counting, and solving problems.

REACHING ALL LEARNERS

Some students may benefit from using the virtual manipulatives on the e-Tools CD-ROM. The e-Tools appropriate for this unit include Place-Value Blocks and Counters. These can be used in place of, or to support the use of, Base Ten Blocks and counters.

DIAGNOSTIC ASSESSMENT

What to Look For	What to Do
✔ Students can choose the appropriate operation (addition, subtraction, multiplication, or division) to solve a problem with whole numbers.	***Extra Support:*** Students who have difficulty choosing the appropriate operation to solve a problem with whole numbers may benefit from modelling the problem with Base Ten Blocks or counters.

Representing, Comparing, and Ordering Numbers

LESSON ORGANIZER

40–50 min

Curriculum Focus: Represent, compare, and order numbers to 999 999. (5m11, 5m14)

Student Materials

- 6-column charts (PM 21)

Vocabulary: expanded form, standard form

Assessment: Master 2.2 Ongoing Observations: Whole Numbers

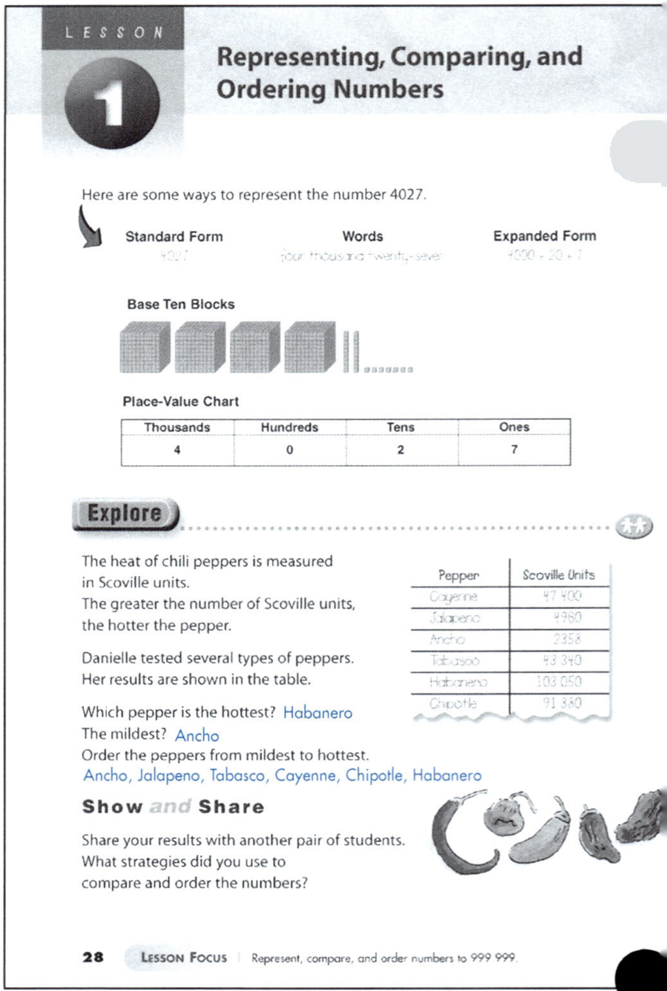

LESSON 1

Representing, Comparing, and Ordering Numbers

Here are some ways to represent the number 4027.

Standard Form — 4027

Words — four thousand twenty-seven

Expanded Form — 4000 + 20 + 7

Base Ten Blocks

Place-Value Chart

Thousands	Hundreds	Tens	Ones
4	0	2	7

Explore

The heat of chili peppers is measured in Scoville units.
The greater the number of Scoville units, the hotter the pepper.

Danielle tested several types of peppers.
Her results are shown in the table.

Pepper	Scoville Units
Cayenne	47 400
Jalapeno	4960
Ancho	2358
Tabasco	43 340
Habanero	103 050
Chipotle	91 880

Which pepper is the hottest? Habanero
The mildest? Ancho
Order the peppers from mildest to hottest.
Ancho, Jalapeno, Tabasco, Cayenne, Chipotle, Habanero

Show and Share

Share your results with another pair of students.
What strategies did you use to compare and order the numbers?

28 LESSON FOCUS | Represent, compare, and order numbers to 999 999.

Key Math Learnings

1. Numbers can be written in many ways.
2. Place-value concepts are used to compare and order numbers.

BEFORE — Get Started

Ask questions, such as:

- What does the digit 4 represent in 4027?
  (4 thousands)
- Which is greater, 4000 or 5000? How do you know?
  (5000 is greater than 4000; 5 is greater than 4, so 5 thousands is greater than 4 thousands.)

Discuss the various ways of representing 4027 shown at the top of page 28 in the Student Book. Ask questions, such as:

- How is modelling 4027 with Base Ten Blocks similar to showing it in a place-value chart? In expanded form?
  (Both the Base Ten Blocks and the place-value chart show that 4027 is made up of 4 thousands, 2 tens, and 7 ones; expanded form shows that 4000 + 20 + 7 is 4027, and Base Ten Blocks show that combining 4 thousands, 2 tens, and 7 ones make 4027.)

Present *Explore*. Be sure students realize that to find the hottest pepper, they need to find the greatest number in the chart.

You may wish to distribute 6-column charts to students to use as place-value charts.

DURING — Explore

Ongoing Assessment: Observe and Listen

Ask questions such as:

- What place value would you look at first to find the greatest number?
  (Hundred thousands)
- Which pepper is the hottest? How do you know?
  (The Habanero pepper is the hottest. 103 050 is the greatest number; it is the only 6-digit number in the list.)

Connect

The table shows the population of some Canadian cities in 2001.

City	Population
St. John's, NL	99 182
Halifax, NS	359 111
Quebec, QC	169 076
Winnipeg, MB	619 544
Edmonton, AB	666 104
Vancouver, BC	545 671

➤ Order the numbers from greatest to least.
Use a place-value chart.

	Thousands			Units		
City	Hundred Thousands	Ten Thousands	One Thousands	Hundreds	Tens	Ones
St. John's, NL		9	9	1	8	2
Halifax, NS	3	5	9	1	1	1
Quebec, QC	1	6	9	0	7	6
Winnipeg, MB	6	1	9	5	4	4
Edmonton, AB	6	6	6	1	0	4
Vancouver, BC	5	4	5	6	7	1

666 104 has the most hundred thousands and ten thousands.
It is the greatest number.

99 182 has no hundred thousands.
It is the least number.

When we write numbers with more than 4 digits in standard form, we put a space between the hundreds digit and the thousands digit.

The order of the numbers from greatest to least is:
666 104, 619 544, 545 671, 359 111, 169 076, 99 182

➤ Edmonton has a population of 666 104.
We can write this in expanded form:
600 000 + 60 000 + 6000 + 100 + 4
and in words: six hundred sixty-six thousand one hundred four

29

REACHING ALL LEARNERS

Early Finishers

Have students find each number:

- the greatest 5-digit number with all different odd digits
- the least 5-digit number with all different even digits

Common Misconceptions

➤Students may ignore zeros as placeholders in a number. For example, they may interpret 4027 as four hundred twenty-seven.

How to Help: Have students use a place-value chart to compare numbers such as 4027 and 427.

- How did you find the least number?
  (*4960 and 2358 have only 4 digits. 2 thousands are less than 4 thousands, so 2358 is the least number. The Ancho is the mildest pepper.*)
- What is the order of the peppers from mildest to hottest?
  (*Ancho, Jalapeno, Tabasco, Cayenne, Chipotle, and Habanero*)

AFTER Connect

Invite students to discuss the strategies they used to order the numbers in *Connect*. Ask:

- How do we know 99 182 is the least number?
  (*It has no hundred thousands.*)
- How can you tell whether Edmonton or Winnipeg has the greater population?
  (*The numbers representing the populations both have 6 hundred thousands. We compare the ten thousands. 6 ten thousands is greater than 1 ten thousand, so 666 104 is greater than 619 544.*)

Practice

Have 6-column charts available for all questions. For question 4, be sure students recall the ">" symbol represents "greater than" and the "<" symbol represents "less than."

Assessment Focus: Question 7

Students should recognize that to make the 6-digit number closest to 100 000, they need to make the least 6-digit number using these digits. To make the least number, they would arrange the digits 1 to 6 from least to greatest. To make the number closest to 500 000, most students will try the greatest number with 4 hundred thousands and the least number with 5 hundred thousands.

Sample Answers

3. From least to greatest:
   40 000 + 700 + 90 + 5; forty thousand seven hundred ninety-five
   400 000 + 6000 + 500 + 80 + 3; four hundred six thousand five hundred eighty-three
   400 000 + 20 000 + 1000 + 30 + 5; four hundred twenty-one thousand thirty-five
   400 000 + 20 000 + 3000 + 4; four hundred twenty-three thousand four
5. 975 310 is the greatest number you can make with all different odd digits and one zero. 9 is the greatest digit and it is in the 100 000s place, 7 is the next greatest digit and it is in the 10 000s place, 5 is the next greatest digit, and so on. 0, which is the smallest digit, is in the units place.
7. c) We got closest to 500 000 because 498 765 is less than 2 000 away from 500 000, but 123 456 is more than 23 000 away from 100 000.

REFLECT: Denis is not correct. In 84 914, the 8 is in the ten thousands place. So, it represents 80 000. In 311 902, the 3 is in the hundred thousands place. So, it represents 300 000. 84 914 has 0 hundred thousands; so, 311 902 is greater than 84 914.

Numbers Every Day

Start at 94; subtract 8 each time.
Start at 48; add 8 each time.
Start at 212; subtract 8 each time.
Start at 89; add 8 each time.

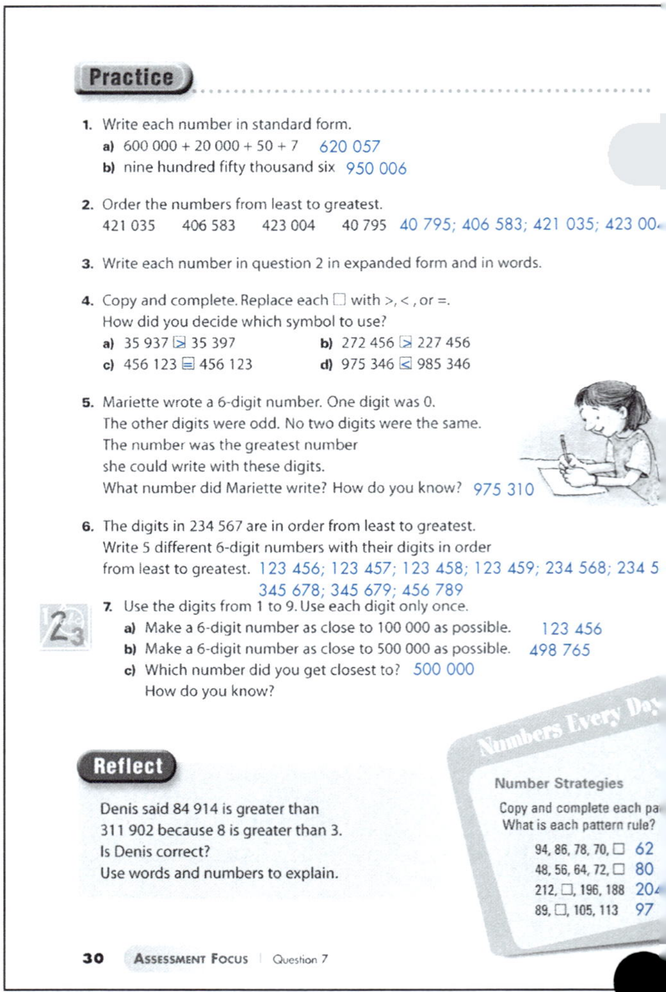

Practice

1. Write each number in standard form.
   a) 600 000 + 20 000 + 50 + 7 620 057
   b) nine hundred fifty thousand six 950 006
2. Order the numbers from least to greatest.
   421 035 406 583 423 004 40 795 40 795; 406 583; 421 035; 423 00
3. Write each number in question 2 in expanded form and in words.
4. Copy and complete. Replace each □ with >, <, or =.
   How did you decide which symbol to use?
   a) 35 937 > 35 397 b) 272 456 > 227 456
   c) 456 123 = 456 123 d) 975 346 < 985 346
5. Mariette wrote a 6-digit number. One digit was 0.
   The other digits were odd. No two digits were the same.
   The number was the greatest number she could write with these digits.
   What number did Mariette write? How do you know? 975 310
6. The digits in 234 567 are in order from least to greatest.
   Write 5 different 6-digit numbers with their digits in order from least to greatest. 123 456; 123 457; 123 458; 123 459; 234 568; 234 5
   345 678; 345 679; 456 789
7. Use the digits from 1 to 9. Use each digit only once.
   a) Make a 6-digit number as close to 100 000 as possible. 123 456
   b) Make a 6-digit number as close to 500 000 as possible. 498 765
   c) Which number did you get closest to? 500 000
   How do you know?

Reflect

Denis said 84 914 is greater than 311 902 because 8 is greater than 3.
Is Denis correct?
Use words and numbers to explain.

Numbers Every Day

Number Strategies

Copy and complete each pa
What is each pattern rule?

94, 86, 78, 70, □ 62
48, 56, 64, 72, □ 80
212, □, 196, 188 204
89, □, 105, 113 97

30 ASSESSMENT FOCUS | Question 7

ASSESSMENT FOR LEARNING

What to Look For	What to Do
Understanding concepts ✔ Students can represent numbers to 999 999 in standard form, expanded form, and words. ✔ Students can compare and order numbers to 999 999.	***Extra Support:*** Students can do the Additional Activity, *Go for the Greatest* (Master 2.9). Students can use Step-by-Step 1 (Master 2.13) to complete question 7. ***Extra Practice:*** Students can complete Extra Practice 1 (Master 2.28). ***Extension:*** Challenge students to write five different 7-digit numbers and order the numbers from least to greatest.

Recording and Reporting
Master 2.2 Ongoing Observations: Whole Numbers

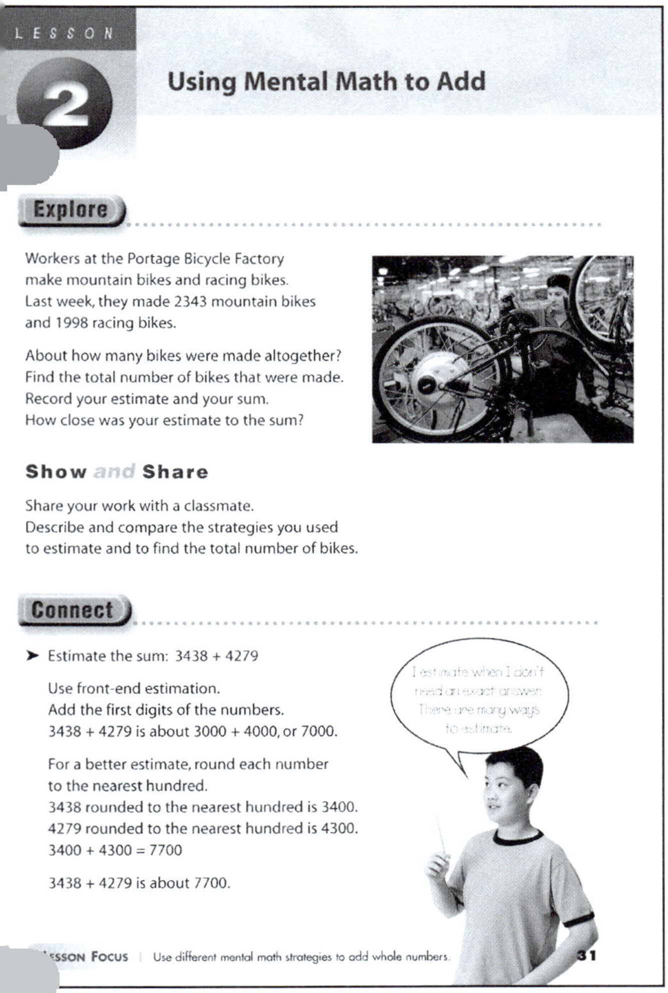
LESSON 2

Using Mental Math to Add

Explore

Workers at the Portage Bicycle Factory make mountain bikes and racing bikes. Last week, they made 2343 mountain bikes and 1998 racing bikes.

About how many bikes were made altogether? Find the total number of bikes that were made. Record your estimate and your sum. How close was your estimate to the sum?

Show and Share

Share your work with a classmate. Describe and compare the strategies you used to estimate and to find the total number of bikes.

Connect

➤ Estimate the sum: 3438 + 4279

Use front-end estimation. Add the first digits of the numbers.
3438 + 4279 is about 3000 + 4000, or 7000.

For a better estimate, round each number to the nearest hundred.
3438 rounded to the nearest hundred is 3400.
4279 rounded to the nearest hundred is 4300.
3400 + 4300 = 7700

3438 + 4279 is about 7700.

SSON FOCUS | Use different mental math strategies to add whole numbers. 31

Using Mental Math to Add

LESSON ORGANIZER (40–50 min)

Curriculum Focus: Use different mental math strategies to add whole numbers. (5m30, 5m36)

Student Materials *Optional*
- Step-by-Step 2 (Master 2.14)
- Extra Practice 1 (Master 2.28)

Vocabulary: compensation

Assessment: Master 2.2 Ongoing Observations: Whole Numbers

Key Math Learnings

1. Estimation is used when an exact answer is not required; mental math is used when an exact answer is required.
2. There are many strategies for estimating sums and adding mentally.

BEFORE Get Started

Have students use mental math to find each sum.
2000 + 1500 (*3500*) 4200 + 2300 (*6500*)

Ask:
- Why was it easy to add these numbers mentally?
  (*The numbers had 0 tens and 0 ones. There was no need for regrouping.*)

Remind students that "friendly numbers" are numbers that are easy to add or to estimate with.

- How can you tell if an exact answer is required or if an estimate will do?
  (*Usually, when an estimate will do, the question asks "About how many ...?"*)

Present *Explore*. Encourage students to think about the mental math strategies they used with smaller numbers.

DURING Explore

Ongoing Assessment: Observe and Listen

Ask questions, such as:
- How did you decide how to estimate the sum?
  (*I prefer to use front-end estimation, but sometimes rounding gives a better estimate. For example, if a number is very close to the next thousand, then front-end estimation "misses" a lot of the number.*)
- If you estimated by rounding, how did you decide how to round the numbers?
  (*Rounding both numbers to the nearest thousand gives numbers that are very easy to add, but the estimate may not be very close to the sum. I estimated by rounding 1998 to the nearest thousand and then adding 2343.*)
- How did you find the sum?
  (*I added 2 to 1998 to make 2000, and took 2 from 2343 to make 2341; 2000 + 2341 = 4341, so 1998 + 2343 = 4341.*)

REACHING ALL LEARNERS

Alternative Explore

Materials: a set of index cards, each with a multiple of 10, 100, or 1000 written on it.

Students work in a group. Students take turns to write a 4-digit number. Each student selects a card, writes an addition statement with the 4-digit number and the number on the card, and then uses mental math to find the sum.

Early Finishers

Have students develop their own number trick, similar to the one in question 4.

➤ Use mental math to add: 2180 + 6432

Use **compensation**.

2180 + 20 = 2200

6432 − 20 = 6412

The sum of 2200 + 6412 is equal to the sum of 2180 + 6432.

2200 + 6412 = 8612

2180 + 6432 = 8612

➤ Use mental math to add: 2625 + 432

Use the strategy of adding on.

Start with the greater number, 2625.

There are 4 hundreds to add.

Count on by 100 four times:

2625 (+100) 2725 (+100) 2825 (+100) 2925 (+100) 3025

There are 3 tens to add.

Count on by 10 three times:

3025 (+10) 3035 (+10) 3045 (+10) 3055

Then add 2:

3055 + 2 = 3057

2625 + 432 = 3057

Practice

Use mental math.

1. Add. Use as many different strategies as you can.
   - **a)** 6145 + 3007 **b)** 3654 + 372 **c)** 500 + 2150
   - **d)** 1999 + 999 **e)** 4003 + 2968 **f)** 7741 + 685

   a) 9152 b) 4026 c)
   d) 2998 e) 6971 f)

2. Find the sums less than 10 000.
   - **a)** 3099 + 5824 **b)** 6489 + 3201 **c)** 4673 + 6595
   - **d)** 9997 + 8763 **e)** 5036 + 297 **f)** 9539 + 470

   a) 8923 b) 9690
   e) 5333

32

AFTER Connect

Invite students to share their estimation strategies and estimates. Compare the estimates to the sum. Discuss which estimation strategy yields the best estimate in this case.

Review the estimation strategies presented in *Connect*. Ask questions, such as:

- Suppose you estimated 3438 + 4279 by rounding to the nearest thousand. How would this estimate compare to one found using front-end estimation? Explain. (*In this case, rounding to the nearest thousand and front-end estimation give the same estimate. Both numbers round down.*)
- Why does rounding to the nearest hundred give a "better" estimate? (*Rounding to a lower place value usually gives an estimate that is closer to the actual sum.*)

Discuss the mental math strategies presented in *Connect*. Ask:

- When would you use compensation as a strategy? (*When one of the numbers is close to a friendly number*)
- When would you use adding on as a strategy? (*When there aren't too many numbers to "count on"*)

Practice

Assessment Focus: Question 4

Students should recognize that Victoria chose numbers that were close to friendly numbers. They should also recognize that the result of subtracting 202 and adding 204 is the same as just adding 2. Adding 498 and 2 means that 500 has been added to the original number. So, subtracting 500 will "bring you back" to the original number.

3. Natalie's school gave a concert last week.
On Friday, 4560 people attended.
On Saturday, 2995 people attended.
How many people attended the concert in all? 7555 people

4. Victoria shows her friends a number trick.
She says:
- Pick any 4-digit number.
  Don't tell me what it is.
- Add 498 to the number.
- Subtract 202 from the sum.
- Add 204 to the difference.
- Tell me what number you have now.
- The number you picked is □.

Victoria subtracts 500 from the number she is told.
This always gives her the original number.

Why does this trick work?
Use words and numbers to explain.

5. A blueberry pie has 2285 calories.
A cherry pie has 2465 calories.
About how many calories are in both pies altogether? About 4800

6. Write an addition problem you can solve using mental math.
Solve your problem.
Which strategy did you use to solve your problem? Why?

Reflect

Describe 2 different ways you could mentally add 4621 + 5393.

Numbers Every Day

Number Strategies

Round each number to the nearest ten, the nearest hundred, and the nearest thousand.
- 6493 6490, 6500, 6000
- 7989 7990, 8000, 8000
- 5091 5090, 5100, 5000
- 8996 9000, 9000, 9000
- 3003 3000, 3000, 3000

ASSESSMENT FOCUS | Question 4 33

Sample Answers

4. The trick works because 498 − 202 + 204 = 500. The trick adds 500 to the original number. If you subtract 500 from the end number, you will get the original number.
6. For example, 4999 + 3021 = 8020. I used compensation. It was easy to add 1 to 4999 and make it 5000, and take one away from 3021 to make it 3020.

REFLECT: I could use compensation.
Add 7 to 5393 to get 5400 and subtract 7 from 4621 to get 4614.
Since 5400 + 4614 = 10 014, then 5393 + 4621 = 10 014
I could also use adding on:
4621 + 5000 = 9621
9621 + 300 = 9921
9921 + 90 = 10 011
10 011 + 3 = 10 014

Numbers Every Day

Have students observe how it is possible that a number rounded to the nearest ten, nearest hundred, and nearest thousand can round to the same number each time.

ASSESSMENT FOR LEARNING

What to Look For

Understanding concepts
- ✔ Students can distinguish between estimation and mental math.
- ✔ Students can mentally add whole numbers up to 4 digits.
- ✔ Students can apply different estimation strategies and different mental math strategies for addition.

What to Do

Extra Support: Have students do some addition questions in which they add multiples of 10, 100, or 1000.
Students can use Step-by-Step 2 (Master 2.14) to complete question 4.

Extra Practice: Students can complete Extra Practice 1 (Master 2.28).

Extension: Have students play in pairs. Player 1 selects a target number between 1000 and 100 000 and a start number less than the target number. Players take turns to add a multiple of 1000, 100, 10, or 1. The goal is to get closest to the target number, without going over. If a player goes over the target number, the other player wins.

Recording and Reporting
Master 2.2 Ongoing Observations: Whole Numbers

Adding 3- and 4-Digit Numbers

LESSON ORGANIZER

40–50 min

Curriculum Focus: Use different strategies to add 3- and 4-digit numbers. (5m18, 5m34, 5m35)

Teacher Materials
- overhead Base Ten Blocks

Student Materials
- Base Ten Blocks

Optional
- Step-by-Step 3 (Master 2.15)
- Extra Practice 2 (Master 2.29)

Assessment: Master 2.2 Ongoing Observations: Whole Numbers

Key Math Learnings

1. A variety of strategies can be used to add 3- and 4-digit numbers.
2. All the strategies for adding 3- and 4-digit numbers are based on place value.

LESSON 3

Adding 3- and 4-Digit Numbers

Explore

Last week, Sarah drank 1196 mL of juice.
Luke drank 937 mL.
How many millilitres of juice did they drink altogether? 2133 mL

Show and Share

Share your solution with another pair of students.
How did you add the numbers?

Connect

Gemma ate 738 g of fruit one week.
In the same week, Devon ate 1452 g of fruit.
How many grams of fruit did they eat altogether?

Add: 738 + 1452

➤ Use Base Ten Blocks on a place-value mat to add.

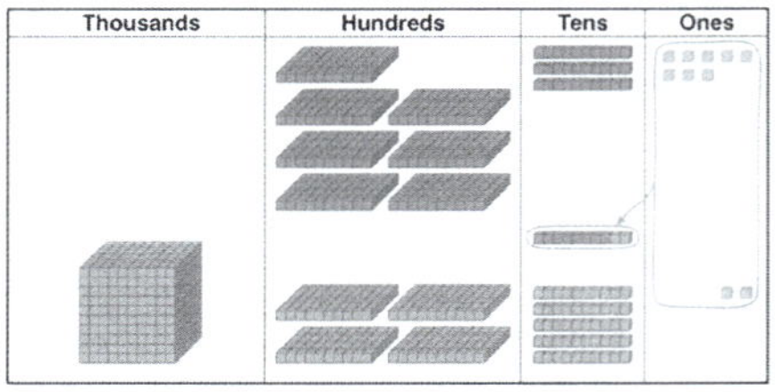

- Trade 10 ones for 1 ten.

34 LESSON FOCUS | Use different strategies to add 3- and 4-digit numbers.

BEFORE Get Started

Ask:
- How can you use Base Ten Blocks to model 297? 143?
  (For 297, use 2 flats, 9 rods, and 7 unit cubes. For 143, use 1 flat, 4 rods, and 3 unit cubes.)
- How can you use Base Ten Blocks to add 297 + 143?
  (Look at the ones. There are 10 ones. Regroup 10 ones as 1 ten. There are no ones. Look at the tens. There are 14 tens. Regroup 10 tens as 1 hundred. There are 4 tens left. Look at the hundreds. There are 4 hundreds.
  297 + 143 = 440)

Present *Explore*. Have Base Ten Blocks available for those students who wish to use them.

DURING Explore

Ongoing Assessment: Observe and Listen

Observe which methods students use to add. Ask questions, such as:
- How much juice did Sarah and Luke drink last week? How did you find out?
  (2133 mL. I used Base Ten Blocks to add. For 1196, I used 1 thousand cube, 1 flat, 9 rods, and 6 unit cubes. For 937, I used 9 flats, 3 rods, and 7 unit cubes. I added the ones: 13 ones. I regrouped 13 ones as 1 ten 3 ones. I added the tens: 13 tens. Then I regrouped 13 tens as 1 hundred 3 tens. I added the hundreds: 11 hundreds. I regrouped 11 hundreds as 1 thousand 1 hundred. Finally, I added the thousands: 2 thousands.)

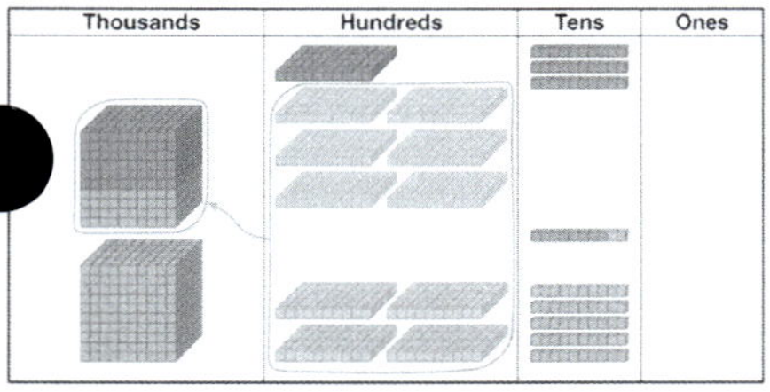

• Trade 10 hundreds for 1 thousand.

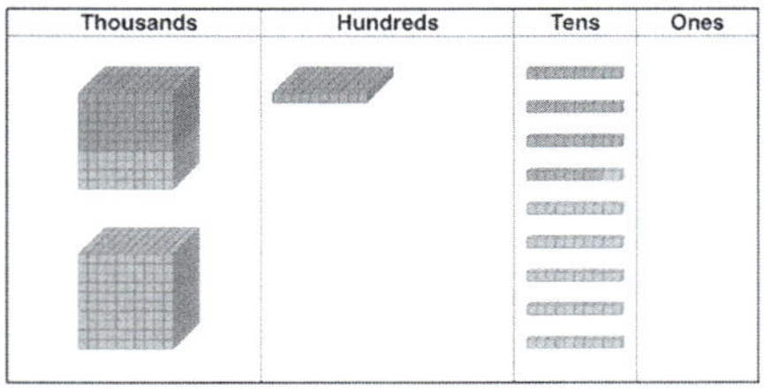

738 + 1452 = 2190

➤ Use expanded form to add.

738	→		+	700	+ 30	+ 8		
+ 1452	→	1000	+	400	+ 50	+ 2		
		1000	+	1100	+ 80	+ 10	= 2100 + 90	= 2190

➤ Use place value to add.

Add the ones: 10 ones. Regroup 10 ones as 1 ten 0 ones.	Add the tens: 9 tens	Add the hundreds: 11 hundreds. Regroup 11 hundreds as 1 thousand 1 hundred.	Add the thousands: 2 thousands
738 + 1452 = 0 (regrouped 1 above tens)	738 + 1452 = 90	738 + 1452 = 190 (regrouped 1 above thousands)	838 + 1452 = 2190

Together Gemma and Devon ate 2190 g of fruit last week.

35

REACHING ALL LEARNERS

Alternative Explore

Materials: play money

Suppose Alex has $2516. He earns $1737. Have students find the total amount of money Alex now has. Have students discuss what regrouping looks like with money (for example, 10 loonies can be traded for one $10 bill; ten $10 bills can be traded for a $100 bill.)

Early Finishers

Have students find different combinations of numbers that work in question 7.

Common Misconceptions

➤ Students forget to regroup when using place value to add.

How to Help: Have students use a place-value chart. Remind them that only one digit can go in each place value on the chart.

➤ Students do not align the numbers correctly when they use place value to add.

How to Help: Have students work on lined paper turned sideways. They print one digit in each column, beginning with the ones digits.

AFTER Connect

Invite students to share the strategies they used to add. If any students used a novel approach, ask them to present their method to the class. Review the strategies presented in *Connect*. Ask:

- How is using place value to add the same as using Base Ten Blocks to add?
  (In both cases, I add the ones and regroup if necessary, then I add the tens and regroup if necessary, then I add the hundreds and regroup if necessary, and finally I add the thousands and regroup if necessary.)
- How do you show regrouping when using place value to add?
  (*Suppose I regroup 15 ones as 1 ten and 5 ones. I write the 5 that represents the number of ones below the ones digits of the numbers being added. I write the 1 that represents 1 ten above the tens digits of the numbers being added.*)

Be sure students realize that all the methods for addition involve place-value concepts.

Practice

Encourage students to do some of the questions using expanded notation, and some using place value. For question 2, encourage students to describe the estimation strategies they used.

Assessment Focus: Question 6

Students should recognize that they need to find the total amount of aluminum delivered by Fairfield and Westdale, and then compare the sum with 2450 kg.

Sample Answers

5. They need $7034; they have raised $7000.
6. 1665 + 795 = 2460; 2460 kg > 2450 kg
7. For example, 5432 + 4000; 8432 + 1000; or 5311 + 4121
   Any two 4-digit numbers will do if their sum is 9432.

REFLECT: I would model 981 with 9 flats, 8 rods, and 1 unit cube. I would model 3131 with 3 thousand cubes, 1 flat, 3 rods, and 1 unit cube. I would add the units:
1 one + 1 one = 2 ones
Then I would add the tens:
8 tens + 3 tens = 11 tens
I would regroup 11 tens as 1 hundred 1 ten.
Next, I would add the hundreds:
1 hundred + 9 hundreds + 1 hundred = 11 hundreds
I would regroup 11 hundreds as 1 thousand 1 hundred.
Finally I would add the thousands:
1 thousand + 3 thousands = 4 thousands
The sum is 4112.

Practice

1. Add.
   a) 8689 + 798 = 9487
   b) 6877 + 2364 = 9241
   c) 4062 + 859 = 4921
   d) 6953 + 5241 = 12 194
2. Estimate. Then find each sum greater than 7000.
   a) 4176 + 2457 — About 6800
   b) 3872 + 5129 = 9001
   c) 5839 + 987 — About 6900
   d) 6518 + 2828 = 9346
3. Keshav collects stamps.
   She has 3845 Canadian stamps and 2690 stamps from other countries.
   How many stamps does she have in all? 6535 stamps

4. Two games were played in the semi-finals of a hockey tournament.
   The attendance at one game was 9847.
   The attendance at the other game was 7788.
   How many people attended the semi-finals? 17 635 people
5. Members of the school council raised $7000.
   They plan to buy sports equipment for $3596 and library books for $3438.
   Did they raise enough money to make the purchases? No
   How do you know?
6. Regional Recycling has a target of 2450 kg of aluminum.
   Suppose Fairfield delivers 1665 kg of aluminum, and Westdale delivers 795 kg of aluminum.
   Will Regional Recycling meet its goal? Explain. Yes
7. Two 4-digit numbers have a sum of 9432.
   What might the numbers be? How do you know?

Reflect

Describe how you would use Base Ten Blocks to add 981 + 3131.

Numbers Every Day

Mental Math

Add. Which strategies did you use?

443 + 268 = 711
114 + 508 = 622
611 + 294 = 905
407 + 342 = 749

36 ASSESSMENT FOCUS Question 6

Numbers Every Day

Some students may prefer to use compensation or adding on. Encourage students to look at the numbers and choose the strategy that works best for these numbers.

ASSESSMENT FOR LEARNING

What to Look For

Understanding concepts

✔ Students can accurately add 3- and 4-digit numbers.

Communicating

✔ Students can describe more than one strategy for adding numbers.

What to Do

Extra Support: Use Base Ten Blocks to model each addition problem and Step-by-Step 3 (Master 2.15) to complete question 6.

Extra Practice: Complete Extra Practice 2 (Master 2.29).

Extension: Challenge students to solve these Cryptarithms.

PIG	FOUR
+ MUD	+ ONE
JOY	FIVE
Solution 1	*Solution 2*
249	*1250*
+ 107	*+ 236*
356	*1486*

Many different solutions are possible. e.g., If P = 2, I = 4, G = 9, M = 1, U = 0, D = 7, J = 3, O = 5, and Y = 6, Solution 1 is an answer. If E = 6, F = 1, I = 4, N = 3, O = 2, R = 0, U = 5, and V = 8, Solution 2 is an answer.

Recording and Reporting

Master 2.2 Ongoing Observations: Whole Numbers

LESSON 4

Adding Three Numbers

LESSON 4

Adding Three Numbers

Some athletes like to participate in stair-climbing competitions.
Some people climb the stairs to raise money for charity.

CN Tower
Toronto, Canada
1776 steps

Sears Tower
Chicago, USA
2109 steps

Central Park Tower
Perth, Australia
1236 steps

Menara Tower
Kuala Lumpur, Malaysia
2058 steps

Explore

Mei participated in stair-climbing events at the Menara Tower, the Central Park Tower, and the CN Tower.

How many steps did she climb altogether? 5070 steps

Show and Share

Share your work with another pair of students.
How did you add the numbers?

LESSON FOCUS | Use different strategies to add 3 or more numbers

37

LESSON ORGANIZER (40–50 min)

Curriculum Focus: Use different strategies to add 3 or more numbers. (5m18, 5m34, 5m35)

Teacher Materials

- clear protractor
- blank transparency
- overhead markers

Student Materials

Optional

- Step-by-Step 4 (Master 2.16)
- Extra Practice 2 (Master 2.29)

Assessment: Master 2.2 Ongoing Observations: Whole Numbers

Key Math Learnings

1. Numbers can be added in any order.
2. A variety of strategies can be used to add 3 or more numbers.

BEFORE Get Started

Have students find this sum:

$$\begin{array}{r} 8 \\ 5 \\ 2 \\ +\ 4 \\ \hline \end{array}$$

Ask:

- How did you find the sum?
  (I know 8 + 2 = 10, so I added these numbers first. 10 + 5 = 15 and 15 + 4 = 19)

Have students look at the illustration at the top of page 37 of the Student Book. Ask:

- Which building has the greatest number of steps? The least number?
  (Sears Tower has the greatest number of steps and Central Park Tower has the least number of steps.)
- Order the towers from the tower with the least number of steps to the tower with the greatest number of steps.
  (The towers, in order from least number of steps to greatest number of steps, are: Central Park Tower, CN Tower, Menara Tower, Sears Tower)
- How did you compare the numbers?
  (First, I looked at the thousands. Both Sears Tower and Menara Tower have 2 thousands. Then I looked at the hundreds. Sears Tower has 1 hundred, but Menara Tower has 0 hundreds. Both CN Tower and Central Park Tower have 1 thousand. CN Tower has 7 hundreds, but Central Park Tower has 2 hundreds, which is less.)

Present *Explore.* Tell students they will use the data at the top of page 37. Have Base Ten Blocks available for students who wish to use them.

REACHING ALL LEARNERS

Alternative Explore

Have students solve this problem:
It is 1503 km from St. John's, NL to Halifax, NS. It is 1788 km from Halifax to Toronto, ON. It is 4412 km from Toronto to Vancouver, BC. Suppose you travelled from St. John's to Vancouver via Halifax and Toronto. How many kilometres would you travel?

Early Finishers

Have students create missing digits problems similar to question 4. Students must make sure that each problem they create *can* be solved with the information they have given.
Students trade problems with a classmate, and solve their classmate's problem.

Connect

Last year, Ahmal climbed the stairs at the CN Tower, the Central Park Tower, and the Sears Tower.
How many steps did he climb altogether?

Add: 1776 + 1236 + 2109

Here are 2 strategies to add.

➤ Add: 1776 + 1236

$$\begin{array}{r} 1776 \\ +\,1236 \\ \hline 3012 \end{array}$$

Then add 2109 to the result.

$$\begin{array}{r} 3012 \\ +\,2109 \\ \hline 5121 \end{array}$$

➤ Use place value to add.

Add the ones: 21 ones
Regroup 21 ones as 2 tens 1 one.

$$\begin{array}{r} {\scriptstyle 2} \\ 1776 \\ 1236 \\ +\,2109 \\ \hline 1 \end{array}$$

Add the tens: 12 tens
Regroup 12 tens as 1 hundred 2 tens

$$\begin{array}{r} {\scriptstyle 1\,2} \\ 1776 \\ 1236 \\ +\,2109 \\ \hline 21 \end{array}$$

Add the hundreds: 11 hundreds
Regroup 11 hundreds as 1 thousand 1 hundred.

$$\begin{array}{r} {\scriptstyle 1\,1\,2} \\ 1776 \\ 1236 \\ +\,2109 \\ \hline 121 \end{array}$$

Add the thousands: 5 thousands

$$\begin{array}{r} {\scriptstyle 1\,1\,2} \\ 1776 \\ 1236 \\ +\,2109 \\ \hline 5121 \end{array}$$

Estimate to check the answer is reasonable.
Both 1776 and 2109 are close to 2000.
1236 is close to 1000.
2000 + 2000 + 1000 = 5000
5121 is a reasonable answer.

Ahmal climbed 5121 steps altogether.

38

DURING Explore

Ongoing Assessment: Observe and Listen

Observe how students find the sum. Some students may add all three numbers; others may add two numbers, and then add the third number to the sum of the first two.

Ask questions, such as:
- Do the numbers have to be added in the order given? Explain.
  (*No, I can add the numbers in any order. I can also find the sum of two of the numbers, and then add the third number to the sum of the first two.*)
- How many steps did Mei climb altogether?
  (*5070 steps*)

AFTER Connect

Invite students to share the strategies they used to add. Ask students who used a novel approach to present their strategy to the class. Have students compare their sums. They should recognize that the sum is the same no matter which strategy was used to add.

Review the strategies presented in *Connect*. Ask:
- When we use place value to add, why do we start with the ones place?
  (*We need to know if there are more than 10 ones. If there are, we need to regroup ones as tens. The same reasoning applies for tens, hundreds, thousands, and so on.*)
- On page 38 of the Student Book, estimation is used to show that the answer is reasonable. How could you check if an answer is correct?
  (*I could add the numbers in a different order to see if I get the same result.*)

Practice

1. Find each sum.

a) 1175	b) 2456	c) 4782
3241	3727	543
+ 829	+ 1104	+ 2368
5245	7287	7693

2. Estimate.
Find each sum less than 6000.

a) 2174	b) 4265	c) 876
263	2120	3154
+ 1768	+ 104	+ 1623
4205	About 6500	5653
d) 2675	e) 998	f) 3610
3125	1365	5285
+ 6400	+ 4745	+ 1495
About 12 000	About 7000	About 10 000

3. Juan drives a truck.
On Monday, he travelled 1639 km from Prince George to Whitehorse.
On Wednesday, he travelled 1222 km from Whitehorse to Inuvik.
He left Inuvik on Saturday and travelled 3149 km to Yellowknife.
How many kilometres did Juan travel altogether? 6010 km

4. The Ajax Bearing Company made 4716 bearings on Wednesday, 3984 bearings on Thursday, and 4125 bearings on Friday.
How many bearings did they make in total for the 3 days? 12 825 bearings

39

Sample Answers

8. Any pair of numbers that add to 7208; for example, 3145 and 4063; 3145 + 4063 + 988 = 8196
9. The number is 5684 because in every place you need to choose the greatest digit that can add to the corresponding digit in 4315 without going over 9; in the 1000s place, the digit is 5 because 4 + 5 = 9; in the 100s place, the digit is 6 because 3 + 6 = 9; in the 10s place, the digit is 8 because 1 + 8 = 9; and in the 1s place, the digit is 4 because 5 + 4 = 9.

Practice

Have Base Ten Blocks available for all questions.

For question 1, have students check that their sums are reasonable. For question 6, students should write three 4-digit numbers and find their sum. Students should erase no more than 1 digit from each place value.

Assessment Focus: Question 5

Students should recognize that they need to begin by looking at the ones digits. They need to find a 1-digit number they can add to 5 + 4 to get a sum with a ones digit of 5. Students must account for the regrouping when they look at the tens digits. In other words, they must find a 1-digit number they can add to 1 + 7 + 5 to get a sum with a ones digit of 1. They should use similar reasoning to find the remaining digits.

10. More than one number is possible, for example, 1836. The ones digit can be 6, 7, 8, or 9; the tens digit can be any number from 2 to 9; the hundreds digit can be 7, 8, or 9; the thousands digit can be 1 or 2.

REFLECT: I look at the numbers to decide which strategy to use.
If the numbers are friendly numbers, I would use mental math.
For example: 2000 + 3000 + 4000
2 thousands + 3 thousands + 4 thousands is 9 thousands or 9000.
If two of the numbers can be added mentally, I would add the two numbers, and then add the third number to the sum of the first two. For example:
1998 + 3405 + 2794; 1998 + 3405 = 5403;
5403 + 2794 = 8197
Usually, I would use place value to add:

```
  4 318
  5 323
+ 6 322
 15 963
```

Numbers Every Day

forty-five thousand three hundred two; 5 thousands
ninety thousand two hundred fifteen; 5 ones
fifty-eight thousand seven hundred sixty; 5 ten thousands
eleven thousand five hundred forty-two; 5 hundreds
thirty thousand fifty-one; 5 tens

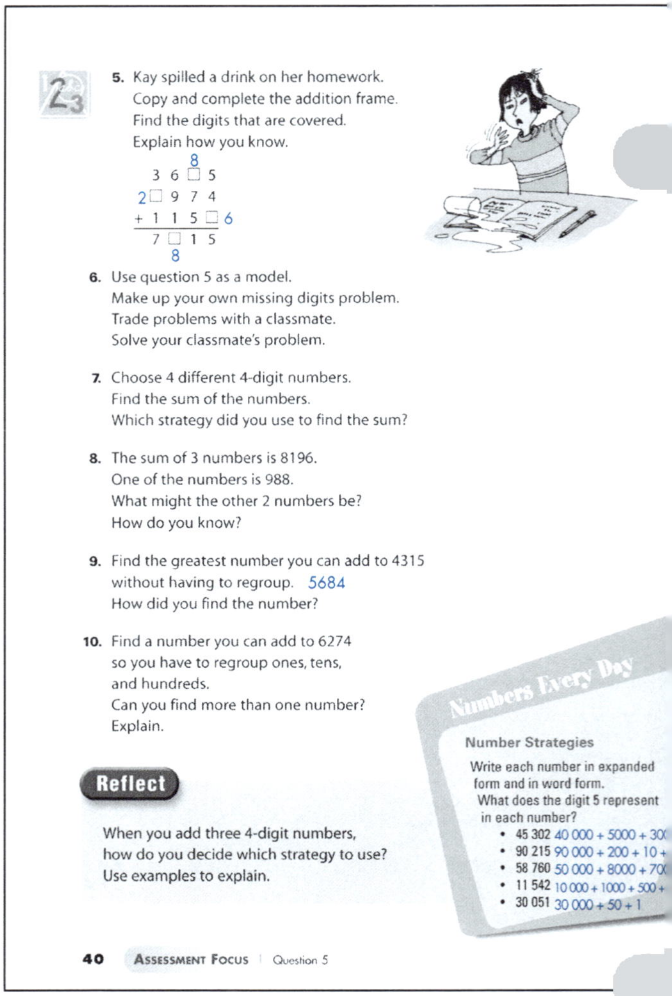
5. Kay spilled a drink on her homework.
Copy and complete the addition frame.
Find the digits that are covered.
Explain how you know.

```
    8
3 6 □ 5
2□ 9 7 4
+ 1 1 5 □ 6
7 □ 1 5
  8
```

6. Use question 5 as a model.
Make up your own missing digits problem.
Trade problems with a classmate.
Solve your classmate's problem.

7. Choose 4 different 4-digit numbers.
Find the sum of the numbers.
Which strategy did you use to find the sum?

8. The sum of 3 numbers is 8196.
One of the numbers is 988.
What might the other 2 numbers be?
How do you know?

9. Find the greatest number you can add to 4315 without having to regroup. 5684
How did you find the number?

10. Find a number you can add to 6274 so you have to regroup ones, tens, and hundreds.
Can you find more than one number?
Explain.

Reflect

When you add three 4-digit numbers, how do you decide which strategy to use?
Use examples to explain.

Numbers Every Day

Number Strategies

Write each number in expanded form and in word form.
What does the digit 5 represent in each number?
- 45 302 40 000 + 5000 + 30
- 90 215 90 000 + 200 + 10 +
- 58 760 50 000 + 8000 + 70
- 11 542 10 000 + 1000 + 500 +
- 30 051 30 000 + 50 + 1

40 ASSESSMENT FOCUS | Question 5

ASSESSMENT FOR LEARNING

What to Look For	What to Do
Understanding concepts ✔ Students can accurately add 3 or more numbers. ***Applying procedures*** ✔ Students can use more than one strategy for finding the sum of 3 or more numbers.	***Extra Support:*** Have students complete this missing digits question before they do question 5. 7 4 / + 5 ○ / ○ 3 2 Students can use Step-by-Step 4 (Master 2.16) to complete question 5. ***Extra Practice:*** Have students find the sums greater than 6000 in question 2. Students can complete Extra Practice 2 (Master 2.29). ***Extension:*** Ask students to solve this Cryptarithm. THIS + IS + VERY = EASY *(3120 + 20 + 4765 = 7905)*

Recording and Reporting
Master 2.2 Ongoing Observations: Whole Numbers

LESSON 5

Using Mental Math to Subtract

Explore

After the first snowfall of the year, 1184 people went snowboarding at Shred City Snowpark. After the second snowfall, 978 people went snowboarding.

➤ About how many more people went snowboarding after the first snowfall than after the second? 200

➤ How many more people went snowboarding after the first snowfall? 206

Record your estimate and the difference. How close was your estimate to the difference?

Show and Share

Share your work with a classmate. Describe and compare the strategies you used to estimate and to find the difference in the number of snowboarders.

Connect

➤ Estimate: 3818 – 2079

Round each number to the nearest hundred.
3818 rounded to the nearest hundred is 3800.
2079 rounded to the nearest hundred is 2100.
3800 – 2100 = 1700

3818 – 2079 is about 1700.

LESSON FOCUS | Use different mental math strategies to subtract whole numbers.

41

Using Mental Math to Subtract

LESSON ORGANIZER 40–50 min

Curriculum Focus: Use different mental math strategies to subtract whole numbers. (5m30, 5m36)

Student Materials *Optional*
- Step-by-Step 5 (Master 2.17)
- Extra Practice 3 (Master 2.30)

Assessment: Master 2.2 Ongoing Observations: Whole Numbers

Key Math Learnings

1. Estimation is used when an exact answer is not required; mental math is used when an exact answer is required.
2. There are many strategies that can be used to mentally subtract numbers.

BEFORE Get Started

Have students use mental math to find each difference:

3400 – 2000 6520 – 5520
7200 – 200 2270 – 1370

Ask:
- Why is it easy to subtract these numbers mentally? (*The numbers have zeros in the ones, tens, and/or hundreds places. Little or no regrouping is required.*)
- What are "friendly numbers?" (*Friendly numbers are numbers that are easy to subtract mentally.*)

Present *Explore*. Encourage students to think about the mental math strategies they used to subtract with 3-digit numbers. Be sure students understand that for the question "About how many more people went ...," an estimate is sufficient; for the question "How many more people went ...," an exact answer is required.

DURING Explore

Ongoing Assessment: Observe and Listen

Ask questions such as:
- Which strategy did you use to estimate the difference? Why? (*I rounded both numbers to the nearest hundred. About 200 more people went snowboarding after the first snowfall. If I round to the nearest thousand or use front-end estimation, the estimated difference would be 0.*)
- How many more people went snowboarding after the first snowfall? How did you find out? (*206; I added 2 to 978 to make 980 and added 2 to 1184 to make 1186. The difference 1186 – 980 is the same as the difference 1184 – 978, which is 206.*)

AFTER Connect

Invite students to share the strategies they used to estimate and to subtract. As a class, discuss the differences in the estimates yielded by

REACHING ALL LEARNERS

Early Finishers

Have students find 5 different problems for question 7. Have them write to describe how they found each problem.

Common Misconceptions

➤ Students compensate incorrectly. For example, they may add a number to the number being subtracted, and subtract that number from the answer.

How to Help: Have students adjust the *question* rather than the answer. For example, 4555 – 1998 is the same as 4557 – 2000.

Making Connections

Math Link: To find how many years Jeanne Louise Calment lived, students should subtract 1875 from 1997. She lived for 122 years.

Sample Answers

6. 5200 – 2998 = 2202
I used friendly numbers to solve this problem.
I added 2 to 2998 to make 3000, and added 2 to 5200 to make 5202; 5202 – 3000 = 2202; so 5200 – 2998 = 2202

➤ Subtract: 2437 – 2298
Make a friendly number.

Add 2 to 2298 to make 2300.
Add 2 to 2437 to make 2439.

Write 2437 – 2298 as:
2439 – 2300 = 139

2437 – 2298 = 139

➤ Use mental math to subtract: 5791 – 3486

Think of 3486 in expanded form:
3000 + 400 + 80 + 6
Subtract each number in turn.

5791 – 3000 = 2791
2791 – 400 = 2391
2391 – 80 = 2311
2311 – 6 = 2305

5791 – 3486 = 2305

Practice

Use mental math.

1. Subtract. Which strategy did you use each time?
a) 7438 – 6002 b) 5002 – 2797 c) 4555 – 1998 a) 1436 b) 2205 c)
d) 4261 – 2256 e) 6848 – 954 f) 3011 – 427 d) 2005 e) 5894 f)

2. Estimate.
Then subtract the numbers for which the difference will be less than 4000.
a) 5437 – 1601 b) 5432 – 370 c) 7715 – 2898 a) 3836 b) About 50
d) 4060 – 256 e) 6227 – 2419 f) 8008 – 5050 c) About 4800
d) 3804 e) 3808 f)

3. George's car has a mass of 1262 kg.
Sue's van has a mass of 1957 kg.
Which vehicle has greater mass? Sue's van
How much greater? 695 kg

42

different strategies. Discuss which strategy produced the estimate closest to the actual difference. Ask:

- Is this always the best strategy to use to estimate a difference? Explain.
(*Not necessarily; the best strategy depends on both the numbers in the question and the context of the question. Sometimes a rough estimate is acceptable, so I would round to the highest place value. Other times a more precise estimate is required, so I would look at the numbers and decide which strategy I think will produce an estimate close to the actual difference.*)

Discuss the estimation strategy presented in *Connect*. Ask:

- Why might you choose to estimate by rounding to the nearest hundred rather than to the nearest thousand?
(*Rounding to the nearest hundred gives a closer estimate while still subtracting friendly numbers.*)

Look at the mental math strategies presented in *Connect*. Be sure students realize that if you add or subtract an amount from one number to make a friendly number, you have to subtract or add the same amount from the other number to compensate. Ask:

- When is it easier to use compensation as a strategy?
(*When the number being subtracted is close to a friendly number*)
- When is it easier to use expanded form to subtract mentally?
(*When there is no regrouping*)

Practice

Assessment Focus: Question 6

Students should write a subtraction problem with numbers that are close to friendly numbers so it is easy to use compensation to make friendly numbers, or they should write a problem that requires little or no regrouping.

Math Link

Your World

Jeanne Louise Calment of France is the oldest woman ever.
She lived from 1875 to 1997.
How many years did she live?

4. Cole has $1307 in his savings account.
Emma has $988 in hers.
How much more money does Cole have than Emma? $319

5. Last Saturday and Sunday, 3741 people visited the art gallery.
On Saturday, 2802 people visited the gallery.
How many people visited the gallery on Sunday? 939 people

6. Write a subtraction problem you can solve using mental math.
Solve the problem.
Describe the strategy you used to solve the problem.
Explain your choice.

7. The answer to a subtraction problem is 2550.
Use mental math to find 2 problems with this answer.
How did you find the problems?

8. a) Find the least 4-digit number you can subtract from 8297 without regrouping. 1000
b) Find the greatest 4-digit number you can subtract from 8297 without regrouping. 8297
c) Which number was easier to find?
Use words and numbers to explain.

Reflect

Describe 2 mental math strategies you could use to subtract 4775 − 2986.
Use words and numbers to explain.

Numbers Every Day

Number Strategies

Order the numbers in each set from least to greatest.

- 25 317, 23 715, 25 731
- 60 324, 62 043, 60 243
- 38 960, 38 906, 38 690

ASSESSMENT FOCUS | Question 6 43

7. I used friendly numbers to find the problems
3550 − 1000 = 2550
4550 − 2000 = 2550

8. c) 8297 is easier to find because the greatest 4-digit number you can subtract from 8297 is 8297 itself. The least 4-digit number is 1000; it can be subtracted from 8297 without regrouping.

REFLECT: I could make friendly numbers. I could add 14 to both numbers to get 4789 − 3000.
Since 4789 − 3000 = 1789, then 4775 − 2986 = 1789
I could also use add on:

2986		3000		4000		4775
	+ 14		**+ 1000**		**+ 775**	

I added a total of 1789.
Since 2986 + 1789 = 4775, then 4775 − 2986 = 1789

Numbers Every Day

Students should compare the ten thousands, then the thousands, then the hundreds, and so on when ordering the numbers. Some students may prefer to write each number in a place-value chart.
23 715, 25 317, 25 731
60 243, 60 324, 62 043
38 690, 38 906, 38 960

ASSESSMENT FOR LEARNING

What to Look For	What to Do
Communicating ✔ Students can describe at least two strategies for subtracting numbers mentally. ✔ Students can explain the difference between estimation and mental math. ***Understanding concepts*** ✔ Students can accurately subtract two 4-digit numbers mentally.	***Extra Support:*** Students can use Step-by-Step 5 (Master 2.17) to complete question 6. ***Extra Practice:*** Have students use mental math to find each difference greater than 4000 in question 2. Students can complete Extra Practice 3 (Master 2.30). ***Extension:*** Challenge students to use mental math to solve this problem: Subtract the greatest/least 3-digit even number from the greatest/least 4-digit even number. *(9998 − 998 = 9000; 1000 − 100 = 900)*

Recording and Reporting

Master 2.2 Ongoing Observations: Whole Numbers

Subtracting with 4-Digit Numbers

LESSON ORGANIZER 40–50 min

Curriculum Focus: Use different strategies to subtract 4-digit numbers. (5m18, 5m34, 5m35)

Teacher Materials
- overhead Base Ten Blocks
- overhead place-value mat

Student Materials
- Base Ten Blocks

Optional
- Step-by-Step 6 (Master 2.18)
- Extra Practice 3 (Master 2.30)

Assessment: Master 2.2 Ongoing Observations: Whole Numbers

LESSON 6

Subtracting with 4-Digit Numbers

A pedometer records the number of steps you take.

Explore

Emma wore a pedometer for 2 hours.
She recorded the number of steps each hour.
The first hour, she took 1347 steps.
The second hour, she took 984 steps.

In which hour did she take more steps?
How many more? 363 steps

Show and Share

Share your work with another pair of students.
How did you subtract the numbers?

Connect

Drake and Carly went for a walk.
They each wore a pedometer.
After 90 minutes, Drake had taken 1276 steps and Carly had taken 1593 steps.
How many more steps did Carly take than Drake?

Subtract: 1593 – 1276

44 LESSON FOCUS | Use different strategies to subtract 4-digit numbers.

Key Math Learnings

1. A variety of strategies can be used to subtract with 4-digit numbers.
2. All subtraction strategies are based on place-value concepts.
3. Add to check if an answer is correct. Estimate to check if an answer is reasonable.

BEFORE Get Started

Ask:

- How would you use Base Ten blocks to model 614?
  (*I would use 6 flats, 1 rod, and 4 unit cubes.*)
- How would you use Base Ten Blocks to subtract 614 – 523?
  (*Look at the ones. Take 3 ones from 4 ones to leave 1 one. Look at the tens. You cannot take 2 tens from 1 ten. Trade 1 hundred for 10 tens. Take 2 tens from 11 tens to leave 9 tens. Look at the hundreds. Take 5 hundreds from 5 hundreds. 614 – 523 = 91*)

Present *Explore*. Tell students they will use what they know about subtracting with 3-digit numbers to subtract with 4-digit numbers. Have Base Ten Blocks available for those students who wish to use them.

DURING Explore

Ongoing Assessment: Observe and Listen

For students using the Base Ten Blocks to subtract, check that they:

- Model 1347 correctly.
- Know that they only have to model 1347.
- Correctly regroup 1 hundred as 10 tens, and 1 thousand as 10 hundreds.

For students trying other strategies, look/listen for evidence that they understand and can use place value as they subtract. Ask questions, such as:

- Did Emma take more steps in the first hour or the second hour?
  (*1347 is greater than 984. Emma took more steps in the first hour.*)
- How did you find out how many more steps she took?
  (*I subtracted 984 from 1347 to get 363.*)

➤ Use Base Ten Blocks on a place-value mat to subtract.

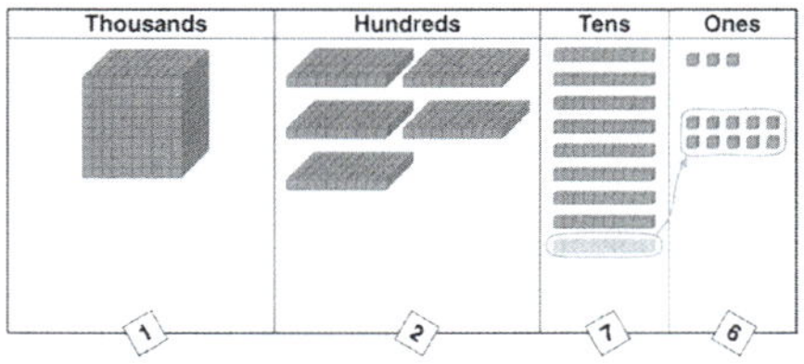

You cannot take 6 ones from 3 ones.

Trade 1 ten for 10 ones.

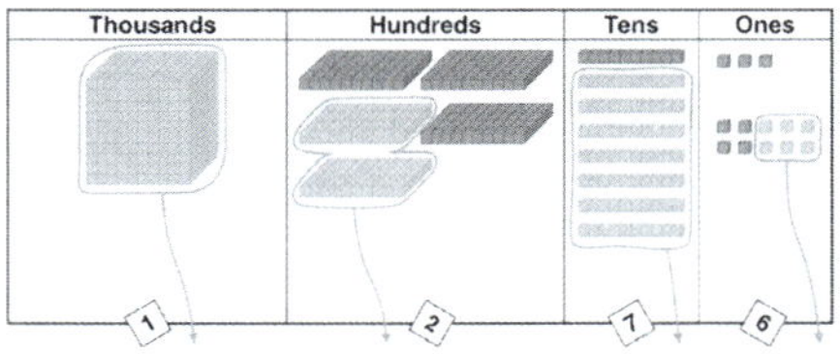

Take away:
- 6 ones
- 7 tens
- 2 hundreds
- 1 thousand

1593 − 1276 = 317

➤ Use place value to subtract.

You cannot take 6 ones from 3 ones.
Regroup 1 ten as 10 ones.

```
   8 13
 1 5 9 3
-1 2 7 6
```

Subtract the ones.
Subtract the tens.
Subtract the hundreds.
Subtract the thousands.

```
   8 13
 1 5 9 3
-1 2 7 6
   3 1 7
```

Carly took 317 more steps than Drake.

45

REACHING ALL LEARNERS

Early Finishers

Have students use the digits 0 to 9. Each digit can be used no more than once in each frame. Students copy and complete each subtraction frame.

```
  ○ ○ ○        ○ ○ ○ ○        ○ ○ ○ ○
− ○ ○ ○      −   ○ ○ ○      −     ○ ○
```

For each frame, students arrange the digits to make the greatest difference and the least difference. Students write about their observations.

Common Misconceptions

➤ Students regroup when it is not necessary.

How to Help: Have students compare the digits in each place. Remind them that if the digit being subtracted is less, then they can just "take away" that many with no need to regroup.

➤ When using place value to subtract, students do not align the digits correctly.

How to Help: Have students write each number in a place-value chart.

AFTER Connect

Invite students to share their strategies and answers from *Explore*. Encourage students to share any different strategies they use to subtract.

Discuss the strategies presented in *Connect*.

Ask questions such as:
- When we subtract, what place value do we usually start with? Why?
  (We usually start with the ones digits. If there are not enough ones, we need to regroup 1 ten as 10 ones.)
- How is subtracting with Base Ten Blocks the same as using place value to subtract?
  (In both cases, I look at the ones first, regroup if necessary, then do the same for tens, hundreds, and thousands.)

To check answers, ensure students understand they can estimate to check if an answer is reasonable; they can add to check if an answer is correct.

Practice

Have Base Ten Blocks available for all questions.

Assessment Focus: Question 5

Students' explanations of how they decided where to place the digit should demonstrate an understanding of place value. Most students should recognize that, to make the greatest difference, they need to subtract the least possible 4-digit number from the greatest possible 4-digit number. To make the least difference, most students will arrange the digits to make two 4-digit numbers; one may be the least number greater than 5000; the other number may be the greatest number less than 5000. Some students may use a guess and check strategy along with place value to find the least difference.

Sample Answers

5. a) To make the greatest difference, the first number should be the greatest possible number and the second number should be the least possible number; 9876 − 1234 = 8642
   b) To make the least difference, the second number must be the greatest possible number that is less than the first number. Here are two possible results:
   5123 − 4987 = 136; 6123 − 5987 = 136
6. a) 9876 − 1234 = 8642
   The greatest 4-digit number less the least 4-digit number gives the greatest difference.
   b) 6123 − 5987 = 136
   For the smallest difference, the thousands digits must be as close as possible. Once the first digit of each number has been selected, complete the first number making it as small as possible and the second number making it as large as possible.

REFLECT: I thought of 1796 in expanded form:

	1000 + 700 + 90 + 6
I subtracted the thousands:	7774 − 1000 = 6774
Then I subtracted the hundreds:	6774 − 700 = 6074
Next I subtracted the tens:	6074 − 90 = 5984
Finally, I subtracted the ones:	5984 − 6 = 5978

Numbers Every Day

Students should recognize that, since one of the numbers is 13, the other two numbers must have a product of 135 (1755 ÷ 13 = 135).

Practice

Use Base Ten Blocks when they help.

1. Subtract. Check your answer.

a)	b)	c)	d)
7774	8350	6432	9808
− 1796	− 2673	− 2798	− 1750
5978	5677	3634	8058

2. Estimate first. Subtract the numbers for which the difference will be greater than 2000.

a)	b)	c)	d)
7985	9824	5632	7162
− 4512	− 7912	− 3554	− 4359
3473	About 1900	2078	2803

3. Mount Alberta, Alberta, is 3620 m above sea level.
   Mount Odin, Nunavut, is 2147 m above sea level.
   How much higher is Mount Alberta than Mount Odin? 1473 m
4. There were 8275 tickets available for a school play.
   Two thousand eight hundred sixty-three tickets were sold.
   How many tickets were left? 5412 tickets
5. Copy and complete the subtraction frame.
   Use the digits 1 to 9.
   Use each digit only once.
   Arrange the digits to make:
   a) the greatest difference
   b) the least difference
   How did you decide where to place the digits?

   □□□□
   − □□□□

6. Suppose you subtract a 4-digit number from a different 4-digit number.
   Which numbers give the greatest difference?
   Which numbers give the least difference?
   How do you know?

Reflect

Choose one of the subtraction questions from question 1.
Explain how you found the difference.

Numbers Every Day

Calculator Skills

The product of 3 numbers is 1755.
One number is 13.
What might the other 2 numbers be?
3 and 45; 5 and 27; 9 and 15

46 ASSESSMENT FOCUS | Question 5

ASSESSMENT FOR LEARNING

What to Look For	What to Do
Applying procedures ✔ Students can use more than one strategy to subtract up to 4-digit numbers. ✔ Students can estimate to check if answers are reasonable, and add to check if answers are correct.	***Extra Support:*** Have students use Base Ten Blocks or a place-value chart. Students can use Step-by-Step 6 (Master 2.18) to complete question 5. ***Extra Practice:*** Students can do the Additional Activity, *What's the Difference?* (Master 2.10). Students can complete Extra Practice 3 (Master 2.30). ***Extension:*** For this problem, have students determine if each number of digits is possible and give an example for each: When you subtract a 4-digit number from a 4-digit number, how many digits are possible in the answer?

Recording and Reporting
Master 2.2 Ongoing Observations: Whole Numbers

Multiplication and Division Facts to 144

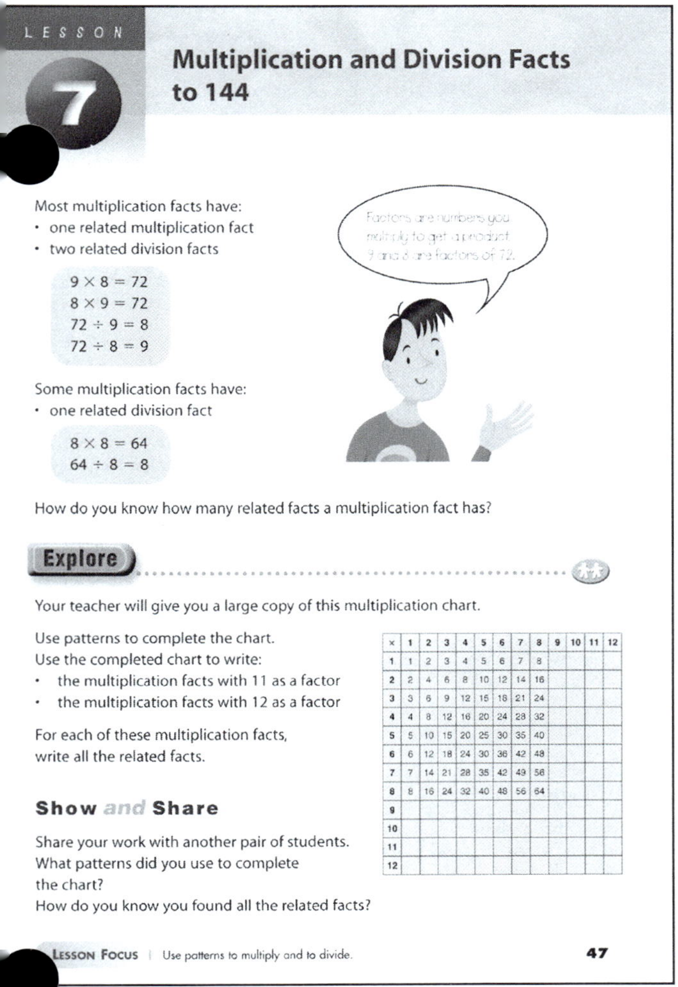

LESSON 7

Multiplication and Division Facts to 144

Most multiplication facts have:

- one related multiplication fact
- two related division facts

$9 \times 8 = 72$
$8 \times 9 = 72$
$72 \div 9 = 8$
$72 \div 8 = 9$

Some multiplication facts have:

- one related division fact

$8 \times 8 = 64$
$64 \div 8 = 8$

Factors are numbers you multiply to get a product. 9 and 8 are factors of 72.

How do you know how many related facts a multiplication fact has?

Explore

Your teacher will give you a large copy of this multiplication chart.

Use patterns to complete the chart.
Use the completed chart to write:

- the multiplication facts with 11 as a factor
- the multiplication facts with 12 as a factor

For each of these multiplication facts, write all the related facts.

×	1	2	3	4	5	6	7	8	9	10	11	12
1	1	2	3	4	5	6	7	8				
2	2	4	6	8	10	12	14	16				
3	3	6	9	12	15	18	21	24				
4	4	8	12	16	20	24	28	32				
5	5	10	15	20	25	30	35	40				
6	6	12	18	24	30	36	42	48				
7	7	14	21	28	35	42	49	56				
8	8	16	24	32	40	48	56	64				
9												
10												
11												
12												

Show and Share

Share your work with another pair of students.
What patterns did you use to complete the chart?
How do you know you found all the related facts?

LESSON FOCUS | Use patterns to multiply and to divide.

47

LESSON ORGANIZER — 40–50 min

Curriculum Focus: Use patterns to multiply and to divide. (5m12, 5m29)

Teacher Materials

- multiplication chart transparency (Master 2.6)

Student Materials

- multiplication charts (Master 2.6)

Optional

- counters
- Step-by-Step 7 (Master 2.19)
- Extra Practice 4 (Master 2.31)

Vocabulary: factors, product, dividend, divisor, quotient

Assessment: Master 2.2 Ongoing Observations: Whole Numbers

Key Math Learnings

1. Different strategies and patterns can be used to master basic multiplication and division facts.
2. Most multiplication facts have a related multiplication fact and two related division facts.

BEFORE — Get Started

Use the multiplication chart transparency. Ensure students remember how to interpret the numbers in the chart.

Review the vocabulary presented at the top of page 47 of the Student Book. Ensure students understand that a multiplication fact with equal factors only has one related division fact.

Present *Explore*. Distribute copies of the multiplication chart. Encourage students to look for patterns.

DURING — Explore

Ongoing Assessment: Observe and Listen

Observe the strategies students use to complete the chart.

Ask questions, such as:

- What are the multiplication facts with 11 as a factor?
  ($1 \times 11 = 11$; $2 \times 11 = 22$; $3 \times 11 = 33$; $4 \times 11 = 44$; … $12 \times 11 = 132$; and $11 \times 1 = 1$; $11 \times 2 = 22$; … $11 \times 12 = 132$)
- What are the multiplication facts with 12 as a factor?
  ($1 \times 12 = 12$; $2 \times 12 = 24$; $3 \times 12 = 36$; … $12 \times 12 = 144$; and $12 \times 1 = 12$; $12 \times 2 = 24$; … $12 \times 12 = 144$)
- Which facts with 11 or 12 as a factor have only one related fact?
  ($11 \times 11 = 121$; $121 \div 11 = 11$; $12 \times 12 = 144$; $144 \div 12 = 12$)

REACHING ALL LEARNERS

Alternative Explore

Materials: 1-cm grid paper (PM 23)

Have students draw rectangles to represent each of the multiplication facts with 11 or 12 as a factor. Students find the area of each rectangle to find each product.

Early Finishers

Have students extend the pattern for products with 11 as a factor. They use the pattern to mentally find products, such as 25 × 11 and 32 × 11.

ESL Strategies

If possible, pair ESL students with the same first language. Have them discuss the patterns in the multiplication chart. This will allow them to identify the patterns without the barrier of language. Have each student in the pair explain the patterns to a classmate with a different first language.

Sample Answers

3. a) 11 × 12 = 132
   12 × 11 = 132
   132 ÷ 11 = 12
   132 ÷ 12 = 11

b) 6 × 11 = 66
   11 × 6 = 66
   66 ÷ 6 = 11
   66 ÷ 11 = 6

c) 3 × 12 = 36
   12 × 3 = 36
   36 ÷ 3 = 12
   36 ÷ 12 = 3

d) 12 × 8 = 96
   8 × 12 = 96
   96 ÷ 12 = 8
   96 ÷ 8 = 12

Connect

Here are some strategies to help you multiply.

➤ Use known facts to multiply.
To find 12 × 8:

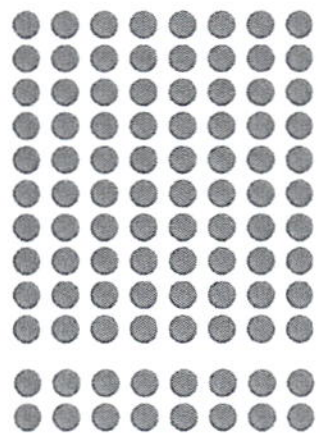

10 × 8 = 80
2 × 8 = 16
80 + 16 = 96
12 × 8 = 96

➤ Use patterns to remember multiplication facts with 11.

1 × 11 = 11
2 × 11 = 22
3 × 11 = 33
4 × 11 = **44** ← The digits of the number multiplied by 11 are the first and last digits of the product.
⋮
9 × 11 = 99
10 × 11 = 110
11 × 11 = 121
12 × 11 = **132** ← The middle digit of the product is the sum of the first and last digits of the product: 1 + 2 = 3

Here is a strategy for division.

➤ Use related multiplication facts to find the quotient.
To find 77 ÷ 11:

Think: 11 times which number is 77?
You know 11 × 7 = 77.
So, 77 ÷ 11 = 7

The **divisor** is 11.
77 ÷ 11 = 7
The **dividend** is 77.
The **quotient** is 7.

48

AFTER Connect

Discuss the first strategy presented in *Connect*. Ask questions such as:

- Why is the array for 12 × 8 separated?
  (*The array has been separated into two arrays. One represents 2 × 8 = 16, the other represents 10 × 8 = 80. These multiplication facts are easy to remember. We can use them to find 12 × 8.*)
- How else might we separate the array for 12 × 8?
  (*We could separate the array into two equal arrays, each representing 6 × 8 = 48.*)

Have students examine the pattern shown for multiplication facts with 11. Be sure students understand how the pattern changes when the product has more than 2 digits.

Look at the last example in *Connect*. Discuss the vocabulary introduced.

Ensure students understand they can multiply to check if their quotient is correct.

Practice

Have counters and grid paper available for all questions.

Assessment Focus: Question 8

Students may show how any array representing a multiplication fact with 12 as a factor can be separated into two equal arrays representing multiplication facts with 6 as a factor.

Practice

1. Multiply.
   a) 8 × 9 72 b) 3 × 12 36 c) 11 × 7 77 d) 12 × 6 72
   e) 10 × 12 120 f) 8 × 11 88 g) 7 × 12 84 h) 12 × 4 48
2. Find each quotient.
   a) 72 ÷ 6 12 b) 110 ÷ 11 10 c) 121 ÷ 11 11 d) 33 ÷ 3 11
   e) 108 ÷ 12 9 f) 12 ÷ 12 1 g) 24 ÷ 12 2 h) 55 ÷ 11 5
3. Write four related facts for each set of numbers.
   a) 11, 12, 132 b) 6, 11, 66 c) 3, 12, 36 d) 12, 8, 96
4. a) Start at 12. Count on by 12s to 144. Write the numbers.
   b) Start at 11. Count on by 11s to 144. Write the numbers.
   c) Compare the numbers you wrote to the numbers in the last 2 rows of the multiplication chart. What do you notice?
5. Write the products for 1 × 12 to 10 × 12.
   Describe all the patterns you see in the products.
   Do the patterns continue for 11 × 12 and 12 × 12? Explain.
6. How can you use the product of 10 × 6 to help you find the product of 11 × 6?
7. Barbara planted 12 rows of corn.
   Each row had the same number of seeds.
   Barbara planted 84 seeds.
   How many did she plant in each row? 7 seeds

8. Kayla finds the multiplication facts for 12 by doubling the multiplication facts for 6.
   Does Kayla's strategy work?
   Use words, numbers, or pictures to explain.

Reflect

Which facts do you find the hardest to remember?
Which strategies do you use to help you?
Use words, numbers, and pictures to explain.

Numbers Every Day

Number Strategies

Which questions have the answer 250?
How do you know?

- 775 ÷ 3 No
- 135 + 115 Yes
- 3875 − 3625 Yes
- 25 × 11 No

ASSESSMENT FOCUS | Question 8   49

4. a) 12, 24, 36, 48, 60, 72, 84, 96, 108, 120, 132, 144
   b) 11, 22, 33, 44, 55, 66, 77, 88, 99, 110, 121, 132, 143
   c) The numbers are the same.
5. 1 × 12 = 12; 2 × 12 = 24; 3 × 12 = 36; 4 × 12 = 48; 5 × 12 = 60; 6 × 12 = 72; 7 × 12 = 84; 8 × 12 = 96; 9 × 12 = 108, 10 × 12 = 120
   There is a repeating pattern in the ones digits. The core is 2, 4, 6, 8, 0. The products are the same as the numbers you say when you count on by 12s.
   11 × 12 = 132; 12 × 12 = 144; the pattern continues for 11 × 12 and 12 × 12.
6. I know that 11 × 6 is one group of 6 more than 10 × 6, so 11 × 6 is 10 × 6 = 60 and 6 more, which is 66.
8. Yes; 12 is 2 × 6 or double 6. The product of 12 and any number is the same as 2 times the product of 6 and that number.

REFLECT: I find the higher facts with 12, like 11 × 12 and 12 × 12, are the hardest to remember.
I use the facts with 10 to help me find 11 × 12 and 12 × 12.
For 11 × 12, I think: 10 × 12 or 120 and 12 more, which is 132.
For 12 × 12, I think: 10 × 12 or 120 and 2 more groups of 12, which is 120 + 24 or 144.

Numbers Every Day

You may wish to have students discuss the mental math strategies they used for each question.

ASSESSMENT FOR LEARNING

What to Look For	What to Do
Understanding concepts ✔ Students can recall multiplication facts up to 12 × 12 = 144. ✔ Students can recall division facts up to 144 ÷ 12 = 12. ***Applying procedures*** ✔ Students can write the related multiplication and division facts for a set of numbers. ***Communicating*** ✔ Students can describe patterns and strategies for multiplication and division clearly, using appropriate language.	***Extra Support:*** Students may benefit from using a multiplication chart, grid paper, or counters to multiply and divide. Students can use Step-by-Step 7 (Master 2.19) to complete question 8. ***Extra Practice:*** Have students write all the related facts for each product in one row of the multiplication chart. Students can complete Extra Practice 4 (Master 2.31). ***Extension:*** Have students extend the multiplication chart to 15 × 15 and describe any patterns they notice.

Recording and Reporting

Master 2.2 Ongoing Observations: Whole Numbers

Banquet Coordinator

Banquet Coordinator

Many large restaurants, halls, and resorts cater weddings and other parties. The banquet coordinator makes sure there is the right amount of food, drink, plates, cutlery, and serving dishes for the event. If there is too much food, the restaurant can lose money. If there is too little food, the guests may complain, and the restaurant may lose future business.

The banquet coordinator works on a per person basis for most calculations. For other items, he relies on experience. For example, he knows the quantity of mineral water to order. He has extra sets of cutlery on hand in case any gets dropped, and he knows how many guests 1 urn of coffee will serve.

Many establishments use spreadsheets to do the calculations. The coordinator enters the number of people attending and the spreadsheet calculates the amounts needed.

50

We use number skills in our daily lives. At home, we use number skills to create and balance a household budget, determine the area of a floor to be carpeted, calculate the mileage on a vehicle, and so on. A well-developed sense of number is a definite asset!

Many careers involve number—both number operations and number sense. Here are some careers that involve number skills.

Banker: A banker calculates the net worth of clients before deciding whether to make a loan. Total assets, such as money in bank accounts, value of home and vehicles, and investments, are compared with total debts, such as existing loans, money owed on credit cards, and mortgage.

Accountant: An accountant prepares financial statements. He tracks expenditures and income and calculates the net position of his client.

Machinist: A machinist works with very precise measurements and blueprints to create metal machine parts. Much of the work may be done on computerized lathes, but the machinist programs the computer with the coded numerical instructions.

Small Business Owner: A small business owner creates a budget for her business. She calculates charges for the product or service she sells, taxes to be paid, whether she can afford new equipment, and determines employees' salaries and benefits.

Land Surveyor: A land surveyor measures lots where houses and apartment buildings are constructed; railway, roadway, and subway routes; the heights of mountains; and the width of rivers. Surveyors also provide the physical information upon which the maps of Canada are based. No matter where you live in Canada, someone has done a survey of the land you are standing on!

Multiplication Tic Tac Toe

Games

You will need 20 each of two colours of markers and 2 paper clips.
Your teacher will give you a copy of the game board and the factor list.

The object of the game is to be the first player to place 3 markers in a row.
The row can be horizontal, vertical, or diagonal.

- Each player chooses a different colour.
- The first player chooses any two factors in the factor list. She marks the factors with paper clips.
- Player 1 multiplies the factors. She finds the product on the game board and covers it with a coloured marker. If the product appears more than once on the game board, she chooses which one to cover.
- Player 2 may move only one of the paper clips on the factor list. He finds the product of the factors. He finds the product on the game board and covers it with a marker.
- Players continue to take turns. Each player may move only one paper clip per turn.
- The first player to place 3 markers in a row wins.

Share your strategies for playing the game.
Talk about how you found products that you did not know automatically.

Variation:
Play 4-in-a-Row.

51

Multiplication Tic-Tac-Toe

LESSON ORGANIZER 20 min

Student Materials
- 2 colours of counters or other objects to use as markers
- paper clips
- game board and factor list (Master 2.7)

BEFORE Get Started

Organize the students into pairs. Provide each pair of students with a copy of the game board and factor list, and 2 paper clips. Each student needs 20 counters or other objects to use as markers. Each student in a pair should use a different colour of marker. Ensure students understand the first player to place 3 markers in a row, horizontally, vertically, or diagonally, is the winner.

DURING Game

As students play, ask questions, such as:
- How did you decide which factor to choose?
  (I looked at the squares in which I needed to put a counter to either get 3 in a row or block my partner from getting 3 in a row. Then I looked at the products in these squares. I chose a factor that would give me one of these products.)
- What strategies did you use to find the products?
  (I used mental math, place value, known facts, and patterns to multiply.)

AFTER

Invite students to share the strategies they used to play and to find the products. You may wish to have students play the game again to further develop their strategic thinking.

Multiplying with Multiples of 10

LESSON ORGANIZER (40–50 min)

Curriculum Focus: Use patterns to multiply with multiples of 10. (5m28, 5m30)

Student Materials
- calculators
- 5-column charts (PM 20)
- 6-column charts (PM 21)

Optional
- Step-by-Step 8 (Master 2.20)
- Extra Practice 4 (Master 2.31)

Vocabulary: multiples

Assessment: Master 2.2 Ongoing Observations: Whole Numbers

Key Math Learning

Patterns can be used to mentally multiply with multiples of 10, 100, and 1000.

LESSON 8

Multiplying with Multiples of 10

Every multiple of 10 has 10 as a factor.
These are multiples of 10:

100 1000 30 300 3000

What are some other multiples of 10?

Explore

You will need a calculator.

➤ Find each product.
Record the products in a place-value chart.

11 × 1	9 × 9	12 × 8
11 × 10	9 × 90	12 × 80
11 × 100	9 × 900	12 × 800
11 × 1000	9 × 9000	12 × 8000

Ten Thousands	Thousands	Hundreds	Tens	Ones

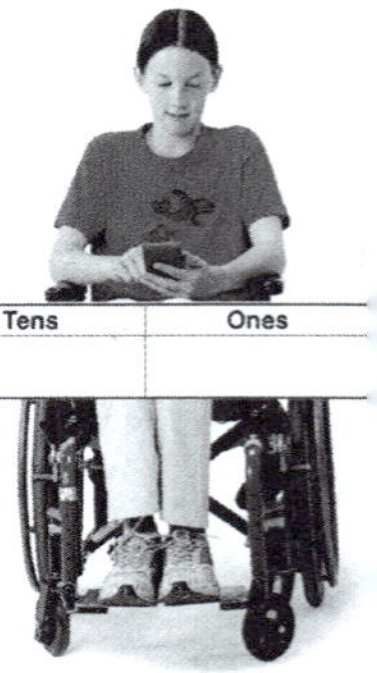

➤ Find each product.
Record the products in a place-value chart.

20 × 9	70 × 7	50 × 6
20 × 90	70 × 70	50 × 60
20 × 900	70 × 700	50 × 600

Show and Share

Share your work with another pair of students.
Describe any patterns you see.
How can you tell how many digits the product will have?
How can you tell which digits in the product will be 0?

52 LESSON FOCUS | Use patterns to multiply with multiples of 10.

BEFORE — Get Started

Have students read the information at the top of page 52 of the Student Book. Ensure students understand what is meant by a "multiple of 10." Ask:

- What are some other multiples of 10?
  (*50, 200, 70, 8000*)
- How can you tell if a number is a multiple of 10, 100, and 1000?
  (*The ones digit of any multiple of 10 is 0. If the number is a multiple of 100, both the tens and ones digits are 0. If the number is a multiple of 1000, the hundreds, tens, and ones digits are all 0.*)
- Is any multiple of 100 also a multiple of 10? How do you know?
  (*Yes, any multiple of 100 has 0 in the ones position.*)

Present *Explore*. Advise students that calculators should only be used to establish a pattern. Students should use the pattern to multiply with multiples of 10, 100, and 1000 mentally. Distribute place-value charts.

DURING — Explore

Ongoing Assessment: Observe and Listen

Ask questions, such as:

- What are the products of the first set of numbers?
  (*11, 110, 1100, 11 000; 81, 810, 8100, 81 000; 96, 960, 9600, 96 000*)
- What are the products of the second set of numbers?
  (*180, 1800, 18 000; 490, 4900, 49 000; 300, 3000, 30 000*)

Connect

➤ Use place value to multiply by 10, 100, and 1000.
Find each product. Record each product in a place-value chart.
25 × 10 25 × 100 25 × 1000

25 × 1 ten = 25 tens
25 × **10** = 25**0**

When you multiply a whole number by 10, the digits move 1 place to the left.

25 × 1 hundred = 25 hundreds
25 × **100** = 25**00**

When you multiply a whole number by 100, the digits move 2 places to the left.

25 × 1 thousand = 25 thousands
25 × **1000** = 25 **000**

When you multiply a whole number by 1000, the digits move 3 places to the left.

Product	Ten Thousands	Thousands	Hundreds	Tens	Ones
250			2	5	0
2500		2	5	0	0
25 000	2	5	0	0	0

➤ Use basic facts and place-value patterns to multiply by multiples of 10, 100, and 1000.
Find each product.
3 × **600** 3 × **6000**

You know 3 × 6 = 18

3 × 6 hundreds = 18 hundreds
3 × **6**00 = **18**00

When you multiply a whole number by a multiple of 100, the digits in the product of the related basic fact move 2 places to the left.

3 × 6 thousands = 18 thousands
3 × **6**000 = **18** 000

When you multiply a whole number by a multiple of 1000, the digits in the product of the related basic fact move 3 places to the left.

➤ Use what you know about multiplying by multiples of 10, 100, and 1000 to multiply two multiples of 10, 100, and 1000.
Find each product.
20 × 30 500 × 40

2 tens × 30 = 60 tens
20 × **30** = **600**

5 hundreds × 40 = 200 hundreds
500 × **40** = **20** 000

53

REACHING ALL LEARNERS

Early Finishers

Have students use a calculator to extend question 6 to find the number of seconds in 1 day and in 1 week. Have them find the approximate number of days 999 999 seconds represent.
(*86 400; 604 800; about 12 days*)

Common Misconceptions

➤ Students have trouble writing the correct number of zeros in the product when one of the factors is a multiple of 10, 100, or 1000.

How to Help: Have students underline the digits in the related basic multiplication fact. For example, for 5 × 6000 = 30 000, the related multiplication fact is 5 × 6 = 30; **5** × **6**000 = **30** 000

- What patterns did you notice?
(*In each case, the product was the same as in the related basic fact, the digits shifted 1 place to the left for multiples of 10, 2 places to the left for multiples of 100, and 3 places to the left for multiples of 1000.*)

AFTER Connect

Ask:
- Without multiplying, how do you know how many digits the product has?
(*The product has the same number of digits as the product of the related basic fact plus the number of zeros in the factor that is a multiple of 10.*)
- How do you know which digits in the product will be 0?
(*If one of the factors is a multiple of 10, the product is also a multiple of 10. If one of the factors is a multiple of 100, the product is also a multiple of 100. If one of the factors is a multiple of 1000, the product is also a multiple of 1000.*)

Discuss the examples presented in *Connect*.

Practice

Have place-value charts available for all questions.

Assessment Focus: Question 5

Students should realize there are 60 seconds in a minute and 60 minutes in an hour. Although the multiplication will likely be done mentally, students should record multiplication sentences.

Sample Answers

5. There are 60 seconds in 1 minute.
   The hummingbird flaps 60 times per second.
   The flaps in 1 minute = 60 × 60 = 3600 times
   There are 60 minutes in 1 hour.
   The hummingbird flaps 3600 times in 1 minute.
   The flaps in 1 hour = 3600 × 60 = 216 000 times
7. A car factory produces 20 000 cars each month. How many cars will be produced each year?
   (20 000 × 12 = 240 000 cars)

REFLECT: When you multiply a number by a multiple of 10, the result is the product of the related basic fact with the digits shifted 1 place to the left. There is a zero in the ones position as a placeholder. When you multiply a number by a multiple of 100, the result is the product of the related basic fact with the digits shifted 2 places to the left. There are zeros in the tens and ones positions as placeholders. When you multiply a number by a multiple of 1000, the result is the product of the related basic fact with the digits shifted 3 places to the left. There are zeros in the hundreds, tens, and ones positions as placeholders.

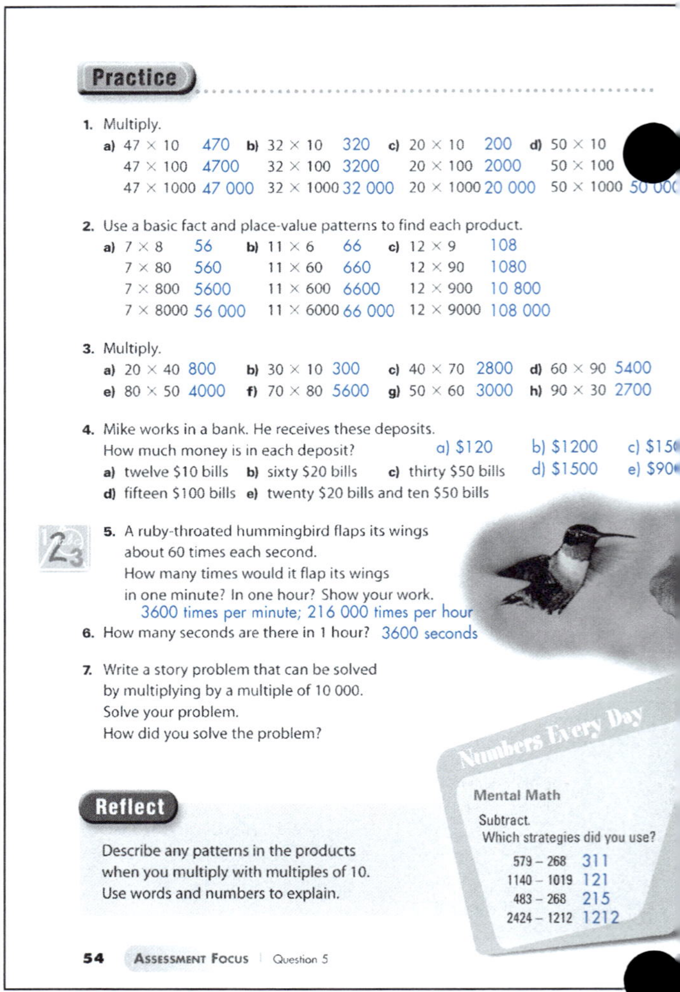

Practice

1. Multiply.
   a) 47 × 10 470; 47 × 100 4700; 47 × 1000 47 000
   b) 32 × 10 320; 32 × 100 3200; 32 × 1000 32 000
   c) 20 × 10 200; 20 × 100 2000; 20 × 1000 20 000
   d) 50 × 10; 50 × 100; 50 × 1000 50 00
2. Use a basic fact and place-value patterns to find each product.
   a) 7 × 8 56; 7 × 80 560; 7 × 800 5600; 7 × 8000 56 000
   b) 11 × 6 66; 11 × 60 660; 11 × 600 6600; 11 × 6000 66 000
   c) 12 × 9 108; 12 × 90 1080; 12 × 900 10 800; 12 × 9000 108 000
3. Multiply.
   a) 20 × 40 800 b) 30 × 10 300 c) 40 × 70 2800 d) 60 × 90 5400
   e) 80 × 50 4000 f) 70 × 80 5600 g) 50 × 60 3000 h) 90 × 30 2700
4. Mike works in a bank. He receives these deposits.
   How much money is in each deposit? a) $120 b) $1200 c) $15 d) $1500 e) $90
   a) twelve $10 bills b) sixty $20 bills c) thirty $50 bills
   d) fifteen $100 bills e) twenty $20 bills and ten $50 bills
5. A ruby-throated hummingbird flaps its wings about 60 times each second.
   How many times would it flap its wings in one minute? In one hour? Show your work.
   3600 times per minute; 216 000 times per hour
6. How many seconds are there in 1 hour? 3600 seconds
7. Write a story problem that can be solved by multiplying by a multiple of 10 000.
   Solve your problem.
   How did you solve the problem?

Reflect

Describe any patterns in the products when you multiply with multiples of 10.
Use words and numbers to explain.

Numbers Every Day

Mental Math

Subtract.
Which strategies did you use?

579 − 268 311
1140 − 1019 121
483 − 268 215
2424 − 1212 1212

54 Assessment Focus | Question 5

Numbers Every Day

Students may use expanded notation, counting on, or friendly numbers to subtract. Have students discuss their choices.

ASSESSMENT FOR LEARNING

What to Look For	What to Do
Applying procedures ✔ Students can use basic facts and place value to mentally multiply 1-digit numbers by multiples of 10, 100, and 1000, and to mentally multiply two multiples of 10, 100, and 1000.	***Extra Support:*** Have students use place-value charts to record their answers. They can also check their answers with a calculator. Students can use Step-by-Step 8 (Master 2.20) to complete question 5. ***Extra Practice:*** Have students write, and then solve, problems similar to question 4. Students can complete Extra Practice 4 (Master 2.31).
Communicating ✔ Students can describe the patterns they observe when multiplying with multiples of 10, 100, and 1000.	***Extension:*** Have students continue the patterns in questions 1 and 2 for multiplication with multiples of 10 000.

Recording and Reporting
Master 2.2 Ongoing Observations: Whole Numbers

LESSON

9

Using Mental Math to Multiply

Explore

How many different ways can you find the product 14 × 26?
Record each way.

Use any materials that help.

Show and Share

Share your work with another pair of students.
Compare the strategies you used to find the product.

Connect

➤ Multiply: 15 × 7

Think of an array for 15 × 7.

The product 15 × 7 is equal to the sum of the products 10 × 7 and 5 × 7.

15 × 7 = (10 × 7) + (5 × 7)
= 70 + 35
= 105

So, 15 × 7 = 105

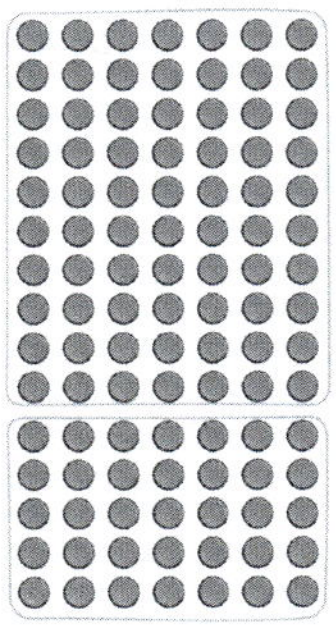

LESSON FOCUS | Use different strategies to mentally multiply 2 numbers. 55

Using Mental Math to Multiply

LESSON ORGANIZER 40–50 min

Curriculum Focus: Use different strategies to mentally multiply 2 numbers. (5m30, 5m36)

Student Materials *Optional*
- Step-by-Step 9 (Master 2.21)
- Extra Practice 5 (Master 2.32)

Vocabulary: halving and doubling friendly numbers

Assessment: Master 2.2 Ongoing Observations: Whole Numbers

Key Math Learning

A variety of strategies can be used to mentally multiply two numbers.

BEFORE Get Started

Ask questions, such as:

- Suppose you have 12 quarters. How much money do you have? *($3)*
- How does knowing 12 quarters is $3 help you find the product 12 × 25?
(I know that 12 quarters is $3 dollars, or 300¢, so 12 × 25 = 300.)

Present *Explore*. Have grid paper and counters available for students who wish to use them.

DURING Explore

Ongoing Assessment: Observe and Listen

Ask questions, such as:

- What are some of the strategies you used to find the product 14 × 26?
(I drew an array with 14 rows and 26 columns. I looked at different ways to separate the large array into smaller arrays. These are some of the multiplication sentences I wrote for the smaller arrays: 10 × 26 = 260 and 4 × 26 = 104; 7 × 26 = 182 and 7 × 26 = 182; 14 × 20 = 280 and 14 × 6 = 84; 14 × 26 = 364
Another strategy I used was to think of 14 × 26 as 14 × 25 and 14 × 1. I know 14 quarters is $3.50 or 350¢, so 14 × 25 = 350. 14 × 1 = 14; so, 14 × 26 = 364)

AFTER Connect

Invite students to share the strategies they used to find the product 14 × 26. Ask students who used a novel strategy to present it to the class.

Discuss the first example in *Connect*. Ask:

- Why might you want to think of 15 × 7 as 10 × 7 and 5 × 7?
(It is easy to multiply mentally by 10, and 5 × 7 is a basic fact.)

REACHING ALL LEARNERS

Alternative Explore

Materials: Base Ten Blocks

Students use Base Ten Blocks to represent 7×15 as many different ways as they can.

Early Finishers

Students remove the 0 card from the set of digit cards. They play a game similar to the one in question 2. This time they make the least product.

➤ Multiply: 16×25
Use the strategy of halving and doubling.

16×25
8 is half of 16 — 50 is double 25
8×50

$8 \times 50 = 400$
So, $16 \times 25 = 400$

➤ Multiply: 28×25
Rewrite 28 as 7×4.

$28 \times 25 = 7 \times 4 \times 25$
$= 7 \times 100$
$= 700$

So, $28 \times 25 = 700$

➤ Jane has one hundred ninety-eight $5 bills.
How many dollars does she have?

Multiply: 198×5

Use friendly numbers.
200 is close to 198.

Multiply: $200 \times 5 = 1000$

200 is 2 more $5 bills than Jane has, so subtract $2 \times 5 = 10$.

$1000 - 10 = 990$
So, $198 \times 5 = 990$
Jane has $990.

Practice

1. Multiply. Use mental math.
   - a) 6×199 1194
   - b) 7×302 2114
   - c) 3×498 1494
   - d) 5×310 1550
   - e) 36×25 900
   - f) 11×34 374
   - g) 24×21 504
   - h) 12×51 612

56

Discuss the second example in *Connect*. Ask:

- How do you know 16×25 and 8×50 have the same product?
  (16 is the same as 8×2. I can rewrite 16×25 as $8 \times 2 \times 25$, or 8×50.)
- Could we halve and double 8×50?
  (Yes, 8×50 is the same as $4 \times 100 = 400$.)

Discuss the last two examples in *Connect*.

Practice

Have grid paper and counters available for all questions.

Assessment Focus: Question 4

Most students will likely use friendly numbers and halving and doubling. Some may prefer to break the number apart to get 10×99 and 6×99.

2. **Who Has the Greater Product?**
You will need a set of shuffled digit cards from 0 to 9.
The goal is to arrange 4 digits to make a multiplication problem with the greatest product.
Each player copies and completes the multiplication grid.
Take turns drawing one card.
As each card is selected, each player writes that digit in any box on his or her grid.
Continue until all the boxes are filled.
Multiply.
The player with the greater product scores a point.
The first player to score 5 points wins.

Game

□□□
× □

3. Describe the strategies you used to play the game *Who Has the Greater Product?*

4. Use mental math.
Find the product of 16 × 99 two different ways.
Describe the strategies you used.

5. A theatre has 16 rows of seats.
Each row has 24 seats.
How many seats are there in the theatre? 384 seats

6. Copy the multiplication frame.
Arrange the digits 2, 3, 4, and 5 to make the greatest product.
Use each digit only once.
How did you decide how to arrange the digits?

□□
× □□

43
× 52
2236

7. Write a multiplication problem that can be solved using mental math. Solve the problem.
Which strategy did you use? Why?

Reflect

Peter says the strategy of halving and doubling works best when you are multiplying even numbers.
Use words and numbers to show why he is correct.

Numbers Every Day

Number Strategies

Find each product.
Describe any patterns in the the factors and in the products.

11 × 9	99
11 × 10	110
11 × 11	121
11 × 12	132

Assessment Focus | Question 4

Sample Answers

3. If I draw an 8 or a 9, I put it in the single-digit box. If I draw a number from between 0 and 4, I put it in the ones place of the 3-digit number.
4. I thought of 16 × 99 as 16 × 100 = 1600, but that's one 16 too many, so I subtracted 16 to get 1584. I found the products 10 × 99 = 990 and 6 × 99 = 594. Then I found the sum of the products, 1584.
6. I knew 4 and 5 had to be in the tens place. I tried all the combinations to see which one gave the greatest product.
7. Martin uses 12 eggs to make 1 cake. How many eggs would he need to make 50 cakes?
(*12 × 50 = 600*)

REFLECT: It is really only possible to use halving and doubling when at least one of the factors is even. For example, 24 × 25 is the same as 12 × 50. You could "half and double" again to make 6 × 100. This is a simple product to find: 6 × 100 = 600, so 24 × 25 = 600
If you have odd numbers, like 17 × 25, neither factor is divisible by 2 with no remainder. You cannot use halving and doubling.

Numbers Every Day

The digits of the number multiplied by 11 are the first and last digits of the product. When the product has 3-digits, the middle digit is the sum of the first and last digits.

ASSESSMENT FOR LEARNING

What to Look For

Applying procedures

✔ Students use a variety of strategies to mentally multiply two numbers.

Communicating

✔ Students can clearly describe the strategies they use for mentally multiplying two numbers.

What to Do

Extra Support: Have students use grid paper or counters to make arrays to model products in *Explore*. They explore different ways to break up the array.
Students can use Step-by-Step 9 (Master 2.21) to complete question 4.

Extra Practice: Students can do the Additional Activity, *Powerful Products* (Master 2.11).
Students can complete Extra Practice 5 (Master 2.32).

Extension: Challenge students to create 3 different problems for question 7. Each problem should be solved using a different mental math strategy.

Recording and Reporting
Master 2.2 Ongoing Observations: Whole Numbers

Multiplying 2-Digit Numbers

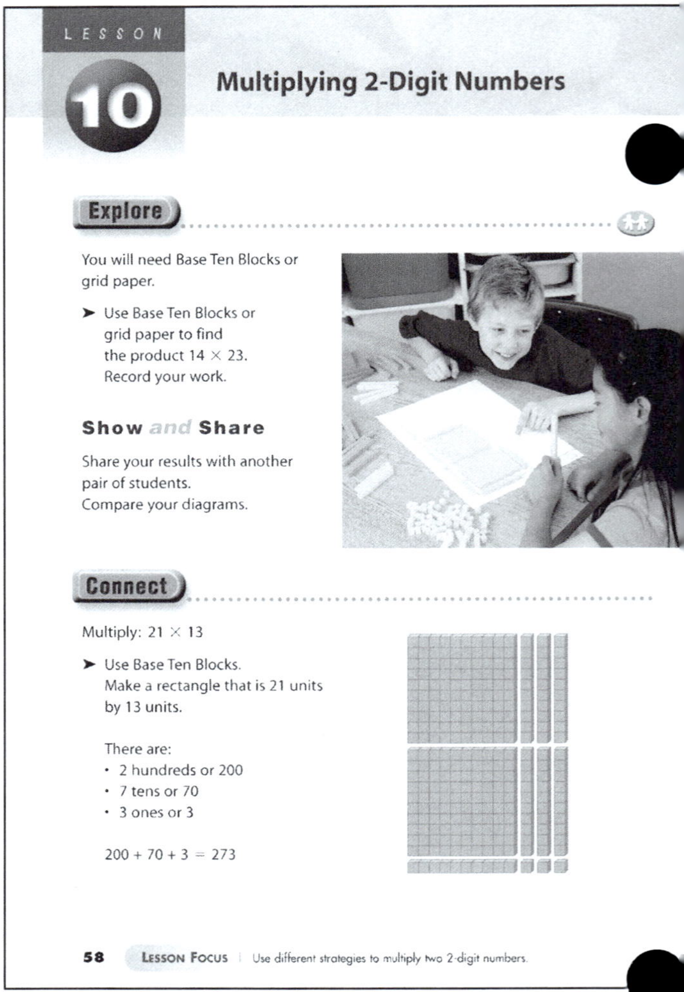
LESSON 10 Multiplying 2-Digit Numbers

Explore

You will need Base Ten Blocks or grid paper.

➤ Use Base Ten Blocks or grid paper to find the product 14 × 23. Record your work.

Show and Share

Share your results with another pair of students. Compare your diagrams.

Connect

Multiply: 21 × 13

➤ Use Base Ten Blocks. Make a rectangle that is 21 units by 13 units.

There are:
- 2 hundreds or 200
- 7 tens or 70
- 3 ones or 3

200 + 70 + 3 = 273

58 LESSON FOCUS | Use different strategies to multiply two 2-digit numbers.

LESSON ORGANIZER 40–50 min

Curriculum Focus: Use different strategies to multiply two 2-digit numbers. (5m18, 5m28, 5m34)

Teacher Materials
- overhead Base Ten Blocks
- 1-cm grid transparency (PM 23)

Student Materials
- Base Ten Blocks
- 1-cm grid paper (PM 23)

Optional
- Step-by-Step 10 (Master 2.22)
- Extra Practice 5 (Master 2.32)

Assessment: Master 2.2 Ongoing Observations: Whole Numbers

Key Math Learnings

1. Many strategies can be used to multiply two 2-digit numbers.
2. All the strategies are based on place-value concepts.

BEFORE Get Started

Have students draw a rectangle on grid paper to show 4 × 12. Ask:
- How many rows of squares are there? (*4*)
- How many squares are in each row? (*12*)
- How many squares are there in all? How do you know? (*48; 4 × 12 = 48*)

Use overhead Base Ten Blocks. Ask:
- Which blocks would you use to show 12? (*1 rod and 2 unit cubes*)
- How could you show 4 × 12? (*I could make 4 groups, each with 1 rod and 2 unit cubes.*)
- How could you find the product 4 × 12? (*Put the blocks together. There are 4 rods and 8 unit cubes, so 4 × 12 = 48.*)

Present *Explore*. Distribute Base Ten Blocks and grid paper.

DURING Explore

Ongoing Assessment: Observe and Listen

Ask questions, such as:
- How could you show 14 × 23 with Base Ten Blocks? (*I could make 14 rows, each with 2 rods and 3 unit cubes. Then I could trade groups of 10 rods for flats.*)
- How could you group the Base Ten Blocks to make them easier to count? (*I could break the rectangle after every 10 rows, and after every 10 columns. I could then count the numbers of hundreds, tens, and ones.*)

AFTER Connect

Invite students to share the strategies they used to find 14 × 23. Have students who used different strategies present them to the class.

➤ You can also use grid paper.
Make a rectangle that is 21 units long by 13 units wide.

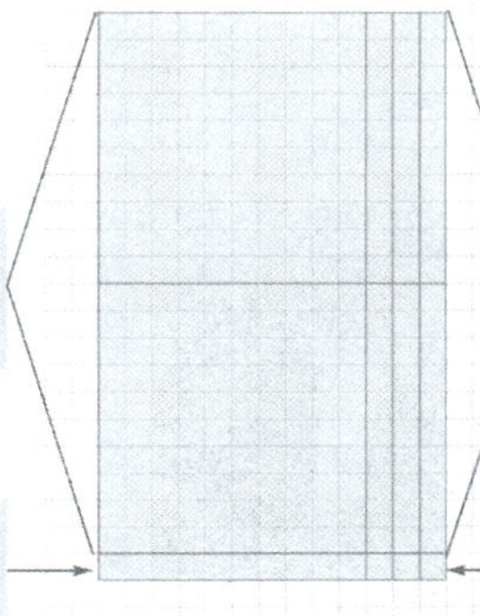

200 + 10 + 60 + 3 = 273

➤ Here is another way to explain the numbers on the grid.
Break a number apart to multiply:

	13
	× 21
Multiply: 1 × 13	13
Multiply: 20 × 13	+ 260
Add.	273

21 × 13 = 273

Practice

1. Multiply.
What do you notice about the products in each pair?
a) 34 × 26 = 884; 26 × 34 = 884
b) 45 × 23 = 1035; 23 × 45 = 1035

Numbers Every Day

Calculator Skills

Suppose the 8 key on your calculator is broken.
How can you find each result?

870 × 8
7.8 + 8.7

59

REACHING ALL LEARNERS

Alternative Explore

Materials: 1-cm grid paper (PM 23)

Students work in pairs. They draw a rectangle that is 12 cm wide and 16 cm long. Students draw horizontal and vertical lines to break the rectangle into tens and ones along the length and the width. Students write a multiplication sentence for each small rectangle. They compare the areas of the small rectangles with the area of the large rectangle.

Early Finishers

Students draw an array on grid paper. They use the array to show why changing the order in which they multiply the factors does not change the product.

Common Misconceptions

➤ When breaking a number apart to multiply, students forget they are multiplying by tens in the second step.

How to Help: Write the problem on a place-value chart, so students can "see" that the number they are multiplying by is in the tens place.

Numbers Every Day

Students may suggest a variety of strategies. For 870 × 78 they may suggest halving and doubling to get 1740 × 39. For 7.8 + 8.7 they may suggest using compensation. For example, add 2.2 to first number and subtract 2.2 from the second to get 10 + 6.5.

Discuss the strategies presented in *Connect*. Ask:

- How is modelling a product with Base Ten Blocks similar to modelling a product with grid paper?
  (In both cases, I break the factors apart into numbers that are easy to multiply, and then add the results.)
- When you use the strategy of "break a number apart" to multiply, what do you do first?
  (I break one factor into tens and ones. Then I multiply the other number by the tens and by the ones, and then add the products.)
- How do you know the next multiplication is 20 × 13, not 2 × 13?
  (The 2 in 21 is in the tens place, so I'm multiplying 20 × 13 = 260.)

Practice

Have Base Ten Blocks and grid paper available for all questions.

Assessment Focus: Question 7

Students may break 45 × 23 apart in different ways, but their work should demonstrate they understand how to apply the distributive property to make the multiplication of 2-digit numbers easier.

Sample Answers

1. a) The products in each pair are equal.
4. I can use mental math for d, for example.
   I could use 17 × 30 = 510 and 17 × 3 = 51, and then add to find the product of 17 × 33.
   510 + 51 = 561
5. a) 25 × 26 = 625 + 25, or 650
   b) 24 × 25 = 625 − 25, or 600
   c) 50 × 25 = 2 × 625, or 1250
6. Sharma's wall has 25 more tiles.
7. I could use 5 × 23 = 115 and 40 × 23 = 920 to find the product 45 × 23.
   I could also use 45 × 20 = 900 and 45 × 3 = 135 to find this product. The product 45 × 23 is 1035.
8. I would use arrangement b. I tried different ways to arrange 4 different digits to make the greatest product. I found that 8 hundreds times 9 equals 72 hundreds, but 80 times 90 also equals 7200. When I tried to multiply the greatest 3-digit number by the greatest one-digit number (876 × 9), this equals 7884. However, when I multiplied two 2-digit numbers (96 × 87) the product was greater; 8352. This is the greatest product.

REFLECT: They are all similar in that all the strategies "break the numbers apart." They are different in the way they show the numbers being broken apart.

---

2. Multiply.
a) 35 × 52 1820 **b)** 65 × 30 1950 **c)** 48 × 25 1200 **d)** 41 × 74 3034
e) 92 × 43 3956 **f)** 14 × 75 1050 **g)** 20 × 54 1080 **h)** 25 × 16 400

3. Find each product.
a) 46 × 64 2944 **b)** 23 × 50 1150 **c)** 61 × 11 671 **d)** 17 × 33 561
e) 29 × 41 1189 **f)** 68 × 12 816 **g)** 80 × 16 1280 **h)** 16 × 77 1232
i) 85 × 58 4930 **j)** 60 × 74 4440 **k)** 13 × 18 234 **l)** 21 × 22 462

4. Can you use mental math to find any of the products in question 3? Explain why or why not.

5. Find the product 25 × 25. 625
How can you use the product 25 × 25 to help you find each product?
a) 25 × 26 **b)** 24 × 25 **c)** 50 × 25

6. Jordan tiled a wall. His wall has 27 rows each with 27 tiles.
Sharma tiled a different wall. Her wall has 26 rows of 29 tiles.
Whose wall has more tiles? How many more?

7. Which multiplication facts can you use to find 45 × 23?
How do you know?
Show your work.

8. Suppose you wanted to arrange 4 different digits to make the greatest product.
Which arrangement would you use? Why?
a) □□□ × □ **b)** □□ × □□

At Home

Measure the dimensions of a rectangular table top to the nearest centimetre.
Find the area of the table top.

Reflect

How are the 3 different strategies for multiplying two 2-digit numbers the same? How are they different? Use words, numbers, and pictures to explain.

60 ASSESSMENT FOCUS | Question 7

ASSESSMENT FOR LEARNING

What to Look For	What to Do
Understanding concepts ✔ Students can multiply a 2-digit number by a 2-digit number.	***Extra Support:*** Students model each multiplication with Base Ten Blocks or grid paper. Students can use Step-by-Step 10 (Master 2.22) to complete question 7.
Applying procedures ✔ Students can use more than one strategy to multiply a 2-digit number by a 2-digit number.	***Extra Practice:*** Students can complete Extra Practice 5 (Master 2.32).
	Extension: Challenge students to solve this Cryptarithm. Each letter represents a different digit.

$$\begin{array}{r} ABC \\ \times \quad C \\ \hline CDE \end{array}$$

(*132 × 2 = 264*)

Recording and Reporting
Master 2.2 Ongoing Observations: Whole Numbers

Estimating Quotients

LESSON 11

Estimating Quotients

Explore

The Leckies drove 1875 km in 4 days.
Suppose they drove the same distance each day.
About how far did they drive in 1 day? About 500 km

Show and Share

Share your estimate with another pair of students.
Describe the strategies you used to estimate.

Connect

Here are some strategies you can use to estimate quotients.

➤ Estimate: 2870 ÷ 6
Look for **compatible numbers**.

2870 is close to 3000.
3000 is 30 hundreds.

30 hundreds ÷ 6 = 5 hundreds
= 500

2870 ÷ 6 is about 500.

LESSON FOCUS | Use different strategies to estimate quotients. 61

LESSON ORGANIZER (40–50 min)

Curriculum Focus: Use different strategies to estimate quotients. (5m30, 5m36)

Student Materials *Optional*
- Step-by-Step 11 (Master 2.23)
- Extra Practice 6 (Master 2.33)

Vocabulary: compatible numbers

Assessment: Master 2.2 Ongoing Observations: Whole Numbers

Key Math Learnings

1. Different strategies can be used to estimate quotients.
2. Estimating a quotient yields an approximate result. Mental math yields an exact answer.

BEFORE Get Started

Review some of the patterns used when multiplying with multiples of 10, 100, and 1000. Have students find each product:

6 × 7   6 × 70   6 × 700   6 × 7000

Ask:
- How can we use what we know about multiplying with multiples of 10, 100, and 1000 to find a quotient, such as: 420 ÷ 6? (*We can look for similar patterns; 420 ÷ 6 is 42 tens ÷ 6 = 7 tens or 70.*)

Present *Explore*. Ensure students understand an exact answer is not required; an estimate is sufficient.

DURING Explore

Ongoing Assessment: Observe and Listen

Observe the strategies the students use. Many students will try guess and check with multiplication. For example, 4 × 200 = 800 (too low)

Others may use a similar strategy, but will try to get closer. For example,
4 × 450 = 1800 (too low, but close)

Ask questions, such as:
- What numbers are close to 1875 and are easily divisible by 4? (*1600 and 2000, but 2000 is closer*)
- How do we know an estimate is sufficient? (*The question says, "About how far did they drive in 1 day?"*)

REACHING ALL LEARNERS

Early Finishers

Have students write to describe how they broke the numbers apart in question 7.

Common Misconceptions

➤ Students round to estimate a quotient rather than finding compatible numbers.

How to Help: For the quotient 2295 ÷ 6, ask students to list numbers of hundreds that are easy to divide by 6 (600, 1200, 1800, 2400). Have them choose the number from the list that is closest to 2295. Point out that rounding to 2300 ÷ 6 does not make the quotient easier to estimate.

➤ Estimate: 4368 ÷ 8
Use front-end estimation.

Find out how many digits the quotient will have.

8 × 100 = 800 too low

8 × 1000 = 8000 too high

The quotient will be in the hundreds.

Estimate the hundreds digit of the quotient.
There are 43 hundreds in 4368.
43 ÷ 8 is between 5 and 6, but closer to 5.

4368 ÷ 8 is about 500.

Here is a mental math strategy for division.

➤ Divide: 336 ÷ 4
Break 336 into 2 numbers you can divide easily by 4.

336 = 320 + 16

320 ÷ 4 = 32 tens ÷ 4 = 8 tens = 80   16 ÷ 4 = 4

336 ÷ 4 = 80 + 4 = 84

Practice

1. Which compatible numbers would you use to estimate each quotient? Why did you choose those numbers?
   a) 238 ÷ 8   b) 193 ÷ 2   a) 240 ÷ 8   b) 200 ÷ 2
   c) 2000 ÷ 7   d) 2132 ÷ 5   c) 2100 ÷ 7   d) 2000 ÷ 5

2. Estimate each quotient. Which strategies did you use?
   a) 185 ÷ 6   b) 3475 ÷ 9   a) About 30   b) About 400
   c) 947 ÷ 3   d) 5400 ÷ 8   c) About 300   d) About 700

62

Sample Answers

1. I chose pairs of numbers I can divide mentally.
2. I found compatible pairs of numbers I can divide mentally.
   a) 185 ÷ 6 is about 180 ÷ 6.
   b) 3475 ÷ 9 is about 3600 ÷ 9.
   c) 947 ÷ 3 is about 900 ÷ 3.
   d) 5400 ÷ 8 is about 5600 ÷ 8.

- What information can we get from the quotients 1600 ÷ 4 and 2000 ÷ 4? (*1600 is less than 1875. 2000 is greater than 1875. The quotient 1600 ÷ 4 = 400 is less than the quotient 1875 ÷ 4. The quotient 2000 ÷ 4 = 500 is greater than the quotient 1875 ÷ 4. We know the quotient 1875 ÷ 4 is between 400 and 500.*)

AFTER Connect

Invite students to share the strategies they used to find the distance travelled each day.

Discuss the first example in *Connect*. Discuss the definition of compatible numbers. Ask:

- Why is 3000 a compatible number for 6? (*Because we can find 3000 ÷ 6 = 500 mentally*)
- What are some other compatible numbers for 6? (*2400, 3600*)
- Why is 3000 the best compatible number to use for this estimate? (*3000 is the closest compatible number to 2870.*)

Discuss the steps used in front-end estimation. Ensure students understand they must first find out how many digits the quotient will have, and then estimate the first digit of the quotient.

Discuss the mental math strategy for division in *Connect*. Ask:

- How is this strategy similar to the estimation strategy on page 61? How is it different? (*Both strategies use compatible numbers. In the first example we estimated the quotient, but this time we are finding an exact answer.*)

Practice

Assessment Focus: Question 6

Students should recognize that Tyler tested products with 4 as one factor and numbers he thought would result in a product close to 3400.

3. a) Two thousand thirty bottles are placed in cartons of 6. About how many cartons are there? About 300 cartons
b) Four thousand one hundred pencils are packaged in boxes of 8. About how many boxes are there? About 500 boxes

4. Kris has 1362 game tokens. He plans to share them among 9 people. About how many tokens will each person get? How did you find out? About 200 tokens

5. Write a story problem that can be solved by estimating a quotient. Trade problems with a classmate. Solve your classmate's problem.

6. Tyler estimated 3495 ÷ 4. He wrote these statements:
- The quotient is between 800 and 900.
- The quotient is greater than 850.

How might Tyler have made his estimates? Use words and numbers to explain.

7. Use mental math to divide.
a) 635 ÷ 5 127 b) 738 ÷ 9 82 c) 444 ÷ 6 74 d) 576 ÷ 8 72

8. Write a division problem that can be solved using mental math. Solve your problem. Which strategy did you use? Why?

Reflect

How is finding compatible numbers different from rounding numbers? Use words and numbers to explain.

Numbers Every Day

Number Strategies

Find the next 3 terms in each pattern. Write each pattern rule.

3, 6, 12, 24, ... 48, 96, 192

384, 192, 96, 48, ... 24, 12, 6

ASSESSMENT FOCUS | Question 6 63

4. I used compatible numbers. 1362 is between 900 and 1800. 1362 is closer to 1800. 1800 ÷ 9 = 200.

5. Crayons come 6 to a package. About how many packages can be made from 1000 crayons? (*About 200*)

6. Tyler may have thought:
3200 ÷ 4 = 800 (too low)
3600 ÷ 4 = 900 (too high)
3400 ÷ 4 = 850
3495 is greater than 3400, so the quotient is greater than 850.

8. An 8-level building is 200 m tall. How tall is each level? (*25 m*)

REFLECT: In rounding numbers, you just take a number up or down to the nearest hundred or thousand, for example, 1920 rounded to the nearest thousand is 2000. Finding compatible numbers in division means not just rounding to the nearest thousand, but to a number that is easy to divide. To estimate 1920 ÷ 3, you would not round to 2000, you would think of a number you can divide easily by 3, such as 1800 ÷ 3 = 600. 1920 ÷ 3 is about 600.

Numbers Every Day

Start at 3. Multiply by 2 each time.
Start at 384. Divide by 2 each time.

ASSESSMENT FOR LEARNING

What to Look For	What to Do
Applying procedures ✔ Students can use a variety of strategies to estimate quotients. ***Communicating*** ✔ Students can clearly describe the difference between estimating quotients and using mental math to divide.	***Extra Support:*** Have students use a multiplication chart and a place-value chart to help them think of compatible numbers. Students can use Step-by-Step 11 (Master 2.23) to complete question 6. ***Extra Practice:*** Students can complete Extra Practice 6 (Master 2.33). ***Extension:*** Students can do the Additional Activity, *The Range Game* (Master 2.12).

Recording and Reporting

Master 2.2 Ongoing Observations: Whole Numbers

Dividing with Whole Numbers

LESSON ORGANIZER 40–50 min

Curriculum Focus: Use different strategies to divide a 4-digit number by a 1-digit number. (5m18, 5m28, 5m34)

Student Materials
- 6-Sector Spinner (Master 2.8)
- 4 numbered cubes, labelled 1 to 6

Optional
- Step-by-Step 12 (Master 2.24)
- Extra Practice 6 (Master 2.33)

Vocabulary: short division

Assessment: Master 2.2 Ongoing Observations: Whole Numbers

Key Math Learnings

1. Different strategies can be used to divide numbers.
2. All the strategies are based on place-value concepts.

LESSON 12

Dividing with Whole Numbers

Explore

A tire factory makes 1248 tires a day. A new car needs a set of 4 tires. How many sets of tires are made each day?

Show and Share

Share your answer with another pair of students. How did you divide to find the number of sets?

Connect

Some vehicles have 5 tires in a set. How many sets of 5 tires can be made with 1127 tires?

Divide: $5\overline{)1127}$

➤ Think multiplication. Estimate the number of sets, then improve the estimate.

64 LESSON FOCUS | Use different strategies to divide a 4-digit number by a 1-digit number.

BEFORE Get Started

Review the front-end estimation strategy with the students. Ask questions, such as:

- How do I know how many digits are in the quotient 3400 ÷ 8?
  (*I can use front-end estimation. 8 × 100 = 800 (too low); 8 × 1000 = 8000 (too high); the quotient will have 3 digits.*)
- How can I estimate the value of the hundreds digit in the quotient?
  (*I can use compatible numbers close to 3400 to estimate the hundreds digit in the quotient. 3200 ÷ 8 = 400 (too low); 4000 ÷ 8 = 500 (too high); the hundreds digit of the quotient is 4.*)
- How can I tell if the quotient 3400 ÷ 8 is closer to 400 or 500?
  (*Look at the compatible numbers used to estimate the hundreds digit. 3400 is much closer to 3200 than it is to 4000. The quotient will be closer to 400 than 500.*)

Present *Explore*. Make sure students understand an exact answer is required.

DURING Explore

Ongoing Assessment: Observe and Listen

Ask questions, such as:

- How can you tell how many digits the quotient has before you divide?
  (*I use front-end estimation. 4 × 100 = 400 (too low); 4 × 1000 = 4000 (too high); the quotient has 3 digits.*)
- Is the quotient greater than or less than 300? How do you know?
  (*The quotient is greater than 300. 4 × 300 = 1200; the number of tires, 1248, is greater than 1200; the quotient is greater than 300.*)

1000 and 1500 are close to 1127.
1000 ÷ 5 = 200   1500 ÷ 5 = 300
1127 is between 1000 and 1500.
The quotient is between 200 and 300.

Make 200 sets of 5.	Make 20 sets of 5.	Make 5 sets of 5.
200 × 5 = 1000	20 × 5 = 100	5 × 5 = 25
Subtract 1000 from 1127.	Subtract 100 from 127.	Subtract 25 from 27. Add the sets.

```
5)1127               5)1127               5)1127
 - 1000 | 200         - 1000 | 200         - 1000 | 200
    127                  127                  127
                       - 100 | 20           - 100 |  20
                          27                   27
                                             - 25 | + 5
                                                2 | 225
```

So, 1127 ÷ 5 = 225 R2

➤ Use place value.

1 thousand 1 hundred is 11 hundreds.	1 hundred 2 tens is 12 tens.	2 tens 7 ones is 27 ones.
Show 11 hundreds in 5 equal groups.	Show 12 tens in 5 equal groups.	Show 27 ones in 5 equal groups.
There are 5 groups each with 2 hundreds.	There are 5 groups each with 2 tens.	There are 5 groups each with 5 ones.
1 hundred is left over.	2 tens are left over.	2 ones are left over.

```
  th h t o             th h t o             th h t o
      2                    2 2                  2 2 5
5 ) 1 1 2 7          5 ) 1 1 2 7          5 ) 1 1 2 7
  - 1 0                - 1 0 ↓              - 1 0 ↓ |
      1                    1 2                  1 2 |
                         - 1 0                - 1 0 ↓
                             2                    2 7
                                                - 2 5
                                                    2
```

So, 1127 ÷ 5 = 225 R2

Two hundred twenty-five sets of tires can be made.
There will be 2 tires left over.

65

REACHING ALL LEARNERS

Alternative Explore

Materials: Base Ten Blocks

Have students use Base Ten Blocks to find the quotient 1248 ÷ 4.

Early Finishers

Have students continue playing *Target No Remainder* from question 7. This time, the player with the greater total is the winner.

- How did you find how many sets of tires are made each day?
  (*I know 1200 tires make 300 sets with 48 left over. 48 tires make 12 more sets. 312 sets of tires are made each day.*)

AFTER Connect

Invite students to share the strategies they used to find the number of sets of tires made each day. Some students may have used mental math to solve the problem. If so, have them show how they broke 1248 up to make numbers they could divide mentally.

Review the methods presented in *Connect*. Some students using multiplication to divide *may* write the number of sets they are making *above* the dividend rather than down the side. It is fine to record the results in this way.

Discuss the second bullet in *Connect*. Ask:

- In the first frame, why is the 2 written in the hundreds place?
  (*We are dividing 11 hundreds into groups of 5. The number of groups is 2 hundreds.*)
- Why is the 2 in the second frame in the tens place?
  (*We are dividing 12 tens into groups of 5. The number of groups is 2 tens.*)
- In the third frame, what does the 5 represent? The 2 at the bottom?
  (*27 ones are divided into groups of 5. There are 5 groups of 5. The 2 shows how many tires are left over.*)

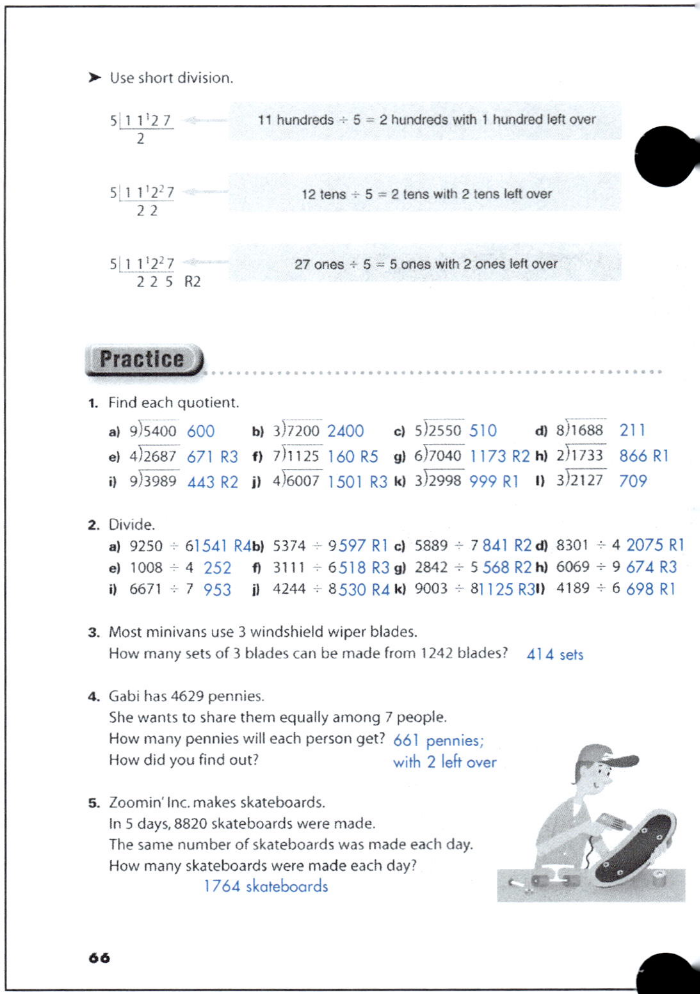
➤ Use short division.

5⌊1 1¹2 7 — 11 hundreds ÷ 5 = 2 hundreds with 1 hundred left over
2

5⌊1 1¹2²7 — 12 tens ÷ 5 = 2 tens with 2 tens left over
2 2

5⌊1 1¹2²7 — 27 ones ÷ 5 = 5 ones with 2 ones left over
2 2 5 R2

Practice

1. Find each quotient.
   a) 9)5400 600 b) 3)7200 2400 c) 5)2550 510 d) 8)1688 211
   e) 4)2687 671 R3 f) 7)1125 160 R5 g) 6)7040 1173 R2 h) 2)1733 866 R1
   i) 9)3989 443 R2 j) 4)6007 1501 R3 k) 3)2998 999 R1 l) 3)2127 709

2. Divide.
   a) 9250 ÷ 6 1541 R4 b) 5374 ÷ 9 597 R1 c) 5889 ÷ 7 841 R2 d) 8301 ÷ 4 2075 R1
   e) 1008 ÷ 4 252 f) 3111 ÷ 6 518 R3 g) 2842 ÷ 5 568 R2 h) 6069 ÷ 9 674 R3
   i) 6671 ÷ 7 953 j) 4244 ÷ 8 530 R4 k) 9003 ÷ 8 1125 R3 l) 4189 ÷ 6 698 R1

3. Most minivans use 3 windshield wiper blades.
   How many sets of 3 blades can be made from 1242 blades? 414 sets

4. Gabi has 4629 pennies.
   She wants to share them equally among 7 people.
   How many pennies will each person get? 661 pennies;
   How did you find out? with 2 left over

5. Zoomin' Inc. makes skateboards.
   In 5 days, 8820 skateboards were made.
   The same number of skateboards was made each day.
   How many skateboards were made each day?
   1764 skateboards

66

Discuss the third bullet in *Connect*. Ask:

- How are the methods shown in the second and third bullets the same?
  (*Both methods use place value and regrouping, starting with hundreds, then tens, and then ones. Short division is simply a short way to record the steps of division.*)

Practice

Question 7 requires a spinner (Master 2.8) and 4 number cubes labelled 1 to 6.

Have Base Ten Blocks available for students who wish to use them.

Assessment Focus: Question 8

Students should have an organized way to list all the 4-digit numbers they can make. Once they have made all the 4-digit numbers, they should check to see which ones are divisible by 7 with no remainder.

6. Write a division problem that can be solved by dividing a 4-digit number by a 1-digit number.
Trade problems with a classmate.
Solve your classmate's problem.

Target No Remainder! Game

You will need:

- a spinner with 6 equal sectors, labelled 4 to 9
- 4 number cubes, each labelled 1 to 6

Take turns.
On your turn, roll all 4 number cubes and spin the spinner.
Arrange the numbers on the number cubes to make a 4-digit number.
Divide the 4-digit number by the number on the spinner.
Record the remainder. This is your score for this turn.
At the end of the game, total your score.
The winner is the player with the lesser total.

8. Use the digits 8, 6, 1, and 4 once each.
Arrange the digits to make a 4-digit number.
How many different 4-digit numbers can you make that are divisible by 7 with no remainder?
How do you know you have found them all?

9. Without dividing, how can you tell how many digits the quotient of 8445 ÷ 9 will have?
Use words and numbers to explain.

Reflect

Look at your answers for question 2.
Which quotients had 3 digits? Which had 4 digits?
How can you tell how many digits the quotient will have before you divide?

Numbers Every Day

Mental Math

Find each sum.

8 + 15 + 12 35
41 + 17 + 3 + 9 70
38 + 12 + 25 75

Which strategies did you use?

Assessment Focus | Question 8 67

Sample Answers

6. Kim arranged 1024 books on 8 shelves. She put the same number of books on each shelf. How many books did she put on each shelf? (*1024 ÷ 8 = 128*)
8. 4186 and 4816; I tried all the possible 4-digit numbers with these digits. These were the only two that were divisible by 7 with no remainder.
9. The quotient 8445 ÷ 9 has 3 digits. The quotient is greater than 100 (9 × 100 = 900, too low), and less than 1000 (9 × 1000 = 9000, too high).

REFLECT: The quotients in 2a, 2d, and 2k had 4 digits. All the other quotients had 3 digits. To find the number of digits a quotient will have, multiply the divisor by 100 and 1000, and compare the product with the dividend. For example, for 9250 ÷ 6, 6 × 1000 = 6000, which is still less than 9250, so the quotient will have 4 digits. For 5374 ÷ 9, 9 × 100 = 900 and 9 × 1000 = 9000, so the quotient is between 100 and 1000; it will have 3 digits.

Numbers Every Day

Students will most likely look for friendly numbers. For example, in the first question, they would likely add 8 and 12 to get 20, and then add 15. In the second question, they might add 41 and 9 to get 50, add 17 and 3 to get 20, and then add 50 + 20. In the third question, students may recognize that the sum of 38 and 12 is 50.

ASSESSMENT FOR LEARNING

What to Look For	What to Do
Understanding concepts ✔ Students can divide a 4-digit number by a 1-digit number. ***Applying procedures*** ✔ Students can use more than one strategy to divide a 4-digit number by a 1-digit number.	***Extra Support:*** Have students use Base Ten Blocks to model each quotient. Students can use Step-by-Step 12 (Master 2.24) to complete question 8. ***Extra Practice:*** Have students choose 4 quotients from question 1 and describe a strategy they could use to divide mentally. Students can complete Extra Practice 6 (Master 2.33). ***Extension:*** Students can do the Additional Activity, *Go for the Greatest* (Master 2.9). This time, they toss the decahedron 6 times and arrange the digits to make a 5-digit by 1-digit division question.

Recording and Reporting

Master 2.2 Ongoing Observations: Whole Numbers

Solving Problems

LESSON ORGANIZER 40–50 min

Curriculum Focus: Solve problems with more than one step. (5m33, 5m35)

Student Materials *Optional*
- Step-by-Step 13 (Master 2.25)
- Extra Practice 7 (Master 2.34)

Assessment: Master 2.2 Ongoing Observations: Whole Numbers

Key Math Learnings

1. Some math problems require more than one computation.
2. Sometimes it is necessary to calculate to find important information to solve a problem.

LESSON 13

Solving Problems

You have used addition, subtraction, multiplication, and division to solve problems with whole numbers.

In this lesson, you will solve problems with more than one step.

Explore

Rhianna mows lawns and shovels driveways.
Last year, she earned $1252.
She mowed 93 lawns for $8 each.
How much money did she earn from shovelling driveways?

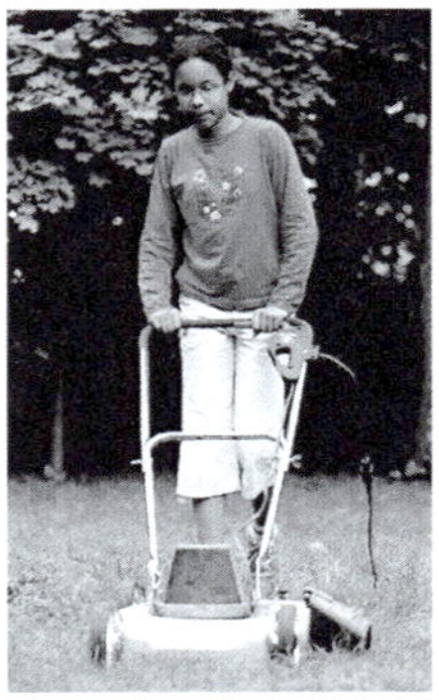

Show and Share

Share your work with another pair of students. Compare your answers and the strategies you used to find them. What did you need to calculate before you could find how much Rhianna earned from shovelling driveways? Explain.

Connect

➤ Rob spent $1478 on stamps and coins.
He bought 14 stamps for $37 each.
How much did Rob spend on coins?

To find the amount Rob spent on coins, we need to find out how much Rob spent on stamps.

68 LESSON FOCUS | Solve problems with more than one step

BEFORE Get Started

Ask:
- How might you solve this problem?
  I spent $5 on lunch today. I had fruit, milk, and a sandwich. The fruit was $1. How much was the sandwich?
  (I don't know how much the milk cost so I cannot find the cost of the sandwich.)
- Suppose the milk cost $1. Can you find the cost of the sandwich now? How?
  (Yes. The fruit and the milk cost $1 dollar each. That is $2 altogether. The sandwich cost $3.)

Present *Explore*. Explain to students they will be solving problems that involve more than one step.

DURING Explore

Ongoing Assessment: Observe and Listen

Ask questions, such as:
- What are you asked to find?
  (The amount Rhianna earned shovelling driveways last year)
- How much did Rhianna earn altogether last year? *($1252)*
- What do you need to know in order to find out how much she earned shovelling driveways?
  (I need to know how much Rhianna earned mowing lawns.)
- How could you find out how much Rhianna earned mowing lawns?
  (I could multiply the number of lawns she mowed by the amount she earned for mowing each lawn; 93 × 8 = 744. Rhianna earned $744 mowing lawns.)

Multiply: 14 × 37

$$\begin{array}{r} 37 \\ \times\ 14 \\ \hline 148 \\ +\ 370 \\ \hline 518 \end{array}$$

Rob spent $518 on stamps.

Find out how much Rob spent on coins.
Subtract the amount he spent on stamps
from the total amount he spent.
Subtract: 1478 − 518

1478 − 518 = 960

Rob spent $960 on coins.

➤ Mackenzie uses 16 m of fabric to make 4 outfits from one pattern.
How much fabric would she need to make 9 outfits from the same pattern?

To find the amount of fabric she needs for 9 outfits,
we first need to know how much fabric she needs for 1 outfit.
Divide: 16 ÷ 4 = 4

Mackenzie needs 4 m of fabric to make 1 outfit.
Multiply the amount of fabric needed for 1 outfit
by the number of outfits, 9.
4 × 9 = 36

Mackenzie needs 36 m of fabric to make 9 outfits from the pattern.

Practice

1. Campbell bought 14 hardcover books. Each book cost $35.
   a) How much did Campbell spend on books? $490
   b) Write a story problem that uses your answer to part a.
   Trade problems with a classmate.
   Solve your classmate's problem.
   c) Compare your problem to your classmate's problem.

69

REACHING ALL LEARNERS

Early Finishers

Have students solve question 3, supposing the choir stood in rows of 15, rows of 18, and rows of 20. Students write to explain how the results changed each time.

Common Misconceptions

➤ Some students think that whenever there are 3 numbers in a problem, they just add the three numbers.

How to Help: Have students summarize what they need to know to solve the problem, and then think of a strategy to find the information they need to know.

Sample Answers

1. b) Campbell spent $650 on books and DVDs. He bought 14 books for $35 each. How much did he spend on DVDs? (*$160*)

- How can you find out how much Rhianna earned shovelling driveways? (*I can subtract the amount she made mowing lawns from the total she earned; 1252 − 744 = 508. Rhianna earned $508 shovelling driveways.*)
- How would the problem change if Mackenzie could make 8 outfits with 16 m of fabric?
(*Each outfit would only need 2 m of fabric. So 18 m would be needed for 9 outfits.*)

AFTER Connect

Discuss the first example in *Connect*. Ask:
- Why did we multiply 14 × 37?
(*Rob bought 14 stamps at $37 each. We need to find the product 14 × 37 to find the amount he spent on stamps.*)

Discuss the second example in *Connect*. Ensure students understand why they need to divide 16 by 4. To be sure students understand, Ask:
- How would you find how much fabric Mackenzie needs for 15 dresses?
(*I would multiply the amount she needs for one dress, 4 m, by the number of dresses she plans to make; 4 × 15 = 60 m.*)

Practice

Assessment Focus: Question 4

Students should realize the cheetah's speed is given in metres per second. To compare the cheetah's speed with Connor's, they first have to find the cheetah's speed in metres per minute, and then compare how far each can run in 1 minute.

2. a) The cost of 1 cartridge at Sam's
   b) The number of minutes in 2 hours
   The total time Karen worked

4. There are 60 seconds in 1 minute.
   The cheetah runs 60 × 29, or 1740 m in 1 minute.
   1740 m − 150 m = 1590 m
   The cheetah runs 1590 m farther in 1 minute.

REFLECT: When you solve a problem with more than one step, you first have to find what information you need to find the final answer. Then you need to calculate to get that information. For example, Tahlia has 121 cans of vegetables and 223 cans of soup. She is putting them in rows of 4 on a shelf. How many rows of cans will she have?
First you need to add to find out how many cans she has altogether. Then you divide the total number of cans by 4.

2. For each problem, describe what you need to find before you can solve the problem.

a) At Sam's Office Supply, a package of 3 colour inkjet cartridges costs $216.
At Ink World, the same brand of cartridge costs $79 each.
How much more does a colour cartridge cost at Ink World? 79 − 72 = 7; $7

b) Karen booked the computer for 2 hours.
She spent 75 minutes typing a report and 32 minutes checking her work. 75 + 32 = 107
How much computer time does Karen have left? 120 − 107 = 13; 13 minutes

3. The Lakeland District choir stood in rows of 12 for a performance.
The people in 2 rows carried red streamers.
The people in 4 rows carried yellow streamers.
The people in 3 rows carried purple streamers.
How many people are in the choir?
108 people

4. Connor runs 150 m every minute.
A cheetah runs 29 m every second.

a) How much farther than Connor will the cheetah run in 1 minute?

b) Explain how you solved the problem.

5. Kamil played a game 3 times.
His first score was 1063 points.
His second score was 129 points lower.
His third score was 251 points higher than his second score.
How many points did Kamil score in his third game? 1185 points

Reflect

Describe how to solve a problem with more than one step.
Use examples to explain.

Numbers Every Day

Number Strategies

Find each product.

25 × 32 800
47 × 50 2350
22 × 88 1936
80 × 60 4800
14 × 19 266

70 ASSESSMENT FOCUS | Question 4

Numbers Every Day

Encourage students to use mental math strategies wherever they can. You may wish to allow some time for students to share the mental math strategies they used.

ASSESSMENT FOR LEARNING

What to Look For	What to Do
Problem solving ✔ Students can solve problems with more than one step.	***Extra Support:*** Scaffold some of the problems for students to model the kind of thinking they need to do. Students can use Step-by-Step 13 (Master 2.25) to complete question 4. ***Extra Practice:*** Students can complete Extra Practice 7 (Master 2.34). ***Extension:*** Students work in pairs. They each write a problem with more than one step. They trade problems with their partner and solve their partner's problem.

Recording and Reporting
Master 2.2 Ongoing Observations: Whole Numbers

Less Is More

You will need a decahedron numbered 0 to 9.

The object of the game is to make a division statement with:
- the least quotient, *and*
- the least remainder

➤ Each player makes a large copy of this division frame.

□ □ □ □ ÷ □

➤ Players take turns to roll the decahedron.
➤ On your turn, record the number that turns up in any square of the division frame.
Once a number is written down, you may not move it.
➤ Continue until each player has filled her or his division frame.
➤ Each player finds the quotient for her or his division frame.
Check each other's work.
Each player with a correct answer scores 1 point.
The player with the least remainder scores 1 point.
The player with the least quotient scores 1 point.
The first player to score 6 points wins.

71

Less Is More

LESSON ORGANIZER 20 min

Student Materials
- decahedrons, labelled 0 to 9

BEFORE — Get Started

Organize the students into groups of 3. Each group requires a decahedron labelled 0 to 9. Invite students to read the game instructions. Ensure students understand they are to try to make a division statement with *both* the least quotient *and* the least remainder.

DURING — Game

As students play, ask questions, such as:
- How did you decide where to place the digits?
  (*If I roll a number that divides into a lot of numbers, such as 2, I write it as the divisor. If I wrote 2 as the divisor, and I roll an even number, I write that as the ones digit of the dividend. This way I know the remainder will be 0. On my 3rd roll, I would write a large number as the tens digit of the dividend and a small number as the hundreds digit.*)
- What strategies did you use to divide?
  (*I used place value and basic multiplication facts.*)

AFTER

Invite students to share the strategies they used to place the digits in the division frame and to divide.

Strategies Toolkit

LESSON ORGANIZER — 40–50 min

Curriculum Focus: Interpret a problem and select an appropriate strategy. (5m35)
Assessment:
PM 1 Inquiry Process Check List
PM 3 Self-Assessment: Problem Solving

Key Math Learnings

1. Making an organized list is a good strategy to use for problems in which more than one pair of numbers must be tried.
2. Using a guess and check strategy together with making an organized list is a good way to solve many problems.

LESSON 14 **Strategies Toolkit**

Explore

Samrina organized a team to participate in a 325-km bike relay.
Half the team members ride 25 km.
The rest ride 40 km.
Including Samrina, how many people are on Samrina's team? 10 people

Show and Share

Describe the strategy you used to solve the problem.
How could you solve the problem a different way?

Connect

Mr. Biegala bought resource books for $28 and bookshelves for $84.
He spent $448 on 12 items.
How many of each item did Mr. Biegala buy? 2 bookshelves and 10 books

Understand

What do you know?
- Resource books cost $28 each.
- Bookshelves cost $84 each.
- The total number of books and bookshelves is 12.
- The total cost is $448.

Plan

Think of a strategy to help you solve the problem:
You could **make an organized list**.
- Find 2 numbers that add to 448.
- One number must be a multiple of 28, the other must be a multiple of 84.

Strategies
- Make a table.
- Use a model.
- Draw a diagram.
- Solve a simpler problem.
- Work backward.
- Guess and check.
- Make an organized list.
- Use a pattern.
- Draw a graph.

72 LESSON FOCUS | Interpret a problem and select an appropriate strategy.

BEFORE — Get Started

As a class, solve this problem:
The product of two numbers is 60. Their sum is 17. What are the numbers?
Find pairs of factors with a product of 60.
Record the information in an organized list:

Numbers	Product	Sum
2, 30	60	32
3, 20	60	23
4, 15	60	19
5, 12	60	17

Present *Explore*.

DURING — Explore

Ongoing Assessment: Observe and Listen

Ask questions such as:
- Suppose there are 6 people on Samrina's team. How many ride 25 km? 40 km? (*3; 3*)
- How far would the members of a 6-person team ride in total? (*195 km*)
- Is there an even or odd number of people on Samrina's team? How do you know? (*Even; an odd number is not divisible by 2.*)
- How many people are on Samrina's team? (*10*)

AFTER — Connect

Review the example in *Connect*. Ask:
- For 1 bookshelf, why is the number of books 11? (*The total number of books and bookshelves must be 12.*)
- How do we know we need to use more than 1 bookshelf? (*The total cost of 1 bookshelf and 11 books is less than $448.*)

Practice

Remind students to refer to the Strategies list and choose an appropriate strategy.

Find the cost of 1 bookshelf.
Find the amount of $448 that is left.
Try to find a number of books whose cost is equal to the amount left.
Record the amounts in an organized list.
Find the cost of 2 bookshelves.
Continue until you find the number of books and the number of bookshelves.

Number of Bookshelves	Cost ($)	Amount Left ($)	Number of Books	Cost ($)
1	84	448 – 84 = 364	11	308

Check your work.
Is the total number of books and bookshelves 12?
Is the total cost of books and bookshelves $448?

Practice

Choose one of the **Strategies**

1. Together, 2 hot tubs cost $6094.
   The difference between their prices is $2304.
   What is the price of the more expensive hot tub? $4199

2. Colin's grandma gave him $100.
   He bought a game for $61.
   He wants to buy another game that costs $47.
   How much more money does Colin need? $8

Reflect

Choose one of the *Practice* questions.
Describe how you solved the problem.

73

REACHING ALL LEARNERS

Alternative Explore

Have students solve this problem:
Rosemary has 14 dimes and quarters. She has $2 altogether. How many of each coin does Rosemary have? (*10 dimes and 4 quarters*)

Early Finishers

Have students repeat the *Explore* question. This time, change the total distance to 455 km. Have students explain why the results are different.

REFLECT: In question 2, I knew Colin started with $100.
He spent $61 on a game, so he had $100 – $61 = $39 left.
The game he wants costs $47.
He needs another $8 because 47 – 39 = 8.

ASSESSMENT FOR LEARNING

What to Look For	What to Do
Applying procedures ✔ Students can select an appropriate strategy for solving a problem.	***Extra Support:*** Have students use play money to model the problem in question 2.
Communicating ✔ Students can describe the strategy clearly.	***Extra Practice:*** Have students solve this problem: I have $100 in $5 and $10 bills. How many of each kind of bill might I have? (*There are many answers to this problem: two $5 bills + nine $10 bills; four $5 bills + eight $10 bills; ⋮ ⋮ eighteen $5 bills + one $10 bill*)
	Extension: Challenge students to make up problems that can be solved by making an organized list. Students trade problems with a classmate and solve their classmate's problem.

Recording and Reporting
PM 1 Inquiry Process Check List
PM 3 Self-Assessment: Problem Solving

LESSON ORGANIZER

40–50 min

Assessment:
Master 2.1 Unit Rubric: Whole Numbers
Master 2.4 Unit Summary: Whole Numbers

Sample Answers

2. 20 000; 300 000 + 20 000 + 70 + 5

7. a) 8 × 12 = 96   96 ÷ 8 = 12
12 × 8 = 96   96 ÷ 12 = 8

b) 11 × 9 = 99   99 ÷ 11 = 9
9 × 11 = 99   99 ÷ 9 = 11

Unit 2 Show What You Know

LESSON 1

1. Write each number in standard form.
   a) 800 000 + 60 000 + 400 + 30 + 7   860 437
   b) seven hundred fifty-four thousand eight   754 008

2. Write the value of the underlined digit.
   Then write the number in expanded form.
   320 075

3. Write the numbers in order from greatest to least:
   437 126   437 162   473 126   473 126, 437 162, 437 126

LESSON 2, 3, 5, 6

4. Estimate first. Then find each sum or difference.
   a) 4729 + 3178 = 7907   About 8000
   b) 2968 − 387 = 2581   About 2600
   c) 9127 − 6988 = 2139   About 2000
   d) 6496 + 7827 = 14 323   About 14 500

LESSON 4, 6

5. Find each sum or difference. Check your answer.
   a) 2471 + 3989 + 4635 = 11095
   b) 7412 − 4386 = 3026
   c) 4003 − 2778 = 1225
   d) 1999 + 1576 + 5814 = 9389

6. Use mental math to add or subtract.
   a) 6647 + 1004 = 7651
   b) 8000 − 3594 = 4406
   c) 2999 + 3998 + 1997 = 8994
   d) 7642 − 3998 = 3644

LESSON 7

7. Write four related facts for each set of numbers.
   a) 8, 12, 96   b) 11, 9, 99

8. Find each product or quotient.
   a) 132 ÷ 12   11   b) 10 × 11   110   c) 108 ÷ 2   54   d) 7 × 11   77

LESSON 8, 9, 10

9. Multiply.
   a) 8 × 7000   56 000   b) 50 × 90   4500   c) 11 × 500   5500   d) 60 × 60   3600
   e) 32 × 75   2400   f) 51 × 78   3978   g) 66 × 33   2178   h) 91 × 23   2093

74

Check If Your Answer Is Reasonable

Encourage students to estimate each answer before they calculate. Students should develop a sense of the reasonableness of each answer. Suppose they multiply 3 × 700 and get 21. They should recognize that it is not reasonable to multiply a number with hundreds and get a product with tens.

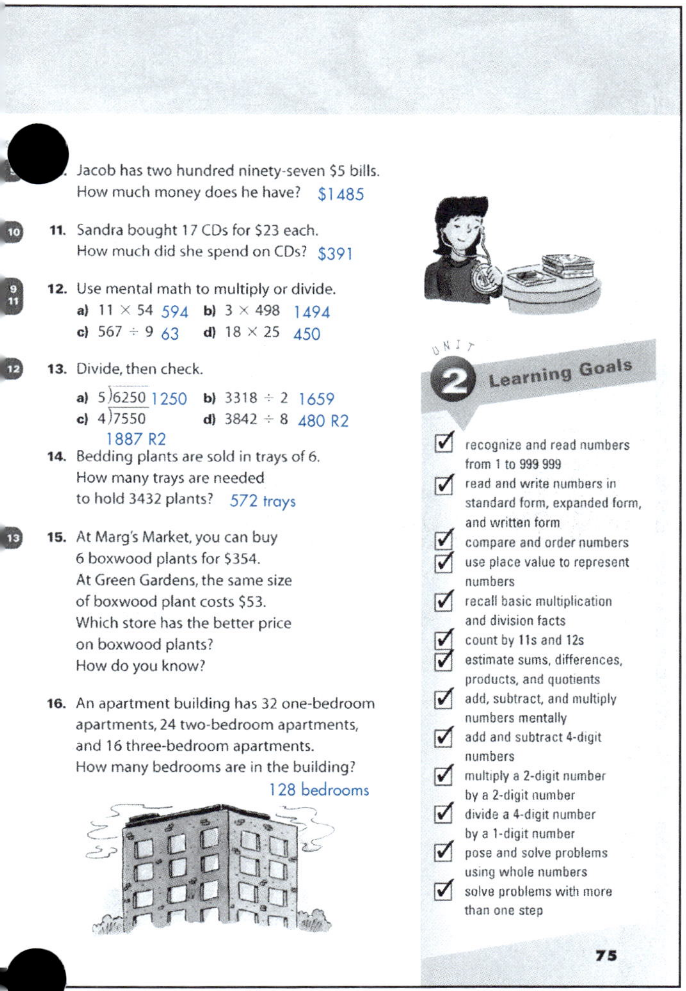

Jacob has two hundred ninety-seven $5 bills. How much money does he have? $1485

10 **11.** Sandra bought 17 CDs for $23 each. How much did she spend on CDs? $391

9 11 **12.** Use mental math to multiply or divide.
a) 11 × 54 594 **b)** 3 × 498 1494
c) 567 ÷ 9 63 **d)** 18 × 25 450

12 **13.** Divide, then check.
a) 5)6250 1250 **b)** 3318 ÷ 2 1659
c) 4)7550 1887 R2 **d)** 3842 ÷ 8 480 R2

14. Bedding plants are sold in trays of 6. How many trays are needed to hold 3432 plants? 572 trays

13 **15.** At Marg's Market, you can buy 6 boxwood plants for $354. At Green Gardens, the same size of boxwood plant costs $53. Which store has the better price on boxwood plants? How do you know?

16. An apartment building has 32 one-bedroom apartments, 24 two-bedroom apartments, and 16 three-bedroom apartments. How many bedrooms are in the building? 128 bedrooms

UNIT 2 Learning Goals

- ☑ recognize and read numbers from 1 to 999 999
- ☑ read and write numbers in standard form, expanded form, and written form
- ☑ compare and order numbers
- ☑ use place value to represent numbers
- ☑ recall basic multiplication and division facts
- ☑ count by 11s and 12s
- ☑ estimate sums, differences, products, and quotients
- ☑ add, subtract, and multiply numbers mentally
- ☑ add and subtract 4-digit numbers
- ☑ multiply a 2-digit number by a 2-digit number
- ☑ divide a 4-digit number by a 1-digit number
- ☑ pose and solve problems using whole numbers
- ☑ solve problems with more than one step

75

15. Green Gardens; at Marg's Market, the cost of 1 plant is $354 ÷ 6 = $59.

ASSESSMENT FOR LEARNING

What to Look For

Understanding of concepts

✔ **Questions 1, 2, and 3:** Student understands that the value of a digit is determined by its position in the number. Student recognizes 0 as a placeholder in numbers such as 320 075.

✔ **Questions 10, 11, and 14:** Student recognizes that the question can be answered by multiplying or by dividing.

Application of mathematical procedures

✔ **Questions 4, 5, and 6:** Student can use a variety of strategies to add and subtract.

✔ **Questions 8, 9, 12, and 13:** Student can use a variety of strategies to multiply or to divide.

Problem solving

✔ **Questions 14, 15, and 16:** Student can solve problems using multiplication and division.

Recording and Reporting

Master 2.1 Unit Rubric: Whole Numbers
Master 2.4 Unit Summary: Whole Numbers

On The Dairy Farm

LESSON ORGANIZER 40–50 min

Student Grouping: Groups of 2
Assessment:
Masters 2.3 Performance Assessment Rubric:
On the Dairy Farm, 2.4 Unit Summary: Whole Numbers

Unit Problem

On the Dairy Farm

Silage is made from green corn plants. The whole plant is harvested, chopped, and fermented in a storage silo.

Haylage is hay that has been cut, chopped, and stored moist.

Each day a cow eats:
- 5 kg of hay
- 9 kg of haylage
- 9 kg of corn silage
- 10 kg of dairy ration

A cow also requires minerals and salt, and 80 to 160 L of water each day.

76

Sample Answers

1. Each day, 1 cow requires 5 + 9 + 9 + 10 = 33 kg of feed.
   Multiply 33 kg by 43 to find the amount of feed required each day for 43 cows.
   $43 \times 33 = 1419$
   Each day Amy will use 1419 kg of feed.
   Multiply the daily amount by 14 to find the amount Amy needs for 2 weeks.
   $1419 \times 14 = 19\,866$
   Amy will use 19 866 kg of feed every 2 weeks.
2. Matthew will divide his field into 6 parts.
   $72 \div 6 = 12$
   Each part will be 12 hectares.
   $4 \times 12 = 48$
   Matthew will use 48 hectares for hay, 12 hectares for corn, and 12 hectares for cow pasture.

Have students turn to the *Unit Launch* on pages 26 and 27 of the Student Book.

Review the Learning Goals for the unit with the students. You may wish to have a brief discussion about each goal.

If you have recorded students' responses to the questions on page 27 on chart paper, you may want to post these responses on the board to review how they found the answers.

Present the *Unit Problem*. Have a volunteer read through the Check List to ensure students know what they are expected to do. Have different volunteers read through the problems. Answer any questions students might have regarding the problems.

You might want to brainstorm with the class about the different story problems. They could write about a dairy farm.

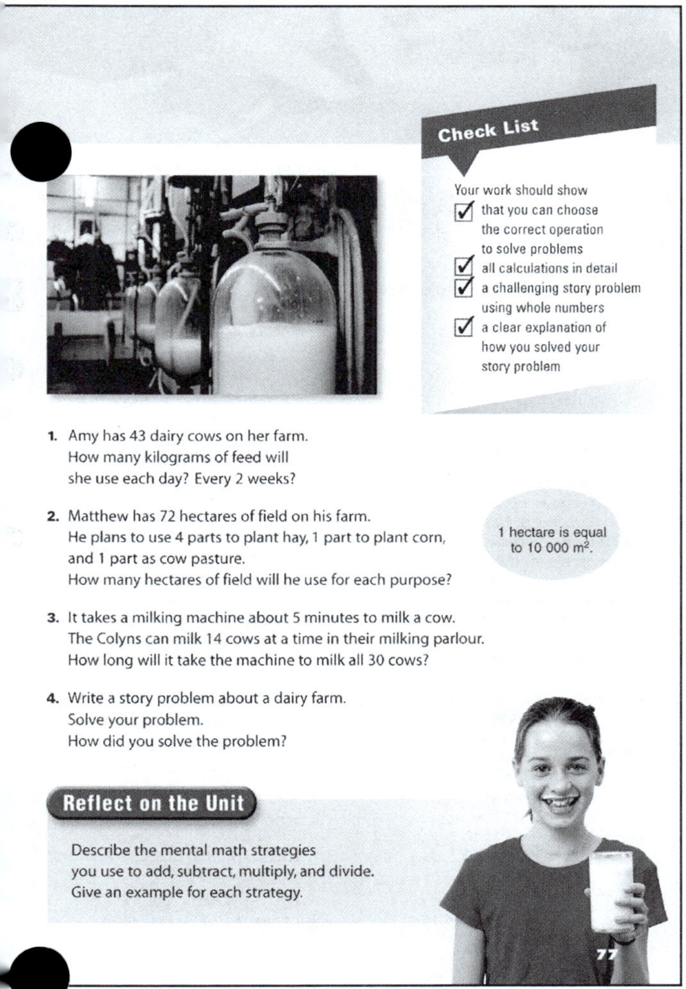

Check List

Your work should show
- ☑ that you can choose the correct operation to solve problems
- ☑ all calculations in detail
- ☑ a challenging story problem using whole numbers
- ☑ a clear explanation of how you solved your story problem

1. Amy has 43 dairy cows on her farm. How many kilograms of feed will she use each day? Every 2 weeks?
2. Matthew has 72 hectares of field on his farm. He plans to use 4 parts to plant hay, 1 part to plant corn, and 1 part as cow pasture. How many hectares of field will he use for each purpose?

1 hectare is equal to 10 000 m^2.

3. It takes a milking machine about 5 minutes to milk a cow. The Colyns can milk 14 cows at a time in their milking parlour. How long will it take the machine to milk all 30 cows?
4. Write a story problem about a dairy farm. Solve your problem. How did you solve the problem?

Reflect on the Unit

Describe the mental math strategies you use to add, subtract, multiply, and divide. Give an example for each strategy.

77

3. Fourteen cows can be milked at a time. At the end of 5 minutes, 14 cows will be milked. At the end of 10 minutes, 28 cows will be milked. There are still 2 cows to be milked. It would take the machine 15 minutes to milk all the cows.
4. How much silage will you need to feed 20 cows for a week?
   (*There are 20 cows. Each cow needs 9 kg of silage each day.*
   20 × 9 = 180
   For 20 cows, you need 180 kg of silage each day.
   There are 7 days in a week.
   180 × 7 = 1260
   For 20 cows, you need 1260 kg of silage each week.)

Reflect on the Unit

To add, I might use compensation. For example, to add 298 + 746, I would add 2 to 298 to make it 300, and take 2 from 746 to make 744; 300 + 744 = 1044, so 298 + 746 = 1044.
To subtract, I might use friendly numbers. For example, to subtract 5001 − 3998, I would make 3998 a friendly number by adding 2, and do the same to 5001; 5003 − 4000 = 1003, so 5001 − 3998 = 1003.
To multiply 16 × 35, I would use halving and doubling to make it 8 × 70 = 560.
To divide 832 ÷ 4, I would break 832 up into 800 + 32 because these numbers are easy to divide by 4. 800 ÷ 4 = 200 and 32 ÷ 4 = 8, so 832 ÷ 4 = 200 + 8, or 208.

ASSESSMENT FOR LEARNING

What to Look For

- ✔ Students can choose the appropriate operation to solve problems with whole numbers.
- ✔ Students can solve problems with more than one step.
- ✔ Students pose and solve problems with whole numbers.

What to Do

Extra Support: Make the problem accessible.
Scaffold the problem for students. For example, for question 2, Ask:
- Into how many parts will Matthew divide his field? How did you find out? (*6; I added the numbers of parts he plans to use for each purpose: 4 + 1 + 1*)
- How large will each part be? (*The field is 72 hectares. It will be divided into 6 parts.*
  72 ÷ 6 = 12; each part will be 12 hectares.)
- How many hectares will Matthew use to plant hay? (*Matthew will use 4 parts to plant hay. Each part is 12 hectares.*
  4 × 12 = 48; Matthew will plant 48 hectares of hay.)

Recording and Reporting
Master 2.3 Performance Assessment Rubric: On the Dairy Farm
Master 2.4 Unit Summary: Whole Numbers

Evaluating Student Learning: Preparing to Report: Unit 2 Whole Numbers

This unit provides an opportunity to report on the **Number Sense and Numeration** strand. *Master 2.4 Unit Summary: Whole Numbers* provides a comprehensive format for recording and summarizing evidence collected.

Here is an example of a completed summary chart for this Unit:

Strand: *Number Sense and Numeration*	**Problem solving**	**Understanding of concepts**	**Application of mathematical procedures**	**Communication**	***Overall***
Ongoing Observations	2	2	3	3	**2/3**
Strategies Toolkit (Lesson 14)	2	2		3	**2**
Work samples or portfolios; conferences	3	2	3	3	**3**
Show What You Know	2	2	3	2	**2**
Unit Test	2	2	3	3	**2/3**
Unit Problem On the Dairy Farm	2	3	2	2	**2**
Achievement Level for reporting					**2**

Recording	**How to Report**
Ongoing Observations	Use *Master 2.2 Ongoing Observations: Whole Numbers* to determine the most consistent level achieved in each category. Enter it in the chart. Choose to summarize by achievement category, or simply to enter an overall level. Observations from late in the Unit should be most heavily weighted.
Strategies Toolkit (problem solving)	Use *PM 1: Inquiry Process Check List* with the Strategies Toolkit (Lesson 14). Transfer results to the summary form. Teachers may choose to enter a level in the Problem solving column and/or Communication.
Portfolios or collections of work samples; conferences or interviews	Use *Master 2.1 Unit Rubric: Whole Numbers* to guide evaluation of collections of work and information gathered in conferences. Teachers may choose to focus particular attention on the Assessment Focus questions. Work from late in the unit should be most heavily weighted.
Show What You Know	Teachers may choose to assign some or all of these questions. *Master 2.1 Unit Rubric: Whole Numbers* may be helpful in determining levels of achievement. #1, 2, 3, 10, 11, and 14 provide evidence of Understanding of concepts; #4, 5, 6, 8, 9, 12, and 13 provide evidence of Application of mathematical procedures; #14, 15, and 16 provide evidence of Problem solving; all provide evidence of Communication.
Unit Test	*Master 2.1 Unit Rubric: Whole Numbers* may be helpful in determining levels of achievement. Part A provides evidence of Application of mathematical procedures; Part B provides evidence of Understanding of concepts; Part C provides evidence of Problem solving; all parts provide evidence of Communication.
Unit performance task	Use *Master 2.3 Performance Assessment Rubric: On the Dairy Farm*. The *Unit Problem* offers a snapshot of students' achievement. In particular, it shows their ability to synthesize and apply what they have learned.
Student Self-Assessment	Note students' perceptions of their own progress. This may take the form of an oral or written comment, or a self-rating.
Comments	Analyse the pattern of achievement to identify strengths and needs. In some cases, specific actions may be planned to support the learner.

Learning Skills	**Ongoing Records**
PM 4: Learning Skills Check List Use to record and report throughout a reporting period, rather than for each unit and/or strand.	*PM 10: Summary Class Record: Strands* *PM 11: Summary Class Record: Achievement Categories* *PM 12: Summary Record: Individual* Use to record and report evaluations of student achievement over several clusters, a reporting period, or a school year. These can also be used in place of the Unit Summary.

Name ____________________ Date ________________

Master 2.1

Unit Rubric: Whole Numbers

	Level 1	Level 2	Level 3	Level 4
Problem solving • chooses and carries out a range of strategies to pose and solve 1- and 2-step problems, and uses estimation to determine the reasonableness of solutions (for example, compatible numbers, rounding, friendly numbers, mental math, making a simpler problem, using calculators, Base Ten Blocks, pictures, lists)	with assistance, chooses and carries out a limited range of appropriate strategies to pose and solve problems and check results; rarely results in an accurate solution	with limited assistance, chooses and carries out appropriate strategies to pose and solve problems and check results; frequently results in an accurate solution	chooses and carries out appropriate strategies to pose and solve problems and check results; usually results in an accurate solution	chooses and carries out appropriate, and often innovative, strategies to pose and solve problems and check results; always results in an accurate solution
Understanding of concepts • shows understanding by appropriately demonstrating and explaining: – place value – estimation of sums, differences, products, and quotients – processes and solutions (for example, multiplication, division) – choice of operation and calculation method – use of numbers in careers	may be unable to demonstrate or explain: – place value – estimation – processes and solutions – choice of operation and calculation method – use of numbers in careers	partially able to demonstrate and explain: – place value – estimation – processes and solutions – choice of operation and calculation method – use of numbers in careers	demonstrates and explains: – place value – estimation – processes and solutions – choice of operation and calculation method – use of numbers in careers	in various contexts, demonstrates and explains: – place value – estimation – processes and solutions – choice of operation and calculation method – use of numbers in careers
Application of mathematical procedures • accurately: – reads, writes, compares, and orders numbers (to 100 000) – counts by 11 and 12 – recalls multiplication and division facts to 144 – uses mental math – adds and subtracts (4-digits) – multiplies (2-digit by 2-digit) and divides (4-digit by 1-digit)	limited accuracy; major errors in: – reading, writing, comparing, ordering – counting by 11 and 12 – recalling multiplication and division facts – using mental math – adding and subtracting – multiplying – dividing	somewhat accurate; makes several minor errors in: – reading, writing, comparing, ordering – counting by 11 and 12 – recalling multiplication and division facts – using mental math – adding and subtracting – multiplying – dividing	generally accurate; makes few minor errors in: – reading, writing, comparing, ordering – counting by 11 and 12 – recalling multiplication and division facts – using mental math – adding and subtracting – multiplying – dividing	accurate; makes no errors in: – reading, writing, comparing, ordering – counting by 11 and 12 – recalling multiplication and division facts – using mental math – adding and subtracting – multiplying – dividing
Communication • presents work, describes procedures, and explains reasoning clearly	often unclear; imprecise; needs assistance to describe procedures and explain reasoning	presents work, describes procedures, and explains reasoning with some clarity and precision	presents work, describes procedures, and explains reasoning with general clarity and precision	presents work, describes procedures, and explains reasoning clearly, precisely, and confidently

Name ____________________ Date ________________

Master 2.2

Ongoing Observations: Whole Numbers

The behaviours described under each heading are examples; they are not intended to be an exhaustive list of all that might be observed. More detailed descriptions are provided in each lesson under *Assessment for Learning.*

STUDENT ACHIEVEMENT: Whole Numbers				
Student	**Problem solving** ▪ Chooses and carries out a range of strategies to pose and solve problems, and check problem solutions	**Understanding of concepts** ▪ Explains place value, estimates, processes, and solutions ▪ Justifies choice of operation and method	**Application of mathematical procedures** ▪ Reads, writes, compares, orders ▪ Adds, subtracts (4-digit numbers) ▪ Multiplies (2-digit by 2-digit) and divides (4-digit by 1-digit)	**Communication** ▪ Explains reasoning clearly ▪ Presents work clearly

Level 1 – very limited; Level 2 – somewhat or limited; Level 3 – satisfactory; Level 4 – thorough

Name ____________________ Date ______________

Master 2.3

Performance Assessment Rubric: On the Dairy Farm

	Level 1	Level 2	Level 3	Level 4
Problem solving • chooses appropriate strategies to solve and create 1- and 2-step problems involving whole numbers, and estimates to check reasonableness of results	uses few simple strategies to solve and create 1- and 2-step problems and check results; limited success	uses some appropriate strategies to solve and create 1- and 2-step problems and check results; some success	uses appropriate strategies to solve and create 1- and 2-step problems, and check results; successful	uses innovative and appropriate strategies to solve and create 1- and 2-step problems and check results; successful and effective
Understanding of concepts • shows understanding of whole numbers by offering reasonable explanations of strategies, procedures, and results	shows very limited understanding by giving inappropriate explanations of strategies, procedures, and results that use few concepts related to whole numbers	shows limited understanding by giving appropriate but incomplete explanations of strategies, procedures, and results using some concepts related to whole numbers	shows understanding by giving appropriate explanations of strategies, procedures, and results using relevant concepts related to whole numbers	shows thorough understanding by giving appropriate and complete explanations of strategies, procedures, and results using relevant concepts related to whole numbers
Application of mathematical procedures • accurately: – multiplies and divides whole numbers (may also add and subtract) – reads and writes whole numbers	makes few accurate calculations; major errors or omissions in: – multiplying and dividing whole numbers (also adding and subtracting if used) – reading and writing whole numbers	makes some accurate calculations with several minor errors or omissions in: – multiplying and dividing whole numbers (also adding and subtracting if used) – reading and writing whole numbers	makes accurate calculations with few minor errors or omissions in: – multiplying and dividing whole numbers (also adding and subtracting if used) – reading and writing whole numbers	makes accurate calculations with no errors or omissions in: – multiplying and dividing whole numbers (also adding and subtracting if used) – reading and writing whole numbers
Communication • explains reasoning clearly, using appropriate mathematical terminology	explains reasoning unclearly and imprecisely	explains reasoning with some clarity	explains reasoning clearly and precisely	explains reasoning clearly, precisely, and confidently

Name ____________________ Date ________________

Master 2.4

Unit Summary: Whole Numbers

Review assessment records to determine the most consistent achievement levels for the assessments conducted. Some cells may be blank. *Overall* achievement levels may be recorded in each row, rather than identifying levels for each achievement category.

	Most Consistent Level of Achievement*				
Strand: *Number Sense and Numeration*	**Problem solving**	**Understanding of concepts**	**Application of mathematical procedure**	**Communication**	***Overall***
Ongoing Observations					
Strategies Toolkit (Lesson 14)					
Work samples or portfolios; conferences					
Show What You Know					
Unit Test					
Unit Problem On the Dairy Farm					
Achievement Level for reporting					

*Use Ontario Achievement Levels 1, 2, 3, 4.

Self-Assessment:

Comments: (Strengths, Needs, Next Steps)

Name ____________________ Date ______________

Master 2.5

To Parents and Adults at Home ...

Your child's class is starting a mathematics unit on whole numbers. Students will develop strategies for adding, subtracting, multiplying, and dividing with whole numbers, and learn when estimation and mental math strategies are appropriate and effective.

In this unit, your child will:

- Recognize and read numbers from 1 to 999 999.
- Read and write numbers in standard form, expanded form, and written form.
- Compare and order numbers.
- Use place value to represent numbers.
- Recall basic multiplication and division facts.
- Count by 11s and 12s.
- Estimate sums, differences, products, and quotients.
- Add, subtract, and multiply numbers mentally.
- Add and subtract 4-digit numbers.
- Multiply a 2-digit number by a 2-digit number.
- Divide a 4-digit number by a 1-digit number.
- Pose and solve problems using whole numbers.
- Solve problems with more than one step.

Students are encouraged to use a variety of different strategies to add, subtract, multiply, and divide with whole numbers, depending on the situation and context. Calculating with number sense means that children look at the numbers and operation involved, and choose the strategy that is most efficient. You may want to ask your child to show you some of the different strategies he or she uses.

Here's a suggestion for a game you can play at home:

Duelling Products

- Remove the jokers and face cards from a deck of playing cards.
  Use Aces as 1 and tens as 0.
  Shuffle the cards and divide them evenly between you.
- Each player turns over 2 cards and multiplies the numbers.
  The player with the greater result takes all the cards.
- If both players get the same result, leave the cards on the table.
  The winner of the next round takes all the cards.

Name ____________________ Date ________________

Master 2.6

Multiplication Chart

×	0	1	2	3	4	5	6	7	8	9	10	11	12
1	0	1	2	3	4	5	6	7	8				
2	0	2	4	6	8	10	12	14	16				
3	0	3	6	9	12	15	18	21	24				
4	0	4	8	12	16	20	24	28	32				
5	0	5	10	15	20	25	30	35	40				
6	0	6	12	18	24	30	36	42	48				
7	0	7	14	21	28	35	42	49	56				
8	0	8	16	24	32	40	48	56	64				
9													
10													
11													
12													

Name ____________________ Date ________________

Master 2.7

Multiplication Tic-Tac-Toe

Game Board

42	33	16	70	64	9	48	24
10	72	50	96	40	22	80	15
60	21	36	120	18	54	27	99
12	90	77	30	132	14	88	4
35	6	40	121	63	100	56	110
50	81	18	84	45	72	25	48
28	16	70	24	60	20	36	144
44	55	8	66	32	108	49	30

Factor List

2	3	4	5	6	7	8	9	10	11	12

Name ______________________ Date ________________

Master 2.8

6-Sector Spinner

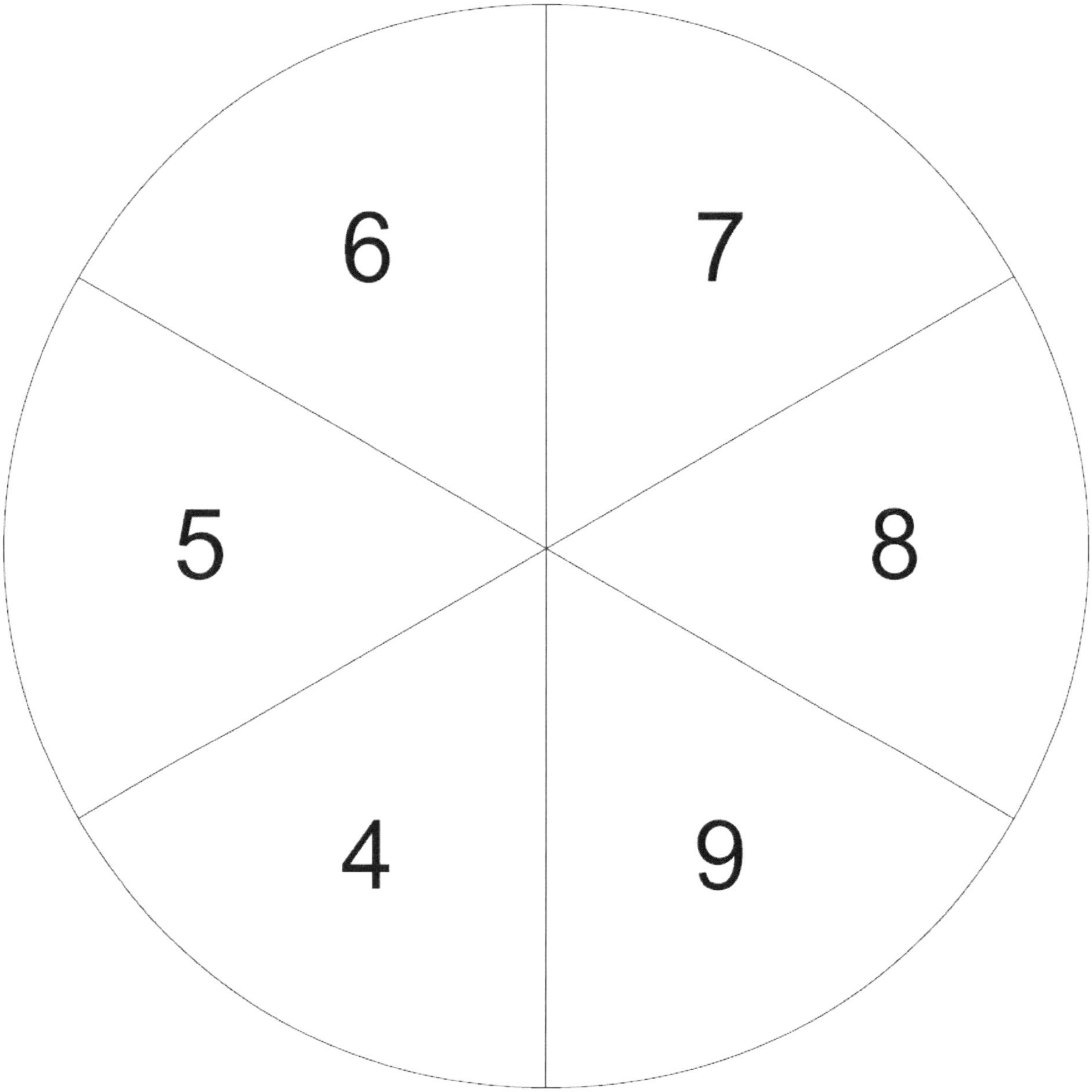

Name ____________________ Date _______________

Master 2.9

Additional Activity 1: Go for the Greatest

Work in a group.
You will need a calculator.
You will need a decahedron numbered 0 to 9.
The goal is to make the greatest number in this number frame.

- Players take turns to roll the decahedron and record the number in any position in their number frame.
  Once a player has recorded a number, he or she cannot move it.

- Play continues until each player has filled her or his number frame.

- The player with the greatest number scores 2 points.
  The player with the least number scores 1 point.
  The first player to score 8 points wins.

Take It Further:
At the end of each round, arrange all the numbers in order from greatest to least.

Name ____________________ Date ________________

Master 2.10

Additional Activity 2: What's the Difference?

Work with a partner.
You will need a set of digit cards numbered 0 to 9.

- Shuffle the digit cards and place them face down on the table.
- Player 1 selects 4 digit cards and makes the least number possible.
- Player 2 turns over 3 cards and makes the greatest number possible. Player 1 finds the difference between the 4-digit number and the 3-digit number.
- Players switch roles.
- The player with the least difference scores 1 point. If there is a tie, both players score 1 point.
- The player with more points after 8 rounds of play is the winner.

Take It Further:
Play the game again. This time, use 4 sets of digit cards.

Name ____________________ Date ________________

Master 2.11

Additional Activity 3: Powerful Products

Work with a partner.
You will need 2 sets of digit cards each numbered 0 to 9.

- Shuffle the digit cards and place them face down on the table.
  Each player takes 3 cards.
- Arrange your cards to make a 2-digit by 1-digit multiplication problem with the greatest product.
  Record your multiplication problem.
- Compare your product and your partner's product.
  The player with the greater product scores 1 point.
- Play continues for 6 rounds.
  The player with the greater score wins.

Take It Further:
Play the game again. This time, take 4 cards each.
Make a 2-digit by 2-digit multiplication problem.
The player with the greater product scores a point.

Name ____________________ Date ________________

Master 2.12a

Additional Activity 4: The Range Game

Play with a partner.
Your teacher will give you a set of range cards.

- Shuffle the range cards and place them facedown in a pile.
  Take turns to select a range card.
- Player 1 chooses a factor and finds the product or quotient.
  If the result is in the range, Player 1 scores a point.
  If not, Player 2 chooses a factor and finds the product or quotient.
- Play continues until one player chooses a factor that gives a result in the range.
  That player scores 1 point.
- The first player to score 5 points wins.

Take It Further:
Make your own set of range cards.
Trade sets with another pair of students and play the game.

Name ____________________ Date ________________

Master 2.12b **Range Cards**

$36 \times \square$ Product is between 1900 and 2000.	$9477 \div \square$ Quotient is between 1050 and 1350.	$73 \times \square$ Product is between 1600 and 2000.
$8188 \div \square$ Quotient is between 1640 and 2040.	$59 \times \square$ Product is between 3050 and 3190.	$2007 \div \square$ Quotient is between 330 and 600.
$14 \times \square$ Product is between 125 and 175.	$7621 \div \square$ Quotient is between 950 and 1270.	$61 \times \square$ Product is between 3900 and 4150.
$6850 \div \square$ Quotient is between 1700 and 2300.	$49 \times \square$ Product is between 780 and 980.	$763 \div \square$ Quotient is between 105 and 155.
$4 \times \square$ Product is between 2730 and 2780.	$5435 \div \square$ Quotient is between 600 and 900.	$9 \times \square$ Product is between 1280 and 1440.

Name ____________________ Date ________________

Master 2.13

Step-by-Step 1

Lesson 1, Question 7

Step 1 Use the digits 1 to 9. Use each digit only once.
Arrange the digits to make a 6-digit number as close to 100 000 as possible.

Step 2 Use the digits 1 to 9. Use each digit only once.
Arrange the digits to make a 6-digit number as close to 500 000 as possible.

Step 3 Find the difference between the number in *Step 1* and 100 000.

____

Step 4 Can you write a number that is close to 100 000? If so, repeat *Step 1*.

Step 5 Find the difference between the number in *Step 2* and 500 000.

____

Step 6 Can you write a number that is close to 500 000? If so, repeat *Step 2*.

Step 7 Did you get closer to 100 000 or to 500 000? ____________________
How do you know?

____

____

Name ____________________ Date ______________

Master 2.14

Step-by-Step 2

Lesson 2, Question 4

Step 1 Begin with 1000. Add 498. ________________________________

Step 2 Subtract 202 from your answer from *Step 1*. ____________________

Step 3 Add 204 to your answer from *Step 2*. ________________________

Step 4 Compare your answer from *Step 3* to the number you started with. What is the difference between the numbers?

____

Step 5 If you subtract 500 from the number in *Step 3*, what will you get?

____

Step 6 How does this compare with the original number you started out with?

____

Step 7 Find 498 – 202 + 204. __________________________________

Step 8 Repeat *Steps 1* through *3* again, but with a different starting number. If you subtract 500 from the number you are told in *Step 3*, will you always get the original number?

____

Step 9 Explain why the number trick works.

____

____

Name ____________________ Date ________________

Master 2.15 **Step-by-Step 3**

Lesson 3, Question 6

Regional Recycling has a target of 2450 kg of aluminum.
Suppose Fairfield delivers 1665 kg of aluminum,
and Westdale delivers 795 kg of aluminum.

Step 1 Find the sum 1665 + 795. ____

Step 2 Compare the sum from *Step 1* with the target of 2450.

____

Step 3 Will Regional Recycling meet its goal? How do you know?

____

____

Name ____________________ Date ______________

Master 2.16 **Step-by-Step 4**

Lesson 4, Question 5

Find the missing digits:

	3	6	□	5
	□	9	7	4
+	1	1	5	□
	7	□	1	5

Step 1 Look at the digits in the ones column.

5 + 4 + □ = ___ 5

What is the least number you could add to 5 + 4 that gives a sum with a 5 in the ones position? __________

Write the tens digit on top of the tens column.

Step 2 Look at the digits in the tens column.

1 + □ + 7 + 5 = ___ 1

What is the least number you could add to the numbers in the tens column that gives a sum with a 1 in the tens position? __________

Write the hundreds digit on top of the hundreds column.

Step 3 Find the sum of the hundreds digits.

Write the thousands digit on top of the thousands column.

Step 4 Look at the digits in the thousands column.

1 + 3 + □ + 1 = 7

What is the least number you could add to the numbers in the thousands column that gives a sum with a 7 in the thousands position? __________

Name ____________________ Date ________________

Master 2.17

Step-by-Step 5

Lesson 5, Question 6

Step 1 Write two 3- or 4-digit numbers you can subtract using mental math.

__________ – __________ = __________

Step 2 Write a story problem using the numbers from *Step 1*.
Make sure it is a subtraction problem.

____

____

____

____

Step 3 Solve the problem.

____

____

____

____

Step 4 What strategy did you use? Why?

____

____

____

____

Name ____________________ Date _______________

Master 2.18

Step-by-Step 6

Lesson 6, Question 5

Use the digits 1 to 9. Use each digit once.

Step 1 What is the greatest 4-digit number you can make? ___ ___ ___ ___

What is the least 4-digit number you can make? ___ ___ ___ ___

Step 2 Write the numbers from *Step 1* below.
What is the difference between the greatest and the least 4-digit numbers?

	□	□	□	□
–	□	□	□	□

Step 3 Write another 4-digit number. ___ ___ ___ ___

Step 4 Write a different 4-digit number that is as close as possible to the number in *Step 3*. ___ ___ ___ ___

Step 5 Write the numbers from *Steps 3* and *4* in the boxes below.
What is their difference?

	□	□	□	□
–	□	□	□	□

Step 6 Can you find 2 numbers with a difference that is less than your answer in *Step 5*? If so, find the numbers.

	□	□	□	□
–	□	□	□	□

Step 7 How did you decide where to place the digits?

____

____

Name ____________________ Date ______________

Master 2.19 **Step-by-Step 7**

Lesson 7, Question 8

You will need counters.

Step 1 Make an array to show 1×12.
Record the array.
Circle 2 groups of 6 counters
to show 1×6 two times.

Step 2 Make an array to show 2×12.
Record the array.
Circle 2 groups of 12 counters
to show 2×6 two times.

Step 3 Make an array to show 3×12.
Record the array.
Circle 3 groups of 12 counters
to show 2×6 three times.

Step 4 Kayla finds the multiplication facts for 12 by doubling the multiplication facts for 6.
Does Kayla's strategy work?
How do you know?

____

____

____

____

Name ____________________ Date ________________

Master 2.20

Step-by-Step 8

Lesson 8, Question 5

Step 1 How many seconds are in 1 minute? _______________

Step 2 A ruby-throated hummingbird flaps its wings about 60 times each second. How many times would it flap its wings in 1 minute?

____

Step 3 How many minutes are in 1 hour? _______________

Step 4 How many times does the hummingbird flap its wings in 1 hour?

____

Name ____________________ Date ________________

Master 2.21

Step-by-Step 9

Lesson 9, Question 4

Step 1 Use mental math. Find the product 16×100. ________________________

Step 2 What is the difference between 100 and 99? __________

Step 3 How can you use your answer from *Step 1* to find the product 16×99?

____

Use this result to find the product 16×99.

____

Step 4 Find each product.

$10 \times 99 =$ ______

$6 \times 99 =$ ______

Step 5 How can you use the products from *Step 4* to find the product 16×99?

____

____

Use these products to find the product 16×99.

____

Step 6 Describe the 2 strategies you used to find the product 16×99.

____

____

____

____

____

____

Name ________________ Date ______________

Master 2.22

Step-by-Step 10

Lesson 10, Question 7

Step 1 Draw an array to show 45 × 23.

Step 2 Draw a line to break the array from *Step 1* into 2 smaller arrays.
The 2 smaller arrays should represent products that are easy to find.
Write down 2 products from *Step 2*.
_______ × _______ = _______ and _______ × _______ = _______

How did you decide where to draw the line?

____

____

Step 3 Use your results from *Step 2*.
Find the product 45 × 23.

____

Name ____________________ Date ________________

Master 2.23

Step-by-Step 11

Lesson 11, Question 6

Step 1 Find each quotient.

$32 \div 4 =$ ______ $36 \div 4 =$ ______

$3200 \div 4 =$ ______ $3600 \div 4 =$ ______

Step 2 Use the quotients from *Step 1* to help you estimate the quotient $3495 \div 4$.

____

____

Step 3 When Tyler estimated $3495 \div 4$, he wrote these statements:

- The quotient is between 800 and 900.
- The quotient is greater than 850.

Look at the second set of quotients you found in *Step 1*.
Explain how Tyler might have made his estimates.

____

____

____

____

Name ____________________ Date ________________

Master 2.24

Step-by-Step 12

Lesson 12, Question 8

Use the digits 8, 6, 1, and 4. Use each digit once.

Step 1 Write all the 4-digit numbers you can make with 8 in the thousands place.

____

Step 2 Divide each number from *Step 1* by 7.
List all the numbers that are divisible by 7 with no remainder.

____

Step 3 Repeat *Step 1*. This time write all the 4-digit numbers you can make with each remaining digit in the thousands place: 6, then 4, then 1.

____

____

____

Step 4 Divide each number from *Step 3* by 7.
List all the numbers that are divisible by 7 with no remainder.

____

____

____

Step 5 How do you know you have found all the 4-digit numbers made from the digits 8, 6,1, 4 that are divisible by 7 with no remainder?

____

____

____

Name ____________________ Date ______________

Master 2.25

Step-by-Step 13

Lesson 13, Question 4

Step 1 How many seconds are in 1 minute? __________

Step 2 A cheetah runs 29 m every second.
How far does the cheetah run in 1 minute?

__________ × __________ = __________

Step 3 Connor runs 150 m in 1 minute.
How much farther than Connor will the cheetah run in 1 minute?

__________ – __________ = __________

How did you find out?

____

____

Name ____________________ Date ________________

Master 2.26a

Unit Test: Unit 2 Whole Numbers

Part A

1. Write each number in standard form.

a) 400 000 + 2000 + 30 + 7

____

b) four hundred twenty thousand thirteen

____

c) 40 000 + 2000 + 300 + 30 + 7

____

2. Order the numbers in question 1 from least to greatest.

____

3. Find each sum.

a) $\begin{array}{r} 8759 \\ +\,1997 \\ \hline \end{array}$ **b)** $\begin{array}{r} 7537 \\ +\,2026 \\ \hline \end{array}$ **c)** $\begin{array}{r} 2792 \\ 3476 \\ +\;\;984 \\ \hline \end{array}$

4. Find each difference.

a) $\begin{array}{r} 7006 \\ -\,3903 \\ \hline \end{array}$ **b)** $\begin{array}{r} 9867 \\ -\,3782 \\ \hline \end{array}$ **c)** $\begin{array}{r} 7465 \\ -\,2342 \\ \hline \end{array}$

5. Multiply.

a) 12×900 **b)** 80×30 **c)** 18×16 **d)** 7×8000

e) $\begin{array}{r} 52 \\ \times\,25 \\ \hline \end{array}$ **f)** $\begin{array}{r} 47 \\ \times\,21 \\ \hline \end{array}$ **g)** $\begin{array}{r} 398 \\ \times\;\;5 \\ \hline \end{array}$ **h)** $\begin{array}{r} 64 \\ \times\,27 \\ \hline \end{array}$

Name ____________________ Date ________________

Master 2.26b

Unit Test continued

6. Find each quotient.
Estimate to check if your answer is reasonable.

a) $6876 \div 5$ **b)** $8406 \div 9$ **c)** $3817 \div 6$ **d)** $9106 \div 8$

Part B

7. a) Arrange the digits 5, 7, 8, 9 to make a 4-digit number.
Use each digit only once.
What is the greatest number you can make? The least number?

____

____

b) Use your numbers from part a.
Find the sum and the difference of the numbers.

____

____

8. A plant can produce 9 strawberries.
These are packed 27 strawberries to a basket.
How many plants will it take to produce 30 baskets of strawberries?

____

____

____

Name ________________ Date ____________

Master 2.26c

Unit Test continued

Part C

9. Katrina has a collection of marbles.
When she places them in groups of 4, she has 3 left over.
When she places them in groups of 5, she has 2 left over.
She has more than 100 marbles, but fewer than 150 marbles.
How many marbles might Katrina have?

____

____

____

____

____

____

Name ____________________ Date ______________

Master 2.27

Sample Answers

Unit Test – Master 2.26

Part A

1. **a)** 402 037 **b)** 420 013 **c)** 42 337

2. 42 337, 402 027, 420 013

3. **a)** 10 756 **b)** 9563 **c)** 7252

4. **a)** 3103 **b)** 6085 **c)** 5123

5. **a)** 10 800 **b)** 2400 **c)** 288
   d) 56 000 **e)** 1300 **f)** 987
   g) 1990 **h)** 1728

6. **a)** 1375 R1 **b)** 934 **c)** 636 R1
   d) 1138 R2

Part B

7. **a)** 9875; 5789
   b) 15 664; 4086

8. 90 plants

Part C

9. Katrina might have 107, 127, or 147 marbles.

Extra Practice Masters 2.28–2.35

Go to the CD-ROM to access editable versions of these Extra Practice Masters.

Name ________ Date ________

Master 2.28 **Extra Practice 1**

Lesson 1: Representing, Comparing, and Ordering Numbers

1. Write each number in standard form.
   a) 300 000 + 2000 + 600 + 40 + 6
   b) five hundred thousand seven hundred twelve
2. Write 990 009 in expanded form and in words.
3. Order the numbers from least to greatest.
   968 342, 689 342, 98 342
4. Write the greatest number with each pattern of even (e) and odd (o) digits.
   Use each digit only once.
   a) eoe oeo b) oee oee

Lesson 2: Using Mental Math to Add

1. Hakim estimated 5285 + 1760 as 7100.
   Is his estimate reasonable? How do you know?
2. Use mental math to add.
   a) 6004 + 3755 b) 4215 + 673 c) 5995 + 8464
   d) 7439 + 370 e) 1492 + 2950 f) 6250 + 2970

Name ________ Date ________

Master 2.29 **Extra Practice 2**

Lesson 3: Adding 3- and 4-Digit Numbers

1. Add. Estimate to check if your answer is reasonable.
   a) 8689 + 798 b) 6877 + 2364 c) 4062 + 859 d) 6953 + 5241
2. The coastline of the island of Newfoundland is 9654 km long.
   Labrador's coastline is 7886 km.
   How many kilometres of coastline are there in the province of Newfoundland and Labrador?
3. Fitch St. School recycled 3285 aluminum tabs.
   Quaker Rd. School recycled 4978 aluminum tabs.
   How many aluminum tabs did the 2 schools recycle altogether?

Lesson 4: Adding Three Numbers

1. Add. Check by adding in a different order.
   a) 1765 + 7447 + 996 b) 5374 + 1697 + 3812 c) 2385 + 3025 + 8200 d) 3295 + 4068 + 7871
2. The students of Wigg School held 3 fundraisers this year.
   The first fundraiser raised $2974.
   The second one raised $4156.
   The third one raised $6744.
   How much money did the students of Wigg School raise this year?

Name ________ Date ________

Master 2.30 **Extra Practice 3**

Lesson 5: Using Mental Math to Subtract

1. Use mental math to subtract.
   a) 5286 – 2004 b) 6973 – 861 c) 7004 – 3050
   d) 4632 – 997 e) 4635 – 1980 f) 4800 – 1750
2. Michelle had $4328 in her chequing account.
   She wrote a cheque for $1003 to pay for car repairs.
   How much money does Michelle have in her chequing account now?

Lesson 6: Subtracting with 4-Digit Numbers

1. Subtract. Use addition to check if your answer is correct.
   a) 9610 – 2312 b) 4006 – 1775 c) 7000 – 1437 d) 5432 – 4654
2. a) Mount Logan has an elevation of 5959 m.
   Fairweather Mountain has an elevation of 4663 m.
   How much higher is Mount Logan than Fairweather Mountain?
   b) Cirque Mountain has an elevation of 1568 m.
   How much higher is Fairweather Mountain than Cirque Mountain?

Name ________ Date ________

Master 2.31 **Extra Practice 4**

Lesson 7: Multiplication and Division Facts to 144

1. How many eggs are in 9 dozen?
2. Write four related facts for each set of numbers.
   a) 5, 12, 60 b) 11, 7, 77
3. How does knowing the product 6 × 7 help you find the product 12 × 7?

Lesson 8: Multiplying with Multiples of 10

1. Multiply.
   a) 7 × 700 b) 90 × 80 c) 12 × 600 d) 30 × 50
2. There are 100 cm in 1 m.
   A piece of fabric is 12 m long.
   How many centimetres is that?
3. Rhianna puts eight $20 bills and fifteen $10 bills into a cash register.
   How much money did she put in the cash register?

Name ________ Date ________

Master 2.32 **Extra Practice 5**

Lesson 9: Using Mental Math to Multiply

1. Use mental math to multiply.
   a) 7 × 397 b) 9 × 502 c) 48 × 25 d) 11 × 62
2. Suhail has thirty-five $10 bills and one hundred three $5 bills.
   How much money does Suhail have?
3. A tile floor has 16 rows of tiles.
   There are 26 tiles in each row.
   How many tiles are in the floor?

Lesson 10: Multiplying 2-Digit Numbers

1. Multiply.
   a) 84 × 44 b) 41 × 87 c) 45 × 37 d) 83 × 70
2. Katelyn made a jigsaw puzzle with 24 rows of 29 pieces.
   Lauren made a puzzle with 26 rows of 27 pieces.
   Whose puzzle has more pieces? How many more?
3. A tile wall has 336 tiles.
   How many rows of tiles might it have?
   How many tiles would be in each row?

Name ________ Date ________

Master 2.33 **Extra Practice 6**

Lesson 11: Estimating Quotients

1. Estimate each quotient.
   a) 4835 ÷ 8 b) 2015 ÷ 5 c) 1897 ÷ 7
   d) 2968 ÷ 4 e) 5038 ÷ 9 f) 4202 ÷ 6
2. Ethna wants to make 4 identical structures using 585 building blocks.
   About how many blocks will be in each structure?
3. Use mental math to divide.
   a) 276 ÷ 3 b) 468 ÷ 9 c) 128 ÷ 4 d) 301 ÷ 7

Lesson 12: Dividing with Whole Numbers

1. Find each quotient greater than 99.
   a) 2640 ÷ 3 b) 5887 ÷ 7 c) 6396 ÷ 4 d) 1744 ÷ 8
2. In a 5-day week, a factory makes 6385 bicycles.
   Suppose the same number of bicycles is made each day.
   How many bicycles are made each day?
3. Find each quotient greater than 1000.
   a) 9258 ÷ 6 b) 3760 ÷ 5 c) 3884 ÷ 2 d) 9308 ÷ 4

Name ________ Date ________

Master 2.34 **Extra Practice 7**

Lesson 13: Solving Problems

1. Tickets to a school play cost $8 for adults and $5 for children.
   Suppose 60 adult tickets and 45 children's tickets were sold.
   How much money was made on the sale of tickets?
2. Katherine's dog, Blackie, eats 21 kg of dog kibble in 3 weeks.
   How much kibble will he eat in 10 weeks?
3. A local restaurant held a draw last weekend.
   Tickets cost $6.
   Two hundred forty-three tickets were sold on Friday,
   397 on Saturday, and 132 on Sunday.
   How much money was collected altogether?

Name ________ Date ________

Master 2.35 **Sample Answers**

Extra Practice 1 – Master 2.28

Lesson 1
1. a) 302 646 b) 500 712
2. 900 000 + 90 000 + 9
   nine hundred ninety thousand nine
3. 98 342, 689 342, 968 342
4. a) 896 745 b) 986 742

Lesson 2
1. Hakim's estimate is reasonable; rounding both numbers to the nearest hundred gives 5300 and 1800: 5300 + 1800 = 7100
2. a) 9759 b) 4888
   c) 14 459 d) 7809
   e) 4442 f) 9220

Extra Practice 2 – Master 2.29

Lesson 3
1. a) 9487 b) 9241
   c) 4921 d) 12 194
2. 17 540 km
3. 8263

Lesson 4
1. a) 10 208 b) 10 883
   c) 13 610 d) 15 234
2. $13 874

Extra Practice 3 – Master 2.30

Lesson 5
1. a) 3282 b) 6112 c) 3954
   d) 3635 e) 2655 f) 2850
2. Michelle has $3325 left in her account.

Lesson 6
1. a) 7298 b) 2231
   c) 5563 d) 778
2. a) 1296 m b) 3095 m

Extra Practice 4 – Master 2.31

Lesson 7
1. 108
2. a) 5 × 12 = 60, 12 × 5 = 60, 60 ÷ 5 = 12, 60 ÷ 12 = 5
   b) 11 × 7 = 77, 7 × 11 = 77, 77 ÷ 7 = 11, 77 ÷ 11 = 7
3. 6 × 7 = 42, so 12 × 7 = 2 × 6 × 7 = 2 × 42 = 84

Lesson 8
1. a) 4900 b) 7200
   c) 7200 d) 1500
2. 1200 cm
3. $310

Extra Practice 5 – Master 2.32

Lesson 9
1. a) 2779 b) 4518
   c) 1200 d) 682
2. $865
3. 416 tiles

Lesson 10
1. a) 3696 b) 3567
   c) 1665 d) 5810
2. Lauren's; 6
3. For example, there may be 12 rows of tiles; each row would have 28 tiles.

Extra Practice 6 – Master 2.33

Lesson 11
1. a) About 600
   b) About 400
   c) About 300
   d) About 700
   e) About 600
   f) About 700
2. About 150
3. a) 92 b) 52
   c) 32 d) 43

Lesson 12
1. a) 880 b) 841 c) 1599 d) 218
2. 1277 bicycles
3. a) 1543 c) 1942 d) 2327

Extra Practice 7 – Master 2.34

Lesson 13
1. $705
2. 70 kg
3. $4632

Addison Wesley
Mathematics
Makes Sense

Program Authors

Peggy Morrow
Ralph Connelly
Bryn Keyes
Jason Johnston
Steve Thomas
Jeananne Thomas
Angela D'Alessandro
Maggie Martin Connell
Don Jones
Michael Davis
Sharon Jeroski
Trevor Brown
Nora Alexander
Cynthia Pratt Nicolson

Printed and bound in Canada

8 9 MP 18 17

PEARSON
Education Canada

ADDISON WESLEY

Ontario

Math Makes Sense 5

Ontario

Teacher Guide

Unit 3: Geometry

PEARSON
Addison Wesley

UNIT 3

Geometry

"Geometry provides a rich context for the development of mathematical reasoning, including inductive and deductive reasoning, making and validating conjectures, and classifying and defining geometric objects."

– NCTM, 2000

FOCUS STRAND
Geometry and Spatial Sense

SUPPORTING STRAND
Measurement

Mathematics Background

What Are the Big Ideas?

- Figures can be classified by attributes, such as the number of sides, the number of parallel sides, the number of equal sides, and angle measure.
- Polygons can be named by their vertices.
- Angles can be measured and constructed using a protractor.
- Triangles can be constructed given side and angle measures.
- Triangles can have congruent angles but be different sizes
- Changing the size of an angle in a triangle changes the lengths of one or more sides. Changing the length of a side in a triangle changes the size of one or more angles.
- Nets show all the faces of a solid, joined in one piece.
- Computer applications can be used to create nets.

How Will the Concepts Develop?

Students measure side lengths of a variety of polygons. They name and sort polygons by the number of sides and by side length.

Students use a protractor to measure and construct angles. They classify angles according to the size of the angles.

Students measure the interior angles in a variety of polygons. They name and sort polygons by the number of angles and by angle measure.

Students use a variety of materials to construct triangles. Students determine if a triangle is possible given side and/or angle measures.

Students identify whether a figure is a net of a solid. They match a net to the solid it represents. Students construct nets of cubes and pyramids.

Why Are These Concepts Important?

Exploring geometric concepts and figures helps students develop relationships between and among different figures. As students explore geometry, they develop spatial sense. This allows them to visualize figures and objects and to "see" an entire object from a two-dimensional drawing of the object. As students sort and classify geometric figures, they develop their logic and reasoning skills. These skills can be applied in other branches of mathematics and in other disciplines.

Curriculum Overview

Cluster 1: Classifying Polygons

Overall Expectations

- Identify, describe, compare, and classify geometric figures. (5m65)
- Use mathematical language effectively to describe geometric concepts, reasoning, and investigations. (5m70)

Specific Expectations

- Sort polygons according to the number of sides, angles, and vertices. (5m75)
- Classify two-dimensional shapes according to angle and side properties. (5m76)
- Measure and construct angles using a protractor. (5m78)
- Use mathematical language to describe geometric ideas. (5m82)
- Discuss geometric concepts with peers and use mathematical language to explain their understanding of the concepts. (5m84)
- Discuss ideas, make conjectures, and articulate hypotheses about geometric properties and relationships. (5m85)

Launch
Bridges

Lesson 1:
Naming and Sorting Polygons by Sides

Lesson 2:
Measuring and Constructing Angles

Lesson 3:
Strategies Toolkit

Lesson 4:
Naming and Sorting Polygons by Angles

Cluster 2: Constructing Figures

Overall Expectation

- Draw and build three-dimensional objects and models. (5m66)

Specific Expectations

- Identify nets for a variety of polyhedra from drawings while holding three-dimensional figures in their hands. (5m71)
- Construct nets of cubes and pyramids using a variety of materials. (5m72)
- Sketch the faces that make up a three-dimensional figure by looking at a three-dimensional figure. (5m73)
- Construct triangles given specific measures of angles and sides, using a variety of tools. (5m79)
- Use a computer application to explore and extend geometric concepts. (5m81)

Lesson 5:
Constructing Triangles

Lesson 6:
Making Nets

Technology:
Using a Computer to Explore Nets

Show What You Know

Unit Problem
Bridges

Curriculum across the Grades

Grade 4	Grade 5	Grade 6
Students measure angles using a protractor. They identify and sort quadrilaterals. Students sort and classify two-dimensional figures according to shape. They identify and sketch the two-dimensional shapes of the faces of three-dimensional figures. Students identify similar and congruent figures and construct congruent figures in a variety of ways. Students design and make skeletons for three-dimensional figures. They model three-dimensional figures of specific volumes using blocks.	Students identify nets for a variety of polyhedra from drawings while holding three-dimensional figures in their hands. Students construct nets of cubes and pyramids using a variety of materials. Students sketch the faces that make up a three-dimensional figure by looking at a three-dimensional figure. Students sort polygons according to the number of sides, angles, and vertices. Students classify two-dimensional shapes according to angle and side properties. Students measure and construct angles using a protractor. Students construct triangles given specific measures of angles and sides, using a variety of tools. Students use a computer application to explore and extend geometric concepts. Students use mathematical language to describe geometric ideas. Students discuss geometric concepts with peers and use mathematical language to explain their understanding of the concepts. Students discuss ideas, make conjectures, and articulate hypotheses about geometric properties and relationships.	Students identify nets for polyhedra from drawings by visualizing the two-dimensional faces of the three-dimensional figures. Students design nets of cubes and pyramids using grid and isometric dot paper. Students sketch the net for a three-dimensional figure. Students build a figure with interlocking cubes and record the design on isometric dot paper. Students classify two-dimensional shapes according to angle and side properties. Students estimate the size of angles. Students construct a variety of two-dimensional shapes given specific measures of angles and sides. Students use a computer application to explore and extend geometric concepts. Students use mathematical language to describe geometric ideas. Students recognize and describe geometric properties and principles in the everyday world. Students discuss geometric concepts using mathematical language. Students explain, make conjectures about, and articulate hypotheses about geometric properties and relationships.

Additional Activities

Partner Polygons

For Extra Practice (Appropriate for use after Lesson 4)
Materials: *Partner Polygons* (Master 3.10), 2-m lengths of fabric elastic, index cards

The work students do: Students work with a group to brainstorm a list of attributes of polygons. They record the attributes from their list on index cards. Students take turns to select a card. They hold a loop of elastic and use it to model a polygon with the attribute described on the card.

Take It Further: Have students model the next polygon using the fewest moves. A move consists of moving only one hand.

Kinesthetic/Social
Group Activity

Pattern Block Properties

For Extra Support (Appropriate for use after Lesson 4)
Materials: *Pattern Block Properties* (Master 3.11), Pattern Blocks, brown paper bags

The work students do: Students work with a partner. They place the Pattern Blocks into the bag. Students take turns to think of a Pattern Block and describe it to their partner, without telling which block it is. Without looking, their partner reaches into the bag try to find the Pattern Block that matches the description.

Take It Further: Have students take turns to think of a polygon. Without telling the name of the polygon, they describe the polygon to their partner. Their partner tries to sketch the polygon described.

Logical/Mathematical
Partner Activity

Explore Paper Triangles

For Extra Practice (Appropriate for use after Lesson 5)
Materials: *Exploring Paper Triangles* (Master 3.12), scissors, paper, rulers, protractors

The work students do: Students work with a partner. They cut out a large triangle from paper. Students measure and record the side lengths and angles. They fold the paper once, parallel to any side. Students measure and record the new side lengths and the angles. They compare the side and angle measures of the original triangle to those of the new triangle.

Take It Further: Have students try different types of triangles and describe what they notice.

Visual/Spatial
Individual Activity

Making Angles and Triangles

For Extension (Appropriate for use after Lesson 5)
Materials: *Making Angles and Triangles* (Master 3.13), paper, scissors, protractors, rulers

The work students do: Students work on their own. They fold, then cut, a piece of paper to make a square. The fold line is one diagonal of the square. Students fold the paper to make the other diagonal. They fold their paper square into 8, then cut a piece from the fold. When they unfold, they describe the cut shapes they see and explain the number.

Take It Further: Students experiment to determine how to make a 90° angle by folding any scrap of paper.

Kinesthetic
Individual Activity

Planning for Unit 3

Planning for Instruction

Suggested Unit time: 2 weeks

Lesson	Time	Materials	Program Support
Launch: Bridges, page 2	15–20 min		
Lesson 1: Naming and Sorting Polygons by Sides, page 4 Name and sort polygons by number of sides and by side length.	40–50 min	millimetre rulers scissors triangles geoboards and geobands square dot paper drinking straws pipe cleaners	PM 25: Square Dot Paper Master 3.6: Triangles for Lesson 1 Master 3.14: Step-by-Step 1 Master 3.21: Extra Practice 1
Lesson 2: Measuring and Constructing Triangles, page 8 Use a protractor to measure and construct angles.	40–50 min	clear protractor overhead projector blank transparency overhead markers millimetre rulers protractors geoboards and geobands square dot paper	PM 25: Square Dot Paper Master 3.15: Step-by-Step 2 Master 3.21: Extra Practice 1
Lesson 3: Strategies Toolkit, page 12 Interpret a problem and select an appropriate strategy.	40–50 min	tangrams Pattern Blocks protractors	PM 29: Tangram PM 28: Pattern Blocks
Lesson 4: Naming and Sorting Polygons by Angles, page 14 Name and sort polygons by number of angles and by angle measure.	40–50 min	clear protractor overhead projector blank transparency overhead markers triangles protractors geoboards and geobands square dot paper millimetre rulers	PM 25: Square Dot Paper Master 3.7: Triangles for Lesson 4 Master 3.16: Step-by-Step 4 Master 3.22: Extra Practice 2
Lesson 5: Constructing Triangles, page 18 Construct triangles given side and angle measures.	40–50 min	overhead projector clear protractor millimetre rulers triangles from a geometry set protractors geoboards and geobands square dot paper	PM 25: Square Dot Paper Master 3.17: Step-by-Step 5 Master 3.22: Extra Practice 2
Lesson 6: Making Nets, page 22 Identify and construct nets of solids.	40–50 min	models of solids pyramids cubes tape millimetre rulers scissors	Master 3.18: Step-by-Step 6 Master 3.23: Extra Practice 3
Technology: Using a Computer to Explore Nets, page 26 Use a computer to create nets.	40–50 min	computer with *AppleWorks* or *The Geometer's Sketchpad*	
Game: What's My Rule?, page 29	40–50 min	scissors labels, string	Master 3.8: What's My Rule? Game Cards
Show What You Know, page 30 Assessment	40–50 min	protractors millimetre rulers	
Unit Problem: Bridges, page 32 Assessment	40–50 min	Bristol board hole punches or compasses paper fasteners centimetre rulers centimetre cubes or standard masses	Master 3.9: Truss Pieces

Planning for Assessment

Purpose	Tools and Process	Recording and Reporting
Diagnostic	*Unit Launch* Question; conference; scaffold problems throughout the unit	PM 8: Conference Prompts
Formative	*Explore* – Ongoing Assessment: Observe and Listen Prompt student's self-assessment *Practice* – Assessment Focus Questions Review student work; provide feedback; scaffold as needed; select key pieces	Master 3.2 Ongoing Observations: Geometry PM 1: Inquiry Process Check List PM 6: Observation Record 1 PM 7: Observation Record 2 PM 8: Conference Prompts PM 2: Self-Assessment PM 3: Self-Assessment: Problem Solving PM 9: Work Sample Records
Summative	*Show What You Know* *Unit Problem* – Performance Assessment Unit Test Review assessment records; add unit results to ongoing records	Master 3.1 Unit Rubric: Geometry Master 3.3 Performance Assessment Rubric: Bridges Master 3.4 Unit Summary: Geometry PM 10: Summary Class Records: Strands PM 11: Summary Class Records: Achievement Categories PM 12: Summary Record: Individual
Learning Skills/Mathematical Disposition	Observe and record throughout the unit	PM 4: Learning Skills Check List PM 5: Mathematical Dispositions and Learning Skills

Program Masters (PM) are in the *Grade 5 Planning and Program Masters* module.
Extra Practice Masters are on the CD-ROM.

Bridges

LESSON ORGANIZER

15–20 min

Curriculum Focus: Activate prior learning about two-dimensional figures, their names and attributes.
Vocabulary: triangles, mass

ASSUMED PRIOR KNOWLEDGE

- ☑ Students can identify and name triangles and other two-dimensional figures.
- ☑ Students can describe the attributes of two-dimensional figures.

ACTIVATE PRIOR LEARNING

Invite students to examine the various truss bridges pictured on page 78 of the Student Book.

Ask students if they have seen any examples of these kinds of bridges, and if so, where?
(*In rural areas to carry cars over small river valleys*)

Ask:

- What other types of bridges do you know of?
  (*Suspension, arch, beam, cable-stayed, cantilever*)
- Why do you think truss bridges are so common?
  (*They are light, strong, and rigid, and look like they would not cost much to build.*)

Discuss the questions in the first bullet in the Student Book.

Record students' answers on chart paper, so they can be referred to in the *Unit Problem*.

(*The most common figure is the triangle. In the Pratt Truss, I see 9 triangles — 3 large and 6 small. In the Double Warren Truss, I see 20 triangles. In the Howe Truss, I see 7 triangles. I see 24 triangles in the Howe Truss with counter braces.*)

Discuss the questions in the second bullet in the Student Book.
(*I see trapezoids, parallelograms, rectangles, and squares in all the trusses. Some of the squares are congruent. Some of the parallelograms have different sizes and are not similar.*)

Discuss the last bullet in the Student Book.
(*The Howe truss with counter braces looks more rigid and solid. I think it could support the greatest mass.*)

Discuss the Learning Goals. Tell students that they will use these skills at the end of the unit to construct a truss bridge.

These are different types of truss bridges.

They were built during the great age of trains, about a hundred years ago.

A truss is a framework.

It is made of wooden beams or metal bars.

The bridges are light, strong, and rigid.

- What is the most common geometric figure you see in the bridges?
  How many triangles can you count in each bridge?
  How are the triangles the same?
  How are they different?
- What other geometric figures do you see?
  How are they the same? How are they different?
- Which bridge do you think would support the greatest mass? Why?

Key Words

polygon
equilateral triangle
isosceles triangle
scalene triangle
acute angle
right angle
obtuse angle
perpendicular
acute triangle
right triangle
obtuse triangle
regular polygon
irregular polygon
net

79

LITERATURE CONNECTIONS FOR THE UNIT

Bridges by Etta Kaner. Kids Can Press 1994.
ISBN: 1550741462
Well illustrated, students can read all about the different types of bridge constructions and their varied uses. Directions are given to build these bridges usually from readily found materials.

Bridge to Terabithia by Katherine Paterson. Trophy 2003.
ISBN: 0064401847
The use of the bridge as a metaphor is the focus in this award-winning novel. Jess Aarons had to be the fastest runner at Lark Creek Elementary School. But when he was challenged by Leslie Burke, a girl, that was just the beginning of a new season in Jess's life. Leslie and her parents were newcomers to the rural community where Jess lived. They were thought to be a bit odd, for they didn't even own a TV, though their house was filled with books.

DIAGNOSTIC ASSESSMENT

What to Look For	What to Do
✔ Students can identify and name triangles and other two-dimensional figures. ✔ Students can describe the attributes of two-dimensional figures.	***Extra Support:*** Some students may have difficulty seeing triangles within triangles. Use the large and small right triangles from several Tangram sets. Manipulate the triangles to show how two triangles can go together to form another larger triangle. *Work on this skill during Lessons 1, 3, and 5.* Some students having difficulty recognizing figures may need to manipulate Pattern Blocks to see how larger, more complex figures may be constructed by combining smaller figures. *Work on this skill during Lessons 3 and 6.*

Naming and Sorting Polygons By Sides

LESSON ORGANIZER — 40–50 min

Curriculum Focus: Name and sort polygons by number of sides and by side length. (5m75, 5m76)

Student Materials
- millimetre rulers
- scissors
- Triangles for Lesson 1 (Master 3.6)
- geoboards and geobands
- square dot paper (PM 25)
- drinking straws
- pipe cleaners

Optional
- Step-by-Step 1 (Master 3.14)
- Extra Practice 1 (Master 3.21)

Vocabulary: polygon, quadrilateral, rectangle, parallelogram, trapezoid, kite, pentagon, hexagon, octagon, equilateral triangle, isosceles triangle, scalene triangle

Assessment: Master 3.2 Ongoing Observations: Geometry

Key Math Learnings
1. Polygons can be named by the number of sides and by side length.
2. Polygons can be named by their vertices.
3. Triangles can be named by the number of equal sides.

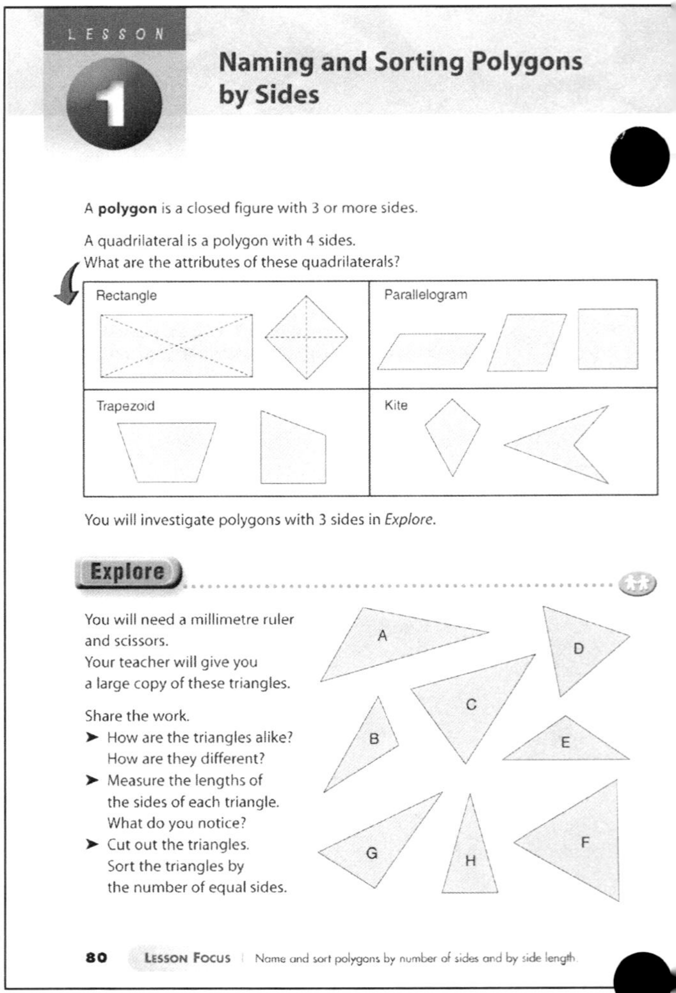
LESSON 1

Naming and Sorting Polygons by Sides

A **polygon** is a closed figure with 3 or more sides.

A quadrilateral is a polygon with 4 sides.
What are the attributes of these quadrilaterals?

You will investigate polygons with 3 sides in *Explore*.

Explore

You will need a millimetre ruler and scissors.
Your teacher will give you a large copy of these triangles.

Share the work.
- How are the triangles alike? How are they different?
- Measure the lengths of the sides of each triangle. What do you notice?
- Cut out the triangles. Sort the triangles by the number of equal sides.

80 LESSON FOCUS | Name and sort polygons by number of sides and by side length

BEFORE — Get Started

Have students look at the quadrilaterals at the top of page 80 in the Student Book. Ask:

- What attributes do all of these polygons share?
  (*They all have 4 sides and 4 angles.*)
- How are the quadrilaterals in each group alike? Different?
  (*All the rectangles have opposite sides equal, equal diagonals, and 4 square corners. The parallelograms have opposite sides parallel and equal, and opposite angles equal. The trapezoids have one pair of parallel sides. The kites have two pairs of adjacent sides equal and pairs of equal angles. Squares and rectangles are parallelograms with 4 equal angles.*)

Introduce *Explore*. Distribute copies of Master 3.6 to pairs of students. Suggest they record the side lengths on the interior of the triangles.

DURING — Explore

Ongoing Assessment: Observe and Listen

As students work, ask questions, such as:
- How are the triangles the same? How are they different?
  (*All the triangles have 3 sides. Some triangles have sides that appear to be equal; others have sides of obviously different lengths.*)
- What are the measures of the sides of the triangles?
  (*Answers should be to the nearest centimetre.*)
- What do you notice about the lengths of the sides of the triangles?
  (*Triangles A, B, and G have no sides equal. Triangles C, E, and H have 2 sides equal. Triangles D and F have all sides equal.*)

As well as measuring with a ruler, you may wish to have students use grid paper, paper folding, or other techniques to compare length of sides.

Show and Share

Compare your sorting with that of another pair of students.
…d you sort the triangles the same way? Explain.

Connect

Here are some ways to name polygons.

➤ Name polygons by the number of sides.

A triangle has 3 sides. | A pentagon has 5 sides. | A hexagon has 6 sides. | An octagon has 8 sides.

➤ Name polygons by their vertices.
Label each vertex with a different capital letter.

This is triangle ABC. | This is quadrilateral MNPQ.

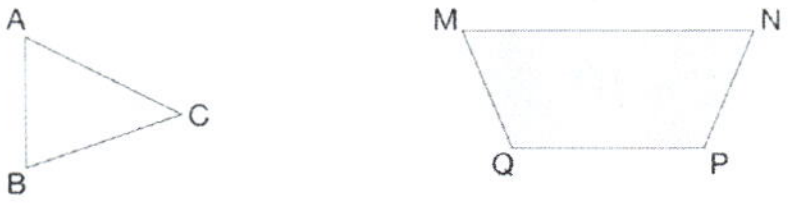

Use the letters to name the sides of the polygon.
Triangle ABC has 3 sides: AB, AC, and BC

➤ Name triangles by the number of equal sides.

An **equilateral triangle** has all sides equal. | An **isosceles triangle** has 2 sides equal. | A **scalene triangle** has no sides equal.

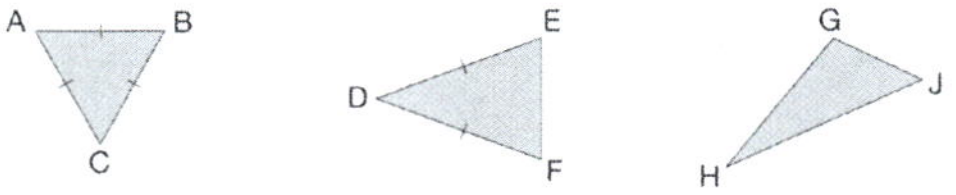

AB = BC = AC | DE = DF

81

REACHING ALL LEARNERS

Alternative Explore

Materials: Triangles for Lesson 1 (Master 3.6)
Students cut out each triangle. They fold the triangles to try to match sides with equal length. Students sort the triangles into groups according to how many different matching folds can be made. They describe the attributes of the triangles in each group.

Common Misconceptions

➤ Students may think all triangles in a particular group need to be congruent or similar.

How to Help: Begin with different-size equilateral triangles. Because the triangles are similar in shape, students will see they belong together. Fold the triangles to match equal sides. Students should see that the lengths of sides *within* the same triangle are all the same even though different triangles may be different sizes. Repeat with different isosceles triangles. Fold the triangles to match equal sides. Only two sides will match. When they fold scalene triangles no sides will match.

➤ Students think the vertical and horizontal distances between points on a geoboard are equal to the diagonal distance between points.

How to Help: Use a ruler to measure the diagonal distance and the horizontal and vertical distances on a geoboard. Measure the distances between points 5 units apart to illustrate the difference more dramatically. Then show the difference with shorter distances.

AFTER Connect

Invite students to share their strategies for sorting.

Ask:

- Why are there only 3 possibilities when you sort triangles by the number of equal sides? (*A triangle has 3 sides. There are only 3 possibilities: no equal sides, 2 equal sides, or 3 equal sides.*)

Review the names of the different polygons. Ask students to name objects that suggest each kind of polygon.

Ask:

- Why is it useful to name a polygon by its vertices? (*Naming a polygon by its vertices gives us an easy way to refer to the polygon. It also gives us a clear way to refer to the sides and angles in the polygon.*)

You may wish to have students sketch a polygon, label the vertices, and challenge their partners to touch the different sides as the name of each side is mentioned.

Practice

Questions 1 and 6 require geoboards, geobands, and square dot paper.

Question 5 requires drinking straws, scissors, a millimetre ruler, and pipe cleaners.

Encourage students to show their thinking in pictures, numbers, and words.

Assessment Focus: Question 5

Students should be able to explain their reasoning for each solution. Oral explanations and discussion should precede written explanations. Students should recognize there is only one possible equilateral triangle (with all sides 5 cm long). Students may construct

ESL Strategies

ESL students benefit from hearing vocabulary repeatedly with visual cues. Use the words frequently in dialogue and point to the word and illustrations from the text as often as possible. Try to associate new vocabulary with known words or ideas (for example, *equil*ateral has all sides *equal*, isosceles sounds like *I saw sillies* and think of 2 silly things, sca*lene* triangles appear to *lean* to one side).

Sample Answers

1. a) The student should make each triangle with all sides different length.
   b) The student should make each triangle with 2 sides equal.
   c) It is not possible to make an equilateral triangle on a geoboard with square arrays of pegs. The diagonal distance between points is longer than the horizontal and vertical distances between points.
3. b) Polygons D and F have 3 sides; polygons A and E have 4 sides; polygons B and C have 5 sides
   c) Polygons D and F have 3 vertices; polygons A and E have 4 vertices; polygons B and C have 5 vertices
   d) A polygon has the same numbers of vertices as sides.

Practice

1. Use a geoboard, geobands, and dot paper.
   a) Make 3 different scalene triangles.
   Record each triangle on dot paper.
   How do you know each triangle is scalene?
   b) Make 3 different isosceles triangles.
   Record each triangle on dot paper.
   How do you know each triangle is isosceles?
   c) Try to make an equilateral triangle.
   What do you notice?

2. Measure the sides of each triangle.
   Name each triangle as equilateral, isosceles, or scalene.

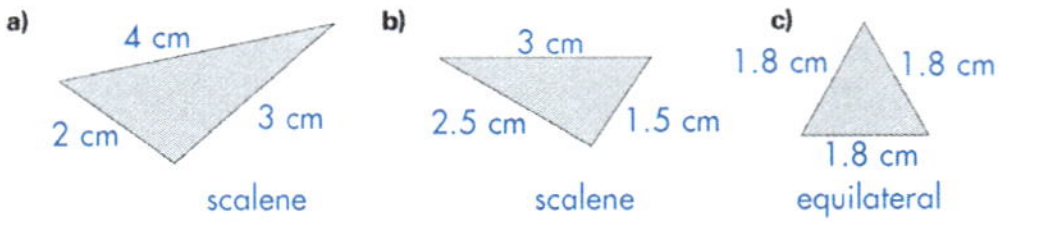

3. a) Name each polygon.

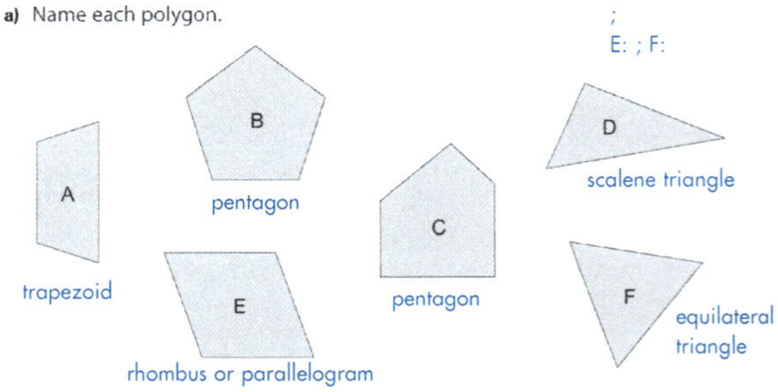

   b) Sort the polygons by the number of sides.
   c) Sort the polygons by the number of vertices.
   d) Compare the two sortings. What do you notice?
   Do you think this is always true? Explain.

82

different isosceles triangles, but should recognize that the triangle with the least perimeter will have the shortest sides. It is possible to construct different scalene triangles, but the triangle with the longest sides will have the greatest perimeter. Students should realize the longest straw must be shorter than the combined length of the other two straws to make a triangle. They should experiment with different combinations but do not need to exhaust all the possibilities.

4. a) Which triangles are isosceles? How do you know? ABC, DEF, RST

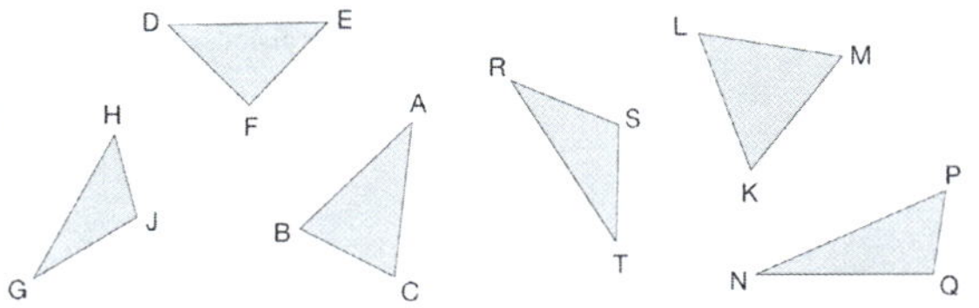

b) For each triangle, name the sides that are the same length. AB = AC; DF = FE; RS = ST

c) Find the perimeter of each triangle. ABC: 6.7 cm; DEF: 6.4 cm; GHJ: 6.1 cm; KLM: 7.2 cm; NPQ: 7.7 cm; RST: 7.0 cm

5. You need drinking straws, scissors, and pipe cleaners.
Cut the straws into 8 pieces as shown.
Use pieces of pipe cleaner as joiners.

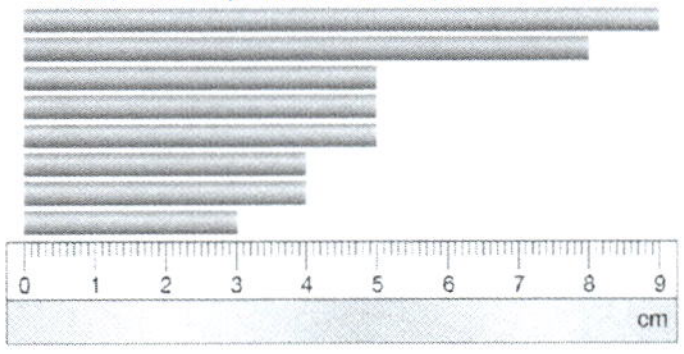

a) Make each triangle. Trace and label your results.
- an equilateral triangle
- an isosceles triangle with the least perimeter
- a scalene triangle with the greatest perimeter

b) Which straws could not be used together to make a triangle? Explain.

6. Use a geoboard, geobands, and dot paper.
a) Make an isosceles triangle. Record the triangle on dot paper.
b) Use the triangle from part a.
Change the triangle so it is scalene.
Describe the changes you made.

Numbers Every Day

Calculator Skills

Find 3 odd numbers that have a product of 693 and a sum of 27. 11, 9, 7

Reflect

How can you use side lengths to name a triangle? Use words and pictures to explain.

ASSESSMENT FOCUS | Question 5 **83**

4. a) Isosceles triangles have two sides equal.

5. a) There are only 3 straws with equal length. The equilateral triangle has sides 5 cm long.
To make the isosceles triangle with the least perimeter, I chose the shortest pair of straws with the same length and the shortest straw.
The side lengths are 4 cm, 4 cm, and 3 cm.
To make the scalene triangle with the greatest perimeter, I chose the 3 longest straws with different lengths.
The side lengths are 5 cm, 8cm, and 9cm.

b) Any combination of straws in which the longest straw is longer than or equal to the combined length of the other two will not make a triangle.
Triangles with these side lengths are not possible:
8, 3, 4; 8, 3, 5; 8, 4, 4; 9, 3, 4; 9, 3, 5; 9, 4, 4; 9, 5, 4.

6. To change an isosceles triangle to a scalene triangle, move one vertex until none of the sides are equal.

REFLECT: A triangle can be named by the number of equal sides it has. An equilateral triangle has 3 equal sides. An isosceles triangle has 2 equal sides. A scalene triangle has no equal sides.

Numbers Every Day

Students may find it helpful to write lists of 3 odd numbers with a sum of 27. They can systematically find the products of the numbers in each list.

ASSESSMENT FOR LEARNING

What to Look For	What to Do
Understanding concepts ✔ Students understand that polygons can be named by the number of sides and by side length. ✔ Students understand that triangles can be named by the number of equal sides (equilateral, isosceles, scalene). ***Applying procedures*** ✔ Students can sort and name polygons according to their side attributes.	***Extra Support:*** Students can use Step-by-Step 1 (Master 3.14) to complete question 5. ***Extra Practice:*** Have pairs of students take turns. One student describes a polygon, without naming it. The other student guesses the name of the polygon. Students can complete Extra Practice 1 (Master 3.21). ***Extension:*** Challenge students to find the number of different isosceles triangles they can make using a circular geoboard or circular dot paper.

Recording and Reporting
Master 3.2 Ongoing Observations: Geometry

LESSON 2

Measuring and Constructing Angles

LESSON ORGANIZER

40–50 min

Curriculum Focus: Use a protractor to measure and construct angles. (5m78)

Teacher Materials
- clear protractor
- overhead projector
- blank transparency
- overhead markers

Student Materials
- millimetre rulers
- protractors
- geoboards and geobands
- square dot paper (PM 25)

Optional
- Step-by-Step 2 (Master 3.15)
- Extra Practice 1 (Master 3.21)

Vocabulary: acute angle, right angle, obtuse angle, perpendicular

Assessment: Master 3.2 Ongoing Observations: Geometry

LESSON 2 **Measuring and Constructing Angles**

Is each angle greater than 90°, less than 90°, or equal to 90°?
What is the measure of each angle?

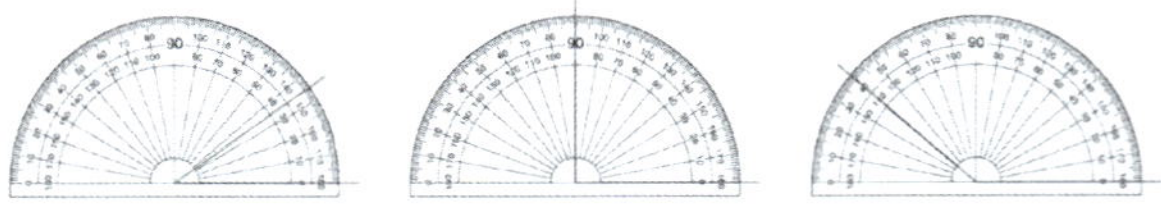

Explore

You will need a ruler and a protractor.

➤ Use a ruler to draw an angle.

➤ Have your partner:
- estimate the size of the angle, in degrees
- measure the angle with a protractor
- record the estimate and the angle measure

➤ Trade roles. Continue until you have 6 different angles.
Try to make angles that are less than 90°, greater than 90°, and equal to 90°.

➤ Order the angles from least to greatest.

Show and Share

Show your work to another pair of students.
How did you use the measure of one angle to estimate the measure of another angle?

84 LESSON FOCUS | Use a protractor to measure and construct angles.

Key Math Learnings

1. Angles can be measured and constructed using a protractor.
2. An angle can be named and sorted according to its measure.

BEFORE Get Started

Students may benefit from using their arms to model angles of different sizes. Ask:

- How could you model a 90° angle using your arms?
  (*I could extend one arm horizontally and the other arm vertically.*)
- How would you adjust your arms to model an angle less than 90°?
  (*I would move my arms closer together.*)
- How could you model an angle greater than 90°?
  (*I could start by modelling a 90° angle, then move my arms further apart.*)

Have pairs of students face one another. Call out different angles. Have students model each angle with their arms. Alternatively, have pairs of students use a length of string. One person holds one end and the middle of the string, the other person holds the other end.

Introduce *Explore*. Ensure students understand that they draw the angle with a ruler. They use the protractor to measure the size of the angle after they have estimated its size.

DURING Explore

Ongoing Assessment: Observe and Listen

As students work on the task, ask:

- What angles can you use as reference angles when estimating?
  (*0°, 45°, 90°, 135°, 180°*)
- Without measuring, how can you tell if an angle is greater than 90°, less than 90°, or equal to 90°?
  (*A 90° angle has a square corner. An angle greater than 90° has a greater distance between the arms than a 90° angle. An angle less than 90° has less distance between its arms than a 90° angle.*)

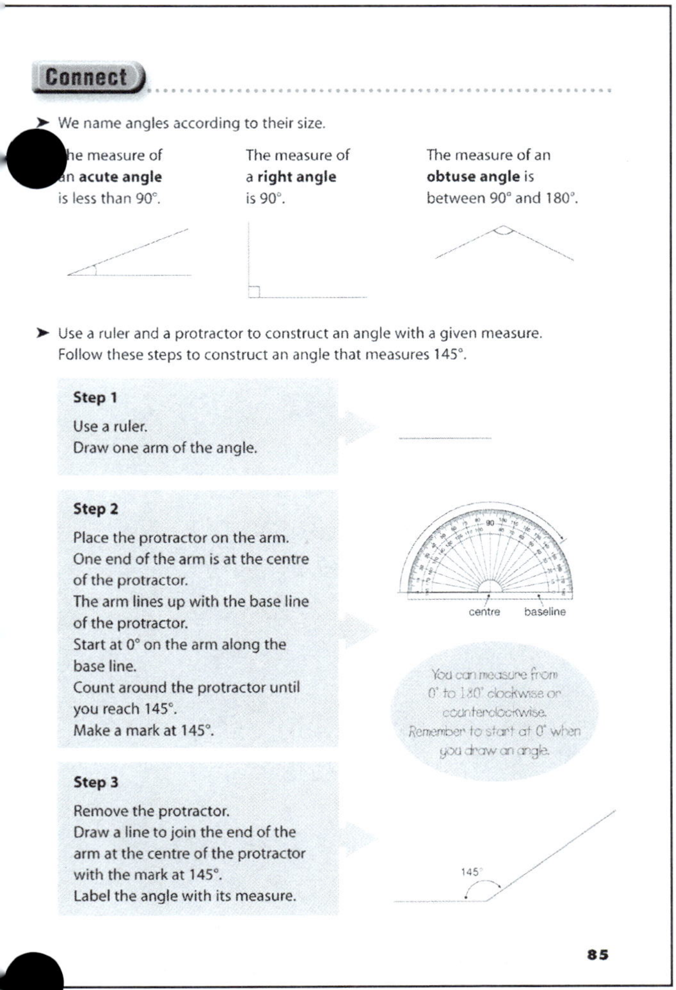

Connect

➤ We name angles according to their size.

The measure of an **acute angle** is less than 90°.

The measure of a **right angle** is 90°.

The measure of an **obtuse angle** is between 90° and 180°.

➤ Use a ruler and a protractor to construct an angle with a given measure.
Follow these steps to construct an angle that measures 145°.

Step 1
Use a ruler.
Draw one arm of the angle.

Step 2
Place the protractor on the arm.
One end of the arm is at the centre of the protractor.
The arm lines up with the base line of the protractor.
Start at 0° on the arm along the base line.
Count around the protractor until you reach 145°.
Make a mark at 145°.

centre baseline

You can measure from 0° to 180° clockwise or counterclockwise.
Remember to start at 0° when you draw an angle.

Step 3
Remove the protractor.
Draw a line to join the end of the arm at the centre of the protractor with the mark at 145°.
Label the angle with its measure.

145°

85

REACHING ALL LEARNERS

Alternative Explore

Materials: protractors and rulers

Have students work in pairs. Remind students how to measure angles using a protractor. Have them reverse the process to try to construct angles measuring 45° and 120° with a protractor and a ruler. Students should measure each angle to be sure they are correct. Have students write to describe the process they used to construct the angles.

Common Misconceptions

➤ Students have difficulty knowing how to orient the protractor on the angle.

How to Help: Have students choose one arm to be the base. They should align the baseline of the protractor with the base of the angle. The vertex of the angle must be at the centre of the protractor. Students require lots of experience measuring angles of different sizes and orientations to become proficient.

➤ Students have difficulty using the upper or lower scale on the protractor.

How to Help: Have students estimate the measure of each angle and identify as acute, obtuse, or right before they measure the angle. Use string, or paper strips fastened at one end with paper fasteners to construct different angles. Ask how each angle compares to 90°.

ESL Strategies

Pair ESL students with stronger English students. Some students may benefit from these mnemonics: acute sounds like *a cute little angle,* obtuse makes your mouth *big* when you say it.

- How can you use what you know about angles to estimate the angle measures?
  (I can compare the angle to other known angles, cut out angles, or trace a known angle and lay it on top).
- Describe 2 ways you could order the angles from least to greatest.
  (I could compare the pictures of the angles. The angle with arms closest together is the least angle. The angle with arms farthest apart is the greatest angle. Alternatively, I could compare the angle measures. I can order the angle measures from the one with the least number of degrees to the one with the greatest number of degrees.)

AFTER Connect

Ask volunteers to share the strategies they used to estimate the size of an angle. If any student had a novel strategy, have her or him share it with the class.

With the class, discuss the definitions of acute angle, right angle, and obtuse angle presented in *Connect*. Have students sort their angles from *Explore* as acute, right, or obtuse. Invite volunteers to share their sorting with the class. Ask students to identify objects in the classroom that have acute angles, right angles, and obtuse angles.

2. b) The lengths of the arms do not affect the size of the angle measure. The distance between the arms determines the size of the angle.

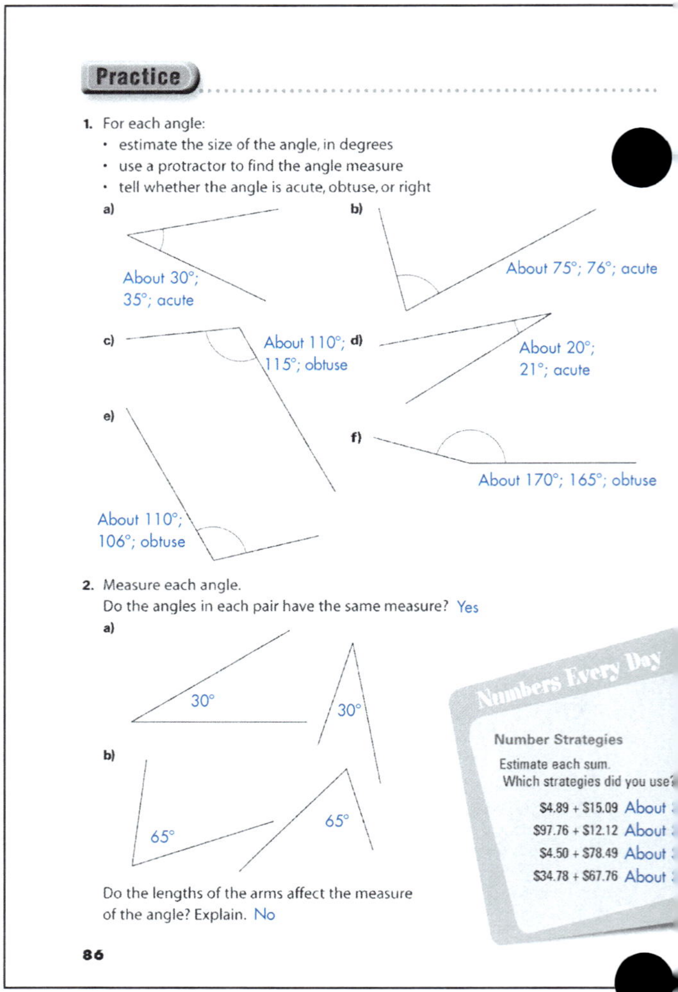

Practice

1. For each angle:
   - estimate the size of the angle, in degrees
   - use a protractor to find the angle measure
   - tell whether the angle is acute, obtuse, or right

a) About 30°; 35°; acute

b) About 75°; 76°; acute

c) About 110°; 115°; obtuse

d) About 20°; 21°; acute

e) About 110°; 106°; obtuse

f) About 170°; 165°; obtuse

2. Measure each angle.
   Do the angles in each pair have the same measure? Yes

a) 30° 30°

b) 65° 65°

Do the lengths of the arms affect the measure of the angle? Explain. No

Numbers Every Day

Number Strategies

Estimate each sum.
Which strategies did you use?

$4.89 + $15.09 About
$97.76 + $12.12 About
$4.50 + $78.49 About
$34.78 + $67.76 About

86

Numbers Every Day

Most students will round to the nearest dollar, then add.

Use an overhead projector, a blank transparency, and a clear protractor to demonstrate the steps for constructing an angle. Students should follow along independently and check each other's work. Remind students to mark the number that is greater than 90° if the angle is obtuse. Similarly, if the angle is acute, students should mark the number that is less than 90°.

Practice

All questions require a protractor.

Question 3 requires a geoboard and geobands or square dot paper.

Question 4 requires a ruler.

Assessment Focus: Question 4

Students should apply the techniques for constructing angles using a protractor. They should recognize that an obtuse angle must be constructed to be larger than 90°. Most students will recognize that a straight line is a 180° angle. This is a labelled angle on the protractor.

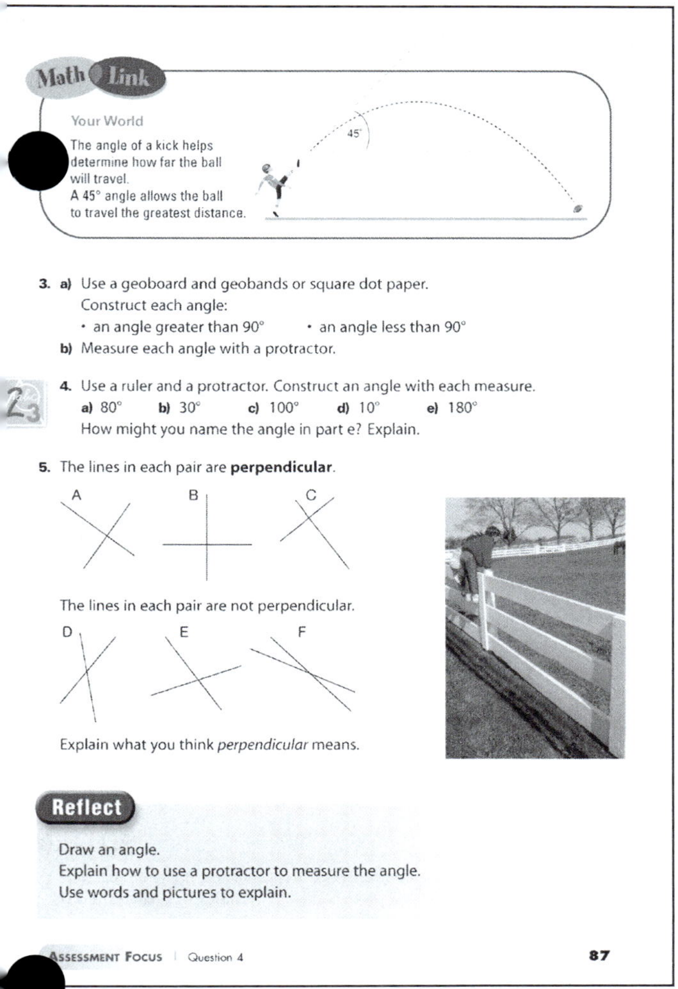
Math Link

Your World

The angle of a kick helps determine how far the ball will travel.
A 45° angle allows the ball to travel the greatest distance.

3. a) Use a geoboard and geobands or square dot paper.
Construct each angle:
• an angle greater than 90° • an angle less than 90°
b) Measure each angle with a protractor.

4. Use a ruler and a protractor. Construct an angle with each measure.
a) 80° b) 30° c) 100° d) 10° e) 180°
How might you name the angle in part e? Explain.

5. The lines in each pair are **perpendicular**.

A B C

The lines in each pair are not perpendicular.

D E F

Explain what you think *perpendicular* means.

Reflect

Draw an angle.
Explain how to use a protractor to measure the angle.
Use words and pictures to explain.

Assessment Focus | Question 4 87

4. e) An angle that measures 180° looks like a straight line. I could call it a straight angle.

5. Perpendicular lines cross at a 90°, or at a right angle.

REFLECT: I place the protractor on top of the angle. I rotate the protractor until the baseline is aligned with one of the arms of the angle. I match the vertex of the angle with the centre of the protractor. Then I look at the place where the other arm goes up through numbers on the protractor. If the angle is acute, I read the scale with the lesser numbers. If the angle is obtuse, I read the scale with the greater numbers.

ASSESSMENT FOR LEARNING

What to Look For	What to Do
Understanding concepts ✔ Students understand that angles can be named as right, acute, or obtuse. ***Applying procedures*** ✔ Students can identify right, acute, and obtuse angles. ✔ Students can measure and construct various angles using a protractor. ***Communicating*** ✔ Students can use appropriate mathematical terms to describe angles.	***Extra Support:*** Copy protractors onto transparencies. Cut the copies into wedges of 30°, 45°, 60°, 90°, 120°, 135°, and 150°. Students use the wedges to estimate the measure of angles and to construct angles. Students can use Step-by-Step 2 (Master 3.15) to complete question 4. ***Extra Practice:*** Have students work in pairs. Each student secretly marks 4 dots on dot paper and labels them 1 to 4. Students connect the dots in order from bottom left to top right. Using only lengths and angle measures, students describe to their partners how to move from the first to the last dot. Students can complete Extra Practice 1 (Master 3.21). ***Extension:*** Challenge students to determine the number of times each day the hands on a clock form a 90° angle.

Recording and Reporting
Master 3.2 Ongoing Observations: Geometry

Strategies Toolkit

LESSON ORGANIZER

40–50 min

Curriculum Focus: Interpret a problem and select an appropriate strategy.

Teacher Materials

- tangram (PM 29)

Student Materials

- tangram (PM 29)
- Pattern Blocks (PM 28)
- protractors

Assessment: PM 1: Inquiry Process Check List
PM 3: Self-Assessment: Problem Solving

Key Math Learning

Maintaining an organized list is an efficient strategy to solve problems; it ensures all possibilities have been considered.

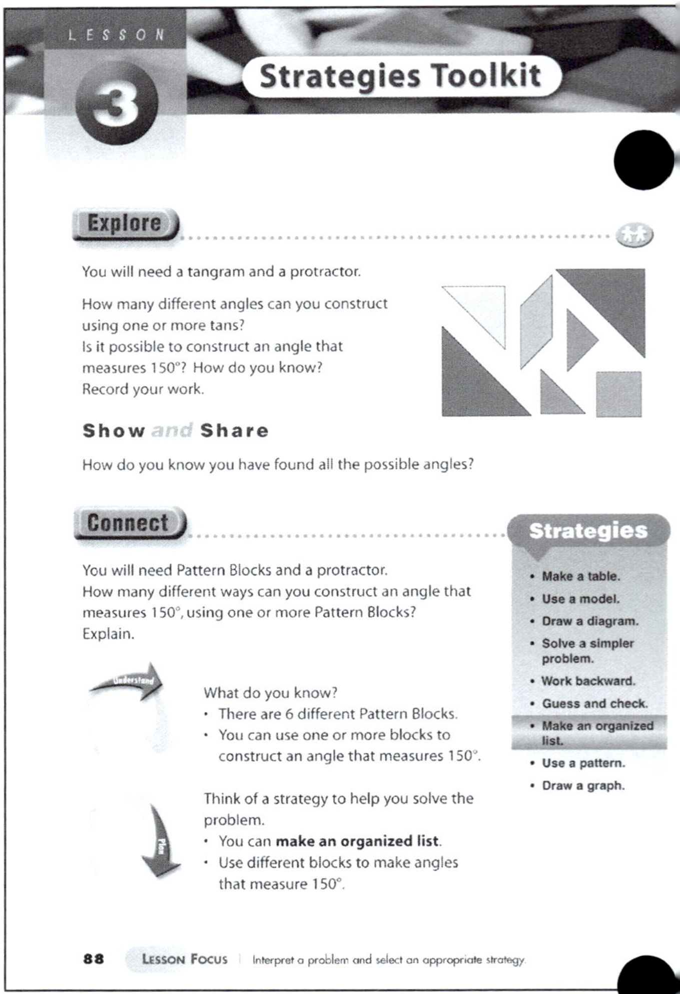

LESSON 3 Strategies Toolkit

Explore

You will need a tangram and a protractor.

How many different angles can you construct using one or more tans?
Is it possible to construct an angle that measures 150°? How do you know?
Record your work.

Show and Share

How do you know you have found all the possible angles?

Connect

You will need Pattern Blocks and a protractor.
How many different ways can you construct an angle that measures 150°, using one or more Pattern Blocks?
Explain.

What do you know?
- There are 6 different Pattern Blocks.
- You can use one or more blocks to construct an angle that measures 150°.

Think of a strategy to help you solve the problem.
- You can **make an organized list**.
- Use different blocks to make angles that measure 150°.

Strategies
- Make a table.
- Use a model.
- Draw a diagram.
- Solve a simpler problem.
- Work backward.
- Guess and check.
- Make an organized list.
- Use a pattern.
- Draw a graph.

88 LESSON FOCUS | Interpret a problem and select an appropriate strategy.

BEFORE Get Started

Use tangram pieces.
Show students how to arrange a triangle and a parallelogram to make an angle that measures 135°.
Present *Explore*.

DURING Explore

Ongoing Assessment: Observe and Listen

Ask questions, such as:

- Which tans are the least helpful in finding the different angles?
  (The triangles are the least helpful. They each have the same angles, 90° and 45°.)
- How can you organize your work to make sure you find all the possible angles?
  (I sketched each tan and recorded the measures of the angles on the sketches.)
- How do you know if you found all possible angles?
  (I started with the smallest angle, then found all the angles I could create using that angle. I repeated the process for the next largest angle. I continued until I had used all the angles. I made these angles: 45°, 90°, 135°, 180°. I also found these angles greater than 180°: 225°, 270°, 315°, 360°)
- Why is it not possible to construct a 150° angle?
  (All the angles in the tans are multiples of 45°; 150 is not a multiple of 45.)

AFTER Connect

Invite volunteers to share the strategies they used to solve the problem. Discuss why they chose a particular strategy and how effective it was. As a class, work through the problem presented in *Connect*. Model the strategy **make an organized list**.

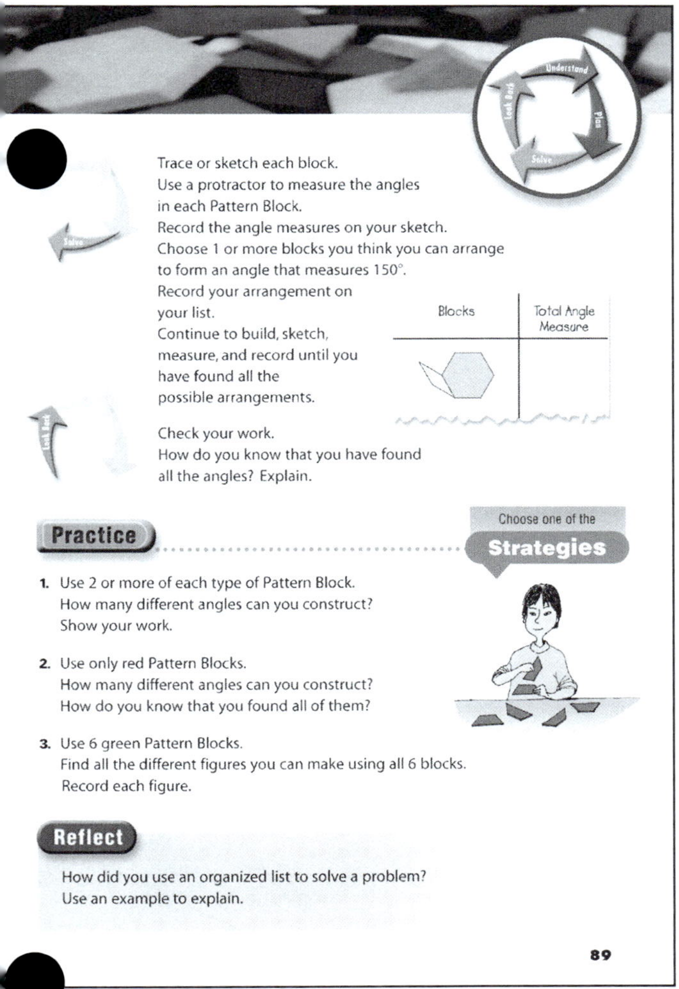

Trace or sketch each block.
Use a protractor to measure the angles in each Pattern Block.
Record the angle measures on your sketch.
Choose 1 or more blocks you think you can arrange to form an angle that measures 150°.
Record your arrangement on your list.
Continue to build, sketch, measure, and record until you have found all the possible arrangements.

Blocks	Total Angle Measure

Check your work.
How do you know that you have found all the angles? Explain.

Practice

Choose one of the **Strategies**

1. Use 2 or more of each type of Pattern Block. How many different angles can you construct? Show your work.
2. Use only red Pattern Blocks. How many different angles can you construct? How do you know that you found all of them?
3. Use 6 green Pattern Blocks. Find all the different figures you can make using all 6 blocks. Record each figure.

Reflect

How did you use an organized list to solve a problem? Use an example to explain.

89

REACHING ALL LEARNERS

Early Finishers

Ask students to design and create a new Pattern Block. The new block should provide a different set of angles than those found in a set of Pattern Blocks. Challenge students to find all the different angles that could be made using their block along with a set of Pattern Blocks.

Sample Answers

1. All the angles in the Pattern Blocks are multiples of 30°. Using 2 Pattern Blocks, the least angle that can be made measures 60°. Other possible angles are 90°, 120°, 150°, 180°, 210°, 240°, 270°, 300°, 330°, and 360°.
2. Red Pattern Blocks have angles of 60° and 120°. The possible angles are multiples of 60°: 60°, 120°, 180°, 240°, 300°, and 360°
3. Here are some of the different figures that can be made with 6 green Pattern Blocks.

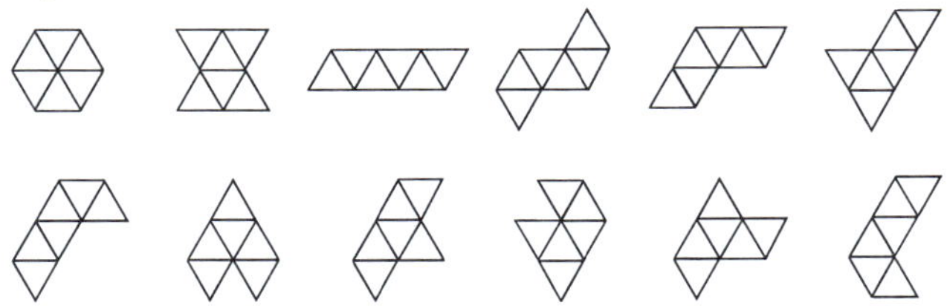

REFLECT: For *Practice* question 2, I drew all the angles possible by tracing them. I organized the drawings in a list. The list allowed me to be sure I had found all the possible angles.

ASSESSMENT FOR LEARNING

What to Look For	What to Do
Problem solving ✔ Students can select an appropriate strategy and use it to solve a problem. ***Communicating*** ✔ Students can organize their work in an efficient way so as to be sure they have found all of the possibilities.	***Extra Support:*** Some students may benefit from having a partially completed organized list. The list should include a sketch of each of the Pattern Blocks with the angle measures indicated. ***Extra Practice:*** Have students solve this problem: A combination lock has four dials. Each dial has five numbers on it from 1 to 5. How many different combinations can there be? (*625*) ***Extension:*** Challenge students to create their own problem using Pattern Blocks. Students can exchange problems with a classmate and solve their classmate's problem.

Recording and Reporting

PM 1 Inquiry Process Check List
PM 3 Self-Assessment: Problem Solving

Naming and Sorting Polygons by Angles

LESSON ORGANIZER

40–50 min

Curriculum Focus: Name and sort polygons by number of angles and by angle measure. (5m75, 5m76)

Teacher Materials
- overhead projector
- clear protractor
- blank transparency
- overhead markers

Student Materials
- Triangles for Lesson 4 (Master 3.7)
- protractors
- millimetre rulers
- geoboards and geobands
- square dot paper (PM 25)

Optional
- Step-by-Step 4 (Master 3.16)
- Extra Practice 2 (Master 3.22)

Vocabulary: acute triangle, right triangle, obtuse triangle, regular polygon, irregular polygon

Assessment: Master 3.2 Ongoing Observations: Geometry

Key Math Learnings

1. Triangles can be sorted by angle measure.
2. Quadrilaterals can be named by number of equal angles.
3. Polygons can be sorted by the number of equal sides and by the number of equal angles.

LESSON 4

Naming and Sorting Polygons by Angles

Explore

You will need a protractor.
Your teacher will give you a large copy of the triangles.

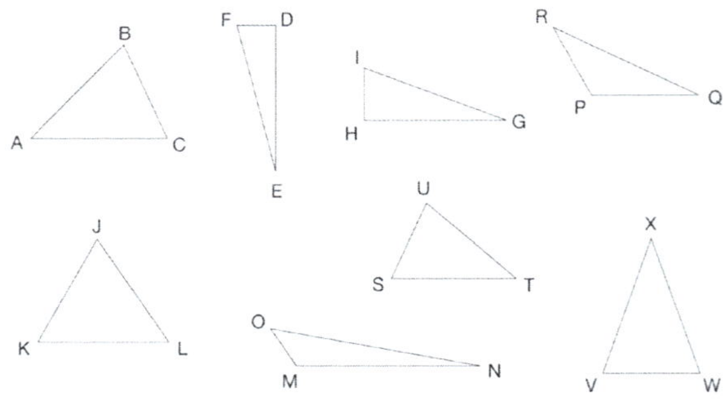

➤ Measure each angle in each triangle.
Record the angle measures.

➤ Sort the triangles according to the measures of their angles.
How are the triangles in each group the same?
How are they different?

Show and Share

Share your work with another pair of students.
Did you sort the triangles the same way? Explain.

90 LESSON FOCUS | Name and sort polygons by number of angles and by angle measure.

BEFORE — Get Started

Draw an angle on a transparency. Ask:

- About how big is this angle?
  (*If the angle is acute, students should estimate an angle measure less than 90°. If the angle is obtuse, students should estimate an angle measure greater than 90°.*)
- How can I measure the size of this angle?
  (*Use a protractor. Align the baseline of the protractor with one arm of the angle. Ensure the vertex of the angle is at the centre of the protractor. Read the angle measure. Be sure to read the appropriate scale. For example, if the angle is acute, the angle measure will be less than 90°.*)

Draw several more angles. Be sure to draw acute and obtuse angles. Invite student volunteers to come up and estimate, then measure the size of the angles.

Present *Explore*. Distribute copies of Master 3.7 *Triangles for Lesson 4*.

DURING — Explore

Watch that students re-orient the baseline of the protractor on each side of the triangles. Help students who need assistance with using protractors.

Ask students to compare their measurements with those of other students.

Ongoing Assessment: Observe and Listen

Ask questions, such as:

- What are the angle measures?
  (*In triangle ABC, $\angle A = 45°$, $\angle B = 70°$, and $\angle C = 65°$*
  In triangle FDE, $\angle D = 90°$, $\angle E = 15°$, and $\angle F = 75°$
  In triangle IGH, $\angle G = 20°$, $\angle H = 90°$, and $\angle I = 70°$
  In triangle KJL, $\angle J = 65°$, $\angle K = 60°$, and $\angle L = 55°$

Connect

➤ We can sort and name triangles by angle measure.

An **acute triangle** has all angles less than 90°.
A **right triangle** has one 90° angle.
An **obtuse triangle** has one angle greater than 90°.

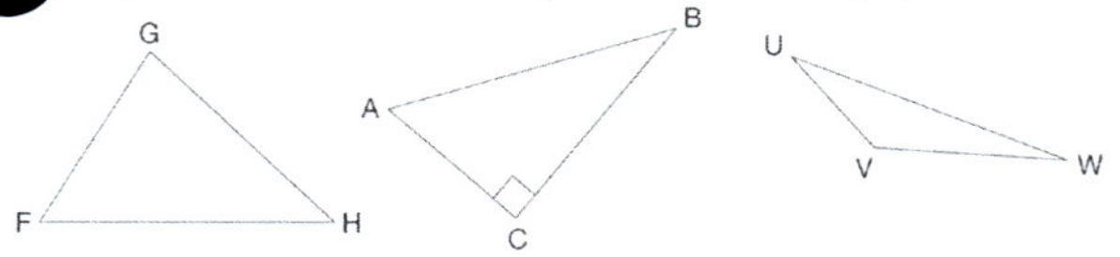

➤ We can sort and name quadrilaterals by angles.

A rectangle has 4 right angles.
A parallelogram has 2 pairs of equal angles.
A kite has 1 pair of equal angles.

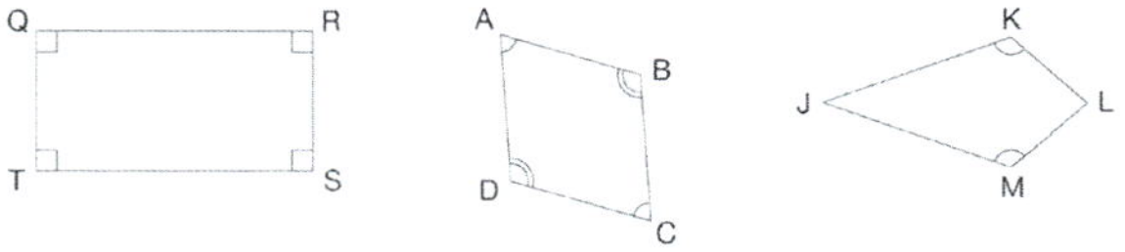

➤ We can sort polygons by the numbers of equal sides and equal angles.

A **regular polygon** has all sides equal and all angles equal.

An equilateral triangle is a regular triangle. It has 3 equal sides. Each angle measures 60°.

A square is a regular rectangle. It has 4 equal sides. Each angle measures 90°.

An **irregular polygon** does not have all sides equal and all angles equal.

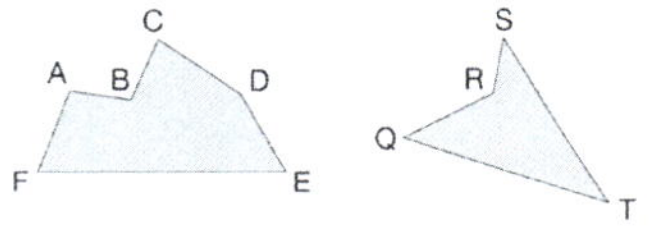

∠G = 90°
The symbol ∠ means angle.

91

REACHING ALL LEARNERS

Alternative Explore

Materials: tracing paper, scissors

Rather than measuring the angles in *Explore* using a protractor, ask students to compare the angles of each triangle in other ways (folding, tracing, cutting) and sort them.

Common Misconceptions

➤ Students may need further assistance using protractors, especially on dot paper or geoboards.

How to Help: Work with individuals or groups as needed. Difficulty using a protractor should not stand in the way of understanding the concept of sorting polygons by angle. Students can compare angles by tracing, cutting out, or folding polygons. They can also compare the angles in the polygons to known angles.

In triangle MON, ∠M = 124°, ∠N = 10°, and ∠O = 46°
In triangle PRQ, ∠P = 120°, ∠R = 35°, and ∠Q = 25°
In triangle UTS, ∠S = 65°, ∠T = 40°, and ∠U = 75°
In triangle VXW, ∠V = 70°, ∠X = 40°, and ∠W = 70°)

- How are the triangles in each group you sorted the same? How are they different? (*The triangles in one group have all angles less than 90°. The triangles in the second group have one right angle. The triangles in the third group have one angle greater than 90°.*)
- How else could you sort the triangles? (*I could also sort the triangles by the number of equal angles they contain. One group of triangles would have no equal angles. The second group would have a pair of equal angles. The third group would have all angles equal.*)

AFTER Connect

Invite students to share the strategies they used to sort the triangles. They can demonstrate using an overhead projector or have students gather around a desk or table.

Discuss *Connect*. Ensure students understand the meaning of the angle symbol, ∠.

Ask students to find examples of regular and irregular polygons in the classroom. If possible, measure the sides and the angles.

Sample Answers

1. a) All the angles in all 3 triangles must be less than 90°.
   b) Each triangle must contain one angle greater than 90°.
   c) Each triangle must contain one 90° angle.
3. a) Irregular; one side is longer than the others
   b) Regular; all sides and all angles are equal
   c) Irregular; not all angles are equal
   d) Irregular; not all angles are equal
4. Figure E has all right angles. Figure D has all obtuse angles. Figure G has all acute angles. Figure C has 2 acute angles and 1 right angle. Figure A has right angles and obtuse angles. Figure B has right angles and an acute angle and an obtuse angle. Figures F, H, and I each have 2 acute and 2 obtuse angles.

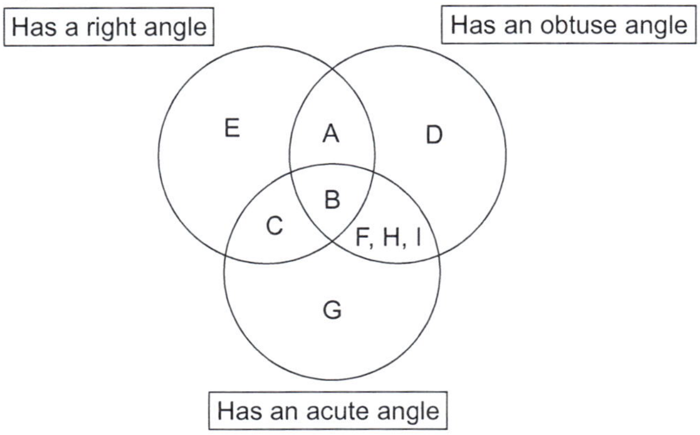

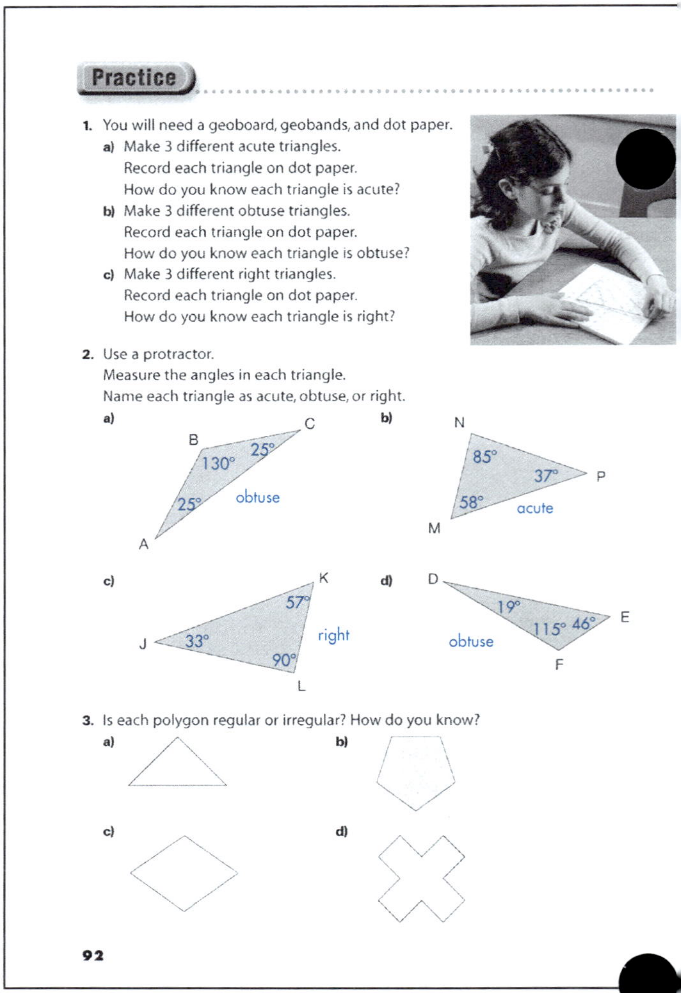

Practice

1. You will need a geoboard, geobands, and dot paper.
   a) Make 3 different acute triangles.
   Record each triangle on dot paper.
   How do you know each triangle is acute?
   b) Make 3 different obtuse triangles.
   Record each triangle on dot paper.
   How do you know each triangle is obtuse?
   c) Make 3 different right triangles.
   Record each triangle on dot paper.
   How do you know each triangle is right?
2. Use a protractor.
   Measure the angles in each triangle.
   Name each triangle as acute, obtuse, or right.
   a) B 130°, C 25°, A 25° obtuse
   b) N 85°, P 37°, M 58° acute
   c) K 57°, J 33°, L 90° right
   d) D 19°, E 46°, F 115° obtuse
3. Is each polygon regular or irregular? How do you know?
   a) b) c) d)

92

Practice

Questions 1 and 5 require a geoboard, geobands, and square dot paper.

Have millimetre rulers and protractors available for all questions.

Assessment Focus: Question 5

Students use the number of angles and angle measures. For part a, students understand that many regular or irregular quadrilaterals can have *only* 2 obtuse angles. Other polygons cannot. For part b, students should recognize that acute triangles are possible, along with many other irregular polygons that have acute, right, and obtuse angles. For part c, students should understand that rectangles contain more than 1 right angle, as do many other irregular polygons. For part d, students should recognize that no figure can be made with *only 1* of each attribute, however they may construct different polygons with *1 or more* of each.

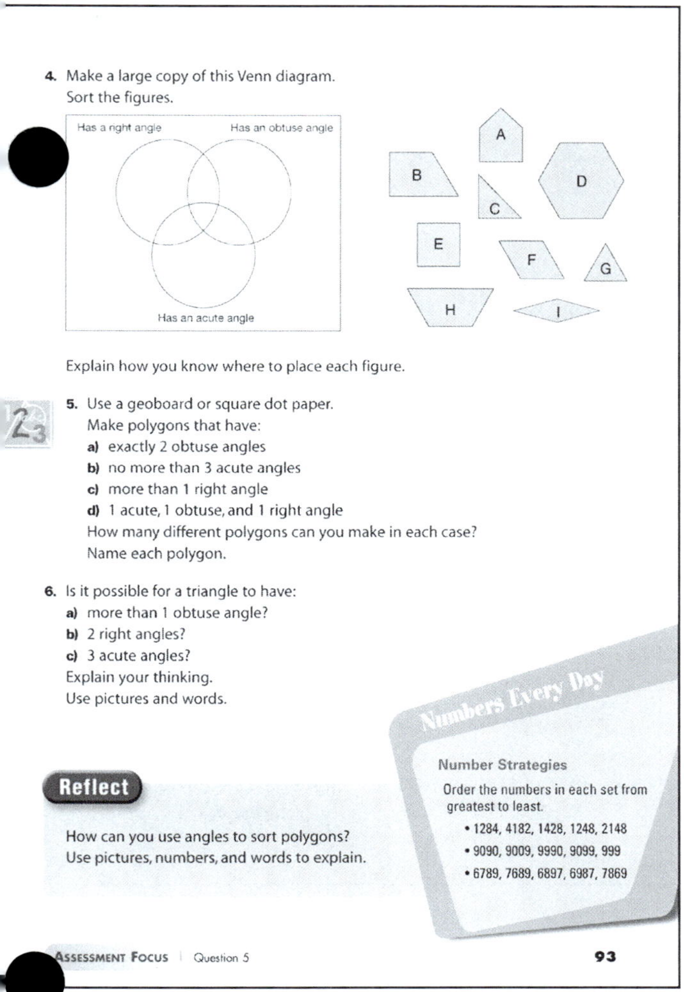

4. Make a large copy of this Venn diagram.
Sort the figures.

Explain how you know where to place each figure.

5. Use a geoboard or square dot paper.
Make polygons that have:
a) exactly 2 obtuse angles
b) no more than 3 acute angles
c) more than 1 right angle
d) 1 acute, 1 obtuse, and 1 right angle
How many different polygons can you make in each case?
Name each polygon.

6. Is it possible for a triangle to have:
a) more than 1 obtuse angle?
b) 2 right angles?
c) 3 acute angles?
Explain your thinking.
Use pictures and words.

Reflect

How can you use angles to sort polygons?
Use pictures, numbers, and words to explain.

Numbers Every Day

Number Strategies

Order the numbers in each set from greatest to least.
- 1284, 4182, 1428, 1248, 2148
- 9090, 9009, 9990, 9099, 999
- 6789, 7689, 6897, 6987, 7869

ASSESSMENT FOCUS | Question 5

93

5. a) The polygons include a parallelogram, a trapezoid, and a kite.
b) The polygons include an acute triangle, a parallelogram, a trapezoid, a right triangle.
c) The polygons include a square and a rectangle.
d) The polygons include a trapezoid with 2 right angles.

6. a) No; the arms of obtuse angles at opposite ends of a line segment will not cross.
b) No; if a figure has 2 right angles, the arms will not cross.
c) Yes; many different triangles have 3 acute angles.

REFLECT: You can sort polygons by the number of obtuse angles, right angles, acute angles, or equal angles. Triangles can be acute, right, or obtuse. Quadrilaterals can have 2 pairs of right angles, 2 pairs of equal angles, or 1 pair of equal angles. Polygons can be regular or irregular.

Numbers Every Day

Students should first compare the thousands digits, then the hundreds, then the tens, and finally the ones.
- 4182, 2148, 1428, 1284, 1248
- 9990, 9099, 9090, 9009, 999
- 7869, 7689, 6987, 6897, 6789

ASSESSMENT FOR LEARNING

What to Look For	What to Do
Understanding concepts ✔ Students understand that triangles can be sorted by angle measure. ✔ Students can identify quadrilaterals by number of equal angles. ✔ Students can identify regular and irregular polygons. ***Communicating*** ✔ Students use appropriate mathematical terms to describe polygons.	***Extra Support:*** Students can do the Additional Activity, *Pattern Block Properties* (Master 3.11). Students can use Step-by-Step 4 (Master 3.16) to complete question 5. ***Extra Practice:*** Students can do the Additional Activity, *Partner Polygons* (Master 3.10). Students can complete Extra Practice 2 (Master 3.22). ***Extension:*** Challenge students to draw 10 different polygons, label each with a letter, and cut them out. Have students sort their polygons 2 ways. For each way, students should draw a Venn diagram with 3 loops.

Recording and Reporting

Master 3.2: Ongoing Observations: Geometry

LESSON 5

Constructing Triangles

LESSON ORGANIZER
40–50 min

Curriculum Focus: Construct triangles given side and angle measures. (5m79)

Teacher Materials
- overhead projector
- clear protractor

Student Materials
- protractors
- millimetre rulers
- triangles from a geometry set
- geoboard and geobands
- square dot paper (PM 25)

Optional
- Step-by-Step 5 (Master 3.17)
- Extra Practice 2 (Master 3.22)

Assessment: Master 3.2 Ongoing Observations: Geometry

LESSON

5

Constructing Triangles

These triangles come with a geometry set.
The measure of each angle is shown.

Explore

You will need:
- a millimetre ruler
- triangles from a geometry set

➤ Construct triangle DEF.
The measure of ∠D is 30°.
The measure of ∠E is 60°.
The measure of ∠F is 90°.
Which side will be the longest?
Try to make more than one triangle DEF.

➤ Construct triangle ABC.
The length of AB is 66 mm.
The measure of ∠A is 120°.
The length of AC is 66 mm.
How long is side BC?
What are the measures of ∠B and ∠C?

➤ Name each triangle 2 ways.
Record your work.

94 Lesson Focus | Construct triangles given side and angle measures.

Key Math Learnings
1. Triangles can be constructed, given side and angle measures.
2. Two triangles can have congruent angles but different side lengths.
3. Changing the measure of an angle in a triangle affects the lengths of the sides and vice versa.

BEFORE Get Started

On the board, draw a large triangle with the vertices labelled D, E, and F. Ask student volunteers to come up and point to each side or angle as you call it out.

Place the triangles from a geometry set on the overhead. Invite students to come up and measure the angles with a protractor.

Present *Explore*. Ensure students understand that they will be using the triangles from a geometry set, rather than a protractor, to construct the angles in each triangle.

DURING Explore

Ongoing Assessment: Observe and Listen

Ask questions. such as:
- What is the first step when you construct triangle DEF?
(*First I draw a line. The line can be any length. I will draw the line about 5 cm long. Next, I need to construct angles from each end of that line.*)
- For triangle DEF, how do you know how long to make each side? Does it matter?
(*I can draw the first side any length. The length does not matter. A longer line will result in a larger triangle; a shorter line will result in a smaller triangle. The lengths of the other 2 sides will be determined by the point where they cross.*)
- What is the first step when you construct a triangle ABC?
(*I would start by drawing side AB or side AC because we know their lengths.*)
- How do you know how to label triangle DEF? (*The vertex with the angle that measures 30° is D. Similarly, the vertices with the angles that measure 60° and 90° are E and F. Side DE is the side between vertices D and E. Side EF is the side between vertices E and F.*)

Show and Share

Compare your triangles with those of another pair of students.
Is it possible to make different triangles ABC? DEF? Explain.

Connect

You can use a ruler and a protractor to construct a triangle.

Construct triangle MNP.
The length of MN is 4.5 cm.
The measure of ∠M is 40°.
The length of MP is 3.7 cm.

Step 1
Sketch the triangle first.
Label each side and angle.
This sketch is *not* accurate.
It shows each given measure.

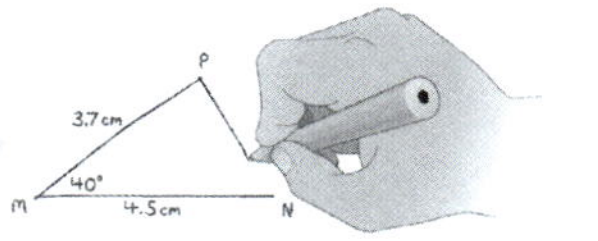

Step 2
Use a ruler to draw side MN
4.5 cm long.

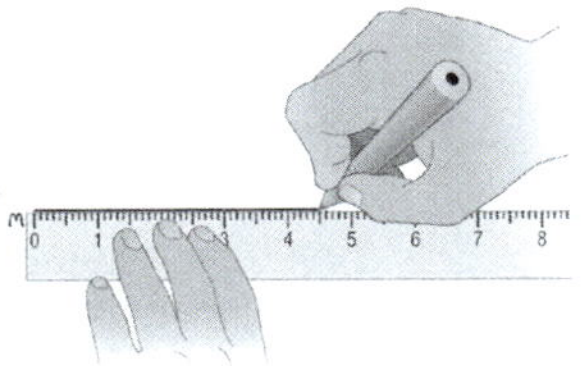

Step 3
Place the protractor on MN,
with its centre at M.
From 0° on the inner circle,
measure an angle of 40° at M.

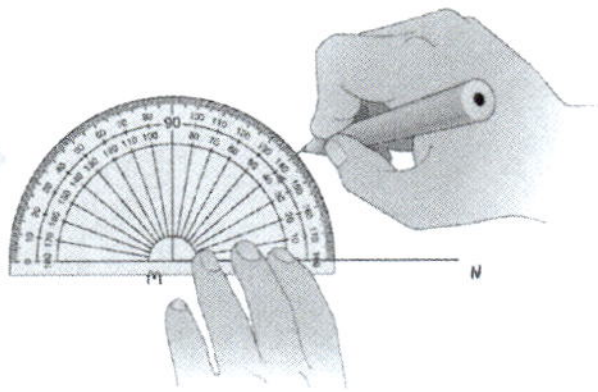

95

REACHING ALL LEARNERS

Alternative Explore

Materials: protractors, millimetre rulers, paper
Ask students to explore triangles that contain one or more of these angles: 45°, 30°, 60°, 90°, 120°. Have students construct different triangles. Each triangle should contain one or more of these angles. For each triangle, students find and record all the side and angle measures. Have students choose one of the triangles and change the measure of one angle or side length. Students describe how the triangle changes.

Common Misconceptions

➤ Some students will have difficulty deciding how long to draw a given side of a triangle if no length is given.
How to Help: Demonstrate how the point where the arms of two angles intersect determines the length of the side. Students should draw the arms of the angles in pencil. The arms should be long enough to intersect. The extra length can be erased.

➤ Some students will find labelling their triangles confusing.
How to Help: Suggest that students start with something that is known, such as: The length of HG is 46 mm. Once they have drawn their triangle, they should check to see that it meets the conditions described in the problem, and then label each vertex, based on each set of instructions given in the problem. They will discover that a triangle may be constructed with different orientations or labels but meet the criteria described in the problem. Students should share their constructions and talk about the similarities and differences.

- Does the order of the letters matter?
  (*No, as long as the lengths and angle measures match the correct letters*)
- How could you name each triangle?
  (*Triangle DEF is a right triangle. All the sides have different length, so it is also scalene. Triangle ABC is an obtuse triangle. Two sides have the same length, so it is also isosceles.*)

AFTER Connect

Invite students to share their triangles. Ask students to share any strategies they developed to help them construct triangles. Have students compare their triangles with those of their classmates. Students should find that all the triangles ABC are congruent. The triangles DEF should all have the same shape, but may have different size.

Ask:
- Why is it possible to draw different triangles DEF?
  (*No side lengths were given, so the size of the triangle is determined by the length chosen for the first side. The first side could have any length.*)
- Why is it not possible to draw different triangles ABC?
  (*The measures of 2 angles were given, along with the length of the side between those 2 angles. The size of the triangle is determined by the length of the first side. The first side must be 66 mm.*)

Discuss *Connect*.

Numbers Every Day

Students could start with basic multiplication facts, then use related facts and halving and doubling to find other multiplication sentences with product 42. Students may use multiplication to find division sentences with quotient 42. For example, $42 \times 3 = 126$, so $126 \div 3 = 42$. Students can find two or more numbers whose sum or difference is 42, then use compensation to find other numbers.

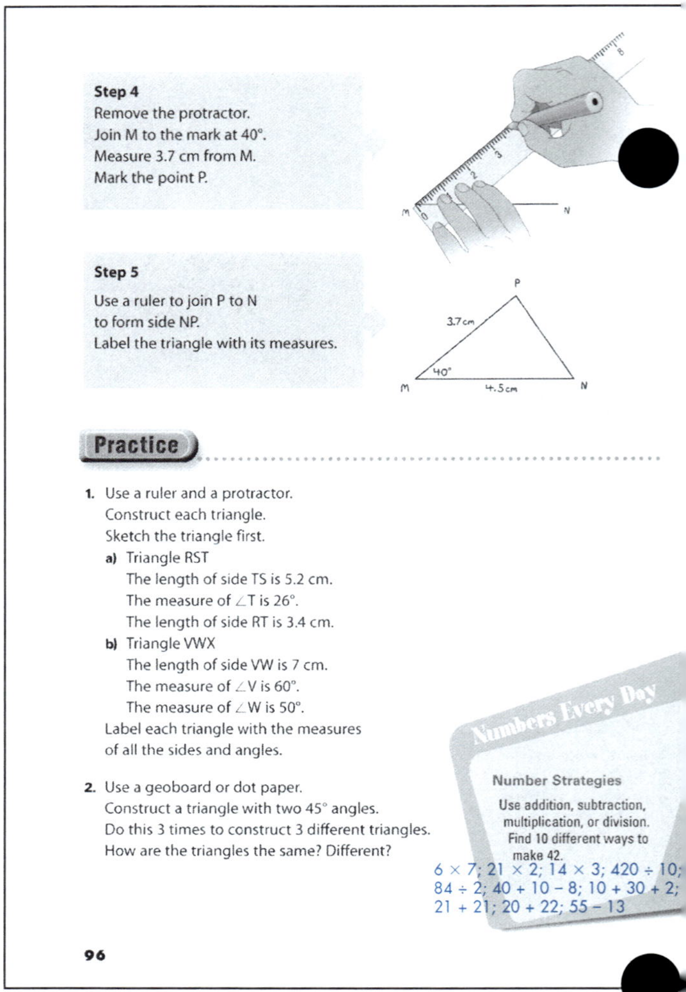

Step 4
Remove the protractor.
Join M to the mark at 40°.
Measure 3.7 cm from M.
Mark the point P.

Step 5
Use a ruler to join P to N
to form side NP.
Label the triangle with its measures.

Practice

1. Use a ruler and a protractor.
   Construct each triangle.
   Sketch the triangle first.
   a) Triangle RST
      The length of side TS is 5.2 cm.
      The measure of ∠T is 26°.
      The length of side RT is 3.4 cm.
   b) Triangle VWX
      The length of side VW is 7 cm.
      The measure of ∠V is 60°.
      The measure of ∠W is 50°.
   Label each triangle with the measures of all the sides and angles.
2. Use a geoboard or dot paper.
   Construct a triangle with two 45° angles.
   Do this 3 times to construct 3 different triangles.
   How are the triangles the same? Different?

Numbers Every Day

Number Strategies

Use addition, subtraction, multiplication, or division.
Find 10 different ways to make 42.

6×7; 21×2; 14×3; $420 \div 10$; $84 \div 2$; $40 + 10 - 8$; $10 + 30 + 2$; $21 + 21$; $20 + 22$; $55 - 13$

96

Sample Answers

All triangles can be shown with different orientations or translations (slide, flip, or turn).

1. Use a ruler and a protractor to check students' triangles.
   a) RS = 7.2 cm, ∠R = 42°, ∠S = 26°
   b) VX = 5.8 cm, XW = 6.5 cm, ∠X = 70°
2. All the triangles are right isosceles. They all have these angle measures: 45°, 45°, 90°. They have the same shape, but different sizes.

Practice

Have millimetre rulers and protractors available for all questions.

Question 2 requires geoboards and geobands, or dot paper.

It may be difficult for students to make precise measurements with protractors and rulers. Expect measurements to be within 2 or 3 degrees or millimetres of those provided.

Assessment Focus: Question 4

Students should use their skill with constructing angles and lines of given length. They should understand that changes to angle measure or side length affect each other. In this case, when side HG is lengthened, ∠H and side HK remain constant. To adjust, ∠K gets larger, while side GK gets longer. Teachers may wish to have students hypothesize and explore the results of combinations of changes to side length or angle.

3. Use a ruler and a protractor.
Construct a triangle with angles 40°, 60°, and 80°.
Compare your triangle with that of a classmate.
Are your triangles congruent?
How could you find out?

4. Construct triangle GHK.
The measure of ∠H is 45°.
The length of side HK is 64 mm.
The length of side HG is 46 mm.
   a) What is the measure of ∠K? 45°
   What is the length of side GK? 46 mm
   b) Suppose the length of side HG is 7 cm.
   What happens to the measure of ∠K?
   What happens to the length of GK?
Show your work.

5. Construct a right triangle with two angles of 55° and 35°.
Can you make more than one triangle? Explain.

6. Try to construct triangle ABC.
Draw AB 42 mm long.
The measure of ∠A is 90°.
The measure of ∠B is 95°.
Can you construct triangle ABC?
How do you know?

7. Can you construct a triangle with three 45° angles?
Explain your thinking.

At Home

Look for triangles in your home.
They could be pictures or objects with triangular faces.
Name each triangle 2 ways.
Choose 1 triangle. Draw it.

Reflect

Which measures do you need to know to be able to draw a triangle?
For each example, draw the triangle.

ASSESSMENT FOCUS | Question 4 97

3. Students' triangles will not necessarily be congruent to those of their classmates. All the triangles should have the same shape, but they may be different sizes.
4. Students will obtain a more precise angle measurement if they make HK 65 mm.
   b) The measure of ∠K increases from 45° to 53°.
   The length of GK increases from 46 mm to 50 mm.
5. Many triangles with these angle measures are possible. All the triangles will have the same shape, but be different sizes.
6. This triangle is not possible.
   AC and BC will not cross.

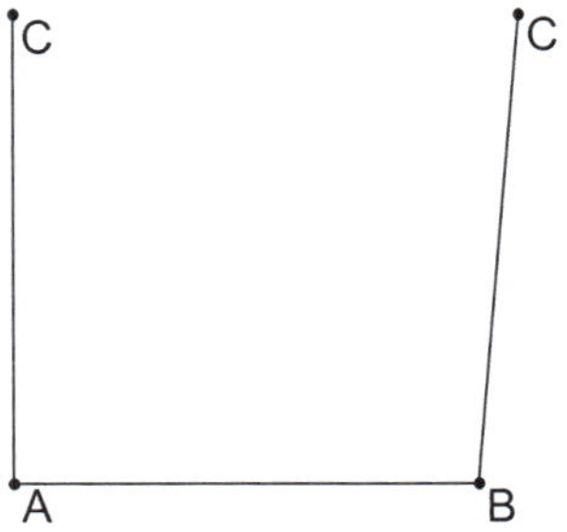

7. No. A triangle can have one or two 45° angles.
   If a triangle has two 45° angles, the other angle must be 90°.
   See examples from questions 2 and 4.

REFLECT: To draw one specific triangle, I need to know the lengths of the sides or the measures of 2 angles and the length of the side between the angles. If I know the measures of all 3 angles, I can draw many different triangles. The triangles all have the same shape, but different sizes.

ASSESSMENT FOR LEARNING

What to Look For	What to Do
Understanding concepts ✔ Students understand that triangles can be constructed from given side and angle measures, and can have congruent angles but different sizes. ✔ Students understand that changes to angle measure or side length affect each other. ***Applying procedures*** ✔ Students can construct triangles, given side and angle measures. ***Communicating*** ✔ Students use mathematical terms to describe triangles and their construction.	***Extra Support:*** Students can use Step-by-Step 5 (Master 3.17) to complete question 4. ***Extra Practice:*** Students can do the Additional Activity, *Exploring Paper Triangles* (Master 3.12). Students can complete Extra Practice 2 (Master 3.22). ***Extension:*** Students can do the Additional Activity, *Making Angles and Triangles* (Master 3.13).

Recording and Reporting
Master 3.2 Ongoing Observations: Geometry

Making Nets

LESSON ORGANIZER 40–50 min

Curriculum Focus: Identify and construct nets of solids. (5m72, 5m73)

Teacher Materials
- models of solids

tudent Materials
- pyramids
- cubes
- tape
- millimetre rulers
- scissors

Optional
- Step-by-Step 6 (Master 3.18)
- Extra Practice 3 (Master 3.23)

Vocabulary: net

Assessment: Master 3.2 Ongoing Observations: Geometry

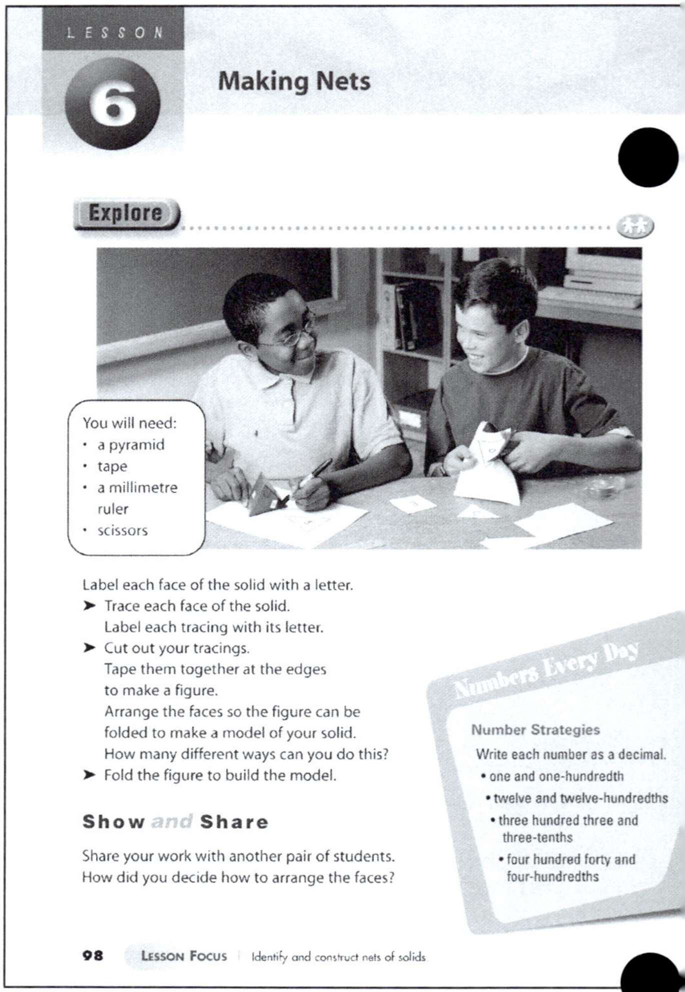
LESSON 6

Making Nets

Explore

You will need:
- a pyramid
- tape
- a millimetre ruler
- scissors

Label each face of the solid with a letter.
➤ Trace each face of the solid.
Label each tracing with its letter.
➤ Cut out your tracings.
Tape them together at the edges to make a figure.
Arrange the faces so the figure can be folded to make a model of your solid.
How many different ways can you do this?
➤ Fold the figure to build the model.

Show and Share

Share your work with another pair of students.
How did you decide how to arrange the faces?

Numbers Every Day

Number Strategies

Write each number as a decimal.
- one and one-hundredth
- twelve and twelve-hundredths
- three hundred three and three-tenths
- four hundred forty and four-hundredths

98 LESSON FOCUS | Identify and construct nets of solids

Key Math Learnings

1. A net is a figure that shows all the faces of a solid.
2. To find which solid a net represents, look at the shapes of the faces in the net.

Numbers Every Day

Some students may benefit from representing each number with Base Ten Blocks or by shading hundredths grids before they write the number as a decimal.

1.01; 12.12; 303.3; 440.04

BEFORE Get Started

Hold up a rectangular pyramid and discuss the properties of this solid.

Ask questions, such as:

- How would you describe the faces of this solid?
  (*It has 5 faces. The base is a rectangle. The other 4 faces are triangles. Pairs of triangles are congruent.*)
- Remember, prisms and pyramids are named by their bases.
  What is the name of this solid?
  (*A rectangular pyramid*)
- Suppose you wanted to create a 2-dimensional model of this solid.
  What figures would you draw?
  (*4 triangles and a rectangle*)

Discuss the photograph on page 98 in the Student Book.

Ask questions, such as:

- Which solid is the student on the left tracing?
  (*A square pyramid*)
- What is the shape of the face he is tracing?
  (*A triangle*)

Present *Explore.* Remind students to arrange the cutout shapes before taping them together, to make sure a pyramid will result.

DURING Explore

Ongoing Assessment: Observe and Listen

Ask questions, such as:

- How do you know you traced all the faces?
  (*The faces of the square pyramid were labelled from A to E. I traced each face, from A to E.*)

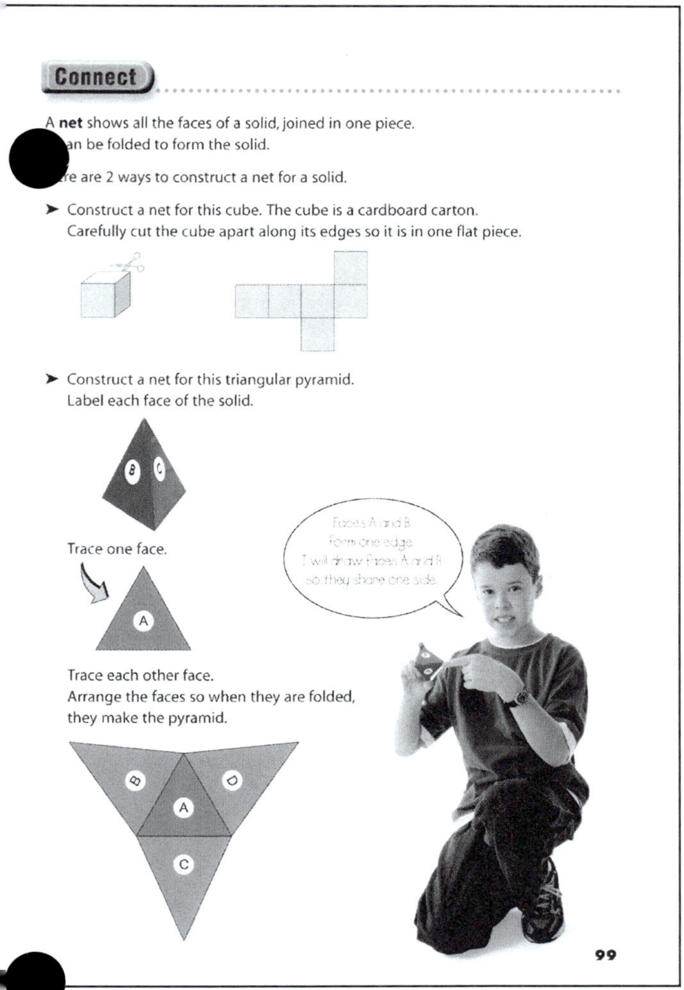

Connect

A **net** shows all the faces of a solid, joined in one piece.
an be folded to form the solid.

re are 2 ways to construct a net for a solid.

➤ Construct a net for this cube. The cube is a cardboard carton.
Carefully cut the cube apart along its edges so it is in one flat piece.

➤ Construct a net for this triangular pyramid.
Label each face of the solid.

Trace one face.

Trace each other face.
Arrange the faces so when they are folded, they make the pyramid.

99

REACHING ALL LEARNERS

Alternative Explore

Materials: Relational Geosolids and Nets for Relational Geosolids

Instead of tracing and combining the faces to make up nets, students use Relational Geosolids and Nets for Relational Geosolids to construct nets or deconstruct solids to make nets. These concrete materials could then be used to demonstrate understanding in *Practice*.

Early Finishers

Have students design nets that can be folded to make boxes for a variety of small classroom objects. Students draw the nets on grid paper, cut them out, and assemble them. They test their design by placing the object inside to confirm the size and shape are appropriate.

Common Misconceptions

➤Students create a net that does not result in an enclosed solid.

How to Help: Have students slowly unfold their net and lay it flat. Turn it over and record a number from 1 to 6 on each of the square faces. Fold the net up again and determine which face is missing or overlapped. Students can then problem solve to decide where the missing face should be relocated.

- How did you decide on the arrangement of the faces before taping them together?
  (*Each triangle connects along two edges with other triangles. The third side of the triangle connects with the base. When the arrangement is folded, the square is connected to all four triangles.*)
- Is there more than one way to arrange the faces to form a net? Explain.
  (*There are many ways. Each arrangement will work as long as all the faces that are joined in the net are faces that form an edge in the pyramid.*)

AFTER Connect

Have student volunteers share their nets with the class. If more than one pair of students constructed a net for the same solid, ask them all to show their nets. Students can compare different nets for the same solid. Ask students to share the strategies they used to figure out how to arrange the faces.

Discuss *Connect*. Ask:

- What is practical about the first method shown for constructing a net? What is not practical?
  (*It is easy to tell how to arrange the faces, because not all the edges need to be cut. It is very difficult to cut neatly along the edge of a solid.*)
- How is the second method for constructing a net shown in *Connect* the same as the method you used in *Explore*? How is it different?
  (*In Explore, I traced each face separately. I cut out each face, then arranged the faces to form a net. In Connect, one face is traced, then the next face is traced with one edge in common. The tracing results in a net.*)

Students who are having difficulty may prefer to cut solids apart to form nets. Ensure students know to look at the lengths of the sides of the faces when they are deciding how to arrange the faces.

Sample Answers

1. a) Square pyramid
   b) Pentagonal prism
   c) Pentagonal pyramid
   d) Triangular prism
2.

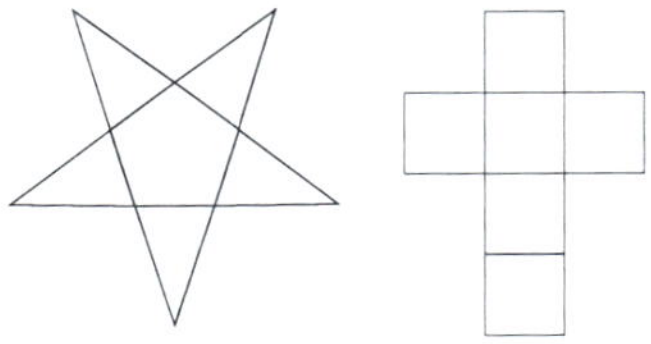

3. a) Rectangular prism; the net has two pairs of long congruent rectangles. The pairs of rectangles have the same length but different widths. There are also two congruent small rectangles. These represent the bases of the prism.
   b) Hexagonal pyramid; the net has six congruent triangles all connected to a hexagon, which is the base.
   c) Triangular prism; the net has three connected congruent rectangles and two congruent triangles, which represent the bases.
   d) Triangular prism: the net has three connected congruent rectangles and two congruent triangles.
4. a) Non-net of a pentagonal prism. Move one of the pentagonal faces to the opposite side of the rectangles.
   b) Rectangular pyramid
   c) Square pyramid
   d) Non-net of a hexagonal pyramid. Change the triangles so they are all congruent. Ensure the heights of the triangles are sufficient to make a 3-dimensional solid when folded.

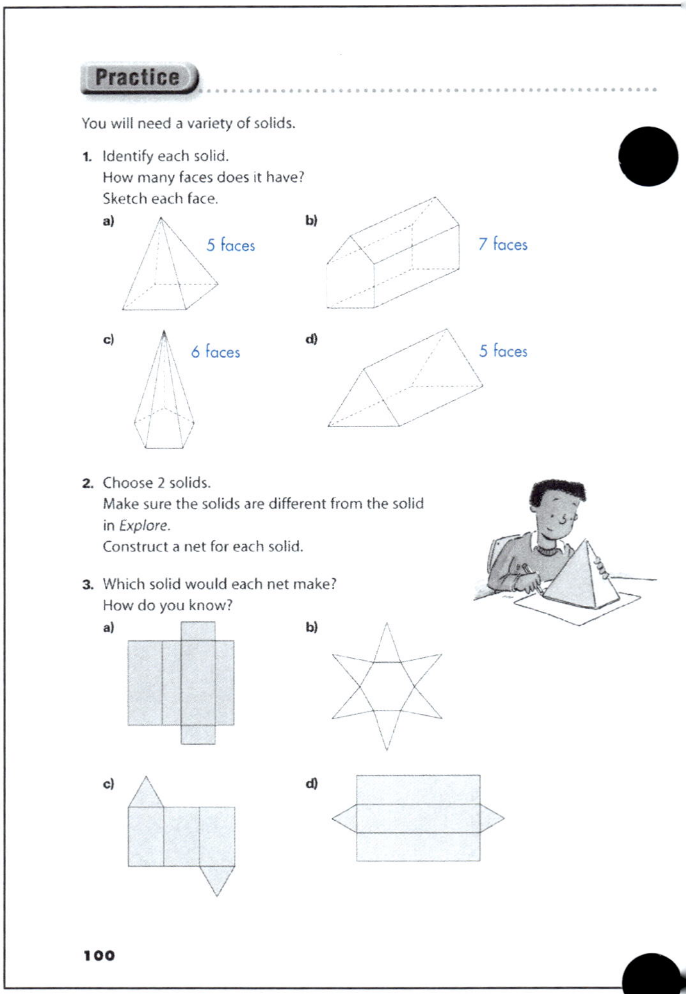

Practice

You will need a variety of solids.

1. Identify each solid.
   How many faces does it have?
   Sketch each face.

   a) 5 faces
   b) 7 faces
   c) 6 faces
   d) 5 faces

2. Choose 2 solids.
   Make sure the solids are different from the solid in *Explore*.
   Construct a net for each solid.

3. Which solid would each net make?
   How do you know?

   a) b) c) d)

100

Practice

For Question 2, students require a variety of cubes and pyramids, paper, scissors, and tape. Question 5 requires grid paper.

Assessment Focus: Question 5

Most students will use trial and error to discover the number of different possible nets for a cube. Students should recognize that the greatest number of squares permissible in a row is 4 or else they will overlap. Students should also recognize that some of their arrangements are transformations of previous solutions.

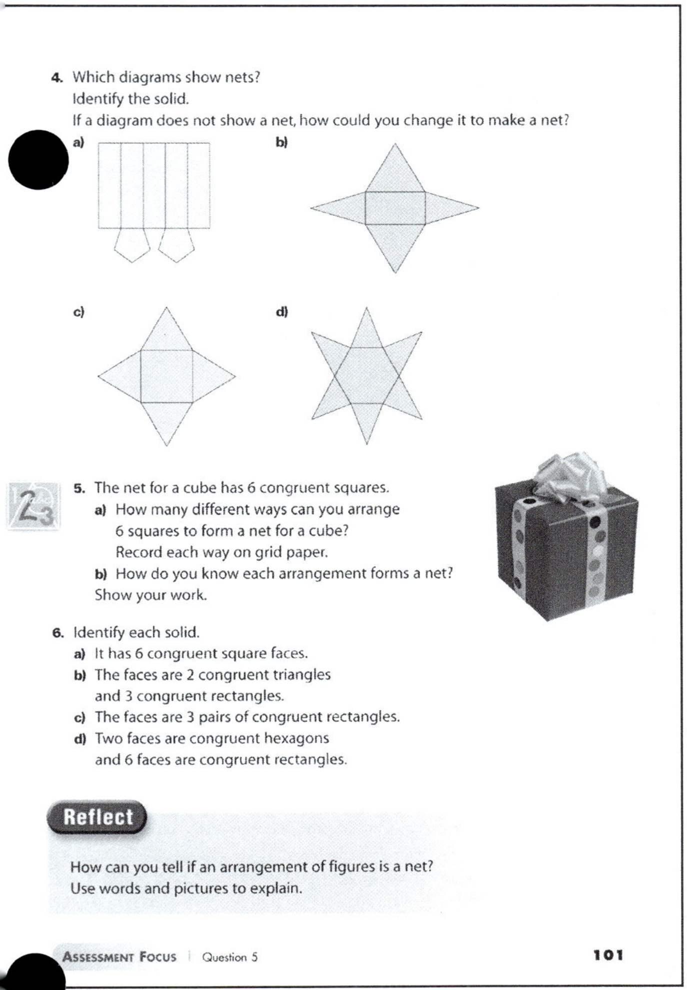

4. Which diagrams show nets?
Identify the solid.
If a diagram does not show a net, how could you change it to make a net?
a)
b)
c)
d)

5. The net for a cube has 6 congruent squares.
a) How many different ways can you arrange 6 squares to form a net for a cube? Record each way on grid paper.
b) How do you know each arrangement forms a net? Show your work.

6. Identify each solid.
a) It has 6 congruent square faces.
b) The faces are 2 congruent triangles and 3 congruent rectangles.
c) The faces are 3 pairs of congruent rectangles.
d) Two faces are congruent hexagons and 6 faces are congruent rectangles.

Reflect

How can you tell if an arrangement of figures is a net? Use words and pictures to explain.

ASSESSMENT FOCUS | Question 5

101

5. a) There are 11 different nets that will make a cube.

b) All of these nets, if cut out and folded, will make a cube. Any further nets would be transformations of one of these.

6. a) Cube **b)** Triangular prism
c) Rectangular prism **d)** Hexagonal prism

REFLECT: To tell if an arrangement of figures is a net of a solid, cut out the net and fold it up. Here is a net for a cube.
Here is an example of a non-net for a cube.

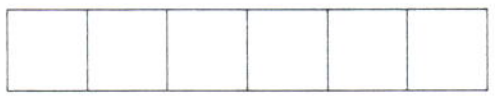

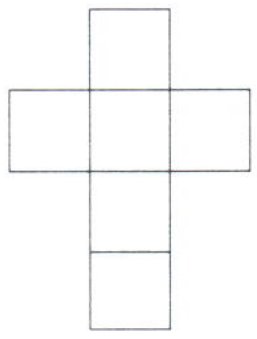

If this was cut out and folded, only 4 sides would be closed. Two faces would be empty and 2 squares would overlap.

ASSESSMENT FOR LEARNING

What to Look For

Understanding concepts
- ✔ Students are able to identify solids from their nets.
- ✔ Students are able to identify solids from a description.

Applying procedures
- ✔ Students can construct solids from nets.
- ✔ Students can construct nets for cubes and pyramids.

Problem solving
- ✔ Students are able to choose an appropriate strategy to solve problems involving geometric models.

What to Do

Extra Support: Students having difficulty can use Relational Geosolids and Nets for Relational Geosolids to construct nets or deconstruct solids to make nets.
Students can use Step-by-Step 6 (Master 3.18) to complete question 5.

Extra Practice: Have students explore the different nets that can be made for a square-based pyramid.
Students can complete Extra Practice 3 (Master 3.23).

Extension: Have each student bring an empty box from home. She should sketch a possible net of the box, then carefully take the box apart to lay it flat in one piece to confirm her sketch. Explanations can be made of students' successes. Students will also see why there is a need for tabs or flaps in box making.

Recording and Reporting
Master 3.2 Ongoing Observations: Geometry

Using a Computer to Explore Nets

LESSON ORGANIZER — 40–50 min

Curriculum Focus: Use a computer to create nets.
Student Materials
- Computer with *AppleWorks* or *The Geometer's Sketchpad*

Key Math Learning
A computer can be used to draw nets.

Using a Computer to Explore Nets

Work with a partner.

Use *AppleWorks*.
Follow these steps to create a net for a cube.

1. Open a new drawing document in *AppleWorks*. Click: Drawing
2. If a grid appears on the screen, go to Step 3.
   If not, click: Options, then click: Show Graphics Grid
3. Check that Autogrid is on. Click: Options
   If **Turn Autogrid Off** appears in the menu, Autogrid is on.
   If not, click: Turn Autogrid On Ctrl+Y
4. Check the ruler settings. Click: Format
   Click: Rulers, then click: Ruler Settings...
   Choose these settings:

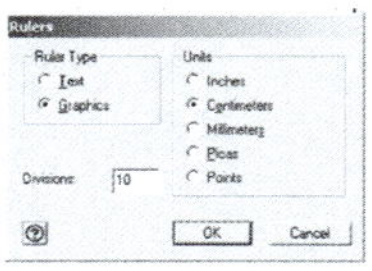

   Click: OK
5. To **draw a square**, click the Rectangle Tool: □
   The cursor will look like this: +
   Hold down the Shift key while you click and hold down the mouse button.
   Drag the cursor. Release the mouse button.

102 LESSON FOCUS | Use a computer to create nets.

BEFORE — Get Started

Tell students they will be using the Draw tools of *AppleWorks* to create a net for a cube. Ask questions, such as:
- How many faces does a cube have? *(6)*
- What shape are the faces of a cube? *(Square)*

DURING — Explore

Ongoing Assessment: Observe and Listen

Ask questions, such as:
- How do you know the arrangement of squares you have drawn will make an enclosed cube?
  (A net for a cube can have a maximum of 4 squares in a row.)

Instructions for creating nets using *The Geometer's Sketchpad*:

1. Open a new sketch in *The Geometer's Sketchpad*.
   Click: **File**, then click: **New Sketch**
2. Select the **Point Tool**.
   Click to draw a point.
   Do this 4 times.
3. Select the **Selection Arrow Tool**.
   Click to select all four points.
   Click: **Construct**, then click: **Segments**
   This connects the points with line segments to form a quadrilateral.
4. Click to select the points and the segments.
   Click: **Measure**, then click: **Length**
   to determine the length of the four segments.

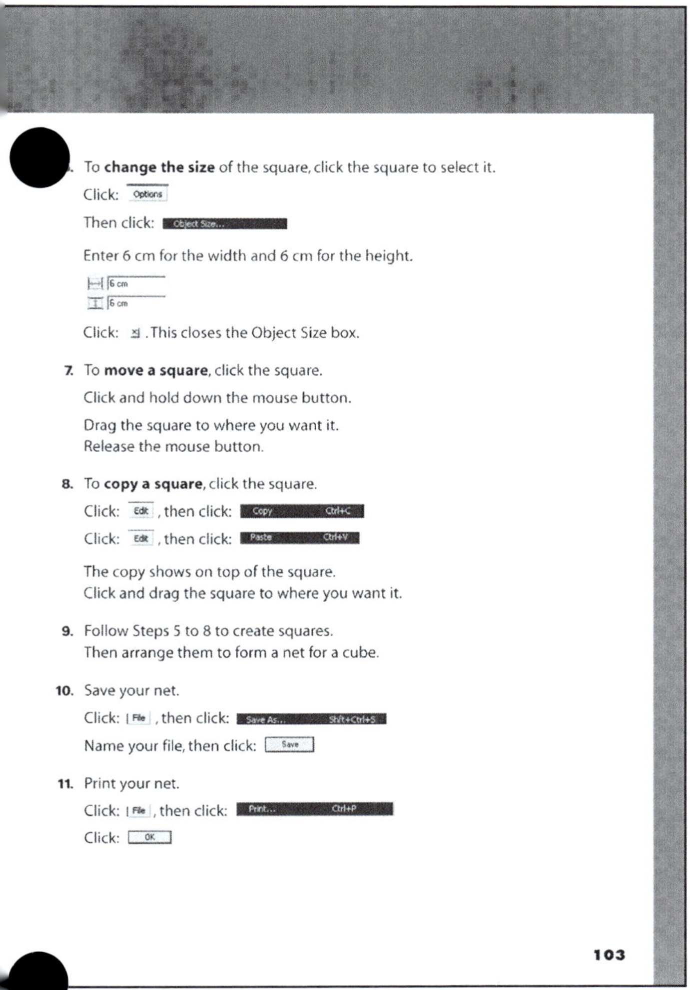

To **change the size** of the square, click the square to select it.

Click: Options

Then click: Object Size...

Enter 6 cm for the width and 6 cm for the height.

6 cm
6 cm

Click: . This closes the Object Size box.

7. To **move a square**, click the square.
Click and hold down the mouse button.
Drag the square to where you want it.
Release the mouse button.

8. To **copy a square**, click the square.
Click: Edit, then click: Copy Ctrl+C
Click: Edit, then click: Paste Ctrl+V
The copy shows on top of the square.
Click and drag the square to where you want it.

9. Follow Steps 5 to 8 to create squares.
Then arrange them to form a net for a cube.

10. Save your net.
Click: File, then click: Save As... Shift+Ctrl+S
Name your file, then click: Save

11. Print your net.
Click: File, then click: Print... Ctrl+P
Click: OK

103

REACHING ALL LEARNERS

Early Finishers

From a selection of pyramids, have students select a solid and attempt to create a net for it. Students can save and print their nets. They can cut out and assemble the net to confirm it is correctly configured.

5. Click outside the quadrilateral to deselect all the points and segments.
To change the size of the quadrilateral:
Click a line segment.
Hold down the mouse button.
Drag the line segment until it is where you want it.
Watch what happens to the measures as you move the line segment.
Release the mouse button.
Continue to select and move line segments until your quadrilateral is a square.

6. Select the **Selection Arrow Tool.**
Click to select all the points and line segments of the square.
Click: **Edit**, then click: **Copy**
Click: **Edit**, then click: **Paste**
Click the copy, and hold down the mouse button.
Drag the copy so that one side aligns with one side of the original square.
Release the mouse button.

7. Repeat Step 6 until you have 6 squares arranged to form a net of a cube.

8. Save your net.
Click: **File**, then click: **Save As**
Give your file a name.
Click: **Save**

9. Print your net.
Click: **File**, then click: **Print**
Click: **OK**

REFLECT: In a previous lesson we made and used nets for cubes. Some arrangements of squares did not make a net for a cube. I made a picture in my head of what the net would look like when it was folded up to make the cube. Four squares need to be in a row with two more squares on either side. This arrangement will make a cube. There are other nets that can be made, but none of them have more than 4 squares in a row.

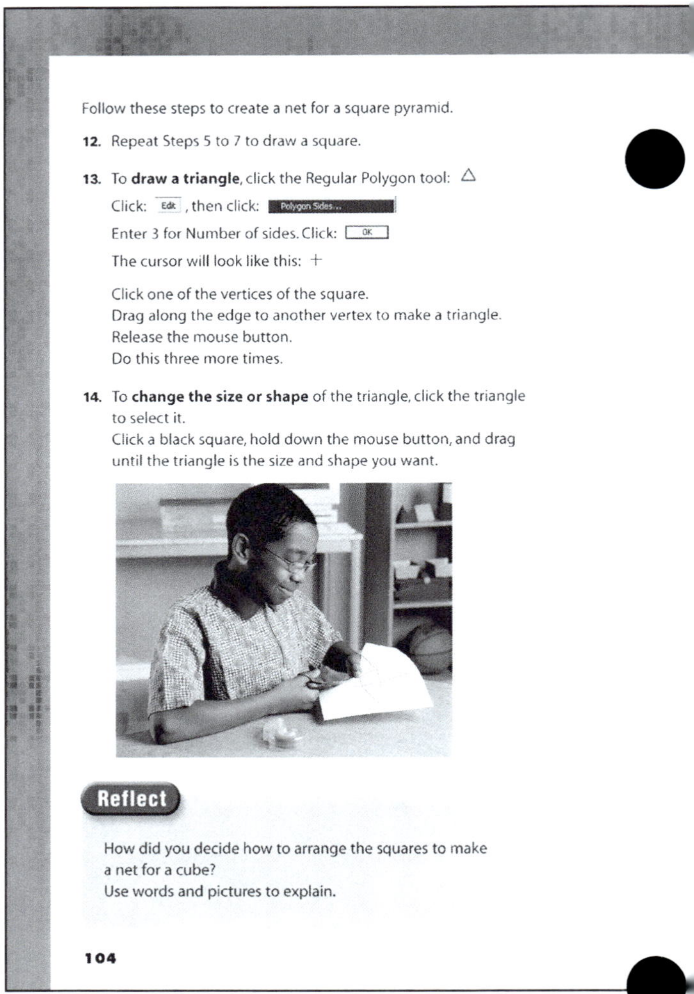

Follow these steps to create a net for a square pyramid.

12. Repeat Steps 5 to 7 to draw a square.
13. To **draw a triangle**, click the Regular Polygon tool: △
    Click: Edit , then click: Polygon Sides...
    Enter 3 for Number of sides. Click: OK
    The cursor will look like this: +
    Click one of the vertices of the square.
    Drag along the edge to another vertex to make a triangle.
    Release the mouse button.
    Do this three more times.
14. To **change the size or shape** of the triangle, click the triangle to select it.
    Click a black square, hold down the mouse button, and drag until the triangle is the size and shape you want.

Reflect

How did you decide how to arrange the squares to make a net for a cube?
Use words and pictures to explain.

104

AFTER Connect

Invite volunteers to share their printouts and discuss how they created their net.

Ask:

- What challenges did you encounter as the net was being created?
  (*Dragging the squares so they meet exactly*)
- Is using a computer a useful way to create nets? Why?
  (*Very useful; the measurements are always exact.*)

Discuss using a computer to make nets. Elicit from students that using the copy and paste function helps make congruent squares quickly.

What's My Rule?

What's My Rule?

You will need a set of *What's My Rule?* game cards, scissors, 2 labels, and two 1-m lengths of string.

Cut out the game cards.
Spread them out, face up.
Use the string to make 2 loops.
Label one loop "Matches" and one loop "Discards."

- Player A thinks of a secret rule that describes some of the polygons on the cards.
  The rule could be:
  - all triangles with a right angle; or
  - all regular polygons; or
  - all quadrilaterals with 1 pair of parallel sides
- Player A chooses 2 game cards.
  One card must fit the rule.
  He places it face up inside the "Matches" loop.
  The other card must not fit the rule.
  He places it face up in the "Discards" loop.
- Player B chooses a game card.
  If she thinks the card fits the rule, she places it inside the "Matches" loop.
  Otherwise, she places it in the "Discards" loop.
- Player A tells Player B whether her placement is correct.
  If the placement is correct, she can guess the rule.
  If the placement is not correct, she cannot make a guess.
- Players C and D continue until someone guesses the secret rule.
- Switch roles. Another player thinks of a secret rule.
  The other players take turns trying to guess the new rule.

The winner takes the fewest turns to guess the rule.

105

LESSON ORGANIZER 20 min

Student Materials
- What's My Rule? Game Cards (Master 3.8)
- scissors
- labels
- string

BEFORE **Get Started**

Organize the students into groups of 4. Provide each group with a copy of the game cards to cut out. This gives students an opportunity to identify each figure. Invite students to read the game instructions and gather the labels and string.

DURING **Game**

As students play, observe student and group behaviour. Ask questions, such as:
- Is the first player able to establish a rule for others to follow?
  (Yes, the second and subsequent players are able to follow the rule.)
- Has the next player been able to make a reasonable guess from the clues given?
  (Yes, the next player has been able to make a reasonable guess from the clues given, even if it is not the rule established by the first player.)

AFTER

After the game has been played, give students an opportunity for discussion. Ask what they liked and disliked. Students may make suggestions about how to make the game more challenging. For example, students develop additional game cards showing different polygons, or students investigate how a third string loop could be integrated into the game, or students have the two loops overlap like a Venn Diagram.

Invite students to determine if this game could be used in other mathematical topics.

Show Your Best

LESSON ORGANIZER — 40–50 min

Student Materials
- protractors
- millimetre rulers

Assessment: Master 3.1 Unit Rubic: Geometry
Master 3.4 Unit Summary: Geometry

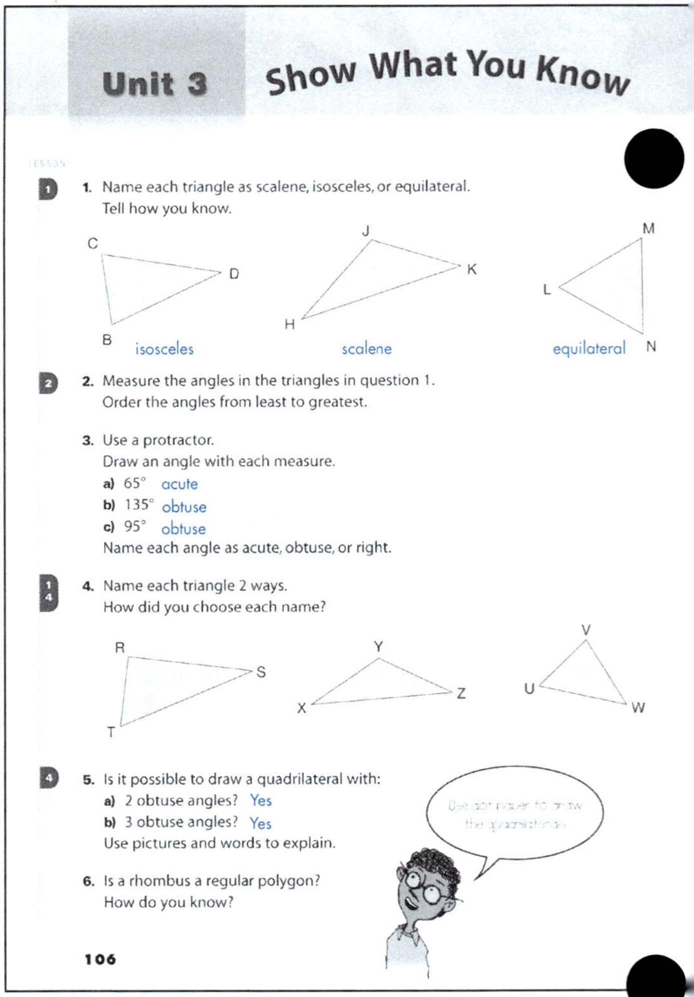

Unit 3 Show What You Know

1. Name each triangle as scalene, isosceles, or equilateral.
   Tell how you know.

2. Measure the angles in the triangles in question 1.
   Order the angles from least to greatest.
3. Use a protractor.
   Draw an angle with each measure.
   a) 65° acute
   b) 135° obtuse
   c) 95° obtuse
   Name each angle as acute, obtuse, or right.
4. Name each triangle 2 ways.
   How did you choose each name?

5. Is it possible to draw a quadrilateral with:
   a) 2 obtuse angles? Yes
   b) 3 obtuse angles? Yes
   Use pictures and words to explain.
6. Is a rhombus a regular polygon?
   How do you know?

106

1. △ BCD: sides CD and DB have equal length.
   △ HJK: all 3 sides have different lengths.
   △ LMN: all 3 sides have equal length.
2. ∠H = 30°, ∠K = 35°, ∠D = 40°, ∠L = ∠M = ∠N = 60°,
   ∠B = ∠C = 70°, ∠J = 115°
3. a) Use a protractor to check the angle is 65°.
   b) Use a protractor to check the angle is 135°.
   c) Use a protractor to check the angle is 95°.
4. △ RST: scalene triangle, right triangle; one angle measures 90°; all sides have different lengths.
   △ XYZ: obtuse triangle, scalene triangle; the measure of ∠Y is greater than 90°; all sides have different lengths.
   △ UVW: acute triangle, scalene triangle; the measure of all angles is less than 90°, and all sides have different lengths.

Be Accurate

Encourage students to work carefully and precisely when drawing and explaining their solutions. They should show all their work and label their drawings accurately. Remind students that the audience for their work may be more than their teacher. Parents, for example, will want to see their work. They should use rulers for measuring and drawing straight lines, and protractors for measuring and constructing angles.

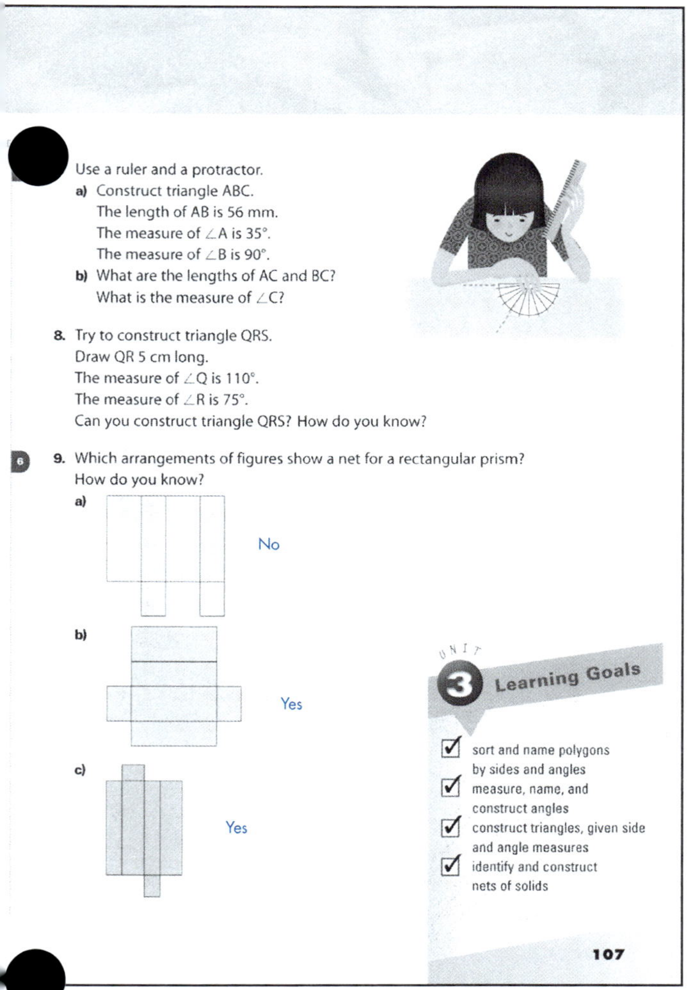
Use a ruler and a protractor.

a) Construct triangle ABC.
The length of AB is 56 mm.
The measure of ∠A is 35°.
The measure of ∠B is 90°.

b) What are the lengths of AC and BC?
What is the measure of ∠C?

8. Try to construct triangle QRS.
Draw QR 5 cm long.
The measure of ∠Q is 110°.
The measure of ∠R is 75°.
Can you construct triangle QRS? How do you know?

9. Which arrangements of figures show a net for a rectangular prism?
How do you know?

a) No

b) Yes

c) Yes

UNIT 3 Learning Goals

- ✓ sort and name polygons by sides and angles
- ✓ measure, name, and construct angles
- ✓ construct triangles, given side and angle measures
- ✓ identify and construct nets of solids

107

5. a) A rhombus has one pair of opposite angles greater than 90°.

   b) A quadrilateral can have these interior angles: 120°, 110°, 100°, 30°.

6. Sometimes; a rhombus has all sides equal, pairs of parallel sides, and opposite angles equal. A square is a rhombus; it is a regular polygon because it has all sides and all angles equal. Any rhombus that is not a square is not a regular polygon.

7. a)

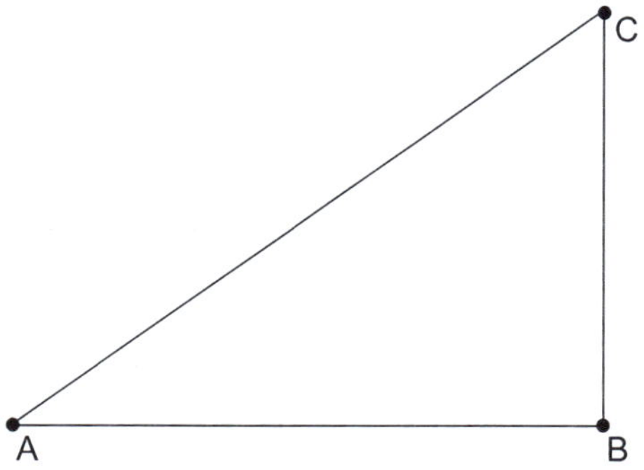

   b) AC = 69 mm; BC = 40 mm; ∠C = 55°

8. No, it impossible to draw a triangle from these measurements. Line segments QS and RS are angled away from each other; these line segments will never meet to make a triangle.

9. a) If figure were cut out and folded, one face would not be complete.

   b) If the figure were cut out and folded, all the faces would be complete.

   c) If the figure were cut out and folded, all the faces would be complete.

ASSESSMENT FOR LEARNING

What to Look For

Understanding of concepts

✔ **Question 9:** Student understands that a net shows all the faces of a solid and can be joined in one piece.

Application of mathematical procedures

✔ **Question 2 and 3:** Student is able to use a protractor to measure and name angles.

✔ **Question 7:** Student is able to construct a triangle given side and angle measures.

Communication

✔ **Question 6:** Student is able to explain what a regular polygon is through its properties, using words and drawings.

Problem solving

✔ **Question 8:** Student can solve problems by interpreting a drawing.

Recording and Reporting

Master 3.1 Unit Rubric: Geometry
Master 3.4 Unit Summary: Geometry

Bridges

LESSON ORGANIZER 40–50 min

Student Grouping:
Groups of 4
Student Materials
- Bristol board
- hole punches or compasses
- paper fasteners
- centimetre rulers
- centimetre cubes or standard masses
- Truss Pieces (Master 3.9)

Assessment: Masters 3.3 Performance Assessment Rubric: Bridges, 3.4 Unit Summary: Geometry

Teaching notes for the Cross Strand Investigation *Triangle, Triangle, Triangle* are in the *Additional Assessment Support* module.

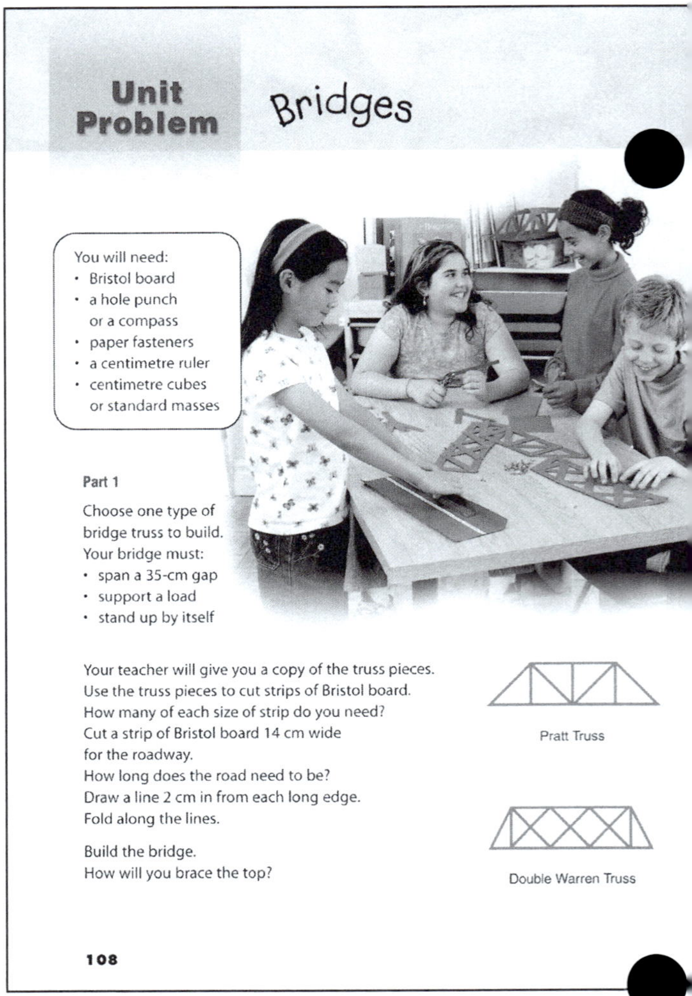
Unit Problem Bridges

You will need:
- Bristol board
- a hole punch or a compass
- paper fasteners
- a centimetre ruler
- centimetre cubes or standard masses

Part 1

Choose one type of bridge truss to build.
Your bridge must:
- span a 35-cm gap
- support a load
- stand up by itself

Your teacher will give you a copy of the truss pieces.
Use the truss pieces to cut strips of Bristol board.
How many of each size of strip do you need?
Cut a strip of Bristol board 14 cm wide for the roadway.
How long does the road need to be?
Draw a line 2 cm in from each long edge.
Fold along the lines.

Build the bridge.
How will you brace the top?

Pratt Truss

Double Warren Truss

108

Display the answers recorded in the *Unit Launch* and review the questions and answers. Refer students to the list of key words and the Learning Goals in the *Unit Launch*.

Invite a volunteer to read Parts 1, 2, and 3 aloud. Students should share the tasks. To save time, you may wish to pre-cut the truss pieces using a paper cutter. Depending on the bridge they choose to build, each group will need 4 to 10 "A" pieces, 8 to 18 "B" pieces, and 4 to 8 "C" pieces. Groups that build a Double Warren Truss bridge also need 4 "D" and 4 "E" pieces. Suggest to students that they arrange the truss pieces on their desks before beginning to join the pieces.

Use the information from the Check List and the Performance Assessment Rubric: Bridges to clarify what is expected from student work. Refer students to the Check List as they complete this performance task.

Observe how students use the materials as they build the bridge. Do they use the truss pieces appropriately? Is the length of the roadway sufficient to clear the 35-cm span?

Observe how students identify the attributes of the bridge. Do they name the different polygons correctly? Can they differentiate regular from irregular polygons?

Observe how the students test their bridges for load support. How do they compare their own bridge to others? Do they recognize the strengths and weaknesses of the various bridges? Do they effectively record their understanding of bridges and the attributes that make them strong?

Check List

Your work should show
- ☑ a clear explanation of what you did and why
- ☑ as many attributes as possible
- ☑ how you used what you know about geometry
- ☑ how you found the greatest mass your bridge could support

Part 2

Look at your bridge.
Identify as many of these attributes as you can:
- congruent figures
- scalene, equilateral, and isosceles triangles
- obtuse, acute, and right angles
- equal angles

Name different polygons you see.
Are any of them regular? Explain.

Part 3

Use two desks or some textbooks to make a 35-cm gap.
Place your bridge across the gap.
Find the load your bridge can support.

Compare your bridge with those of other groups.
Which type of bridge can support the greatest mass?

Write about the bridges and the attributes that make them strong.

Howe Truss

Howe Truss with counter braces

Reflect on the Unit

How can you use what you know about triangles and other polygons to
- draw nets of solids?
- identify solids from their nets?

109

Sample Response

Part 1

The truss bridge should meet the given constraints; it must span a 35-cm gap, support a load, and be self-standing. The truss bridges will look similar to one of the bridges depicted. Students should recognize that the roadway must be longer than 35 cm for the bridge to span a 35-cm gap. Students should also realize they need to brace the bridge across the top. Triangles provide great strength and rigidity.

Part 2

Students should identify congruent triangles, parallelograms, and/or squares, depending on the bridge they constructed. They name the triangles according to side lengths and angle measures. Students identify regular polygons in their bridge.

Part 3

Students use appropriate loads for their bridges. They start with small masses and gradually increase the load. They compare bridges using appropriate attributes. Students identify a specific bridge as being able to support the greatest mass and support their choice.

Reflect on the Unit

When I make a net of a solid, every face of the solid must be represented. Faces that form an edge in the solid should be adjacent to one another in the net. The figures in the net must be congruent to the faces of the solid. I can identify a solid from its net by looking at the polygons that make up the net.

ASSESSMENT FOR LEARNING

What to Look For

Understanding concepts
- ✔ Students can correctly identify and name polygons related to the bridges built.
- ✔ Students can identify regular polygons.

Applying procedures
- ✔ Students can construct triangles from materials and use them to build bridges.

Communicating
- ✔ Students give a clear explanation of the attributes of a bridge.

What to Do

Extra Support: Make the problem accessible.
Some students may require more direction to complete Parts 1 and 2. Refer them to the criteria for building the truss bridge. Suggest they study the artwork in the Student Book and refer back to the notes from the *Unit Launch*.

Recording and Reporting
Master 3.3 Performance Assessment Rubric: Bridges
Master 3.4 Unit Summary: Geometry

Evaluating Student Learning: Preparing to Report: Unit 3 Geometry

This unit provides an opportunity to report on the **Geometry and Spatial Sense** strand. *Master 3.4 Unit Summary: Geometry* provides a comprehensive format for recording and summarizing evidence collected.

Here is an example of a completed summary chart for this Unit:

Strand: *Geometry and Spatial Sense*	Problem solving	Understanding of concepts	Application of mathematical procedures	Communication	*Overall*
Ongoing Observations	3	2	2	3	2/3
Strategies Toolkit (Lesson 3)			3		3
Work samples or portfolios; conferences	3	3	2	3	3
Show What You Know	3	3	3	3	3
Unit Test	3	2	2	3	2/3
Unit Problem *Bridges*	3	3	3	2	3
Achievement Level for reporting					3

Recording	How to Report
Ongoing Observations	Use *Master 3.2 Ongoing Observations: Geometry* to determine the most consistent level achieved in each category. Enter it in the chart. Choose to summarize by achievement category, or simply to enter an overall level. Observations from late in the unit should be most heavily weighted.
Strategies Toolkit (problem solving)	Use *PM 1: Inquiry Process Check List* with the Strategies Toolkit (Lesson 3). Transfer results to the summary form. Teachers may choose to enter a level in the Problem solving column and/or Communication.
Portfolios or collections of work samples; conferences, or interviews	Use *Master 3.1 Unit Rubric: Geometry* to guide evaluation of collections of work and information gathered in conferences. Teachers may choose to focus particular attention on the *Assessment Focus* questions. Work from late in the unit should be most heavily weighted.
Show What You Know	Teachers may choose to assign some or all of these questions. *Master 3.1 Unit Rubric: Geometry* may be helpful in determining levels of achievement. #9 provides evidence of Understanding of concepts; #2, 3, and 7 provide evidence of Application of mathematical procedures; #4 provides evidence of Problem solving; #6 provides evidence of Communication.
Unit Test	*Master 3.1 Unit Rubric: Geometry* may be helpful in determining levels of achievement. Part A provides evidence of Accuracy of procedures; Part B provides evidence of Reasoning; Applying concepts; Part C provides evidence of Problem solving; all parts provide evidence of Communication.
Unit performance task	Use *Master 3.3 Performance Assessment Rubric: Bridges.* The *Unit Problem* offers a snapshot of students' achievement. In particular, it shows their ability to synthesize and apply what they have learned.
Student Self-Assessment	Note students' perceptions of their own progress. This may take the form of an oral or written comment, or a self-rating.
Comments	Analyse the pattern of achievement to identify strengths and needs. In some cases, specific actions may be planned to support the learner.

Learning Skills	Ongoing Records
PM 4: Learning Skills Check List Use to record and report throughout a reporting period, rather than for each unit and/or strand.	*PM 10: Summary Class Records: Strands* *PM 11: Summary Class Records: Achievement Categories* *PM 12: Summary Record: Individual* Use to record and report evaluations of student achievement over several clusters, a reporting period, or a school year. These can also be used in place of the Unit Summary.

Name ____________________ Date ________________

Master 3.1

Unit Rubric: Geometry

<table>
<tr><th></th><th>Level 1</th><th>Level 2</th><th>Level 3</th><th>Level 4</th></tr>
<tr><td>Problem solving
• chooses and carries out appropriate strategies, such as: drawing; creating models, constructions, nets, computer programs to solve problems in geometry</td><td>with assistance, chooses and carries out a limited range of appropriate strategies to solve geometric problems, rarely resulting in an accurate solution</td><td>with limited assistance, chooses and carries out some appropriate strategies to solve geometric problems, frequently resulting in an accurate solution</td><td>chooses and carries out appropriate strategies to solve geometric problems, usually resulting in an accurate solution</td><td>chooses and carries out appropriate strategies to solve geometric problems accurately; may be innovative</td></tr>
<tr><td>Understanding of concepts
• shows understanding by creating and explaining:
– nets of cubes and pyramids
– sketches of faces of 3-D solids
– angles
– triangles</td><td>may be unable to create or explain:
– nets and sketches of cubes and pyramids
– angles and triangles</td><td>partially able to create and explain:
– nets and sketches of cubes and pyramids
– angles and triangles</td><td>appropriately creates and explains:
– nets and sketches of cubes and pyramids
– angles and triangles</td><td>in various contexts, consistently and appropriately creates and explains:
– nets and sketches of cubes and pyramids
– angles and triangles</td></tr>
<tr><td>• shows understanding by discussing and explaining:
– geometric properties and principles in the everyday world
– ideas, conjectures, and hypotheses about geometric properties and relationships</td><td>may be unable to discuss and explain geometric properties, principles, and relationships</td><td>partially able to discuss and explain geometric properties, principles, and relationships</td><td>appropriately explains geometric properties, principles, and relationships</td><td>in various contexts, offers appropriate and complete explanations of geometric properties, principles, and relationships</td></tr>
<tr><td>Application of mathematical procedures
• uses appropriate procedures to accurately:
– sort and name polygons
– measure and name angles
– identify and create nets of solids</td><td>limited accuracy; major errors or omissions in:
– sorting and naming polygons
– measuring and naming angles
– identifying and creating nets</td><td>somewhat accurate; makes frequent minor errors/omissions in:
– sorting and naming polygons
– measuring and naming angles
– identifying and creating nets</td><td>generally accurate; makes few errors/ omissions in:
– sorting and naming polygons
– measuring and naming angles
– identifying and creating nets</td><td>accurate; rarely makes errors/omissions in:
– sorting and naming polygons
– measuring and naming angles
– identifying and creating nets</td></tr>
<tr><td>Communication
• presents work, describes procedures, and explains reasoning clearly, using appropriate mathematical symbols and terms (e.g., equilateral, isosceles, scalene, acute, obtuse, polygon)</td><td>work is often unclear and imprecise; needs assistance to describe procedures and explain reasoning; often unclear and imprecise</td><td>work is presented with some clarity and precision; describes procedures and explains reasoning with some clarity, precision, and appropriate terminology</td><td>work is generally clear and precise; describes procedures and explains reasoning with general clarity and precision, and appropriate terminology</td><td>work is clear and precise; describes procedures and explains reasoning clearly, precisely, and confidently, using the most appropriate terminology</td></tr>
</table>

Name ____________________ Date ______________

Master 3.2

Ongoing Observations: Geometry

The behaviours described under each heading are examples; they are not intended to be an exhaustive list of all that might be observed. More detailed descriptions are provided in each lesson under *Assessment for Learning*.

STUDENT ACHIEVEMENT: Geometry				
Student	**Problem solving** ▪ Uses appropriate strategies to solve problems, including construction of figures and solids	**Understanding of concepts** ▪ Creates and explains nets, sketches, 3-D solids, angles, and triangles ▪ Offers ideas about geometric properties and relationships	**Application of mathematical procedures** ▪ Sorts and names polygons and angles ▪ Measures angles ▪ Identifies nets	**Communication** ▪ Presents work, procedures, and reasoning clearly ▪ Uses appropraite geometric terminology

Level 1 – very limited; Level 2 – somewhat or limited; Level 3 – satisfactory; Level 4 – thorough

Name ____________________ Date ______________

Master 3.3

Performance Assessment Rubric: Bridges

	Level 1	Level 2	Level 3	Level 4
Problem solving • chooses and carries out appropriate strategies (e.g., estimating, measuring, sketching) to create a bridge, identify attributes, and determine the load the bridge can support	chooses and carries out simple or inappropriate strategies that lead to inaccurate solutions	chooses and carries out some appropriate strategies with partial success to: – create the bridge – identify attributes – determine the load	chooses and carries out appropriate and effective strategies to: – create the bridge – identify attributes – determine the load	chooses innovative, appropriate, and effective strategies to: – create the bridge – identify attributes – determine the load
Understanding of concepts • shows understanding by discussing and explaining geometric properties, principles, and relationships and their application (e.g., in creating strong bridges)	shows very limited understanding by giving inappropriate explanations (of the bridges and the attributes that make them strong)	shows limited understanding by giving appropriate but incomplete explanations (of the bridges and the attributes that make them strong)	shows understanding by giving appropriate explanations (of the bridges and the attributes that make them strong)	shows thorough understanding by giving appropriate and complete explanations (of the bridges and the attributes that make them strong)
Application of mathematical procedures • uses appropriate procedures to accurately identify: – length of the roadway – congruent figures – scalene, equilateral, and isosceles triangles – obtuse, acute, and right angles – equal angles – polygons	limited accuracy; major errors or omissions in identifying: – length of the roadway – attributes of the bridge	somewhat accurate; several minor errors or omissions in identifying: – length of the roadway – attributes of the bridge	generally accurate; few errors or omissions in identifying: – length of the roadway – attributes of the bridge	accurate; very few or no errors or omissions in identifying: – length of the roadway – attributes of the bridge
Communication • provides clear explanations and descriptions • uses mathematical terminology, including units and symbols, correctly (e.g., polygon, right angle, perpendicular)	explanations and descriptions are unclear and imprecise; uses few appropriate mathematical terms and symbols	explanations and descriptions are partially clear and precise; uses some appropriate mathematical terms and symbols	explanations and descriptions are generally clear and precise; uses appropriate mathematical terms and symbols	explanations and descriptions are clear, precise, and confident; uses the most appropriate mathematical terminology and symbols

Name ______________________ Date ________________

Master 3.4

Unit Summary: Geometry

Review assessment records to determine the most consistent achievement levels for the assessments conducted. Some cells may be blank. *Overall* achievement levels may be recorded in each row, rather than identifying levels for each achievement category.

	Most Consistent Level of Achievement*				
Strand: *Geometry and Spatial Sense*	**Problem solving**	**Understanding of concepts**	**Application of mathematical procedures**	**Communication**	***Overall***
Ongoing Observations					
Strategies Toolkit (Lesson 3)					
Work samples or portfolios; conferences					
Show What You Know					
Unit Test					
Unit Problem: Bridges					
Achievement Level for reporting					

*Use Ontario Achievement Levels 1, 2, 3, 4.

Self-Assessment:

Comments: (Strengths, Needs, Next Steps)

Name ____________________ Date ______________

Master 3.5

To Parents and Adults at Home ...

Your child's class is beginning a mathematics unit on geometry. Through daily activities, students will explore different two-dimensional figures. They will investigate the characteristics of different figures, and explore relationships between vertices (corners), side length, and angle measurement of these figures.

In this unit, your child will:

- Sort and name polygons by sides and angles.
- Measure, name, and construct angles.
- Construct triangles, given side and angle measures.
- Identify and construct nets of solids.

Geometry is an important part of a student's mathematical experience. Geometry provides students with a strong link between the mathematics they learn in the classroom and the real world.

Here are some suggestions for activities to do at home.

- Before recycling cardboard boxes or containers, carefully take them apart to see how they are constructed.
- Cut cardboard strips of different lengths, and explore different figures that can be made from them. Compare the angles that result.

Name ____________________ Date ________________

Master 3.6

Triangles for Lesson 1

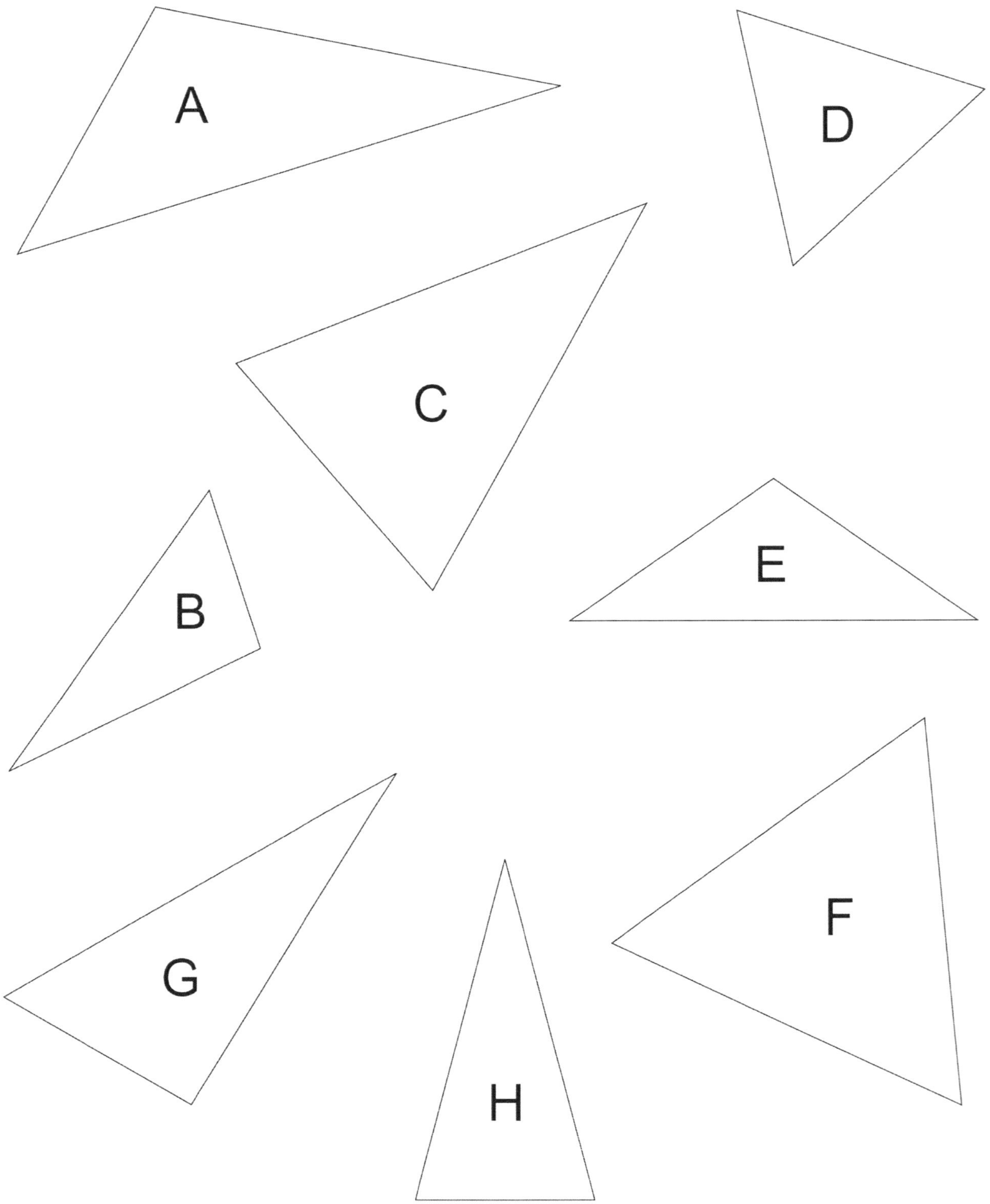

Name ____________________ Date ________________

Master 3.7

Triangles for Lesson 4

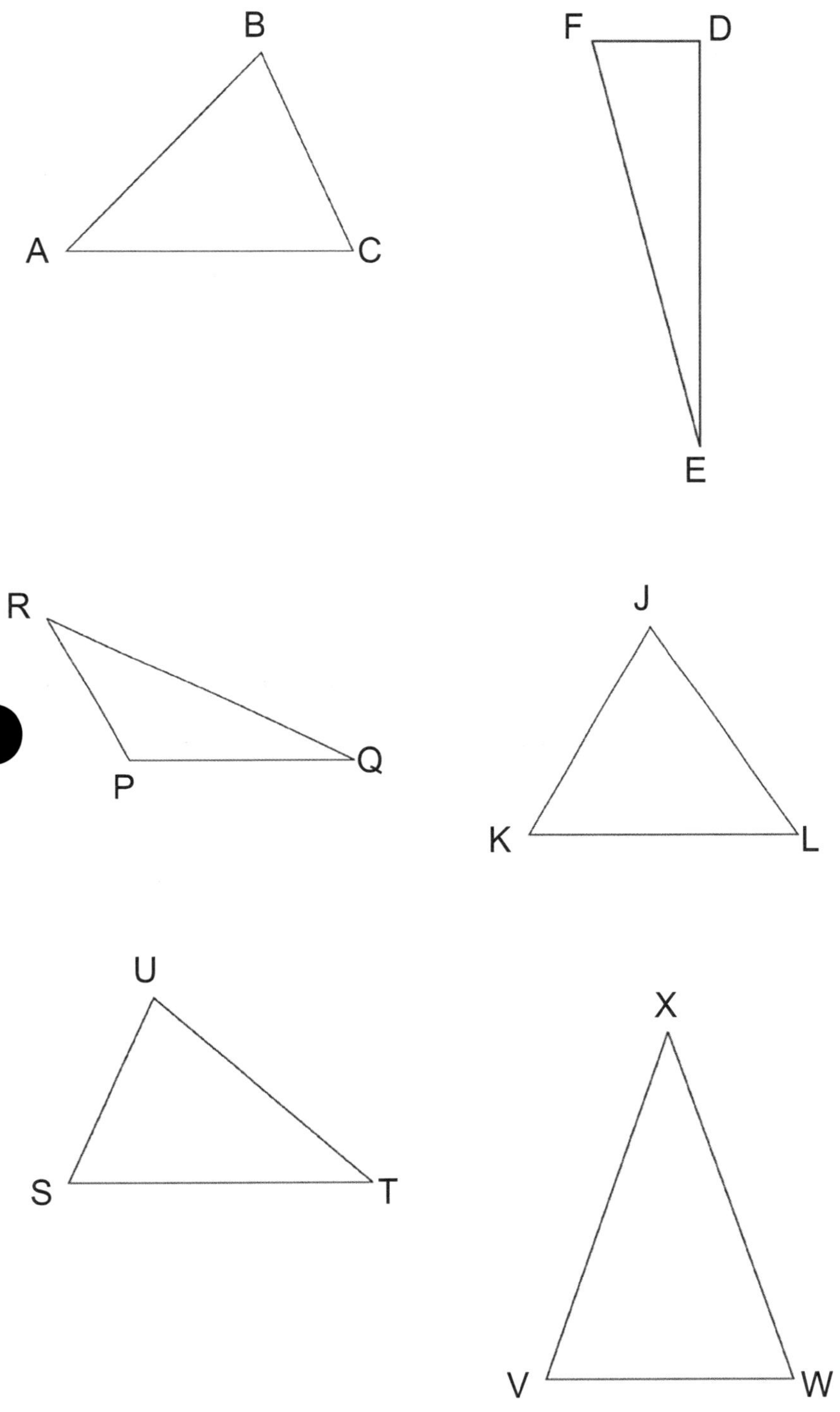

Name ____________________ Date ________________

Master 3.8

What's My Rule? Game Cards

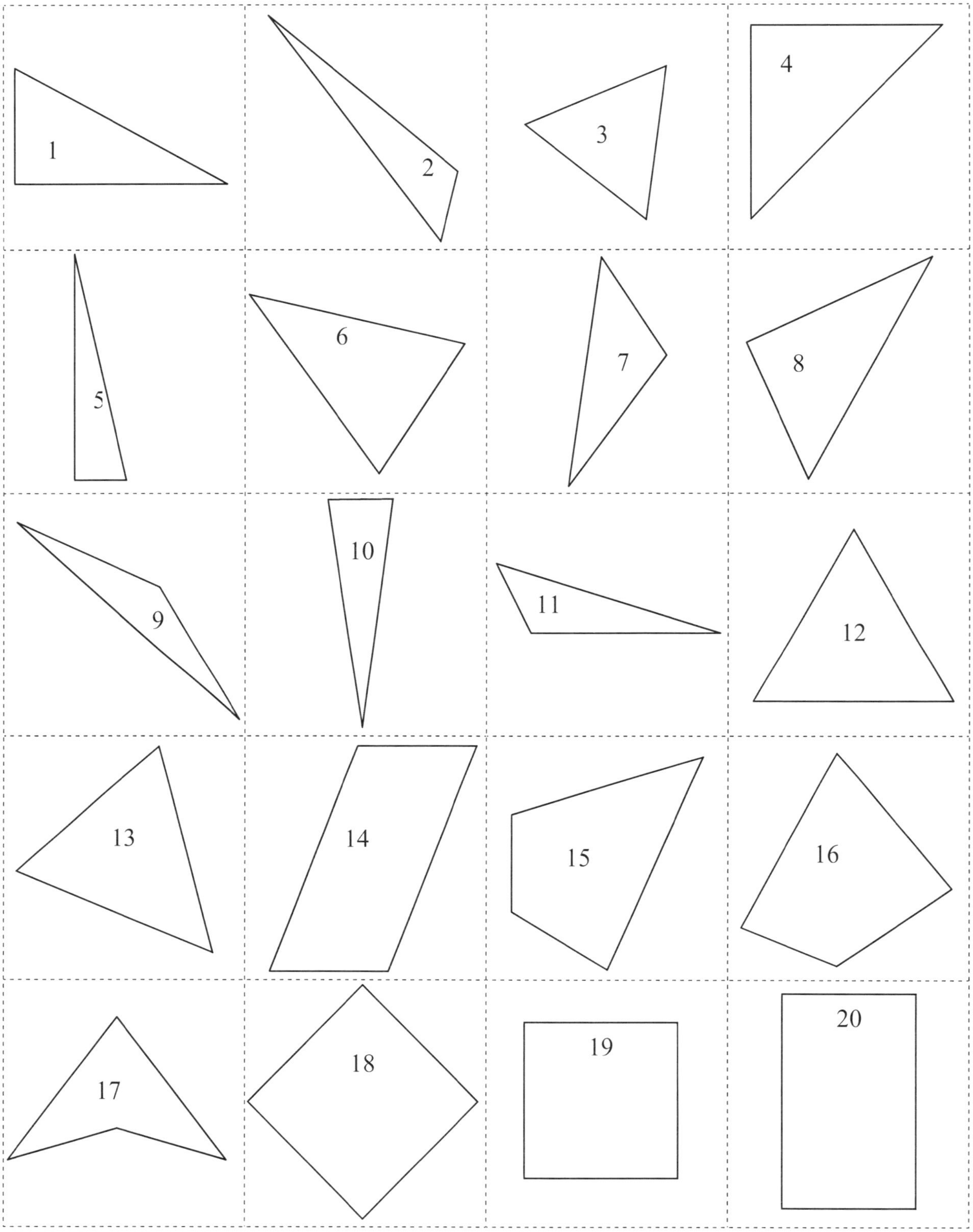

Name ____________________ Date ________________

Master 3.9

Truss Pieces

All the bridges require
pieces A, B, and C.
The Double Warren Truss
also requires pieces D and E.

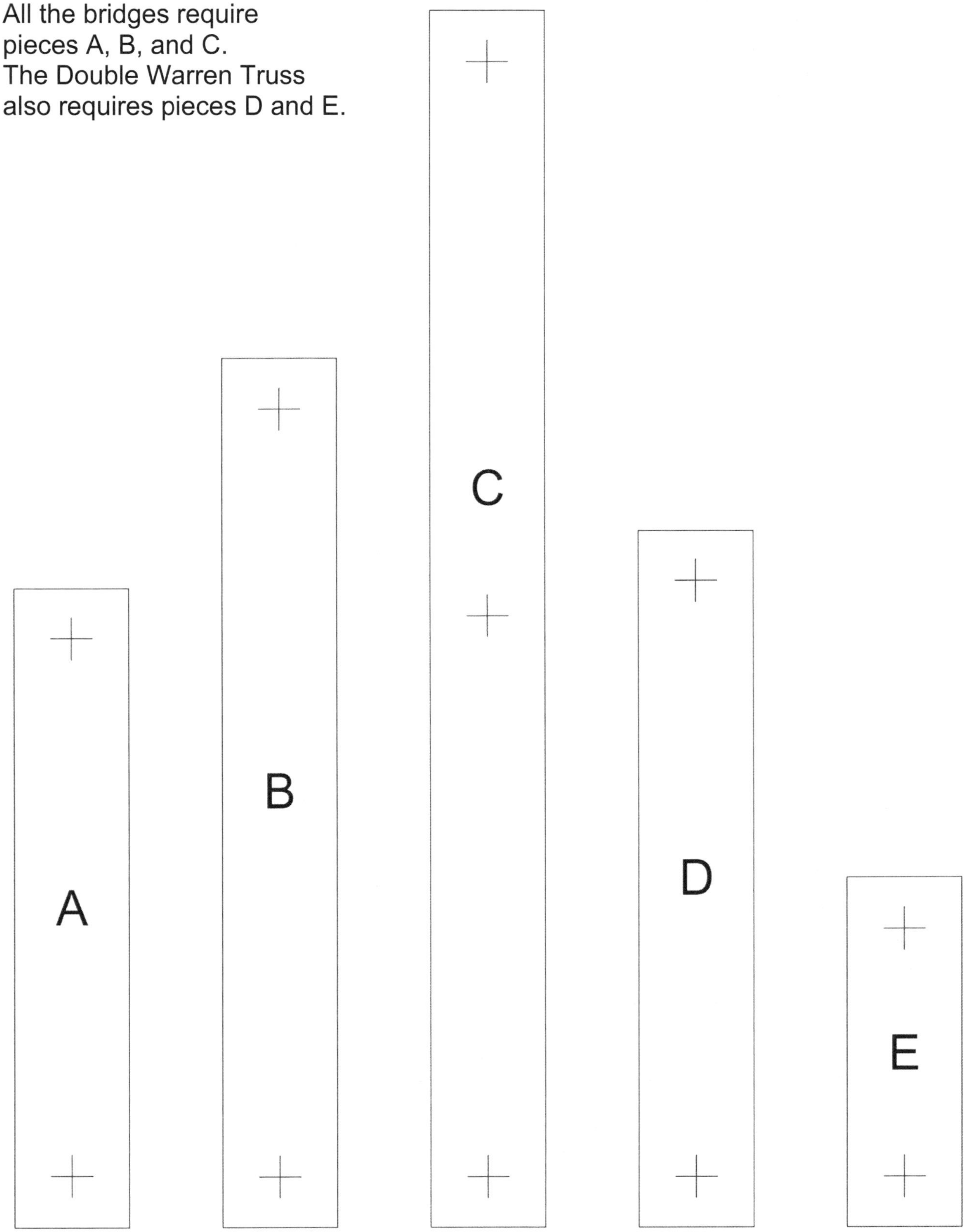

Name ____________________ Date _______________

Master 3.10

Additional Activity 1: Partner Polygons

Work with a group.

You will need a 2-m length of fabric elastic and index cards.

- Brainstorm a list of attributes of polygons.
  You may include attributes such as,
  2 pairs of parallel sides, all angles equal, and number of sides.
  Write the attributes from your list on index cards.
  Shuffle the index cards and place them face down in a pile.

- Tie the elastic to form a large loop.
  Take turns to draw a card from the pile.
  Loop the elastic around your hands.
  Model a polygon with the attribute described on the card.
  If it is not possible, draw another card to include with the previous card.

Take It Further:
Try to create the next polygon or angle using the fewest moves.
A move consists of moving only one hand.

Name ____________________ Date _______________

Master 3.11

Additional Activity 2: Pattern Block Properties

Work with a partner.
You will need Pattern Blocks and a brown paper bag.

- Place the Pattern Blocks in the bag.

- Take turns to think of a Pattern Block.
  Do not tell which block you are thinking of.
  When it is your turn, describe the block you are thinking of.
  Do not tell what shape it is.
  Talk about the sides and the angles in your description.

- Without looking, your partner reaches into the bag and tries to find the Pattern Block that matches your description.

Take It Further:
Take turns to think of a polygon.
Without telling the name of the polygon, describe the polygon to your partner.
Your partner tries to sketch the polygon you described.

Name ____________________ Date ________________

Master 3.12

Additional Activity 3: Exploring Paper Triangles

Work with a partner.
You will need scissors, paper, a ruler, and a protractor.

- Cut out a large paper triangle.
  Measure the side lengths and the angles.
  Record the measures on the triangle.

- Fold one side of the triangle.
  The fold line should be parallel to one side of the triangle, as shown.

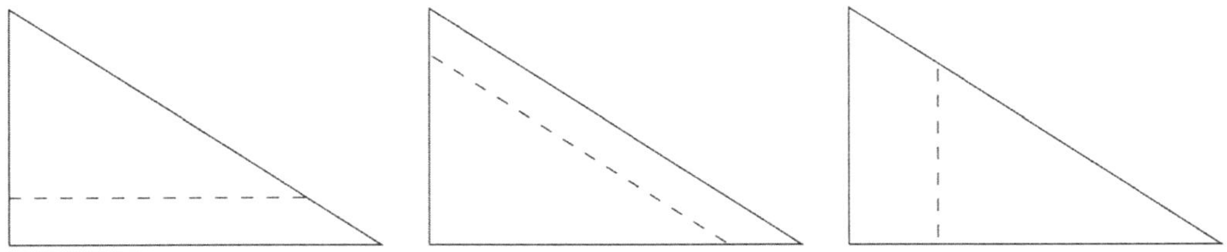

- Measure the side lengths and angles of the new triangle.
  Record the new measures.

- Compare the side lengths and angles of the original triangle to the side lengths and angles of the smaller triangle formed by folding.
  What do you notice?

Take It Further
Try different types of triangles, such as scalene and obtuse.
What do you notice?

Name ____________________ Date ______________

Master 3.13

Additional Activity 4: Making Angles and Triangles

Work on your own.
You will need scissors, paper, a ruler, and a protractor.

- Fold a piece of paper as shown.
  Unfold the paper. Cut the rectangle off the end to form a square.

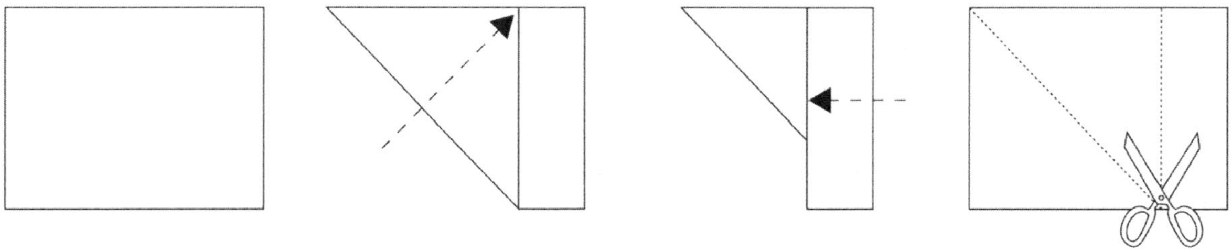

  Describe the triangles you see.
  Find the measures of the sides and angles of the triangles.

- Fold the square to make the other diagonal.
  Find the measures of the sides and angles of the triangles.
  Name all the triangles you see.

- Fold your paper square into 4 along the diagonals.
  This forms a right isosceles triangle.
  Fold the triangle so the equal sides align.
  Cut a piece from the fold line.

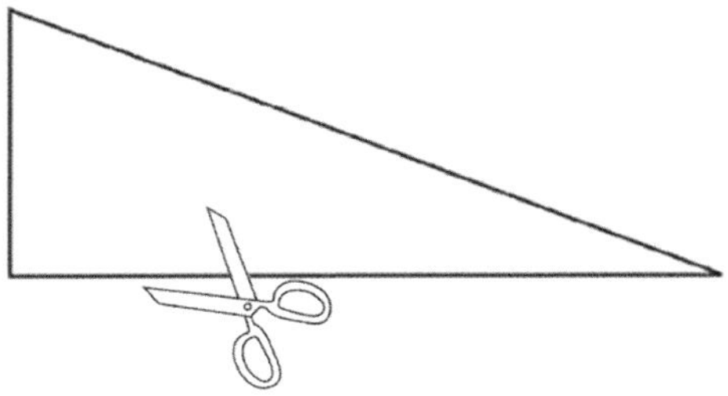

- Unfold the paper.
  Describe the cut shapes you see.
  How many are there? Why?

Take It Further:
How can you make a 90° angle by folding any scrap of paper?

Name ____________________ Date ________________

Master 3.14

Step-by-Step 1

Lesson 1, Question 5

You need pipe cleaners and drinking straws cut to these lengths:

- 1 piece 3 cm long
- 2 pieces 4 cm long
- 3 pieces 5 cm long
- 1 piece 8 cm long
- 1 piece 9 cm long

Step 1 Choose 3 straws with the same length.
Arrange the straws to make an equilateral triangle.
Trace the triangle. Label it "equilateral."

Step 2 Choose the 2 shortest straws with equal length.
Choose the shortest straw with a different length.
Arrange the straws to make an isosceles triangle.
Trace and label your triangle.

Step 3 Choose 3 straws with different lengths.
Choose the longest straws possible.
Arrange the straws to make a scalene triangle.
Trace and label your triangle.

Step 4 Which straws could not be used together to make a triangle?
Why not?

____

____

Name ____________________ Date _______________

Master 3.15

Step-by-Step 2

Lesson 2, Question 4

Step 1 To construct a 80° angle:
Use a ruler.
Draw a horizontal line. This is one arm of the angle.

Step 2 Use a protractor.
Place the middle of the protractor at the left end of the arm you drew in *Step 1*.
Start at the 0° on the arm.
Count around the protractor until you reach the angle you are looking for.
Make a mark at the angle.

Step 3 Draw a line joining the left end of the arm with the mark.
Label the angle with its measure.

Step 4 Repeat *Steps 1* to *3* to make a 30° angle.

Step 5 Repeat *Steps 1* to *3* to make a 100° angle.

Step 6 Repeat *Steps 1* to *3* to make a 10° angle.

Step 7 Repeat *Steps 1* to *3* to make a 180° angle.

Step 8 Look at the angle that measures 180°.

What does this angle look like? ________________________________

How might you name an angle that measures 180°?

____

Name ____________________ Date ________________

Master 3.16

Step-by-Step 4

Lesson 4, Question 5

Use square dot paper, or a geoboard and geobands.

Step 1 Draw an obtuse angle.
At the end of one arm, draw another obtuse angle.
Join the ends of the arms to make a polygon.
Write the name of the polygon inside it.

Step 2 Draw an acute angle.
At the end of one arm, draw another acute angle.
Join the ends of the arms to make a polygon.
Write the name of the polygon inside it.

Step 3 Draw a right angle.
At one end of the arm, draw another right angle.
Join the ends of the arms to make a polygon.
Write the name of the polygon inside it.

Step 4 Draw an acute angle.
At the end of one arm draw an obtuse angle.
At the end of one arm, draw a right angle.
Join the ends of the arms to make a polygon.
Write the name of the polygon inside it.

Step 5 Look at the instructions for each polygon in the Student Book.
Draw different polygons that match these instructions.

Name ____________________ Date _______________

Master 3.17

Step-by-Step 5

Lesson 5, Question 4

Step 1 Construct triangle GHK.
Use the line segment HK, below left.
Use a protractor. Construct a 45° angle at H.
Use a ruler to mark 46 mm along the arm you drew.
Label the end of this segment G.
Use a ruler to join G to K.

Step 2 For the triangle in *Step 1*:

What is the length of side GK? ______________

What is the measure of ∠K? ______________

Record the measures on the triangle in *Step 1*.

Step 3 Repeat *Step 1* for line segment HK, above right.
This time, make HG 7 cm long.
Draw a new line segment to connect G to K to complete the triangle.

Step 4 For the triangle in *Step 3*:
What is the new side length of GK? ______________
Is it greater than or less than the
length of GK in the triangle in *Step 1*? ______________

What is the new measure of ∠K? ______________

Is it greater than or less than ∠K for *Step 2*? ______________
Record these measures on the triangle.

Name ____________________ Date ________________

Master 3.18

Step-by-Step 6

Lesson 6, Question 5

You will need 2-cm grid paper.
Look at the net for a cube on page 99.

Step 1 Draw the squares again on grid paper, with one square in a different position.

Is this new picture a net? ____________________
Cut out and fold to check.

Step 2 If it is a net, record the net on another piece of grid paper.

Step 3 Repeat *Steps 1* and *2* for a different square.

Step 4 Repeat *Steps 1* and *2* for the same square but moved to a different position.

Step 5 Use *Steps 1* to *4* to find as many nets as you can.
How do you know the nets are different?

____

____

Name ____________________ Date ________________

Master 3.19

Unit Test: Unit 3 Geometry

Part A

1. Name each polygon.
Use as many names as you can for each polygon.

a) 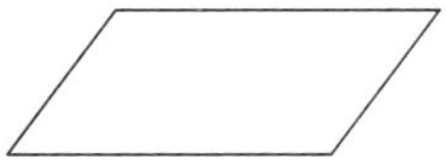	**b)** 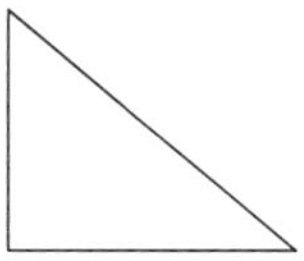	**c)** 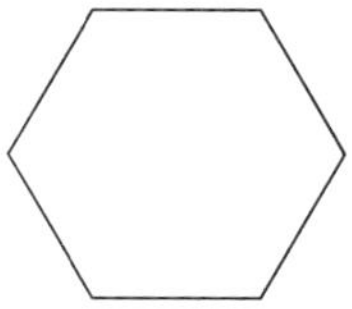	**d)** 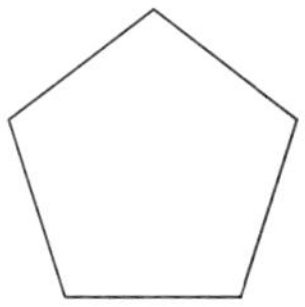

2. For each angle:
Estimate the size of the angle, in degrees.
Use a protractor to measure the angle. Mark the angle on each drawing.
Name the angle as acute, obtuse, or right.

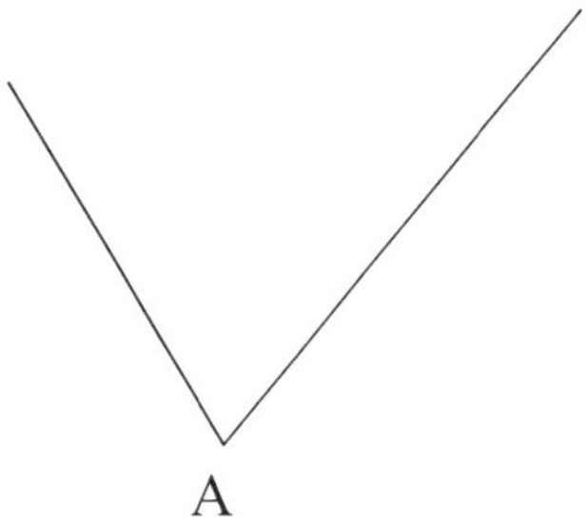

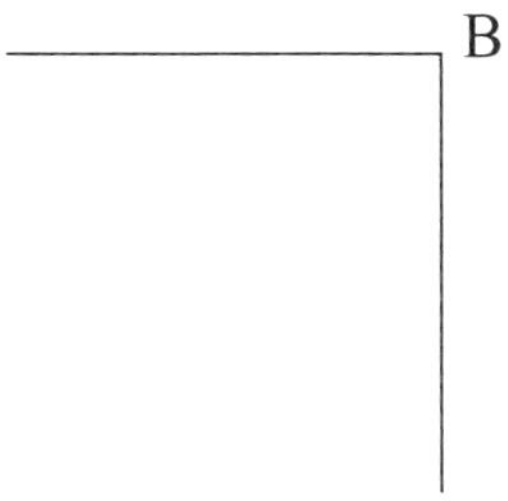

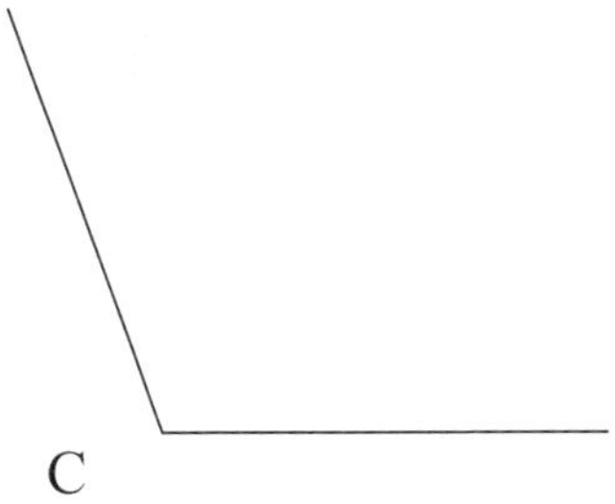

____________________ ____________________ ____________________

3. Measure the sides of each triangle.
Name each triangle. Use the words equilateral, isosceles, or scalene.

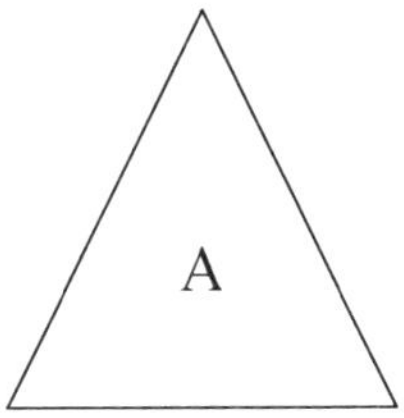

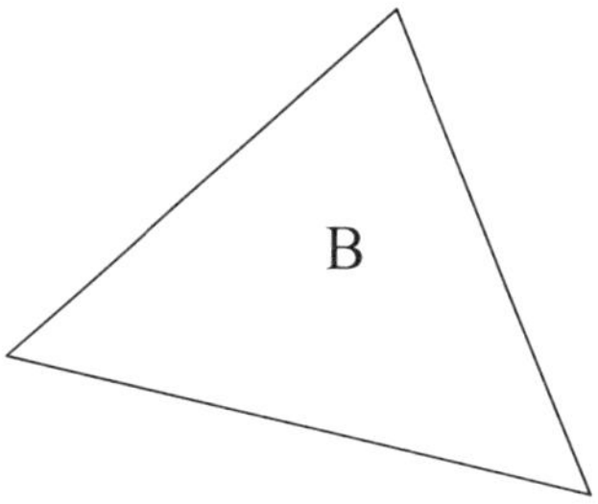

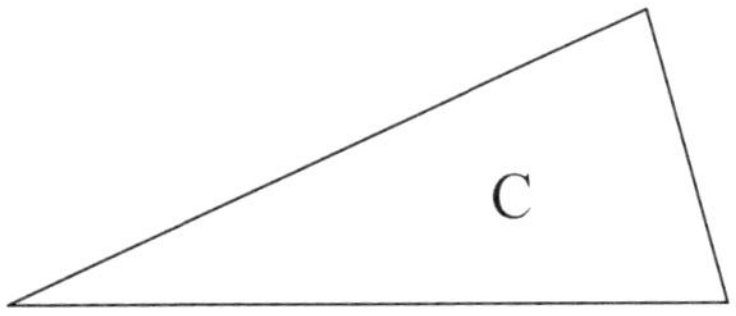

____________________ ____________________ ____________________

Name ____________________ Date ________________

Master 3.19b

Unit Test continued

Part B

4. Use square dot paper. Draw a polygon that has:

a) Exactly 2 right angles **b)** Exactly 3 acute angles

5. Use a ruler and a protractor.
Construct an angle with each measure. Label each angle with its measure.

a) 60° **b)** 20° **c)** 130°

6. Use a ruler and a protractor. Construct each triangle.

a) The measure of ∠B is 30°. The length of side AB is 5 cm. The length of side BC is 3 cm.	**b)** The measure of ∠X is 60°. The measure of ∠Y is 50°. The length of side XY is 5 cm.

c) Is triangle ABC scalene? Triangle XYZ? How do you know?

____

____

Name ______________________ Date ________________

Master 3.19c

Unit Test continued

Part C

7. Which solid would each net make? How do you know?

a)

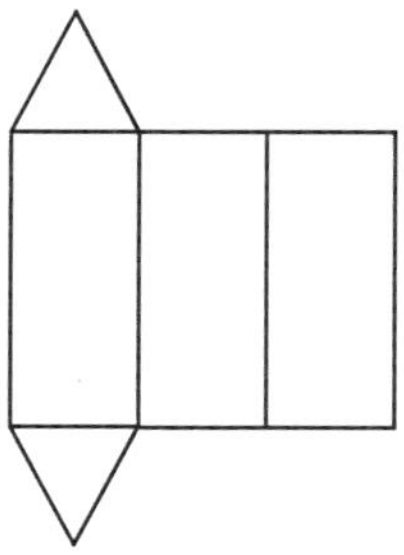

b)

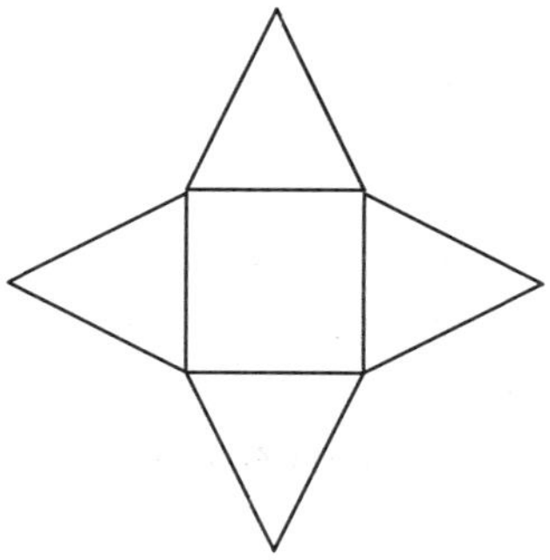

____

____

____

____

8. Which figures are nets for a cube? How do you know?

a)

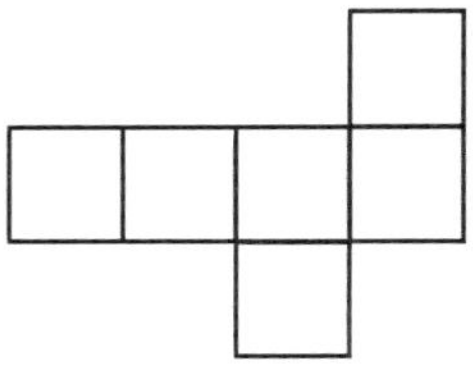

b)

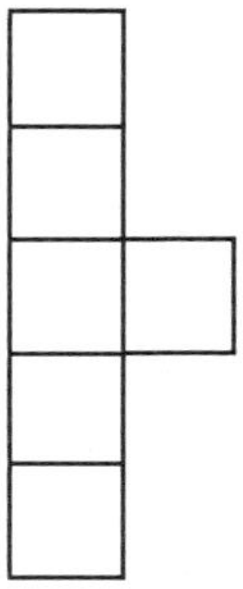

c)

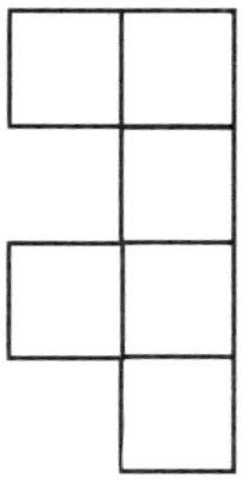

d)

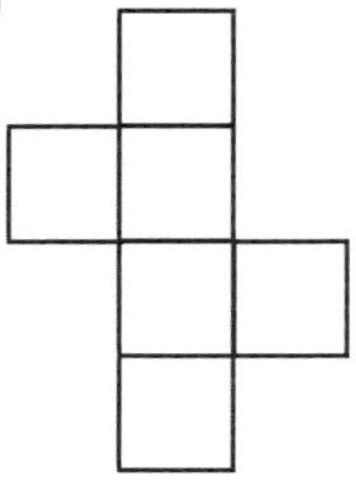

____

____

____

____

Name ____________________ Date ________________

Master 3.20

Sample Answers

Part A

1. a) Quadrilateral, parallelogram
   b) Triangle, right triangle, isosceles triangle
   c) Regular polygon, regular hexagon
   d) Regular polygon, regular pentagon
2. a) About 60°; 70°; acute
   b) About 90°; 90°, right
   c) About 105°; 110°; obtuse
3. a) 2.9 cm, 2.9 cm, 2.6 cm; isosceles
   b) 3.6 cm, 3.6 cm, 4.2 cm; isosceles
   c) 4.6 cm, 4.8 cm, 2.0 cm; scalene

Part B

4. Students may draw polygons such as these.

a)

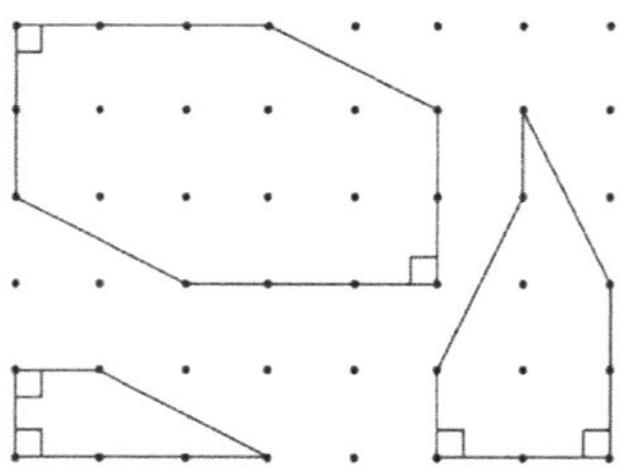

b)

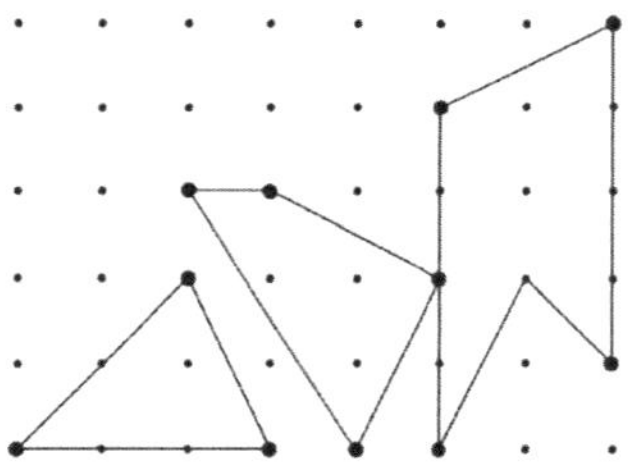

5. a)

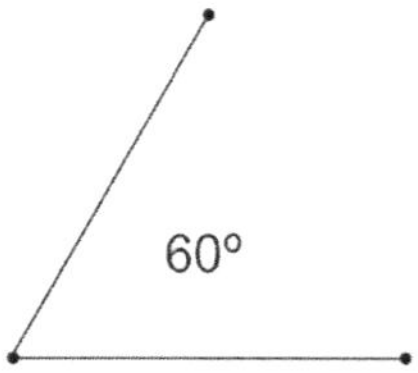

b)

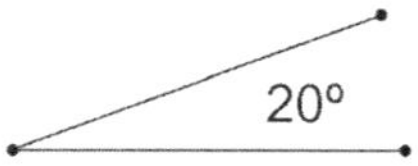

c)

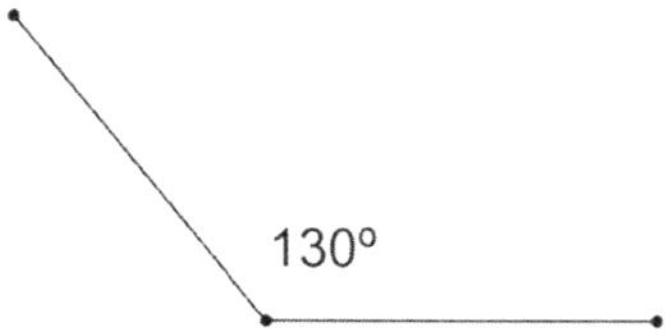

6. Students should draw triangles with these measures:

a)

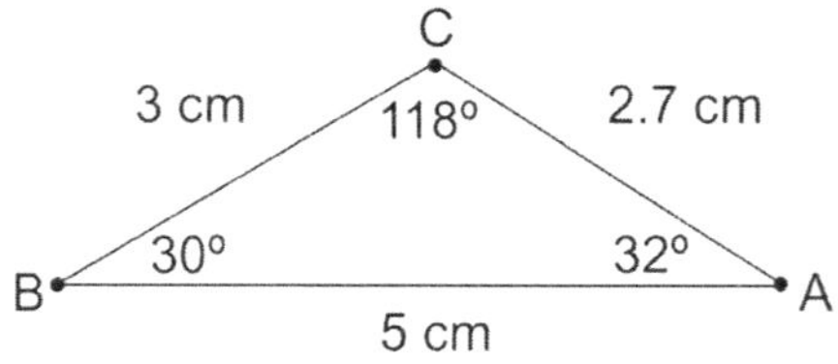

b)

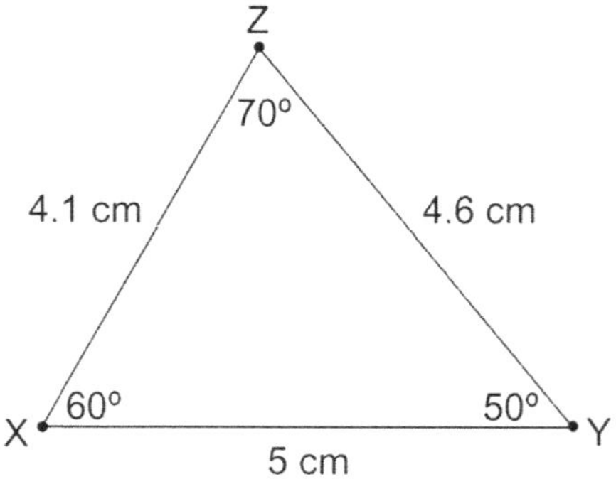

c) Both triangles are scalene; all sides have different length.

Part C

7. a) Triangular prism; there are 3 congruent rectangles and 2 congruent triangles
   b) Square pyramid; there are 4 congruent triangles each sharing one side with a square
8. a) Yes; there are 4 sides and 2 ends
   b) No; there are 5 sides and 1 end
   c) No; there are 4 sides and 2 overlapping ends
   d) Yes; there are 4 sides and 2 ends

Extra Practice Masters 3.21–3.24

Go to the CD-ROM to access editable versions of these Extra Practice Masters.

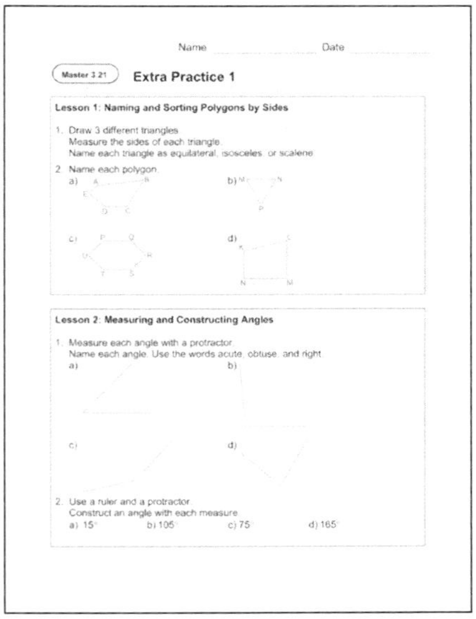

Name ______ Date ______

Master 3.21 **Extra Practice 1**

Lesson 1: Naming and Sorting Polygons by Sides

1. Draw 3 different triangles. Measure the sides of each triangle. Name each triangle as equilateral, isosceles, or scalene.
2. Name each polygon.
a) b) c) d)

Lesson 2: Measuring and Constructing Angles

1. Measure each angle with a protractor. Name each angle. Use the words acute, obtuse, and right.
a) b) c) d)
2. Use a ruler and a protractor. Construct an angle with each measure.
a) 15° b) 105° c) 75° d) 165°

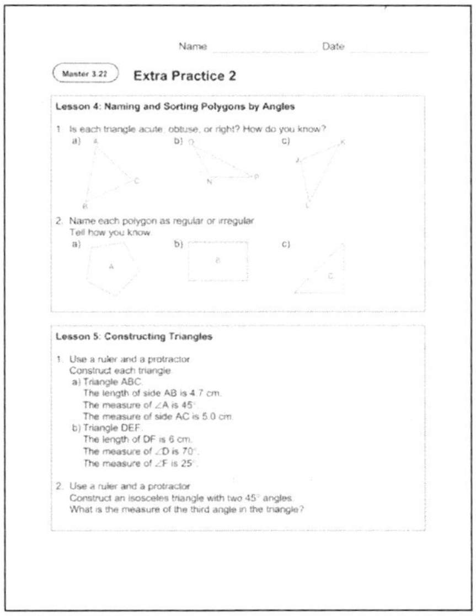

Name ______ Date ______

Master 3.22 **Extra Practice 2**

Lesson 4: Naming and Sorting Polygons by Angles

1. Is each triangle acute, obtuse, or right? How do you know?
a) b) c)
2. Name each polygon as regular or irregular. Tell how you know.
a) b) c)

Lesson 5: Constructing Triangles

1. Use a ruler and a protractor. Construct each triangle.
a) Triangle ABC
The length of side AB is 4.7 cm.
The measure of ∠A is 45°.
The measure of side AC is 5.0 cm.
b) Triangle DEF
The length of DF is 6 cm.
The measure of ∠D is 70°.
The measure of ∠F is 25°.
2. Use a ruler and a protractor. Construct an isosceles triangle with two 45° angles. What is the measure of the third angle in the triangle?

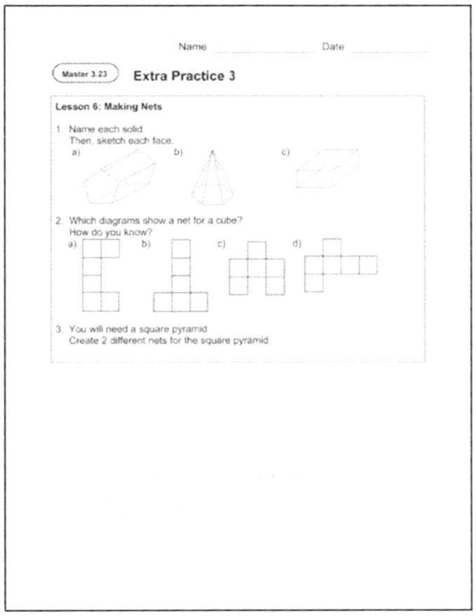

Name ______ Date ______

Master 3.23 **Extra Practice 3**

Lesson 6: Making Nets

1. Name each solid. Then, sketch each face.
a) b) c)
2. Which diagrams show a net for a cube? How do you know?
a) b) c) d)
3. You will need a square pyramid. Create 2 different nets for the square pyramid.

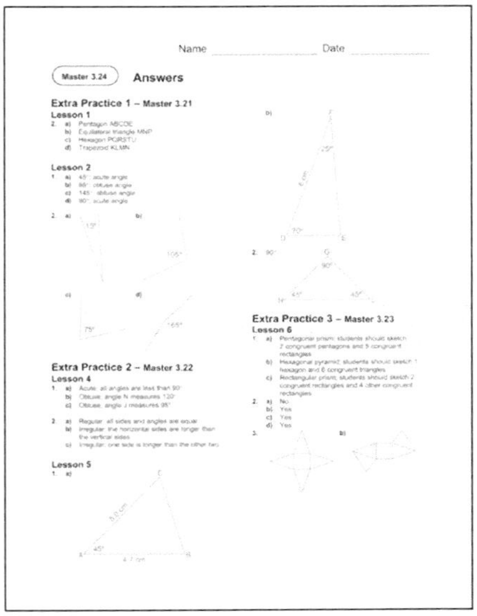

Name ______ Date ______

Master 3.24 **Answers**

Extra Practice 1 – Master 3.21
Lesson 1
2. a) Pentagon ABCDE
b) Equilateral triangle MNP
c) Hexagon PQRSTU
d) Trapezoid KLMN

Lesson 2
1. a) 45°; acute angle
b) 86°; obtuse angle
c) 145°; obtuse angle
d) 80°; acute angle
2. a) b) c) d)

Extra Practice 2 – Master 3.22
Lesson 4
1. a) Acute: all angles are less than 90°
b) Obtuse: angle N measures 120°
c) Obtuse: angle J measures 95°
2. a) Regular: all sides and angles are equal
b) Irregular: the horizontal sides are longer than the vertical sides
c) Irregular: one side is longer than the other two

Lesson 5
1. a) b)
2. 90°

Extra Practice 3 – Master 3.23
Lesson 6
1. a) Pentagonal prism; students should sketch 2 congruent pentagons and 5 congruent rectangles
b) Hexagonal pyramid; students should sketch 1 hexagon and 6 congruent triangles
c) Rectangular prism; students should sketch 2 congruent rectangles and 4 other congruent rectangles
2. a) No
b) Yes
c) Yes
d) Yes
3. b)

Addison Wesley
Mathematics
Makes Sense

Program Authors

Peggy Morrow
Ralph Connelly
Bryn Keyes
Jason Johnston
Steve Thomas
Jeananne Thomas
Angela D'Alessandro
Maggie Martin Connell
Don Jones
Michael Davis
Sharon Jeroski
Trevor Brown
Nora Alexander
Cynthia Pratt Nicolson

Printed and bound in Canada

8 9 MP 18 17

PEARSON
Education Canada

ADDISON WESLEY

Ontario

Math Makes Sense 5

Ontario

Teacher Guide

Unit 4: Decimals

PEARSON
Addison Wesley

UNIT 4

Decimals

"Students can develop a deep understanding of rational numbers through experiences with a variety of models, such as fraction strips, number lines, 10 × 10 grids, area models, and objects. These models offer students concrete representations of abstract ideas and support students' meaningful use of representations and their flexible movement among them to solve problems."

— *Principles and Standards for School Mathematics*, pp. 215–216, National Council of Teachers of Mathematics, 2000

FOCUS STRAND
Number Sense and Numeration

SUPPORTING STRAND
Measurement

Mathematics Background

What Are the Big Ideas?

- A decimal number is just another way to write a fraction.
- The base-ten place-value system extends infinitely in both directions. Between any two place values, the ten-to-one ratio remains the same.
- Addition and subtraction with decimals involve adding and subtracting the numbers using place value, as in whole number addition and subtraction.
- Estimation plays a central role in decimal computation.

How Will the Concepts Develop?

Students use Base Ten Blocks, place-value charts, and hundredths grids to model metric measures expressed in decimals, and to explore equivalent decimals. Students use these same models, along with number lines, to compare and order decimals and to round a decimal to the nearest whole number.

Students begin their investigation of decimal operations by developing rounding strategies to estimate decimal sums and differences. They use a variety of models to develop computational procedures and algorithms for adding and subtracting decimals. The parallels between whole number and decimal computations are emphasized. Students are encouraged to use estimation to check the reasonableness of their answers.

Students use calculators to explore multiplying decimals by 10 and 100, and dividing decimals by 10. By noting the shift in place-value positions in the decimals, students develop strategies for performing these operations mentally. Students will continue their investigation of decimal operations in Unit 8.

Why Are These Concepts Important?

The use of the metric system and the increased use of technology have made an understanding of and facility with decimals increasingly important. Work with decimal concepts and computations prepares students for work in future grades with rational and irrational numbers.

Curriculum Overview

Cluster 1: Understanding Decimals

Overall Expectations
- Represent, and explore relationships between, decimals, mixed numbers, and fractions using concrete materials and drawings. (5m1)
- Compare, order, and represent...decimals...using concrete materials and drawings. (5m2)
- Understand the significance of numbers within the surrounding environment. (5m5)
- Solve problems involving decimals... and describe and explain the variety of strategies used. (5m8)

Specific Expectations
- Recognize and read numbers from 0.01.... (5m10)
- Compare, order, and represent the place value of...decimals from 0.01...using concrete materials, drawings, and symbols. (5m14)
- Relate a fraction with a denominator of 10 or 100 to a decimal using concrete materials, drawings, and symbols. (5m24)
- Read and write decimal numbers to hundredths. (5m26)
- Demonstrate the equivalence of decimals using concrete materials, drawings, and symbols. (5m27)
- Explain their thinking when solving problems involving...decimals. (5m35)

Cluster 2: Decimal Computations

Overall Expectations
- Understand and explain basic operations of decimals by modelling and discussing a variety of problem situations. (5m3)
- Develop proficiency in multiplying tenths and hundredths and dividing by tenths. (5m4)
- Select and perform computation techniques appropriate to specific problems involving...decimals... and determine whether the results are reasonable. (5m7)
- Solve problems involving decimals...and describe and explain the variety of strategies used. (5m8)
- Justify in oral and written expression the method chosen for calculations: estimation, mental computation, concrete materials, algorithms, or calculators. (5m9)

Specific Expectations
- Mentally multiply decimal numbers by 10 and 100. (5m15)
- Mentally divide decimal numbers by 10. (5m16)
- Explain processes and solutions with...decimals using mathematical language. (5m18)
- Use mental computation strategies to solve number problems. (5m30)
- Add and subtract decimal numbers to hundredths using concrete materials, drawings, and symbols. (5m31)
- Select operations and solve two-step problems involving...decimals with and without a calculator. (5m33)
- Pose problems involving...decimals and solve them using the appropriate calculation method: pencil and paper, or calculator or computer. (5m34)
- Explain their thinking when solving problems involving...decimals. (5m35)
- Use and explain estimation strategies to determine the reasonableness of solutions to problems, and justify the choice of strategies. (5m36)

Launch
Coins Up Close

Lesson 1: Tenths and Hundredths
Lesson 2: Equivalent Decimals
Lesson 3: Comparing and Ordering Decimals
Lesson 4: Rounding Decimals

Lesson 5: Estimating Sums and Differences
Lesson 6: Adding Decimals
Lesson 7: Subtracting Decimals
Lesson 8: Multiplying Decimals by 10 and 100
Lesson 9: Dividing Decimals by 10
Lesson 10: Strategies Toolkit

Show What You Know

Unit Problem
Coins Up Close

Curriculum across the Grades

Grade 4	Grade 5	Grade 6
Students read and write decimal numbers to hundredths. Students represent the place value of, and compare and order decimals to, hundredths. Students connect proper fractions with decimals. They explore fraction-decimal relationships using a calculator. Students add and subtract decimal numbers.	Students read and write decimal numbers to hundredths. Students represent the place value of, and compare, order, and round, decimals. Students relate fractions to decimals. They explore relationships between fractions and decimals using a calculator. Students demonstrate the equivalence of decimals. Students add and subtract decimal numbers. They multiply decimals by 10 and 100, and divide decimals by 10.	Students read and write decimal numbers to thousandths in standard and expanded form. They represent the place value of, and compare and order decimals to, thousandths. Students relate decimals in fractions, percents, rates, and ratios. Students add and subtract decimals to thousandths. They multiply and divide decimals to thousandths by a 1-digit whole number. They multiply decimals by 1000 and whole numbers by 0.1, 0.01, and 0.001. They divide decimals by 100.

Materials for This Unit

You may need a 50¢ coin for Lesson 5.
Use large sheets of light cardboard to make place-value mats with columns for tens, ones, tenths, and hundredths (Lessons 6, 7, 8).

Additional Activities

Decimal Designs

For Extra Practice (Appropriate for use after Lesson 1)
Materials: Hundredths Grids (PM 15), *Decimal Designs* (Master 4.8)

The work students do: Students work in pairs. Students create a design on a 10 by 10 grid using 3 different colours. Students use a decimal and a fraction to describe each colour of their design.

Take It Further: Students fold a 10 by 10 grid in half to make a line of symmetry. They work together to make a 4-colour symmetrical design. They describe each colour of their design using a decimal and a fraction.

Social
Partner Activity

Spin for One

For Extra Support (Appropriate for use after Lesson 2)
Materials: 10-Part Spinner (Master 4.9b), Hundredths Grids (PM 15), pencil crayons, *Spin for One* (Master 4.9a)

The work students do: Students play this game in pairs. Each person needs a hundredths grid to represent one whole and a 10-part spinner.

Students take turns to spin the pointer. The number that comes up tells how many tenths or hundredths to colour on the grid. For example, if a student spins a 2, she may colour 2 hundredths *or* 2 tenths.
Each student has 6 turns. The student who comes closest to colouring the whole grid without going over wins.

Take It Further: Students play again, using two hundredths grids.

Logical/Mathematical
Partner Activity

Guess the Decimal

For Enrichment (Appropriate for use after Lesson 3)
Materials: *Guess the Decimal* (Master 4.10)

The work students do: Students work in groups of 3 or 4. One student (the leader) secretly writes a decimal with tenths, between 1 and 10. The other students take turns to guess the number. To each guess, the leader responds, "Greater" or "Less." The student who guesses the number becomes the leader, and the activity is repeated.

Take It Further: Students repeat the activity using decimals with hundredths.

Linguistic
Group Activity

Closing in on 2

For Extra Practice (Appropriate for use after Lesson 7)
Materials: number cube labelled 1 to 6, *Closing in on 2* (Master 4.11)

The work students do: Students play this game in pairs. Students take turns rolling the number cube twice to get a 2-digit decimal with tenths. The number is recorded. Students take 2 more turns. They then choose 2 of their 3 decimals to add or subtract. The student whose sum or difference is closer to 2 gets a point. Students play 4 more rounds.

Take It Further: Students play again, rolling the number cube 3 times to make a decimal with hundredths.

Logical/Mathematical
Partner Activity

Planning for Unit 4

Planning for Instruction

Suggested Unit time: 3 weeks

Lesson	Time	Materials	Program Support
Launch: Coins Up Close, page 2	20–25 min	Base Ten Blocks	
Lesson 1: Tenths and Hundredths, page 4 Explore decimals with tenths and hundredths.	40–50 min	Base Ten Blocks hundredths grids	PM 15: Hundredths Grids Master 4.12: Step-by-Step 1 Master 4.23: Extra Practice 1
Lesson 2: Equivalent Decimals, page 8 Identify equivalent decimals.	40–50 min	Base Ten Blocks hundredths grids and transparency pencil crayons	PM 15: Hundredths Grids Master 4.13: Step-by-Step 2 Master 4.23: Extra Practice 1
Lesson 3: Comparing and Ordering Decimals, page 10 Compare and order decimals to hundredths.	40–50 min	Base Ten Blocks blank number lines	PM 16: Number Lines Master 4.14: Step-by-Step 3 Master 4.24: Extra Practice 2
Lesson 4: Rounding Decimals, page 14 Round decimals to the nearest whole number.	40–50 min	blank number lines and transparency hundredths grids play money	PM 16: Number Lines PM 15: Hundredths Grids PM 30: Play Money Master 4.15: Step-by-Step 4 Master 4.24: Extra Practice 2
Lesson 5: Estimating Sums and Differences, page 17 Estimate sums and differences of decimals.	40–50 min	50¢ coin (optional)	Master 4.16: Step-by-Step 5 Master 4.25: Extra Practice 3
Lesson 6: Adding Decimals, page 20 Add decimals to hundredths.	40–50 min	Base Ten Blocks place-value mats catalogues	Master 4.17: Step-by-Step 6 Master 4.25: Extra Practice 3
Game: Make 2!, page 23	20 min	coloured markers decimal cards hundredths grids	PM 15: Hundredths Grids Master 4.6: Decimal Cards
Game: Spinning Decimals, page 24	20 min	Base Ten Blocks place-value mats spinners	Master 4.7: Spinner
Lesson 7: Subtracting Decimals, page 25 Subtract decimals to hundredths.	40–50 min	Base Ten Blocks place-value mats calculators hundredths grids crayons or markers	PM 15: Hundredths Grids Master 4.18: Step-by-Step 7 Master 4.26: Extra Practice 4
Lesson 8: Multiplying Decimals by 10 and 100, page 29 Mentally multiply decimals with tenths and hundredths by 10 and 100.	40–50 min	calculators overhead calculator (optional) Base Ten Blocks place-value mats	Master 4.19: Step-by-Step 8 Master 4.26: Extra Practice 4
Lesson 9: Dividing Decimals by 10, page 33 Mentally divide decimals with tenths by 10.	40–50 min	calculators Base Ten Blocks	Master 4.20: Step-by-Step 9 Master 4.27: Extra Practice 5
Lesson 10: Strategies Toolkit, page 36 Interpret a problem and select an appropriate strategy.	40–50 min	play money	PM 30: Play Money

Lesson	Time	Materials	Program Support
Show What You Know, page 38 Assessment	40–50 min	calculators	
Unit Problem: Coins Up Close, page 40 Assessment	40–50 min	calculators	

Planning for Assessment

Purpose	Tools and Process	Recording and Reporting
Diagnostic	*Unit Launch* Question; conference; scaffold problems throughout the unit	PM 8: Conference Prompts
Formative	*Explore* – Ongoing Assessment: Observe and Listen Prompt student's self-assessment *Practice* – Assessment Focus Questions Review student work; provide feedback; scaffold as needed; select key pieces	Master 4.2 Ongoing Observations: Decimals PM 1: Inquiry Process Check List PM 6: Observation Record 1 PM 7: Observation Record 2 PM 8: Conference Prompts PM 2: Self-Assessment PM 3: Self-Assessment: Problem Solving PM 9: Work Sample Records
Summative	*Show What You Know* *Unit Problem* – Performance Assessment Unit Test Review assessment records; add unit results to ongoing records	Master 4.1 Unit Rubric: Decimals Master 4.3 Performance Assessment Rubric: Coins Up Close Master 4.4 Unit Summary: Decimals PM 10: Summary Class Records: Strands PM 11: Summary Class Records: Achievement Categories PM 12: Summary Record: Individual
Learning Skills/Mathematical Disposition	Observe and record throughout unit	PM 4: Learning Skills Check List PM 5: Mathematical Dispositions and Learning Skills

Program Masters (PM) are in the *Grade 5 Planning and Program Masters* module.
Extra Practice Masters are on the CD-ROM.

Coins Up Close

LESSON ORGANIZER (20–25 min)

Curriculum Focus: Demonstrate prior knowledge of decimals.

Student Materials

- Base Ten Blocks

ASSUMED PRIOR KNOWLEDGE

- ✓ Students can read and write decimal numbers to hundredths.
- ✓ Students can represent the place value of decimal numbers.
- ✓ Students can compare and order decimal numbers.
- ✓ Students can relate decimals to fractions with denominators of 10 and 100.
- ✓ Students can add and subtract decimals to tenths.

UNIT 4

Decimals

Coins Up Close

Learning Goals

- represent, read, and write decimals to hundredths
- explore equivalent decimals
- compare and order decimals
- round decimals to the nearest whole number
- estimate decimal sums and differences
- add, subtract, multiply, and divide decimals
- pose and solve problems involving decimals

The coins we use are made at the Royal Canadian Mint in Winnipeg, Manitoba. Coin blanks are punched from large sheets of thin metal. These blanks pass through machines that stamp designs on both sides. The coins are inspected, then loaded into machines that count and package them. The coins are now ready for your pocket or piggy bank.

112

ACTIVATE PRIOR LEARNING

Together, read and discuss the information presented about the Royal Canadian Mint.

Ask questions such as:

- Why do you think each coin has to have the exact size, thickness, and mass?
  (*To prevent counterfeiting*)
- Which coin do you think the Mint makes the fewest of? Explain.
  (*The 50¢ coin because it is rarely seen.*)

Draw students' attention to the chart of data. Elicit from them that most of the measurements are given in decimal notation. Invite volunteers to find and read a measurement given as:

- a decimal with tenths
  (*For example, 1.8 mm or 26.5 mm*)
- a decimal with hundredths
  (*For example, 18.03 mm*)
- a whole number
  (*For example, 7 g*)

If necessary, model the proper way to read a decimal (for example, three and ninety-five hundredths).

Have students work in pairs to choose one decimal with tenths from the chart and to model it using Base Ten Blocks. Repeat with a decimal with hundredths. Take note of those students who experience difficulty modelling the numbers.

Invite volunteers to answer the questions beneath the chart and to explain how they know, or how they got their answer. Use students' responses to informally assess their ability to read, compare, and round numbers, and to estimate sums and differences.

Tell students that in this unit they will learn more about decimal numbers and operations with decimals, and that they will use what they learn to solve problems about coins.

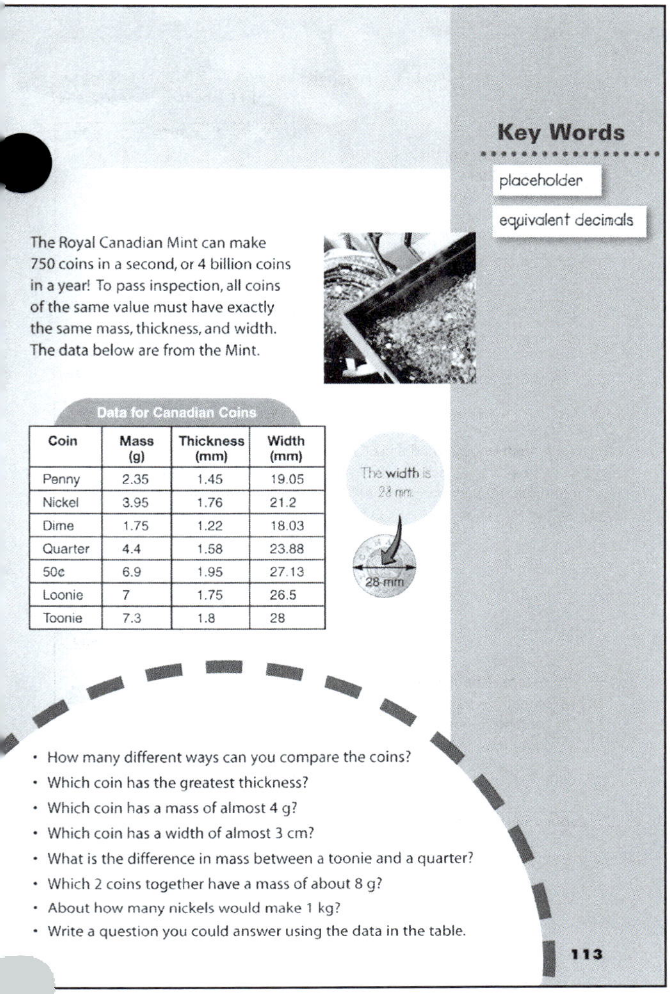
Key Words

placeholder

equivalent decimals

The Royal Canadian Mint can make 750 coins in a second, or 4 billion coins in a year! To pass inspection, all coins of the same value must have exactly the same mass, thickness, and width. The data below are from the Mint.

Data for Canadian Coins

Coin	Mass (g)	Thickness (mm)	Width (mm)
Penny	2.35	1.45	19.05
Nickel	3.95	1.76	21.2
Dime	1.75	1.22	18.03
Quarter	4.4	1.58	23.88
50¢	6.9	1.95	27.13
Loonie	7	1.75	26.5
Toonie	7.3	1.8	28

- How many different ways can you compare the coins?
- Which coin has the greatest thickness?
- Which coin has a mass of almost 4 g?
- Which coin has a width of almost 3 cm?
- What is the difference in mass between a toonie and a quarter?
- Which 2 coins together have a mass of about 8 g?
- About how many nickels would make 1 kg?
- Write a question you could answer using the data in the table.

113

LITERATURE CONNECTIONS FOR THE UNIT

The Phantom Tollbooth by Norton Juster. Random House Books for Young Readers, 1961.
ISBN 0394815009
This is the story of Milo, a bored ten-year old boy who drives through a large toy tollbooth and begins a memorable journey to Expectations. He meets such characters as the kings Dictionopolis and Digitopolis, Humbug, the Mathemagician, and the "Which," Faintly Macabre, who gives Milo the "impossible" mission of returning two princesses to the Kingdom of Wisdom.

The Dewey Decimal System by Allan Fowler. Children's Press, 1997.
ISBN 0516261304
In this book, Fowler explains how the Dewey Decimal system for classifying library books works and how it was developed.

REACHING ALL LEARNERS

e-tools Some students may benefit from the virtual manipulatives on the e-Tools CD-ROM. The e-Tools appropriate for this unit include Place-Value Blocks.

DIAGNOSTIC ASSESSMENT

What to Look For	What to Do
✔ Students can read and interpret decimals. ✔ Students can model decimals with Base Ten Blocks. ✔ Students can compare decimals.	***Extra Support:*** Students who appear to have little understanding of decimals may not have made the connection between fractions and decimals. Provide them with many opportunities to use Base Ten Blocks and hundredths grids to model fractions with denominators of 10 and 100 and to record the numbers in both fraction and decimal form.

LESSON 1

Tenths and Hundredths

LESSON ORGANIZER 40–50 min

Curriculum Focus: Explore decimals with tenths and hundredths. (5m10, 5m14, 5m26)

Teacher Materials
- Base Ten Blocks for the overhead projector (optional)

Student Materials
- Base Ten Blocks
- hundredths grids (PM 15)

Optional
- Step-by-Step 1 (Master 4.12)
- Extra Practice 1 (Master 4.23)

Vocabulary: decimal, tenths, hundredths

Assessment: Master 4.2 Ongoing Observations: Decimals

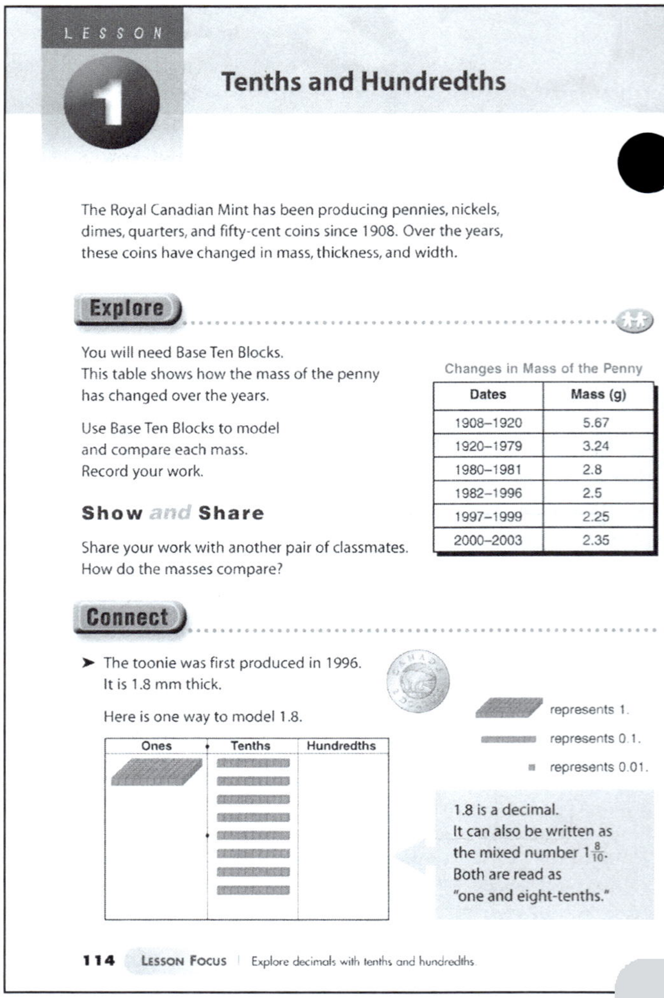

LESSON

1

Tenths and Hundredths

The Royal Canadian Mint has been producing pennies, nickels, dimes, quarters, and fifty-cent coins since 1908. Over the years, these coins have changed in mass, thickness, and width.

Explore

You will need Base Ten Blocks.
This table shows how the mass of the penny has changed over the years.

Use Base Ten Blocks to model and compare each mass.
Record your work.

Changes in Mass of the Penny

Dates	Mass (g)
1908–1920	5.67
1920–1979	3.24
1980–1981	2.8
1982–1996	2.5
1997–1999	2.25
2000–2003	2.35

Show and Share

Share your work with another pair of classmates.
How do the masses compare?

Connect

➤ The toonie was first produced in 1996.
It is 1.8 mm thick.

Here is one way to model 1.8.

1.8 is a decimal.
It can also be written as the mixed number $1\frac{8}{10}$.
Both are read as "one and eight-tenths."

114 LESSON FOCUS | Explore decimals with tenths and hundredths

Key Math Learnings

1. Decimals are another way of writing fractions.
2. Decimals are read in the same way as fractions are read.
3. The decimal point separates the whole number part and the fraction part of a decimal number.
4. For a decimal less than 1, a 0 is written in the ones place.

BEFORE Get Started

Invite a volunteer to read the introduction to the lesson.

Ask questions, such as:
- About how long ago did the Mint start making coins? (*About 100 years*)
- The coins that are minted now are smaller, thinner, and lighter than in 1908. Why do you suppose this is? (*To conserve metal*)

Have students examine the table of masses in *Explore*.

Ask:
- What is the difference in mass between the 1908 penny and the 2003 penny? (*3.32 g*)
- Between which two time periods did the penny increase in mass? (*1997–1999 and 2000–2003*)

Present the *Explore* activity. Students should record their work either by sketching and using a place-value chart or by drawing pictures of the Base Ten Blocks. Remind students to use simple squares, sticks, and dots to represent flats, rods, and unit cubes.

Emphasize to students that in this lesson a flat represents 1, a rod represents 0.1, and a unit cube represents 0.01. Students should become flexible in the ways they use Base Ten Blocks to represent place value. The value of the blocks can be anything you wish, as long as they maintain their order in terms of place value.

Think of a place-value chart. As long as the Base Ten Blocks maintain their order, we can slide them left or right to change the value each type of block represents.

➤ You can also say that the toonie has a thickness of 0.18 cm.
Here is one way to model 0.18.

1.8 mm = 0.18 cm

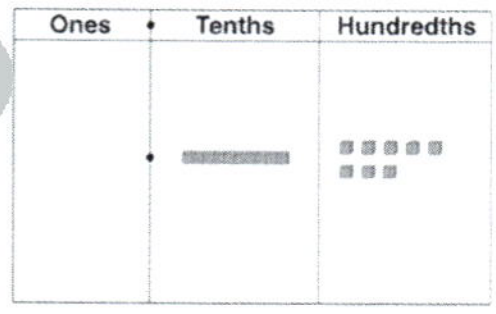

For a decimal less than 1, you write a 0 in the ones place for 0 ones.
0.18 can be written as a fraction: $\frac{18}{100}$
Both are read as "eighteen-hundredths."

➤ The loonie was first produced in 1987.
Loonies made since 1988 have a thickness of 1.75 mm.
Here is one way to model 1.75.

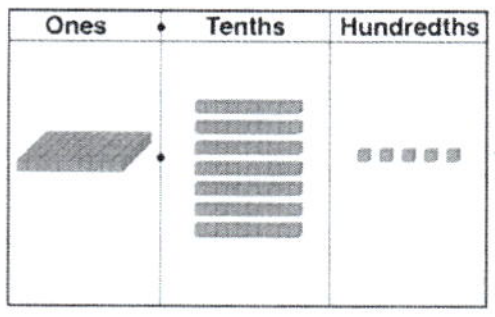

1.75 can be written as the mixed number $1\frac{75}{100}$. Both are read as "one and seventy-five hundredths."

➤ From 1968 to 1999, the dime had a mass of 2.07 g.
Here is one way to model 2.07.

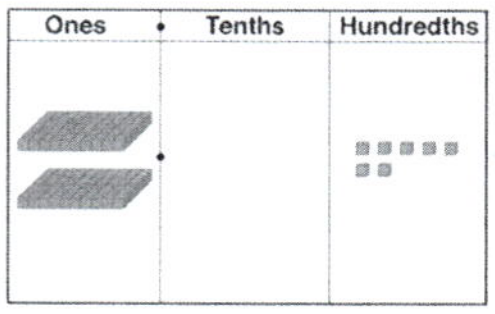

2.07 can be written as the mixed number $2\frac{7}{100}$. Both are read as "two and seven-hundredths."

➤ You can use a place-value chart to show decimals.

Ones	•	Tenths	Hundredths
1	•	8	
0	•	1	8
1	•	7	5
2	•	0	7

115

REACHING ALL LEARNERS

Alternative Explore

Materials: Hundredths grids (PM 15)

Have students model the following decimals and then write a fraction or mixed number for each: 1.43, 2.7, 0.8, 1.06, 0.05, 3.62

Early Finishers

Have students write a mixed number for each of the decimals they modelled.

Common Misconceptions

➤ Students have difficulty modelling decimals with hundredths using the least number of blocks.

How to Help: Provide students with place-value mats with columns for ones, tenths, and hundredths. Have them model 1.01, 1.02, 1.03, ..., 1.10. Once they place 10 unit cubes in the hundredths column, have them trade the cubes for a rod and move it to the tenths column. Continue with 1.11, 1.12, etc.

ESL Strategies

Pair English learners with a partner to develop an illustrated reference chart of words such as *decimal*, *decimal point*, *fraction*, *mixed number*, and *place-value chart*.

Hundreds	Tens	Ones	•	Tenths	Hundredths
❒	|	•	•		
	❒	|	•	•	
			•		

In the first row, a unit cube represents 1 one, a rod represents 10 ones, and a flat represents 10 of 10 ones or 100 ones. In the second row, a unit cube represents 1 tenth, a rod represents 10 tenths or 1, and a flat represents 100 tenths or 10. In the third row, a unit cube represents 1 hundredth, a rod represents 10 hundredths or 1 tenth, and a flat represents 100 hundredths or 1.

DURING Explore

Ongoing Assessment: Observe and Listen

Watch to see how students model hundredths. Are they using all unit cubes or do they realize that they can use a rod in place of 10 cubes?

Ask questions, such as:

- How can you decide how to define the value each Base Ten Block represents?
  (*Base Ten Blocks represent counting "somethings" into groups of 10. You can decide what you want the "something" to be. For example, you could say that a unit cube represents 1 "something." So, a rod represents 10 "somethings" and a flat represents 100 "somethings." The "something" could be ones, tens, tenths, hundredths, and so on.*)
- What is the value of the 5 in 2.5? ($\frac{5}{10}$)
  What blocks will you use to show that?
  (*5 rods*)
- How will you show 25 hundredths?
  (*25 unit cubes*)
  Could you show it another way?
  (*2 rods and 5 cubes*)
- Which decimal took the most blocks to model? (5.67) What does that tell you?
  (*It's the greatest number.*)

Sample Answers

3. a) | | | | : : :   b) ❑❑❑: :   c) ❑| | | | | | | | |

d) ❑: : : : .   e) ❑❑❑| | | : : .

4.

	Ones	Tenths	Hundredths
a)		|	. .
b)	❑	| |	: : : .
c)		| | | | | |	
d)			: :
e)	❑❑❑❑❑❑ ❑	| | | | | | | |	: : : : .
f)	❑❑	| | | |	

8.

4 . 5 8 $4\frac{58}{100}$	4 . 8 5 $4\frac{85}{100}$	5 . 4 8 $5\frac{48}{100}$
5 . 8 4 $5\frac{84}{100}$	8 . 4 5 $8\frac{45}{100}$	8 . 5 4 $8\frac{54}{100}$
4 5 . 8 $45\frac{8}{10}$	4 8 . 5 $48\frac{5}{10}$	5 4 . 8 $54\frac{8}{10}$
5 8 . 4 $58\frac{4}{10}$	8 4 . 5 $84\frac{5}{10}$	8 5 . 4 $85\frac{4}{10}$

Practice

Use Base Ten Blocks when they help.

1. Write a decimal and a fraction or mixed number for each picture.

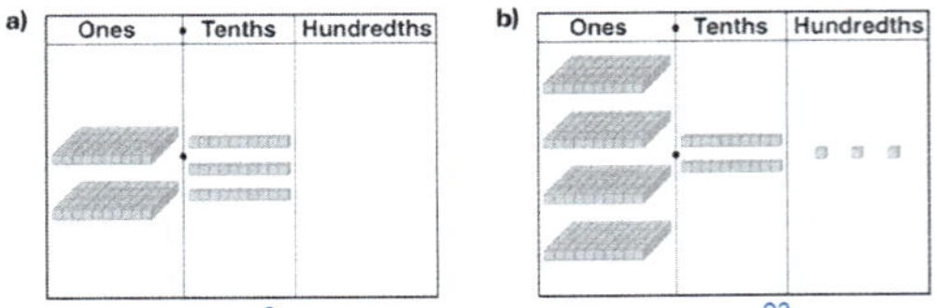

a) 2.3, $2\frac{3}{10}$ b) 4.23, $4\frac{23}{100}$

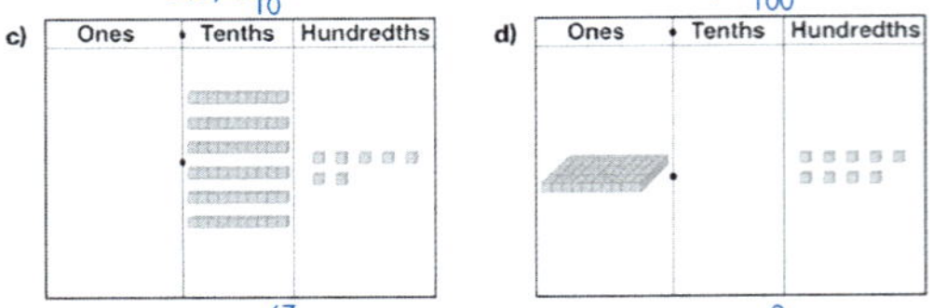

c) 0.67, $\frac{67}{100}$ d) 1.09, $1\frac{9}{100}$

2. Colour hundredths grids to show each decimal.
   Write it as a fraction or a mixed number.
   a) 3.17 $3\frac{17}{100}$ b) 2.06 $2\frac{6}{100}$
   c) 0.78 $\frac{78}{100}$ d) 1.4 $1\frac{4}{10}$

3. Model each decimal with Base Ten Blocks.
   Make a sketch to record your work.
   a) 0.46   b) 3.04   c) 1.9   d) 1.09   e) 3.35

4. Sketch a place-value mat.
   Show each number on it.
   a) 12 hundredths
   b) 1 and 27 hundredths
   c) 6 tenths
   d) 4 hundredths
   e) 7 and 89 hundredths
   f) 2 and 4 tenths

Ones	Tenths	Hundredths

116

AFTER Connect

Invite volunteers to choose one of the decimals to model on the overhead projector and to then call on a classmate to identify the number and record it on the board, both as a decimal and as a mixed number. If a student models hundredths using all unit cubes, ask if anyone can model it another way using fewer blocks.

Have students use Base Ten Blocks to model 21 hundredths using the least number of blocks (2 rods and 1 unit cube). Record 0.21 in a place-value chart:

Ones	Tenths	Hundredths
0	2	1

Emphasize that 0.21 is read as 21 hundredths, even though the chart shows 2 tenths and 1 hundredth. Draw attention as well to the convention of writing a 0 in the ones place for decimals less than 1.

Practice

Provide students with hundredths grids to complete question 2.

Assessment Focus: Question 8

Students understand that they must combine the 3 digits in as many ways as they can to form decimals with hundredths and with tenths. Students realize they can use each combination to make 2 numbers—one with hundredths and one with tenths. Some students may work randomly to find the combinations while others may use a systematic, organized approach. Students realize that the fraction equivalents of each decimal are determined by the number of digits to the right of the decimal point.

5. Use Base Ten Blocks to model each fraction or mixed number.
Then write it as a decimal.
a) $\frac{85}{100}$ 0.85 b) $4\frac{6}{10}$ 4.6 c) $\frac{9}{10}$ 0.9 d) $2\frac{8}{100}$ 2.08 e) $7\frac{7}{100}$ 7.07

Write each number as a decimal.
a) forty-six hundredths 0.46
b) five and six-hundredths 5.06
c) two and eight-tenths 2.8
d) nine and forty-nine hundredths 9.49

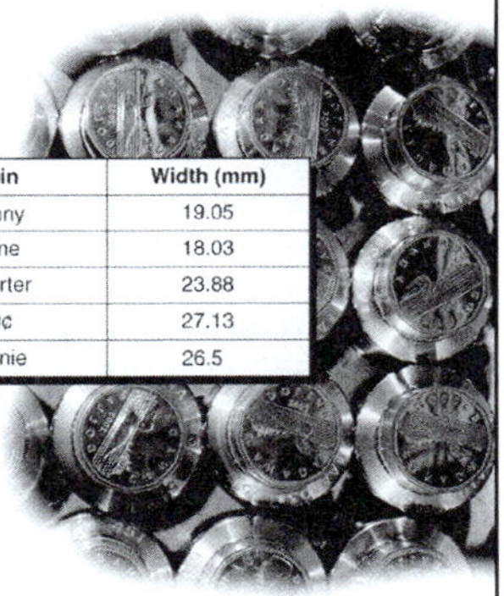

7. Use the data in the table.
a) Write the number that has a 5 in the hundredths place. 19.05
b) Write the number that has a 3 in the ones place. 23.88
c) Write a number that has a 3 in the hundredths place. 18.03 or 27.13

Coin	Width (mm)
Penny	19.05
Dime	18.03
Quarter	23.88
50¢	27.13
Loonie	26.5

8. Draw boxes like these:
□.□□ and □□.□
Use the digits 4, 5, and 8.
a) Write these digits in the boxes to make as many different decimals as you can.
b) Write a mixed number for each of your decimals.
c) Arrange your numbers to show you have found all possible decimals.

9. The dime is 1.22 mm thick.
Sketch Base Ten Blocks to show the decimal 1.22 in as many different ways as you can.

Reflect

What is the purpose of the decimal point in a decimal?
Use words and numbers to explain.

Numbers Every Day

Number Strategies
Write each number in expanded form, and in words.
2005
20 500
250 000

ASSESSMENT FOCUS | Question 8

117

9. 

REFLECT: The decimal point comes after the ones in a decimal number. It shows where the whole number part ends and the fraction part begins.

Numbers Every Day

Some students may benefit from writing each number in a place-value chart before they write it in expanded form or in words.
2000 + 5; two thousand five
20 000 + 500; twenty thousand five hundred
200 000 + 50 000; two hundred fifty thousand

ASSESSMENT FOR LEARNING

What to Look For	What to Do
Understanding concepts ✔ Students understand that decimals are another way of writing fractions with denominators of 10 and 100. ✔ Students understand that tenths and hundredths are fractional parts of a whole. ✔ Students understand decimal place value. ***Applying procedures*** ✔ Students model decimal numbers with tenths and hundredths.	***Extra Support:*** Model decimals such as 2.5, 4.25, 0.9, and 0.64 with Base Ten Blocks on a place-value mat. Have students say and write the decimal, and write the fraction or mixed number. Students can use Step-by-Step 1 (Master 4.12) to complete question 8. ***Extra Practice:*** Students can complete the Additional Activity, *Decimal Designs* (Master 4.8). Students can complete Extra Practice 1 (Master 4.23). ***Extension:*** Have students describe each of the following lengths as a part of a metre: 7 cm, 84 cm, 2 dm, 4.3 dm

Recording and Reporting
Master 4.2 Ongoing Observations: Decimals

Equivalent Decimals

LESSON ORGANIZER — 40–50 min

Curriculum Focus: Identify equivalent decimals. (5m27)

Teacher Materials
- hundredths grids transparency (PM 15)
- Base Ten Blocks for the overhead projector (optional)

Student Materials
- Base Ten Blocks
- hundredths grids (PM 15)
- pencil crayons

Optional
- Step-by-Step 2 (Master 4.13)
- Extra Practice 1 (Master 4.23)
- metre sticks

Vocabulary: equivalent decimals

Assessment: Master 4.2 Ongoing Observations: Decimals

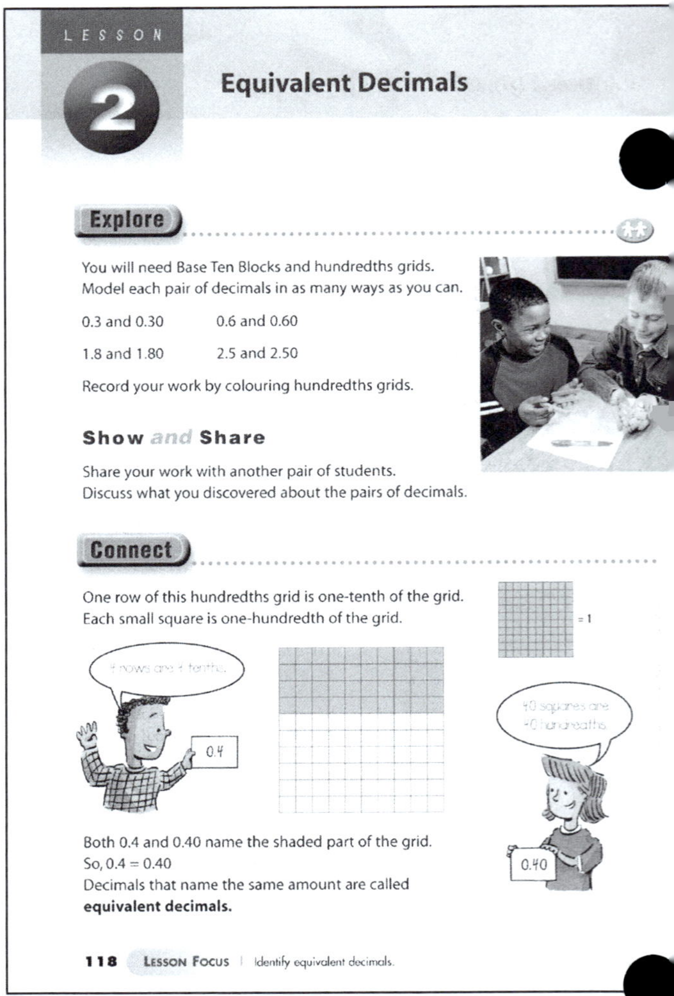
LESSON 2

Equivalent Decimals

Explore

You will need Base Ten Blocks and hundredths grids.
Model each pair of decimals in as many ways as you can.

0.3 and 0.30 — 0.6 and 0.60

1.8 and 1.80 — 2.5 and 2.50

Record your work by colouring hundredths grids.

Show and Share

Share your work with another pair of students.
Discuss what you discovered about the pairs of decimals.

Connect

One row of this hundredths grid is one-tenth of the grid.
Each small square is one-hundredth of the grid.

Both 0.4 and 0.40 name the shaded part of the grid.
So, 0.4 = 0.40
Decimals that name the same amount are called **equivalent decimals.**

118 LESSON FOCUS | Identify equivalent decimals.

Key Math Learning

Equivalent decimals name the same amount.

Sample Answers

5. 0.9 and 0.90 are equivalent decimals, so both bottles contain the same amount of oil. The bottle for $5.89 is the better buy.
6. Ruby is not correct. 8.40 and 8.4 are equivalent decimals. The 40 in 8.40 means 40 hundredths. The 4 in 8.4 means 4 tenths. 40 hundredths and 4 tenths are equal.

REFLECT: 7 tenths on a hundredths grid is 7 rows and 70 hundredths on a hundredths grid is 70 small squares, which is the same as 7 rows.

BEFORE — Get Started

Review with students the values we assign to the Base Ten Blocks when modelling decimals. (flat = 1, rod = 1 tenth, unit cube = 1 hundredth)

DURING — Explore

Ongoing Assessment: Observe and Listen

Ask questions, such as:
- How will you show 3 tenths on the grid? (*Colour 3 rows or 3 columns.*)
- How will you show 30 hundredths? (*Colour 30 small squares.*)
- How will you show 1 and 8 tenths? (*Colour one whole grid and 8 rows of another.*)

AFTER — Connect

Invite volunteers to demonstrate on the overhead projector some of the ways they modelled the pairs of decimals.

Ask:
- What did you discover about the pairs of decimals? (*They are equal.*)
- How can you prove that 6 tenths and 60 hundredths are equal? (*I colour the same number of squares in each case.*)

Practice

Students will need hundredths grids to complete question 2.

Assessment Focus: Question 6

Students should recognize that 0.40 represents 40 hundredths and 0.4 represents 4 tenths. Some students may wish to use Base Ten Blocks or hundredths grids.

Practice

1. Write two equivalent decimals that name the shaded part of each grid.

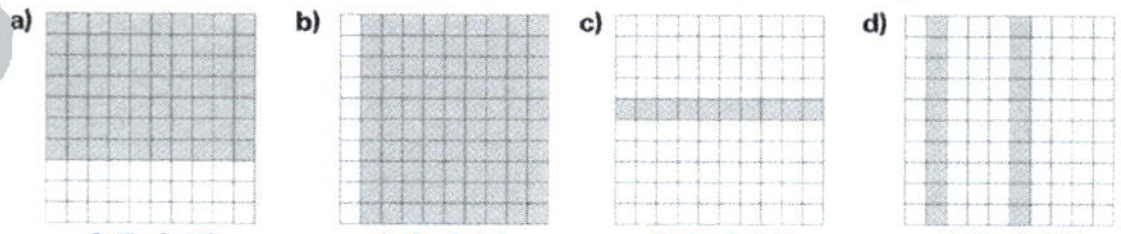

a) 0.7, 0.70 b) 0.9, 0.90 c) 0.1, 0.10 d) 0.2, 0.20

2. Colour hundredths grids to show each number.
Write an equivalent decimal.
a) 0.20 0.2 b) 0.9 0.9 c) 0.70 0.7 d) 0.5 0.50

3. Write an equivalent decimal for each number.
a) 0.5 0.50 b) 0.80 0.8 c) 0.30 0.3 d) 0.6 0.60 e) 2.4 2.40
f) 1.70 1.7 g) 4.9 4.90 h) 7.20 7.2 i) 5.50 5.5 j) 0.10 0.1

4. Find the equivalent decimals in each group.
a) 0.5 0.05 0.50 0.5, 0.50 b) 0.70 0.7 0.07 0.70, 0.7
c) 4.8 4.08 4.80 4.8, 4.80 d) 6.04 6.40 6.4 6.40, 6.4

5. Which bottle of olive oil is the better buy? Explain how you know.

6. Ruby said that 8.40 is greater than 8.4 because 40 is greater than 4. Was Ruby correct? Use words, pictures, or numbers to explain.

Reflect

Use numbers, pictures, or words to explain why 7 tenths is the same as 70 hundredths.

Numbers Every Day

Number Strategies

Estimate each sum.

4567 + 7654 + 6547 18 800
1234 + 4321 + 3214 8700
8009 + 9008 + 8090 25 100

Which strategies did you use?
Round to nearest hundred

ASSESSMENT FOCUS | Question 6

119

REACHING ALL LEARNERS

Alternative Explore

Materials: metre sticks

Have students locate the following pairs of lengths on a metre stick and write what they discovered about the pairs of lengths: 0.4 m and 0.40 m, 0.7 m and 0.70 m, 0.2 m and 0.20 m, and 0.5 m and 0.50 m.

Early Finishers

Have students work in pairs. One student records a decimal number with tenths or hundredths. The other student records an equivalent decimal. Students continue the activity, switching roles at each turn.

Common Misconceptions

➤ Students have difficulty identifying the equivalent decimals in question 4.

How to Help: Have students model the trio of decimals with Base Ten Blocks and then find the two that show the same amount.

Numbers Every Day

Most students will round each number to the nearest hundred, then add. Others may prefer to round to the nearest thousand. Some students may use front-end estimation. You may wish to initiate a discussion about the results of the different estimation strategies and how students might determine which strategy gives the "best" estimate in each case.

ASSESSMENT FOR LEARNING

What to Look For

Understanding concepts

✔ Students understand that equivalent decimals name the same amount.

Applying procedures

✔ Students can, given a decimal with tenths or hundredths, name an equivalent decimal.

What to Do

Extra Support: Have students complete the Additional Activity, *Spin for One* (Master 4.9).

Students can use Step-by-Step 2 (Master 4.13) to complete question 6.

Extra Practice: Have students find the equivalent decimals in sets of decimals such as 1.04, 1.40, and 1.4.

Students can complete Extra Practice 1 (Master 4.23).

Extension: Have students explain why 0.4 = 0.40, but 0.40 > 0.04.

Recording and Reporting

Master 4.2 Ongoing Observations: Decimals

Comparing and Ordering Decimals

LESSON ORGANIZER (40–50 min)

Curriculum Focus: Compare and order decimals to hundredths. (5m14)

Student Materials
- Base Ten Blocks

Optional
- Step-by-Step 3 (Master 4.14)
- Extra Practice 2 (Master 4.24)
- blank number lines (PM 16)

Assessment: Master 4.2 Ongoing Observations: Decimals

Key Math Learning
Place value can be used to compare and order decimals.

LESSON 3

Comparing and Ordering Decimals

Olympic medal winners in racing events often beat their competitors by fractions of a second. Very small numbers can make a huge difference!

In the 2002 Winter Olympics, the gold medal-winning bobsled team from Germany beat one American team by 0.3 of a second and another by 0.35 of a second.

Explore

Here are the top 5 results of the 2000 Summer Olympics women's 100-m dash.

➤ Who finished first? Who finished last?

➤ Order the runners from first to last. Use any materials or strategies you wish.

➤ Suppose you do not have enough Base Ten Blocks. How can you order the decimals?

Women's 100-m Dash

Athlete	Time (seconds)
M. Jones (USA)	10.75
T. Lawrence (Jamaica)	11.18
M. Ottey (Jamaica)	11.19
Z. Pintusevych (Ukraine)	11.2
E. Thanou (Greece)	11.12

Show and Share

Share your results with another pair of students. Discuss the strategies you used to order the times.

120 LESSON FOCUS | Compare and order decimals to hundredths

BEFORE Get Started

Together, read the introduction to the lesson. If you have a clock with a second hand, have students observe the hand's movement to get a sense of one second, and to imagine how short a fraction of a second is.

Ask:
- Which is longer, 3 tenths of a second or 35 hundredths of a second? Explain. *(35 hundredths of a second is longer than 3 tenths of a second. 3 tenths is equivalent to 30 hundredths. 35 hundredths is greater than 30 hundredths.)*

Present *Explore*. Ensure students understand that gold, silver, and bronze medals are awarded to athletes in first, second, and third positions. Have Base Ten Blocks available for students who wish to use them. Remind students to record their work and to be prepared to explain the strategies they used.

DURING Explore

Ongoing Assessment: Observe and Listen

Ask questions, such as:
- How will you determine who finished first? *(The person who finished first had the shortest time. I compared the numbers by first looking at the tens digits, then the ones digits. M. Jones finished first with a time of 10.75 seconds.)*
- How did you determine who finished last? *(The person who finished last has the longest time. Again, I compared the tens digits, then the ones digits, then the tenths digits. Z. Pintusevych finished last with a time of 11.2 seconds.)*

Connect

Women's Pole Vault

Athlete	Height (m)
S. Dragila (USA)	4.6
V. Flosadottir (Iceland)	4.5
T. Grigorieva (Australia)	4.55

Here are the top 3 results of the 2000 Olympics women's pole vault.

Here are 3 ways to find who won gold, silver, and bronze:

➤ Use Base Ten Blocks to model the height of each pole vault, then put the heights in order.

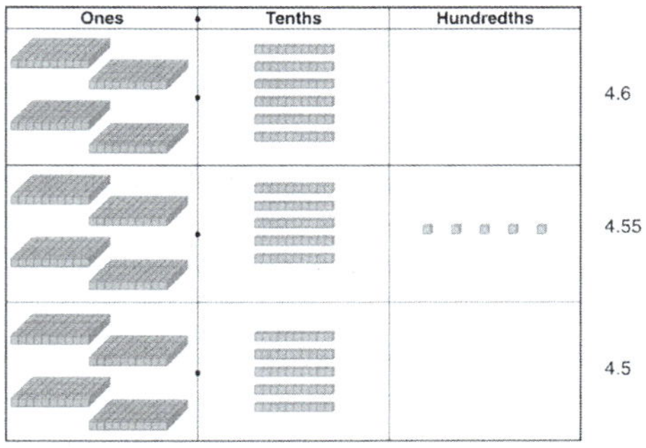

➤ Write each decimal in a place-value chart.

Ones		Tenths	Hundredths
4	•	6	0
4	•	5	0
4	•	5	5

Use equivalent decimals.
6 tenths is 60 hundredths.
5 tenths is 50 hundredths.

Look at the whole number parts. All 3 numbers have 4 ones.

Compare the decimal parts. 60 hundredths is the greatest. 50 hundredths is the least.

So, the heights from greatest to least are:
4.6 m, 4.55 m, 4.5 m

121

REACHING ALL LEARNERS

Alternative Explore

Materials: Blank number lines (PM 16)

Have students label one number line from 9.80 to 10.10 and another one from 10.70 to 11.30. Students then locate and label the positions of the times for the men's and women's 100-m dashes on the number lines. Use the results to identify the 3 medal winners from each chart.

Early Finishers

Have students write a time that might have come between the 1st and 2nd, the 2nd and 3rd place times in the men's and women's 100-m dash events.

Common Misconceptions

➤ Students believe that 11.12, 11.18, and 11.19 are greater than 11.2 because 12, 18, and 19 are greater than 2.

How to Help: Point out to students that 11.12, 11.18, and 11.19 have hundredths and 11.2 has tenths. Remind them of how to write an equivalent number for 11.2.

- How did you order the runners?
  (I used a place-value chart to order the times from least to greatest. The times in order are: 10.75 seconds, 11.12 seconds, 11.18 seconds, 11.19 seconds, 11.2 seconds. The runners in order from first to last are: M. Jones, E. Thanou, T. Lawrence, M. Ottey, and Z. Pintusevych.)

Watch for students who are struggling to order the times. Suggest that modelling the numbers with Base Ten Blocks or writing the decimals in a place-value chart may help.

AFTER Connect

Invite volunteers to share their solutions and describe or demonstrate the strategies they used.

Ask questions, such as:

- How much higher was the jump of the winner of the women's gold than the winner of the silver? How did you find out?
  (I subtracted the silver medal height from the gold medal height. 4.6 – 4.55 = 0.05; the difference was 0.05 m.)
- How much higher was her jump than the jump of the athlete who came in 3rd?
  (0.10 m)
- How did you compare 4.6 m to 4.55 m?
  (I changed 4.6 to 4.60 m.)

Use *Connect* to illustrate 3 possible ways to compare and order decimals. Have students compare these methods to the ones they used. Suggest that students may want to try using one of them in the future.

Sample Answers

6. e) The sequence from fastest to slowest would be: Bolden, Thompson, Drummond, Greene, Chambers

7. a) Paulette, Luca, and Arthur.

b) Chelsey and Holly.

8. d) ninety-nine hundredths, five and nine-tenths, four and ninety-four hundredths
twenty-four hundredths, six and two-tenths, five and six-tenths
ninety-two hundredths, seven and five-tenths, five and seven-tenths

REFLECT: 2.3 is equivalent to 2.30 and 2.30 is greater than 2.27.

➤ Use a number line.
Mark a dot for each number on the number line.

Since the best result is the greatest height, read the numbers from right to left: 4.6, 4.55, 4.5

So, Dragila won gold, Grigorieva won silver, and Flosadottir won bronze.

Practice

Use Base Ten Blocks or a number line to model and compare decimals.

1. Choose the decimal that best describes the amount in each glass.

a) 0.35 0.60 0.85 **b)** 0.95 0.38 0.50 **c)** 0.35 0.10 0.01

 0.60 0.95 0.10

2. Copy and complete. Use >, <, or =.

a) 0.60 = 0.6 **b)** 0.45 < 0.62 **c)** 4.07 < 4.12
d) 5.60 > 5.12 **e)** 3.08 < 3.8 **f)** 1.27 > 0.99

3. Write the decimals in order from least to greatest.

a) 1.47, 1.82, 1.31 **b)** 2.07, 2.01, 1.85 a) 1.31, 1.47, 1.82 b) 1.85, 2.01, 2.0
c) 0.83, 0.73, 1.04 **d)** 7.30, 7.62, 6.80 c) 0.73, 0.83, 1.04 d) 6.80, 7.30, 7.6

4. Write the decimals in order from greatest to least.
Think about equivalent decimals when you need to.

a) 0.5, 0.40, 0.52 **b)** 16.4, 14.79, 14.09 a) 0.52, 0.5, 0.40 b) 16.4, 14.79,
c) 0.43, 0.6, 0.55 **d)** 0.5, 1.4, 1.16 c) 0.6, 0.55, 0.43 d) 1.4, 1.16, 0..

5. Copy. Then write a decimal to make each statement true.
How did you decide which decimal to write?

a) 0.45 > □ 0.03 **b)** 12.7 < □ 12.9 **c)** 7.01 > □ 6.99
d) 1.3 < □ 2.8 **e)** 3.24 > □ 2.07 **f)** 0.09 < □ 0.10

122

Practice

Have Base Ten Blocks and blank number lines (PM 16) available for students who wish to use them.

Assessment Focus: Question 6

Students realize that the athlete with the shortest time was the fastest. Students compare the decimals to find the least number and the greatest. Students find the decimal that falls between 10.09 and 10.04. Students may compare the numbers by modelling them with Base Ten Blocks, by using a place-value chart, or by organizing the decimals on a number line. Some students may use visual inspection and their knowledge of place values.

YOUR NOTES

6. Use the data in the table.
  a) Which sprinter was fastest? Greene
  b) Which sprinter was slowest? Drummond
  c) Whose time was faster than Drummond's, but slower than Thompson's? Chambers
  d) Look at the number line. Match each letter with the sprinter who made that time.

Men's 100-m Dash

Athlete	Time (seconds)
A. Bolden (Trinidad & Tobago)	9.99
D. Chambers (Great Britain)	10.08
J. Drummond (USA)	10.09
M. Greene (USA)	9.87
O. Thompson (Barbados)	10.04

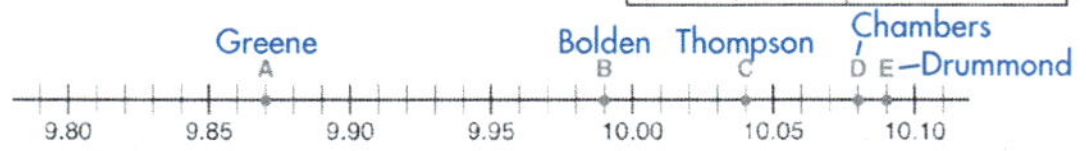

  e) Suppose they raced again. Chambers and Greene took 1 second longer. The others ran in the same time as in the first race. How would this affect the race results? Explain.

7. The average Canadian eats 23 kg of beef each year. This is about 0.44 kg each week. Look at the list.
  a) Who eats less than the weekly average?
  b) Who eats more?

Beef Eaten Each Week
Paulette - 0.4 kg
Luca - 0.43 kg
Chelsey - 0.49 kg
Arthur - 0.09 kg
Holly - 0.52 kg

8. a) Write 3 decimals less than 1.01. 0.99, 0.24, 0.92
  b) Write 3 decimals greater than 5.8. 5.9, 6.2, 7.5
  c) Write 3 decimals greater than 4.81 and less than 5.73. 4.94, 5.6, 5.7
  d) Write your answers to parts a, b, and c in words.

Reflect

How do you know 2.3 is greater than 2.27? Use pictures, numbers, or words to explain.

Numbers Every Day

Calculator Skills

Find two 5-digit numbers:
- with a sum of 35 428
- with a difference of 35 428

ASSESSMENT FOCUS | Question 6

Numbers Every Day

Some students may recognize that an easy way to find the numbers is to add or subtract 10 000.
For example, _____ + 10 000 = 35 428 and
_____ − 10 000 = 35 428
20 000 + 15 428 = 35 428
52 628 − 17 200 = 35 428

ASSESSMENT FOR LEARNING

What to Look For	What to Do
Applying procedures ✔ Students compare and order decimals to hundredths. ✔ Students can name decimals greater than and less than a given decimal.	***Extra Support:*** Have students record decimals dictated to them in a place-value chart, then order the decimals from least to greatest. Students can use Step-by-Step 3 (Master 4.14) to complete question 6.
Problem solving ✔ Students choose an appropriate strategy and solve problems that involve comparing and/or ordering decimals.	***Extra Practice:*** Have students colour hundredths grids to show 0.4, 0.91, and 0.17. Students then order the numbers from greatest to least. Students can complete Extra Practice 2 (Master 4.24).
Communicating ✔ Students describe their thinking and their strategies clearly and concisely.	***Extension:*** Have students work in pairs to complete the Additional Activity, *Guess the Decimal* (Master 4.10).

Recording and Reporting

Master 4.2 Ongoing Observations: Decimals

Rounding Decimals

LESSON ORGANIZER (40–50 min)

Curriculum Focus: Round decimals to the nearest whole number. (5m14)

Teacher Materials
- hundredths grids transparency (PM 15)
- number lines transparency (PM 16)

Student Materials
- hundredths grids (PM 15)
- number lines (PM 16)

Optional
- Step-by-Step 4 (Master 4.15)
- Extra Practice 2 (Master 4.24)
- play money (PM 30)

Assessment: Master 4.2 Ongoing Observations: Decimals

Key Math Learning
The strategies used to round whole numbers can be used to round decimals.

Numbers Every Day
Students multiply each number of books by 10.

LESSON 4 Rounding Decimals

Suppose there were 5362 spectators at an Olympic swimming event.
Round this number to the nearest ten and nearest hundred.
What strategies did you use?
You can use the same strategies to round decimals.

Explore

This table shows the winning times of seven gold medal winners at the 2000 Sydney Olympics.

Event	Athlete	Time (seconds)
Women's 50-m Freestyle Swimming	I. De Bruijn	24.32
Men's 50-m Freestyle Swimming	G. Hall Jr. and A. Ervin	21.98
Women's 100-m Dash	M. Jones	10.75
Men's 100-m Dash	M. Greene	9.87
Women's 100-m Freestyle Swimming	I. De Bruijn	53.83
Men's 100-m Freestyle Swimming	P. van den Hoogenband	48.30

Suppose times were recorded in whole seconds.
What would each person's time be?
Use any materials you need to help you.

Show and Share

Share your rounded times with a classmate.
Discuss the strategies you used to round.
Why might you want to round the times to the nearest second?

Numbers Every Day

Mental Math

One book costs $10.
How much would each number of books cost?

7 $70
35 $350
128 $1280
4327 $43 270

124 LESSON FOCUS | Round decimals to the nearest whole number

BEFORE Get Started

Invite a student to read the introduction. Have students work in pairs to round 5362 to the nearest ten and nearest hundred. Then have volunteers name the rounded numbers and explain the strategies they used. Repeat the process with 5365 and 5350.

Present the *Explore*. Make blank number lines and hundredths grids available for students who wish to use them.

DURING Explore

Ongoing Assessment: Observe and Listen

Ask questions, such as:
- Which 2 whole numbers is 24.32 between? (*24 and 25*)
- Is 24.32 closer to 24 or to 25? (*24*) How do you know? (*0.32 rounds down because it is less than 0.50.*)
- How can you use a number line to help you? (*Plot 24.32 on the line. You will see it is closer to 24.*) What numbers would you put on the ends of the number line? (*24 and 25*)
- Suppose you used a grid to show the hundredths part of that decimal. How would you know whether the number would round up or down? (*If less than half of the grid is coloured, the number would round down. If half or more is coloured, the number would round up.*)

AFTER Connect

Invite volunteers to share their rounded numbers and the strategies they used. Call on any students who used a number line or hundredths grids to demonstrate their strategies on the overhead projector.

Display a blank number line on the overhead projector. Ask:

Connect

➤ In the women's 100-m dash, the gold medal time was 10.75 seconds. The silver medal time was 11.12 seconds.

These times are measured to the nearest hundredth of a second. To write an estimate of these times, you can *round* to the nearest second.

Here are 2 ways to round 10.75 and 11.12 to the nearest second.

- Use a number line.

10.75 is between 10 and 11, but closer to 11.
So, 10.75 seconds rounds up to 11 seconds.

11.12 is between 11 and 12, but closer to 11.
So, 11.12 seconds rounds down to 11 seconds.

- Use what you know about decimal hundredths.

Look at the hundredths in 10.75.
You know that 75 hundredths is closer to 1 than to 0.
So, 10.75 rounds up to 11.

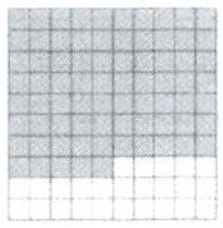

Look at the hundredths in 11.12.
You know that 12 hundredths is closer to 0 than to 1.
So, 11.12 rounds down to 11.

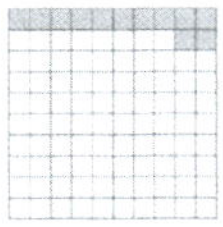

➤ One swimmer had a time of 56.50 seconds in the men's 100-m backstroke.

To round 56.50 seconds to the nearest second:

Think: Since 50 hundredths is halfway between 0 and 1, you round up.
So, 56.50 seconds rounds to 57 seconds.

125

REACHING ALL LEARNERS

Alternative Explore

Materials: play money (PM30)

Have students model money amounts, such as $5.95, $1.50, and $2.21, and then round each amount to the nearest dollar. Have students describe their strategies.

Early Finishers

Have students copy 4 or 5 prices from an advertisement and round each amount to the nearest dollar.

Common Misconceptions

➤ Students do not understand what it means to "round to the nearest whole number."

How to Help: Have students record decimal numbers in a place-value chart. Point out that the digits in hundreds, tens, and/or ones place form the whole number part of the number and the tenths and hundredths form the fractional part. Highlighting the whole number part of a decimal in colour may also be helpful.

ESL Strategies

Be on the lookout for words with which beginning English learners may not be familiar (for example, spectators, dash, earthworm). Provide explanations as needed.

- Suppose an athlete had a time of 9.50 seconds. Which 2 whole numbers is 9.50 between? (*9 and 10*)

Invite a volunteer to label the ends of the number line and find the 9.50 mark. Elicit from students that since 9.50 falls halfway between 9 and 10, we round up to 10.

To summarize the key points of the lesson, ask:

- What is the first thing you think about when rounding decimals to the nearest whole number?
  (*I think about which 2 whole numbers the decimal falls between.*)
- How do you decide whether to round up to the next whole number or down to the whole number part of the decimal?
  (*I round up if the decimal part is half or more of one whole. I round down if the decimal part is less than half of one whole.*)

Practice

Provide hundredths grids and blank number lines to students who wish to use them.

Assessment Focus: Question 8

Students realize that a decimal less than 5 which rounds to 5 will have a 4 in the ones place and 50 to 99 hundredths. They realize that a decimal greater than 5 which rounds to 5 will have a 5 in the ones place and 1 to 49 hundredths. Some students may use a number line or hundredths grids to show their work. Others may perform the task mentally, showing only their answers.

Sample Answers

7. Fastest time: 11.49 seconds
   Slowest time: 10.50 seconds

REFLECT: Here is how I would round 2.04 to the nearest whole number: 2.04 is between 2 and 3. I know that 4 hundredths is closer to 0 than to 1. So 2.04 rounds down to 2.

Practice

1. Round to the nearest whole number.
   a) 4.78 5 b) 6.31 6 c) 5.09 5 d) 1.98 2 e) 3.2 3 f) 12.50 13
   g) 7.49 7 h) 11.71 12 i) 40.12 40 j) 4.47 4 k) 1.25 1 l) 3.62 4
2. Round to the nearest dollar.
   a) \$4.78 \$5.00 b) \$1.22 \$1.00 c) \$7.50 \$8.00 d) \$3.99 \$4.00
   e) \$6.27 \$6.00 f) \$4.49 \$4.00 g) \$0.97 \$1.00 h) \$21.55 \$22.00
3. Which decimals could be rounded to each circled number? Explain.
   a) ⑦ 6.42, 7.1, 6.08 7.1 b) ⑨ 8.50, 9.43, 9.01 8.50, 9.43, 9.01
   c) ② 1.9, 2.8, 1.50 1.9, 1.50 d) ④ 0.09, 3.89, 4.44 3.89, 4.44
4. The toonie has a mass of 7.3 g and a thickness of 1.8 mm.
   Round each measurement to the nearest whole number. 7 g, 2 mm
5. The 1908 penny has a mass of 5.67 g and a width of 25.4 mm.
   Round each measurement to the nearest whole number. 6 g, 25 mm
6. The biggest earthworm ever found was 6.7 m long and 2.03 cm wide.
   Round each measurement to the nearest whole number. 7m, 2 cm
7. A runner's time in the 100-m dash is about 11 seconds when rounded to the nearest second.
   Suppose the time was recorded to the nearest hundredth of a second.
   What are the fastest and slowest possible times?

8. Use the digits 4, 5, and 6.
   a) Write as many decimals as you can that round to 5 when rounded to the nearest whole number. 4.56, 4.65, 5.46
   b) Order the decimals from least to greatest. 4.56, 4.65, 5.46
   c) Suppose the digit 5 was replaced with 3.
      How would this affect your results? Explain. 4.63

Reflect

Choose a number with a digit in the hundredths place.
How would you round your number to the nearest whole number?

126 ASSESSMENT FOCUS | Question 8

ASSESSMENT FOR LEARNING

What to Look For	What to Do
Understanding concepts ✔ Students understand that a decimal number falls between 2 whole numbers. ✔ Students understand that to round a decimal number to the nearest whole number, one must determine which whole number it is closer to.	***Extra Support:*** Provide students with a list of decimals. Have them name the 2 whole numbers each decimal falls between. Or, provide pairs of consecutive numbers. Have them name decimals that fall between each pair. Students can use Step-by-Step 4 (Master 4.15) to complete question 8. ***Extra Practice:*** Students can use rulers or metre sticks to round the following lengths to the nearest whole number: 6.23 cm, 8.2 dm, 0.78 m, 0.6 m Students can complete Extra Practice 2 (Master 4.24).
Applying procedures ✔ Students round decimals to hundredths to the nearest whole number. ✔ Students name decimals that would round to a given whole number.	***Extension:*** Provide students with a list of decimals with hundredths (for example, 2.76, 10.42, 6.18). Challenge students to round each number to the nearest tenth and to the nearest whole number.

Recording and Reporting
Master 4.2 Ongoing Observations: Decimals

LESSON 5

Estimating Sums and Differences

The 50¢ coin was the first coin produced in Canada.
In recent decades, 50¢ coins have not been widely used.
Nowadays, most of them are purchased by coin collectors.

Explore

Use the data in the table.

➤ Estimate the combined mass of:
- a 50¢ coin and a quarter
- a 50¢ coin and a nickel
- a 50¢ coin and a dime

➤ Estimate the difference in widths of:
- a 50¢ coin and a penny
- a 50¢ coin and a quarter
- a 50¢ coin and a nickel

Coin	Mass (g)	Width (mm)
Penny	2.35	19.05
Nickel	3.95	21.2
Dime	1.75	18.03
Quarter	4.4	23.88
50¢	6.9	27.13
Loonie	7	26.5
Toonie	7.3	28

Show and Share

Compare your estimates with those of another pair of classmates.
Discuss the strategies you used to estimate the sums and differences.

Connect

➤ The toonie has a mass of 7.3 g. The 50¢ coin has a mass of 6.9 g.
To estimate the combined mass of these coins:
Estimate: 7.3 + 6.9

Round each decimal to the nearest whole number.
7.3 rounds to 7.
6.9 rounds to 7.
Add the rounded numbers: 7 + 7 = 14
The combined mass of a toonie and a 50¢ coin is about 14 g.

You get another estimate if you round just 1 number:
7 + 6.9 = 13.9
So, 7.3 + 6.9 is about 13.9.

LESSON FOCUS | Estimate sums and differences of decimals. 127

Estimating Sums and Differences

LESSON ORGANIZER 40–50 min

Curriculum Focus: Estimate sums and differences of decimals. (5m18, 5m36)

Teacher Materials
- a 50¢ coin (optional)

Student Materials *Optional*
- Step-by-Step 5 (Master 4.16)
- Extra Practice 3 (Master 4.25)

Assessment: Master 4.2 Ongoing Observations: Decimals

Key Math Learning

Rounding can be used to estimate sums and differences of decimals.

BEFORE Get Started

Together, read and discuss the opening passage. If you have a 50¢ coin available, pass it around for the students to see. Invite volunteers to describe the coin.

Ask:
- Why do you think the 50¢ coin never became highly used? (*People did not really see it as useful to exchange 2 quarters for a 50¢ coin. The mass of the 50¢ coin is less than 2 g less than the mass of the 2 quarters.*)
- Do you think any other coins will eventually not be used? Why? (*I think the penny will eventually not be used. Now that $1 and $2 coins are in use, there is too much change to carry around. Also, the mass of 5 pennies is 11.75 g whereas the mass of a nickel is 3.95 g, for a difference of 7.8 g.*)

Present *Explore*. Ensure students know what is meant by "combined mass." Ensure as well students understand that exact answers are not what is expected. Rather, they must estimate, recording only the approximate sums and differences.

DURING Explore

Ongoing Assessment: Observe and Listen

Ask questions, such as:
- What strategy are you using to estimate? (*Rounding each number to the nearest whole gram.*)
- Which coins are you using in your calculations? (*A 50-cent piece and a quarter*)
- Which two numbers did you add (subtract) to get your estimate? (*7 and 4*) What is your estimated mass? (*7 g + 4 g = 11 g*)

REACHING ALL LEARNERS

Alternative Explore

Materials: A collection of objects labelled with prices
Students choose pairs of objects and estimate their combined prices, and the differences in their prices.

Early Finishers

Have students write questions like those in *Practice* questions 7 and 8. Students trade papers and estimate the answers to their partner's questions.

Common Misconceptions

➤ Students consistently round down to estimate sums and differences.

How to Help: Have students find the exact answers to a few questions and compare them with their estimates. This should help them to see that rounding to the nearest whole numbers produces better estimates.

➤ The mass of a penny is 2.35 g.
The mass of a dime is 1.75 g.
To estimate the difference in these masses:
Estimate: 2.35 − 1.75

Round one or both decimals to a "nice number."
Round 2.35 down to 2.25.
2.25 − 1.75 = 0.50
So, 2.35 − 1.75 is about 0.50.

The difference in masses of a penny and a dime is about 0.50 g.

You get another estimate if you round up to a "nice number."
Round 2.35 up to 2.50.
2.50 − 1.75 = 0.75
So, 2.35 − 1.75 is about 0.75.

Numbers Every Day

Number Strategies
Write each pattern rule.
1, 3, 7, 13, 21, 31, 43, … 57, 7
100, 90, 81, 73, 66, 60, … 55,
Write the next 3 terms in each pattern.

Practice

1. Estimate each sum.
   a) 4.6 + 9.8 About 15 b) $2.31 + $8.79 About $11.00
   c) 5.99 + 1.40 About 7 d) 11.20 + 6.31 About 17
   e) $12.36 + $4.08 About $16.00 f) 7.1 + 4.2 About 11
2. Estimate each difference.
   a) 4.7 − 3.8 About 1 b) 8.07 − 7.91 About 0
   c) 10.82 − 6.99 About 4 d) $12.99 − $8.50 About $4.00
   e) 4.04 − 2.96 About 1 f) 12.1 − 8.8 About 3
3. Estimate each sum or difference.
   a) 9.75 + 5.5 About 16 b) 5.25 − 1.4 About 4
   c) 9.9 + 6.42 About 16 d) 7.1 − 2.96 About 4
4. Use the data in the poster.
   a) About how much would 2 adult tickets cost? About $28.00
   b) About how much would tickets for a 14-year-old and a 9-year-old cost? About $20.00
   c) About how much more is an adult ticket than a senior ticket? About $6.00

128

Making Connections

Measurement Strand: Have students measure and record, in parts of a metre, the lengths of 2 objects. Students then estimate to find the combined length.

Numbers Every Day

Start at 1. Add 2 to get the next term, then increase the number added by 2 each time.
Start at 100. Subtract 10 to get the next term, then subtract 1 less each time.

- Do you think the exact answer is less than or greater than your estimate? Explain.
  (*I think my answer is less than the estimate because in both cases where I rounded, the actual number is larger.*)

Watch for students who find exact answers and then round to produce an estimate. Remind them that the idea is to estimate only.

AFTER Connect

Have volunteers share their estimates and the strategies they used. Ask:

- Why is rounding to the nearest whole numbers a good way to estimate?
  (*It is easier to add and subtract whole numbers than decimals.*)
- Suppose you rounded just 1 of the numbers to estimate a sum. How would your estimate be different than if you rounded both numbers?
  (*It would be closer to the actual answer.*)
- If you wanted to round just 1 number to subtract, which one would you round?
  (*The one you subtract.*) Why? (*It is harder to subtract from zeros.*)

Practice

Assessment Focus: Question 6

Some students will use different estimation strategies to find the sum. They will then compare the resulting estimates with Kenichi's and Ariel's estimates to determine how each student estimated. Some students may recognize that Kenichi rounded both numbers to the nearest 10 to estimate and Ariel rounded only 11.14 to the nearest 10.

5. Agnes has $50 in her pocket.
Explain how Agnes might estimate to check
if she has enough money to buy the sweater and the jeans.

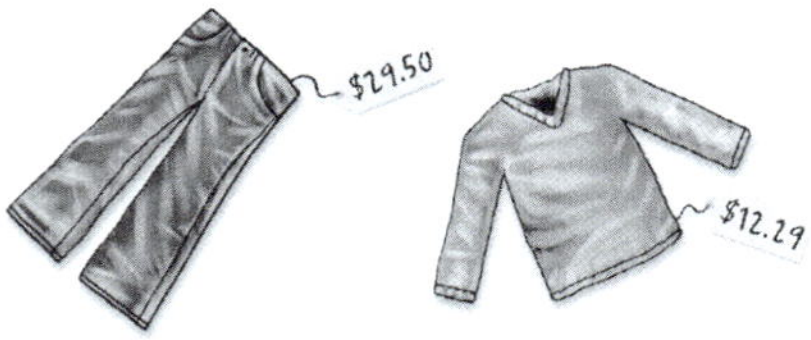

6. Kenichi estimated that 23.58 + 11.14 is about 35.
Ariel's estimate was 34.58.
   a) How did each student estimate the sum?
   Use numbers and words to explain.
   b) Use a different strategy to estimate the sum.
   How is your estimate different?

7. Jamel is saving up for a helmet that costs $39.99.
So far, he has saved $14.10.
About how much more money does Jamel need to save? About $26.00

8. An insect's body is 2.34 cm long. Its antennae are 4.58 cm long.
Estimate the total length of the insect. Show your work. About 7 cm

9. Choose the better estimate. Explain your thinking.
   a) 9.2 − 3.8   4, 5, or 6   5
   b) 19.6 + 12.2   31, 32, or 33   32
   c) 10.53 − 4.99   5, 6, or 7   6

Reflect

Explain how estimating decimal sums and differences is the same as estimating whole-number sums and differences. How is it different?

At Home

Talk with family members.
When do they estimate?
How do they estimate?
Write about what you found out.

ASSESSMENT FOCUS | Question 6   129

Sample Answers

5. Agnes could round $12.29 to $12.00 and $29.50 to $30, and then add.

6. a) Kenichi estimated by rounding 23.58 to 24 and 11.14 to 11, then adding.
Ariel estimated by rounding 11.14 to 11, then adding 11 + 23.58.

REFLECT: Estimating the sums and differences of decimal numbers is like estimating the sums and differences of whole numbers because you use rounding for both. The estimating is different because with decimals you round to the nearest whole number, and with whole numbers you round to the nearest 10 or 100.

ASSESSMENT FOR LEARNING

What to Look For	What to Do
Understanding concepts ✔ Students understand that rounding decimals before adding or subtracting produces a reasonable estimate. ***Applying procedures*** ✔ Students use rounding to estimate the sums and differences of decimals. ***Communicating*** ✔ Students explain clearly the strategies they use to estimate. They use appropriate mathematical language.	***Extra Support:*** Students may benefit from estimating sums and differences of decimals with tenths before proceeding to decimals with hundredths. Students can use Step-by-Step 5 (Master 4.16) to complete question 6. ***Extra Practice:*** Students work in pairs. Each student writes 5 decimals on separate slips of paper. They put the papers in a bag and take turns to draw 2 papers and estimate the sum and then the difference. Students can complete Extra Practice 3 (Master 4.25). ***Extension:*** Have students estimate the sums of 3 or 4 decimals.

Recording and Reporting
Master 4.2 Ongoing Observations: Decimals

Adding Decimals

LESSON ORGANIZER

40–50 min

Curriculum Focus: Add decimals to hundredths. (5m18, 5m31, 5m34)

Student Materials
- Base Ten Blocks
- place-value mats

Optional
- Step-by-Step 6 (Master 4.17)
- Extra Practice 3 (Master 4.25)
- catalogues

Assessment: Master 4.2 Ongoing Observations: Decimals

Key Math Learning

Addition with decimals is an extension of addition with whole numbers.

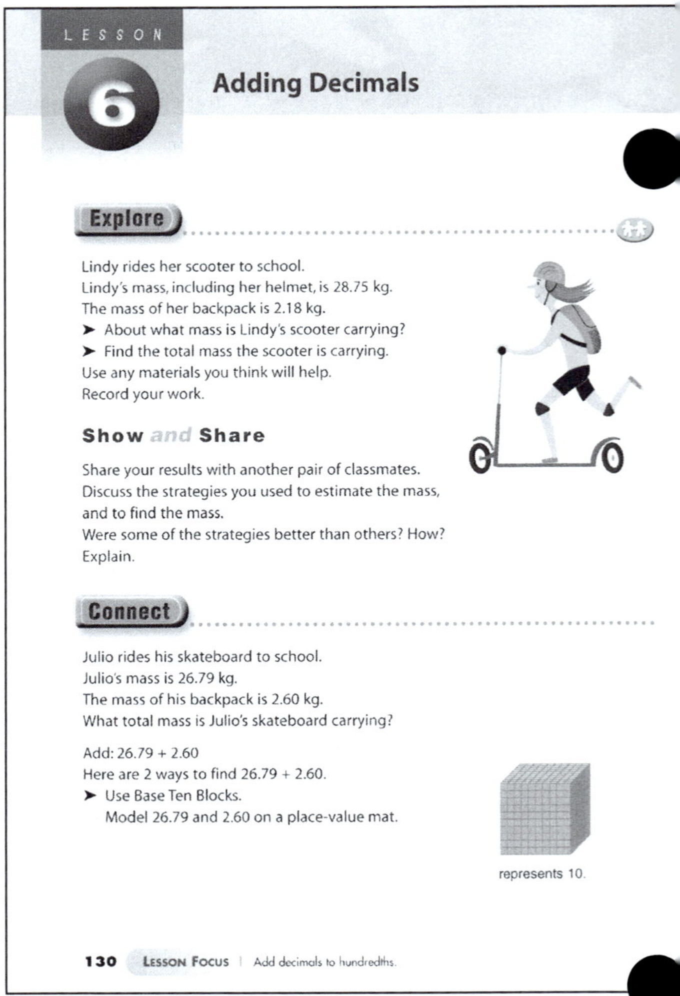
LESSON 6

Adding Decimals

Explore

Lindy rides her scooter to school.
Lindy's mass, including her helmet, is 28.75 kg.
The mass of her backpack is 2.18 kg.
➤ About what mass is Lindy's scooter carrying?
➤ Find the total mass the scooter is carrying.
Use any materials you think will help.
Record your work.

Show and Share

Share your results with another pair of classmates.
Discuss the strategies you used to estimate the mass, and to find the mass.
Were some of the strategies better than others? How? Explain.

Connect

Julio rides his skateboard to school.
Julio's mass is 26.79 kg.
The mass of his backpack is 2.60 kg.
What total mass is Julio's skateboard carrying?

Add: 26.79 + 2.60
Here are 2 ways to find 26.79 + 2.60.
➤ Use Base Ten Blocks.
Model 26.79 and 2.60 on a place-value mat.

represents 10.

130 LESSON FOCUS | Add decimals to hundredths.

BEFORE Get Started

Invite a volunteer to read the problem in *Explore*. Ask:
- What is the problem asking you to do? (*To find the approximate mass Lindy's scooter is carrying and then to find the actual total mass*)
- What do we do to find an approximate answer? (*Estimate.*)
- What do we do to find a total? (*Add.*)

Make Base Ten Blocks and place-value mats available for students who wish to use them. Review the values assigned to the blocks when modelling decimal numbers.

DURING Explore

Ongoing Assessment: Observe and Listen

Ask questions, such as:
- What will you do to estimate the total mass? (*Round the decimals and add.*)
- How could you get a closer estimate? (*Round just one of the decimals.*)
- How could you use Base Ten Blocks to help? (*Model the decimals.*)
- Which blocks will you use to represent the 2 in 28.75? (*The big cubes*) The 2 in 2.18? (*The flats*)

Watch for students who add without the use of materials. Are they adding digits of like values? Are they getting an answer close to their estimate? With students who are having difficulties, suggest they sketch a place-value chart and record the decimals on it.

AFTER Connect

Have students share their estimates and describe their estimation strategies. Then call on individuals to demonstrate the strategies they used to find the actual total. As Base Ten Blocks and a place-value mat are used, model

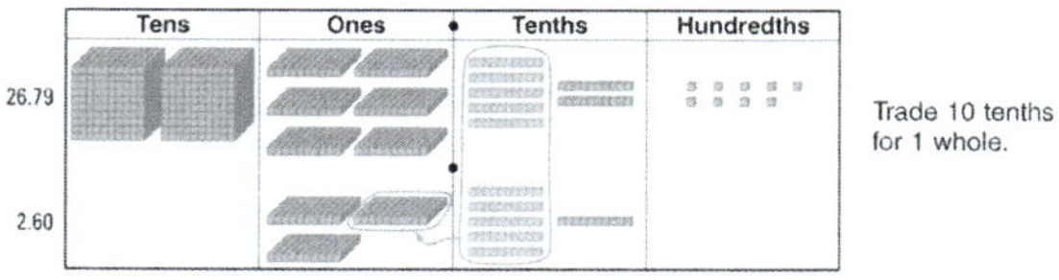

26.79 + 2.60 = 29.39
So, the total mass is 29.39 kg.

➤ Use place value.

Estimate.
26.79 rounds to 27.
2.60 rounds to 3.
27 + 3 = 30

Tens	Ones	Tenths	Hundredths
2	6	7	9
	2	6	0

Step 1: Record the numbers. Align the numbers as you aligned the blocks on the place-value mat.

$$\begin{array}{r} 26.79 \\ +\ 2.60 \\ \hline \end{array}$$

Step 2: Add as you would with whole numbers.

$$\begin{array}{r} ^{1}\ \ \ \ \ \\ 26.79 \\ +\ 2.60 \\ \hline 29.39 \end{array}$$

29.39 is close to 30, so the answer is reasonable.

Practice

1. Estimate first. Then add.

a) 4.6 + 2.3 — About 7; 6.9

b) 9.5 + 5.4 — About 15; 14.9

c) \$6.25 + \$3.92 — About \$10.00; \$10.17

d) 5.24 + 6.99 — About 12; 12.23

131

REACHING ALL LEARNERS

Alternative Explore

Materials: catalogues

Have students find 2 items that cost less than \$100 in a catalogue, then add to find the total cost.

Early Finishers

Have students work in pairs. Each student rolls a number cube 3 times to generate a decimal number with hundredths. Students record both decimals and add.

Common Misconceptions

➤ Students fail to align the digits of like value when recording an addition in vertical form.

How to Help: Provide students with 1-cm grid paper to help them align the digits. The columns can also be labelled to highlight the place value of each digit as shown.

T	O	Tth	Hth
2	4	6	7
	5	6	8

ESL Strategies

English learners could respond to question 10 by drawing pictures of 2 items with price tags and a plus sign between them.

how each step is recorded. Emphasize the importance of aligning the digits in the same way the blocks are aligned on the mat.

Ask:

- Why is it important to line up the digits of the same value?
  (*To add like values*)
- How is adding decimals like adding whole numbers?
  (*You add digits with the same place value and convert between place values the same way.*)
  How is it different?
  (*You have to consider the placement of the decimal.*)
- How do you know your answer is reasonable?
  (*I estimate to check.*)

Assign one or two additions for students to try on their own on paper. Have students check one another's work.

Practice

Ensure students understand the term "vertically" in question 2. Have Base Ten Blocks and place-value mats available.

Assessment Focus: Question 6

Students should recognize there are many different pairs of possible lengths. They should give some examples with a whole number length, 2 lengths with tenths, and 2 lengths with hundredths. Most students will determine the pairs of lengths by subtracting.

Sample Answers

4. Tagak estimated to check his answer. He saw that the sum should have been about 4. The correct sum is 4.61.
6. Answers will vary. 2.3 m and 2.6 m or 1.5 m and 3.4 m
9. Answers will vary. The rectangle might be 20 cm long and 17.1 cm wide.
   20 cm + 17.1 cm + 20 cm + 17.1 cm = 74.2 cm
10. Jerri had 2 pieces of rope. One was 4.25 m long. The other was 7.38 m long. How many metres of rope did Jerri have?

$$\begin{array}{r} 4.25 \\ +\,7.38 \\ \hline 11.63 \end{array}$$

   Jerri had 11.63 m of rope.

REFLECT: The sum of 2 decimals with hundredths can be a decimal with tenths. 6.28 + 1.42 = 7.70. 7.70 is equivalent to 7.7.

Numbers Every Day

Students should start with a simple pair of numbers, such as 10 × 72. They can then use strategies such as halving and doubling to find the other pairs.
10 × 72 = 720; 20 × 36 = 720; 30 × 24 = 720;
40 × 18 = 720; 12 × 60 = 720; 15 × 48 = 720;
16 × 45 = 720

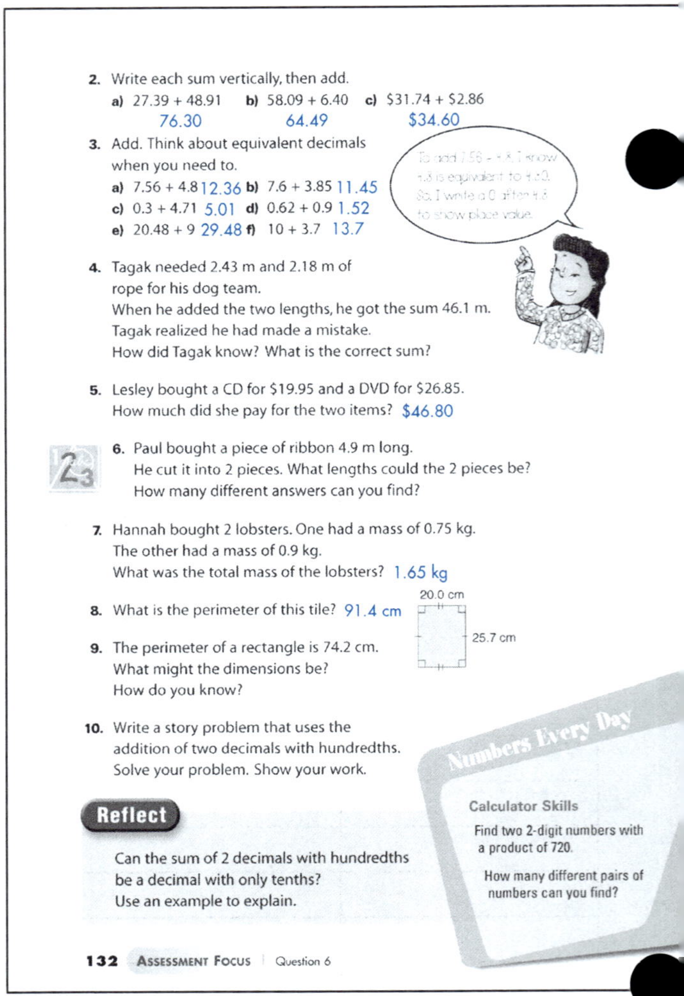

2. Write each sum vertically, then add.
   a) 27.39 + 48.91 76.30 b) 58.09 + 6.40 64.49 c) $31.74 + $2.86 $34.60
3. Add. Think about equivalent decimals when you need to.
   a) 7.56 + 4.8 12.36 b) 7.6 + 3.85 11.45
   c) 0.3 + 4.71 5.01 d) 0.62 + 0.9 1.52
   e) 20.48 + 9 29.48 f) 10 + 3.7 13.7

4. Tagak needed 2.43 m and 2.18 m of rope for his dog team.
   When he added the two lengths, he got the sum 46.1 m.
   Tagak realized he had made a mistake.
   How did Tagak know? What is the correct sum?
5. Lesley bought a CD for $19.95 and a DVD for $26.85.
   How much did she pay for the two items? $46.80
6. Paul bought a piece of ribbon 4.9 m long.
   He cut it into 2 pieces. What lengths could the 2 pieces be?
   How many different answers can you find?
7. Hannah bought 2 lobsters. One had a mass of 0.75 kg.
   The other had a mass of 0.9 kg.
   What was the total mass of the lobsters? 1.65 kg
8. What is the perimeter of this tile? 91.4 cm

9. The perimeter of a rectangle is 74.2 cm.
   What might the dimensions be?
   How do you know?
10. Write a story problem that uses the addition of two decimals with hundredths.
   Solve your problem. Show your work.

Reflect

Can the sum of 2 decimals with hundredths be a decimal with only tenths?
Use an example to explain.

Numbers Every Day

Calculator Skills

Find two 2-digit numbers with a product of 720.

How many different pairs of numbers can you find?

132 ASSESSMENT FOCUS | Question 6

ASSESSMENT FOR LEARNING

What to Look For	What to Do
Understanding concepts ✔ Students understand that addition of decimals involves adding digits of like values.	***Extra Support:*** Provide students with additional opportunities to use Base Ten Blocks to model additions with decimal numbers. Encourage them to articulate each step of the procedure. Students can use Step-by-Step 6 (Master 4.17) to complete question 6.
Applying procedures ✔ Students can record in vertical form an addition involving decimals. ✔ Students can add decimal numbers, regrouping where required.	***Extra Practice:*** Have students write in vertical form and add: 24.36 + 13.95; 6.27 + 4.3; 85.7 + 4.84 Students can complete Extra Practice 3 (Master 4.25).
Problem solving ✔ Students select an appropriate strategy and solve problems involving the addition of decimals.	***Extension:*** Challenge students to find the missing digits in questions like: ❏ 6.4 ❏ + 3 ❏.5 9 = 6 1.❏7

Recording and Reporting

Master 4.2 Ongoing Observations: Decimals

Make 2!

u will need coloured markers.
ur teacher will give you a set of decimal cards
and hundredths grids.

The object of the game is to shade hundredths grids
to represent a decimal that is as close to 2 as possible.

- Shuffle the decimal cards.
  Place the cards face down in a pile.
  Turn over the top 4 cards.
- Players take turns choosing one of the 4 cards displayed.
  Each time, the card is replaced with the top card in the deck.
- On your turn, represent the decimal on one of the hundredths grids.
  Use a different colour for each decimal.
  You may not represent part of the decimal on one grid
  and the other part on the second grid.
  You may not represent a decimal that would more than fill a grid.
  If each of the decimals on the 4 cards is greater than either decimal
  left on your grids, you lose your turn.
- Continue playing until neither player can choose a card.
  Find the sum of the decimals you coloured on your grids.
  The player whose sum is closer to 2 is the winner.

133

Make 2!

LESSON ORGANIZER 20 min

Student Materials
- coloured markers
- sets of decimal cards (Master 4.6)
- hundredths grids (PM 15)

BEFORE Get Started

Organize the students into pairs. Distribute a set of decimal cards and hundredths grids to each pair. Invite students to read the game instructions. Tell students they will shade a pair of hundredths grids to make a decimal that is as close to 2 as possible, without going over. Be sure students understand they must represent each decimal *entirely* on one grid. If a player does not have enough empty squares on her grid to represent any of the decimals that are turned up, she loses her turn.

DURING Game

As students play, ask questions, such as:
- How did you decide which card to choose? (*At first, I chose cards with decimals that were close to 1. As I shaded more squares on each grid, I chose cards with decimals that were less than 0.5.*)
- How did you decide where to represent each decimal? (*I represented each decimal on the hundredths grid that had the fewest empty squares. If the decimal would not fit on that grid, I represented it on the other grid.*)
- What strategies did you use to find the sum? (*I counted the shaded squares on the hundredths grid to find the sum, then I checked by adding the decimals.*)

AFTER

Engage students in a discussion of the strategies they used to choose each decimal card, decide where to represent each decimal, and add. Students who found the sum by counting squares on the hundredths grids should check by adding the decimals and vice versa.

Spinning Decimals

LESSON ORGANIZER 20 min

Student Materials
- Base Ten Blocks
- place-value mats
- spinners (Master 4.7)

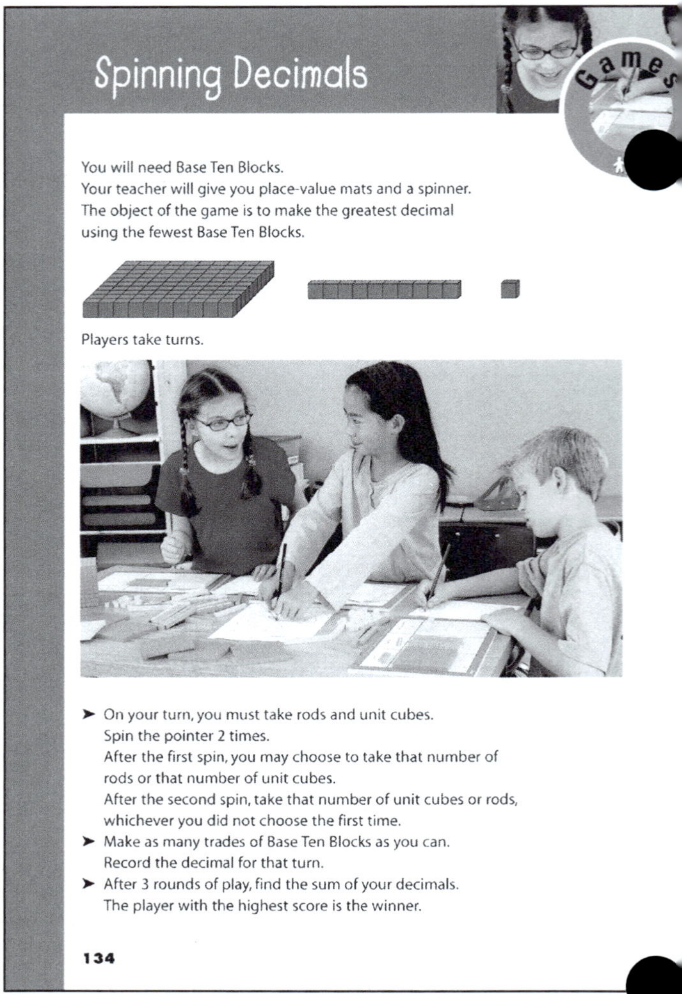
Spinning Decimals

You will need Base Ten Blocks.
Your teacher will give you place-value mats and a spinner.
The object of the game is to make the greatest decimal using the fewest Base Ten Blocks.

Players take turns.

- On your turn, you must take rods and unit cubes.
Spin the pointer 2 times.
After the first spin, you may choose to take that number of rods or that number of unit cubes.
After the second spin, take that number of unit cubes or rods, whichever you did not choose the first time.
- Make as many trades of Base Ten Blocks as you can.
Record the decimal for that turn.
- After 3 rounds of play, find the sum of your decimals.
The player with the highest score is the winner.

134

BEFORE — Get Started

Organize the students into groups of 3. Each group requires a spinner and each student requires Base Ten Blocks and a place-value mat. Invite students to read the game instructions. Ensure students understand they are to use the fewest Base Ten Blocks to make the greatest decimal.

DURING — Game

As students play, ask questions, such as:
- On your first spin, how did you decide whether to take unit cubes or rods?
(*The object of the game is to make the greatest decimal. If the pointer landed on one of the greater numbers — 15 to 19 — I took rods. Otherwise, I took unit cubes.*)
- How do you know you have used the fewest Base Ten Blocks?
(*I counted the number of each type of block. If there were fewer than 10 of each, no more trades were possible.*)
- What strategies did you use to add?
(*I found the sum of 2 of the decimals, then I added the third decimal to the sum.*)

AFTER

Invite students to share the strategies they used to make each decimal and find each sum.

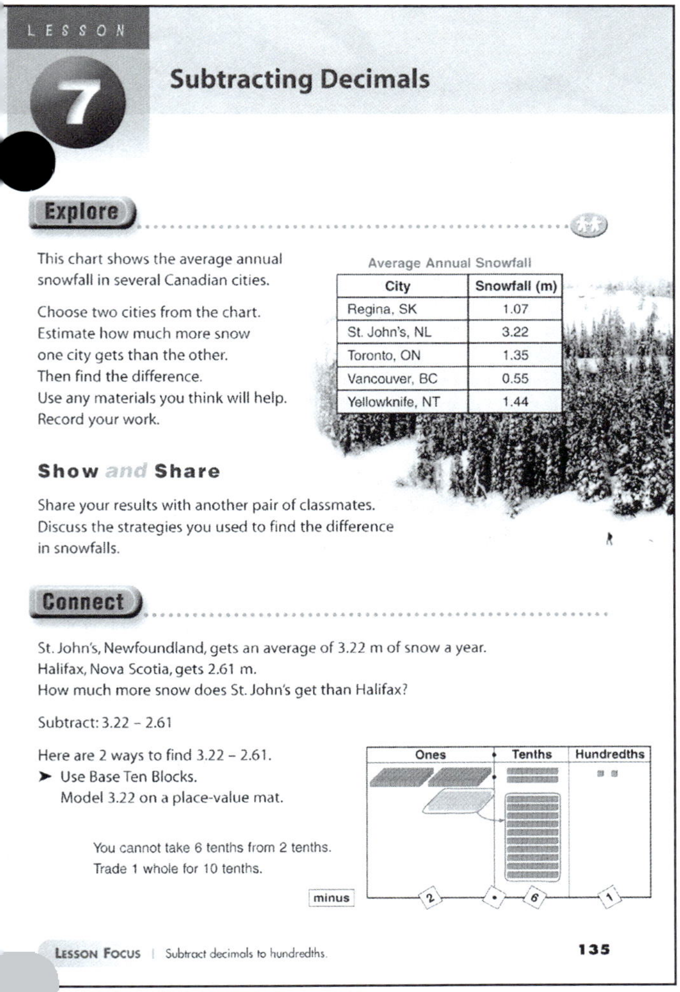
LESSON 7

Subtracting Decimals

Explore

This chart shows the average annual snowfall in several Canadian cities.

Average Annual Snowfall

City	Snowfall (m)
Regina, SK	1.07
St. John's, NL	3.22
Toronto, ON	1.35
Vancouver, BC	0.55
Yellowknife, NT	1.44

Choose two cities from the chart.
Estimate how much more snow one city gets than the other.
Then find the difference.
Use any materials you think will help.
Record your work.

Show and Share

Share your results with another pair of classmates.
Discuss the strategies you used to find the difference in snowfalls.

Connect

St. John's, Newfoundland, gets an average of 3.22 m of snow a year.
Halifax, Nova Scotia, gets 2.61 m.
How much more snow does St. John's get than Halifax?

Subtract: 3.22 – 2.61

Here are 2 ways to find 3.22 – 2.61.
➤ Use Base Ten Blocks.
Model 3.22 on a place-value mat.

You cannot take 6 tenths from 2 tenths.
Trade 1 whole for 10 tenths.

Lesson Focus | Subtract decimals to hundredths.   135

LESSON 7

Subtracting Decimals

LESSON ORGANIZER 40–50 min

Curriculum Focus: Subtract decimals to hundredths. (5m18, 5m31, 5m34)

Student Materials
- Base Ten Blocks
- place-value mats
- calculators

Optional
- Step-by-Step 7 (Master 4.18)
- Extra Practice 4 (Master 4.26)
- hundredths grids (PM 15)
- crayons or markers

Assessment: Master 4.2 Ongoing Observations: Decimals

Key Math Learning

Subtraction with decimals is an extension of subtraction with whole numbers.

BEFORE Get Started

Remind students of the strategies they used to subtract whole numbers. As a class, find this difference:

$$\begin{array}{r} 5921 \\ \underline{-\ 846} \end{array}$$

Ask:

- Why is the 8 from 846 written below the 9 of 5921 rather than below the 5?
  (When we subtract we use place value. We align the ones digits, the tens digits, and so on. In 5921 the 9 represents 9 hundreds. In 846 the 8 is in the hundreds place.)
- What strategies can you use to find this difference?
  (I could use Base Ten Blocks on a place-value mat, or a place-value chart.)

Invite students to examine the data in the Average Annual Snowfall chart.

Ask:

- What do you think "average annual snowfall" means?
  (In some years, we get a lot of snow and in other years we get very little. The average is the number that best represents the amount of snow each year.)

If necessary, explain that the data in the chart were found by adding the amounts of snow that fell each year for a number of years and then dividing by the number of years.

Present *Explore*. Have Base Ten Blocks and place-value mats available for students who wish to use them. Remind students to show all their work and to be ready to explain the strategies they used.

REACHING ALL LEARNERS

Alternative Explore

Materials: hundredths grids, crayons or markers

Have students model the subtraction of decimals by colouring hundredths grids. They colour grids to show the greater decimal, then cross out portions of the coloured parts to take away the lesser decimal.

Early Finishers

Have students choose 2 more cities from the chart and find the difference in their average annual snowfall.

Common Misconceptions

➤ Students regroup incorrectly as they subtract.

How to Help: Use Base Ten Blocks on a place-value mat to remind students that in subtraction, any regrouping must be done before subtracting from the top number.

ESL Strategies

Support beginning English speakers by reading the questions to them, rephrasing and explaining vocabulary as needed.

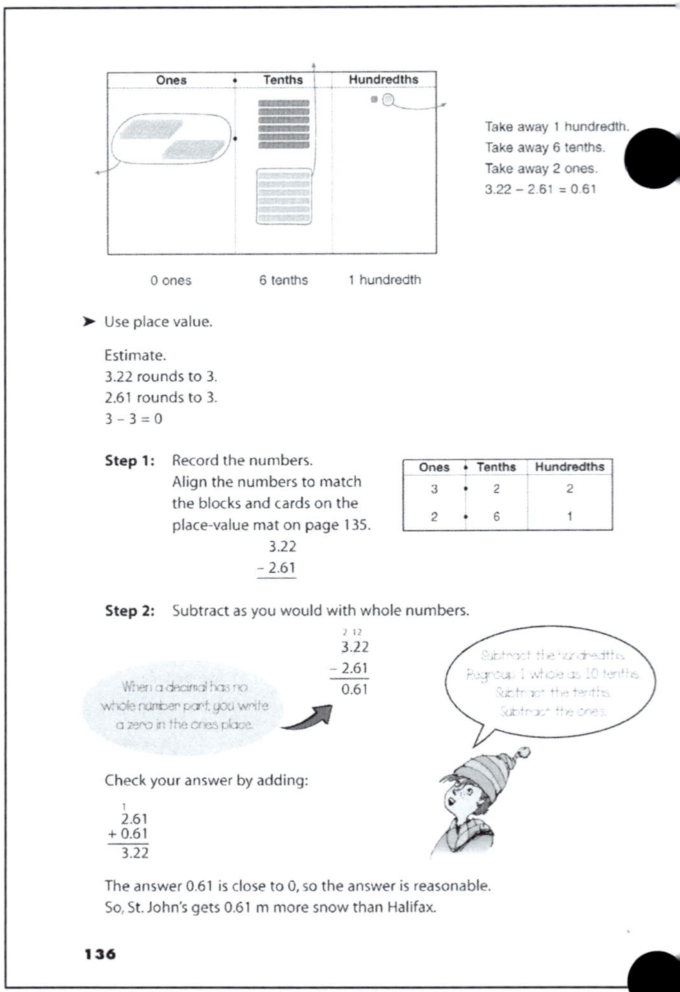
Ones • Tenths Hundredths

0 ones 6 tenths 1 hundredth

Take away 1 hundredth.
Take away 6 tenths.
Take away 2 ones.
3.22 – 2.61 = 0.61

➤ Use place value.

Estimate.
3.22 rounds to 3.
2.61 rounds to 3.
3 – 3 = 0

Step 1: Record the numbers.
Align the numbers to match the blocks and cards on the place-value mat on page 135.

Ones	•	Tenths	Hundredths
3	•	2	2
2	•	6	1

$$\begin{array}{r} 3.22 \\ -\,2.61 \\ \hline \end{array}$$

Step 2: Subtract as you would with whole numbers.

$$\begin{array}{r} \scriptstyle 2\ 12 \\ 3.22 \\ -\,2.61 \\ \hline 0.61 \end{array}$$

Check your answer by adding:

$$\begin{array}{r} \scriptstyle 1 \\ 2.61 \\ +\,0.61 \\ \hline 3.22 \end{array}$$

The answer 0.61 is close to 0, so the answer is reasonable.
So, St. John's gets 0.61 m more snow than Halifax.

136

Making Connections

Science: Have students research to find the average annual snowfall in their city and in other cities of their choice. Students can then find the differences between their city and the other cities.

DURING Explore

Ongoing Assessment: Observe and Listen

Ask questions, such as:

- Which two cities did you choose? (*Yellowknife and Regina*) Which one has the greater amount of snowfall? (*Yellowknife*) How do you know? (*1.44 > 1.07*)
- How did you make your estimate? (*I rounded to the nearest one.*)
- How could you get a closer estimate? (*Round to the nearest tenth.*)
- What will you do to find the differences? (*Subtract.*)
- How could you show the subtraction with the Base Ten Blocks? (*Model the greater number, then take away the lesser.*)

Watch for students who subtract without the aid of Base Ten Blocks. Ensure they are aligning the digits.

AFTER Connect

Invite volunteers to name the cities they chose and demonstrate the procedures they used to subtract. As Base Ten Blocks and a place-value mat are used, model how to record each step on the board, pointing out that you are aligning the digits in the same way the blocks are aligned on the place-value mat.

Ask:

- How is subtracting decimals like subtracting whole numbers? (*You subtract numbers with the same place value.*) How is it different? (*You have to be concerned about the placement of the decimal point in the answer.*)

Record one or two subtractions on the board in horizontal form (for example, 8.43 – 5.09). Have students record them in vertical form on paper and subtract. Students should check one another's work.

Practice

Use Base Ten Blocks to model the decimals.
Write the differences vertically if it helps.

1. Estimate first. Then subtract.
   a) 7.8 − 2.3 About 6, 5.5
   b) 6.7 − 3.8 About 3, 2.9
   c) 9.35 − 4.26 About 5, 5.09
   d) $10.62 − $4.07 About $7, $6.55
2. Subtract.
   a) 6.04 − 3.78 2.26
   b) 2.76 − 0.98 1.78
   c) $9.03 − $7.28 $1.75
   d) 11.09 − 9.29 1.80
   e) 12.26 − 3.91 8.35
   f) 73.40 − 54.23 19.17
3. Subtract. Think about equivalent decimals when you need to.
   a) 0.56 − 0.4 0.16
   b) $16 − $4.26 $11.74
   c) 0.8 − 0.36 0.44
4. Erin subtracted 12 from 37.8 and got a difference of 36.6.
   How did Erin know she had made a mistake?
   What is the correct answer? 25.8
5. Use the data in the table.

Average Annual Precipitation

City	Precipitation (cm)
Calgary, AB	39.88
Victoria, BC	85.80
Montreal, QC	93.97
Whitehorse, YT	26.90
Winnipeg, MB	50.44

   a) What is the difference in precipitation between Calgary and Whitehorse? 12.98 cm
   b) How much more precipitation does Montreal get than Winnipeg? 43.53 cm
   c) How much less precipitation does Whitehorse get than Winnipeg? 23.54 cm
   d) What is the difference in precipitation between the cities with the greatest and the least precipitation? 67.07 cm
6. Use the data in question 5.
   Find which two cities have a difference in precipitation of:
   a) 45.92 cm
   b) 8.17 cm
   c) 54.09 cm

137

Sample Answers

4. Erin knew she made a mistake because if you subtract 12 from 37, the answer is 25. If you subtract 12 from 37.8, the answer should be about 25.
6. a) Victoria and Calgary
   b) Victoria and Montreal
   c) Calgary and Montreal

Practice

Have Base Ten Blocks and place-value mats available for all questions.

Calculators are required for question 6.

Assessment Focus: Question 10

Students realize that if they round the decimals to the nearest whole number and subtract, the answer will be 10. By using visual inspection, students see that there would be some hundredths left after subtracting because 9 hundredths are to be taken away from 42 hundredths. Students conclude that the difference is greater than 10.

YOUR NOTES

9. Waterloo got 3.85 cm of rain in July and 5.09 cm of rain in August. How much more rain did Waterloo get in August than in July?

$$\begin{array}{r} \overset{4}{\cancel{5}}.09 \\ -\ 3.85 \\ \hline 1.24 \end{array}$$

Waterloo got 1.24 cm more rain in August than in July.

10. The difference is greater than 10. If you round 11.42 to 11 and 1.09 to 1 and subtract, the answer is 10. But 11.42 has more hundredths than 1.09, so the answer will be 10 and some hundredths.

REFLECT: Subtracting decimals is like subtracting whole numbers because in both you have to subtract the digits with the same place value. It is different because when you subtract decimals, there are digits in the tenths and hundredths and you use a decimal point between the whole number part and the decimal part.

Numbers Every Day

Students should compare consecutive terms to determine the pattern rule. They can then apply the pattern rule to find the missing terms.

Math Link

Media

A headline in a newspaper writes a large number like this:

1.5 Million People Affected by Power Cut

We say 1.5 million as "one point five million" or "one and a half million." 1.5 million is one million five hundred thousand, or 1 500 000.

7. In the men's long jump event, Marty jumped 8.26 m in the first trial and 8.55 m in the second trial. What is the difference between his jumps? 0.29 m

8. Candida got a $50 bill for her birthday. She bought a camera for $29.95 and a wallet for $9.29. How much of the $50 is left? $10.76

9. Write a story problem that uses the subtraction of two decimals with hundredths. Trade problems with a classmate. Solve your classmate's problem.

10. Brad estimated the difference between 11.42 and 1.09 as less than 10. Is Brad correct? Show 2 different ways to estimate that support your answer.

Reflect

How is subtracting decimals like subtracting whole numbers? How is it different? Use words, pictures, or numbers to explain.

Numbers Every Day

Mental Math

Copy and complete each number pattern.

22, 33, □, 55, □, □ (44, 66, 77)

24, □, 48, 60, □, □ (36, 72, 84)

138 ASSESSMENT FOCUS | Question 10

ASSESSMENT FOR LEARNING

What to Look For	What to Do
Understanding concepts ✔ Students understand that subtraction of decimals involves subtracting digits of like values. ***Applying procedures*** ✔ Students can record a subtraction involving decimals in vertical form, annexing zeros where necessary. ✔ Students can subtract decimal numbers, regrouping where required. ***Problem solving*** ✔ Students choose an appropriate strategy and solve problems involving the subtraction of decimals.	***Extra Support:*** Provide students with grid paper to use in recording subtractions to ensure that digits of like value are aligned. Students can use Step-by-Step 7 (Master 4.18) to complete question 10. ***Extra Practice:*** Students can complete the Additional Activity, *Closing in on 2* (Master 4.11). Students can complete Extra Practice 4 (Master 4.26). ***Extension:*** Challenge students to find 2 decimals with hundredths whose difference is 16.09.

Recording and Reporting

Master 4.2 Ongoing Observations: Decimals

LESSON 8

Multiplying Decimals by 10 and 100

Explore

You will need a calculator.

➤ Use a calculator to find each product.

2.5 × 10	43.7 × 10	2.76 × 10	14.81 × 10
2.5 × 100	43.7 × 100	2.76 × 100	14.81 × 100

Record the products in a place-value chart.

Thousands	Hundreds	Tens	Ones	Tenths

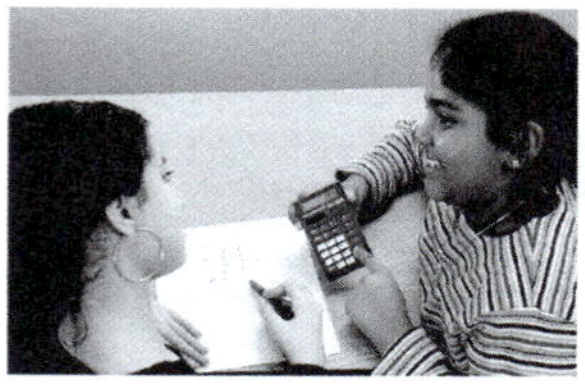

How can you predict the product when you multiply by 10? By 100?

➤ Find each product. Then check with a calculator.

4.8 × 10	26.8 × 10	3.8 × 10	24.68 × 10
4.8 × 100	26.8 × 100	3.8 × 100	24.68 × 100

Show and Share

Share what you discovered with another pair of classmates.
What patterns do you see?
How can you mentally multiply a decimal by 10?
How can you mentally multiply a decimal by 100?

LESSON FOCUS | Mentally multiply decimals with tenths and hundredths by 10 and 100.

139

Multiplying Decimals by 10 and 100

LESSON ORGANIZER

40–50 min

Curriculum Focus: Mentally multiply decimals with tenths and hundredths by 10 and 100. (5m15, 5m30)

Teacher Materials

- overhead calculator (optional)

Student Materials

- calculators
- Base Ten Blocks
- place-value mats

Optional

- Step-by-Step 8 (Master 4.19)
- Extra Practice 4 (Master 4.26)

Assessment: Master 4.2 Ongoing Observations: Decimals

Key Math Learnings

1. Multiplying a decimal by 10 results in the digits of the decimal shifting one place to the left.
2. Multiplying a decimal by 100 results in the digits of the decimal shifting two places to the left.
3. When the product is a whole number, the decimal point is omitted.

BEFORE Get Started

Post the following questions and have students find each product:

4 × 10	86 × 10	124 × 10
4 × 100	86 × 100	124 × 100

Call on students to give the products of one pair of questions. Ask:

- How did you find each product? (*I used place value to multiply. For example, 4 × 100 = 4 × 1 hundred = 4 hundreds, or 400.*)
- What pattern do you notice in the products? (*The product has the same number of zeros as the second factor.*)
- Do you think multiplying decimals by 10 and 100 will produce a similar pattern? Why? (*Yes. The only difference between decimals and whole numbers is place value. The patterns and operations work the same way.*)

Present *Explore.* Students should complete the first part of the activity and talk with their partners about what they discovered. They should then use what they found out to complete the second part of the activity, and use the calculator only to check their answers.

DURING Explore

Ongoing Assessment: Observe and Listen

Observe if students are noticing the shifting of the digits to the left as they multiply by 10 and 100.

Have students examine the products they found with a calculator. Ask questions, such as:

- Think about a place-value chart. In what place is the 2 in 2.5? (*Ones*)
  In what place is the 2 in the product 25? (*Tens*) In what place is the 5 in 2.5? (*Tenths*) And in the product 25? (*Ones*)

REACHING ALL LEARNERS

Early Finishers

Post a list of items and their prices (for example, popcorn, $0.75; hot dogs, $2.25; party hats, $0.65). Have students use mental math to find the cost of 10 and 100 of each item.

Common Misconceptions

➤ Students insert an unnecessary decimal point after the final digit in a whole number product.

How to Help: Explain that the decimal point is only used when there are digits in the tenths or hundredths places.

➤ Students fail to put a zero in the ones place when multiplying a decimal with tenths by 100.

How to Help: Use a place-value chart to illustrate that the digits shift 2 places to the left when multiplying a decimal by 100, and omitting the zero means that the digits have shifted just 1 place to the left.

Making Connections

Measurement Strand: Students can convert measurements reported in metres to decimetres and centimetres by mentally multiplying by 10 and 100.

Connect

➤ You can use Base Ten Blocks to multiply.
Multiply: 3.6 × 10
Use Base Ten Blocks.
Model 10 groups of 3.6.

Make [rod] equal 1, so [flat] is 10, and [unit] is 0.1.

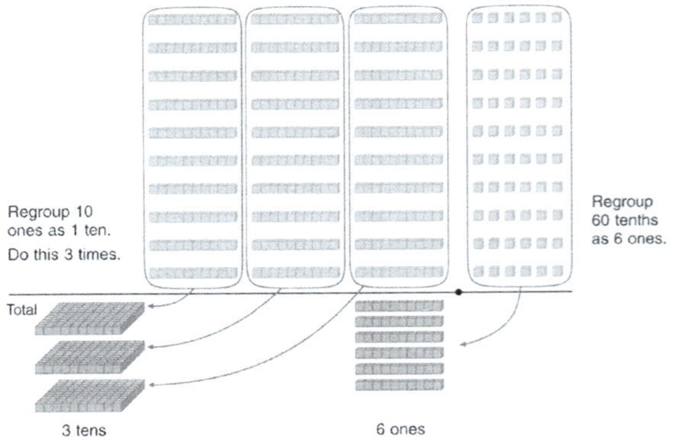

So, 3.6 × 10 = 36

You can use place value to understand what happens when you multiply a decimal by 10 and by 100.

➤ Multiply by 10.
- Multiply: 3.6 × 10
  3.6 = 3 ones and 6 tenths

Tens	Ones	•	Tenths
	3	•	6

3 ones × 10 = 30 ones = 3 tens
6 tenths × 10 = 60 tenths = 6 ones
3 tens + 6 ones = 36
So, 3.6 × 10 = 36

Tens	Ones	•	Tenths
	3	•	6
3	6	•	

140

- How can you find 4.8 × 100 without using a calculator? *(Shift the digits two places to the left.)* In what place will the 4 be? (*Hundreds*) The 8? (*Tens*) What will be in the ones place? (*Zero*)

AFTER Connect

Invite students to share the discoveries they made and to explain how they used what they found out to mentally multiply decimals by 10 and by 100.

Ask questions, such as:

- When you multiply a decimal with tenths by 10, what do you notice about the product? (*It has the same digits as the decimal, but it is a whole number.*)
- And when you multiply a decimal with hundredths by 10? (*It has the same digits, but they shift one place to the left.*)

Follow a similar line of questioning for decimals with hundredths.

Tell students that Base Ten Blocks can be used to model multiplying decimal numbers. Provide students with blocks and place-value mats. Work together to model 2.3 × 10, one step at a time. Lead students to see how the blocks, once the regrouping has been completed, show that the digits in 2.3 have shifted one place to the left.

Conclude by asking:

- How is multiplying a decimal by 10 and 100 like multiplying a whole number by 10 and 100? How is it different? (*I use the same strategies and processes to multiply both decimals and whole numbers by 10 and by 100. When I multiply decimals by 10 and by 100, I must think about where to place the decimal point in the product.*)

- You can use mental math to multiply a decimal by 10.

$2.47 \times 10 = 24.7$

$6.8 \times 10 = 68$ ← You do not have to put a decimal point after a whole number.

$14.81 \times 10 = 148.1$

➤ Multiply by 100.

- Multiply: 3.6×100

3 ones × 100 = 300 ones
= 30 tens
= 3 hundreds
6 tenths × 100 = 600 tenths
= 60 ones
= 6 tens
3 hundreds + 6 tens = 360
So, 3.6 × 100 = 360

Hundreds	Tens	Ones	Tenths
		3 .	6
3	6	0 .	

- You can use mental math to multiply a decimal by 100.

$2.47 \times 100 = 247$

$6.8 \times 100 = 680$ ← You write a zero when there are no digits in the ones place.

$14.81 \times 100 = 1481$

141

- When might you have to multiply a decimal by 10 or 100?
(I would have to multiply a decimal by 10 or by 100 to convert a length measured in metres to decimetres or centimetres and to convert an amount in dollars to an amount in cents.)

Practice

Students should use mental math to complete all questions.

Assessment Focus: Question 4

Students should recognize that to find the number of litres Ana bought and the price she paid, they must multiply the capacity of the can and the price by 10. Similarly, to find the number of litres Hans bought and the price he paid, students must multiply the capacity and price by 100.

YOUR NOTES

Sample Answers

1.

	Thousands	Hundreds	Tens	Ones	• Tenths
a)			7	9 •	
b)			2	6 •	7
c)			7	0 •	
d)	4	2	3	0 •	

5. To find how tall 18.59 m is in centimetres, you have to multiply by 100.
18.59 m × 100 = 1859 cm

7. 10 nickels have a mass of 39.5 g.
20 dimes have a mass of 35 g.
39.5 > 35, so the nickels have the greater mass.

REFLECT: To multiply 8.93 by 10, I shift the digits one place to the left. 8.93 × 10 = 89.3
To multiply 8.93 by 100, I shift the digits two places to the left. 8.93 × 100 = 893

Numbers Every Day

Students may round one or both factors to the nearest ten, hundred, or thousand.

Practice

1. Use a place-value chart. Record each product in the chart.
a) 7.9 × 10 79 b) 2.67 × 10 26.7 c) 0.7 × 100 70 d) 42.3 × 100 4230

2. Multiply. Use mental math.
a) 4.7 × 10 47; 4.7 × 100 470 b) 62.8 × 10 628; 62.8 × 100 6280 c) 3.85 × 10 38.5; 3.85 × 100 385 d) 17.45 × 10 174.5; 17.45 × 100 1745

3. Use mental math to multiply.
a) 1.6 × 10 16 b) 4.82 × 10 48.2 c) 53.7 × 10 537 d) 26.31 × 10 263.1
e) 3.05 × 100 305 f) 56.73 × 100 5673 g) 0.5 × 10 5 h) 0.09 × 100 9

Use mental math to solve each problem.

4. a) Ana bought 10 cans of apple juice.
How many litres did she buy? 13.6 L
How much did Ana pay? $12.90
b) Hans bought 100 cans of apple juice.
How many litres did he buy? 136 L
How much did Hans pay? $129.00

5. Fiona read about a man in India who grew a bush 18.59 m tall in his garden.
Fiona said the bush was 185.9 cm tall.
Was she correct? Explain. No.

6. A hot dog at the ballpark sells for $2.75.
The vendor sold 100 hot dogs.
How much money did she collect? $275.00

7. A nickel has a mass of 3.95 g.
A dime has a mass of 1.75 g.
Which has the greater mass:
10 nickels or 20 dimes? 10 nickels

Reflect

Explain how to use mental math to multiply 8.93 by 10 and by 100.

Numbers Every Day

Number Strategies

Estimate each product.

348 × 9 About 2700
7125 × 5 About 35 000
25 × 35 About 1200

Which strategies did you use?

142 ASSESSMENT FOCUS Question 4

ASSESSMENT FOR LEARNING

What to Look For	What to Do
Understanding concepts ✔ Students understand that multiplying a decimal by 10 or 100 results in the digits shifting to the left. ***Applying procedures*** ✔ Students can mentally multiply a decimal with tenths or hundredths by 10 and 100.	***Extra Support:*** Provide students with a place-value chart and small 0 to 9 cards. Students use the cards on the chart to show a given decimal, then move the digits to show the product of the decimal times 10 or 100. [chart below] Students can use Step-by-Step 8 (Master 4.19) to complete question 4. ***Extra Practice:*** Have students write 3 decimals with tenths and 3 with hundredths. They exchange papers with a partner and multiply each decimal by 10 and 100. Students can complete Extra Practice 4 (Master 4.26). ***Extension:*** Have students write to explain how they could use mental math to multiply 7.63 by 1000.

H	T	O •	Tth	Hth
	2	5 •	7	

Recording and Reporting

Master 4.2 Ongoing Observations: Decimals

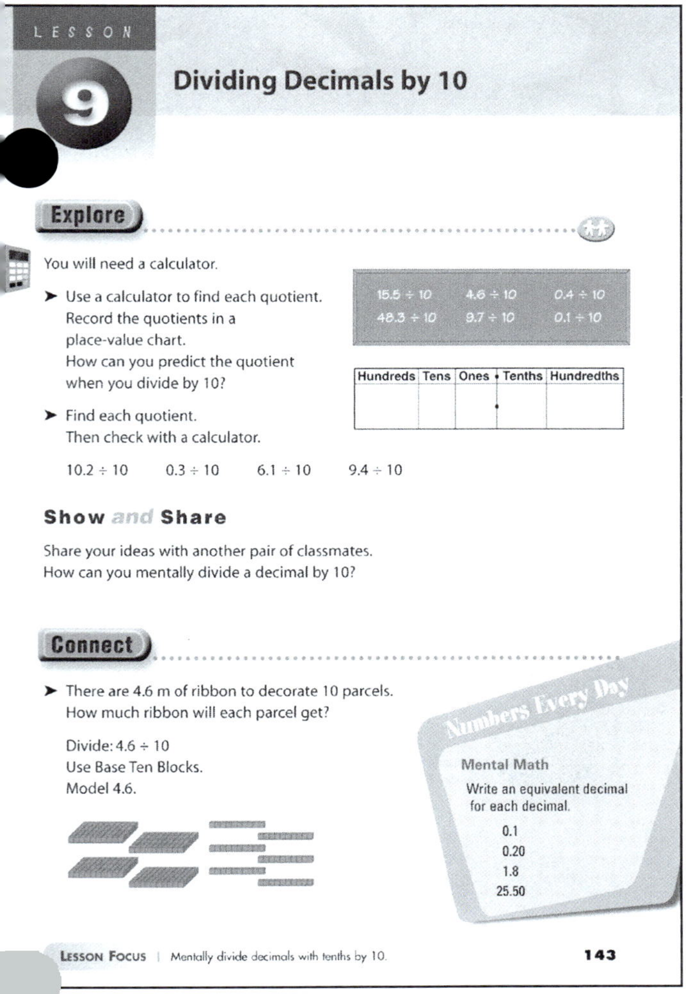

LESSON 9

Dividing Decimals by 10

Explore

You will need a calculator.

➤ Use a calculator to find each quotient.
Record the quotients in a place-value chart.
How can you predict the quotient when you divide by 10?

15.5 ÷ 10	4.6 ÷ 10	0.4 ÷ 10
48.3 ÷ 10	9.7 ÷ 10	0.1 ÷ 10

Hundreds	Tens	Ones	Tenths	Hundredths

➤ Find each quotient.
Then check with a calculator.

10.2 ÷ 10   0.3 ÷ 10   6.1 ÷ 10   9.4 ÷ 10

Show and Share

Share your ideas with another pair of classmates.
How can you mentally divide a decimal by 10?

Connect

➤ There are 4.6 m of ribbon to decorate 10 parcels.
How much ribbon will each parcel get?

Divide: 4.6 ÷ 10
Use Base Ten Blocks.
Model 4.6.

Numbers Every Day

Mental Math

Write an equivalent decimal for each decimal.

0.1
0.20
1.8
25.50

LESSON FOCUS | Mentally divide decimals with tenths by 10.   143

LESSON 9

Dividing Decimals by 10

LESSON ORGANIZER   40–50 min

Curriculum Focus: Mentally divide decimals with tenths by 10. (5m16, 5m30)

Student Materials	*Optional*
■ calculators	■ Step-by-Step 9 (Master 4.20)
■ Base Ten Blocks	■ Extra Practice 5 (Master 4.27)

Assessment: Master 4.2 Ongoing Observations: Decimals

Key Math Learning

Dividing a decimal by 10 results in the digits of the decimal shifting one place to the right.

Numbers Every Day

Students may wish to use hundredths grids to represent the decimals.
0.10, 0.2, 1.80, 25.5

BEFORE   Get Started

Use the following questions to briefly review multiplying a decimal by 10:

4.9 × 10   63.2 × 10   25.4 × 10

Ask:

- What happens to the digits in the decimal when you multiply by 10?
  (*They shift one place to the left.*)
- What do you think will happen when you divide a decimal by 10?
  (*The numbers will get smaller. Maybe the digits will shift to the right.*)

Present *Explore*. Ensure students recall the meaning of the word *quotient*. Students should complete the first part of the activity and discuss their findings, then use what they discovered to complete the second part of the activity.

DURING   Explore

Ongoing Assessment: Observe and Listen

Ask questions, such as:

- Look at the decimal 4.6. In what place-value position is the 4? (*Ones*) The 6? (*Tenths*)
- Where is the 4 in the quotient?
  (*In the tenths place*)
  The 6? (*In the hundredths place*)
- What happened to the digits in 4.6 when you divided by 10?
  (*They shifted one place to the right.*)

Listen for students who are focusing on the position of the decimal point rather than on the digits. Use a place-value chart to show that it is the digits that shift, not the decimal point.

REACHING ALL LEARNERS

Early Finishers

Have students work in pairs. One student uses Base Ten Blocks to model a decimal with tenths. The other student divides the blocks into 10 equal groups, trading as needed. Students reverse roles and repeat the activity.

Common Misconceptions

➤ Students fail to put a zero in the ones place when dividing a decimal such as 9.7 by 10.

How to Help: Remind students that when there are no ones in a decimal, a zero precedes the decimal point.

Making Connections

Measurement Strand: Students can convert measurements reported in millimetres to centimetres or measurements reported in metres to decimetres by mentally dividing by 10.

To divide these blocks into 10 equal groups,
first trade each 1 whole for 10 tenths.

There are 46 tenths.
Divide these into 10 equal groups.
There are 4 tenths in each group, with 6 tenths left over.

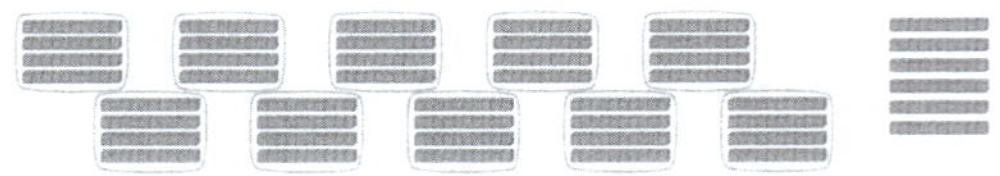

Trade each 1 tenth for 10 hundredths.
There are 60 hundredths.

Divide these 60 hundredths among the 10 equal groups.

There are 4 tenths and 6 hundredths, or 46 hundredths in each group.
So, $4.6 \div 10 = 0.46$
Each parcel gets 0.46 m of ribbon.

➤ You can use place value to understand what happens when you divide a decimal by 10.

Divide: $4.6 \div 10$

4.6 = 4 ones and 6 tenths
= 46 tenths
= 460 hundredths

460 hundredths ÷ 10 = 46 hundredths
So, $4.6 \div 10 = 0.46$

Ones	.	Tenths	Hundredths
4	.	6	
0	.	4	6

144

AFTER Connect

Invite volunteers to share what they found out.

Ask questions, such as:

- What happens when you divide a decimal by 10?
  (*The quotient has the same digits and it is a decimal number. The digits in the decimal shift one place to the right.*)
- How can you divide a decimal by 10 mentally? (*Shift the digits one place to the right.*)
- What must you remember to do when the quotient has no ones?
  (*Put a zero in the ones place.*)

Ask students:

- How can we use Base Ten Blocks to show how to divide a decimal by 10?
  (*Model the decimal and divide the blocks into 10 equal groups.*)

Provide students with Base Ten Blocks. Together, work to model 3.7 ÷ 10, one step at a time. Lead students to see how the blocks, once the trading and dividing have been completed, show that the digits in 3.7 have shifted one place to the right.

Practice

Students should use mental math to complete all questions.

Assessment Focus: Question 5

Students use mental math to divide 2.8 by 10. They record an equation using the division sign. They realize that the quotient has no ones, and they indicate this by preceding the decimal point with a zero.

➤ You can use mental math to divide a decimal by 10.

26.5 ÷ 10 = 2.65

427.9 ÷ 10 = 42.79

8.4 ÷ 10 = 0.84

0.7 ÷ 10 = 0.07

When there are no ones, you use zero as a **placeholder**. Sometimes you need zero as a placeholder in the tenths place.

Practice

1. Use a place-value chart. Record each quotient in the chart.
   a) 8.8 ÷ 10 0.88 **b)** 4.2 ÷ 10 0.42 **c)** 25.1 ÷ 10 2.51 **d)** 16.7 ÷ 10 1.67

2. Use Base Ten Blocks to divide.
   a) 25.3 ÷ 10 2.53 **b)** 185.3 ÷ 10 18.53 **c)** 8.2 ÷ 10 0.82 **d)** 0.9 ÷ 10 0.09

Use mental math to solve each problem.

3. Luke jogged 10 laps around the track. He jogged a total of 7.5 km. How far is it around the track? 0.75 km

4. Ten Grade 5 spelling books have a mass of 4.5 kg. What is the mass of 1 spelling book? 0.45 kg

5. Jen has 2.8 m of fabric. She will make 10 placemats, all the same size. How long will each mat be? 0.28 m

6. Stanley divided a 2.5-kg bag of dog food equally among his 10 dogs. How much food did each dog get? Show your work. 0.25 kg

Reflect

Use Base Ten Blocks to find 14.7 ÷ 10.
Explain how this model shows how to divide by 10 mentally.

ASSESSMENT FOCUS | Question 5 **145**

Sample Answers

1.

	Ones	•	Tenths	Hundredths
a)	0	•	8	8
b)	0	•	4	2
c)	2	•	5	1
d)	1	•	6	7

6. 2.5 kg ÷ 10 = 0.25 kg

REFLECT: When I used Base Ten Blocks to model 14.7, I had 1 ten, 4 ones, and 7 tenths. After I made all the trades, I had no tens, 10 ones, 40 tenths, and 70 hundredths. When I put the blocks into 10 equal groups, each group had 1 one, 4 tenths, and 7 hundredths. This shows that to divide 14.7 by 10 mentally, I just shift the digits one place to the right.

ASSESSMENT FOR LEARNING

What to Look For

Understanding concepts

✔ Students understand that dividing a decimal by 10 results in the digits shifting one place to the right.

Applying procedures

✔ Students can divide a decimal with tenths mentally.

What to Do

Extra Support: Have students use a place-value chart and digit cards to show the shifting of the digits when a decimal is divided by 10. (See Lesson 8, Extra Support.)
Students can use Step-by-Step 9 (Master 4.20) to complete question 5.

Extra Practice: Provide a list of division questions (for example, 2.8 ÷ 10, 25.3 ÷ 10). Have students work in pairs. One student uses mental math to find the quotient while her partner uses a calculator. Students compare answers.
Students can complete Extra Practice 5 (Master 4.27).

Extension: Have students create word problems involving the division of decimals with tenths by 10. Students trade and solve one another's problems.

Recording and Reporting

Master 4.2 Ongoing Observations: Decimals

Strategies Toolkit

LESSON ORGANIZER 40–50 min

Curriculum Focus: Interpret a problem and select an appropriate strategy. (5m33, 5m35)
Student Materials
- play money (PM 30)

Assessment: PM 1: Inquiry Process Check List
PM 3: Self-Assessment: Problem Solving

Key Math Learnings

1. Interpret a problem involving decimals.
2. Solve a problem involving decimals using a work backward strategy.

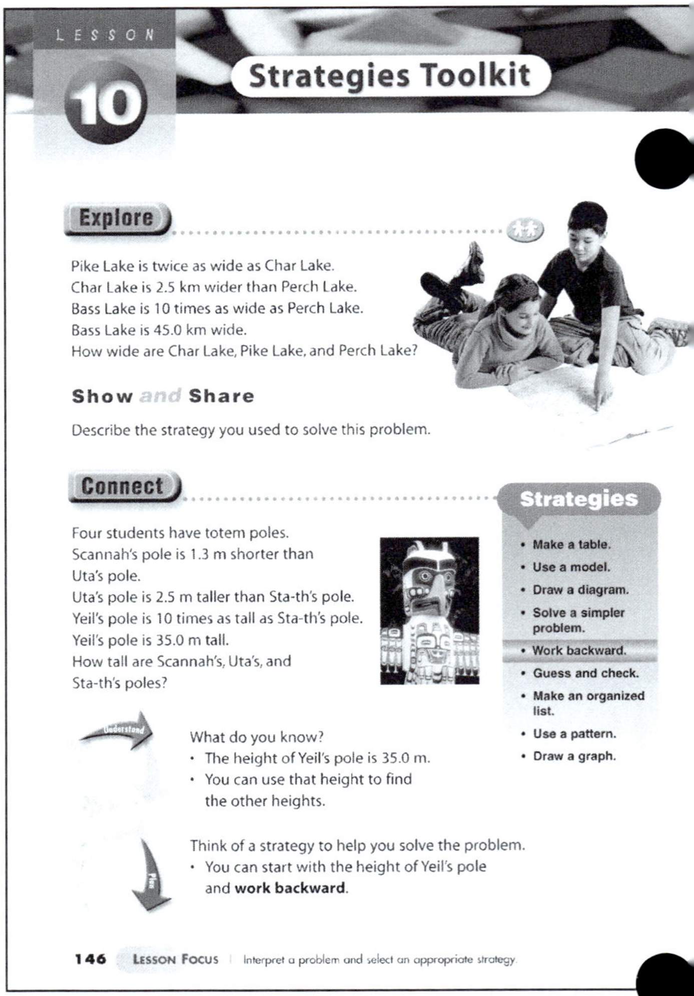
LESSON 10 Strategies Toolkit

Explore

Pike Lake is twice as wide as Char Lake.
Char Lake is 2.5 km wider than Perch Lake.
Bass Lake is 10 times as wide as Perch Lake.
Bass Lake is 45.0 km wide.
How wide are Char Lake, Pike Lake, and Perch Lake?

Show and Share

Describe the strategy you used to solve this problem.

Connect

Four students have totem poles.
Scannah's pole is 1.3 m shorter than Uta's pole.
Uta's pole is 2.5 m taller than Sta-th's pole.
Yeil's pole is 10 times as tall as Sta-th's pole.
Yeil's pole is 35.0 m tall.
How tall are Scannah's, Uta's, and Sta-th's poles?

Strategies
- Make a table.
- Use a model.
- Draw a diagram.
- Solve a simpler problem.
- Work backward.
- Guess and check.
- Make an organized list.
- Use a pattern.
- Draw a graph.

Understand

What do you know?
- The height of Yeil's pole is 35.0 m.
- You can use that height to find the other heights.

Plan

Think of a strategy to help you solve the problem.
- You can start with the height of Yeil's pole and **work backward**.

146 LESSON FOCUS | Interpret a problem and select an appropriate strategy

BEFORE Get Started

Present the problem in *Explore*. Review the main steps in problem solving: understand the problem, plan how to solve the problem, solve it, then look back to check the solution.

DURING Explore

Ongoing Assessment: Observe and Listen

Watch for students who don't seem to know how to get started. Ask:
- For which lake do you know the width? (*Bass Lake*)
- What else do you know about Bass Lake? (*It's 10 times as wide as Perch Lake.*)
- How can you find the width of Perch Lake? (*Divide 45.0 by 10.*)

Have students share their solutions with the class and explain the strategies they used.

AFTER Connect

Work through the problem in *Connect* with the class. Have volunteers explain how to find the height of each pole in the "Solve" stage. Ask:
- How can we be sure our heights are correct? (*We can see if our answers match the information given in the problem.*)
- When do you think to work backward is a good strategy to use? (*When we have information that can be used to figure out earlier clues*)

Practice

Students should change litres to millilitres to solve question 2. Have play money available for question 3.

Use the height of Yeil's pole to find the height of Sta-th's pole.
Use the height of Sta-th's pole to find the height of Uta's pole.
Use the height of Uta's pole to find the height of Scannah's pole.
How tall is each pole?

How can you check your answer?
How could you have solved this problem another way?

Practice

Choose one of the **Strategies**

1. Karl swam the length of the swimming pool 10 times.
He swam a total distance of 166.5 m.
How long is the pool? 16.65 m

2. Lamar opened a 1-L can of tomato juice.
He poured an equal amount into each of 3 glasses.
Lamar had 0.4 L left. How much did Lamar pour into each glass? 0.2 L or 200 mL

3. Last weekend, Inga earned money by mowing lawns.
After her first job, Inga had twice the amount of money she had when she left home.
After her second job, Inga doubled her money again.
When Inga got home, she had $18.60.
How much money did Inga have when she first left home?
$4.65

Reflect

Choose one of the problems in this lesson.
Use words, pictures, or numbers to explain how you solved it.

147

REACHING ALL LEARNERS

Common Misconceptions

➤Students mistakenly interpret the statement, "Bass Lake is 10 times as wide as Perch Lake" as a signal to multiply.

How to Help: Lead students to see that Bass Lake is wider than Perch Lake, so they must divide to find the width of Perch Lake.

REFLECT: For question 2, I needed to find out how much juice Lamar poured into each of 3 glasses. First, I subtracted the amount of juice left in the can from the amount that was in the can at the start. Then, I divided the result by 3.

ASSESSMENT FOR LEARNING

What to Look For	What to Do
Problem solving ✔ Students use the steps of the problem-solving process to solve a problem. ✔ Students can use a work backward strategy to solve a problem involving decimals.	***Extra Support:*** Some students may benefit from having a classmate as a mentor to guide them through the problem-solving process. ***Extra Practice:*** Have students write and solve problems of their own involving decimals. ***Extension:*** Challenge students to change the numbers in each of the questions and solve.

Recording and Reporting
PM 1: Inquiry Process Check List
PM 3: Self-Assessment: Problem Solving

LESSON ORGANIZER (40–50 min)

Student Materials

- calculators

Assessment: Masters 4.1 Unit Rubric: Decimals, 4.4 Unit Summary: Decimals

Unit 4 Show What You Know

Use Base Ten Blocks when they help.

1 **1.** Write each fraction or mixed number as a decimal.
a) $\frac{9}{10}$ 0.9 **b)** $3\frac{14}{100}$ 3.14 **c)** $20\frac{1}{100}$ 20.01 **d)** $\frac{67}{100}$ 0.67

2. Use the digits 1, 3, 4, 8, and a decimal point.
Write the number that is closest to 40. 41.38

2 **3.** Write an equivalent decimal for each decimal.
a) 0.8 0.80 **b)** 7.20 7.2 **c)** 1.1 1.10 **d)** 0.60 0.6

4. a) When would you write 7.50 instead of 7.5?
b) When would you write 7.5 instead of 7.50?

3 **5.** Use the digits 3, 4, 5, and a decimal point.
Write all the possible decimals.
Order these decimals from least to greatest.

6. Use the digits 0, 5, 8 in these boxes: ☐.☐☐
a) Write the greatest number. 8.50
b) Write the least number. 0.58

2 3 **7.** Copy and complete. Use >, <, or =.
a) 3.04 [<] 3.19 **b)** 0.40 [=] 0.4 **c)** 1.7 [>] 1.25

3 **8.** Write the decimals in order from greatest to least.
a) 5.62, 5.9, 5.30 5.9, 5.62, 5.3 **b)** 0.95, 0.6, 1.3 1.3, 0.95, 0.6

9. Copy each statement. Write a decimal to make the statement true.
a) 0.85 > ☐ 0.4 **b)** 7.62 < ☐ 7.94 **c)** 0.04 > ☐ 0.01

4 **10.** Round each decimal to the nearest whole number.
a) 2.34 2 **b)** 0.6 1 **c)** 0.84 1 **d)** 5.5 6

11. An athlete's long jump, rounded to the nearest metre, was 8 m.
What are the longest and shortest lengths the jump could have been, in decimals to the hundredths? 8.49 m; 7.50 m

148

Sample Answers

4. a) When I subtract 2.25 from 7.5
   b) When I multiply 0.75 by 10
5. 3.45, 3.54, 4.35, 4.53, 5.34, 5.43, 34.5, 35.4, 43.5, 45.3, 53.4, 54.3

12. Estimate each sum or difference.
a) 1.7 + 4.9 About 7 b) 7.3 − 2.45 About 5 c) 28.1 + 3.14 About 31
d) 12.98 − 4.01 About 9 e) 6.78 + 3.12 About 10 f) 7.8 − 0.9 About 7

6 7 13. Add or subtract.
a) 3.48 + 7.62 11.10 b) 14.7 − 8.35 6.35 c) 1.98 + 6.3 8.28

6 14. Tran wrote 4 numbers on 4 counters and placed them in a paper bag.
He drew 2 counters and added the numbers.
He replaced the counters and repeated the steps 4 more times.
The sums were: 2.4, 2.5, 2.6, 2.7, 2.8
Which 4 numbers did Tran write on the counters? 1.1, 1.3, 1.4, 1.5 or 1.1, 1.2, 1.3, 1.5

6 7 15. Lisa saved $9.26. Her grandpa gave her $4.75 more.
a) How much money does Lisa have? $14.01
b) How much more money does Lisa need to buy a remote control car that costs $19.95? $5.94

8 16. A canoe is 5.67 m long.
How many centimetres is that? 567 cm

17. A nickel is 21.2 mm wide.
Suppose 100 nickels were laid side by side in a line.
How long would the line of nickels be? 2120 mm

9 18. Leonardo lives in a 10-storey apartment building. The building is 121 m tall.
All the storeys have the same height.
How high is each storey? 12.1 m

8 9 19. Use mental math to multiply or divide.
a) 2.7 × 10 27 b) 8.46 × 100 846
c) 15.8 ÷ 10 1.58 d) 32.4 ÷ 10 3.24
e) 52.73 × 10 527.3 f) 0.2 ÷ 10 0.02

UNIT 4 Learning Goals

- ✓ use place value to represent decimals to hundredths
- ✓ explore equivalent decimals
- ✓ compare and order decimals
- ✓ round decimals to the nearest whole number
- ✓ estimate decimal sums and differences
- ✓ add, subtract, multiply, and divide decimals
- ✓ solve problems involving decimals

Unit 4 **147**

ASSESSMENT FOR LEARNING

What to Look For

Reasoning; Applying concepts

✔ **Question 1:** Student understands that decimals are another way of writing fractions.
✔ **Questions 2, 5, and 6:** Student understands that the decimal point separates the whole number part from the fractional part of a number.
✔ **Questions 3 and 4:** Student understands the equivalence of decimals.

Accuracy of procedures

✔ **Questions 7, 8, and 9:** Student can compare and order decimals.
✔ **Questions 10, 11, and 12:** Student can round decimals to nearest whole number.
✔ **Question 12:** Student can estimate sums and differences of decimals.
✔ **Questions 13, 14, and 15:** Student can add and subtract decimals.
✔ **Questions 16, 17, 18, and 19:** Student can multiply decimals by 10 and 100, and divide decimals by 10.

Problem solving

✔ **Questions 11, 14, and 15:** Student can solve problems that include decimals.

Recording and Reporting

Master 4.1 Unit Rubric: Decimals
Master 4.4 Unit Summary: Decimals

Coins Up Close

LESSON ORGANIZER — 40–50 min

Student Materials
- calculators

Assessment: Master 4.3 Performance Assessment Rubric: Coins Up Close, Master 4.4 Unit Summary: Decimals

Unit Problem Coins Up Close

Use a calculator when it helps.

1. Gloria, Lino, and Lisette worked together doing odd jobs for their neighbours. At the end of the day, they had earned exactly 6 of each of the 7 kinds of coins.
   a) How much money did they earn? $23.46
   b) The children shared the money equally. How much money did each child get? $7.82

2. One toonie has a mass of 7.3 g. Use these data to find the masses of all the numbers of toonies in the table. Copy and complete the table. You may add, subtract, or multiply. Award yourself points for each solution using this point system:
   - 5 points for multiplying
   - 3 points for subtracting
   - 1 point for adding

   What strategy can you use to get the most points? Explain your strategy.

Number of Toonies	Total Mass (g)
1	7.3
2	14.6
3	21.9
4	29.2
5	36.5
6	43.8
7	51.1
8	58.4
9	65.7
10	73

3. Could you lift $10 000 in toonies? Explain.

150

Have students turn to the Launch on pages 112 and 113 to review the context of the *Unit Problem*. Use the lists of *Learning Goals* and *Key Words* to have students recall some of the skills and concepts they learned throughout the unit.

Present the *Unit Problem*. Have students read the five questions to ensure they understand what is being asked of them. Suggest that students may use a calculator when necessary.

Have a volunteer read the Check List so all students are aware of what is expected of them. Discuss possible ways in which students might present their work.

Sample Response

1. a) Gloria, Lino, and Lisette earned
   $6 \times 1¢ + 6 \times 5¢ + 6 \times 10¢ + 6 \times 25¢ + 6 \times 50¢ + 6 \times \$1 + 6 \times \$2$
   $= \$0.06 + \$0.30 + \$0.60 + \$1.50 + \$3.00 + \$6.00 + \$12.00$
   $= \$23.46$

   b) To find how much each person got, I divide the total amount by 3.
   Each person received $\$23.46 \div 3 = \$7.82$
2. Mulitplying produces the most points. So, I chose to multiply the mass of 1 toonie by each number of toonies in turn. This gave me 9×5, or 45 points.
3. Toonies with the value of $10 000 is 10 000 ÷ 2, or 5000 toonies.
   The mass of 5000 toonies is 5000×7.3 g, or 36 500 g.
   1000 g = 1 kg, so 36 500 g = 36.5 kg
4. To find the width on earth, divide each measurement by 10.
   a) 265 mm ÷ 10 = 26.5 mm.
   From the table, the coin is a loonie.
   b) 15.8 mm ÷ 10 = 1.58 mm.
   From the table, the coin is a quarter.
   c) On the Planet of the Giants:
   The height of 1 loonie = $1.75 \text{ mm} \times 10 = 17.5 \text{ mm}$
   The height of 100 loonies = $100 \times 17.5 \text{ mm} = 1750 \text{ mm}$
   10 mm = 1 cm, so $1750 \text{ mm} = \frac{1750}{10} \text{ cm} = 175 \text{ cm}$
   100 mm = 1 dm, so $1750 \text{ mm} = \frac{1750}{100} \text{ dm} = 17.5 \text{ dm}$

Check List

Your work should show
- ☑ the strategies you used to solve each problem
- ☑ how you added, subtracted, multiplied, or divided to find your answers
- ☑ a clear explanation of each answer
- ☑ the correct use of mathematical language and symbols

Coin	Thickness (mm)	Width (mm)
Penny	1.45	19.05
Nickel	1.76	21.2
Dime	1.22	18.03
Quarter	1.58	23.88
50¢	1.95	27.13
Loonie	1.75	26.5
Toonie	1.8	28

4. On the Planet of the Giants, all objects are 10 times as long, wide, and tall as they are on Earth.
Use the table of coin data to answer these questions.
   a) One giant's coin has a width of 265 mm. Which coin is it? Loonie
   b) Another giant's coin is 15.8 mm thick. Which coin is it? Quarter
   c) How high would a stack of 100 loonies be on the Planet of the Giants? Write your answer in millimetres, centimetres, and decimetres. 1750 mm, 175 cm, 17.5 dm

5. Make up your own problem about the coins on the Planet of the Giants. Solve your problem.

Reflect on the Unit

Explain why estimating is important when working with decimals.

Sample Answers

3. $10 000 in toonies is 5000 toonies.
   5000 toonies would have a mass of 36.5 kg.
   I could not lift that much mass on my own.
5. Which 2 coins would have a total thickness of 35.30 mm?
   A quarter would be 15.80 mm thick. A 50¢ coin would be 19.50 mm thick. Together that makes 35.30 mm.

Reflect on the Unit

You can check to see if your answers make sense by estimating.

ASSESSMENT FOR LEARNING

What to Look For

Application of mathematical procedures

✔ Students add, subtract, and multiply decimal numbers.

Problem solving

✔ Students select appropriate operations and solve multistep problems involving decimal computation.

Communicating

✔ Students use appropriate mathematical terminology and symbols related to decimals.

What to Do

Extra Support: Make the problems accessible.
Some students may have difficulty reading and/or interpreting the questions. If necessary, read or paraphrase for them.

Some students may be unable to deal with multistep problems. Break the problem down into manageable steps for them.

Some students may be unsure of whether to multiply or divide to express millimetres in centimetres and in decimetres. Use a ruler to demonstrate that centimetres and decimetres are bigger than millimetres, so there will be fewer of them. Thus, to convert requires dividing by 10.

Recording and Reporting
Master 4.2 Ongoing Observations: Decimals

Cumulative Review

Units 1–4 Cumulative Review

UNIT 1

1. The first 2 terms of a pattern are 3 and 5.
Write 5 different patterns that start with these 2 terms.
List the first 6 terms for each pattern.
Write each pattern rule.

2. Copy and complete the table for this Input/Output machine.
Choose 5 input numbers.
Find each output number.

Input	Output

3. Here is a pattern of figures made with congruent squares.
The side length of each square is 1 unit.

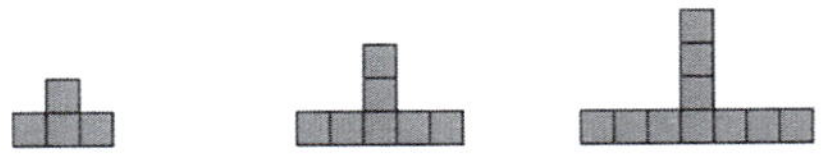

a) Find the perimeters of the figures in the first 3 frames. 10, 16, 22
Record the frame numbers and the perimeters in a table.
b) Write the pattern rule for the perimeters. Start at 10. Add 6 each time.
c) Use the pattern to predict the perimeter of the figure in Frame 12. 76

UNIT 2

4. Write each number in standard form.
a) 600 000 + 40 000 + 3000 + 10 643 010
b) five hundred three thousand nine hundred two 503 902

5. Find each sum or difference.
Use mental math when you can.
a) 7081 + 1199 = 8280
b) 4576 − 4149 = 427
c) 8879 − 988 = 7891
d) 1213 + 2208 = 3421

6. Find each product or quotient.
a) 4 × 6000 24 000
b) 30 × 20 600
c) 11 × 300 3300
d) 132 ÷ 12 11
e) 27 × 68 1836
f) 3576 ÷ 8 447
g) 74 × 55 4070
h) 9198 ÷ 7 1314

152

1. 3, 5, 7, 9, 11, 13 . . .
Start at 3. Add 2 each time.
3, 5, 8, 12, 17, 23 . . .
Start at 3. Add 2. Increase the number added by 1 each time.
3, 5, 4, 6, 5, 7 . . .
Start at 3. Alternately add 2, then subtract 1.
3, 5, 9, 15, 23, 33
Start at 3. Add 2. Increase the number added by 2 each time.
3, 5, 8, 10, 13, 15
Start at 3. Alternately add 2, then add 3.

2.

Input	Output
10	6
11	7
12	8
13	9
14	10

3. a)

Frame Number	Perimeter
1	10
2	16
3	22

8. a) A: No equal sides; scalene triangle
B: 2 equal sides; isosceles triangle
C: 3 equal sides; equilateral triangle
D: No equal sides; scalene triangle
b) A: 3 acute angles; acute triangle
B: 2 acute angles, 1 obtuse angle; obtuse triangle
C: 3 acute angles; acute triangle
D: 2 acute angles, 1 right angle: right triangle

9.

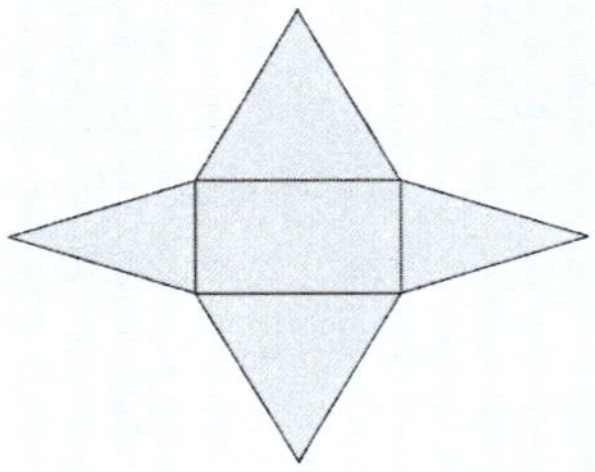

10. a) 67 531, 635 710, 651 370, 653 107, 670 153

7. Caleb has 2691 marbles to share among 9 people.
How many marbles will each person get? 299

8. Use a ruler and a protractor.
Measure the sides and the angles of each triangle.

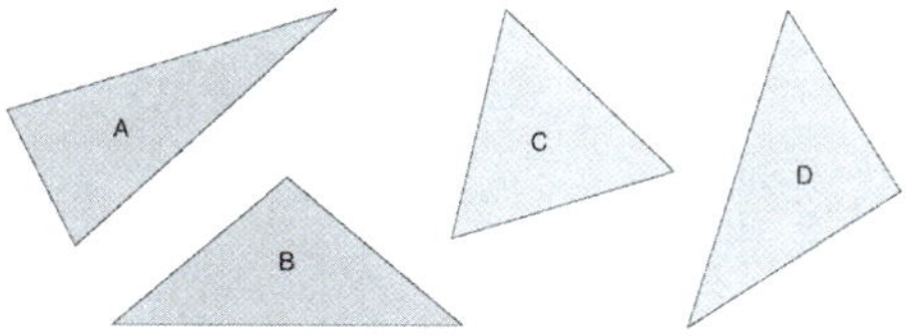

a) Name each triangle by the number of equal sides.
Use the words: scalene, equilateral, isosceles
b) Name each triangle by the angle measures.
Use the words: acute, right, obtuse

9. You will need a pyramid.
Construct a net for the pyramid.

10. Order the numbers in each set from least to greatest.
a) 653 107, 651 370, 635 710, 670 153, 67 531
b) 3.7, 3.68, 3.86, 3.2 3.2, 3.68, 3.7, 3.86
c) 0.75, 0.8, 0.57, 0.6 0.57, 0.6, 0.75, 0.8

11. Write an equivalent decimal for each decimal.
a) 0.50 0.5 b) 3.2 3.20 c) 6.70 6.7 d) 0.3 0.30

12. Find each sum or difference.
a) 4.3 + 6.8 11.1 b) 31.5 − 3.15 28.35 c) 26.07 + 3.46 29.53 d) 8.3 − 0.68 7.62

13. Sophia had $10.47. She spent $4.69.
How much money does she have left? $5.78

14. Carter is 183 cm tall.
What is Carter's height in metres? 1.83 m

Evaluating Student Learning: Preparing to Report: Unit 4 Decimals

This unit provides an opportunity to report on the **Number Sense and Numeration** strand. *Master 4.4 Unit Summary: Decimals* provides a comprehensive format for recording and summarizing evidence collected.

Here is an example of a completed summary chart for this Unit:

Strand: *Number Sense and Numeration*	**Problem solving**	**Understanding of concepts**	**Application of mathematical procedures**	**Communication**	***Overall***
Ongoing Observations	3	2	2	3	**2/3**
Strategies Toolkit (Lesson 10)			3		**3**
Work samples or portfolios; conferences	3	3	2	3	**3**
Show What You Know	3	3	3	3	**3**
Unit Test	3	2	2	3	**2/3**
Unit Problem Coins Up Close	3	3	3	2	**3**
Achievement Level for reporting					**3**

Recording	How to Report
Ongoing Observations	Use *Master 4.2 Ongoing Observations: Decimals* to determine the most consistent level achieved in each category. Enter it in the chart. Choose to summarize by achievement category, or simply to enter an overall level. Observations from late in the unit should be most heavily weighted.
Strategies Toolkit (problem solving)	Use *PM 1: Inquiry Process Check List* with the Strategies Toolkit (Lesson 10). Transfer results to the summary form. Teachers may choose to enter a level in the Problem solving column and/or Communication.
Portfolios or collections of work samples; conferences, or interviews	Use *Master 4.1 Unit Rubric: Decimals* to guide evaluation of collections of work and information gathered in conferences. Teachers may choose to focus particular attention on the *Assessment Focus* questions. Work from late in the unit should be most heavily weighted.
Show What You Know	*Master 4.1 Unit Rubric: Decimals* may be helpful in determining levels of achievement. #1–6 provide evidence of Understanding of concepts; #7–19 provide evidence of Application of mathematical procedures; #11, 14, 15 provide evidence of Problem solving; all parts provide evidence of Communication.
Unit Test	*Master 4.1 Unit Rubric: Decimals* may be helpful in determining levels of achievement. *Part A* provides evidence of Application of mathematical procedures; Part B provides evidence of Understanding of concepts; Part C provides evidence of Problem solving; all parts provide evidence of Communication.
Unit performance task	Use *Master 4.3 Performance Assessment Rubric: Coins Up Close*. The *Unit Problem* offers a snapshot of students' achievement. In particular, it shows their ability to synthesize and apply what they have learned.
Student Self-Assessment	Note students' perceptions of their own progress. This may take the form of an oral or written comment, or a self-rating.
Comments	Analyse the pattern of achievement to identify strengths and needs. In some cases, specific actions may be planned to support the learner.

Learning Skills	Ongoing Records
PM 4: Learning Skills Check List Use to record and report throughout a reporting period, rather than for each unit and/or strand.	*PM 10: Summary Class Records: Strands* *PM 11: Summary Class Records: Achievement Categories* *PM 12: Summary Record: Individual* Use to record and report evaluations of student achievement over several clusters, a reporting period, or a school year. These can also be used in place of the Unit Summary.

Name ____________________ Date ______________

Master 4.1

Unit Rubric: Decimals

	Level 1	Level 2	Level 3	Level 4
Problem solving • chooses and carries out a range of strategies to pose and solve problems with decimals	with assistance, chooses and carries out a limited range of appropriate strategies, rarely resulting in an accurate solution	with limited assistance, chooses and carries out appropriate strategies that frequently result in an accurate solution	chooses and carries out appropriate strategies to pose and solve problems with decimals that usually result in an accurate solution	chooses and accurately carries out appropriate strategies to pose and solve problems with decimals; may offer an innovative approach
Understanding of concepts • shows understanding by appropriately demonstrating and explaining: – equivalent decimals – processes and solutions with decimals – justification of methods chosen	may be unable to demonstrate or explain: – equivalent decimals – processes and solutions with decimals – justification of methods chosen	partially able to demonstrate and explain: – equivalent decimals – processes and solutions with decimals – justification of methods chosen	demonstrates and explains: – equivalent decimals – processes and solutions with decimals – justification of methods chosen	in various contexts, demonstrates and explains: – equivalent decimals – processes and solutions with decimals – justification of methods chosen
Application of mathematical procedures • when working with decimal numbers to 100ths, accurately: – compares and orders – reads and writes decimals – mentally multiplies by 10 and 100 and divides by 10 – adds and subtracts – multiplies and divides by a 1-digit whole number	limited accuracy; major errors in: – comparing and ordering – reading and writing decimals – mentally multiplying by 10 and 100 and dividing by 10 – adding and subtracting – multiplying and dividing by a 1-digit whole number	somewhat accurate; makes some minor errors in: – comparing and ordering – reading and writing decimals – mentally multiplying by 10 and 100 and dividing by 10 – adding and subtracting – multiplying and dividing by a 1-digit whole number	generally accurate; makes few minor errors in: – comparing and ordering – reading and writing decimals – mentally multiplying by 10 and 100 and dividing by 10 – adding and subtracting – multiplying and dividing by a 1-digit whole number	accurate; makes very few or no errors in: – comparing and ordering – reading and writing decimals – mentally multiplying by 10 and 100 and dividing by 10 – adding and subtracting – multiplying and dividing by a 1-digit whole number
Communication • presents work, describes procedures, and explains reasoning clearly	work is often unclear and imprecise needs assistance to describe procedures and explain reasoning; often unclear and imprecise	work is presented with some clarity and precision describes procedures and explains reasoning with some clarity and precision	work is generally clear and precise describes procedures and explains reasoning with general clarity and precision	work is clear and precise describes procedures and explains reasoning clearly, precisely, and confidently

Name ____________________ Date ________________

Master 4.2

Ongoing Observations: Decimals

The behaviours described under each heading are examples; they are not intended to be an exhaustive list of all that might be observed. More detailed descriptions are provided in each lesson under *Assessment for Learning.*

STUDENT ACHIEVEMENT: Decimals				
Student	**Problem solving** ▪ Chooses and carries out a range of strategies to pose and solve problems with decimals	**Understanding of concepts** ▪ Demonstrates and explains equivalent decimals ▪ Explains processes and solutions; justifies methods	**Application of mathematical procedures** ▪ Reads, writes, compares, and orders decimals ▪ Adds and subtracts decimals ▪ Multiplies by 10 and 100 and divides by 10	**Communication** ▪ Explains reasoning clearly ▪ Presents work clearly

Level 1 – very limited; Level 2 – somewhat or limited; Level 3 – satisfactory; Level 4 – thorough

Name ____________________ Date ______________

Master 4.3

Performance Assessment Rubric: Coins Up Close

	Level 1	Level 2	Level 3	Level 4
Problem solving • chooses appropriate strategies to solve and create problems involving decimals in working with the value, mass, thickness, width, and diameter of coins	uses few simple strategies to solve and create problems involving decimals; limited success	uses some appropriate strategies to solve and create problems involving decimals; some success	uses appropriate strategies to solve and create problems involving decimals; successful	uses innovative and appropriate strategies to solve and create problems involving decimals; successful and effective
Understanding of concepts • shows understanding of decimals by offering reasonable explanations of strategies, procedures, and results	shows very limited understanding by giving inappropriate explanations of strategies, procedures, and results using few concepts related to decimals	shows limited understanding by giving appropriate but incomplete explanations of strategies, procedures, and results using some concepts related to decimals	shows understanding by giving appropriate explanations of strategies, procedures, and results using relevant concepts related to decimals	shows thorough understanding by giving appropriate and complete explanations of strategies, procedures, and results using all relevant concepts related to decimals
Application of mathematical procedures • adds, subtracts, multiplies, and divides decimals • reads and writes decimals (to 100ths) • multiplies and divides decimals by 10 and 100 • writes money values	makes few accurate calculations; major errors or omissions in: – adding, subtracting, multiplying, and dividing decimals – reading and writing decimals and money values	makes some accurate calculations; several minor errors or omissions in: – adding, subtracting, multiplying, and dividing decimals – reading and writing decimals and money values	makes accurate calculations; few minor errors or omissions in: – adding, subtracting, multiplying, and dividing decimals – reading and writing decimals and money values	makes accurate calculations; practically no minor errors or omissions in: – adding, subtracting, multiplying, and dividing decimals – reading and writing decimals and money values
Communication • uses mathematical terminology, including units and symbols, correctly (e.g., decimal, decimal point, $, mm, cm, dm) • explains reasoning clearly	uses few appropriate mathematical terms and symbols explains reasoning unclearly and imprecisely	uses some appropriate mathematical terms and symbols explains reasoning with some clarity	uses appropriate mathematical terms and symbols explains reasoning clearly and precisely	uses a range of appropriate mathematical terminology and symbols clearly and precisely explains reasoning clearly, precisely, and confidently

Name ____________________ Date ________________

Master 4.4

Unit Summary: Decimals

Review assessment records to determine the most consistent achievement levels for the assessments conducted. Some cells may be blank. *Overall* achievement levels may be recorded in each row, rather than identifying levels for each achievement category.

	Most Consistent Level of Achievement*				
Strand: *Number Sense and Numeration*	**Problem solving**	**Understanding of concepts**	**Application of mathematical procedures**	**Communication**	***Overall***
Ongoing Observations					
Strategies Toolkit (Lesson 10)					
Work samples or portfolios; conferences					
Show What You Know					
Unit Test					
Unit Problem: Coins Up Close					
Achievement Level for reporting					

* Use Ontario Achievement Levels 1, 2, 3, 4.

Self-Assessment:

Comments: (Strengths, Needs, Next Steps)

Name ____________________ Date ________________

Master 4.5

To Parents and Adults at Home …

Your child's class is starting a mathematics unit on decimals.

We use decimals every day in a wide variety of ways. Shopping trips, sports events, weather reports, and news stories are all places we encounter decimals on a regular basis. This unit includes many concepts your child will already be familiar with from daily life.

In this unit, your child will:

- Represent, read, and write decimals to hundredths.
- Explore equivalent decimals.
- Compare and order decimals.
- Round decimals to the nearest whole number.
- Estimate decimal sums and differences.
- Add, subtract, multiply, and divide decimals.
- Pose and solve problems involving decimals.

Classroom work in this unit will build on understandings children are already developing.

There are many activities you can do with your child that will improve her or his understanding in these areas.

For example, when grocery shopping with your child:

- Ask your child to round the price of an item to the nearest dollar.
- Have your child order items from lowest to highest price.
- Encourage your child to estimate the sum of two prices.
- Ask your child "How much would 10 of these cost? How much would 100 cost?"
- Ask your child to estimate how much change would be given for a certain purchase.
- Have your child decide which items he or she could buy for $10.

Name ____________________ Date ____________________

Master 4.6

Decimal Cards

0.05	0.1	0.11	0.16
0.2	0.25	0.3	0.37
0.4	0.46	0.5	0.55
0.6	0.69	0.7	0.79
0.8	0.84	0.9	0.91

Name ____________________ Date ________________

Master 4.7

Spinner

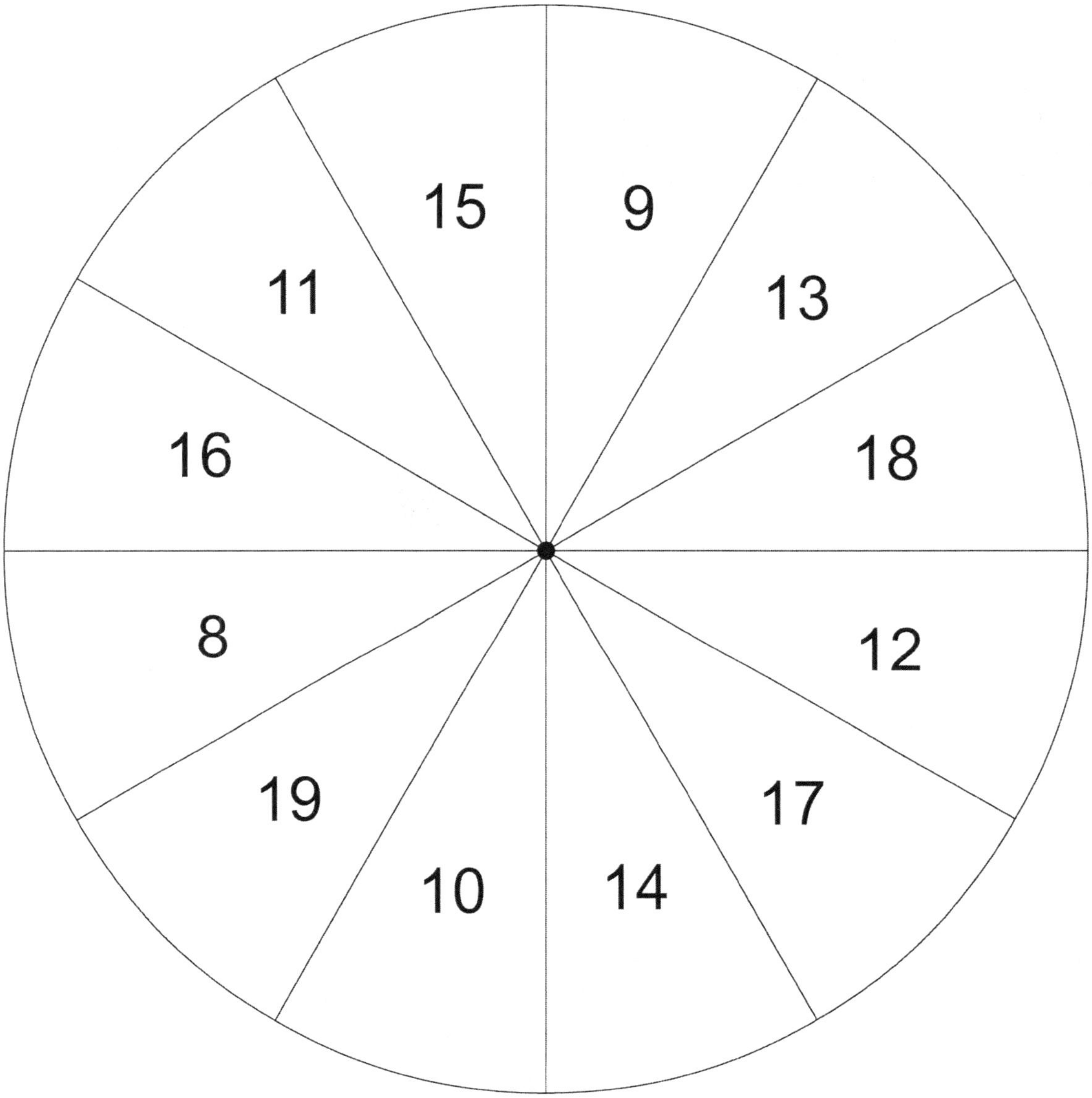

Name ____________________ Date ________________

Master 4.8

Additional Activity 1: Decimal Designs

Work with a partner.

You will need hundredths grids and 3 colours of pencil crayons.

- Create a design on a hundredths grid. Use 3 different colours.
- Write a fraction and a decimal to describe each colour of your design.
- Repeat with another 3-colour design.

Take It Further:

Fold a 10 by 10 grid in half to make a line of symmetry.
Work together to create a 4-colour symmetrical design.
Write a fraction and a decimal to describe each colour of your design.

Name ____________________ Date ________________

Master 4.9a

Additional Activity 2: Spin for One

Play with a partner.

You will need:
- a 10-part spinner labelled 0 to 9
- a paper clip as a pointer
- hundredths grids
- pencil crayons

How to play:

- ➢ Each of you takes a hundredths grid.
  The grid represents one whole.

- ➢ Take turns to spin the pointer.
  The number the pointer lands on tells how many tenths or hundredths to colour on the grid.
  For example, if you spin 4, you may colour 4 tenths *or* 4 hundredths.

- ➢ Take 6 turns each.

- ➢ The player who comes closest to colouring the whole grid in 6 turns without going over wins.

Take It Further:

Play *Spin for Two* using two hundredths grids.

Name ____________________ Date ________________

Master 4.9b

10-Part Spinner

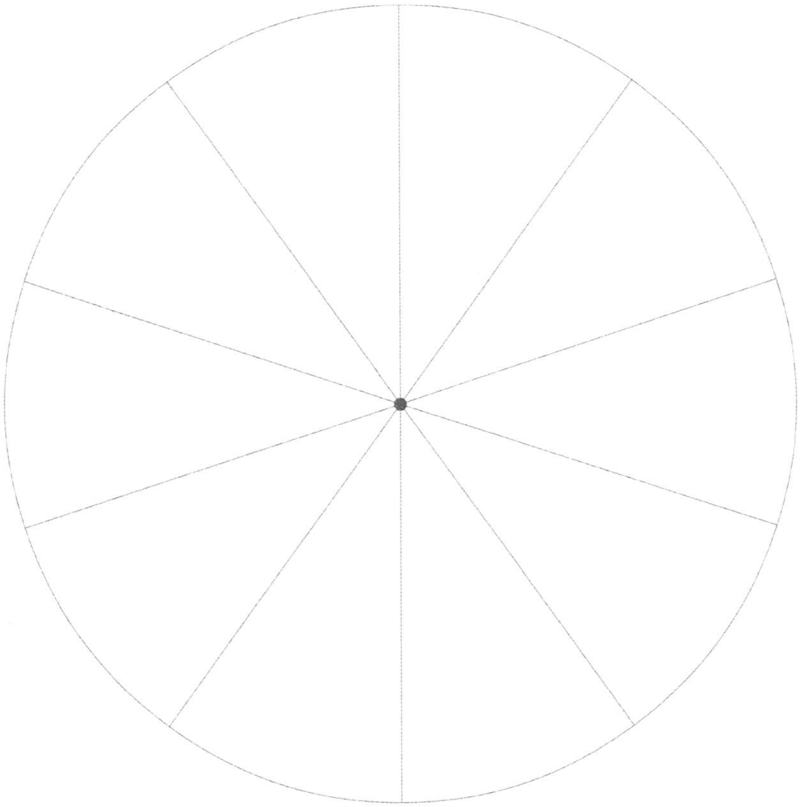

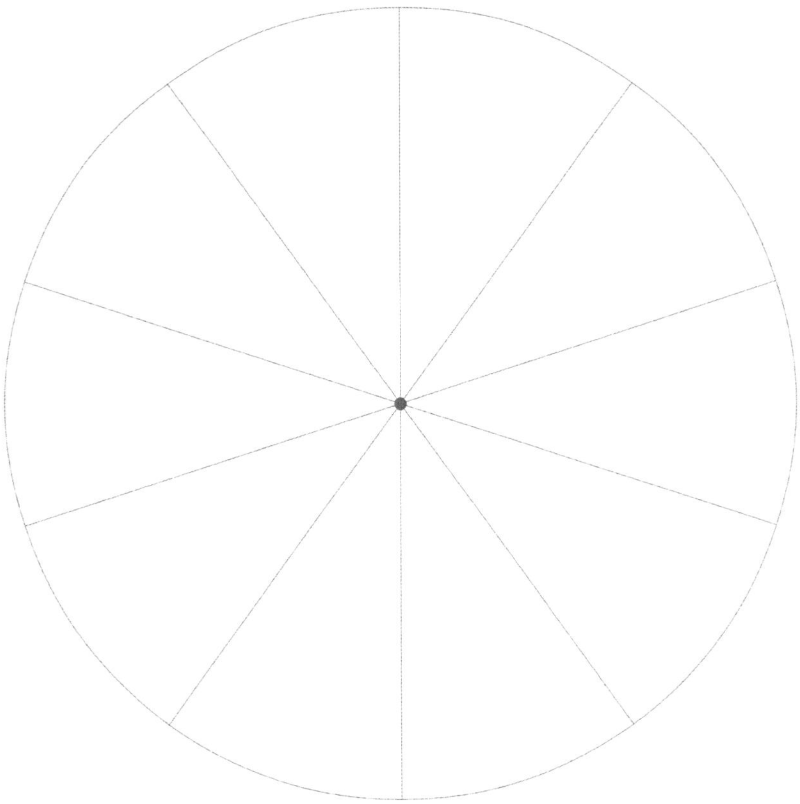

Name ____________________ Date ________________

Master 4.10

Additional Activity 3: Guess the Decimal

Play in a group of 3 or 4.

You will need paper and pencils.

How to play:

- Choose a leader to start the game.
- The leader secretly writes a decimal with tenths, between 1 and 10.
- The other players take turns to try to guess the number.
  For each guess, the leader says, "Greater" or "Less."
- Players continue to take turns until someone guesses the number.
  That player becomes the leader for another game.

Take It Further:

Repeat the activity using decimals with hundredths.

Name ____________________ Date ________________

Master 4.11

Additional Activity 4: Closing in on 2

Play with a partner.

You will need a number cube labelled 1 to 6, paper, and pencils.

How to play:

- Take turns to roll the number cube 2 times.
  Use the numbers in the order rolled to make a decimal with tenths.
  Record the number.

- Take 2 more turns each.

- Choose 2 of your 3 numbers to add or subtract.

- The player whose sum or difference is closer to 2 gets a point.

- Play 4 more rounds. The player with the most points wins.

Take It Further:
Play the game again.
This time, roll the number cube 3 times to make a decimal
with hundredths.

Name ____________________ Date ________________

Master 4.12

Step-by-Step 1

Lesson 1, Question 8

Use the digits 4, 5, and 8. Use each digit once.

Step 1 How many decimals can you write with a 4 in the first position?
Fill in the missing numbers.

Have you found all of them? ________
How do you know?

____

____

Decimal	Mixed Number
4.58	$4\frac{58}{100}$
4._ _	
4 _ . _	
48.5	$48\frac{5}{10}$

Step 2 How many decimals can you write with a 5 in the first position?
Fill in the missing numbers.

Decimal	Mixed Number
5._ _	
5._ _	
5 _ . _	
5 _ . _	

Step 3 How many decimals can you write with an 8 in the first position?
Fill in the table.

Decimal	Mixed Number

Step 4 How many decimals did you write altogether? ________________
How can you arrange your numbers to show you found all possible decimals?

____

____

Name ____________________ Date ______________

Master 4.13 **Step-by-Step 2**

Lesson 2, Question 6

You will need two hundredths grids.

Step 1 One row represents 0.1.
How many rows represent 0.4? ________
Colour a hundredths grid to show the decimal 0.4.

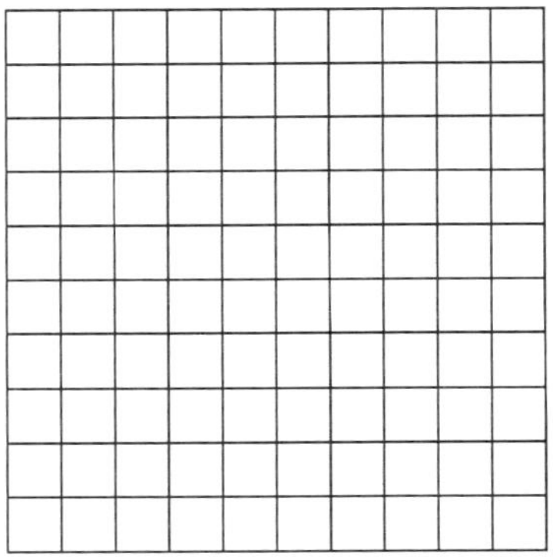

Step 2 One square represents 0.01.
How many squares represent 0.40? ________
Colour a hundredths grid to show the decimal 0.40.

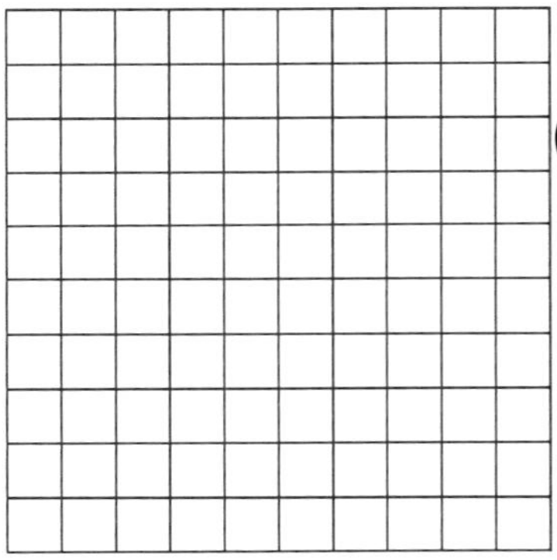

Step 3 Look at your two hundredths grids.
Compare the shaded areas for 0.4 or 0.40. Which one is larger?

____

How do the decimals 0.4 and 0.40 compare?

____

Ruby said 8.40 is greater than 8.4. Was Ruby correct?

____

Name ____________________ Date ______________

Master 4.14

Step-by-Step 3

Lesson 3, Question 6

Refer to the table on page 123 of your math text.

Step 1 Write the numbers from the table in a place-value chart.

Tens	Ones	Tenths	Hundredths

Step 2 Order the numbers from least to greatest.

____

Step 3 Look at the number line.

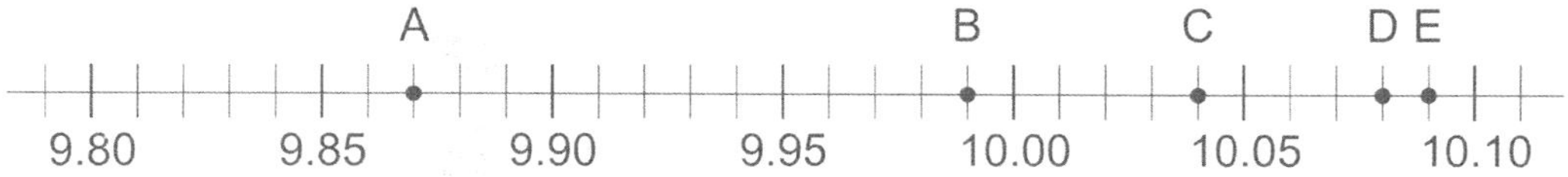

Which letter represents the least time? ________

Which sprinter's time is this? ________________

Which letter represents the greatest time? ________

Which sprinter's time is this? ________________

Which sprinter's time does letter B show? ________________

What about C and D? ______________________________

Step 4 Whose time was faster than Drummond's, but slower than Thompson's? ______________________________

Step 5 Use this number line to plot the times of the sprinters.
This time Chambers ran in 11.08 seconds and
Greene ran in 10.87 seconds.
The others ran in the same times as before.

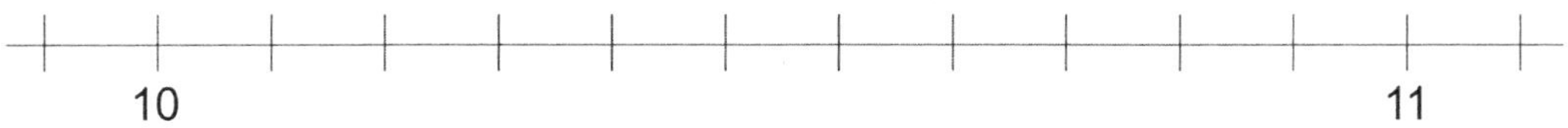

How did the race results change?

____

Name ________________ Date ____________

Master 4.15

Step-by-Step 4

Lesson 4, Question 8

Use the digits 4, 5, and 6. Use each digit once.

Step 1 How many decimals can you write with 4 in the ones place? _________
What do you get when you round each to the nearest whole number?
Fill in the table.

Decimal	Rounds to
4. __ __	
4. __ __	

How many decimals have you written that start with 4 and round to 5? _________

Step 2 How many decimals can you write with 5 in the ones place? _________
What do you get when you round each to the nearest whole number?
Fill in the table.

Decimal	Rounds to

How many decimals have you written that start with 5 and round to 5? _________

Step 3 Can you write a decimal that starts with 6 and rounds to 5? _________
Explain.

____

Step 4 How many decimals have you written that round to 5? _________
Order these decimals from least to greatest.

____

Step 5 Suppose you used the numbers 3, 4, and 6 instead.
How many decimals could you write that round to 5? _________

Name ____________________ Date ________________

Master 4.16

Step-by-Step 5

Lesson 5, Question 6

Kenichi estimated that 23.58 + 11.14 is about 35.
Ariel's estimate was 34.58.

Step 1 Round each decimal to the nearest whole number.
Fill in the table.

Decimal	Rounds to
23.58	
11.14	

Step 2 Look at the table.
Which 2 numbers add to 35?

____

How did Kenichi estimate the sum? Explain.

____

Step 3 Look at the table.
Which 2 numbers add to 34.58?

____

How did Ariel estimate the sum? Explain.

____

Step 4 Use a different strategy to round the 2 numbers.
You could round to the nearest tenth, or round to a "nice" number.

____

Estimate the sum. How does your estimate compare to Ariel's and Kenichi's?

____

____

Name ____________________ Date _______________

Master 4.17

Step-by-Step 6

Lesson 6, Question 6

You may use a calculator.

Write two decimals that add to 4.9.

Step 1 Choose a decimal less than 4.9. _______
Subtract this decimal from 4.9.

4.9 – _______ = _______

Two possible lengths are _______ and _______.

Step 2 Choose a different decimal.
Subtract this decimal from 4.9.

4.9 – _______ = _______

Two possible lengths are _______ and _______.

Step 3 Repeat Step 2 at least four more times.

____

____

____

____

____

____

____

____

Step 4 How many different answers did you find? ______________________
Do you think there are more possible answers? Explain.

____

____

Name ____________________ Date ________________

Master 4.18

Step-by-Step 7

Lesson 7, Question 10

Step 1 Round both numbers to the nearest whole number. ________________
Subtract the rounded numbers.

________ – ________ = ________

Is your estimate less than 10? ________

Step 2 Round 1.09 to the nearest whole number. ________
Subtract the rounded number from 11.42.

11.42 – ________ = ________

Is your estimate less than 10? ________

Step 3 Brad estimated the difference between 11.42 and 1.09 as less than 10.
Is he correct?

____

____

Name ____________________ Date ________________

Master 4.19

Step-by-Step 8

Lesson 8, Question 4

Ana bought 10 cans of apple juice.
Each can holds 1.36 L, and costs $1.29.

Step 1 Write a multiplication statement for the number of litres Ana bought.

__________ × __________

Step 2 When you multiply a decimal by 10, what happens to the digits?

____

Step 3 Answer the multiplication statement in *Step 1*.

____

How much did Ana pay for 10 cans?

____

Step 4 Hans bought 100 cans of apple juice.
When you multiply a decimal by 100, what happens to the digits?

____

Step 5 How many litres of apple juice did Hans buy? ______________________

How much did he pay? ____

Name ____________________ Date ________________

Master 4.20

Step-by-Step 9

Lesson 9, Question 5

Jen has 2.8 m of fabric.
She will make 10 placemats, all the same size.

Step 1 Model 2.8 with Base Ten Blocks.

Step 2 Trade blocks to make 10 equal groups.

Step 3 Write a division statement for the length of each placemat.

_______ ÷ _______

How long will each placemat be? ______________________________

Name ____________________ Date ______________

Master 4.21

Unit Test: Unit 4 Decimals

Part A

1. Write a fraction or mixed number for each decimal.

a) 0.29 ________ b) 1.78 ________ c) 3.6 ________ d) 0.04 ________

2. Write a decimal for each fraction or mixed number.

a) $1\frac{5}{10}$ ________ b) $\frac{6}{100}$ ________ c) $2\frac{89}{100}$ ________ d) $\frac{3}{10}$ ________

3. Compare. Use >, <, or =.

a) 1.67 ☐ 1.6 b) 4.3 ☐ 4.30 c) 6.09 ☐ 6.1

4. Order the decimals from least to greatest.

a) 2.64, 2.95, 1.99 ______________ b) 0.6, 0.44, 0.9 ______________

5. Round to the nearest whole number.

a) 2.12 ________ b) 77.96 ________ c) 1.50 ________ d) 0.89 ________

6. Estimate each sum or difference.

a) 5.9 – 2.8 ________ b) 0.8 + 4.3 ________ c) 9.45 – 2.84 ________ d) 2.40 + 1.35 ________

e) 19.8 + 3.9 ________ f) 20.97 + 8.01 ________ g) $13.24 – $6.11 ________ h) 8.04 – 0.96 ________

7. Add or subtract.

a) $\begin{array}{r} 7.36 \\ +\ 4.95 \\ \hline \end{array}$ b) $\begin{array}{r} 16.91 \\ -\ 4.38 \\ \hline \end{array}$ c) $\begin{array}{r} 0.97 \\ -\ 0.88 \\ \hline \end{array}$ d) $\begin{array}{r} \$0.89 \\ +\ 4.76 \\ \hline \end{array}$

Name ____________________ Date ______________

Master 4.21b **Unit Test continued**

8. Use mental math to find each product or quotient.

a) $4.3 \times 10 =$ ________ **b)** $16.8 \times 100 =$ ________ **c)** $8.6 \div 10 =$ ________

Part B

9. Henry's patio is 5.6 m long and 2.3 m wide.
What is the perimeter of Henry's patio?
Show all your work.

____

____

____

10. Use the digits 3, 7, and 6 to make as many decimals as you can.

____

____

11. Margaret has a pocketful of change.
Rounded to the nearest dollar, Margaret has $14.
What is the least money Margaret could have? ____________________
What is the most money? How do you know?

____

____

12. Patu bought 10 pairs of socks for $3.79 a pair plus taxes.
How much did Patu pay for the socks before taxes?

____

____

Name ____________________ Date ________________

Master 4.21c **Unit Test continued**

13. Ezio bought 7.5 m of material.
He made 10 matching chair cushions and had 0.7 m of material left over.
How much material was used for each chair cushion?
Explain how you got your answer.

____

____

____

____

Part C

14. Use pictures, numbers, or words.
Show and describe 2.65 in as many ways as you can.

____

____

____

____

____

____

____

____

____

____

____

Name ____________________ Date ______________

Master 4.22

Sample Answers

Unit Test – Master 4.21

Part A

1. a) $\frac{29}{100}$ **b)** $1\frac{78}{100}$ **c)** $3\frac{6}{10}$ **d)** $\frac{4}{100}$
2. a) 1.5 **b)** 0.06 **c)** 2.89 **d)** 0.3
3. a) 1.67 > 1.6 **b)** 4.3 = 4.30 **c)** 6.09 < 6.1
4. a) 1.99, 2.64, 2.95 **b)** 0.44, 0.6, 0.9
5. a) 2 **b)** 78 **c)** 2 **d)** 1
6. a) 3 **b)** 5 **c)** 6 **d)** 3
e) 24 **f)** 29 **g)** $7 **h)** 7
7. a) 12.31 **b)** 12.53 **c)** 0.09 **d)** $5.65
8. a) 43 **b)** 1680 **c)** 0.86

Part B

9. 5.6 m + 2.3 m + 5.6 m + 2.3 m = 15.8 m
The perimeter is 15.8 m.

10. Possible answers: 3.76, 3.67, 7.36, 7.63, 6.37, 6.73, 36.7, 37.6, 73.6, 76.3, 63.7, 67.3

11. Least money: $13.50
Most money: $14.49

12. $3.79 × 10 = $37.90
Patu paid $37.90 for the socks.

13. It took 0.68 m to make each chair cushion.
First, I subtracted 0.7 m from 7.5 m.
7.5 m – 0.7 m = 6.8 m
This told me that it took 6.8 m to make 10 cushions.
Then I divided 6.8 m by 10 to find out how much material each cushion took.
6.8 m ÷ 10 = 0.68 m

Part C

14. Many answers are possible.
Examples:
- 2.65 is a decimal.
  It means two and sixty-five hundredths.
- $2\frac{65}{100}$
- 
  2 ones 6 tenths 5 hundredths
Ones	Tenths	Hundredths
2	6	5
- 
  2 ones 5 tenths 15 hundredths
- 2.65 is between 2 and 3, but closer to 3.
- 2.65 rounded to nearest whole number is 3.
- 2.65 comes between 2.64 and 2.66.
- 2.65 is greater than 2.45.
  2.65 is less than 2.69.
- 2.65 is the sum of 1.40 and 1.25.
- I could show 2.65 by colouring two hundredths grids and 65 small squares on another hundredths grid.
- 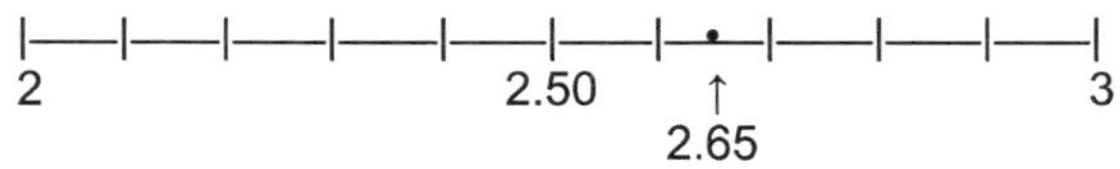

Extra Practice Masters 4.24–4.29

Go to the CD-ROM to access editable versions of these Extra Practice Masters.

Name ______ Date ______

Master 4.24 **Extra Practice 1**

Lesson 1: Tenths and Hundredths

1. Write each fraction or mixed number as a decimal.
   a) $\frac{17}{100}$ b) $4\frac{3}{10}$ c) $\frac{2}{100}$
   d) $\frac{9}{10}$ e) $\frac{99}{100}$ f) $41\frac{7}{100}$
2. Write each decimal as a fraction or mixed number.
   a) 17.02 b) 8.4 c) 0.13
   d) 1.34 e) 0.91 f) 6.7
3. Use the numbers 3, 6, and 9.
   Make as many decimals as you can.

Lesson 2: Equivalent Decimals

1. Colour hundredths grids to show each decimal.
   Write an equivalent decimal.
   a) 1.6 b) 0.40 c) 2.1
2. Write an equivalent decimal for each decimal.
   a) 9.70 b) 4.3 c) 2.20
   d) 0.8 e) 0.10 f) 18.5
3. Circle the equivalent decimals in each group.
   a) 0.3 0.30 0.03 b) 2.01 2.1 2.10
   c) 9.7 9.70 9.07 d) 15.3 15.03 15.30

Name ______ Date ______

Master 4.25 **Extra Practice 2**

Lesson 3: Comparing and Ordering Decimals

1. Write >, <, or = in each box.
   a) 4.70 □ 4.7 b) 3.8 □ 3.6 c) 5.01 □ 5.10
   d) 1.47 □ 1.74 e) 7.50 □ 7.5 f) 2.38 □ 2.4
2. Write the decimals in order from least to greatest.
   a) 5.2, 8.9, 3.6 b) 3.04, 3.41, 3.01
   c) 0.8, 0.43, 0.11 d) 2.3, 2.81, 2.76
3. Write a decimal to make each statement true.
   a) 0.25 < □ b) 8.5 = □ c) 1.5 > □
   d) 0.02 > □ e) 7.67 < □ f) 6.80 = □

Lesson 4: Rounding Decimals

1. Round to the nearest whole number.
   a) 2.78 b) 1.41 c) 0.88
   d) 4.5 e) 18.6 f) 17.50
2. Round to the nearest dollar.
   a) \$0.76 b) \$18.50 c) \$7.49
   d) \$5.89 e) \$37.14 f) \$85.62
3. Name 2 decimals with hundredths that would round to 15 when rounded to the nearest whole number.

Name ______ Date ______

Master 4.26 **Extra Practice 3**

Lesson 5: Estimating Sums and Differences

1. Estimate each sum.
   a) 2.8 + 3.9 b) 6.97 + 5.40
   c) \$1.95 + \$0.06 d) 7.75 + 3.21
2. Estimate each difference.
   a) 9.6 – 3.1 b) 8.7 – 5.9
   c) 2.14 – 1.65 d) \$9.11 – \$6.41
3. Estimate each sum or difference.
   a) 7.4 – 3.8 b) 5.04 + 7.02
   c) 16.81 – 12.33 d) 8.75 + 6.01

Lesson 6: Adding Decimals

1. Add.
   a) 5.3 + 8.2 b) 5.7 + 9.3 c) 6.9 + 8.4 d) 23.08 + 14.99 e) 6.35 + 4.65
2. Write vertically, then add.
   a) 14.26 + 37.98 b) 6.94 + 8.3 c) 52.46 + 34.25

Name ______ Date ______

Master 4.27 **Extra Practice 4**

Lesson 7: Subtracting Decimals

1. Subtract.
   a) 8.4 – 3.1 b) 7.5 – 1.8 c) 6.85 – 3.94 d) 11.04 – 4.18 e) \$9.56 – 2.08
2. Write vertically, then subtract.
   a) 10.08 – 6.9 b) 0.85 – 0.3 c) 5.7 – 2.63

Lesson 8: Multiplying Decimals by 10 and 100

1. Multiply. Use mental math.
   a) 6.3 × 10 = b) 5.82 × 10 = c) 6.72 × 10 =
   d) 31.2 × 100 = e) 0.4 × 100 = f) 8.09 × 100 =
2. Record each product in the place-value chart.

a) 0.04 × 100
b) 6.25 × 10
c) 0.3 × 100
d) 6.8 × 10
e) 2.39 × 10

Tens	Ones	•	Tenths	Hundredths
		•		
		•		
		•		
		•		
		•		

Name ______ Date ______

Master 4.28 **Extra Practice 5**

Lesson 9: Dividing Decimals by 10

1. Use mental math to divide.
   a) 84.2 ÷ 10 = b) 263.4 ÷ 10 = c) 0.7 ÷ 10 =
   d) 0.1 ÷ 10 = e) 8.5 ÷ 10 = f) 173.8 ÷ 10 =
   g) 7.7 ÷ 10 = h) 0.4 ÷ 10 = i) 2.6 ÷ 10 =
2. Ten pennies have a mass of 23.5 g.
   What is the mass of 1 penny?
3. Ten dimes have a mass of 17.5 g. What is the mass of 1 dime?

Name ______ Date ______

Master 4.29 **Sample Answers**

Extra Practice 1 – Master 4.24

Lesson 1
1. a) 0.17 b) 4.3 c) 0.02 d) 0.9 e) 0.99 f) 41.07
2. a) $17\frac{2}{100}$ b) $8\frac{4}{10}$ c) $\frac{13}{100}$ d) $1\frac{34}{100}$ e) $\frac{91}{100}$ f) $6\frac{7}{10}$
3. 3.69, 3.96, 6.39, 6.93, 9.36, 9.63, 36.9, 39.6, 63.9, 69.3, 93.6, 96.3

Lesson 2
1. a) 1.60 b) 0.4 c) 2.10
2. a) 9.7 b) 4.30 c) 2.2 d) 0.80 e) 0.1 f) 18.50
3. a) 0.3 and 0.30 b) 2.1 and 2.10 c) 9.7 and 9.70 d) 15.3 and 15.30

Extra Practice 2 – Master 4.25

Lesson 3
1. a) 4.70 = 4.7 b) 3.8 > 3.6 c) 5.01 < 5.10 d) 1.47 < 1.74 e) 7.50 = 7.5 f) 2.38 < 2.40
2. a) 3.6, 5.2, 8.9 b) 3.01, 3.04, 3.41 c) 0.11, 0.43, 0.8 d) 2.3, 2.76, 2.81
3. Answers may vary.
   a) 0.25 < 0.84 b) 8.5 = 8.50 c) 1.5 > 0.2 d) 0.02 > 0.01 e) 7.67 < 7.9 f) 6.80 = 6.8

Lesson 4
1. a) 3 b) 1 c) 1 d) 5 e) 19 f) 18
2. a) \$1 b) \$19 c) \$7 d) \$6 e) \$37 f) \$86
3. Answers may vary. 14.75 and 15.04

Extra Practice 3 – Master 4.26

Lesson 5
1. a) About 7 b) About 12 c) About \$2 d) About 11
2. a) About 7 b) About 3 c) About 0 d) About \$3
3. a) About 3 b) About 12 c) About 5 d) About 15

Lesson 6
1. a) 13.5 b) 15.0 c) 15.3 d) 38.07 e) 11.00
2. a) 52.24 b) 15.24 c) 86.71

Extra Practice 4 – Master 4.27

Lesson 7
1. a) 5.3 b) 5.7 c) 2.91 d) 6.86 e) \$7.48
2. a) 3.18 b) 0.55 c) 3.07

Lesson 8
1. a) 63 b) 58.2 c) 67.2 d) 3120 e) 40 f) 809
2.

	Tens	Ones	•	Tenths	Hundredths
a)		4			
b)	6	2	•	5	
c)	3	0			
d)	6	8			
e)	2	3	•	9	

Extra Practice 5 – Master 4.28

Lesson 9
1. a) 8.42 b) 26.34 c) 0.07 d) 0.01 e) 0.85 f) 17.38 g) 0.77 h) 0.04 i) 0.26
2. 2.35 g
3. 1.75 g

Addison Wesley
Mathematics
Makes Sense

Program Authors

Peggy Morrow
Ralph Connelly
Bryn Keyes
Jason Johnston
Steve Thomas
Jeananne Thomas
Angela D'Alessandro
Maggie Martin Connell
Don Jones
Michael Davis
Sharon Jeroski
Trevor Brown
Nora Alexander
Cynthia Pratt Nicolson

Printed and bound in Canada

8 9 MP 18 17

ISBN 0-321-31261-9

9 780321 312617

PEARSON
Education Canada

ADDISON WESLEY

Ontario

Math Makes Sense 5

Ontario

Teacher Guide

Unit 5: Data Management

PEARSON
Addison Wesley

UNIT 5

Data Management

"Once a graph is constructed, the most important activity is discussing what it tells the people who see it."

– John A. Van de Walle

FOCUS STRAND
Data Management and Probability

SUPPORTING STRAND
Number Sense and Numeration

Mathematics Background

What Are the Big Ideas?

- Tables and graphs can be interpreted as data.
- Data can be displayed in a variety of ways.
- Data can be collected and organized.
- A set of data has a mean (an average value, or the balance point of the set), and a mode (a value that occurs most often). Both the mean and the mode are averages.
- Data can be collected from a sample, rather than from an entire population.
- Data can be displayed with a bias, showing the data in a way someone else wants you to see them.
- Data can be used to make predictions.

How Will the Concepts Develop?

Students begin by interpreting tables and graphs. They interpret the data shown by asking and answering questions about them.

Students analyse data by calculating the mean and the mode.

Students create spreadsheets on computers. Students draw graphs by hand and with a computer, choosing appropriate scales and keys.

Students investigate bias in the way that data are displayed. Students examine how surveys are conducted and understand what a sample of a population means. They formulate questions, make inferences, and develop new ideas about the data gathered in a survey. Students complete the unit by conducting an experiment and using the results to answer questions.

Why Are These Concepts Important?

The ability to understand and interpret data is an important skill. It will provide a foundation for future mathematics learning, as well as prepare students to analyse the data they encounter in everyday life.

When students explore surveys and conduct experiments, they learn more about themselves and the world around them. By conducting an experiment, students are developing organizational skills, which are an asset in all areas of their lives.

Curriculum Overview

Cluster 1: Interpreting Data

Overall Expectations
- Interpret displays of data and present the information using mathematical terms. (5m109)

Specific Expectations
- Calculate the mean and the mode of a set of data. (5m117)
- Evaluate data presented on tables, charts, and graphs and use the information in discussion. (5m120)

Cluster 2: Displaying Data

Overall Expectations
- Evaluate and use data from graphic organizers. (5m110)

Specific Expectations
- Display data on graphs by hand and by using computer applications. (5m114)
- Explain the choice of intervals used to construct a bar graph or the choice of symbols on a pictograph. (5m116)
- Construct labelled graphs both by hand and by using computer applications. (5m119)

Cluster 3: Evaluating Results

Overall Expectations
- Use computer applications to record the results of data collected. (5m107)
- Predict the validity of the results of data collected. (5m108)

Specific Expectations
- Recognize that graphs, tables, and charts can present data with accuracy or bias. (5m118)
- Design surveys, collect data, and record the results on given spreadsheets or tally charts. (5m113)
- Analyse how data were collected and discuss the reasonableness of the results. (5m115)

Launch
In the Lab

Lesson 1:
Interpreting Data

Lesson 2:
Mean and Mode

Technology:
Creating Spreadsheets Using *AppleWorks*

Lesson 3:
Drawing Bar Graphs

Technology:
Drawing Circle Graphs and Bar Graphs Using *AppleWorks*

Lesson 4:
Line Graphs

Technology:
Drawing Line Graphs Using *AppleWorks*

Lesson 5:
Interpreting Survey Results

Lesson 6:
Bias in Displaying Data

Lesson 7:
Strategies Toolkit

Show What You Know

Unit Problem
In the Lab

Curriculum across the Grades

Grade 4	Grade 5	Grade 6
Students collect and organize data and identify their use. They identify examples of the use of data in the world around them. Before gathering data, students predict the possible results of a survey, based on their experiences. They conduct surveys and record data on tally charts. They explain how data were collected and describe the results of a survey. Students display data by hand and using technology. They create bar graphs and pictographs with many-to-one correspondence. They use conventional symbols, titles, and labels when displaying data. Students recognize the purpose of different parts of a graph. They read and interpret data presented on tables, charts, and graphs and discuss the important features, using mathematical terms. They find the range of data values.	Students design surveys, collect data, and record the results on given spreadsheets or tally charts. They analyse how data were collected and discuss the reasonableness of the results. Students display data on line graphs, bar graphs, pictographs, and circle graphs by hand and by using computer applications. They explain the choice of intervals used to construct a bar graph or the choice of symbols on a pictograph. Students calculate the mean and mode of a set of data. They evaluate data presented on tables, charts, and graphs and use the information in discussion. They recognize that graphs, tables, and charts can present data with accuracy or bias.	Students design surveys, organize the data into self-selected categories and ranges, and record the data on spreadsheets or tally charts. They experiment with a variety of displays of the same data using computer applications, and select the type of graph that best represents the data. Students evaluate and explore how data were collected and how the results represent the population. They explain how the choice of intervals affects the appearance of data in comparing two graphs drawn with different intervals by hand or by using graphing calculators or computers. They calculate the median of a set of data. Students recognize that different types of graphs can present the same data differently. They construct line graphs, bar graphs, and scatter plots both by hand and by using computer applications. They make inferences and convincing arguments based on the analysis of tables, charts, and graphs.

Additional Activities

Word Find

For Extra Practice (Appropriate for use after Lesson 3)
Materials: 1-cm grid paper (PM 23), 2-column chart (PM 17), *Word Find* (Master 5.6)

The work students do: Students work individually. Students make as many different words as possible from the letters in the words DATA MANAGEMENT. Students use a chart to record the number of letters in each word, and draw a bar graph to show the results.

Take It Further: Have each student compare her or his graph with a classmate's. Students can write 3 things they learn from each other's graphs.

Linguistic
Individual Activity

Story of Mrs. D.

Extension (Appropriate for use after Lesson 4)
Materials: *Story of Mrs. D.* (Master 5.7)

The work students do: Students work in pairs. They will write a story about Mrs. D. using the line graph on the activity sheet.
Students will make the connection that when the line graph shows an increase, Mrs. D. is moving away from her home. When the line graph shows a decrease, she is moving toward her home. When there is no change, she has stopped.

Take It Further: Have the students draw their own line graph and write a story about themselves according to the line graph.

Linguistic/Interpersonal
Partner Activity

Concrete Bars

For Extra Support (Appropriate for use after Lesson 5)
Materials: *Concrete Bars* (Master 5.8), a class list, 6 skewers, 6 strips of paper, 30 Cheerios, Plasticine

The work students do: Students work in pairs. Students will survey their class, using skewers and Cheerios to construct a concrete bar graph.
Each classmate the student surveys will place a Cheerio on the skewer that answers his or her question. When all the classmates have been surveyed, have the student write 3 things they have learned about their classmates.

Take It Further: Have students conduct a second survey.

Visual/Interpersonal
Partner Activity

Paper Search

For Extra Support (Appropriate for use after Lesson 6)
Materials: 1-cm grid paper (PM 23), *Paper Search* (Master 5.9), newspapers, magazines

The work students do: Students work in pairs. They look through newspapers or magazines to find a graph that shows bias. They discuss the bias in the graph, and describe what they would change to remove the bias. They write 3 questions about the graph and answer their questions.

Take It Further: Students redraw the graph to show no bias.

Visual/Logical
Partner Activity

Planning for Unit 5

Planning for Instruction

Suggested Unit time: About 2–3 weeks

Lesson	Time	Materials	Program Support
Launch: In the Lab, page 2	15–20 min		
Lesson 1: Interpreting Data, page 4 Read and interpret data in tables and graphs.	40–50 min		Master 5.10: Step-by-Step 1 Master 5.18: Extra Practice 1
Lesson 2: Mean and Mode, page 8 Calculate the mean and the mode of data.	40–50 min	counters linking cubes	Master 5.11: Step-by-Step 2 Master 5.19: Extra Practice 2
Technology: Creating Spreadsheets Using *AppleWorks*, page 11 Use a computer to create spreadsheets.	40–50 min	*AppleWorks*	
Lesson 3: Drawing Bar Graphs, page 14 Draw bar graphs by hand.	40–50 min	measuring tape or metre stick 1-cm grid paper	PM 23: 1-cm Grid Paper Master 5.12: Step-by-Step 3 Master 5.20: Extra Practice 3
Technology: Drawing Circle Graphs and Bar Graphs Using *AppleWorks*, page 17 Use a computer to draw bar graphs and circle graphs.	40–50 min	*AppleWorks*	
Lesson 4: Line Graphs, page 20 Draw line graphs by hand.	40–50 min	1-cm grid paper	PM 23: 1-cm Grid Paper Master 5.13: Step-by-Step 4 Master 5.21: Extra Practice 4
Technology: Drawing Line Graphs Using *AppleWorks*, page 24 Use a computer to draw line graphs.	40–50 min	*AppleWorks*	
Lesson 5: Interpreting Survey Results, page 26 Conduct a survey an interpret survey results.	40–50 min	1-cm grid paper	PM 23: 1-cm Grid Paper Master 5.14: Step-by-Step 5 Master 5.22: Extra Practice 5
Lesson 6: Bias in Displaying Data, page 30 Investigate bias in the way data are displayed.	40–50 min		Master 5.15: Step-by-Step 6 Master 5.23: Extra Practice 6
Lesson 7: Strategies Toolkit, page 34 Interpret a problem and select an appropriate strategy.	40–50 min		
Show What You Know, page 36 Assessment	40–50 min	1-cm grid paper	PM 23: 1-cm Grid Paper
Unit Problem: In the Lab, page 38 Assessment	80–100 min	1-cm grid paper	PM 23: 1-cm Grid Paper

Planning for Assessment

Purpose	Tools and Process	Recording and Reporting
Diagnostic	*Unit Launch* Question; conference; scaffold problems throughout the unit	PM 8: Conference Prompts
Formative	*Explore* – Ongoing Assessment: Observe and Listen	Master 5.2 Ongoing Observations: Data Management PM 1: Inquiry Process Check List PM 6: Observation Record 1 PM 7: Observation Record 2 PM 8: Conference Prompts
	Prompt student's self-assessment	PM 2: Self-Assessment PM 3: Self-Assessment: Problem Solving
	Practice – Assessment Focus Questions	PM 9: Work Sample Records
	Review student work; provide feedback; scaffold as needed; select key pieces	
Summative	*Show What You Know* *Unit Problem* – Performance Assessment Unit Test	Master 5.1 Unit Rubric: Data Management Master 5.3 Performance Assessment Rubric: In the Lab Master 5.4 Unit Summary: Data Management
	Review assessment records; add unit results to ongoing records	PM 10: Summary Class Records: Strands PM 11: Summary Class Records: Achievement Categories PM 12: Summary Record: Individual
Learning Skills/Mathematical Disposition	Observe and record throughout unit	PM 4: Learning Skills Check List PM 5: Mathematical Dispositions and Learning Skills

Program Masters (PM) are in the *Grade 5 Planning and Program Masters* module.
Extra Practice Masters are on the CD-ROM.

In the Lab

LESSON ORGANIZER

15–20 min

Curriculum Focus: Activate prior learning about data management.

Vocabulary: pictograph, bar graph, title, labels, axis, key, scale, range

ASSUMED PRIOR KNOWLEDGE

- ✓ Students understand that data can be collected to make a set of data.
- ✓ Students can sort and classify objects and data.
- ✓ Students can interpret displays of data, such as tables and graphs.

ACTIVATE PRIOR LEARNING

Initiate a discussion about collecting data. Ask:

- When have you collected data? (*I asked my friends when was the best date to have my party.*)
- How did you record your data? (*I made a chart with the names of my friends in one column and the dates they suggested in another column.*)

Draw students' attention to the table in the Student Book.

Point out that the table has a title, and each column is clearly labelled so we know what the table shows.

Discuss the first question in the Student Book. (*September*)

Ask:

- How do you know that month had the most rainfall? (*It has the greatest number.*)

Discuss the second question in the Student Book. (*February*)

Ask:

- How do you know that month had the least rainfall? (*It has the least number.*)

Discuss the third question in the Student Book. (*Pictograph, line graph, circle graph*)

Discuss the fourth question in the Student Book. (*Throughout the school year, a class used a rain gauge to measure the amount of rain each month.*)

Discuss the fifth question in the Student Book. (*Number of sunny days, amount of precipitation, daily high or low temperatures*)

Tell the students that, in this unit, they will investigate how to collect, organize, and display data. At the end of the unit, students will conduct an experiment, organize their data, and present their results to the class.

Key Words

- range
- mean
- average
- mode
- intervals
- line graph
- sample
- bias

Students collected data about the amount of rainfall.

Monthly Rainfall for One School Year

Month	Amount (mm)
September	70
October	63
November	67
December	62
January	47
February	46
March	58
April	65
May	67

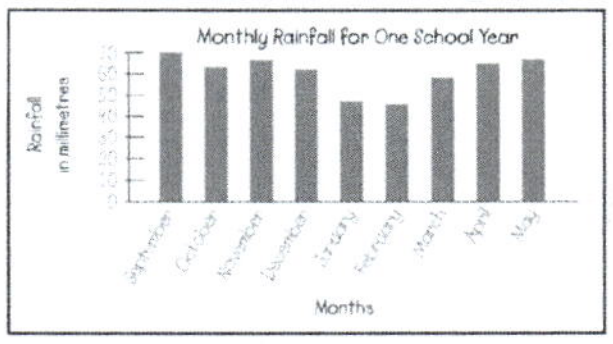

- In which month did the most rain fall?
- In which month did the least rain fall?
- How else could you display the data?
- How do you think these data were collected?
- What other weather data might you record?

155

LITERATURE CONNECTIONS FOR THE UNIT

Tiger Math: Learning to Graph from a Baby Tiger by Ann Nagda. Henry Holt & Company Inc., 2002.
ISBN 080507161X
Learn to graph while following the growth of T.J., an orphaned Siberian tiger cub. The narrative follows the little tiger as he grows into a strong, healthy, and happy adult. The text is paired with picture, circle, bar, and line graphs that display information about T.J.'s progress and tigers in general.

Math Games for Middle School: Challenges & Skill-Builders for Students at Every Level by Mario Salvadori and Joseph P. Wright. Chicago Review Press, Incorporated, 1998.
ISBN 1556522886
This book explains middle-school math with problems that kids want to solve. Each chapter begins with an introduction explaining the concept, followed by a list of problems for readers to solve. Intriguing facts about the history of math capture students' interest.

REACHING ALL LEARNERS

e-tools

Some students may benefit from using the virtual manipulatives on the e-Tools CD-ROM. The e-Tools appropriate for this unit include Spreadsheet/Data/Grapher. Students can use these e-Tools to organize data in tables, to sort data, and in place of the graphing software *Graphers* (for bar graphs only).

DIAGNOSTIC ASSESSMENT

What to Look For	What to Do
✔ Students understand that data are facts that are collected and recorded. ✔ Students understand that tables and graphs display data in an organized way. ✔ Students can read a table and get relevant information from it.	***Extra Support:*** Students who have difficulty reading a table may benefit from running their fingers along the rows and down the columns to help them read information from the table correctly. Encourage students to use a ruler or a straightedge to help read tables and graphs. *Work on this skill throughout the unit.*

Interpreting Data

LESSON ORGANIZER — 40–50 min

Curriculum Focus: Read and interpret data in tables and graphs. (5m120)

Student Materials

Optional
- Step-by-Step 1 (Master 5.10)
- Extra Practice 1 (Master 5.18)

Vocabulary: key, sector, range

Assessment: Master 5.2 Ongoing Observations: Data Management

Key Math Learnings

1. Tables, pictographs, bar graphs, and circle graphs each show data in an organized way.
2. The title of the graph tells you what data are displayed.

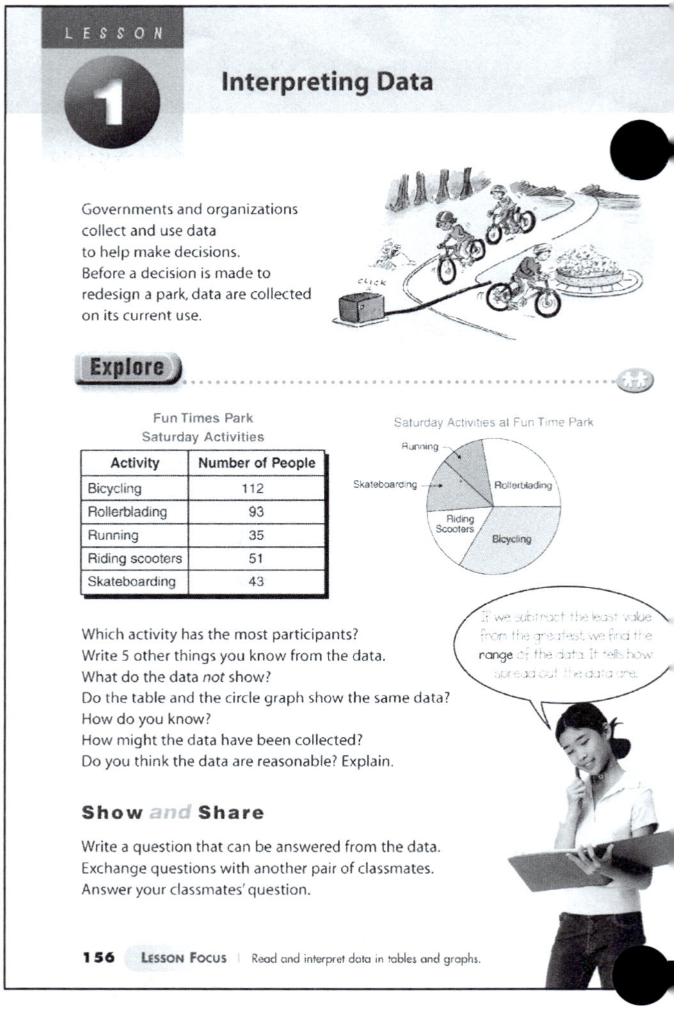

LESSON 1 Interpreting Data

Governments and organizations collect and use data to help make decisions. Before a decision is made to redesign a park, data are collected on its current use.

Explore

Fun Times Park
Saturday Activities

Activity	Number of People
Bicycling	112
Rollerblading	93
Running	35
Riding scooters	51
Skateboarding	43

Which activity has the most participants?
Write 5 other things you know from the data.
What do the data *not* show?
Do the table and the circle graph show the same data?
How do you know?
How might the data have been collected?
Do you think the data are reasonable? Explain.

Show and Share

Write a question that can be answered from the data.
Exchange questions with another pair of classmates.
Answer your classmates' question.

156 LESSON FOCUS | Read and interpret data in tables and graphs.

BEFORE — Get Started

Discuss with students why someone might collect data. Ask:

- Why do people need to collect data?
  (*To help them make decisions; to improve products; to find out what people like or use the most*)
- What are some ways large corporations might collect data?
  (*Through telephone surveys; mail-out surveys; by asking people at random on the street*)
- What things could the principal ask the students at this school to help her or him make decisions?
  (*How should we encourage more students to participate in next year's Jump Rope for Heart event? Should we have a bake sale during lunch and have the profits go to the class trip?*)
- What things could a teacher ask her or his students to help them make decisions?
  (*Should the class have a free period if everyone is prepared for class for a week? Should the class get a treat if everyone has their homework done for a month?*)

Read the introduction, and discuss what data are being collected in the illustration.
(*The number of bicycles using a certain path*)

Present *Explore*. Have students work in pairs to answer the questions. Students should record answers in their notebooks.

DURING — Explore

Ongoing Assessment: Observe and Listen

Ask questions, such as:

- Which activity is most popular? (*Bicycling*)
  How can you tell? (*It has the highest number.*)

Connect

Fun Times Park rents equipment.
The rental data are displayed in graphs.

Tables, pictographs, bar graphs, and circle graphs each show data in an organized way.
The title of the graph tells you what data are displayed.
Each graph presents the same data.

> **Numbers Every Day**
>
> **Number Strategies**
>
> Write an equivalent decimal for each number.
> - 0.3 0.30
> - 1.9 1.90
> - 2.60 2.6
> - 9.80 9.8
> - 6.5 6.50

➤ In a pictograph, symbols show the data.
A key shows what each symbol represents. In the pictograph,

represents 20 rentals.

To find the number of scooters rented, count the and multiply by 20.

There are $8\frac{1}{2}$.

$8 \times 20 = 160$

represents 10 rentals.

$160 + 10 = 170$
So, 170 scooters were rented.

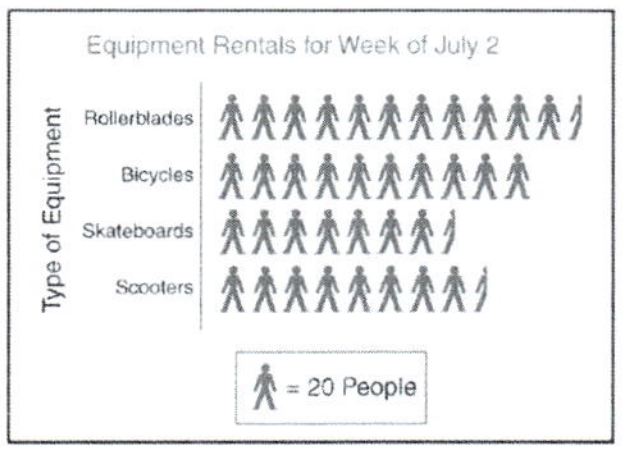

➤ In a bar graph, bars show the data.
The numbers on the vertical axis show the scale.
In this bar graph, the bar for rollerblade rentals is about halfway between 220 and 240.
So, the rollerblade rentals are about 230.
From the bar graph, the greatest number of rentals is 230.
The least number of rentals is about 150.
So, the range is about 230 – 150, or about 80.

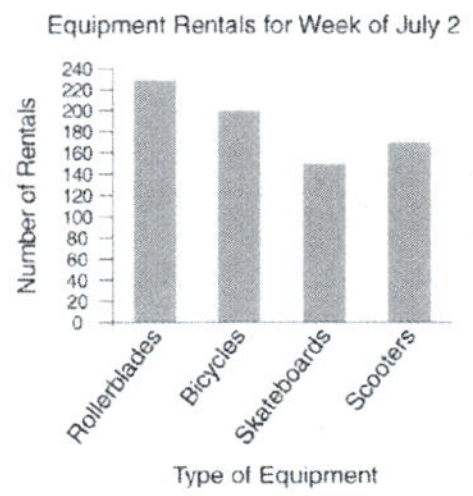

157

REACHING ALL LEARNERS

Alternative Explore

Materials: index cards

Have groups of 3 or 4 students write down questions relating to the Fun Times Park table. The students should write each question on an index card. Have each group trade cards with another group. Have the students read aloud the question and answer to the class.

Early Finishers

Students can write more questions and answers for *Practice* questions 1, 2, and 3.

Common Misconceptions

➤ In a pictograph, students will count the number of symbols as the number of items.

How to Help: Have students locate the key first, then count according to the key. For example, in *Practice* question 3, have students count on by 4s.

Numbers Every Day

Students can add a zero in the hundredths place, or remove the zero from the hundredths place.

- How are the table and the circle graph alike?
  (*They both show Saturday activities at the Fun Time Park.*)
- How are the table and the circle graph different?
  (*The table displays the actual numbers; the circle graph shows the fraction of results in each category.*)
- How do you think the data were collected?
  (*The employees counted the participants, or counted how many people did each activity.*)
- Which type of display is better? Why?
  (*The table, because it shows the actual data; the circle graph, because you can see the data without comparing all the numbers.*)
- Do you think the results would be different if the data were collected on a Monday?
  (*Yes. Fewer people would participate in the activities, because they would be at school or at work. The size of the sectors in the circle graph might stay about the same, but the numbers the sectors represent would be smaller.*)

AFTER Connect

Ask for volunteers to read their questions and answers from *Show and Share*. Discuss which questions can be answered easily, and which require calculations.

Have students review the pictograph in *Connect*. Ask:

- Does the pictograph show the same data as the table and the circle graph?
  (*No. The table and the circle graph show the total number of participants in each activity. The pictograph shows how many people rented equipment. Also, the table and the circle graph are for one day, while the pictograph is for an entire week.*)

Discuss the different parts of the pictograph, the table, and the circle graph. Discuss which features are similar and different.

Sample Answers

1. a) Quebec City; Calgary
   b) Charlottetown; Victoria
   c) Charlottetown, Quebec City, Vancouver
   d) Which cities have about the same number of wet days? (*Answer: Charlottetown and Quebec City*)
   How many more wet days did Vancouver have than Victoria? (*Answer: 11*)
   e) I could display the data in a bar graph, a pictograph, or a circle graph.
3. d) There would be half as many houses.
4. c) Key: 1 vegetable = 20 days

Vegetable	Number of symbols
Cabbage	5
Leek	7
Lettuce	4
Onion	$6\frac{1}{2}$
Spinach	$2\frac{1}{2}$
Peas	$3\frac{1}{2}$
Turnip	3

REFLECT: A graph is easier to read because I can see the data visually, instead of just seeing the numbers.

➤ In a circle graph, data are shown as parts of a whole.
This circle graph shows the same data as in the pictograph.
The sector for bicycle rentals is about $\frac{1}{4}$ of the circle.
About $\frac{1}{4}$ of the people who rented equipment rented bicycles.

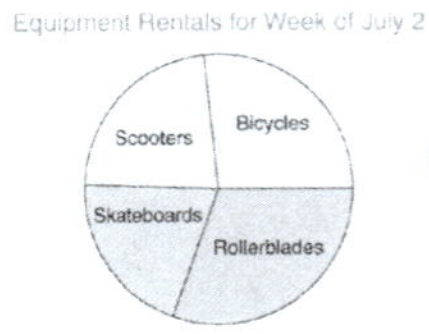

Practice

1. Look at this table of weather data in Canada.
   a) Which city has the most wet days? The fewest?
   b) Which city has the greatest snowfall? The least?
   c) Which cities have about 3 times as much precipitation as Calgary?
   d) Write 2 other questions that can be answered from the data. Answer the questions.
   e) Describe other ways you could display these data.

Average Annual Precipitation in Canadian Cities

City	Snowfall (cm)	Total Precipitation (mm)	Wet Days
Charlottetown, PE	338.7	1201	177
Quebec City, QC	337.0	1208	178
Ottawa, ON	221.5	911	159
Calgary, AB	135.4	399	111
Vancouver, BC	54.9	1167	164
Victoria, BC	46.9	858	153

2. The circle graph shows the after-school activities students chose at Allgood Elementary School.
   a) Which activity was chosen by the most students? Dance and Fitness Club
   The fewest? Choir, Science Club
   b) Estimate the fraction of students that chose the homework club. $\frac{1}{4}$
   c) Which 2 activities were chosen by about the same fraction of students? Choir, Science Club

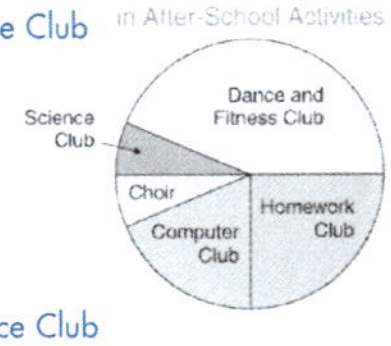

158

Have students suggest a different key to be used for the pictograph. Ask:

- What would happen if the symbol represented 10 people instead of 20? How would the graph change?
  (*There would be twice as many symbols in each row.*)
- Does the pictograph show the same data when the key has changed? Explain.
  (*Yes; the data do not change, just the number of symbols representing the data has changed.*)

Draw students' attention to the bar graph. Ask:

- How are the bar graph and the pictograph similar?
  (*They show the same data.*)
- How are they different?
  (*On the bar graph, you read the numbers off the vertical scale; on the pictograph, you count the symbols.*)

Ensure students understand that a table, a pictograph, and a bar graph show the exact data, while a circle graph shows the fraction of the whole in each category.

Review the concept of range. Ask:

- How do you calculate the range of the data?
  (*You subtract the least number from the greatest number.*)
- Why do you need to know the range of the data?
  (*When you graph the data, the range tells you how large to make your vertical scale.*)

Practice

Students may use a calculator for questions 3 and 4.

Assessment Focus: Question 4

Students understand how to calculate the range and how to convert data into a reasonable key.

3. This pictograph shows the number of days Members of Parliament (MPs) sat in the House of Commons in one year.

a) What months are not shown? July, August
Why do you think they are not shown? Holidays

b) How many days did MPs sit in the House of Commons in March? 11 days

c) How many days did MPs sit during the year?

d) Suppose the graph was redrawn with this key. 133 days
🏛 = 8 days
How would the graph change?

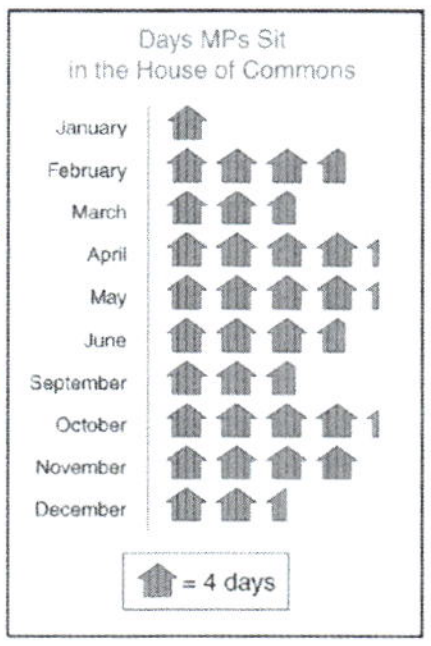

4. This bar graph shows the number of days vegetables grow before they are picked.

a) Which vegetable takes longest to grow? Leek

b) What is the range of the data? 90 days

c) Suppose you wanted to display these data as a pictograph.
What key would you use?
How many symbols would you need for each vegetable?

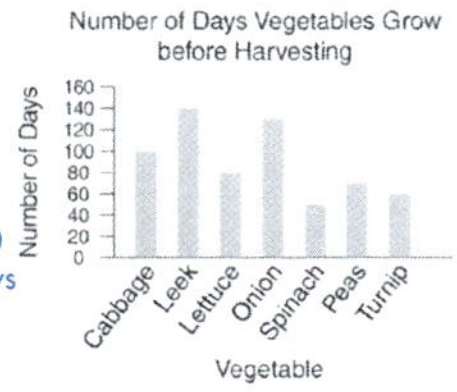

Reflect

Which do you find easier to read: a graph or a table? Explain.

At Home

Look through newspapers and magazines, or search the Internet. Find a table of data you can graph. Graph the data. Give reasons for your choice of graph.

ASSESSMENT FOCUS | Question 4   159

ASSESSMENT FOR LEARNING

What to Look For	What to Do
Understanding concepts ✔ Students understand how to calculate the range. ✔ Students understand that a table, a pictograph, and a bar graph show exact data, while a circle graph shows parts of a whole. ***Applying procedures*** ✔ Students can read and interpret tables, pictographs, bar graphs, and circle graphs.	***Extra Support:*** Students can use Step-by-Step 1 (Master 5.10) to complete question 4. ***Extra Practice:*** Students can complete Extra Practice 1 (Master 5.18). ***Extension:*** Students can find graphs in magazines and newspapers, and read and interpret the data displayed.

Recording and Reporting
Master 5.2 Ongoing Observations: Data Management

LESSON 2

Mean and Mode

LESSON ORGANIZER — 40–50 min

Curriculum Focus: Calculate the mean and the mode of data. (5m117)

Teacher Materials
- overhead counters

Student Materials
- 12 counters
- linking cubes

Optional
- Step-by-Step 2 (Master 5.11)
- Extra Practice 2 (Master 5.19)

Vocabulary: mean, mode

Assessment: Master 5.2 Ongoing Observations: Data Management

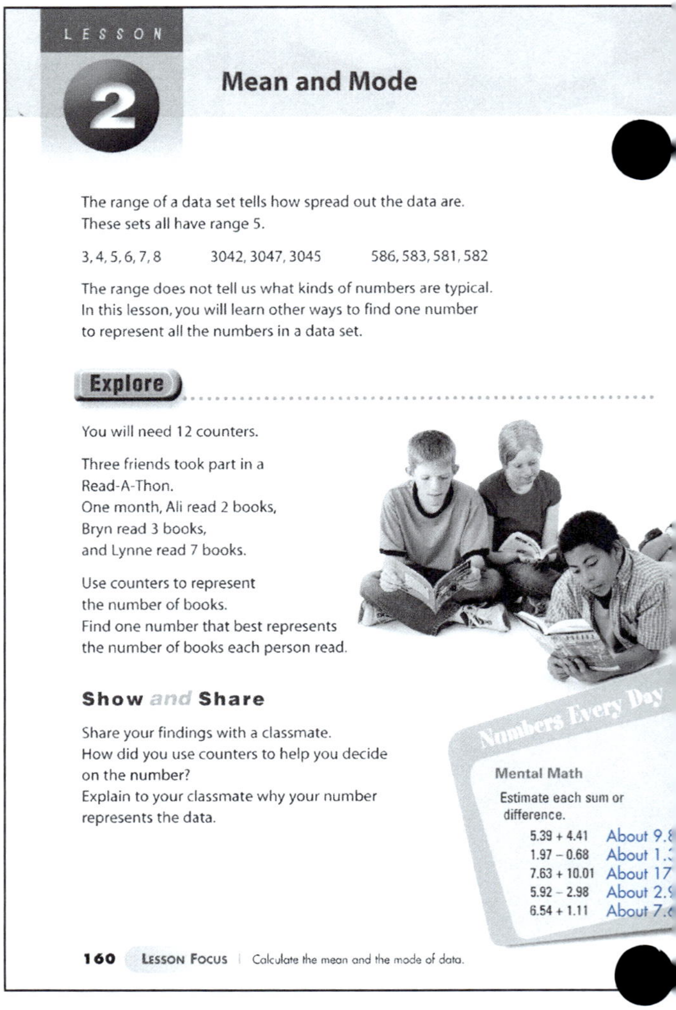
LESSON 2

Mean and Mode

The range of a data set tells how spread out the data are.
These sets all have range 5.

3, 4, 5, 6, 7, 8 3042, 3047, 3045 586, 583, 581, 582

The range does not tell us what kinds of numbers are typical.
In this lesson, you will learn other ways to find one number to represent all the numbers in a data set.

Explore

You will need 12 counters.

Three friends took part in a Read-A-Thon.
One month, Ali read 2 books, Bryn read 3 books, and Lynne read 7 books.

Use counters to represent the number of books.
Find one number that best represents the number of books each person read.

Show and Share

Share your findings with a classmate.
How did you use counters to help you decide on the number?
Explain to your classmate why your number represents the data.

Numbers Every Day

Mental Math

Estimate each sum or difference.

5.39 + 4.41 About 9.
1.97 − 0.68 About 1.
7.63 + 10.01 About 17
5.92 − 2.98 About 2.
6.54 + 1.11 About 7.

160 LESSON FOCUS | Calculate the mean and the mode of data.

Key Math Learnings

1. The mean of a set of numbers is the number that is the balance point of the set.
2. The mode is the number that occurs most often in the data.

Numbers Every Day

Have students round each number to the nearest tenth.

BEFORE — Get Started

Review with students the idea of range. Point out that the data sets in the introduction all have the same range, even though the numbers are very different. Elicit from students that it would be helpful to know the centre of a data set.

Use overhead counters to illustrate the numbers in a set of data. Ask:

- How could you use counters to represent the number of books students read?
  (*I could use 1 counter to represent each book. I could make 1 group for each student. If a student read 5 books, I would make 1 group of 5 counters.*)
- How else could you display these data?
  (*In a table, a pictograph, or a bar graph*)

Present *Explore*. Have students work in pairs to answer the questions. Remind students they need to find one number that best represents the number of books read by each person. Suggest that students try moving the counters around.

DURING — Explore

Ongoing Assessment: Observe and Listen

Ask questions, such as:

- How are you arranging the counters? (*In rows*)
- Can you move the counters around to other rows? (*Yes. I can rearrange the counters, as long as I don't add or remove any.*)
- How many counters are there in total?
  (*12; 2 + 3 + 7 = 12*)
- How many rows will you make? (*3 rows*)
- Can you make 3 rows that have the same number of counters in them?
  (*Yes. I can put 4 counters in each row.*)
- What number best represents the number of books each person read?
  (*Four best represents the number of books each person read. There are 4 counters in each row.*)

Ensure students understand the total number of books read is the same as it would be if everyone had read exactly 4 books.

Connect

The **mean** is a number that represents the centre
set of numbers.
the balance point of the numbers.

Mary surveyed 4 friends on the number of first cousins each has.
She used linking cubes to represent the number of cousins.

Ahmed
Maria
Luis
Marlyn

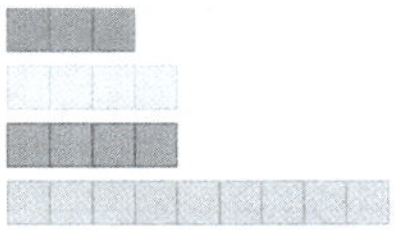

➤ One way to find the mean is to make rows of equal length.

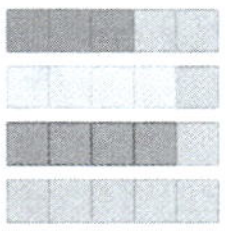

The mean number of first cousins is 5.

When you make equal rows or columns,
the total number of cubes does not change.
You can use this total to calculate the mean.

➤ The number of cubes in each row is 3, 4, 4, 9.
Add these numbers together: $3 + 4 + 4 + 9 = 20$
Then divide by the number of rows, 4: $20 \div 4 = 5$

The mean is 5.

The **mode** is the number that occurs most often in the data.

➤ To find the mode, determine which answer occurs most often.
In Mary's data, the number 4 occurs twice.
The mode is 4 cousins.
Two people have 4 cousins.

161

REACHING ALL LEARNERS

Common Misconceptions

➤ When using counters to find the mean, students make three rows, but cannot turn these into rows of equal length.

How to Help: Have students first combine all the tiles into one group, then make three equal rows.

AFTER Connect

Have students share their strategies for solving the question, and discuss the strategies they observed in *Show and Share.*

Present *Connect.* Have students use counters to model the answer.

Work through the example of finding the mean arithmetically. Show students that this is like putting all the counters into 1 group, then dividing them into 4 equal rows.

Present the idea of mode.

Ensure that students understand mean is the one number that best represents all the data, and mode is the number that occurs most often. A set of numbers can have no mode, one mode, or many modes. A memory strategy students may find helpful is that the first two letters of mode, "mo," begin the word *most.*

Practice

Students will need linking cubes or counters, and a calculator for question 4.

Some students may benefit from using a calculator for questions 2, 3, and 5.

Assessment Focus: Question 5

Students understand how to find the mode from a bar graph, and how to calculate the mean from a bar graph.

Sample Answers

4. a) Round the mean to the nearest whole number.

	Mean	Mode
Games Played	30	34
Field Goals	202	no mode
Free Throws	121	no mode
Total Points	561	no mode

b) I think Jackson is the best player because she has the most points.

5. a) Volleyball and soccer
   b) I could count the number of bars that have the same length.
   c) 1035

REFLECT: The mean is the number that is the balance point of the data set, and could be a number that isn't part of the data set. The mode is the most frequent number that appears in the set of data.
For example, in the data set 3, 3, 3, 5, 6, the mean is 4, which doesn't appear in the data at all. The mode is 3.

Practice

1. Use linking cubes to find the mean of each set of data.
   a) 3, 4, 4, 5 — 4 b) 1, 7, 3, 3, 1 — 3 c) 2, 2, 6, 1, 3, 4 — 3
2. Calculate the mean of each set of data.
   a) 2, 4, 7, 4, 8, 9, 12, 4, 7, 3 — 6 b) 24, 34, 44, 31, 39, 32 — 34
3. Here are the weekly allowances of 10 Grade 5 students:
   $4, $6, $8, $10, $15, $5, $7, $10, $5, $10
   a) What is the mean allowance? $8
   b) What is the mode of the allowances? $10
   c) Suppose two allowances of $14 and $20 are added to the list.
   What is the new mean? What happens to the mode? No change
   $11.40
4. This table shows data for the Women's National Basketball Association.
   a) Calculate each mean and mode:
      - Games Played
      - Field Goals
      - Free Throws
      - Total Points
   b) Who do you think is the best player? Why?

Top 6 WNBA Scorers in 2003

Name	Games Played	Field Goals	Free Throws	Total Points
Catchings	34	221	155	671
Holdsclaw	27	204	140	554
Jackson	33	254	151	698
Leslie	34	194	116	548
Smith	23	165	82	424
Thompson	28	176	81	472

5. The graph shows the most popular sports among people older than 15 in Sportsdale.
   a) Which sports are equally popular?
   b) How could you use the bar graph to find the mode?
   Explain and show your work.
   c) Calculate the mean.
   Use estimated values from the graph.

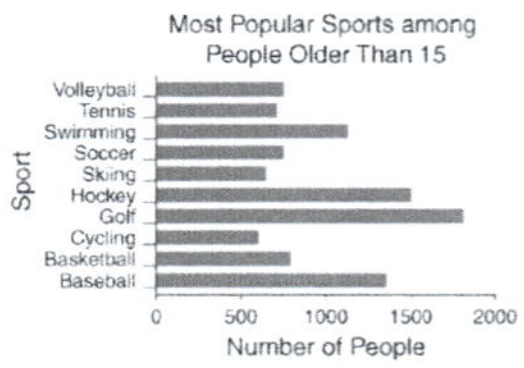

Reflect

What is the difference between mean and mode?
Use a set of data to explain.

162 ASSESSMENT FOCUS | Question 5

ASSESSMENT FOR LEARNING

What to Look For	What to Do
Understanding concepts ✔ Students understand how to calculate the mean of a data set. ✔ Students understand how find the mode of a data set. ***Applying procedures*** ✔ Students can find the mean and the mode from reading a bar graph.	***Extra Support:*** Students can use Step-by-Step 2 (Master 5.11) to complete question 5. ***Extra Practice:*** Students can roll a number cube 10 times, record the results, and calculate the mean and the mode of the data. Students can complete Extra Practice 2 (Master 5.19). ***Extension:*** Students can find data sets in magazines and newspapers, and calculate the mean and the mode of the data.

Recording and Reporting
Master 5.2 Ongoing Observations: Data Management

Creating Spreadsheets Using *AppleWorks*

k with a partner.

The town library tracks the number of books people sign out.

Town Library Sign Out Records

Season	Number of Books
Winter	1488
Spring	1151
Summer	976
Fall	1259

Use *AppleWorks*.
Follow these steps to display these data in a spreadsheet.

1. Open a new spreadsheet in *AppleWorks*. Click: Spreadsheet
2. To **enter the data**:
   Click cell A1 to select it.
   Type: Town Library Sign Out Records
   Press Enter.
   Click cell A2 to select it.
   Type: Season
   Press Enter.
   Click cell A3 to select it.
   Type: Winter
   Press Enter.
   Enter the rest of the seasons in cells A4 to A6.
   Click cell B2 to select it.
   Type: Number of Books
   Press Enter.
   Click cell B3 to select it.
   Type the data for Winter: 1488
   Press Enter.
   Enter the data for the rest of the seasons in cells B4 to B6.

SSON FOCUS | Use a computer to create spreadsheets. 163

Creating Spreadsheets Using *AppleWorks*

LESSON ORGANIZER

40–50 min

Curriculum Focus: Use a computer to create spreadsheets. (5m114)

Student Materials

- *AppleWorks* or *Microsoft Excel*

Vocabulary: spreadsheet

Assessment: Computers can be used to create spreadsheets.

Key Math Learning

Computers can be used to create spreadsheets.

BEFORE

Discuss with students how computer programs can be used to learn mathematics, organize data, and perform calculations.

Have students think about different occupations that use computers as mathematical tools.

Explain to students that they will use a computer to create a spreadsheet. Ask:

- What is a spreadsheet?
  (*A spreadsheet is a way of organizing data in a grid.*)
- Where have you seen a spreadsheet used?
  (*My parents use a spreadsheet for accounting. You use one to keep track of our marks!*)

Note: *AppleWorks* and many other computer programs were developed in the United States. Point out to students that in the United States, the word centimetre is spelled *centimeter* and will appear spelled this way in most computer programs.

DURING

Ongoing Assessment: Observe and Listen

Watch to ensure students read and follow the instructions carefully.

Instructions for creating spreadsheets using *Microsoft Excel*:

1. Open a new spreadsheet in *Microsoft Excel*.
2. To **enter the data:**
   Click cell A1 to select it, if it is not already selected.
   Type: Town Library Sign Out Records
   Press Enter.

   Cell A2 should now be selected.
   If it is not, click cell A2 to select it.
   Type: Season
   Press Enter.

REACHING ALL LEARNERS

Early Finishers

Have students use *AppleWorks* to create a spreadsheet using the data from Lesson 1, *Practice* question 1.

3. To **calculate the total number of books**:

   Click cell A7 to select it.
   Type: Total
   Press Enter.

   Click cell B7 to select it.
   Type: =SUM(B3..B6)
   Press Enter.

   You have entered the formula to find a sum.
   The sum of the numbers in cells B3 to B6 will be displayed.
   All formulas must begin with an "=" sign.

4. To **calculate the mean**:

   Click cell A8 to select it.
   Type: Mean
   Press Enter.

   Click cell B8 to select it.

   Click: Format , then click: Number... Shift+Ctrl+N

   Select Fixed as the Number option.
   Enter 2 for Decimal Precision.

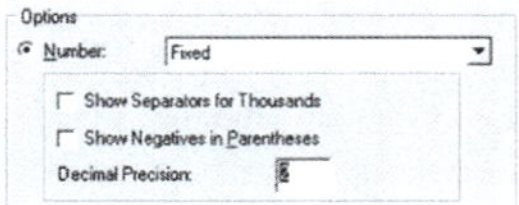

   Click: OK
   The number in this cell will be displayed to the nearest hundredth.
   Type: =B7/4
   Press Enter.

   You have entered a formula for division.
   The sum in cell B7 will be divided by 4 (the number of data).
   The result is the mean of the data.

164

Cell A3 should now be selected.
Type: Winter
Press Enter.

Enter the rest of the seasons in cells A4 to A6.

Click cell B2 to select it.
Type: Number of Books
Press Enter.

Cell B3 should now be selected.
Type the data for Winter: 1488
Press Enter.

Enter the data for the rest of the seasons in cells B4 to B6.

3. To **calculate the total number of books:**

   Click cell A7 to select it.
   Type: Total
   Press Enter.

   Click cell B7 to select it.
   Type: =SUM(B3..B6)
   Press Enter.

   You have entered the formula to find a sum.
   The sum of the numbers in cells B3 to B6 will be displayed.
   All formulas must begin with an "=" sign.

4. To **calculate the mean:**

   Click cell A8 to select it.
   Type: Mean
   Press Enter.

   Click cell B8 to select it.
   Type: =AVERAGE(B3..B6)
   Press Enter.

   You have entered the formula to find a mean.
   The mean of the numbers in cells B3 to B6 will be displayed.

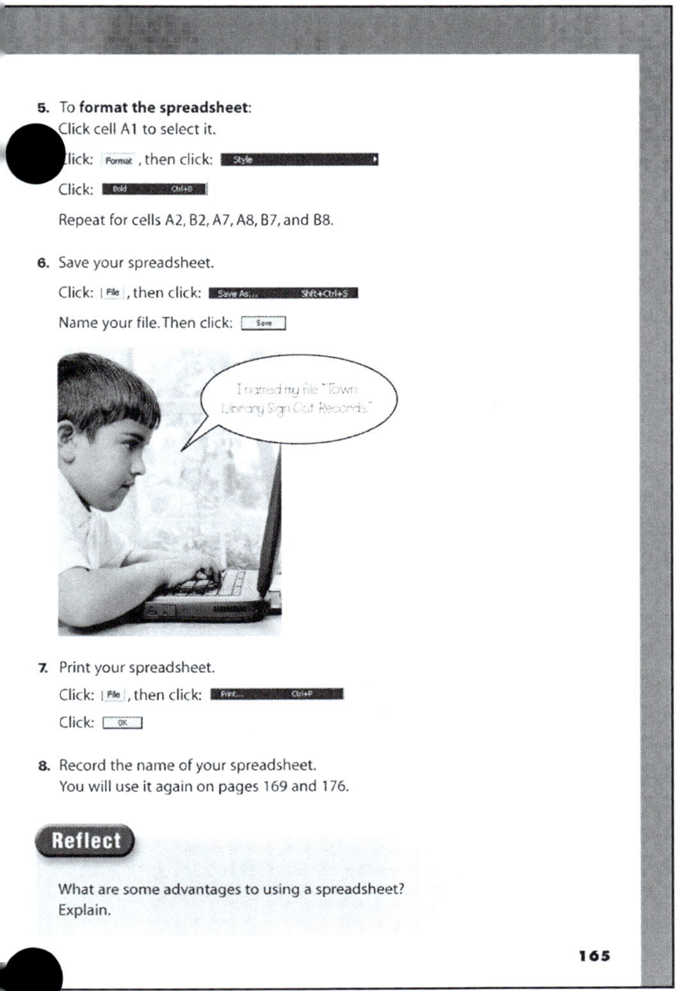

5. To **format the spreadsheet**:
Click cell A1 to select it.
Click: Format, then click: Style
Click: Bold Ctrl+B
Repeat for cells A2, B2, A7, A8, B7, and B8.

6. Save your spreadsheet.
Click: File, then click: Save As... Shft+Ctrl+S
Name your file. Then click: Save

7. Print your spreadsheet.
Click: File, then click: Print... Ctrl+P
Click: OK

8. Record the name of your spreadsheet.
You will use it again on pages 169 and 176.

Reflect

What are some advantages to using a spreadsheet? Explain.

165

REFLECT: One advantage to using a spreadsheet is that the computer will do all the calculations. If you change a number in the spreadsheet, the computer will automatically change any calculations that use that number.

5. To **format the spreadsheet:**
   Click cell A1 to select it.
   Click: **Format**, then click: **Cells**
   Click the tab marked **Font.**
   Under **Font Style,** select **Bold.**
   Click **OK.**
   Repeat for cells A2, B2, A7, A8, B7, and B8.
6. Save your spreadsheet.
   Click: **File**, then click: **Save As...**
   Name your file. Then click: **Save**
7. Print your spreadsheet.
   Click: **File**, then click: **Print...**
   Click: **OK**
8. Record the name of your spreadsheet.
   You will use it again in further technology lessons.

AFTER

Invite volunteers to share any strategies they found helpful.

LESSON 3

Drawing Bar Graphs

LESSON ORGANIZER — 40–50 min

Curriculum Focus: Draw bar graphs by hand. (5m114, 5m116, 5m119)

Student Materials
- 1-cm grid paper (PM 23)
- measuring tape or metre stick

Optional
- Step-by-Step 3 (Master 5.12)
- Extra Practice 3 (Master 5.20)

Vocabulary: intervals

Assessment: Master 5.2 Ongoing Observations: Data Management

Key Math Learnings

1. When there are too many pieces of data to graph each separately, you can group them into equal intervals.
2. When drawing a bar graph, choose an appropriate scale.

Numbers Every Day

Students could round numbers to the nearest ten.

LESSON 3

Drawing Bar Graphs

When you collect data it is important to make sure your data are accurate. Always make sure the numbers or measurements you collect are reasonable. Check any that seem unlikely.

Explore

You will need a measuring tape or a metre stick.
Measure each other's height.
Record the heights on the board.
Look at the class data. Are the results reasonable?
What would make you think a result was not reasonable? Explain.
Order the data for the class.
Draw a bar graph to display the data.

Show and Share

Show your graph to another pair of classmates.
Ask them questions about your graph.
Compare your graph with your classmates' graph.
How are your graphs the same? Different?

Connect

Ms. Lindt teaches math to 25 Grade 5 students.
She ordered the marks her students received from the least to the greatest.

54, 55, 58, 61,
63, 65, 66, 67, 68,
71, 72, 73, 73, 74,
75, 76, 77, 78,
79, 81, 86, 87,
88, 91, 95

She wants to display these data in a bar graph.

➤ There were too many pieces of data to graph each mark separately.
First, she grouped the marks into equal **intervals**.

BEFORE — Get Started

Ask for a volunteer to read aloud the introduction. Ask:

- What are some different ways you could collect data?
  (*I could physically collect it, by doing an experiment or measuring items. I could conduct a survey. I could observe something and record my observations.*)
- What do you need to be sure of when you are collecting data? (*I need to be sure that the data I am collecting are accurate.*)
- How can you ensure your data are accurate?
  (*I can double-check measurements and counts. In a survey, I can make sure to ask questions with reasonable answers.*)

Display a 1-cm grid transparency on an overhead projector. Using a ruler, model how to draw 2 axes on grid paper.

Discuss the features of a bar graph: title, scale, and labels.

Present *Explore*. Have students work in pairs. Students should have 1-cm grid paper available to draw their graphs.

DURING — Explore

Ongoing Assessment: Observe and Listen

Ask questions, such as:

- Does each of the measurements look reasonable?(*Yes, they are all close to each other. No, some of the numbers look way off, compared to the rest of the data.*)
- How could you order the data?
  (*We could order the data from shortest bar to tallest — the least number to the greatest.*)
- What is the range of the data? (*31 cm*)
  How did you calculate it?
  (*I subtracted the least number from the greatest.*)
- What features does a bar graph have?
  (*Vertical and horizontal axes; each axis has a scale; each axis is labelled to show what it represents; a*

Marks of Students in Grade 5

Marks	Number of Students
91–100	2
81–90	4
71–80	10
61–70	6
51–60	3

➤ She chose the scale
1 square represents 1 student.
She labelled one axis
"Number of Students"
and the other "Marks."
Then she drew a bar for each
interval of marks and wrote a title.

Marks of Students in Grade 5

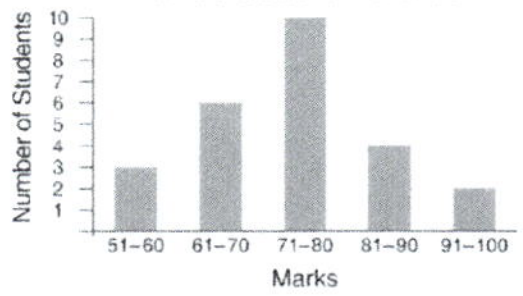

Practice

1. Which of these 3 sets of data would you group into intervals? Why?
How would you group the data into intervals?
Draw the bar graph for the data you grouped in intervals.

a) Election Results
Hillside Public School

Name	Number of Votes
Ho	32
Kake	26
Marr	80
Neigh	30
O'Neil	24
Young	40

b) Number of Books Read
Students at Flanshaw School

Number of Books	Number of Students
One a week	62
One a month	72
One every 3 months	36
One every 6 months	17
One a year	13

c) Masses of parcels in a mail room:
27 kg, 29 kg, 30 kg, 31 kg, 31 kg, 31 kg, 32 kg, 33 kg, 34 kg,
35 kg, 36 kg, 37 kg, 37 kg, 38 kg, 39 kg, 41 kg, 42 kg

167

REACHING ALL LEARNERS

Alternative Explore

In a chart on the board, have the students record the number of siblings they have. Organize the data by frequency (number of students with no siblings, number with 1 sibling, and so on). Look at the data and discuss whether the data are reasonable. Create a bar graph to display the data.

Early Finishers

Have students draw a pictograph for the data collected.

Common Misconceptions

➤ Students will make unequal intervals, or leave out intervals if no data fall into that range.

How to Help: Stress that the intervals must be equal, and must cover all values from the least to the greatest, whether they appear in the data or not.

Sample Answers

1. Group the data in part c into intervals of size 4, because there are too many numbers to graph.

Masses of Parcels in a Mail Room

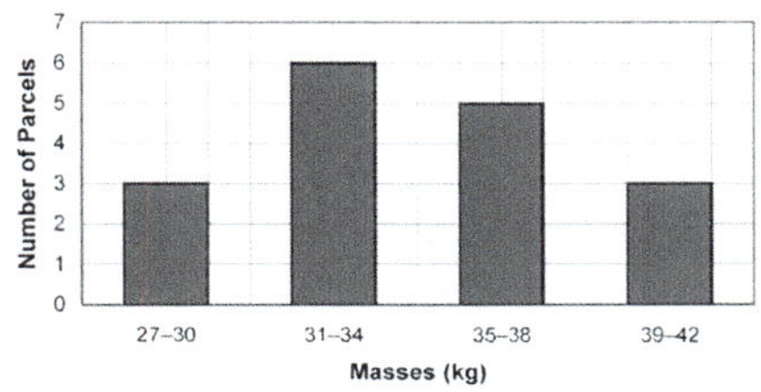

2. b) A bar graph makes it easier to compare the numbers.
c) Quebec's bar is twice as tall as British Columbia's bar.

title to indicate what the bar graph is showing; bars to display the number of results in each category.)

- How could you show so many heights on one graph? (*I could group the data into equal intervals.*)
- What would happen if you didn't group the data? (*There would be too many bars; some bars that represent the same data would repeat, and each bar would be 1 unit in height.*)

AFTER Connect

Invite students to share their graphs. Display each graph on the board. Discuss the differences students observed in *Show and Share.*

Ask:

- How are the graphs the same? (*They show the same data.*) Different? (*They have different intervals, scales, labels, and titles.*)
- How would your graph change if there were more intervals or fewer intervals? (*More intervals would mean you would have more bars, and the bars would be shorter. Fewer intervals would mean you would have fewer bars, and the bars would be taller.*)

Review the concepts in *Connect* regarding choosing intervals for a bar graph. Stress that intervals must be equal in size, and must cover the entire range.

Practice

Students will need 1-cm grid paper for all questions.

Some students might benefit from using a calculator for questions 2 and 3. They should round the mean to the nearest whole number.

Assessment Focus: Question 4

Students choose appropriate intervals for their bar graph. The intervals are equal in size, and cover all the data. Students draw a bar graph that accurately displays the data.

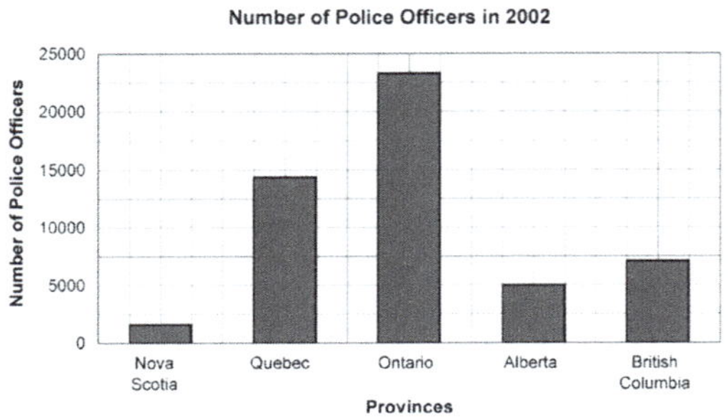

3. a) Mean: about 31; modes: 26, 27, 30, 43, 44

b) I chose a bar graph because I could group the data into intervals.

c) Students may choose to show the mean on the bar graph by shading the bar that contains the mean.

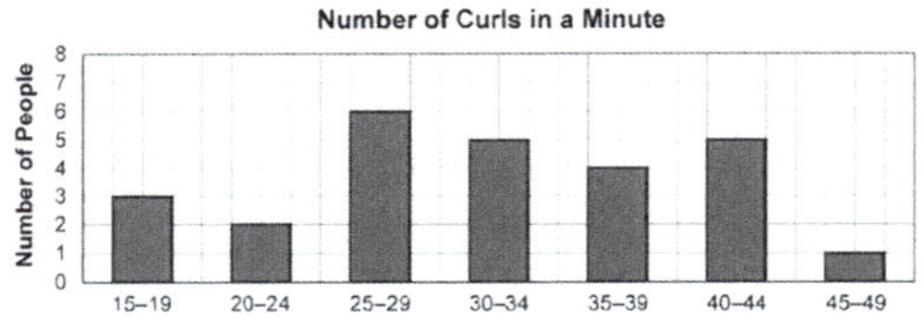

d) The mean is more typical. It shows the centre of the data.

4. b)

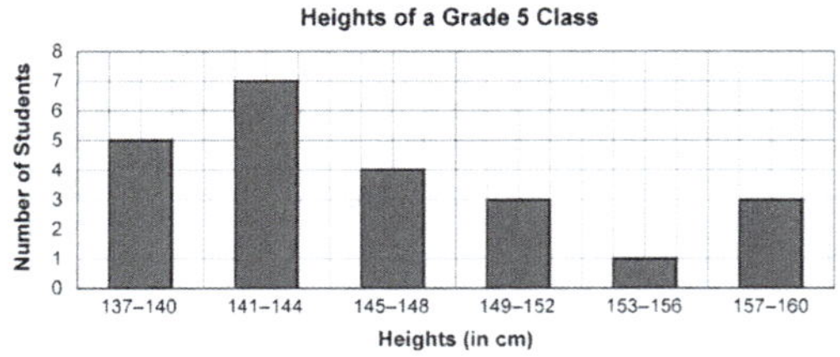

c) More students are in the interval 141–144 cm. There are more students above this interval than below it.

2. Use the table.

a) What is the range of the data? 21 720
The mean? 10 282

b) Round these data to the nearest 100. Then graph the rounded data. Which type of graph did you choose to draw? Why?

c) Which province has about double the number of police officers as British Columbia? Quebec
How does your graph show this?

Number of Police Officers in 2002

Province	Number of Police Officers	Rounded
Nova Scotia	1 608	1 600
Quebec	14 368	14 400
Ontario	23 328	23 300
Alberta	4 999	5 000
British Columbia	7 106	7 100

3. A group fitness test showed the number of curls each person could do in 1 minute:
30, 45, 25, 18, 15, 35, 27, 34, 26, 32, 43, 39, 29, 31, 43, 44, 26, 16, 20, 40, 44, 22, 27, 30, 36, 37

a) Calculate the mean and the mode.

b) Choose a suitable graph to display the data. Explain your choice.

c) Draw the graph. Show the mean on your graph.

d) Which average, the mean or the mode, is more typical of the data? Explain.

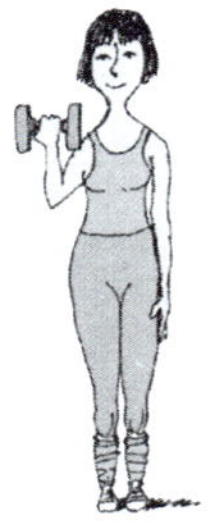

4. The students in a Grade 5 class recorded their heights in centimetres:
137, 139, 139, 140, 140, 141, 142, 142, 142, 143, 144, 144, 146, 147, 148, 148, 149, 150, 152, 154, 158, 159, 160

a) Arrange the data into intervals. Create a table to display the data.

Intervals in cm	137–140	141–144	145–148	149–152	153–156	157–160
Number of Students	5	7	4	3	1	3

b) Display the data in a bar graph.

c) Write 2 things you can learn from the graph.

Numbers Every Day

Mental Math

Estimate each product.
Which strategies did you use?

148 × 9 About 1500
211 × 19 About 400
39 × 32 About 1200
98 × 102 About 10 000

Reflect

Grouping data into intervals makes the data more manageable. Use an example to show why the choice of the interval width is important.

If the intervals are too small, you will have too many bars and it would be hard to make conclusions about the data. If the intervals are too large, you will have too few bars and it would also be hard to make conclusions.

168 ASSESSMENT FOCUS Question 4

ASSESSMENT FOR LEARNING

What to Look For	What to Do
Understanding concepts ✔ Students understand how to collect data in intervals. ✔ Students understand that the scale of a bar graph depends on the data given. ***Applying procedures*** ✔ Students can choose an appropriate interval to represent data in a bar graph. ✔ Students can create a bar graph to display a set of data, using an appropriate scale.	***Extra Support:*** Students can use Step-by-Step 3 (Master 5.12) to complete question 4. ***Extra Practice:*** Have students draw a bar graph for the data in question 1. Students can complete the Additional Activity, *Word Find* (Master 5.6). Students can complete Extra Practice 3 (Master 5.20). ***Extension:*** Challenge students to draw a second bar graph for question 2, using a different scale.

Recording and Reporting

Master 5.2 Ongoing Observations: Data Management

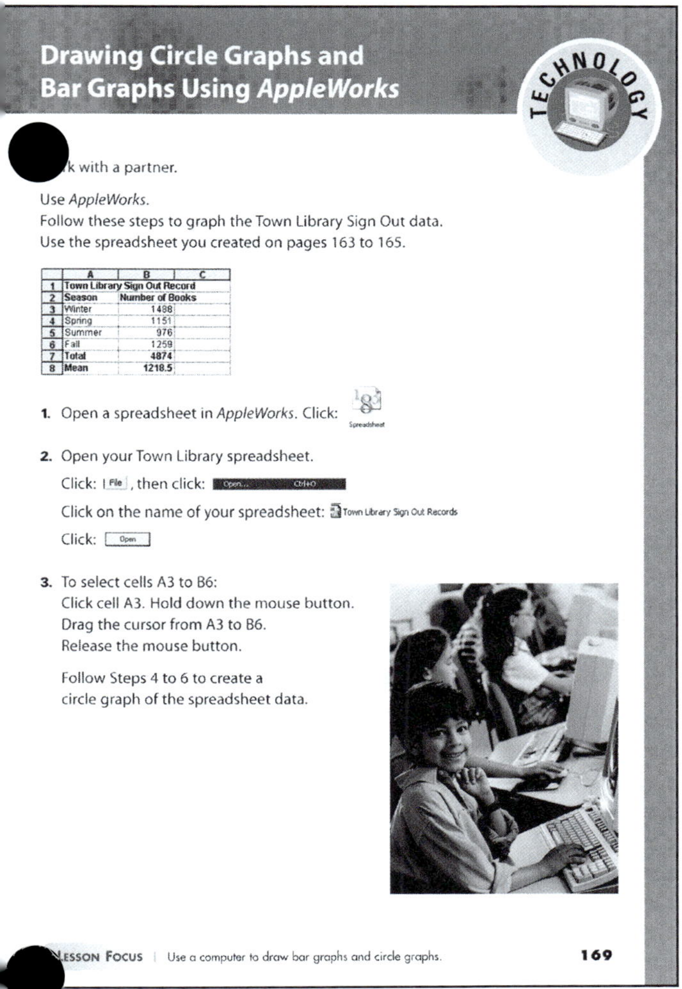

Drawing Circle Graphs and Bar Graphs Using *AppleWorks*

TECHNOLOGY

…k with a partner.

Use *AppleWorks*.
Follow these steps to graph the Town Library Sign Out data.
Use the spreadsheet you created on pages 163 to 165.

	A	B	C
1	**Town Library Sign Out Record**		
2	**Season**	**Number of Books**	
3	Winter	1488	
4	Spring	1151	
5	Summer	976	
6	Fall	1259	
7	**Total**	**4874**	
8	**Mean**	**1218.5**	

1. Open a spreadsheet in *AppleWorks*. Click: Spreadsheet
2. Open your Town Library spreadsheet.
   Click: File, then click: Open... Ctrl+O
   Click on the name of your spreadsheet: Town Library Sign Out Records
   Click: Open
3. To select cells A3 to B6:
   Click cell A3. Hold down the mouse button.
   Drag the cursor from A3 to B6.
   Release the mouse button.

   Follow Steps 4 to 6 to create a circle graph of the spreadsheet data.

…esson Focus | Use a computer to draw bar graphs and circle graphs. 169

Drawing Circle Graphs and Bar Graphs Using *AppleWorks*

LESSON ORGANIZER — 40–50 min

Curriculum Focus: Use a computer to draw bar graphs and circle graphs. (5m114, 5m119)

Student Materials

- *AppleWorks* or *Microsoft Excel*

Key Math Learning

A computer can be used to draw bar graphs and circle graphs.

BEFORE

Discuss with students how computer programs can be used to learn mathematics, organize data, and perform calculations.

Have students think about different occupations that use computers as mathematical tools.

Explain to students that they will use a computer to create circle and bar graphs from the spreadsheet they already made.

Note: Point out to students that, in *Microsoft Excel*, circle graphs are called *pie charts* and bar graphs are called *column charts.*

DURING — Explore

Ongoing Assessment: Observe and Listen

Watch to ensure that students read and follow the instructions carefully.

Instructions for drawing bar graphs and circle graphs using *Microsoft Excel*:

1. Open your Town Library spreadsheet in Microsoft Excel.
   Click: **File**, then click: **Open...**
   Click on the name of your spreadsheet.
   Click: **Open**
2. To select cells A3 to B6:
   Click cell A3. Hold down the mouse button.
   Drag the cursor from A3 to B6.
   Release the mouse button.

   Follow steps 3 to 5 to create a circle graph of the spreadsheet data.
3. To create a circle graph:
   Click: **Insert**, then click: **Chart...**
   Under **Chart type,** choose **Pie.**
   Choose the first **Chart sub-type,** if it is not already highlighted.
   Click: **Next**
   Click **Next** again.

REACHING ALL LEARNERS

Early Finishers

Have students use *AppleWorks* to create a bar graph and a circle graph using the data from Lesson 3, *Practice* questions 2, 3, or 4. Have them compare their drawn graph to the computer-generated graphs.

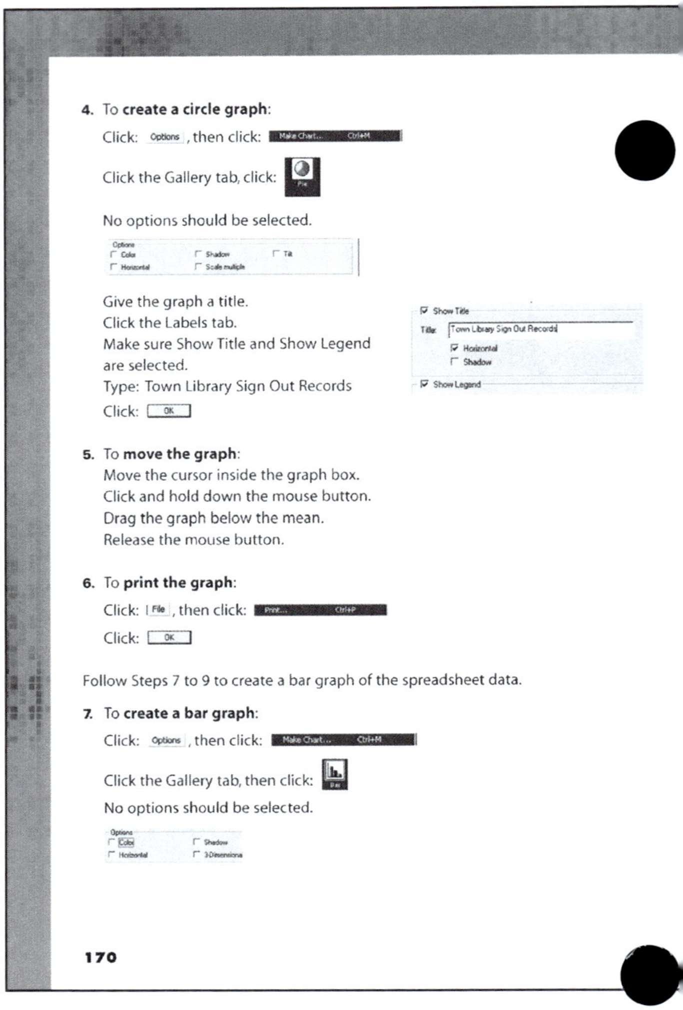

4. To **create a circle graph**:
   Click: Options, then click: Make Chart... Ctrl+M
   Click the Gallery tab, click: Pie
   No options should be selected.
   Give the graph a title.
   Click the Labels tab.
   Make sure Show Title and Show Legend are selected.
   Type: Town Library Sign Out Records
   Click: OK
5. To **move the graph**:
   Move the cursor inside the graph box.
   Click and hold down the mouse button.
   Drag the graph below the mean.
   Release the mouse button.
6. To **print the graph**:
   Click: File, then click: Print... Ctrl+P
   Click: OK

Follow Steps 7 to 9 to create a bar graph of the spreadsheet data.

7. To **create a bar graph**:
   Click: Options, then click: Make Chart... Ctrl+M
   Click the Gallery tab, then click: Bar
   No options should be selected.

170

Click inside the **Chart title** box.
Type: Town Library Sign Out Records
Click: **Next**
Select the **As object in** option.
This means your graph will be part of the spreadsheet, instead of a separate file.
Click: **Finish**

4. To **move the graph:**
   Move the cursor inside the graph box.
   Position the cursor over empty space—not the graph, the legend, or the title.
   Click and hold down the mouse button.
   Drag the graph below the mean.
   Release the mouse button.
5. To **print the graph:**
   Click: **File**, then click: **Print...**
   Click: **OK**

Follow steps 6 to 8 to create a bar graph of the spreadsheet data.

6. To **create a bar graph:**
   Click: **Insert**, then click: **Chart...**
   Under **Chart type,** choose **Column.**
   Choose the first **Chart sub-type.**
   Click: **Next**
   Click **Next** again.
   Click inside the **Chart title** box.
   Type: Town Library Sign Out Records
   Click inside the **Category (X) axis** box.
   Type: Season
   Click inside the **Value (Y) axis** box.
   Type: Number of Books
   Click: **Next**
   Select the **As object in** option.
   This means your graph will be part of the spreadsheet, instead of a separate file.
   Click: **Finish**

Give the graph a title.
Click the Labels tab. Select Show Title.
Make sure Show Legend is not selected.
Type: Town Library Sign Out Records

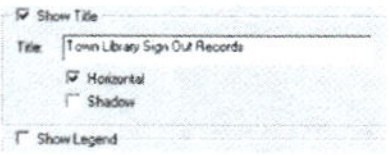

Label the axes.
Click the Axes tab. Select X axis.
Type the Axis label: Season

Select Y axis. Type the Axis label: Number of Books

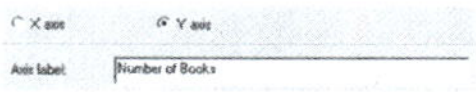

Enter these settings: Minimum: 0 Maximum: 2000 Step size: 500

Click: OK

8. Save your graphs. Click: File
   Then click: Save As... Shift+Ctrl+S
   Give your file a new name.
   Then click: Save

9. Repeat Steps 5 and 6 to move and print your graph.

Reflect

What are some advantages of graphing data using a computer?

171

REFLECT: It is faster to create a graph using a computer, the graphs are more accurate than when drawn by hand, and you can easily change an item of data.

7. **To save your graphs:**
   Click: **File**
   Then click: **Save As...**
   Give your file a new name.
   Then click: **Save**

8. Repeat steps 4 and 5 to move and print your graph.

AFTER

Invite volunteers to share any strategies they found helpful.

Line Graphs

LESSON ORGANIZER

40–50 min

Curriculum Focus: Draw line graphs by hand. (5m114, 5m119)

Student Materials
- 1-cm grid paper

Optional
- Step-by-Step 4 (Master 5.13)
- Extra Practice 4 (Master 5.21)

Vocabulary: line graph, line segment

Assessment: Master 5.2 Ongoing Observations: Data Management

Key Math Learnings

1. A line graph shows data points joined by line segments.
2. A jagged line on the axis indicates that not all the numbers are shown.

Numbers Every Day

Remind students to consider not just the digits, but their place values.

LESSON 4

Line Graphs

Meteorologists record data regularly over time.
In this lesson, you will learn to graph data to show the change in the data.

Explore

Look at this graph.

What does this graph show?
How is it different from other graphs you have seen?
How do the maximum temperatures in May and November compare?
Which months have the same maximum temperature?
Write 4 other questions you can answer from the graph.

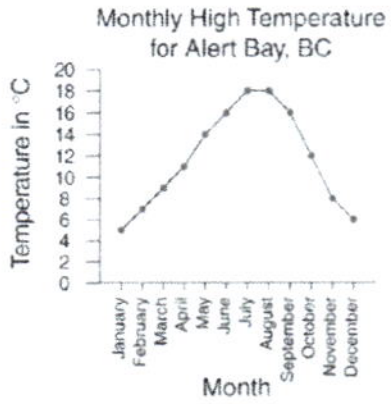

Show and Share

Trade questions with another pair of classmates.
Answer your classmates' questions.
How is this graph the same as a bar graph?
A pictograph? How is it different?

Numbers Every Day

Number Strategies

Order the decimals in each set from least to greatest.

0.68, 0.80, 0.86 • 0.68, 0.86, 0.80
1.35, 5.13, 5.31 • 1.35, 5.31, 5.13
6.74, 7.64, 67.4 • 67.4, 6.74, 7.64
1.23, 2.13, 2.31 • 2.31, 1.23, 2.13

172 LESSON FOCUS | Draw line graphs by hand

BEFORE Get Started

Discuss with students what a line graph looks like. Ask:

- When have you seen a line graph?
  (On the weather, they use a line graph to show the temperature over a 1-week period. In a newspaper, a line graph might show the number of cars sold each month.)

Read the introduction to the lesson. Ask:

- What sort of information would a meteorologist record?
  (A meteorologist records data about the weather. For example, the high temperature every day for a month; the amount of precipitation each month for a year; the number of sunny days in a year)

Ensure students understand that a bar graph visually compares results, while a line graph shows the change between individual results.

Present *Explore*. Have students work in pairs to answer the questions. Students should record answers in their notebooks.

Ensure students understand how to locate a point on a line graph. Illustrate that if you follow the lines through the horizontal and vertical values, they intersect at the point. Begin to model the idea of taking the horizontal value first, then the vertical value; this will help prepare students for later work with graphs.

DURING Explore

Ongoing Assessment: Observe and Listen

Ask questions, such as:

- How can you find the maximum temperature for January?
  (I look for January on the horizontal axis, and follow the line up until I reach the point. Then I follow the line across to the temperature scale, and read the number.)

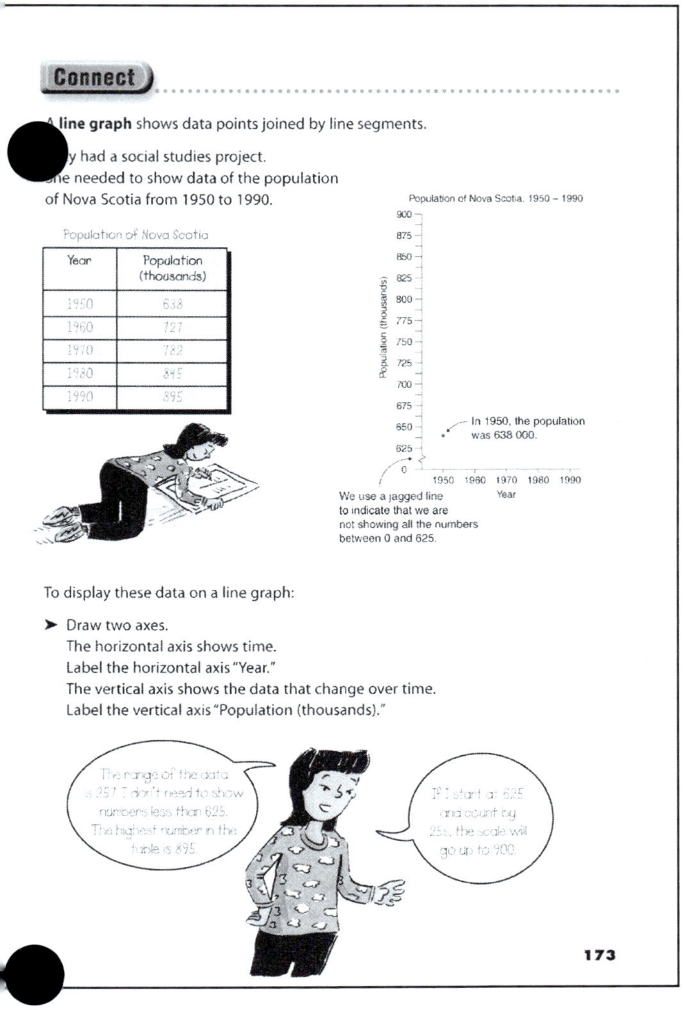

Connect

A **line graph** shows data points joined by line segments.

…y had a social studies project.
…e needed to show data of the population of Nova Scotia from 1950 to 1990.

Population of Nova Scotia

Year	Population (thousands)
1950	638
1960	727
1970	782
1980	845
1990	895

To display these data on a line graph:

➤ Draw two axes.
The horizontal axis shows time.
Label the horizontal axis "Year."
The vertical axis shows the data that change over time.
Label the vertical axis "Population (thousands)."

173

REACHING ALL LEARNERS

Early Finishers

Have students draw a table showing the data from the line graph in *Explore*.

Common Misconceptions

➤ When drawing a line graph, students mark the vertical axis with the numbers in the table, rather than a uniform scale.

How to Help: Have students decide on a scale first, then count by that number until they have reached the greatest number in the data.

- How can you find the maximum temperature for the whole year?
  (*I look for the highest point on the graph.*)
- In which month did the maximum temperature occur?
  (*In both July and August*)
- What was the maximum temperature for the whole year? (*18°C*) How do you know?
  (*That's the value on the vertical axis for July and August.*)
- How do you know when two or more months have the same temperature?
  (*Their values are on the same horizontal line.*)
- What does a horizontal line tell you?
  (*There is no change in the data.*)
- Where do you see a horizontal line on the graph?
  (*There is a horizontal line from July to August.*)
- What happened to the high temperature from September to October?
  (*It went down by 4°C.*)
  How did you find the answer?
  (*I found the value for September, which was 16, and subtracted the value for October, which was 12. The difference is 4.*)

Discuss what students learned from *Show and Share*. Ask:

- How is drawing a line graph similar to drawing a bar graph?
  (*You draw the vertical and horizontal axes. You label both axes. You label the vertical axis with a scale. You title the graph.*)
- How is drawing a line graph different from drawing a bar graph?
  (*In a line graph, you draw a point to indicate each value. You don't sort the data into intervals, as you would in a bar graph. In a line graph, you connect the points with line segments to show an increase or decrease in the values. A line graph shows change, and a bar graph shows a comparison.*)

Sample Answers

1. a)

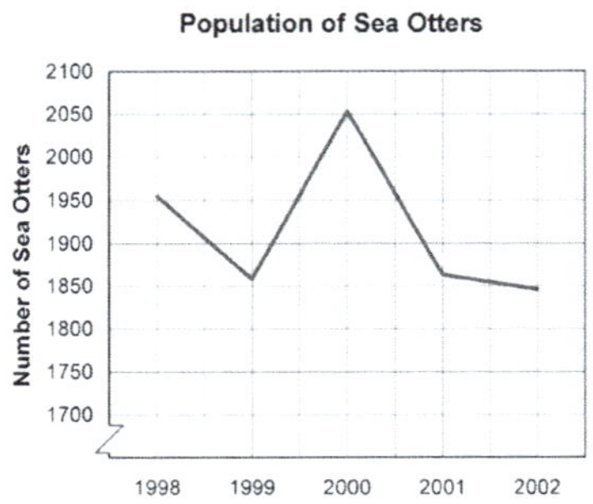

b) I used a scale of 1 square = 50. That made the values close enough to fit on my graph, but spread out enough to see the increases and decreases. I used a jagged line, and started at 1700.

c) The number of sea otters decreased, increased, then decreased again. On the graph, when you move to the right, the line segments go down, then up, then down.

2. a)

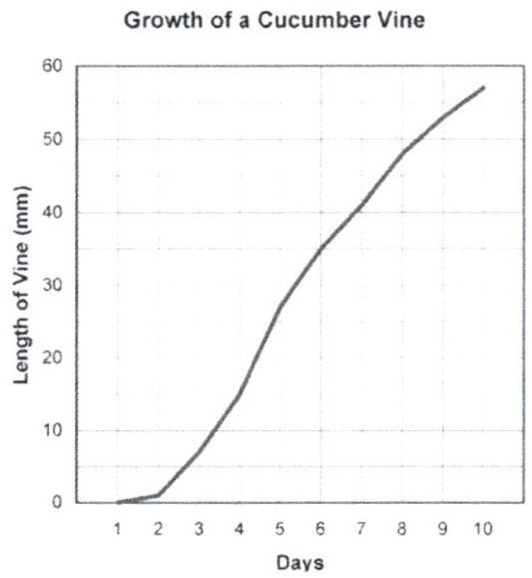

➤ Choose an appropriate scale.
Count by 10s for the scale on the horizontal axis.
The horizontal scale is 3 squares represent 10 years.
Count by 25s for the scale on the vertical axis.
The vertical scale is 2 squares represent 25.

➤ Mark a point for 1950 at 638.
Then mark points for the rest of the data in the same way.

➤ Use a ruler to connect each consecutive pair of points, from left to right.

➤ Give the graph a title.

➤ On a line graph, when the line segments:
- go up to the right, the graph is increasing
- go down to the right, the graph is decreasing

The graph goes up to the right.
The population in Nova Scotia increased from 1950 to 1990.

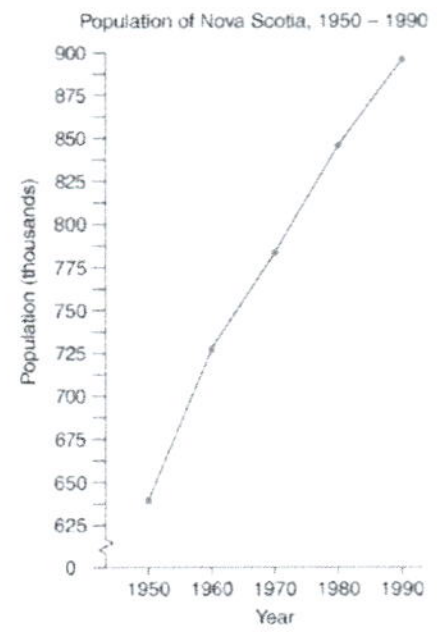

Practice

You will need grid paper.

1. A survey of the population of southern sea otters is done each year. The table shows the results from 1998 to 2002.
   a) Draw a line graph to display these data.
   b) Explain how you chose the vertical scale.
   c) What happened to the number of sea otters from 1998 to 2002? How can you tell from the graph?

Year	Number of Otters
1998	1955
1999	1858
2000	2053
2001	1863
2002	1846

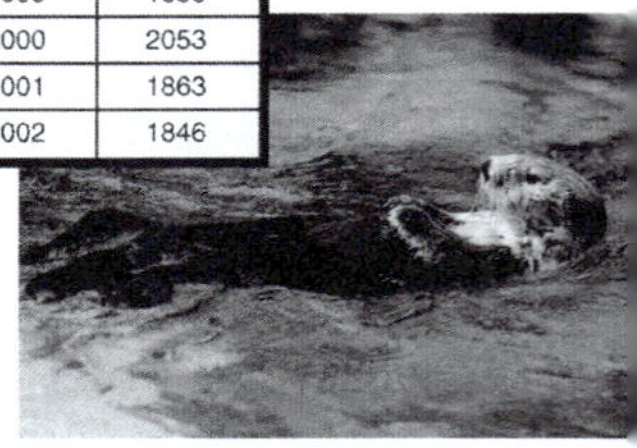

174

AFTER Connect

Invite students to ask the class their questions. On chart paper or the board, record the similarities and differences between a bar graph and a line graph.

Ask:

- What is happening to the temperatures from January to July?
  (*The temperatures are increasing.*)
- How does the line graph show an increase in temperature?
  (*The line segments go up to the right.*)
- What is happening to the temperatures from August to December?
  (*The temperatures are decreasing.*)
- How does the line graph show a decrease in temperature?
  (*The line segments go down to the right.*)

Present *Connect*. Explain the use of the jagged line on the vertical axis.

Practice

Students will need grid paper for all questions.

Assessment Focus: Question 3

Note: Assume the number of beekeepers in Ontario in 2002 is 3000.

Students understand that a line segment going up to the right shows an increase and a line segment going down to the right shows a decrease. Data are shown in a line graph by drawing points connected by line segments.

2. This table shows the growth of Rajiv's cucumber vine.

Day	1	2	3	4	5	6	7	8	9	10
Length of Vine (mm)	0	1	7	15	27	35	41	48	53	57

a) Draw a line graph to display these data.
b) What does the line on the graph show?
c) Write 2 things you know from the graph.

3. This table shows the number of beekeepers in Ontario from 1994 to 2003. The numbers are rounded to the nearest 100.
a) Draw a line graph to display these data.
b) How did you choose the scale?
c) What is happening to the number of beekeepers in Ontario? How does your graph show this?
d) How many beekeepers do you think there will be in Ontario in 2004? Explain your prediction.

Year	Number of Beekeepers
1994	4500
1995	4300
1996	4100
1997	4100
1998	4000
1999	3600
2000	3000
2001	3000
2003	2650

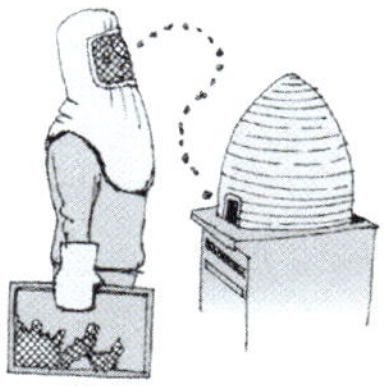

Reflect

You can display data using a line graph, a bar graph, or a pictograph. Describe a situation that best suits each type of graph. Explain your thinking.

At Home

Look through newspapers and magazines, or on the Internet. Find a line graph. Describe the graph. What information do you get from the graph?

ASSESSMENT FOCUS | Question 3

175

b) The length of the vine is increasing. The line segments go up to the right.
c) The length doubled from day 3 to day 4. The biggest increase was between day 4 and day 5.

3. a)

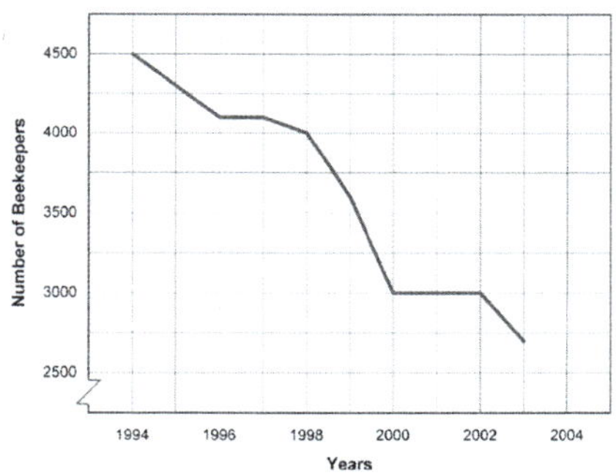

b) I chose the scale 1 square = 250 because then I could show the data without using too much space.
c) The number of beekeepers in Ontario is decreasing; on the graph, the line segments mostly go down to the right.
d) 2500. The number of beekeepers goes down by about 1000 every 4 years.

REFLECT: Line graph: the number of cars produced over several years; you can see the increase or decrease by the way the line segments go up or down.
Bar graph: sales of various types of sports drinks; you can see the exact amount just by looking at the height of the bars.
Pictograph: the number of cavities students in a grade 5 class have; the key can represent a group of people.

ASSESSMENT FOR LEARNING

What to Look For	What to Do
Understanding concepts ✔ Students understand how to represent one piece of data as a point in a line graph.	***Extra Support:*** Students can use Step-by-Step 4 (Master 5.13) to complete question 3.
Communication ✔ Students can use appropriate mathematical terminology to describe the changes in a line graph.	***Extra Practice:*** Have students draw new line graphs for question 2, using different scales. Students can complete Extra Practice 4 (Master 5.21).
	Extension: Have students complete the Additional Activity, *Story of Mrs. D.* (Master 5.7).

Recording and Reporting
Master 5.2 Ongoing Observations: Data Management

Drawing Line Graphs Using *AppleWorks*

LESSON ORGANIZER — 40–50 min

Curriculum Focus: Use a computer to draw line graphs. (5m114, 5m119)

Student Materials

- *AppleWorks* or *Microsoft Excel*

Key Math Learning

A computer can be used to draw line graphs.

Drawing Line Graphs Using *AppleWorks*

Work with a partner.

Use *AppleWorks*.
Follow these steps to draw a line graph of the Town Library Sign Out data.
Use the spreadsheet you created on pages 163 to 165.

	A	B
1	Town Library Sign Out Record	
2	Season	Number of Books
3	Winter	1488
4	Spring	1151
5	Summer	976
6	Fall	1259
7	Total	4874
8	Mean	1218.5

1. Open a spreadsheet in *AppleWorks*. Click: Spreadsheet
2. Open your Town Library spreadsheet.
   Click: File, then click: Open... Ctrl+O
   Click on the name of your spreadsheet: Town Library Sign Out Records
   Click: Open
3. To select cells A3 to B6:
   Click cell A3. Hold down the mouse.
   Drag the cursor from A3 to B6.
   Release the mouse button.
4. To **create a line graph**:
   Click: Options, then click: Make Chart... Ctrl+M
   Click the Gallery tab, then click: Line
   No options should be selected.
   Options: Color, Shadow, Horizontal

   Give the graph a title.
   Click the Labels tab. Select Show Title.
   Make sure Show Legend is not selected.
   Type: Town Library Sign Out Records
   (Show Title; Title: Town Library Sign Out Records)

   Label the axes. Click the Axes tab.
   Select X axis.
   Type the Axis label: Season
   (X axis, Y axis; Axis label: Season)

   Select Y axis.
   Type the Axis label: Number of Books
   (X axis, Y axis; Axis label: Number of Books)

176 LESSON FOCUS | Use a computer to draw line graphs.

BEFORE

Point out to students that, in *Microsoft Excel*, graphs are called *charts*.

DURING

Ongoing Assessment: Observe and Listen

Watch to ensure that students read and follow the instructions carefully.

Instructions for drawing line graphs using *Microsoft Excel*:

1. Open your Town Library Sign Out Records spreadsheet in *Microsoft Excel*.
   Click: **File**, then click: **Open...**
   Click on the name of your spreadsheet.
   Click: **Open**
2. To select cells A3 to B6:
   Click cell A3. Hold down the mouse button.
   Drag the cursor from A3 to B6.
   Release the mouse button.
3. To create a line graph:
   Click: **Insert**, then click: **Chart...**
   Under **Chart type**, choose **Line**.
   Under **Chart sub-type**, choose the second chart in the first column.
   Click: **Next**
   Click: **Next** again.
   Click inside the **Chart title** box.
   Type: Town Library Sign Out Records
   Click inside the **Category (X) axis** box.
   Type: Season
   Click inside the **Value (Y) axis** box.
   Type: Number of Books
   Click: **Next**
   Select the **As object in** option.
   This means your graph will be part of the spreadsheet, instead of a separate file.
   Click: **Finish**

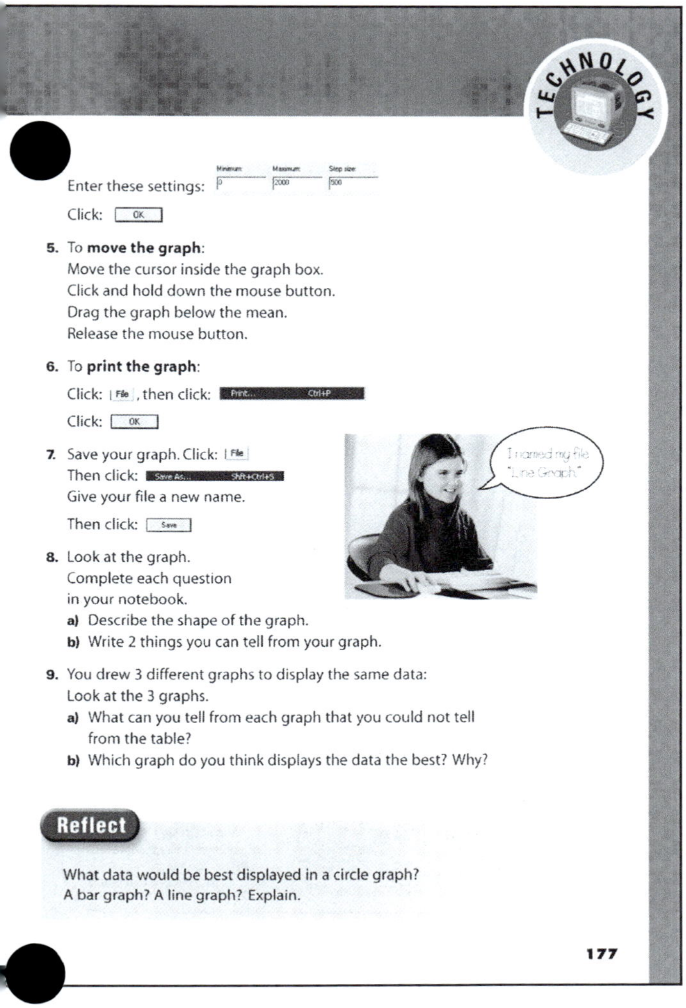

TECHNOLOGY

Enter these settings: Minimum: 0 Maximum: 2000 Step size: 500

Click: OK

5. To **move the graph**:
Move the cursor inside the graph box.
Click and hold down the mouse button.
Drag the graph below the mean.
Release the mouse button.

6. To **print the graph**:
Click: File, then click: Print... Ctrl+P
Click: OK

7. Save your graph. Click: File
Then click: Save As... Shft+Ctrl+S
Give your file a new name.
Then click: Save

8. Look at the graph.
Complete each question in your notebook.
a) Describe the shape of the graph.
b) Write 2 things you can tell from your graph.

9. You drew 3 different graphs to display the same data:
Look at the 3 graphs.
a) What can you tell from each graph that you could not tell from the table?
b) Which graph do you think displays the data the best? Why?

Reflect

What data would be best displayed in a circle graph? A bar graph? A line graph? Explain.

177

REACHING ALL LEARNERS

Early Finishers

Have students use *AppleWorks* to draw line graphs from the data from Lesson 4, questions 1, 2, and 3. Have them compare their drawn graph to the computer-generated graphs.

REFLECT: I would use a circle graph to show how I spent my weekly allowance, or a breakdown of the activities I do in a day. I would use a bar graph to show how many of each colour jellybean are in a bag. I would use a line graph to show the average temperature each month for a year.

4. To **move the graph:**
Move the cursor inside the graph box.
Position the cursor over empty space—not the graph, the legend, or the title.
Click and hold down the mouse button.
Drag the graph below the mean.
Release the mouse button.

5. To **print the graph:**
Click: **File**, then click: **Print...**
Click: **OK**

6. Save your graphs. Click: **File**
Then click: **Save As...**
Give your file a new name.
Then click: **Save**

AFTER

Invite volunteers to share any strategies they found helpful.

Interpreting Survey Results

LESSON ORGANIZER

40–50 min

Curriculum Focus: Conduct a survey and interpret survey results. (5m113, 5m115)

Student Materials
- 1-cm grid paper (PM 23)

Optional
- Step-by-Step 5 (Master 5.14)
- Extra Practice 5 (Master 5.22)

Vocabulary: sample, bias

Assessment: Master 5.2 Ongoing Observations: Data Management

Key Math Learnings

1. A sample is a small group chosen from the entire group.
2. A sample that does not truly represent the group is biased.

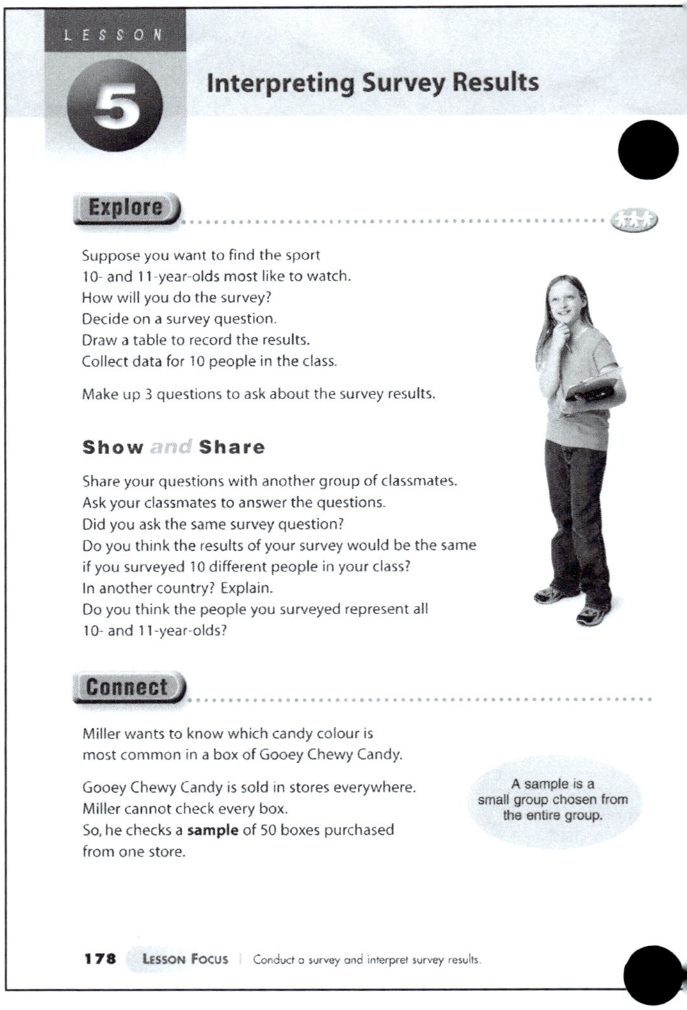
LESSON 5

Interpreting Survey Results

Explore

Suppose you want to find the sport
10- and 11-year-olds most like to watch.
How will you do the survey?
Decide on a survey question.
Draw a table to record the results.
Collect data for 10 people in the class.

Make up 3 questions to ask about the survey results.

Show and Share

Share your questions with another group of classmates.
Ask your classmates to answer the questions.
Did you ask the same survey question?
Do you think the results of your survey would be the same if you surveyed 10 different people in your class?
In another country? Explain.
Do you think the people you surveyed represent all 10- and 11-year-olds?

Connect

Miller wants to know which candy colour is most common in a box of Gooey Chewy Candy.

Gooey Chewy Candy is sold in stores everywhere.
Miller cannot check every box.
So, he checks a **sample** of 50 boxes purchased from one store.

A sample is a small group chosen from the entire group.

178 LESSON FOCUS | Conduct a survey and interpret survey results.

BEFORE — Get Started

Discuss with the class why you might conduct a survey. Ask:

- What would you like to learn about your classmates?
  (*How many brothers and sisters each one has, what their favourite colour is, where they live, what dessert they like best.*)
- How would you conduct your survey?
  (*I would write down my question and list five predicted answers to the question. I would then draw a chart to record my data. To display the results, I would draw a graph.*)
- Suppose you only wanted to ask 10 people. How would you chose which 10 people to ask?
  (*I would only ask my friends. I would ask the students that sit close to me. I would ask the first 10 people that came up to me to ask me their question.*)

Present *Explore*. Ensure students understand that they will only survey 10 classmates, and that they will not display the data in a graph.

DURING — Explore

Ongoing Assessment: Observe and Listen

Ask questions, such as:

- What question will you ask in your survey?
  (*What sport do you most like to watch live?*)
- What different answers will you allow?
  (*We will allow the answers soccer, hockey, baseball, basketball, and golf.*)
- Who are you going to ask?
  (*The students in the first row of desks*)

AFTER — Connect

Invite students to share their questions and possible answers. Discuss the results of the

Here are Miller's findings:

- Miller discovered red was he most common colour of ooey Chewy Candy. The mode colour was red.
- He calculated the mean number of candies of each colour in 50 boxes to be 82.

Gooey Chewy Candy in 50 Boxes

Colour	Number of Candies
Red	138
Blue	16
Yellow	95
Orange	82
Green	56
White	105

Miller had expected the number of each colour of candy to be about the same in each box.
He thought he should sample other stores to see if their results were similar before concluding that there were always more red and white candies than green or blue in a box.

A sample that does not truly represent the group is biased.

Practice

1. Write a survey question for each topic.
   Give 4 possible answers for each question.
   a) favourite food b) favourite athlete c) species of pet

2. How could you conduct a school survey without questioning every student in the school?
   Explain how you could make sure the sample was not biased.

Math Link

Your World

Statistics Canada collects data on many topics, such as the economy and the size of the population. Politicians and researchers use these data to learn more about our country and to make decisions.

179

REACHING ALL LEARNERS

Early Finishers

Have students draw a graph to display the results of their survey.

ESL Strategies

Pair a student for whom English is a second language with a student whose written and verbal language skills are good, in order to help with language comprehension.

Sample Answers

1. a) What fruit do you like best: apple, banana, grapes, or orange?
   b) Which athlete is your favourite: Vince Carter, Tiger Woods, Serena Williams, or Alex Rodriguez?
   c) Which pet do you have at home: dog, cat, hamster, or none of the above?
2. I would randomly pick two students in each class, one boy and one girl. This sample would not be biased because I would ask the same number of students in each class and each grade, and I would randomly choose the students.
3. a) Where do you use a computer at home?
   i) Kitchen ii) Bedroom
   iii) Family room iv) I don't have a computer at home.
   b) 49 students; That is the total number of responses if I add up the heights of all the bars.
   c) I think it was a sample, because most classes have fewer than 49 students and most schools have more than 49 students.

survey. Invite students to share their responses to *Show and Share*. Ask:

- Would the results be different if you surveyed 10 students in a different class? Explain.
  (*Yes, I think so, because different people like different sports. Ten students is a small sample.*)
- Would the results be different if you asked students in a different country?
  (*Yes, students in Europe would probably say soccer was their favourite sport, because it's more popular there than in Canada.*)
- Do you think the people you surveyed represented all 10- and 11-year-olds?
  (*No, because the results would be different in different communities, towns, and cities.*)
- Why would you only survey a small number of students?
  (*I wouldn't have time to ask everyone in the class.*)
- Why would people choose not to survey everyone in a group?
  (*They might not have the time or resources to ask everyone. Maybe they want to show the data a certain way, so they ask people who they think will give the answer they want.*)

Present *Connect*. Ensure students understand that when a sample does not truly represent the group, it is biased.

Practice

Students can use a calculator to find the mean in question 4.

Assessment Focus: Question 3

Students draw conclusions from the survey and speculate how the data were collected.

d) Most students have a computer at home. More students use the computer in their family room than anywhere else in the house.

4. a) Bike sales are increasing because the line segments are going up to the right. This is happening because more people buy bikes during the summer.

c) I think 15 bicycles will be sold in September. Sales will drop because summer is over and students are going back to school.

REFLECT: I might not have the time to ask everyone in a large group.

3. This graph shows the results of a student survey.
   a) Write what the survey question might have been.
   b) How many students do you think were surveyed? Explain.
   c) Do you think a sample or an entire group was surveyed? Why?
   d) Write 2 things you know from this survey.

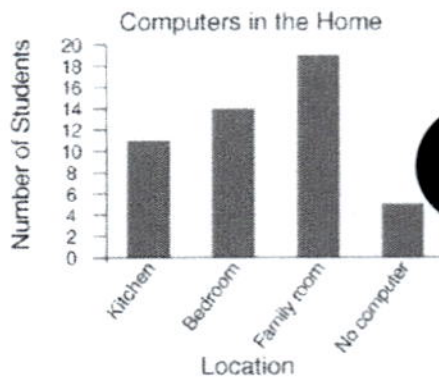

4. Best Bicycle Company surveyed 10 bike stores in Ontario. It wants to find out how many of their bikes have been sold in the last 6 months. Here are the results:

   a) What is happening to bike sales? Why do you think this is happening?
   b) Find the mean number of bicycles sold during this period. 21
   c) Predict sales for September. Give reasons for your prediction.

Reflect

Why might you survey a sample rather than an entire group? Explain.

Numbers Every Day

Number Strategies

Round to the nearest dollar.

\$ 7.78	\$8.00
\$12.62	\$13.00
\$ 1.40	\$1.00
\$25.35	\$25.00
\$14.55	\$15.00

180 ASSESSMENT FOCUS | Question 3

Numbers Every Day

Have students look at the tenths digit to help them round to the nearest dollar.

ASSESSMENT FOR LEARNING

What to Look For

Understanding concepts

✔ Students understand that a survey is conducted to collect and record data.

✔ Students understand that a sample represents a group.

✔ Students understand that a sample can be biased.

Applying procedures

✔ Students can create a survey question, along with appropriate answers.

Communication

✔ Students can describe the results of a survey and write what they learned from the results.

What to Do

Extra Support: Students can use Step-by-Step 5 (Master 5.14) to complete question 3.
Have students complete the Additional Activity, *Concrete Bars* (Master 5.8).

Extra Practice: Have students conduct one of the surveys from question 1.
Students can complete Extra Practice 5 (Master 5.22).

Recording and Reporting

Master 5.2 Ongoing Observations: Data Management

Medical Researcher

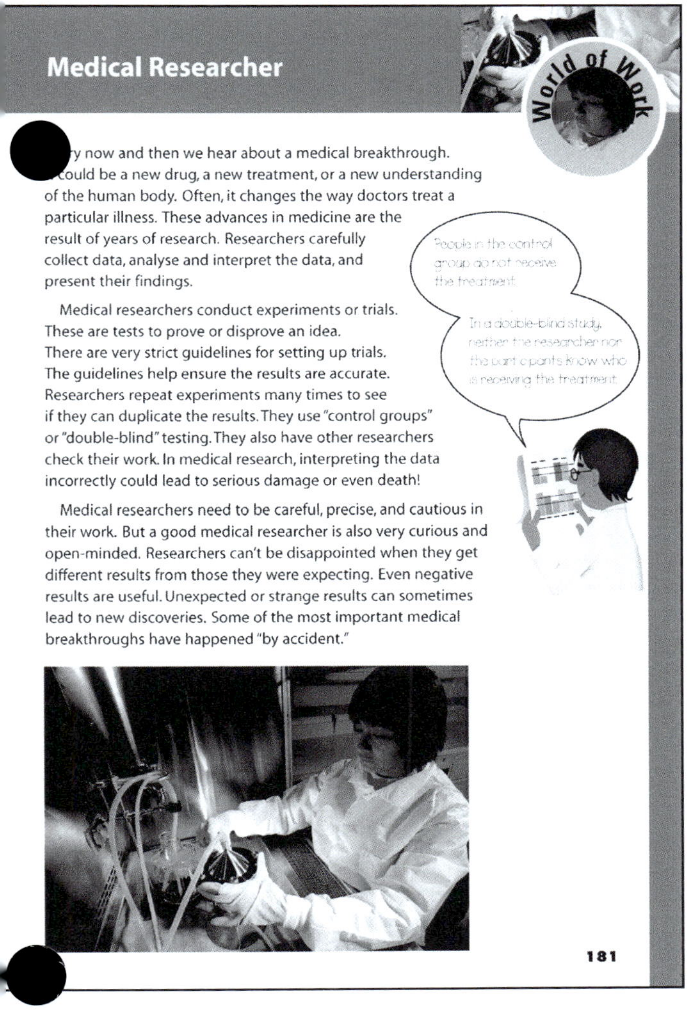

Medical Researcher

World of Work

…y now and then we hear about a medical breakthrough. …could be a new drug, a new treatment, or a new understanding of the human body. Often, it changes the way doctors treat a particular illness. These advances in medicine are the result of years of research. Researchers carefully collect data, analyse and interpret the data, and present their findings.

Medical researchers conduct experiments or trials. These are tests to prove or disprove an idea. There are very strict guidelines for setting up trials. The guidelines help ensure the results are accurate. Researchers repeat experiments many times to see if they can duplicate the results. They use "control groups" or "double-blind" testing. They also have other researchers check their work. In medical research, interpreting the data incorrectly could lead to serious damage or even death!

People in the control group do not receive the treatment.

In a double-blind study, neither the researcher nor the participants know who is receiving the treatment.

Medical researchers need to be careful, precise, and cautious in their work. But a good medical researcher is also very curious and open-minded. Researchers can't be disappointed when they get different results from those they were expecting. Even negative results are useful. Unexpected or strange results can sometimes lead to new discoveries. Some of the most important medical breakthroughs have happened "by accident."

181

Have students brainstorm a list of careers that require data collection or analysis. Invite students to share information about their parents' or other relatives' careers. Here are some careers that require the collection and analysis of data.

Computer Scientists: A computer scientist researches and develops ways to use computer technology to solve complicated problems. They design computer parts and software.

Astronomers: An astronomer studies space, including the sun, the moon, planets, stars, and galaxies. They use satellites and other instruments to observe and collect data. The Hubble Space Telescope has provided a tremendous amount of astronomical data.

Trial lawyers: A trial lawyer specializes in defending clients before a court of law. Trial lawyers spend most of their time outside the courtroom conducting research, interviewing clients and witnesses, and preparing for trial.

Journalists: A journalist creates news stories for television, newspapers, or magazines. Journalists gather information, prepare stories, and make broadcasts that inform us about world events. They examine, interpret, and analyse information received from various sources.

Discuss with students the importance of accurate data in these careers.

LESSON 6

Bias in Displaying Data

LESSON ORGANIZER 40–50 min

Curriculum Focus: Investigate bias in the way data are displayed. (5m118)

Student Materials

Optional
- Step-by-Step 6 (Master 5.15)
- Extra Practice 6 (Master 5.23)

Vocabulary: bias

Assessment: Master 5.2 Ongoing Observations: Data Management

Key Math Learning

Graphs can show data with bias. Bias shows data in a way that someone else wants you to see them.

LESSON 6

Bias in Displaying Data

In the previous lesson, you learned that the data produced by a particular sample might not truly represent the entire group. Sometimes, data are displayed to suggest a particular result.

Explore

The points scored by 3 basketball players are shown in the table. The data are displayed in two graphs.

Points Scored in a Season

Player	Points
Abrams	280
Kiski	300
Snell	250

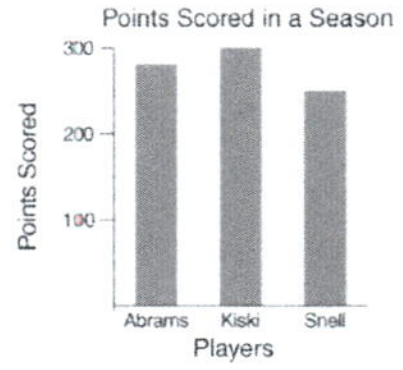

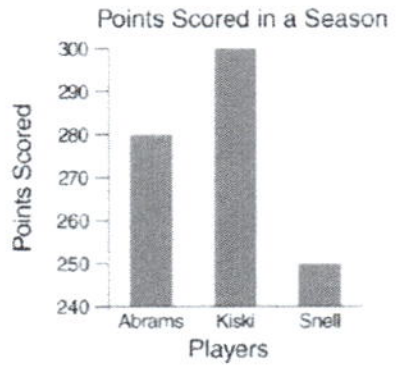

From the table, does there appear to be a great difference in the points each player scored?
What is the range of the points?
Compare Graph A and Graph B.
In which graph does the range seem small?
In which graph does the range seem great?
How are the graphs the same? How are they different?

BEFORE Get Started

Discuss what was discovered in the previous lesson. Ask questions, such as:

- What is a sample? (*A sample is a selected few who are surveyed, rather than the whole group.*)
- Why might someone use a sample? (*To save time and money. A sample can also be used to persuade the reader. A sample that does not truly represent the group is biased.*)
- What does bias mean? (*Bias means that the data are shown in a way that persuades the reader. The data suggest a particular result.*)
- How could a sample have bias? (*You could ask only your friends the question.*)
- Why would someone want a biased sample? (*So they could get results that show a positive view of their service, product, or political point of view*)

Present *Explore*. Students should record their answers to the questions in *Explore*, and any other new information from their discussion with their classmates in *Show and Share*, in their notebooks. Remind students to look at the vertical scale to help them answer the questions.

DURING Explore

Ongoing Assessment: Observe and Listen

Move around the classroom, listening to students' discussions. When one student doesn't understand how both graphs show the same data, is the other student able to explain? If necessary, draw students' attention to the vertical scale. Suggest they should focus on the aspects where the two graphs differ.

Ask questions, such as:

- Do both graphs show the same data? (*Yes*)
- How can you tell that both graphs show the same data? (*In both graphs, Abrams scored 280 point, Kiski scored 300 points, and Snell scored 250 points.*)

Show and Share

Discuss your answers with another pair of students.
Discuss how the vertical scale makes the two graphs look different.
Why might you choose to use Graph A? Graph B?

Numbers Every Day

Mental Math

Write 5 different number sentences with the answer 375.

405 – 30 = 375
25 × 15 = 375
75 × 5 = 375
750 ÷ 2 = 375
374 + 1 = 375

Connect

In a survey, 1000 people were asked to choose between 2 brands of shampoo.
The results are displayed in two different graphs.

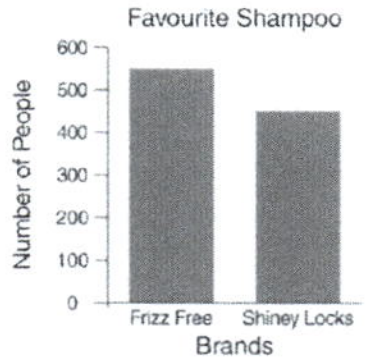

Graph A

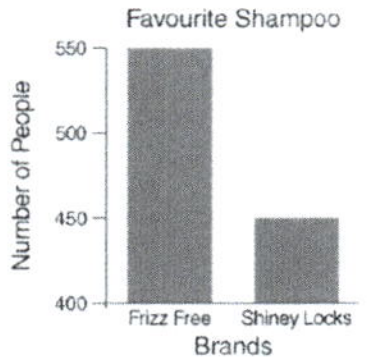

Graph B

➤ Graphs show data in a way that is easy to see.
However, graphs can also show data with **bias**.
Bias shows data in a way that someone else wants you to see them.

➤ Look at Graph A.
The difference between the numbers of people that chose Frizz Free or Shiny Locks shampoo is not very large.
From Graph B, however, it appears that 3 times more people chose Frizz Free over Shiny Locks.
Graph B is biased.
Suppose you were advertising Frizz Free shampoo.
Graph B creates the impression that Frizz Free is much more popular with customers.

183

REACHING ALL LEARNERS

Common Misconceptions

➤Students do not pay attention to the vertical scale.

How to Help: Remind students to look at where the scale begins. Does it start at 0 or another number? Does the vertical axis have a jagged line?

Numbers Every Day

Have the students use the Guess and Check strategy. Remind them they can use all four operations: add, subtract, multiply, and divide.

- Are the ranges different for the two graphs?
  (No, the ranges are the same. In both graphs, the range is 300 – 250 = 50 points.)
- If the ranges are the same, why do the graphs look different?
  (The graphs look different because they use different scales on the vertical axis. In the first graph, the vertical scale goes by hundreds from 0 to 300. In the second graph, the vertical scale goes by tens from 240 to 300.)
- What effect does this have?
  (The second graph makes it look like Kiski is a much better player than Abrams and Snell, when they're really all close to the same.)
- What does one graph have that the other doesn't have?
  (Graph B has a bias; Graph A does not.)

AFTER Connect

Invite students to share their answers with the class. Record students' answers on chart paper or on the board.

Make a list to show the similarities and differences between the graphs. Ask:

- What is the biggest difference between the two graphs?
  (The vertical scale is the biggest difference. Graph A's scale begins at 0 and Graph B's scale begins at 240.)
- How does this change the appearance of the graph?
  (In Graph B, it looks like there is a larger difference between the players than there really is.)
- Who might want to use Graph B?
  (Anyone wanting to emphasize that Kiski was the highest scorer.)

Sample Answers

1. c) Mark spends a bigger fraction of his allowance on movies, but you can't tell who actually spends more because you don't know the total amount of money each student started out with.
2. a) The graphs are alike because both show the same data. They are different because they use different scales on the vertical and horizontal axes.
   c) Graph B makes it look like profits are going up more quickly.
3. c) The scale starts at 140, so it looks like Krunchie had a bigger lead over Tasty Tater and Delish than it really did. The scale should start at 0 to do a comparison.
   e) Graph B makes it look like Krunchie had a bigger advantage because the graph only deals with the number of people from 140–200 on the vertical axis. Graph A shows all 200 people on the vertical axis so it is more compressed.

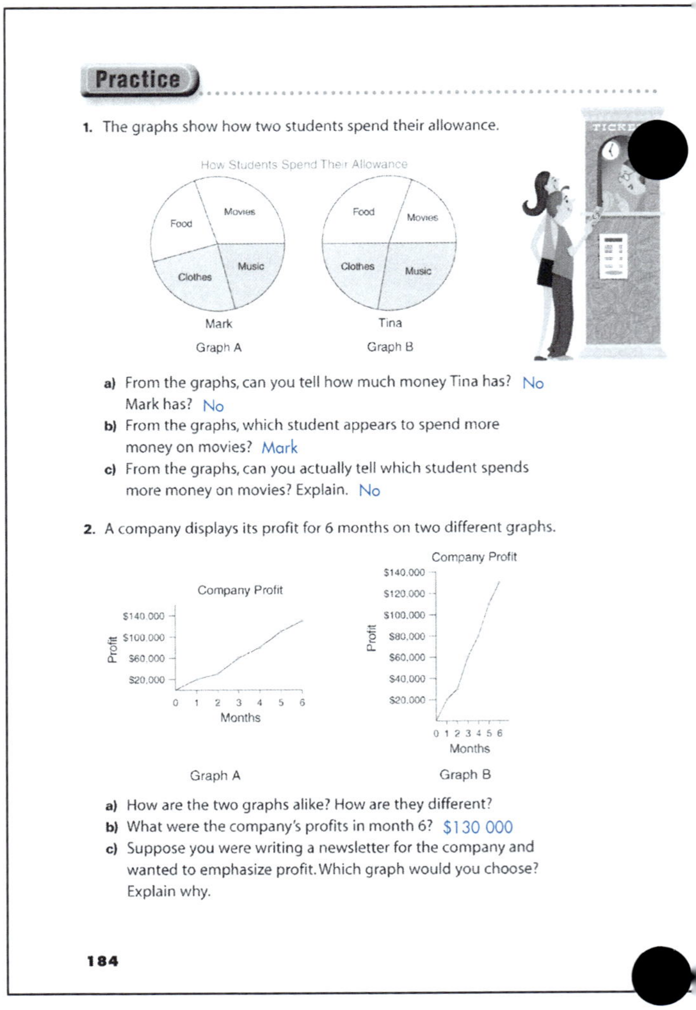
Practice

1. The graphs show how two students spend their allowance.

a) From the graphs, can you tell how much money Tina has? No Mark has? No
b) From the graphs, which student appears to spend more money on movies? Mark
c) From the graphs, can you actually tell which student spends more money on movies? Explain. No

2. A company displays its profit for 6 months on two different graphs.

a) How are the two graphs alike? How are they different?
b) What were the company's profits in month 6? $130 000
c) Suppose you were writing a newsletter for the company and wanted to emphasize profit. Which graph would you choose? Explain why.

184

- Why would businesses display data with bias?
  (To persuade or influence people to buy their products, or to give the impression their products are better)
- Why would politicians display data with bias?
  (To convince people to vote for them during an election campaign)
- How could you show bias in a pictograph?
  (By changing the key. If the symbol represented 100 items instead of 10, it would look like there was less difference in the results.)
- How could you show bias in a line graph?
  (The vertical scale could start at a number other than 0, or the scale could have a different range.)

Present *Connect*. Ensure students understand that graphs can show data with bias. Bias shows data in a way that someone else wants you to see them. Point out to students that a biased graph is not wrong; it still displays the data correctly.

Practice

Assessment Focus: Question 3

Students understand how bias changes the appearance of a graph to influence people the way the author wants. They understand that the two graphs show the same data but look different.

3. In a survey, 5000 people were asked to name their favourite potato chip.
The graphs show the results of a survey.

Graph A

Graph B

a) Look at Graph A. Does there appear to be much difference in the number of people who chose Krunchie over Tasty Tater or Delish? No

b) Use Graph A. How many people chose Krunchie?
How many chose Tasty Tater? How many chose Delish? 200; 150; 170

c) In Graph B, the bar for Krunchie is twice as high as the bars for the other brands.
Can you say that twice as many people prefer Krunchie? No
Explain.

d) Use Graph B. How many people chose Krunchie?
How many chose Tasty Tater? How many chose Delish? 200; 150; 170

e) Suppose you were advertising Krunchie.
Which graph makes the range appear to be larger than it really is? Explain. Graph B

Reflect

Suppose that a graph is drawn to show bias.
Does this mean that the data in the graph are incorrect? Explain.

At Home

Look through newspapers and magazines. Find an advertisement that uses graphs. Is there any bias?

ASSESSMENT FOCUS | Question 3 **185**

REFLECT: No, it means that the data are displayed the way someone else wants you to see them.

ASSESSMENT FOR LEARNING

What to Look For	What to Do
Understanding concepts ✔ Students understand that two graphs can show the same data but look different. ✔ Students understand that a biased graph shows data in a way that someone else wants you to see them. ***Communication*** ✔ Students can explain concepts using appropriate mathematical terminology.	***Extra Support:*** Students can use Step-by-Step 6 (Master 5.15) to complete question 3. Have students complete the Additional Activity, *Paper Search* (Master 5.9). ***Extra Practice:*** Have students draw two graphs of the Gooey Chewy Candy data from Lesson 5, one with bias and one without bias. Students can complete Extra Practice 6 (Master 5.23).

Recording and Reporting
Master 5.2 Ongoing Observations: Data Management

LESSON 7

Strategies Toolkit

LESSON ORGANIZER 40–50 min

Curriculum Focus: Interpret a problem and select an appropriate strategy. (5m33)

Student Materials *Optional*
- play money (PM 30)

Assessment: PM 1 Inquiry Process Check List, PM 3 Self-Assessment: Problem Solving

Key Math Learning

Solve a problem by working backward.

LESSON 7 Strategies Toolkit

Explore

Greg was playing marbles with his friends.
In the first game, he lost 2 marbles.
In the second game, he lost twice as many as in the first game.
In the last game, he won 8 marbles.
Greg finished with 25 marbles.
How many marbles did he start with? 23

Show and Share

Describe the strategy you used to solve the problem.

Connect

At school, Jasmin bought chocolate milk for $0.75, a hot dog for $1.00, and a bottle of water for $1.07.
On the way home, she found a quarter on the sidewalk.
At the end of the day, she had $1.37 in her wallet.
How much money did Jasmin start with? $3.94

Understand

What do you know?
- Jasmin finished with $1.37.
- Jasmin spent $0.75, $1.00, and $1.07.
- Jasmin found $0.25.

Plan

Think of a strategy to help you solve the problem.
- You can **work backward**.
- Start with $1.37.
- Subtract what she found.
- Add what she spent.

Strategies
- Make a table.
- Use a model.
- Draw a diagram.
- Solve a simpler problem.
- Work backward.
- Guess and check.
- Make an organized list.
- Use a pattern.
- Draw a graph.

186 LESSON FOCUS | Interpret a problem and select an appropriate strategy.

BEFORE Get Started

Present *Explore*. Review the key steps in problem solving: understand the problem, plan how to solve the problem, solve the problem, then look back to check the solution.

Ask:
- What is the question asking you to find? (*The number of marbles Greg started with before he began playing with his friends*)

DURING Explore

Ongoing Assessment: Observe and Listen

Ask questions, such as:
- How many marbles did Greg lose in the second game? (*He lost 4, because he lost twice as many as in the first game.*)
- What number will you start with? (*Because I am working backward, I will start with 25. That is how many marbles Greg finished with.*)
- What operation will you do first to 25? (*I will subtract 8.*)
- Why did you subtract 8 instead of adding 8? (*Since Greg won 8 marbles in the last game, he would have had 8 fewer marbles before the game than after.*)

AFTER Connect

Invite students to share their strategies for solving the problem, as well as what they learned about their classmates' strategies in *Show and Share*.

Use the problem in *Connect* to introduce the strategy of working backward.

Practice

Encourage students to refer to the Strategies list to assist in selecting an appropriate strategy.

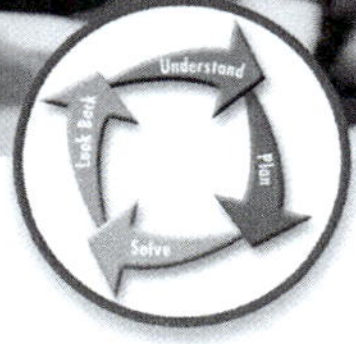

- Subtract $0.25 from $1.37.
- Add $1.07, $0.75, and $1.00.
- How much money did Jasmin start with?

How can you check your answer?
How could you have solved this problem another way?

Practice

Choose one of the **Strategies**

1. On Saturday Jo walked her dog for 20 minutes more than she did on Sunday. For both days she walked a total of 1 hour 15 minutes.
   For how long did Jo walk her dog on Saturday? 47.5 minutes

2. All 5 students in Carlo's group saved some money each week toward the cost of a trip. The mean amount of money saved one week by the group was $2.50.
   Suppose each student saved a different amount.
   How much might each have saved that week?
   $2.30, $2.40, $2.50, $2.60, $2.70

3. Ari lines up his hockey cards with the same number of cards in each row. The card in the middle of the array has 5 cards above, below, to the right, and to the left.
   How many cards does Ari have? 121 cards

Reflect

How can working backward help you solve a problem?
Use words and numbers to explain.

187

REACHING ALL LEARNERS

Common Misconceptions

➤When solving a problem, students will add when they should subtract, and subtract when they should add.

How to Help: Have students realize that working backward means you will be doing the opposite operations as if you were working through the problem from the beginning.

ESL Strategies

Some students for whom English is a second language may find it hard to keep track of all the information presented in a question. Have students underline the key words in a problem. Connect the underlined words to the information needed to solve the problem.

Sample Answers

1. If Jo walked her dog 37.5 minutes both days, that would make 75 minutes, or 1 hour 15 minutes. If I add 10 minutes to Saturday and take 10 minutes away from Sunday, the total time will still be 75 minutes. That would make 47.5 minutes on Saturday and 27.5 minutes on Sunday. So, Jo walked her dog for 47.5 minutes on Saturday.
3. There must be 11 rows of 11 cards each. That makes 121 cards.

REFLECT: You start at the end, so you start with something you already know. Going step by step, you work your way back to the beginning.

ASSESSMENT FOR LEARNING

What to Look For

Problem solving

✔ Students can follow the "understand, plan, solve, and look back" steps to solve a problem.

✔ Students can trace the steps of a problem backward.

Communication

✔ Students can explain why you perform the opposite operation when you work backward.

What to Do

Extra Support: Students may benefit from modelling the questions with play money or counters.

Extension: Each student writes her or his own question. He trades questions with a partner, and they answer each other's questions.

Recording and Reporting

PM 1: Inquiry Process Check List
PM 3: Self-Assessment: Problem Solving

LESSON ORGANIZER

Student Materials

- Questions 3 and 4: 1-cm grid paper (PM 23)
- Questions 2 and 3: 4-function calculators

Assessment: Master 5.1 Unit Rubric: Data Management
Master 5.4 Unit Summary: Data Management

Sample Answers

1. a) Nuclear, coal, and hydroelectric are the largest sectors in the graph.

2. b)

Intervals	26–30	31–35	36–40	41–45
Number of Students	3	8	10	4

I selected the intervals by looking at the range of the data. The lowest mass is 26 kg and the highest is 43 kg. The range is 18 kg, so to show the data in groupings of 5 kg seemed reasonable.

c)

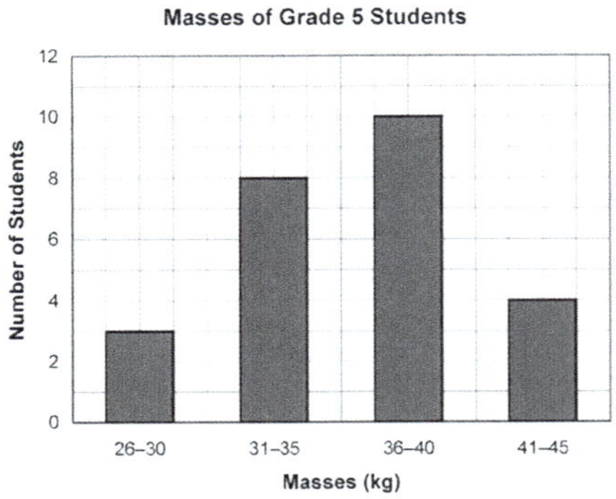

d) What is the most common weight interval?
How many more students weigh between 31–35 kg than 41–45 kg?
How many students were surveyed?

e) The most common weight interval is 36–40 kg.
There are 4 more (or twice as many) Grade 5 students who weigh between 31–35 kg than 41–45 kg.
25 students were surveyed.

3. d)

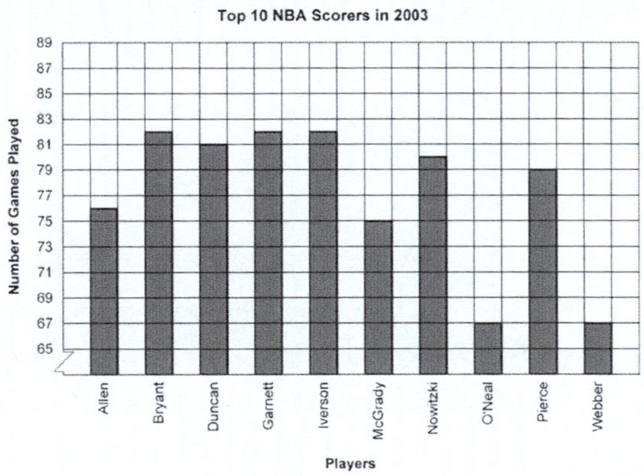

4. a)

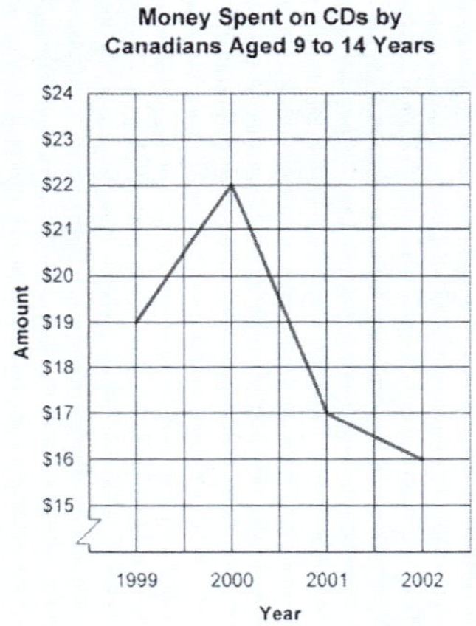

b) The amount increased between 1999 and 2000, because the line segments go up to the right, then decreased, because the line segments go down to the right.

c) $15, because the graph shows a slow decrease.

Unit 5 Show What You Know

1\. This graph shows the sources of Ontario's electricity in 2003.

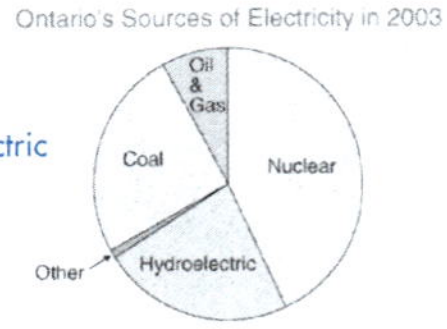

a) Which sources each provide most of Ontario's electricity? Nuclear, coal, hydroelectric
How does the graph show this?

b) Which sources each provide less than $\frac{1}{4}$ of Ontario's electricity? Oil and gas, other

c) About what fraction of Ontario's electricity comes from oil and gas? $\frac{1}{12}$

2\. Here are the masses, to the nearest kilogram, of a group of Grade 5 students:
26, 28, 30, 32, 32, 32, 33, 33, 34, 35, 35, 36, 37, 37, 37, 37, 38, 38, 39, 39, 40, 41, 42, 43, 43

a) What is the mean mass? About 36 kg

b) Arrange the data into intervals.
How did you decide on the intervals?

c) Display the data in a bar graph.

d) Write 3 questions you can answer using the graph.

e) Answer your questions.

3\. This table shows the number of games the top 10 National Basketball Association scorers played in 2003.

a) Find the mean number of games played. About 77

b) Find the mode. 82

c) Find the range of the data. 15

d) Display these data in a graph.

Name	Games Played
Allen	76
Bryant	82
Duncan	81
Garnett	82
Iverson	82
McGrady	75
Nowitzki	80
O'Neal	67
Pierce	79
Webber	67

188

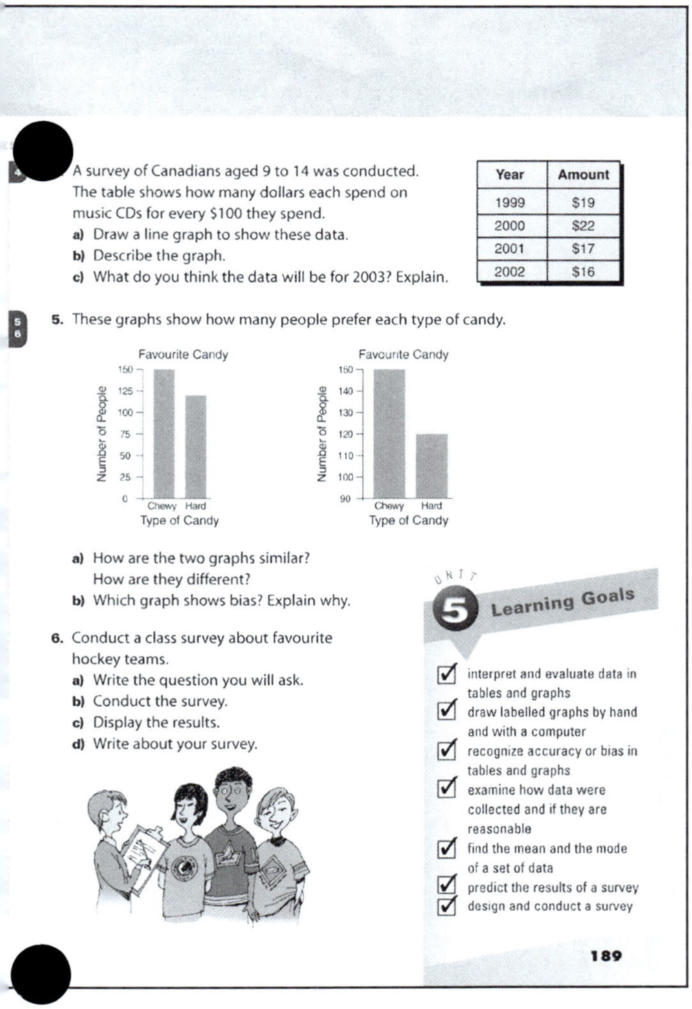
4. A survey of Canadians aged 9 to 14 was conducted. The table shows how many dollars each spend on music CDs for every $100 they spend.
a) Draw a line graph to show these data.
b) Describe the graph.
c) What do you think the data will be for 2003? Explain.

Year	Amount
1999	$19
2000	$22
2001	$17
2002	$16

5. These graphs show how many people prefer each type of candy.

a) How are the two graphs similar? How are they different?
b) Which graph shows bias? Explain why.

6. Conduct a class survey about favourite hockey teams.
a) Write the question you will ask.
b) Conduct the survey.
c) Display the results.
d) Write about your survey.

UNIT 5 Learning Goals
- interpret and evaluate data in tables and graphs
- draw labelled graphs by hand and with a computer
- recognize accuracy or bias in tables and graphs
- examine how data were collected and if they are reasonable
- find the mean and the mode of a set of data
- predict the results of a survey
- design and conduct a survey

189

5. a) They are similar because they both show the same data, and have the same title and labels; They are different because they have different vertical scales.
   b) The second graph shows bias. The vertical scale doesn't start at 0, so it makes the difference in the height of the bars look larger than it really is.

6. a) Students should provide possible answers to the survey question. They should predict which answer will be the most popular.
   b) Students should conduct the survey and record the results in a tally chart. They should choose a sample of the class, and try to ensure that their sample isn't biased.
   c) Students should display the results by constructing a graph.
   d) Students should describe the results of the survey. They should draw conclusions about the most and least favourite hockey teams, or they should rank the teams in order from the most favourite to the least favourite.

ASSESSMENT FOR LEARNING

What to Look For

Understanding of concepts

✔ **Question 5:** Student understands that graphs, tables, and charts can present data with accuracy or bias.

Application of mathematical procedures

✔ **Question 3:** Student can calculate the mean and the mode of a set of data.

✔ **Questions 4 and 6:** Student can organize and display data in a variety of ways.

Problem solving

✔ **Question 4:** Student can organize information about data management and use it to solve a problem.

Recording and Reporting

Master 5.1 Unit Rubric: Data Management
Master 5.4 Unit Summary: Data Management

In the Lab

LESSON ORGANIZER

80–100 min

Student Grouping
3 or 4
Student Materials
- 1-cm grid paper

Assessment: Master 5.3 Performance Assessment Rubric: In the Lab
Master 5.4 Unit Summary: Data Management

Sample Response

Part 1

I decided to perform an experiment to determine the most commonly hit ring on a target game board.

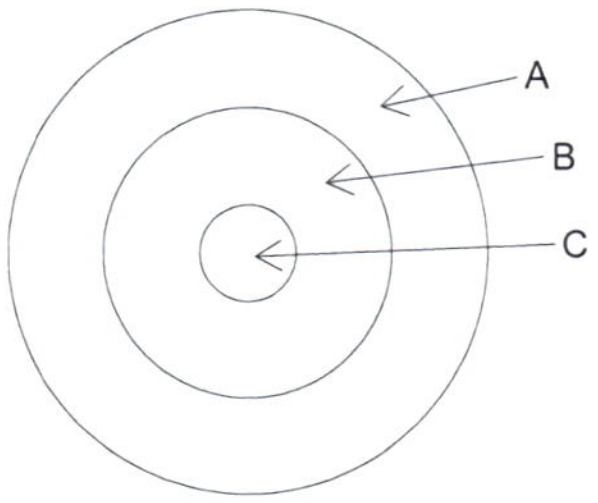

My question is: Which zone will be hit most frequently: A, B, or C?

In my experiment, I will have 10 students each throw a tennis ball at a target game board. I will use a table to record where the tennis ball hits the board. I will have each student make 3 throws, so I will have 30 results altogether.

I expect that zone A will be hit most frequently, because it has the largest area.

Unit Problem

In the Lab

When scientists conduct experiments they collect and study data.
You will conduct an experiment to collect and study data.

Part 1

Work in a group.
Decide on a question that may be answered by doing an experiment.
Design the experiment.
What do you expect the results might be?

Part 2

Conduct the experiment.
Remember to:
- Write down what you want to find out.
- List each step of the experiment.
- List any materials you need.
- Record your data in a table.
- Draw and label a graph to display your data.
- Write the results of the experiment.

190

Remind students of the questions they answered about data management in the *Unit Launch*.

Discuss with students the list of learning goals. Invite a volunteer to explain what each goal means.

Present the *Unit Problem*. Invite volunteers to read aloud the instructions for each part of the problem. Clarify any points.

Have one student read aloud the Check List to ensure all students understand what their work should include. Discuss possible ways in which students might present their work.

Remind students to include titles and scales on a bar graph and a line graph, and a key on a pictograph.

Suggest early finishers display their data on two different types of graphs.

Check List

Your work should show
- ✓ that you created a plan to answer your experiment question
- ✓ how you collected and recorded data accurately
- ✓ a graph that is easy to understand, with labels and title
- ✓ a clear explanation of your results

	M	T	W	T	F	S	S
WEEK 1	14	16	17	18			
WEEK 2							
WEEK 3							
WEEK 4							

CUBE SIZE	MELTING TIME
Small	
Medium	
Large	

Part 3

Trade results with another group.
Check each other's work.
Are the results reasonable?
Discuss why or why not.

Part 4

Present your results to the class.
Discuss what you learned from your experiment.

Reflect on the Unit

Describe some ways you can display data.
When would you use each way?
Use examples to explain.

191

Part 2

Steps

1. Make the target board.
2. Get a tennis ball.
3. Conduct the experiment. Have each student throw the ball at the target 3 times, and record the results in a table.

Materials

- Cardboard
- Markers
- Tape
- Tennis ball

Letter Hit	A	B	C	outside board
Number of Hits	13	8	4	5

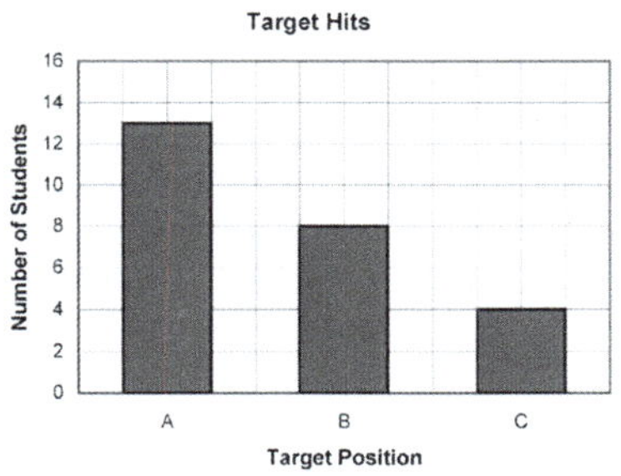

I did not graph the throws that missed the target board. Most students hit the largest part of the target, which was A. Few students hit the centre of the target, C. My prediction was correct.

Reflect on the Unit

I would use a table if there were a small data set. I would use a pictograph or a bar graph to compare things. I would use a circle graph to show how something was divided up; for example, how students spend their allowances.

I would use a line graph to show change when there was only a small data set; for example, how much a bean plant grew in 10 days.

ASSESSMENT FOR LEARNING

What to Look For

Understanding concepts

- ✔ Students understand that they can use an experiment to collect data.
- ✔ Students understand that organizing data enables them to draw conclusions.

Applying procedures

- ✔ Students collect data and display the data on a graph.

Communicating

- ✔ Students explain clearly what the experiment told them about their topic.
- ✔ Students use mathematical terminology.

What to Do

Extra Support: Make the problem accessible.
Discuss possible experiments students can perform, such as how many times a ball bounces at different heights, how long it takes different sizes of ice cubes to melt, how much mass it takes to collapse various cardboard polyhedra, and so on.

Students who have difficulties drawing a graph may benefit from using a computer. Alternatively, provide students with a blank grid that indicates where they should place the title and the axis labels.

Provide questions and hints to elicit from students what factors might affect the outcome of their experiments.

Recording and Reporting

Master 5.3 Performance Assessment Rubric: In the Lab
Master 5.4 Unit Summary: Data Management

Evaluating Student Learning: Preparing to Report: Unit 5 Data Management

This unit provides an opportunity to report on the **Data Management and Probability** strand. *Master 5.4 Unit Summary: Data Management* provides a comprehensive format for recording and summarizing evidence collected.

Here is an example of a completed summary chart for this Unit:

Strand: *Data Management and Probability*	**Problem solving**	**Understanding of concepts**	**Application of mathematical procedures**	**Communication**	***Overall***
Ongoing Observations	3	2	2	3	**2/3**
Strategies Toolkit (Lesson 7)			3		**3**
Work samples or portfolios; conferences	3	3	2	3	**3**
Show What You Know	3	3	3	3	**3**
Unit Test	3	2	2	3	**2/3**
Unit Problem In the Lab	3	3	3	2	**3**
Achievement Level for reporting					**3**

Recording	**How to Report**
Ongoing Observations	Use *Master 5.2 Ongoing Observations: Data Management* to determine the most consistent level achieved in each category. Enter it in the chart. Choose to summarize by achievement category, or simply to enter an overall level. Observations from late in the unit should be most heavily weighted.
Strategies Toolkit (problem solving)	Use *PM 1: Inquiry Process Check List* with the Strategies Toolkit (Lesson 7). Transfer results to the summary form. Teachers may choose to enter a level in the Problem solving column and/or Communication.
Portfolios or collections of work samples; conferences, or interviews	Use *Master 5.1 Unit Rubric: Sorting and Data Management* to guide evaluation of collections of work and information gathered in conferences. Teachers may choose to focus particular attention on the Assessment Focus questions. Work from late in the unit should be most heavily weighted.
Show What You Know	*Master 5.1 Unit Rubric: Data Management* may be helpful in determining levels of achievement. #5 provides evidence of Understanding of concepts; #3, 4, and 6 provide evidence of Application of mathematical procedures; #4 provides evidence of Problem solving; all provide evidence of Communication.
Unit Test	*Master 5.1 Unit Rubric: Data Management* may be helpful in determining levels of achievement. *Part A* provides evidence of Application of mathematical procedures; Part B provides evidence of Understanding of concepts; Part C provides evidence of Problem solving; all parts provide evidence of Communication. *Master 5.1 Unit Rubric: Data Management* may be helpful in determining levels of achievement.
Unit performance task	Use *Master 5.3 Performance Assessment Rubric: In the Lab* The *Unit Problem* offers a snapshot of students' achievement. In particular, it shows their ability to synthesize and apply what they have learned.
Student Self-Assessment	Note students' perceptions of their own progress. This may take the form of an oral or written comment, or a self-rating.
Comments	Analyse the pattern of achievement to identify strengths and needs. In some cases, specific actions may need to be planned to support the learner.

Learning Skills	**Ongoing Records**
PM 4: Learning Skills Check List Use to record and report throughout a reporting period, rather than for each unit and/or strand.	*PM 10: Summary Class Records: Strands* *PM 11: Summary Class Records: Achievement Categories* *PM 12: Summary Record: Individual* Use to record and report evaluations of student achievement over several clusters, a reporting period, or a school year. These can also be used in place of the Unit Summary.

Name ____________________ Date ______________

Master 5.1

Unit Rubric: Data Management

	Level 1	Level 2	Level 3	Level 4
Problem solving • chooses and carries out appropriate strategies for conducting surveys and other inquiries to answer questions and solve problems	with assistance, chooses and carries out a limited range of appropriate strategies for conducting surveys and other inquiries, rarely producing useful results	with limited assistance, chooses and carries out some appropriate strategies for conducting surveys and other inquiries, frequently producing useful results	chooses and carries out appropriate strategies for conducting surveys and other inquiries, usually producing useful results	chooses and carries out appropriate strategies for conducting surveys and other inquiries, that produce useful and often insightful results; may be innovative
Understanding of concepts • shows understanding by appropriately analysing and explaining: – predictions of survey results – reasonableness of results – choice of intervals (bar graph) or symbols (pictograph) – accuracy or bias of a data display (graph, table, chart) – patterns and results in a data display	may be unable to analyse or explain: – predictions of survey results – reasonableness of results – choice of intervals (bar graph) or symbols (pictograph) – accuracy or bias of a data display (graph, table, chart) – patterns and results in a data display	partially able to analyse and explain: – predictions of survey results – reasonableness of results – choice of intervals (bar graph) or symbols (pictograph) – accuracy or bias of a data display (graph, table, chart) – patterns and results in a data display	appropriately analyses and explains: – predictions of survey results – reasonableness of results – choice of intervals (bar graph) or symbols (pictograph) – accuracy or bias of a data display (graph, table, chart) – patterns and results in a data display	in various contexts, consistently and appropriately analyses and explains: – predictions of survey results – reasonableness of results – choice of intervals (bar graph) or symbols (pictograph) – accuracy or bias of a data display (graph, table, chart) – patterns and results in a data display
Application of mathematical procedures • uses appropriate procedures to accurately: – record data on spreadsheets or tally charts – construct line, bar, circle, and pictographs (by hand or computer) – calculate mean and mode	limited accuracy; major errors or omissions in: – recording data on spreadsheets or tally charts – constructing line, bar, circle, and pictographs (by hand or computer) – calculating mean and mode	somewhat accurate; makes frequent minor errors or omissions in: – recording data on spreadsheets or tally charts – constructing line, bar, circle, and pictographs (by hand or computer) – calculating mean and mode	generally accurate; makes few errors or omissions in: – recording data on spreadsheets or tally charts – constructing line, bar, circle, and pictographs (by hand or computer) – calculating mean and mode	accurate; rarely makes errors or omissions in: – recording data on spreadsheets or tally charts – constructing line, bar, circle, and pictographs (by hand or computer) – calculating mean and mode
Communication • discusses procedures, results, and reasoning clearly, including appropriate terminology (range, mean, mode, interval, sample, bias)	needs assistance to describe procedures, discuss results, and explain reasoning; often unclear and imprecise	describes procedures, discusses results, and explains reasoning with some clarity and precision	describes procedures, discusses results, and explains reasoning clearly and precisely	describes procedures, discusses results, and explains reasoning clearly, precisely, and confidently
• presents work clearly	presents work with little clarity	presents work with some clarity	presents most work clearly and precisely	presents work clearly and precisely

Name ____________________ Date ______________

Master 5.2

Ongoing Observations: Data Management

The behaviours described under each heading are examples; they are not intended to be an exhaustive list of all that might be observed. More detailed descriptions are provided in each lesson under *Assessment for Learning.*

STUDENT ACHIEVEMENT: Data Management				
Student	**Problem solving** ▪ Uses appropriate strategies to conduct surveys and other inquiries	**Understanding of concepts** ▪ Predicts, analyses, interprets, and evaluates results	**Application of mathematical procedures** ▪ Records data on spreadsheets or tally charts ▪ Constructs graphs ▪ Calculates mean and mode	**Communication** ▪ Discusses procedures, results, and reasoning clearly ▪ Presents work clearly

Level 1 – very limited; Level 2 – somewhat or limited; Level 3 – satisfactory; Level 4 – thorough

Name ____________________ Date ______________

Master 5.3

Performance Assessment Rubric: In the Lab

	Level 1	Level 2	Level 3	Level 4
Problem solving • chooses and carries out appropriate strategies to design an experiment to collect and study data	with assistance, chooses and carries out a limited range of appropriate strategies to design and conduct an experiment; does not produce useful results	chooses and carries out some appropriate strategies to design and conduct an experiment; results partially answer the question posed; results are flawed	chooses and carries out appropriate strategies to design and conduct an experiment that meets the requirements; results answer the question posed	chooses and carries out appropriate strategies to design and conduct an experiment with some complexity or innovation; results fully answer the question posed and may offer some insight
Understanding of concepts • shows understanding by analysing and explaining: – predicted results – another group's results (are they reasonable?) – own results (what they learned)	shows very limited understanding by giving inappropriate explanations of: – predicted results – another group's results – own results	shows limited understanding by giving appropriate but incomplete explanations of: – predicted results – another group's results – own results	shows understanding by giving appropriate explanations of: – predicted results – another group's results – own results	shows thorough understanding by giving appropriate and complete explanations of: – predicted results – another group's results – own results
Application of mathematical procedures • uses appropriate procedures to accurately: – collect and record data in a table – construct a graph – summarize results	limited accuracy; major errors or omissions in: – collecting and recording data in a table – constructing a graph – summarizing results	somewhat accurate; several minor errors or omissions in: – collecting and recording data in a table – constructing a graph – summarizing results	generally accurate; few errors or omissions in: – collecting and recording data in a table – constructing a graph – summarizing results	accurate; very few or no errors or omissions in: – collecting and recording data in a table – constructing a graph – summarizing results
Communication • provides a clear presentation and explanation of results • uses mathematical terminology (mean, mode, sample, bias)	presentation and discussion are unclear and imprecise uses few appropriate mathematical terms	presentation and discussion are partially clear and precise uses some appropriate mathematical terms	presentation and discussion are generally clear and precise uses appropriate mathematical terms	presentation and discussion are clear, precise, and confident consistently uses the most appropriate mathematical terminology

Name ____________________ Date ________________

Master 5.4

Unit Summary: Data Management

Review assessment records to determine the most consistent achievement levels for the assessments conducted. Some cells may be blank. *Overall* achievement levels may be recorded in each row, rather than identifying levels for each achievement category.

	Most Consistent Level of Achievement*				
Strand: *Data Management and Probability*	**Problem solving**	**Understanding of concepts**	**Application of mathematical procedures**	**Communication**	***Overall***
Ongoing Observations					
Strategies Toolkit (Lesson 7)					
Work samples or portfolios; conferences					
Show What You Know					
Unit Test					
Unit Problem In the Lab					
Achievement Level for reporting					

*Use Ontario Achievement Levels 1, 2, 3, 4.

Self-Assessment:

Comments: (Strengths, Needs, Next Steps)

Name ____________________ Date _______________

Master 5.5

To Parents and Adults at Home …

Your child's class is starting a mathematics unit on data management.

Data management is interpreting, collecting, and organizing data in tables and graphs. This unit includes many concepts and themes your child already encounters in the world. Your child will be interpreting, designing, and conducting surveys, and displaying the results in graphs. Your child will also be introduced to the idea that data can be displayed with bias.

In this unit, your child will:

- Interpret and evaluate data in tables and graphs.
- Draw labelled graphs by hand and with a computer.
- Recognize accuracy or bias in the way data are presented.
- Examine how data were collected and if they are reasonable.
- Find the mean and the mode of a set of data.
- Predict the results of a survey.
- Design and conduct a survey.

There are many activities you can do at home that will improve your child's understanding in these areas. Consider:

- Encouraging your child to discuss any surveys you hear mentioned in the news.
- Asking your child to interpret data displayed in tables, charts, or graphs found in newspapers, magazines, or on the Internet.

Name ____________________ Date ______________

Master 5.6

Additional Activity 1: Word Find

Work on your own.
You will need 1-cm grid paper and a 2-column chart.

- Make as many words as you can from the letters
  DATA MANAGEMENT
  Write the words in one column of your chart.
  Do you think you found all the words? Why or why not?

- In the second column of your chart, write the length of each word.
  For example, one row of your chart might have "magnate" in the word column and "7" in the length column.
  What is the longest word you could find?

- Count how many words of each length you have.

- Using grid paper, display your results in a bar graph.

Take It Further:
Compare your graph with that of a classmate.
How are the graphs the same?
How are they different?
Write 3 things you learned from your classmate's graph.

Name ____________________ Date _______________

Master 5.7

Additional Activity 2
Story of Mrs. D

Work with a partner.

- Mrs. D. likes to record everything she does in different types of graphs.
  When she goes out to do errands, she records her distance from home and displays the data in a line graph.
  Here is the graph of Mrs. D.'s activities for one day.

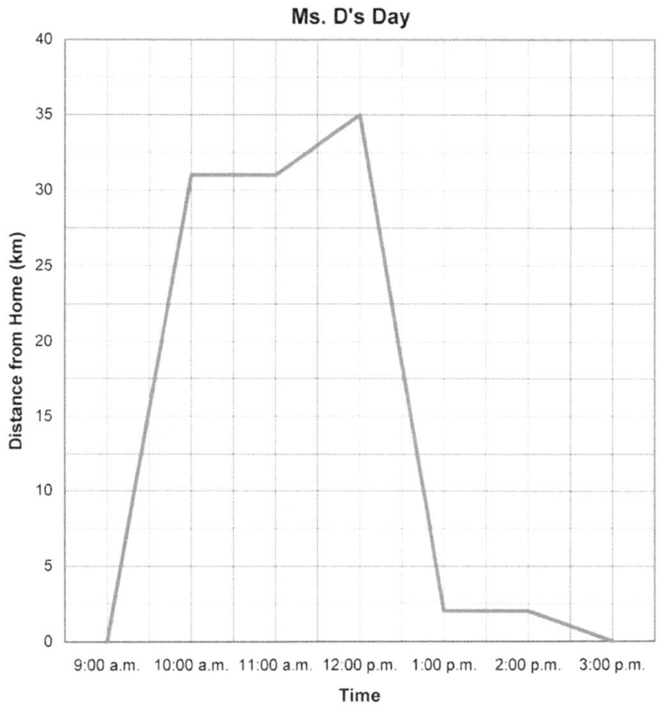

- Look at the graph.
  When is Mrs. D. getting further away from home? How can you tell?
  When is she getting closer to home? How can you tell?
  When is Mrs. D. staying in the same place? How is this shown on the graph?

- Write a story about Mrs. D.'s activities that fits the graph.
  Be specific about time and distance.

Take It Further:
Draw your own line graph and write a story about yourself that fits the graph.

Name ____________________ Date ______________

Master 5.8

Additional Activity 3
Concrete Bars

Work with a partner.
You will need a class list, 6 skewers, 6 strips of paper, 30 Cheerios, and Plasticine.

- With your partner, design a survey question you would like to ask your classmates.
  Your question should have 5 or 6 possible answers, which you will select in advance.
  Record your question and answers.

- Make a block out of Plasticine.
  Stick in 1 skewer for each possible answer to your question.
  Using the strips of paper, label each skewer with the corresponding answer.

- Survey your classmates.
  When you ask a classmate your question, give her or him a Cheerio.
  Have your classmate place the Cheerio on the skewer that represents her or his answer.
  As you survey your classmates, check off their names on the class list.
  Make sure you survey each of your classmates once.

- Look at your skewers.
  What kind of graph is this like?

- Write 3 things you learned about your classmates.

Take It Further:
Conduct a second survey with a different number of possible responses.

Name ____________________ Date ________________

Master 5.9

Additional Activity 4
Paper Search

Work with a partner.
You will need 1-cm grid paper and newspapers or magazines.

- With your partner, look through newspapers or magazines to find a graph that shows bias.
  What data does the graph show?

- Discuss with your partner the bias of the graph.
  Why do you think the graph is biased?
  Who does the bias benefit? Who do you think chose this graph?
  What could you change on the graph to remove the bias?

- Write 3 questions about your graph.

- Answer your questions.

Take It Further:
Redraw the graph without bias.

Name ____________________ Date _______________

Master 5.10

Step-by-Step 1

Lesson 1, Question 4

Step 1 Look at the graph on page 159.
Which vegetable has the highest bar? ___________________

Which vegetable takes the longest to grow? ___________________

Step 2 What is the greatest number of days? _______________

What is the least number of days? _________________

The range of the data is the greatest number minus the least number.

What is the range of this data? ______ – ______ = ______

Step 3 Use the graph on page 159.
Find the number of days each vegetable grows before harvesting.

Vegetable	Number of Days
Cabbage	
Leek	
Lettuce	
Onion	
Spinach	

Vegetable	Number of Symbols
Cabbage	
Leek	
Lettuce	
Onion	
Spinach	

What number divides into each number in the second column? ___________

What key would you use? ____

Step 4 If you used that key, how many symbols would you need for each vegetable?

____

____

Name ____________________ Date ______________

Master 5.11

Step-by-Step 2

Lesson 2, Question 5

Use the graph on page 162.

Step 1 Which sports have the same length bars?

____

Which sports are equally popular?

____

Step 2 The mode of a set of data is the number that occurs most often.
Which bars on the graph are the same length?

____

What does that tell you about these sports?

____

How could you use the graph to find the mode?

____

Step 3 Estimate the length of each bar in the graph.
Fill in the missing numbers.

Sport	Number of People	Sport	Number of People
Volleyball		Hockey	
Tennis		Golf	
Swimming		Cycling	
Soccer		Basketball	
Skiing		Baseball	
Total		**Total**	

Step 4 The mean is an average for the data. One way to calculate the mean is to find the total number of people and divide by the number of sports.

What is the total number of people? _____ + _____ = _____

How many sports are there altogether? ______

Calculate the mean: _____ ÷ _____ = _____

Name ____________________ Date _______________

Master 5.12

Step-by-Step 3

Lesson 3, Question 4

Step 1 See the data on page 168. What is the greatest number? _____

What is the least number? _____

The range is the difference between the greatest and least numbers.

What is the range of the data? _____ – _____ = _____

Step 2 Choose 5 equal intervals. ______ ______ ______ ______ ______

Do your intervals cover the entire range? _______

Are they completely separate (with no overlap)? _______

Step 3 Fill in the table below.

Interval (Heights in cm)					
Number of Students					

Step 4 Construct a bar graph using the data in the table.

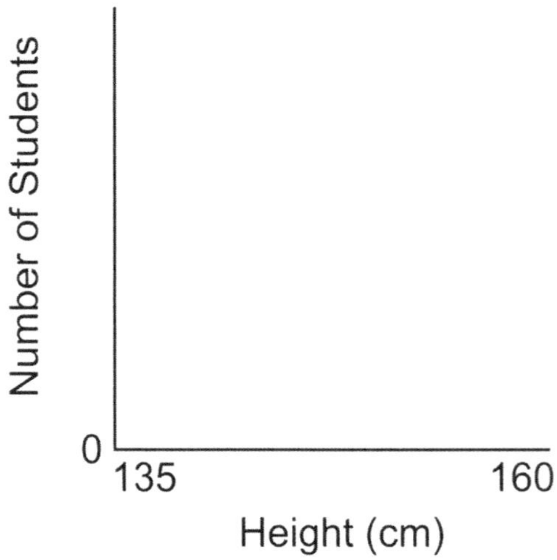

Step 5 Write 2 things you can learn from your graph.

1. ____

2. ____

Name ________________ Date ____________

Master 5.13

Step-by-Step 4

Lesson 4, Question 3

Look at the table on page 175.

Step 1 What is the greatest number? ________

What is the least number? ________

What is the range of the data? ________

Step 2 Use the range from *Step 1*.
Choose a scale for the vertical axis.
How many beekeepers for 1 square on the grid? ________
Use a scale of 1 square for 1 year on the horizontal axis.

Step 3 On grid paper, draw a line graph to display the data.

Step 4 How does the number of beekeepers change?

____

How does the graph show this change?

____

Step 5 How many beekeepers do you think there will be in Ontario in 2004?
Explain.

____

____

Name ____________________ Date _______________

Master 5.14

Step-by-Step 5

Lesson 5, Question 3

Look at the graph on page 180.

Step 1 What does the graph show?

____

Step 2 What were the possible answers to the survey question?

____

Step 3 What might the survey question have been?

____

Step 4 How many students gave each answer? Fill in the chart.

Location	Number of Students
Kitchen	
Bedroom	
Family room	
No computer	

Step 5 How many students were surveyed altogether? ________

Step 6 How many students are usually in a classroom? ________

How many students are usually in a school? ________

Do you think a sample or an entire group was surveyed? ________

Step 7 Write 2 things you learned from this survey.

1. ____

2. ____

Name ____________________ Date _______________

Master 5.15

Step-by-Step 6

Lesson 6, Question 3

Look at the graphs on page 185.

Step 1 Use Graph A. Fill in the table below.

Brands	Number of People
Krunchie	
Tasty Tater	
Delish	

Step 2 Use Graph B. Fill in the table below.

Brands	Number of People
Krunchie	
Tasty Tater	
Delish	

Step 3 Look at Graph B.
Is Krunchie twice as popular as the others? ________
Look at the table you completed in *Step 2*.

Is Krunchie twice as popular? ________

Why do the graph and the table appear to show different data?

____

Step 4 Which graph makes Krunchie look more popular?

____

If you were advertising Krunchie, which graph would you use? Why?

____

Name ____________________ Date ______________

Master 5.16a

Unit Test: Unit 5 Data Management

Part A

1. The gumdrops in a bag are sorted by colour.

Colour	Number of Gumdrops	Colour	Number of Gumdrops
Red	9	Purple	15
Yellow	16	White	18
Orange	15	Pink	16
Green	8	Brown	15
Black	10		

a) How many gumdrops are in the bag? _______

b) What is the mean? Show your work. ______________________

c) What is the mode? How do you know? ______________________

d) What is the range of the data? Show your work. ______________________

e) Use 1-cm grid paper. Draw a bar graph to display these data.

f) Which colour has one-half as many gumdrops as white? ______________

How can you tell this from the graph? ______________________

Part B

2. This table shows how many students were absent at Terple School in one year.

Month	Number of Absentees	Month	Number of Absentees
September	12	February	46
October	23	March	58
November	25	April	39
December	27	May	23
January	33	June	11

a) Why are all the months not shown on the table?

____

b) Use 1-cm grid paper. Draw a line graph for the data.

Name ____________ Date ____________

Master 5.16b

Unit Test continued

c) What trend do you see in the graph?

____

d) Write two things you can tell from the graph.

____

____

3. This circle graphs shows where the bones in your head are.

Bones in Your Head

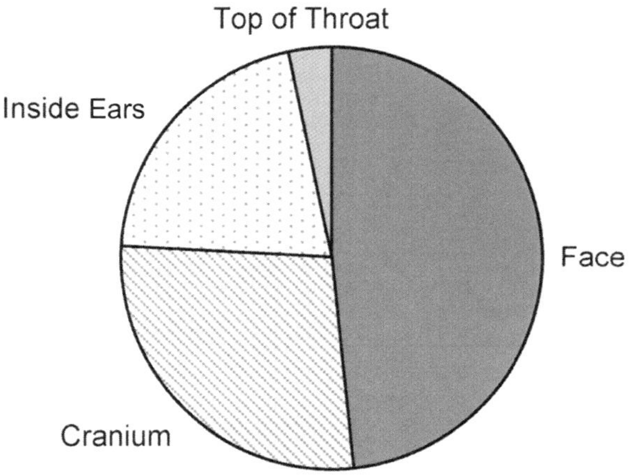

a) Which part of the head has the most bones? ____________

What fraction shows this? ____________

b) Which part of the head has about $\frac{1}{4}$ of the bones in your head?

How do you know this? ____________

c) There are 8 bones in your cranium.

About how many are in your face? ____________

Inside your ears? ____________

At the top of your throat? ____________

Name ____________________ Date ______________

Master 5.16c

Unit Test continued

Part C

4. These two graphs show the price of popcorn at the Tasty Theatre during the last 6 years.

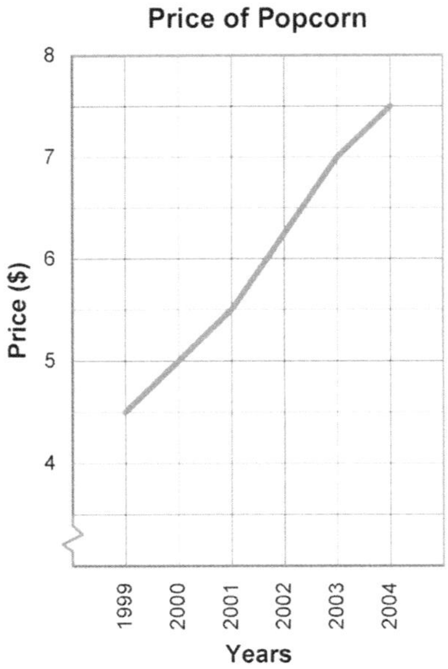

Graph A

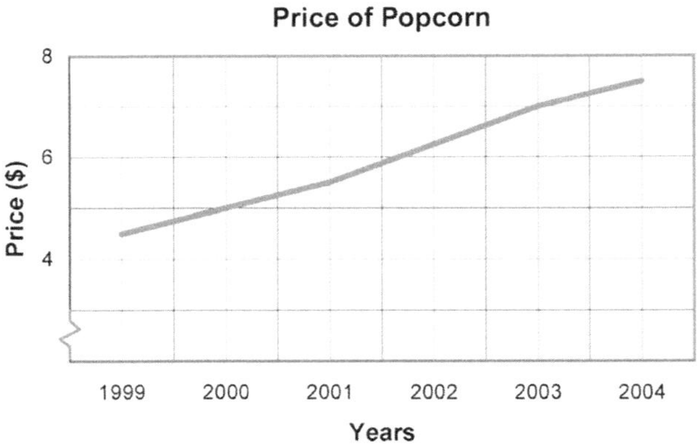

Graph B

a) How are the graphs similar?

____

b) How are the graphs different?

____

c) Do the graphs show the same data? Explain.

____

d) Do you think either graph shows bias? Explain.

____

e) Which graph do you think shows the data better? Explain your answer.

____

____

Name ____________________ Date ______________

Master 5.17

Sample Answers

Unit Test – Master 5.16

Part A

1. a) 122
   b) 122 ÷ 9 = 13.6, or about 14
   c) 15; it is the most common number.
   d) 18 – 8 = 10
   e)

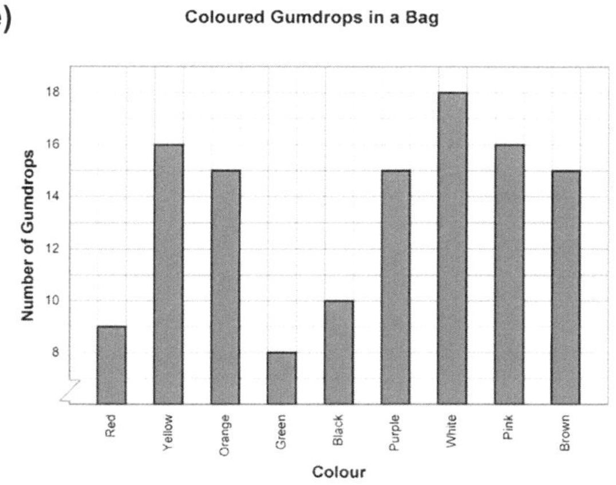

   f) Red; the bar for red is half the height of the bar for white.

Part B

2. a) Children don't go to school in July and August.
   b)

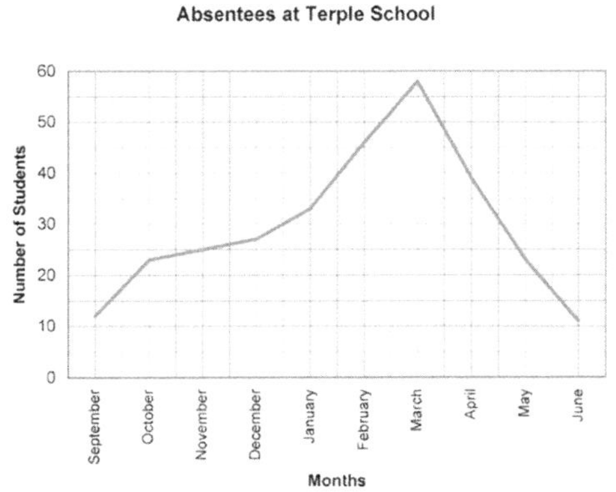

   c) The number of absentees increases until March, then decreases for the rest of the school year.
   d) The most students are absent in March. The fewest students are absent in June.

3. a) The face; it has about $\frac{1}{2}$ of the bones in your head.
   b) The cranium; the area shaded is a little more than $\frac{1}{4}$.
   c) About 14; 6; 1

Part C

4. a) The graphs show the same data; both show an increase.
   b) The scales on the vertical axes are different.
   c) Yes. They both show the data: 1999 \$4.50, 2000 \$5, 2001 \$5.50, 2002 \$6.25, 2003 \$7.00, 2004 \$7.50
   d) The graphs use different scales, which makes them look different. This is not necessarily bias, unless the graphs are used to persuade or influence in a specific way.
   e) Opinions can be given to support either graph.

Extra Practice Masters 5.18–5.24

Go to the CD-ROM to access editable versions of these Extra Practice Masters

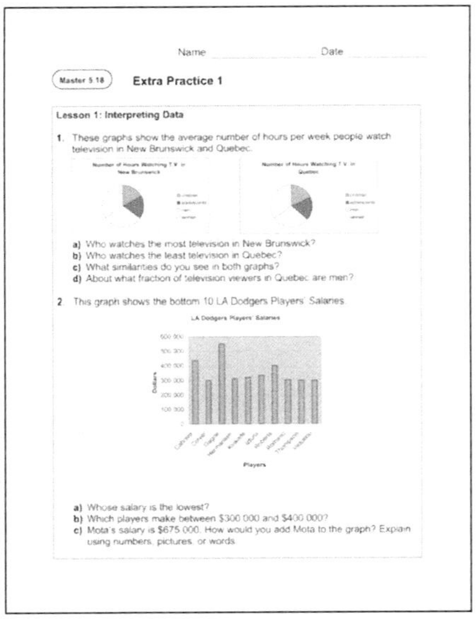
Name ______ Date ______

Master 5.18 **Extra Practice 1**

Lesson 1: Interpreting Data

1. These graphs show the average number of hours per week people watch television in New Brunswick and Quebec.
   a) Who watches the most television in New Brunswick?
   b) Who watches the least television in Quebec?
   c) What similarities do you see in both graphs?
   d) About what fraction of television viewers in Quebec are men?
2. This graph shows the bottom 10 LA Dodgers Players' Salaries.
   a) Whose salary is the lowest?
   b) Which players make between $300 000 and $400 000?
   c) Mota's salary is $675 000. How would you add Mota to the graph? Explain using numbers, pictures, or words.

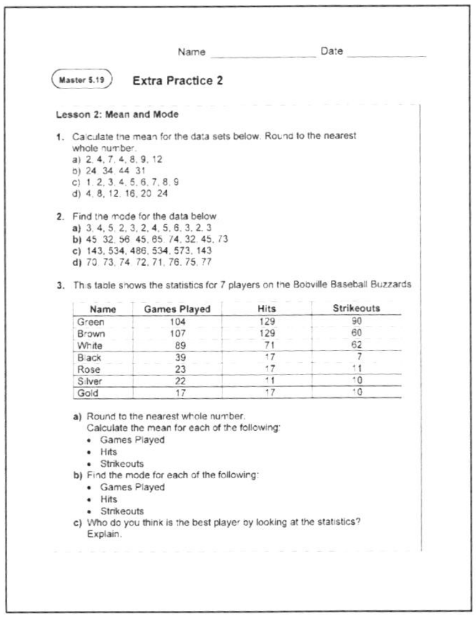
Name ______ Date ______

Master 5.19 **Extra Practice 2**

Lesson 2: Mean and Mode

1. Calculate the mean for the data sets below. Round to the nearest whole number.
   a) 2, 4, 7, 4, 8, 9, 12
   b) 24, 34, 44, 31
   c) 1, 2, 3, 4, 5, 6, 7, 8, 9
   d) 4, 8, 12, 16, 20, 24
2. Find the mode for the data below.
   a) 3, 4, 5, 2, 3, 2, 4, 5, 6, 3, 2, 3
   b) 45, 32, 56, 45, 65, 74, 32, 45, 73
   c) 143, 534, 486, 534, 573, 143
   d) 70, 73, 74, 72, 71, 76, 75, 77
3. This table shows the statistics for 7 players on the Booville Baseball Buzzards.

Name	Games Played	Hits	Strikeouts
Green	104	129	90
Brown	107	129	60
White	89	71	62
Black	39	17	7
Rose	23	17	11
Silver	22	11	10
Gold	17	17	10

   a) Round to the nearest whole number. Calculate the mean for each of the following:
      - Games Played
      - Hits
      - Strikeouts
   b) Find the mode for each of the following:
      - Games Played
      - Hits
      - Strikeouts
   c) Who do you think is the best player by looking at the statistics? Explain.

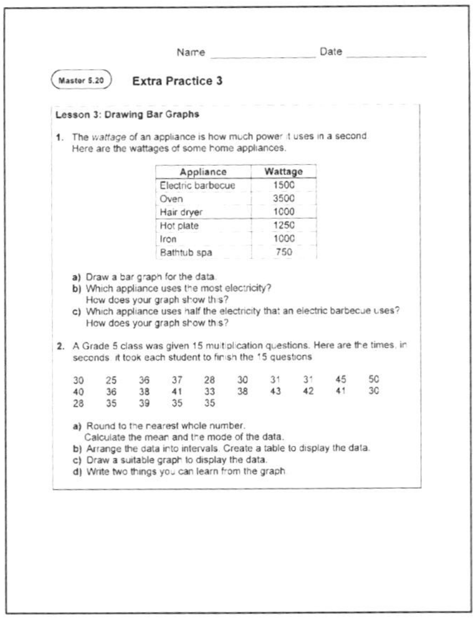
Name ______ Date ______

Master 5.20 **Extra Practice 3**

Lesson 3: Drawing Bar Graphs

1. The wattage of an appliance is how much power it uses in a second. Here are the wattages of some home appliances.

Appliance	Wattage
Electric barbecue	1500
Oven	3500
Hair dryer	1000
Hot plate	1250
Iron	1000
Bathtub spa	750

   a) Draw a bar graph for the data.
   b) Which appliance uses the most electricity? How does your graph show this?
   c) Which appliance uses half the electricity that an electric barbecue uses? How does your graph show this?
2. A Grade 5 class was given 15 multiplication questions. Here are the times, in seconds, it took each student to finish the 15 questions.

30	25	36	37	28	30	31	31	45	50
40	36	38	41	33	38	43	42	41	30
28	35	39	35	35					

   a) Round to the nearest whole number. Calculate the mean and the mode of the data.
   b) Arrange the data into intervals. Create a table to display the data.
   c) Draw a suitable graph to display the data.
   d) Write two things you can learn from the graph.

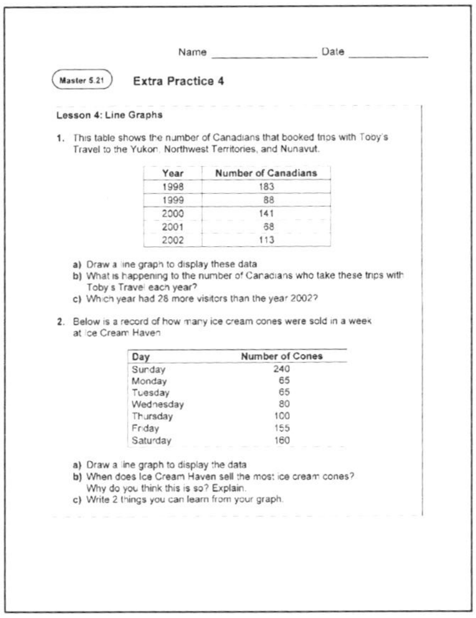
Name ______ Date ______

Master 5.21 **Extra Practice 4**

Lesson 4: Line Graphs

1. This table shows the number of Canadians that booked trips with Toby's Travel to the Yukon, Northwest Territories, and Nunavut.

Year	Number of Canadians
1998	183
1999	88
2000	141
2001	68
2002	113

   a) Draw a line graph to display these data.
   b) What is happening to the number of Canadians who take these trips with Toby's Travel each year?
   c) Which year had 28 more visitors than the year 2002?
2. Below is a record of how many ice cream cones were sold in a week at Ice Cream Haven.

Day	Number of Cones
Sunday	240
Monday	65
Tuesday	65
Wednesday	80
Thursday	100
Friday	155
Saturday	160

   a) Draw a line graph to display the data.
   b) When does Ice Cream Haven sell the most ice cream cones? Why do you think this is so? Explain.
   c) Write 2 things you can learn from your graph.

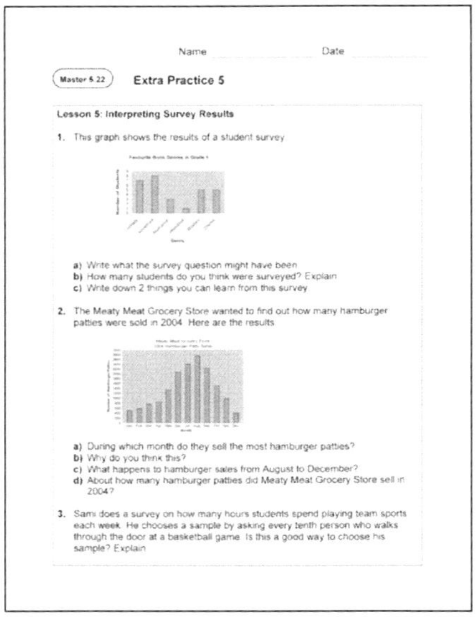
Name ______ Date ______

Master 5.22 **Extra Practice 5**

Lesson 5: Interpreting Survey Results

1. This graph shows the results of a student survey.
   a) Write what the survey question might have been.
   b) How many students do you think were surveyed? Explain.
   c) Write down 2 things you can learn from this survey.
2. The Meaty Meat Grocery Store wanted to find out how many hamburger patties were sold in 2004. Here are the results.
   a) During which month do they sell the most hamburger patties?
   b) Why do you think this?
   c) What happens to hamburger sales from August to December?
   d) About how many hamburger patties did Meaty Meat Grocery Store sell in 2004?
3. Sam does a survey on how many hours students spend playing team sports each week. He chooses a sample by asking every tenth person who walks through the door at a basketball game. Is this a good way to choose his sample? Explain.

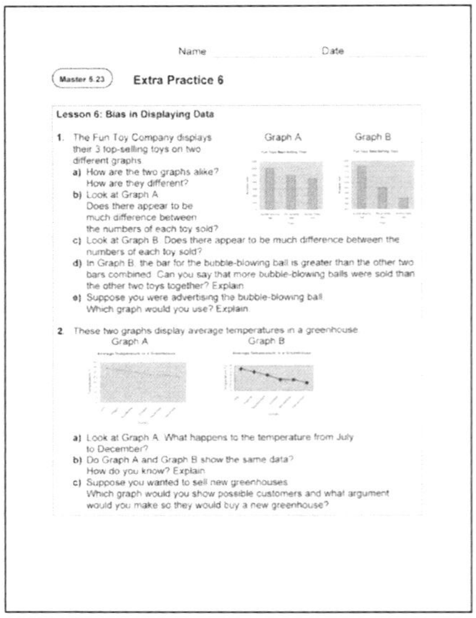
Name ______ Date ______

Master 5.23 **Extra Practice 6**

Lesson 6: Bias in Displaying Data

1. The Fun Toy Company displays their 3 top-selling toys on two different graphs.
   Graph A Graph B
   a) How are the two graphs alike? How are they different?
   b) Look at Graph A. Does there appear to be much difference between the numbers of each toy sold?
   c) Look at Graph B. Does there appear to be much difference between the numbers of each toy sold?
   d) In Graph B, the bar for the bubble-blowing ball is greater than the other two bars combined. Can you say that more bubble-blowing balls were sold than the other two toys together? Explain.
   e) Suppose you were advertising the bubble-blowing ball. Which graph would you use? Explain.
2. These two graphs display average temperatures in a greenhouse.
   Graph A Graph B
   a) Look at Graph A. What happens to the temperature from July to December?
   b) Do Graph A and Graph B show the same data? How do you know? Explain.
   c) Suppose you wanted to sell new greenhouses. Which graph would you show possible customers and what argument would you make so they would buy a new greenhouse?

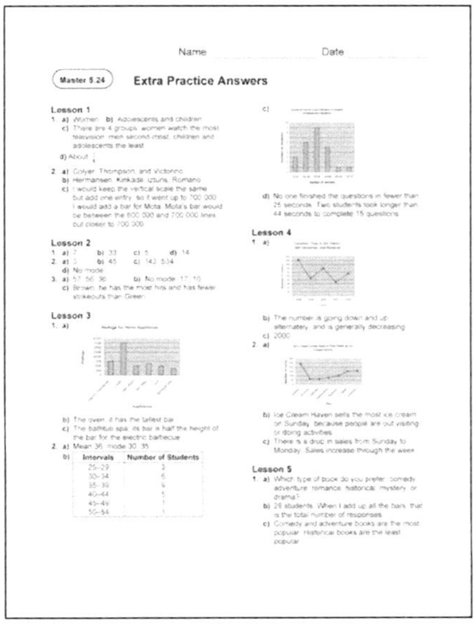
Name ______ Date ______

Master 5.24 **Extra Practice Answers**

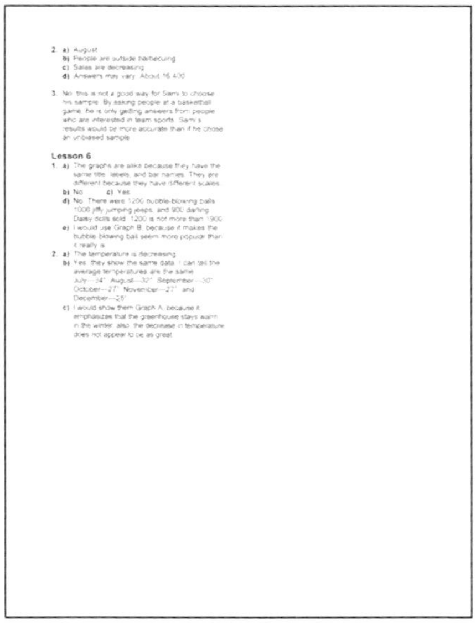

Addison Wesley
Mathematics
Makes Sense

Program Authors

Peggy Morrow
Ralph Connelly
Bryn Keyes
Jason Johnston
Steve Thomas
Jeananne Thomas
Angela D'Alessandro
Maggie Martin Connell
Don Jones
Michael Davis
Sharon Jeroski
Trevor Brown
Nora Alexander
Cynthia Pratt Nicolson

Printed and bound in Canada

8 9 MP 18 17

PEARSON
Education Canada

ADDISON WESLEY

Ontario

Math Makes Sense 5

Ontario

Teacher Guide

Unit 6: Measurement

PEARSON
Addison Wesley

UNIT 6

Measurement

"... measurement helps connect ideas within areas of mathematics and between mathematics and other disciplines. It can serve as a context to help students introduce and develop important mathematical concepts such as fractions, decimals, and proportional reasoning."

– *Principles and Standards for School Mathematics*, NCTM, 1998

FOCUS STRAND
Measurement

SUPPORTING STRAND
Number Sense and Numeration

Mathematics Background

What Are the Big Ideas?

- Measurements of mass, volume, and capacity are made with greater attention to degree of accuracy. Mass is measured in grams. Capacity is measured in litres. Volume is measured in cubic centimetres.
- Time is measured to the second and is recorded using SI notation.
- *Volume* is the amount of space an object occupies. *Capacity* is the amount a container can hold.
- Students count money, and estimate and provide correct change for purchases.
- The relationship between time and distance is known as *speed*. Speed is the measure of how fast an object is moving.

How Will the Concepts Develop?

Students estimate and measure time intervals to the nearest second and record the time in standard notation. They explore the relationship between time and distance.

Students refine their skills in estimating and counting money and learn different strategies for making change for items.

Students build upon their previous understanding of millilitre and litre. They reflect upon their estimates of capacity and make predictions based upon their observations.

Students make predictions, then measure and order a variety of solids by volume, using centimetre cubes. They explore the relationship between volume and capacity, using centimetre cubes and solid objects, by measuring the displacement of water. Students predict the volume of solids, and make conversions between millilitres and cubic centimetres.

Students measure, estimate, and compare mass in milligrams, grams, and kilograms. They investigate large masses and examine the relationship between kilograms and metric tonnes.

Why Are These Concepts Important?

Measurement is an important mathematics strand because of its practicality, its role in linking mathematics to the real world, and its connections to other areas of mathematics. As students investigate relationships between and among measurement concepts, their work is closely connected with other mathematical strands, especially Number Sense and Numeration.

Curriculum Overview

Cluster 1: Exploring Time and Money

Overall Expectations
- Students identify relationships between and among measurement concepts. (5m38)

Specific Expectations
- Students estimate and measure time intervals to the nearest second. (5m47)
- Students read and write dates and times using SI notation. (5m48)
- Students read an analog clock to the nearest second and write the time to the nearest minute. (5m49)
- Students estimate the amount of money in a collection of coins and bills to $1000 and count to determine the total value. (5m50)
- Students read and write money values to $1000. (5m51)
- Students make purchases of and change for items up to $100. (5m52)
- Students identify the relationship between the movement of objects and speed. (5m53)

Launch
All Aboard!

Lesson 1: Measuring Time
Lesson 2: Exploring Time and Distance
Lesson 3: Strategies Toolkit
Lesson 4: Estimating and Counting Money
Lesson 5: Making Change

Cluster 2: Measuring Capacity, Volume, and Mass

Overall Expectations
- Students demonstrate an understanding of and ability to apply appropriate metric prefixes in measurement and estimation activities. (5m37)
- Students estimate, measure, and record the capacity of containers, the mass of familiar objects, and the volume of irregular three-dimensional figures, and compare the measures. (5m40)

Specific Expectations
- Students use prefixes in the metric system correctly. (5m41)
- Students measure containers by volume using standard units: cubic centimetres. (5m59)
- Students determine the relationship between capacity and volume by measuring the volume of various objects and by determining the displacement of liquid by each object. (5m60)
- Students relate the volume of an irregular three-dimensional figure to its capacity. (5m61)
- Students describe the relationship between millilitres and cubic centimetres. (5m62)
- Students determine the relationship between kilograms and metric tonnes. (5m63)
- Students select the most appropriate standard unit to measure mass. (5m64)

Lesson 6: Capacity
Lesson 7: Volume
Lesson 8: Relating Capacity and Volume
Lesson 9: Measuring Mass
Lesson 10: Exploring Large Masses

Show What You Know

Unit Problem
All Aboard!

Curriculum across the Grades

Grade 4	Grade 5	Grade 6
Students are introduced to the decade, the century, and the millennium, and their relationships. They estimate and measure time intervals to the nearest minute.	Students estimate and measure time intervals to the nearest second, read an analog clock to the nearest second, and write the time to the nearest minute.	Students describe the relationship between a 12-hour clock and a 24-hour clock.
Students estimate and count money, make purchases and change, and read and write money values to $50.	Students estimate and count money, and read and write money values to $1000. They make purchases of and change for items up to $100.	Students estimate and count money, and read and write money values to $10 000. They represent amounts of money under $100 using the smallest possible number of coins and bills.
Students select the most appropriate standard unit to measure the capacity of containers (millilitres or litres) and to measure mass (grams or kilograms). They describe the relationships between grams and kilograms, and millilitres and litres.	Students determine the relationship between capacity and volume and describe the relationship between millilitres and cubic centimetres. They measure containers by volume using cubic centimetres.	Students determine the relationship between and among measurement concepts. They select among commonly used SI units of mass and capacity to solve problems.
Students estimate, measure, and record the mass of objects using standard units (grams or kilograms), compare the measures, and order objects by mass.	Students select the most appropriate standard unit to measure mass and determine the relationship between kilograms and tonnes.	Students make simple conversions between metric units and determine the relationship between milligrams, grams, and kilograms.

Materials for This Unit

In this unit you will need a small medicine measuring cup (cough medicine), an envelope, a ping-pong ball, 50 pennies.

Additional Activities

Walk the Walk

Extension (Appropriate for use after Lesson 2)
Materials: clocks or stopwatches, calculators, metre sticks, *Walk the Walk* (Master 6.7)

The work students do: Students work in pairs. They estimate how long it will take to walk 1 km. They measure a distance of 10 m and then record the time it takes each partner to walk that distance. The time is recorded in seconds and then converted to minutes or hours (if necessary).

Take It Further: Students may try to determine the time it will take to travel 10 km, 100 km, or further. Students may also try to determine running time instead of walking time.

Kinesthetic
Partner Activity

Money Matters

For Extra Support (Appropriate for use after Lesson 4)
Materials: play money, calculator, *Money Matters* (Master 6.8a), *Money Matters Price Cards* (Master 6.8b)

The work students do: Students score points by being the first person to correctly count out the proper amount of change from $100. Each student starts the game with coins and bills adding up to $100. Students turn over two price cards from the stack, add them up, and find the required change.

Take It Further: Students may start with more money and draw 3 or more cards.

Logical/Mathematical/Social
Group Activity

Millilitre Mania

For Extra Practice (Appropriate for use after Lesson 6)
Materials: plastic container, water, measuring container, *Millilitre Mania* (Master 6.9a), *Capacity Cards for Millilitre Mania* (Master 6.9b)

The work students do: Students score points by estimating and measuring various amounts of water. Students take turns drawing capacity cards and attempting to pour the amount listed on the card into an unmarked container. The water is then measured for scoring. Students receive 15 points if they pour within 5 mL, 5 points within 25 mL, and 3 points within 50 mL. The game is over after a specified number of rounds or when a time limit has been reached.

Take It Further: Have students measure and estimate greater capacities.

Kinesthetic/Social
Partner Activity

Muddling Through Mass

For Extra Practice (Appropriate for use after Lesson 10)
Materials: paper, balance scales, standard masses, calculators, rulers, 1-cm grid paper (PM 23), *Muddling Through Mass* (Master 6.10)

The work students do: Students find the height of a 100-kg stack of paper. Using sheets of paper and balance scales, students measure the mass of various stacks of paper. Students should try to determine the mass of 1 kg of paper, measure the height of the stack and then multiply the height by 100. The relationship can be shown on a line graph.

Take It Further: Students may try to find the height of 1 t of stacked paper. Students can explain how to use their measurements to find the mass of one sheet of paper.

Kinesthetic/Social
Partner Activity

Planning for Unit 6

Planning for Instruction

Suggested Unit time: 2–3 weeks

Lesson	Time	Materials	Program Support
Launch: All Aboard!, page 2	10–15 min		
Lesson 1: Measuring Time, page 4 Tell time to the nearest second.	40–50 min	stopwatches	Master 6.11: Step-by-Step 1 Master 6.22: Extra Practice 1
Lesson 2: Exploring Time and Distance, page 7 Explore time and distance relationships.	40–50 min	books masking tape marbles metre sticks stopwatches Bristol board	Master 6.12: Step-by-Step 2 Master 6.22: Extra Practice 1
Lesson 3: Strategies Toolkit, page 10 Interpret a problem and select an appropriate strategy.	40–50 min	1-cm grid paper	PM 23: 1-cm Grid Paper
Lesson 4: Estimating and Counting Money, page 12 Estimate and count money to $1000.	40–50 min	play money envelope containing $1000 in play money calculator	PM 30: Play Money Master 6.13: Step-by-Step 4 Master 6.23: Extra Practice 2
Lesson 5: Making Change, page 15 Make purchases and make change from $100.	40–50 min	play money auction cards	PM 30: Play Money Master 6.6: Auction Cards Master 6.14: Step-by-Step 5 Master 6.23: Extra Practice 2
Lesson 6: Capacity, page 18 Estimate, measure, and compare capacities in millilitres and litres.	40–50 min	small medicine cup assorted graduated cylinders different-sized containers measuring spoons bucket of water	Master 6.15: Step-by-Step 6 Master 6.24: Extra Practice 3
Lesson 7: Volume, page 20 Use centimetre cubes to measure volume.	40–50 min	1-cm interlocking cubes	Master 6.16: Step-by-Step 7 Master 6.24: Extra Practice 3
Lesson 8: Relating Capacity and Volume, page 23 Explore the relationship between millilitres and cubic centimetres.	40–50 min	500-mL graduated cylinders centimetre cubes assorted small solid objects 50 pennies dimes ping-pong ball 500-g mass modelling clay counters 3-column charts	PM 18: 3-Column Chart Master 6.17: Step-by-Step 8 Master 6.25: Extra Practice 4
Lesson 9: Measuring Mass, page 26 Measure and compare mass in milligrams, grams, and kilograms.	40–50 min	balance scales standard masses	Master 6.18: Step-by-Step 9 Master 6.25: Extra Practice 4
Lesson 10: Exploring Large Masses, page 29 Use tonnes to measure mass.	40–50 min	metric bathroom scales	Master 6.19: Step-by-Step 10 Master 6.26: Extra Practice 5

Lesson	Time	Materials	Program Support
Show What You Know, page 32 Assessment	40–50 min		
Unit Problem: All Aboard!, page 34 Assessment	40–50 min	drinking straws (rigid and flexible) scissors Bristol board pencil crayons or markers glue tape calculators centimetre cubes 4-column charts	PM 19: 4-Column Chart

Planning for Assessment

Purpose	Tools and Process	Recording and Reporting
Diagnostic	*Unit Launch* Question; conference; scaffold problems throughout the unit	PM 8: Conference Prompts
Formative	*Explore* – Ongoing Assessment: Observe and Listen	Master 6.2 Ongoing Observations: Measurement PM 1: Inquiry Process Check List PM 6: Observation Record 1 PM 7: Observation Record 2 PM 8: Conference Prompts
	Prompt student's self-assessment	PM 2: Self-Assessment PM 3: Self-Assessment: Problem Solving
	Practice – Assessment Focus Questions	PM 9: Work Sample Records
	Review student work; provide feedback; scaffold as needed; select key pieces	
Summative	*Show What You Know* *Unit Problem* – Performance Assessment Unit Test	Master 6.1 Unit Rubric: Measurement Master 6.3 Performance Assessment Rubric: All Aboard! Master 6.4 Unit Summary: Measurement
	Review assessment records; add unit results to ongoing records	PM 10: Summary Class Records: Strands PM 11: Summary Class Records: Achievement Categories PM 12: Summary Record: Individual
Learning Skills/ Mathematical Disposition	Observe and record throughout unit	PM 4: Learning Skills Check List PM 5: Mathematical Dispositions and Learning Skills

Program Masters (PM) are in the *Grade 5 Planning and Program Masters* module.
Extra Practice Masters are on the CD-ROM.

All Aboard!

LESSON ORGANIZER

10–15 min

Curriculum Focus: Activate prior learning about measurement.
Vocabulary: mass, kilogram, volume, capacity, cubic centimetre

ASSUMED PRIOR KNOWLEDGE

- ✓ Students can identify relationships between and among measurement concepts.
- ✓ Students can select the most appropriate standard unit to measure mass and capacity.

UNIT 6

Measurement

All Aboard!

Learning Goals

- tell time to the nearest second
- explore the relationship between time and distance
- count money and make change
- estimate, measure, and compare mass, volume, and capacity
- relate volume and capacity

192

ACTIVATE PRIOR LEARNING

Have students read the *Unit Launch*. Encourage students to look carefully at all illustrations.

Ask questions, such as:

- What does the table show?
  (*It shows when trains leave.*)
- Why is time important in the train business?
  (*People need to know when their train will leave and when it will arrive.*)
- How is the distance a train travels related to time?
  (*Usually, the farther a train travels, the longer it takes.*)

Discuss the first question in the Student Book. (*Time is measured on a clock; by minutes and hours in a table; using 12-hour and 24-hour systems.*)

Discuss the second question in the Student Book. (*She could buy pieces of track, model train cars and engines, and model buildings and landscaping features.*)

Discuss the third question in the Student Book. (*A model train could carry toy figures or other small objects. A real boxcar could carry people, large boxes, or cars.*)

Students can be guided toward thinking about the mass and size of objects. Discuss the fourth question in the Student Book.
(*Model trains carry objects with small masses measured in grams, while real trains carry objects with large masses measured in kilograms.*)

Discuss the last question in the Student Book. (*I could count how many boxes of a certain volume or capacity it holds.*)

Tell students that, in this unit, they will learn more about measuring time, capacity, and mass as well as counting money and making change. At the end of the unit, students will solve problems related to real and model trains.

Aislinn has come to the model train show.

- How is time measured in these pictures?
- How may Aislinn spend her money at the show?
- What objects can a model train boxcar carry? A real boxcar carry?
- How do the masses of the objects compare?
- How could you measure the capacity of a boxcar?

Key Words

- seconds
- SI notation
- speed
- volume
- cubic centimetre (cm^3)
- displacement
- milligrams
- tonnes

193

LITERATURE CONNECTIONS FOR THE UNIT

G Is for Googol: A Math Alphabet Book by David Schwartz.
Tricycle Press, 1999.
ISBN 1883672589
Beginning with "A is for Abacus" and ending with "Z is for Zillion," the author takes readers on a roller-coaster ride through important terms and concepts in mathematics. This smorgasbord of math concepts and trivia is ideal for the budding young mathematician. The text includes "W is for `When are we ever gonna use this stuff, anyway?'" The cartoon illustrations are colourful, amusing, and informative.

Millions to Measure by David M. Schwartz and Steven Kellogg.
HarperCollins Publishers, 2003.
ISBN 0688129161
Another mathematical adventure with Marvelosissimo! The wizard leads readers on an eye-opening exploration of measurement, from before standardization to modern methods. Special emphasis is placed on the metric system.

DIAGNOSTIC ASSESSMENT

What to Look For	What to Do
✔ Students can identify relationships between and among measurement concepts. ✔ Students can select the most appropriate standard unit to measure mass and capacity.	***Extra Support:*** Students who have difficulty identifying relationships between and among measurement concepts may be aided by posting charts that summarize previous learning. *Work on this skill throughout the unit.* Students who have difficulty selecting the most appropriate standard unit to measure mass and capacity may benefit from a chart that shows metric conversions. *Work on this skill during Lessons 6–10.*

Measuring Time

LESSON ORGANIZER — 40–50 min

Curriculum Focus: Tell time to the nearest second. (5m47, 5m48, 5m49)

Teacher Materials
- stopwatch

Student Materials
- stopwatches

Optional
- Step-by-Step 1 (Master 6.11)
- Extra Practice 1 (Master 6.22)

Vocabulary: seconds, SI notation

Assessment: Master 6.2 Ongoing Observations: Measurement

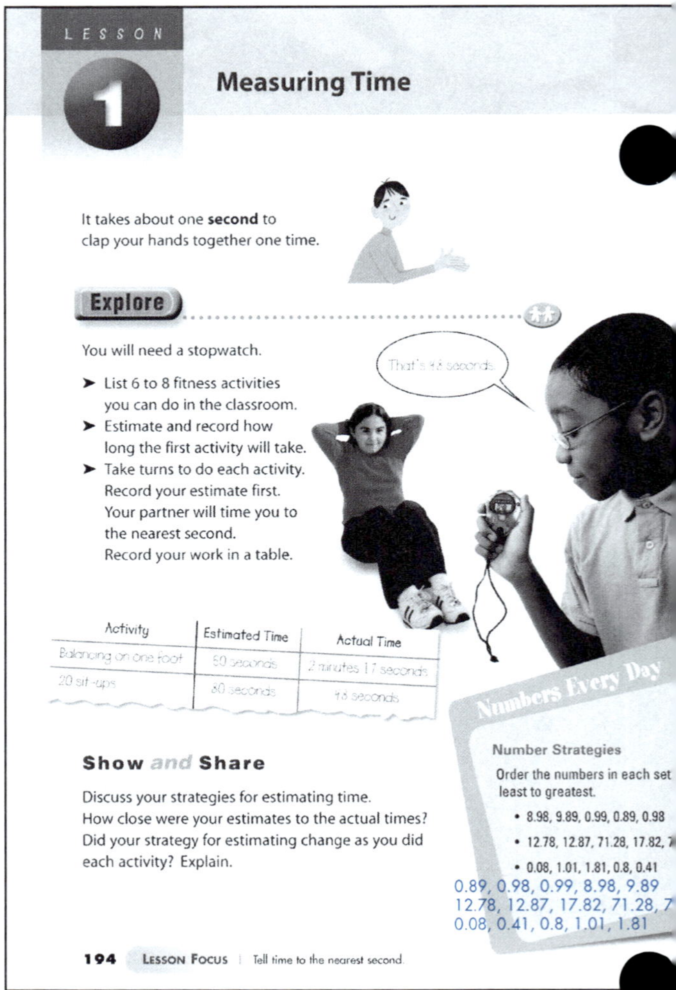

LESSON 1

Measuring Time

It takes about one **second** to clap your hands together one time.

Explore

You will need a stopwatch.

- List 6 to 8 fitness activities you can do in the classroom.
- Estimate and record how long the first activity will take.
- Take turns to do each activity. Record your estimate first. Your partner will time you to the nearest second. Record your work in a table.

Activity	Estimated Time	Actual Time
Balancing on one foot	60 seconds	2 minutes 17 seconds
20 sit-ups	80 seconds	48 seconds

Show and Share

Discuss your strategies for estimating time.
How close were your estimates to the actual times?
Did your strategy for estimating change as you did each activity? Explain.

Numbers Every Day

Number Strategies

Order the numbers in each set least to greatest.

- 8.98, 9.89, 0.99, 0.89, 0.98
- 12.78, 12.87, 71.28, 17.82, 7
- 0.08, 1.01, 1.81, 0.8, 0.41

0.89, 0.98, 0.99, 8.98, 9.89
12.78, 12.87, 17.82, 71.28, 7
0.08, 0.41, 0.8, 1.01, 1.81

194 LESSON FOCUS | Tell time to the nearest second.

Key Math Learnings

1. To measure time, we start counting units of time when the activity begins and stop counting when the activity ends.
2. The second is a small unit of time. It usually takes several seconds to measure the duration of an activity.

Numbers Every Day

Students should use their knowledge of place value to order the numbers in each set.

BEFORE — Get Started

Invite students to think about the time interval of 1 s. Ask them to share strategies they use for counting seconds (*for example, 1 thunder, 2 thunder, …*). Discuss the types of activities that are measured in seconds.

To give students the sense of the length of 10 s, have them close their eyes when you say "start" and open them when you say "stop" 10 s later. Ask:

- Are 10 s longer or shorter than you thought?
- How long do you think it would take you to write your full name? (*6 s*) To tie both shoes? (*15 s*) To pass out workbooks to the class? (*60 s*)

Present *Explore*. Brainstorm a list of fitness activities students could do. Limit the duration of activities by specifying a certain number of repetitions; for example, 20 jumping jacks.

Record the list on the board. Invite a volunteer to try an activity while you demonstrate timing it to the nearest second using a stopwatch.

Emphasize that students should record an estimate before they time each activity.

DURING — Explore

Ongoing Assessment: Observe and Listen

Watch students as they time each other's activities. Ask:

- How does your actual time compare with your estimate?
  (*Some activities took longer than I thought and some took less time.*)
- How can you use the time it took to complete one activity to help you estimate how long it will take to complete a different activity?
  (*I can decide whether the second activity will take more or less time than the first activity.*)

Connect

Many analog clocks show time in hours, minutes, and seconds.

➤ This clock shows a time of 4 hours 32 minutes 10 seconds.
We write: 4 h 32 min 10 s
In **SI notation**, we write: 04:32:10

04:32:10

➤ One second is a very small unit of time.
There are 60 seconds in one minute.
It takes 60 s for the second hand to move all the way around the clock.

60 s = 1 min

Often, we do not need to tell time to the nearest second.
We can round time to the nearest minute.

There are 30 s in half a minute.

When there are less than 30 s on the clock, round time back to the full minute.

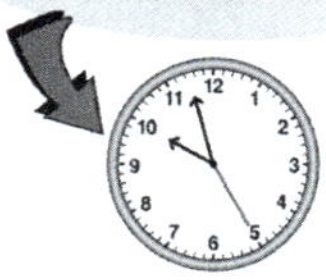

About 09:57

When there are 30 s or more on the clock, round time forward to the next full minute.

About 05:18

➤ The circled date is October 24th, 2006.
October is the 10th month of the year.
In SI notation, we write: 2006 10 24

2006 10 24

195

REACHING ALL LEARNERS

Early Finishers

Ask students to look back at the table they made for *Explore*. Have them make a list of fitness activities they believe they could accomplish in 30 s, then check by timing.

Common Misconceptions

➤ Students have difficulty determining how much time has passed between two given times on an analog clock.

How to Help: Give students an analog clock with a movable second hand to demonstrate the passage of time. Have students display the start time on the clock, then count off the seconds as the hands move to the finish time.

- How many of those do you think you could do in 30 s?
  (*I did 20 sit-ups in 48 s, so I think I could do about 14 sit-ups in 30 s.*)

AFTER Connect

Invite volunteers to share their strategies for estimating time.

Ask:

- Which activities took less than 30 s? Which took more? (*It took less than 30 s to do 10 jumping jacks; it took more than 30 s to do 20 sit-ups.*)
- When might you need to record time to the nearest second? (*When you are timing a race*)
  To the nearest minute?
  (*When you are making a speech*)

Rounding off to the nearest minute is presented in *Connect*, as well as SI notation for times and dates. Have students record their birthdays in SI notation.

Practice

Assessment Focus: Question 5

Students will determine the actual time it took Jack to jog to his friend's house, and compare the actual time to the estimate. They will determine whether the estimate was reasonable. Students will draw an analog watch face clearly showing the time 3:53:45, and they will effectively communicate their thinking.

Sample Answers

1. a) This is reasonable because I know from playing jump rope that I can hop that long.
   b) This is not reasonable because our schoolyard is very large. I think it would take 4 min 30 s.
4. a) 02:50:17, or about 02:50
   b) 11:42:50, or about 11:43
   c) 12:14:30, or about 12:15
5. b) Yes, his estimate was reasonable, because both times would be rounded to 1 min.
   c) Student should draw an analog watch face showing 03:53:45.
   d) I think it took him 1 min 25 s because he was tired and would not run as fast as he did on the way over.

REFLECT: On track and field day it was important to tell time to the nearest second so that we knew if someone beat the school record for the 100-m race. On Book Fair Day, we just needed to know our class's time to shop to the nearest minute.

Practice

1. Is each time estimate reasonable? Explain.
   a) Hop on one foot: 45 s
   b) Run all the way around the schoolyard: 2 min 20 s

2. Write each date in SI notation.
   a) June 23, 1966 — 1966 06 23
   b) your birthday — 1995 07 17
   c) the first day of next month — 2005 10 01
3. Write each date in words.
   a) 1994 07 16 — July 16, 1994
   b) 2000 01 01 — January 1, 2000
   c) 2004 11 09 — November 9, 2004
   d) 2026 03 31 — March 31, 2026
4. Look at each clock.
   In SI notation, write the exact time and the time to the nearest minute.
   a) b) c)

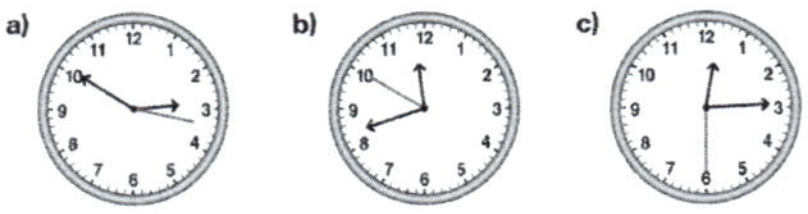

5. Jack estimated it would take 50 s to jog to his friend's house.
   When he left, his watch looked like this:

   When he arrived, his watch looked like this:

   a) How long did it take Jack to jog to his friend's house? 75 s or 1 min 15 s
   b) Was Jack's estimate reasonable? Explain.
   c) Jack knocked at the door. He waited 30 s before someone answered. What did his watch look like then? Draw it.
   d) His friend was not home. So, Jack jogged home. How long do you think it took him? Explain.

Reflect

Tell about a day when knowing time to the nearest second was important. Tell about another day when it was not important to know the time to the nearest second.

196 ASSESSMENT FOCUS | Question 5

ASSESSMENT FOR LEARNING

What to Look For	What to Do
Understanding concepts ✔ Students understand how seconds are used to measure short intervals of time. ✔ Students have a sense of how long one second is. ***Applying procedures*** ✔ Students can measure time intervals to the nearest second. ✔ Students can read and write dates and times using SI notation.	***Extra Support:*** Students can use Step-by-Step 1 (Master 6.11) to complete question 5. ***Extra Practice:*** Students can complete Extra Practice 1 (Master 6.22). ***Extension:*** Challenge students to research and report on a sporting event that is recorded in seconds.

Recording and Reporting
Master 6.2 Ongoing Observations: Measurement

LESSON

2

Exploring Time and Distance

Explore

You will need:
- books to raise a ramp
- a marble
- Bristol board, 30 cm by 10 cm
- a metre stick
- masking tape
- a stopwatch

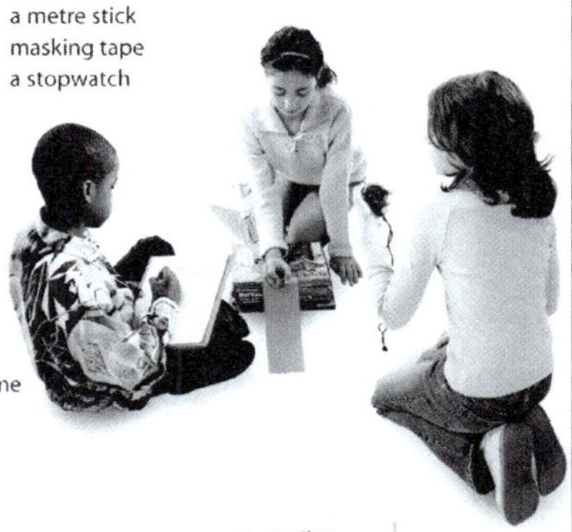

➤ Create a 10-cm high ramp.
Use the Bristol board, books, and masking tape as shown.
Mark distances of 2 m, 4 m, 6 m, and 8 m from the end of the ramp.

➤ One student lets the marble go at the top of the ramp.
Another student measures the time the marble takes to travel 2 m.
A third student records the time and distance in a table.

➤ Change roles. Repeat the steps.
Measure the times for the marble to travel 4 m, 6 m, and 8 m.

➤ Look at the data in your table.
What patterns do you see?
Estimate the time the marble would take to travel each distance: 10 m, 12 m, 14 m

Marble Rolling

Time (s)	Distance (cm)

Show and Share

Compare your results with those of another group.
Describe your strategy to estimate the times for the marble to travel 10 m, 12 m, and 14 m.
How is the distance the marble travels related to the time it takes?

LESSON FOCUS | Explore time and distance relationships. 197

LESSON 2

Exploring Time and Distance

LESSON ORGANIZER 40–50 min

Curriculum Focus: Explore time and distance relationships. (5m53)

Student Materials
- books
- masking tape
- Bristol board strips, 30 cm by 10 cm
- metre sticks
- stopwatches
- marbles

Optional
- Step-by-Step 2 (Master 6.12)
- Extra Practice 1 (Master 6.22)

Vocabulary: speed, distance

Assessment: Master 6.2 Ongoing Observations: Measurement

Key Math Learnings

1. There is a relationship between time and distance.
2. Simple comparisons between time and distance provide a foundation for the concept of speed.

BEFORE Get Started

Hold a marble up to the class and ask them to describe it. List various attributes such as size, shape, and mass. Discuss how these attributes could be measured. Ask questions, such as:

- What attributes of this marble could you measure? (*Size, mass*)
- How would you measure these attributes? (*I would measure size with a measuring tape or ruler, and mass with a scale.*)

Instruct students to watch carefully. Roll the marble across the surface of a desk or along a board ledge. Ask students to describe the marble now. Repeat the marble roll as often as required to elicit student responses. Ask:

- What is different? (*The marble is moving.*)
- What else can you measure now? (*I can measure the distance the marble travels and the time it takes for the marble to travel that distance.*)

Emphasize to students that, although the marble has remained the same, there are now more opportunities for measurement.

Tell students they will be working with marbles to investigate time and distance.

Present *Explore*. Ensure students understand how to make the ramp and that each student makes a personal record of the data. It may be necessary to glue two pieces of Bristol board together to make the ramp rigid.

DURING Explore

Ongoing Assessment: Observe and Listen

Ensure that each group uses tape to mark flat distances of 2 m, 4 m, 6 m, and 8 m from the end of the ramp before beginning their experiment. Make sure students are using a hard, smooth surface for their experiment, such as a bare floor, the hallway, or even the gym floor.

REACHING ALL LEARNERS

Alternative Explore

Materials: stopwatch

In small groups, time individual students as they walk or run measured distances of 10 m, 20 m, and 50 m. Have students estimate how long it would take them to travel 1000 m.

Early Finishers

Have students make a collage of things that have a time and distance relationship. Students should group items by speed or other characteristics. On the back of the collage, students can explain their sorting rule.

Sample Answers

2. The ball will hit the pins 5 s after it is thrown. 5 m × 5 = 25 m
3. The car will take 5 h to travel 400 km; 5 × 80 km = 400 km
4. a) Campbell: 80 m, 400 m, 1600 m, 4800 m
   Tyler: 85 m, 425 m, 1700 m, 5100 m
   b) Tyler is walking faster. Each minute, he goes 5 m farther than Campbell.
5. Car B is moving faster than Car A. The line representing the distance travelled by Car B reached the 12-cm mark first.
6. Jillian swims slower. Each second, Alyssa swims 0.03 m farther than Jillian.
7. I estimate that it would take the Cheung family 7 h.
   (1 h for 100 km + 5 h for 400 km 1 h for two half-hour breaks)

Connect

Speed is a measure of how fast an object is moving.

➤ Helen's marble travels 50 cm every second.
At this speed, it will go:
50 cm in 1 s
100 cm in 2 s
150 cm in 3 s
200 cm in 4 s, and so on.

We can show this:

• In a table

Time (s)	Distance (cm)
1	50
2	100
3	150
4	200

• On a graph

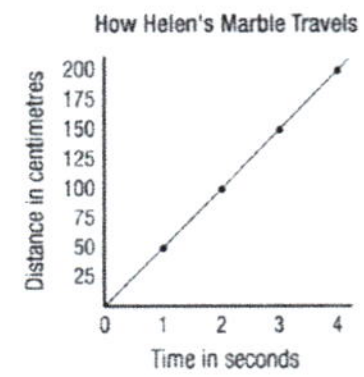

➤ Hannah's marble travels 60 cm every second.
Hannah's marble goes farther each second than Helen's marble.

➤ Colin's marble travels 45 cm every second.
Colin's marble does not go as far each second as Hannah's marble or Helen's marble.

198

While students are recording the time it takes for their marble to roll various distances, facilitate discussion by asking:

- Why must the marble be released from the top of the ramp, not pushed?
  (*So the marble always reaches the flat surface at the same speed*)
- What would happen to the results if the ramp height was raised?
  (*The marble would travel farther because it would be moving faster when it reaches the ground.*)
- What would happen to the results if the ramp height was lowered?
  (*The marble would not travel as far because it would be moving slower when it reaches the ground.*)
- What patterns do you notice?
  (*With the ramp at the same height, the time taken to travel 4 m is approximately double the time taken to travel 2 m.*)

Remind students to record data only to a distance of 8 m.

AFTER Connect

Invite students to share their estimates for 10 m, 12 m, and 14 m. Students may use graphs to present their findings.

Read and discuss the examples in *Connect*. Use the tables to provide links to student experience.

Practice

Students may benefit from using tables to complete the questions. Question 5 requires students to interpret a distance versus time graph.

Assessment Focus: Question 7

Students should recognize that different roads have different speed limits. Some students may select travel along a major highway with only one rest stop, while others may select a combination of roads with various breaks and activities along the way.

Practice

1. A toy car travels 5 cm every second.
At this speed, how far will it go in 1 s? 2 s? 3 s? 10 s?
5 cm, 10 cm, 15 cm, 50 cm

2. A bowling alley is 25 m long.
The bowling ball travels 5 m in 1 s and 10 m in 2 s.
The speed of the ball does not change.
When will the ball hit the pins? Show your work. In 5 s

3. A car travels 80 km in 1 h and 160 km in 2 h.
Suppose the car continues at the same speed.
How long will it take to travel 400 km? Explain. 5 h

4. Campbell walks 80 m every minute.
Tyler walks 85 m every minute.
   a) How far will each person walk in 1 min? 5 min? 20 min? 1 h?
   b) Who is walking faster? How do you know?

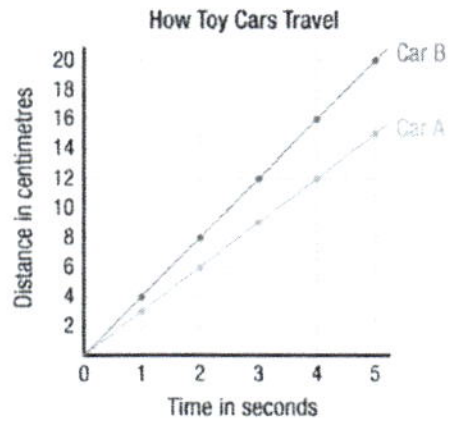

5. a) When has Car A travelled 12 cm? In 4 s.
   b) When has Car B travelled 12 cm? In 3 s.
   c) Which car is moving faster? How do you know?

6. Alyssa swims 0.75 m every second.
Jillian swims 0.72 m every second.
Which girl swims slower? How do you know?

7. The Cheung family plans to drive 500 km to a vacation resort.
How long do you estimate the trip will take?
Use pictures, numbers, and words to show your thinking.

Numbers Every Day

Mental Math

Find the next number in each pattern.
Write each pattern rule.
- 1.2, 1.4, 1.6, 1.8, □ 2.0
- 9000, 900, 90, 9, □ 0.9
- 0.05, 0.5, 5, □ 50
- 0.2, 0.9, 1.6, □ 2.3

Reflect

Suppose you ride your bicycle down the road.
Describe how the time you take and the distance you travel are related.

ASSESSMENT FOCUS | Question 7 199

REFLECT: If you travel at the same speed all the time, a numerical pattern describes the distance you travel for various lengths of time. You will be able to create a line graph with the data that will allow you to predict times for distances not covered or for intermediate distances not actually timed in the original collection of data. You can also predict distances for amounts of time cycled.

Numbers Every Day

The patterns represent basic growing and shrinking patterns. Students may need to be reminded of what it means to multiply or divide by multiples of 10.

Answers:

Start at 1.2; add 0.2.
Start at 9000; divide by 10.
Start at 0.05; multiply by 10.
Start at 0.2; add 0.7.

ASSESSMENT FOR LEARNING

What to Look For	What to Do
Understanding concepts ✔ Students understand the relationship between time and distance. ***Applying procedures*** ✔ Students can recognize and apply patterning rules to determine time or distance measurements.	***Extra Support:*** Have students work with basic Input/Output patterning tables, substituting time and distance values where necessary. Students can use Step-by-Step 2 (Master 6.12) to complete question 7. ***Extra Practice:*** Ask students to create their own distance versus time problem. Students can communicate their own solution to the problem. Students can complete Extra Practice 1 (Master 6.22). ***Extension:*** Students can complete the Additional Activity, *Walk the Walk* (Master 6.7).

Recording and Reporting

Master 6.2 Ongoing Observations: Measurement

Strategies Toolkit

LESSON ORGANIZER 40–50 min

Curriculum Focus: Interpret a problem and select an appropriate strategy. (5m53)

Student Materials

- 1-cm grid paper (PM 23)

Assessment: PM 1 Inquiry Process Check List, PM 3 Self-Assessment: Problem Solving

Key Math Learning

Distance-time problems can be solved using graphs.

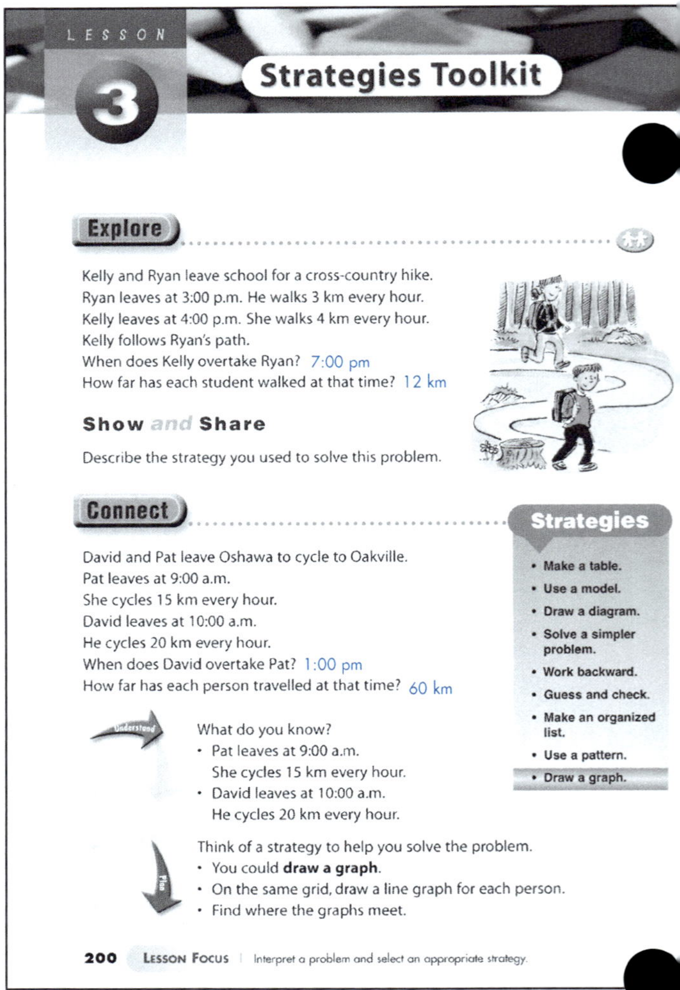

LESSON 3 Strategies Toolkit

Explore

Kelly and Ryan leave school for a cross-country hike.
Ryan leaves at 3:00 p.m. He walks 3 km every hour.
Kelly leaves at 4:00 p.m. She walks 4 km every hour.
Kelly follows Ryan's path.
When does Kelly overtake Ryan? 7:00 pm
How far has each student walked at that time? 12 km

Show and Share

Describe the strategy you used to solve this problem.

Connect

David and Pat leave Oshawa to cycle to Oakville.
Pat leaves at 9:00 a.m.
She cycles 15 km every hour.
David leaves at 10:00 a.m.
He cycles 20 km every hour.
When does David overtake Pat? 1:00 pm
How far has each person travelled at that time? 60 km

What do you know?

- Pat leaves at 9:00 a.m. She cycles 15 km every hour.
- David leaves at 10:00 a.m. He cycles 20 km every hour.

Think of a strategy to help you solve the problem.

- You could **draw a graph**.
- On the same grid, draw a line graph for each person.
- Find where the graphs meet.

Strategies

- Make a table.
- Use a model.
- Draw a diagram.
- Solve a simpler problem.
- Work backward.
- Guess and check.
- Make an organized list.
- Use a pattern.
- Draw a graph.

200 LESSON FOCUS Interpret a problem and select an appropriate strategy.

BEFORE Get Started

Present *Explore*. Ensure students understand the question. Review the key steps in problem solving. Have students work through and discuss the problem with a partner.

DURING Explore

Ongoing Assessment: Observe and Listen

While students are working on the problem, facilitate understanding by asking:

- What are the important facts? (*Ryan leaves at 3:00 p.m. and walks 3 km every hour. Kelly leaves at 4:00 p.m. and walks 4 km every hour.*)
- What patterns can you find in the data? (*Ryan travels 3 km every hour; Kelly travels 4 km every hour.*)
- When will Kelly overtake Ryan? (*When they have travelled the same number of kilometres*)

Watch for students who have difficulty finding patterns in the data.

Have students share their solutions with the class and explain the strategy they used.

AFTER Connect

Work through the problem in *Connect* with the class. Record each problem-solving step on the board and refer to it as you proceed.

Use a table to display the data, then show students how a graph can display the results more effectively. Ask:

- What other strategies might we use to solve this problem? (*Make a table; guess and check*)

Practice

Remind students to refer to the Strategies list as they complete the questions. Have 1-cm grid paper available for all questions.

Find how far Pat has gone at 10:00 a.m., 11:00 a.m., noon, and so on.
Record the times and distances in a table.
Mark a point on the graph for each time and distance.
Draw a line through the points.
Repeat this strategy for David.
Where do Pat and David meet?
How far has each person gone?
What time is it then?

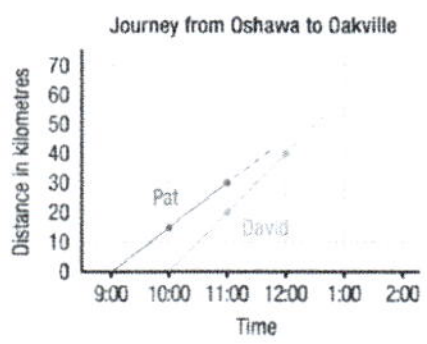

How could you have solved this problem another way?

Practice

Choose one of the **Strategies**

1. A freight train travels 100 km every hour.
   It passes over a river at 10:00 a.m.
   Four hours later, a passenger train passes over the same river.
   The passenger train travels 150 km every hour.
   When does the passenger train overtake the freight train? 10:00 p.m.
   How far are they from the river? 1200 km

2. Erica leaves Deer Lake to travel 300 km to Gander.
   She drives 80 km every hour.
   Gerry leaves Deer Lake for Gander one hour later.
   He drives 90 km every hour.
   Who reaches Gander first? How do you know? Erica

Reflect

When can you use the strategy of draw a graph to solve a problem?
Use an example to explain.

201

REACHING ALL LEARNERS

Common Misconceptions

➤Students do not understand the problem.
How to Help: Have partners describe the problem to each other to help clarify their understanding.

➤Students experience visual/perceptual difficulties graphing coordinate pairs or creating a graph with the correct scale.
How to Help: Encourage students to use a 2-column chart (PM 17) to organize data. Have students look at the range of values to determine what values are needed on the graph. Some students may benefit from using two rulers, one for each axis, to find and locate coordinate points on the graph.

Sample Answer

2. Erica reaches Deer Lake after 3 h 45 min of driving. Gerry reaches Deer Lake after 3 h 20 min. Since he leaves 1 h later and uses only 25 min less driving time, Gerry arrives later.

REFLECT: I can draw a graph whenever the data involve two different but related measurements. An example would be time and money for someone paid an hourly wage. The more hours worked, the more money earned.

ASSESSMENT FOR LEARNING

What to Look For	What to Do
Problem solving ✔ Students can follow the "understand, plan, solve, and look back" steps to solve a problem. ✔ Students can select an appropriate strategy for solving a problem. ✔ Students can justify their solutions. ***Communicating*** ✔ Students can describe their strategy clearly, using appropriate language.	***Extra Support:*** Students may benefit from graphing 3 or 4 sets of distance versus time values. ***Extra Practice:*** Students can change the values in question 1 to 4 km per hour and 8 km per hour respectively. ***Extension:*** For question 2, ask students to tell what speed Gerry would have to travel to arrive in Gander at the same time as Erica. Permit students to use a calculator. *(109 km per hour; Gerry would have to arrive in 2 h and 45 min. 300 km divided by 2.75 h = 109 km per hour)*

Recording and Reporting
PM 1 Inquiry Process Check List
PM 3 Self-Assessment: Problem Solving

Estimating and Counting Money

LESSON ORGANIZER — 40–50 min

Curriculum Focus: Estimate and count money to $1000. (5m50, 5m51)

Teacher Materials

- an envelope containing $1000 in play money (PM 30)

Student Materials

- play money (PM 30)
- calculator

Optional

- Step-by-Step 4 (Master 6.13)
- Extra Practice 2 (Master 6.23)

Assessment: Master 6.2 Ongoing Observations: Measurement

Key Math Learning

A variety of strategies can be used to sort and count money.

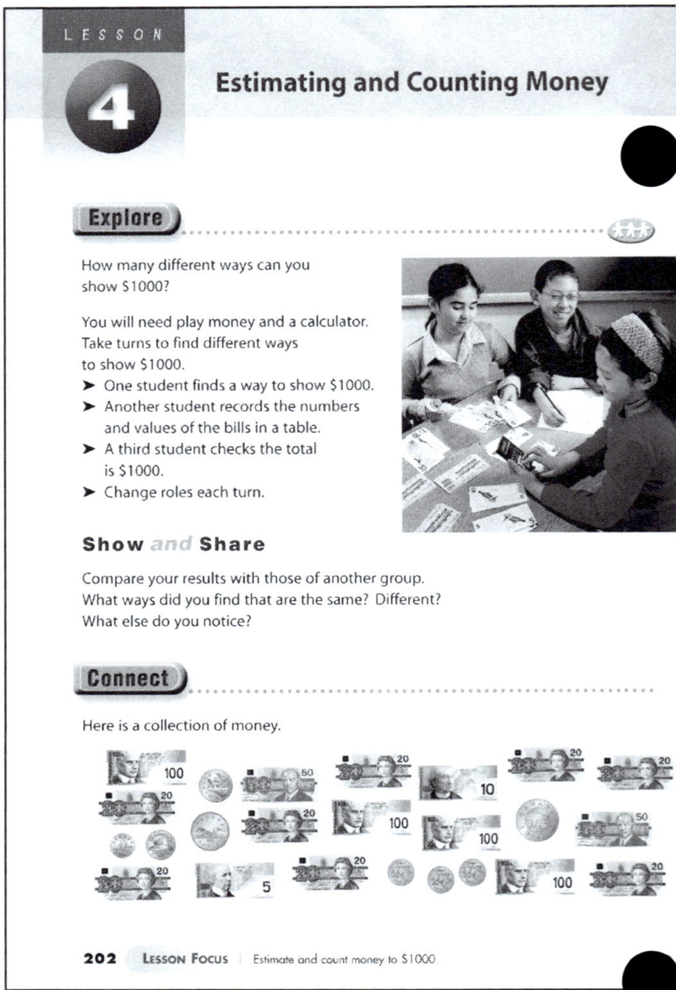

LESSON 4

Estimating and Counting Money

Explore

How many different ways can you show $1000?

You will need play money and a calculator.
Take turns to find different ways to show $1000.

- One student finds a way to show $1000.
- Another student records the numbers and values of the bills in a table.
- A third student checks the total is $1000.
- Change roles each turn.

Show and Share

Compare your results with those of another group.
What ways did you find that are the same? Different?
What else do you notice?

Connect

Here is a collection of money.

202 LESSON FOCUS | Estimate and count money to $1000

BEFORE — Get Started

Show students an envelope labelled $1000 that contains that amount of play money. Ask them to guess the combination of bills and coins in the envelope. List the bills and coins suggested by the students.

Distribute about $350 of play money in bills and coins to each student.

Present *Explore*. Organize students into groups of three. Have each group pool its collection of money. Make sure students understand they are to use different combinations of bills and coins to show exactly $1000.

DURING — Explore

Ongoing Assessment: Observe and Listen

Watch to ensure everyone participates and alternates roles in the activity. As students organize and count the money, watch and listen to their strategies. Are they able to skip count and to shift from one skip count to another? Can they record the money values in a table appropriately? Do they enter money values correctly into the calculator to check their work?

Ask questions, such as:

- How did you decide which coins and bills to use?
  (*I used up all the $100 bills first, then I used the $50s, and then the $20s. I needed fewer bills that way.*)
- How did you count the money?
  (*I counted each type of money to find out how much there was. Then I added the totals together.*)

Here's how Raisa counts the money.

➤ First, she sorts the bills and coins into groups.

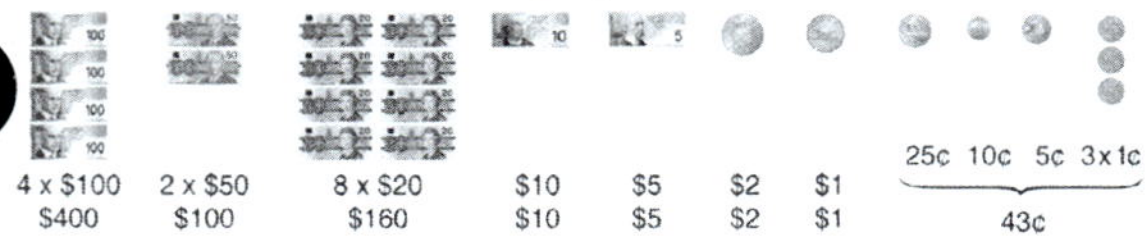

➤ Then, she counts the bills and coins.

➤ Next, she adds the values of the bills and coins:

$400 + $100 + $160 + $10 + $5 + $2 + $1 + $0.43 = $678.43

Here's how Daniel counts the money.

➤ First, he sorts the bills and coins into piles that total $100.

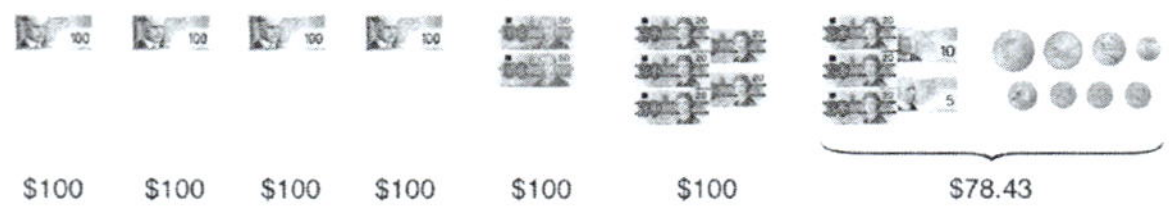

➤ Then, he counts: "1, 2, 3, 4, 5, 6 hundred dollars"

➤ Next, he adds on the value of the remaining bills and coins:

$600 + $78.43 = $678.43

Practice

Use play money when it helps.

1. Estimate, then count. Record each estimate and amount.

a)

About $36, $35.85

b)

About $885, $855, 70

2. Make each amount using the fewest bills and coins.
Record the numbers of bills and coins in a table.
a) $75.50 **b)** $166.13 **c)** $542.86 **d)** $989.48

203

REACHING ALL LEARNERS

Alternative Explore

Materials: play money

Students work behind barriers. Each person makes a collection of play money and records the total value. When a group is ready, students remove the barriers. The students estimate and order the collections from least to greatest value. Then they count each collection to check. Repeat the activity.

Early Finishers

Students randomly select some bills and coins from a collection of play money. After a quick glance, they record their estimates of the total value. Then they count to find the actual total.

Common Misconceptions

➤ Students have difficulty shifting from one skip count to another when counting money.

How to Help: Have students practise skip counting in small groups. Students will start skip counting by 20s. When they hear a signal, they switch to skip counting by 10s. Continue with 5s, then 1s.

Sample Answers

2. a) to d)

Amount	$100	$50	$20	$10	$5	$2	$1	25¢	10¢	5¢	1¢
$75.50		1	1		1			2			
$166.13	1	1		1	1		1		1		3
$542.86	5		2			1		3	1		1
$989.48	9	1	1	1	1	2		1	2		3

AFTER Connect

Invite students to share the strategies they used for showing different ways to make $1000. Record some of their strategies on chart paper or the board.

Open the envelope labelled $1000. Ask:

- How can I make sure the money in the envelope totals $1000?
  (*Sort the money into groups and add the totals of the groups together.*)

Two strategies for counting a collection of money are presented in *Connect*. Have students work through the examples and compare these strategies to the ones they used. Use the bills from the envelope to demonstrate strategies for counting $1000.

Practice

Have play money available for students to use as needed.

Assessment Focus: Question 8

Many students will find the difference of the amount the man started with and the amount he has now ($355 – $290 = $65). Some students may represent that amount using the fewest number of bills only (3 × $20 + 1 × $5), while others will include coins in their answers. There are many possible combinations of 4 bills and various coins that solve the problem.

3. The least price is $20.
(2 $5 bills + 1 $10 bill)
The greatest price is $80.
(1 $50 bill + 1 $20 bill + 1 $10 bill)

$50	$20	$10	$5
1	1	1	0
1	1	0	1
1	0	1	1
0	1	1	1
1	0	0	2
0	1	0	2
0	0	1	2

5. 8 $100, 3 $20, 1 $10, 1 loonie, 2 quarters, 6 pennies
8 $100, 1 $50, 1 $20, 6 quarters, 1 nickel, 1 penny
7 $100, 3 $50, 2 $10, 1 loonie, 5 dimes, 6 pennies
6. Each person gets $33.33 (1 $20 bill, 1 $10 bill, 1 toonie, 1 loonie, 1 quarter, 1 nickel, and 3 pennies), with 1 penny left over.
7. c) Skye could group like bills and coins, then count her money into $10 piles.
8. 3 $20 bills, 1 $5 bill
2 $20 bills, 2 $10 bills, 2 toonies, 1 loonie
2 $20 bills, 1 $10 bill, 1 $5 bill, 5 toonies

REFLECT: You need to know the exact amount of money when you pay for something at a store.
An estimate is good enough when you think about how much money you may earn in the next month.

Numbers Every Day

The first problem can be solved by looking for obvious factors, while the second problem can be solved by repeated subtraction of easy numbers. Many answers are possible in both cases.

3. Callum had a $50 bill, a $20 bill, a $10 bill, and two $5 bills.
He used 3 bills to buy earrings for his mother.
Show all the possible combinations of bills he may have used.
What is the least price for the earrings? The greatest price? $20; $80

4. Abby counts the coins in her piggy bank.
The total is $83.77.
What is the fewest number of coins she could have? 41 toonies, 1 loonie, 3 quarter and 2 pennies
Show your work.

5. Show three different ways to make $871.56.
Use pictures, numbers, or words to record each way.

6. Three people have a $100 bill to share.
How can they share the money?

7. Skye sold some old toys at a yard sale.
Her little brother helped her wash the toys and set up.
Skye promised that for every $10 she earned, she would give her brother $1.
a) Look at the shoebox.
About how much money do you think Skye made at the yard sale? About $65.00
b) About how much does Skye owe her brother?
Explain. About $6.50
c) Skye wants to know exactly how much money she made. How could she count the money?

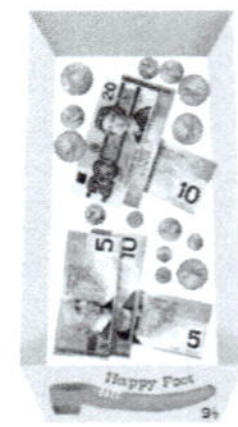

8. A man leaves for the mall with $355 in bills and coins in his pocket.
When he reaches in his pocket, he finds he only has $290.
He knows he is missing 4 bills.
Which bills and coins might he have lost?
Show at least three possible answers.

Reflect

When do you need to know the exact amount of money?
When is an estimate good enough?

Numbers Every Day

Calculator Skills

Find three numbers with a product of 15 600.
$156 \times 10 \times 10 = 15\,600$
Find three odd numbers with a sum of 345.
$111 + 21 + 213 = 345$

204 ASSESSMENT FOCUS | Question 8

ASSESSMENT FOR LEARNING

What to Look For	What to Do
Understanding concepts ✔ Students understand the relationships among different bills and coins. ***Applying procedures*** ✔ Students can estimate and count sums of money to $1000. ***Communicating*** ✔ Students can explain and justify, orally and in writing, their choices of coins and bills to make a sum of money.	***Extra Support:*** Students who need extra practice counting money may choose items priced under $1000 from catalogues and flyers and use play money to model their prices. Students can use Step-by-Step 4 (Master 6.13) to complete question 8. ***Extra Practice:*** Students can complete Extra Practice 2 (Master 6.23). ***Extension:*** Students work in pairs to play *What's in the Envelope?* One student puts a collection of money into an envelope and records the bills and coins used. He announces the total value of the money in the envelope. The second student guesses which bills and coins are in the envelope. Any part of her guess that is correct is identified, and she guesses again. She tries to identify the bills and coins in the fewest number of guesses.

Recording and Reporting
Master 6.2 Ongoing Observations: Measurement

Making Change

LESSON 5

Making Change

Explore — Game

The Auction Game

The goal is to spend the least amount and buy the most fish and decorations for your fish tank.
You will need assorted play money and a set of auction cards.

- Each player starts with $100 and 3 auction cards dealt face down.
- Players take turns being the auctioneer.
- The auctioneer turns over a card for other players to bid on. The highest bidder buys the item. The auctioneer makes change and keeps the money from the sale. Any card not sold is kept by its auctioneer.
- Play continues around the table until each card has been turned over and bid on.

Show and Share

Discuss the strategies you used to bid for items.
What strategies did you use to make change?
How did you know the change you got was correct?

LESSON FOCUS | Make purchases and make change from $100. 205

LESSON ORGANIZER (40–50 min)

Curriculum Focus: Make purchases and make change from $100. (5m52)

Student Materials
- play money (PM 30)
- 1 set of auction cards per group (Master 6.6)

Optional
- Step-by-Step 5 (Master 6.14)
- Extra Practice 2 (Master 6.23)

Assessment: Master 6.2 Ongoing Observations: Measurement

Key Math Learning

The amount of change can be determined by counting on from the cost of the purchase to the amount used to pay for it.

BEFORE Get Started

Explain how an auction works. Provide examples of some specialty auctions that might interest students (for example, baseball cards and music memorabilia).

Ask questions, such as:

- Where have you seen auctions before?
  (*On television; in movies; my parents took me to one.*)
- What kind of an auction would you like to go to?
  (*A comic book auction*)
- How would you decide when to stop bidding on an item?
  (*I would decide in advance the most I would pay for the item.*)

Present *Explore.* Have each student take three $20 bills, two $10 bills, two $5 bills, 3 toonies, and 4 loonies. The rest of the money can be used as a bank if students need to trade bills or coins to make change.

DURING Explore

Ongoing Assessment: Observe and Listen

Observe the methods students use to make change. Do they count on from the auction price of the item to the amount used to pay for it? Are they able to shift from one skip-counting pattern to another as they make change?

Ask:

- About how much change will you get?
  (*A little less than $10*) How do you know?
  (*The item cost a little more than $30 and I paid with two $20 bills.*)
- How many items do you think you will be able to buy?
  (*6 items*)
- How do you know how much change to give?
  (*I count from the price of the item to the amount I was given.*)

REACHING ALL LEARNERS

Alternative Explore

Materials: flyers or catalogues, play money

Students work in pairs. Each one has $100 in play money to spend. One student purchases an item from a flyer or catalogue. The other makes the appropriate change. Change roles. After 15 min, players find the total value of their purchases and the amount of money they have.

Early Finishers

Students can set their own prices for the items shown on the auction cards. With $100 of play money to spend, students make purchases, estimate, and then count out the change they would receive.

Common Misconceptions

➤Students have difficulty counting on to make change.
How to Help: Provide scenarios with prices and amounts paid that require students to switch skip-counting patterns only once. Gradually increase the number of switches required.

ESL Strategies

Emphasize the visual link between the bills and coins being counted and the verbal counting patterns used.

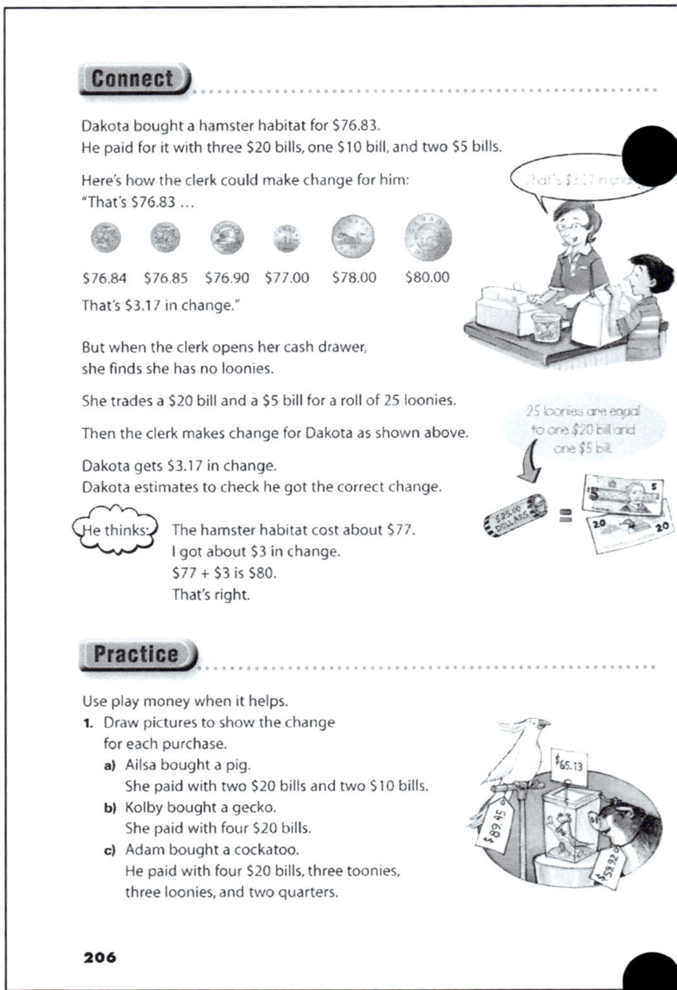

Connect

Dakota bought a hamster habitat for $76.83.
He paid for it with three $20 bills, one $10 bill, and two $5 bills.

Here's how the clerk could make change for him:
"That's $76.83 ...

$76.84 $76.85 $76.90 $77.00 $78.00 $80.00

That's $3.17 in change."

But when the clerk opens her cash drawer, she finds she has no loonies.

She trades a $20 bill and a $5 bill for a roll of 25 loonies.

Then the clerk makes change for Dakota as shown above.

Dakota gets $3.17 in change.
Dakota estimates to check he got the correct change.

He thinks: The hamster habitat cost about $77.
I got about $3 in change.
$77 + $3 is $80.
That's right.

Practice

Use play money when it helps.

1. Draw pictures to show the change for each purchase.
   a) Ailsa bought a pig.
   She paid with two $20 bills and two $10 bills.
   b) Kolby bought a gecko.
   She paid with four $20 bills.
   c) Adam bought a cockatoo.
   He paid with four $20 bills, three toonies, three loonies, and two quarters.

206

- Are you able to pay for that item using exact change?
  (*No. The item costs $7 and I have no coins left.*)

AFTER Connect

Invite volunteers to describe how they chose which bills and coins they used to pay for their auction items. Ask other volunteers to demonstrate the strategies they used to make change.

Read through *Connect* as a class. Have students compare this strategy with the strategies they used to make change.

Practice

Students may use play money when needed.

Assessment Focus: Question 5

Most students will be able to estimate that Michel has enough money by looking at the bills alone. Some may count all the money; others may stop counting as soon as they get over $82.27. Some students will attempt to use exact change, while others will use only bills to pay.

2. Mr. Kwan's class adopted a rabbit from the local animal shelter. They bought these supplies.
The students paid for the items with five \$20 bills.
They were given two bills and eight coins as change.
What bills and coins were they given?

3. Zoe's grandma bought a pair of lovebirds for \$98.26. She was given \$2 change.
   a) How much money did Zoe's grandma give the clerk? \$100.26
   b) Why do you think she gave this amount?

4. Ms. Allen has \$100 to spend on dog food. Each bag of food costs \$32.79.
   a) How many bags of dog food can she buy? 3 bags
   b) How much change will she get? \$1.63

5. Michel is saving to buy an aquarium. It costs \$82.27. Michel has this money.

   a) Does Michel have enough money? Do you need to count it all to find out? Explain.
   b) Which bills and coins could Michel use to pay for the aquarium? What is his change?
   c) How could Michel pay for the aquarium in a different way? What change would he get? Show your work.

Reflect

When you make a purchase, how can you check you get the correct change? Use an example to explain your strategy.

Numbers Every Day

Number Strategies

Estimate each sum.

0.54 + 1.72	About 2.20
5.69 + 2.48	About 8.20
12.33 + 9.11	About 21.40
9.48 + 2.13	About 11.60

ASSESSMENT FOCUS | Question 5

207

Sample Answers

1. Students should draw these coins.
   a) 1 nickel, 3 pennies
   b) one \$10 bill, 2 toonies, 3 quarters, 1 dime, 2 pennies
   c) 1 nickel
2. one \$10 bill, one \$5 bill, 1 toonie, 2 quarters, 1 dime, 1 nickel, 3 pennies
3. b) She wanted to get fewer coins back as change.
5. a) Yes, Michel has enough money. By looking at the number of \$20 bills and \$10 bills you can tell that he has more than \$82.27.
   b) Michel could use three \$20 bills, two \$10 bills, and 3 loonies. His change would be \$0.73.
   c) Michel could use two \$20 bills, three \$10 bills, two \$5 bills, 2 loonies, 1 quarter, and 2 pennies. He would not receive any change.

REFLECT: You could round the price and the change, then add these values to see if they are about the amount you paid. For example, if you bought a fish bowl for \$12.82 and you paid \$15, you would receive \$2.18 change. If you round to the nearest dollar and add, \$13 + \$2 = \$15.

Numbers Every Day

Round the numbers to the nearest tenth and add.

ASSESSMENT FOR LEARNING

What to Look For	What to Do
Applying procedures ✔ Students can select an appropriate number of bills and/or coins to make a purchase. ✔ Students can count on to make change. ***Problem solving*** ✔ Students can show the least number of bills and coins needed to make an amount of money.	***Extra Support:*** Have students use play money to model each question. Students can use Step-by-Step 5 (Master 6.14) to complete question 5. Students can do the Additional Activity, *Money Matters* (Master 6.8). ***Extra Practice:*** Students can complete Extra Practice 2 (Master 6.23). ***Extension:*** Have students write problems that involve purchasing items and getting change. Students trade problems with a classmate and solve their classmate's problems.

Recording and Reporting

Master 6.2 Ongoing Observations: Measurement

LESSON 6

Capacity

LESSON ORGANIZER — 40–50 min

Curriculum Focus: Estimate, measure, and compare capacities in millilitres and litres. (5m41)

Teacher Materials
- small medicine measuring cup (cough medicine)
- 25-mL graduated cylinder

Student Materials
- different-sized containers
- measuring spoons
- assorted graduated cylinders
- bucket of water

Optional
- Step-by-Step 6 (Master 6.15)
- Extra Practice 3 (Master 6.24)

Vocabulary: graduated, capacity, millilitre, litre, benchmark

Assessment: Master 6.2 Ongoing Observations: Measurement

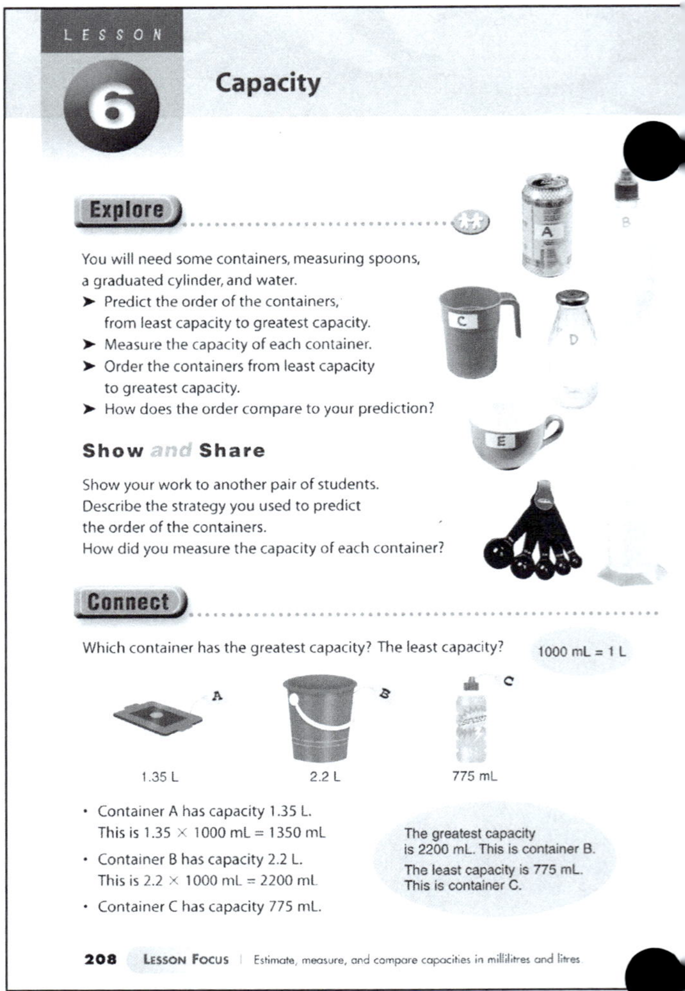

LESSON 6

Capacity

Explore

You will need some containers, measuring spoons, a graduated cylinder, and water.
➤ Predict the order of the containers, from least capacity to greatest capacity.
➤ Measure the capacity of each container.
➤ Order the containers from least capacity to greatest capacity.
➤ How does the order compare to your prediction?

Show and Share

Show your work to another pair of students.
Describe the strategy you used to predict the order of the containers.
How did you measure the capacity of each container?

Connect

Which container has the greatest capacity? The least capacity?

1000 mL = 1 L

A 1.35 L
B 2.2 L
C 775 mL

- Container A has capacity 1.35 L.
This is 1.35 × 1000 mL = 1350 mL
- Container B has capacity 2.2 L.
This is 2.2 × 1000 mL = 2200 mL
- Container C has capacity 775 mL.

The greatest capacity is 2200 mL. This is container B.
The least capacity is 775 mL. This is container C.

208 LESSON FOCUS | Estimate, measure, and compare capacities in millilitres and litres

Key Math Learnings

1. The capacity of a container is the amount it can hold.
2. The width and height of a container affect its capacity.

Materials

Students may use sand in place of water.

BEFORE — Get Started

Have students recall what they know about capacity. Ensure they know 1000 mL = 1 L.

Have students guess the capacity of a small medicine cup. Fill the medicine cup with water and pour it into a small graduated cylinder. Read the water level to find the cup's capacity.

Present *Explore.*

DURING — Explore

Observe how students measure large containers. Do they fill the containers a litre at a time or do they pour the content into smaller containers of known capacities?

AFTER — Connect

Invite students to share their results and explain the differences in capacities measured.

Practice

Questions 1, 4, and 5 require students to use materials from *Explore.*

Assessment Focus: Question 4

Students demonstrate a sense of how capacity relates to the size and shape of a container.

Practice

You will need some containers, a graduated cylinder, and water.

1. Choose three different containers.
   a) Estimate and record the capacity of each container.
   b) Measure and record each capacity.
   c) How do the estimates and measures compare?

2. Order these capacities from least to greatest. c, b, a
   a) 3.45 L b) 2120 mL c) 1.75 L

3. Write each capacity in millilitres.
   a) 5.25 L 5250 mL b) 2.5 L 2500 mL c) 4.38 L 4380 mL

4. Choose one container as a benchmark.
   a) Predict how you would sort the other containers into three groups: greater capacity, lesser capacity, and equal capacity
   b) Describe how you could check your sorting. Show your work.

5. Choose a small container and a large container.
   a) Measure the capacity of each container. Fill the large container with water.
   b) Predict the number of times you can fill the small container using the water from the large container.
   c) Find how many times you can fill the small container using the water from the large container.
   d) How do your results compare to your prediction?

Numbers Every Day

Calculator Skills

Use the digits 5, 6, 7, 8, and 9. Find the product closest to 55 000.

□ □ □ 568
× □ □ × 97
55 096

Reflect

Describe how you would compare the capacities of two containers. Use words and pictures to explain.

ASSESSMENT FOCUS | Question 4

209

REACHING ALL LEARNERS

Alternative Explore

Materials: Bristol board, tape, rice, 500-mL graduated cylinder

Using only Bristol board and tape, students attempt to create 2 totally different containers that will each hold 300 mL of rice. When finished, students communicate their thinking about how the width and height of a container affect its capacity.

Early Finishers/Extra Practice

Students select 4 different-sized containers and estimate how many of the smallest one will fit into each of the larger ones. They measure the capacity of the smallest container to calculate the capacity of each larger container. Students then measure the capacity of each larger container to check.

Common Misconceptions

➤ Students have difficulty ordering capacities, some in millilitres and others in litres, from least to greatest.

How to Help: Suggest students convert all capacities measured in litres to millilitres.

REFLECT: Assuming both containers hold a litre or less, I would fill both containers with water and then pour each one into a 1-L graduated cylinder. I would record the measurement for each and then find the difference.

Numbers Every Day

Start by considering obvious factors of 55 000.

ASSESSMENT FOR LEARNING

What to Look For	What to Do
Understanding concepts ✔ Students understand that the capacity of a container is the amount it can hold. ✔ Students can choose an appropriate unit to measure capacity. ***Applying procedures*** ✔ Students can estimate and measure capacity.	***Extra Support:*** Have students estimate and measure the capacity of different containers using only a 250-mL measuring cup. Students can use Step-by-Step 6 (Master 6.15) to complete question 4. ***Extra Practice:*** Students can complete the Additional Activity, *Millilitre Mania* (Master 6.9). Students can complete Extra Practice 3 (Master 6.24). ***Extension:*** Have students measure the height of a graduated cylinder that contains 500 mL of water. Pour the water into a large-diameter glass bowl. Ask students to measure the new height of the water and to explain the reason for the difference.

Recording and Reporting

Master 6.2 Ongoing Observations: Measurement

Volume

LESSON ORGANIZER — 40–50 min

Curriculum Focus: Use centimetre cubes to measure volume. (5m59)

Student Materials
- 1-cm interlocking cubes

Optional
- Step-by-Step 7 (Master 6.16)
- Extra Practice 3 (Master 6.24)

Vocabulary: volume, cubic centimetre (cm^3)

Assessment: Master 6.2 Ongoing Observations: Measurement

Key Math Learnings

1. The volume of an object is a measure of the space it takes up.
2. Models help solve problems involving volume.
3. Volume can be measured in cubic centimetres (cm^3).

LESSON 7

Volume

How could you find out how much space this shoebox takes up?

Explore

You will need interlocking cubes.

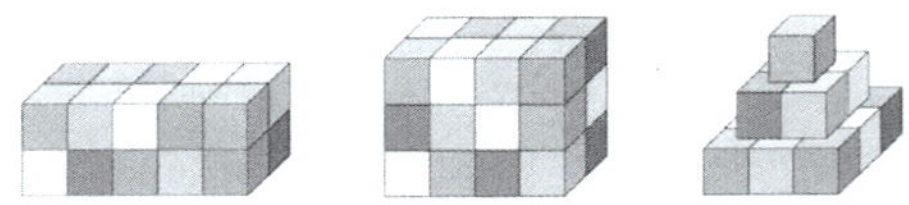

- Estimate how many cubes you need to build each solid.
- Build each solid. Record the number of cubes you used each time.
- Build your own solid. Label it D. Find the number of cubes needed to build your solid.
- Order the solids, from the one that takes up the most space to the one that takes up the least space.

Show and Share

Share your work with another pair of students. How did you order the solids?

210 LESSON FOCUS | Use centimetre cubes to measure volume.

BEFORE — Get Started

Show students a shoebox or a rectangular solid.

Ask questions, such as:
- How could you describe this shoebox? *(It has 6 rectangular faces, 8 vertices, and 12 edges.)*
- Which geometric solid does it look like? *(A rectangular prism)*

Focus students' attention on the following challenge: How could you find out how much space this shoebox takes up? Ask:
- Why would you want to know how much space an object occupies? *(To see if it will fit into a box or a package)*

Brainstorm possible ways to solve this problem and record the ideas on the board. List the tools and materials students suggest.

Suggest using interlocking cubes to determine the amount of space a solid takes up.

Present *Explore*.

Remind students that they need to estimate the number of cubes it will take to make each solid before they start to build.

DURING — Explore

Ongoing Assessment: Observe and Listen

As students are engaged in the activity, observe their methods of constructing the solids.

Ask questions, such as:
- How do you know this solid is the same as the one in the picture? *(I counted the rows of cubes and matched them to the picture.)*
- Does the solid you built take up more or less space than you estimated? *(More space than I estimated)*

Connect

The **volume** of an object is a measure of the space it takes up.

The length of each edge of this centimetre cube is 1 cm.

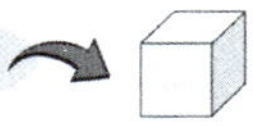

A centimetre cube has a volume of one **cubic centimetre** (1 cm^3).

We can use centimetre cubes to measure volume.

➤ This rectangular prism has 4 rows of 5 cubes, or 20 cubes.
The volume of this prism is 20 cubic centimetres, or 20 cm^3.

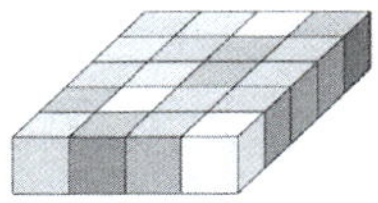

➤ This object has 8 cubes in the bottom layer and 3 cubes in the top layer.
The volume of this solid is 11 cubic centimetres, or 11 cm^3.

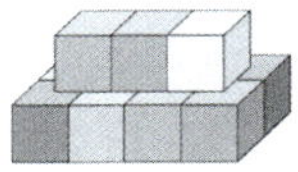

Practice

You will need centimetre cubes.

1. Each prism is made with centimetre cubes.
Find the volume of each prism.
Order the prisms from least to greatest volume. c, a, f, b, e, d

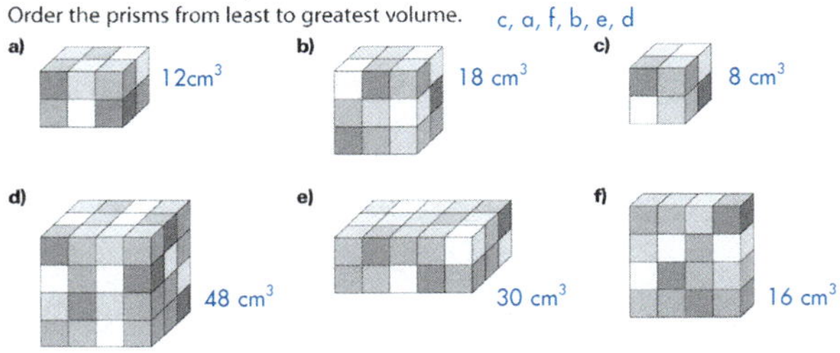

211

REACHING ALL LEARNERS

Alternative Explore

Materials: small boxes or rectangular prisms, centimetre cubes
Give pairs of students a small box or rectangular prism to work with. Challenge them to use centimetre cubes to build a model that has a volume as close to the solid as they can make it.

Common Misconceptions

➤ Students have difficulty visualizing the amount of space taken up by an object as its volume.

How to Help: Students need more experience constructing solids with centimetre cubes. Make sure to call the cubes "cubic centimetres." Have students practise using a fixed number of cubic centimetres to make various solids that have different shapes, but the same volume.

- How do you know you have ordered your solids correctly?
(We counted the cubes in each one, then ordered them from greatest to least number of cubes.)

AFTER Connect

Invite volunteers to share the solids they labelled D. Ask the class to estimate the number of cubes used in each pair's solid. After several pairs have shared, have the students order the solids, from the one that takes up the least space to the one that takes up the most space.

Tell students that when you find out how much space a solid takes up you are measuring its **volume.** Introduce the unit **cubic centimetre** (cm^3). Explain that a cube with each edge 1 cm long is a cubic centimetre, and that its volume is 1 cm^3.

Ask:

- What are the volumes of the solids you modelled in *Explore*?
(20 cm^3, 24 cm^3, and 14 cm^3)

Use *Connect* to solidify the relationship between the number of cubes required to model a solid and its volume in cubic centimetres.

Practice

Students will need centimetre cubes to complete the questions.

Assessment Focus: Question 4

Most students will only list prisms that use exactly 18 cubes. A few students may also consider prisms that use fewer than 18 cubes. Some students will work systematically to find all the different possible prisms. Students should recognize that a 1 by 2 by 9 prism is the same as a 2 by 1 by 9 prism.

Sample Answers

4. Four prisms can be made using exactly 18 centimetre cubes (1 by 1 by 18, 1 by 2 by 9, 1 by 3 by 6, 2 by 3 by 3). The volume of each prism is 18 cm^3. To find all possible prisms, I use the factors of 18, which are 1, 2, 3, 6, 9, 18. Where students used fewer than 18 centimetre cubes, the volume they give should match the number of cubes used.
5. Using 20 centimetre cubes, students may make any configuration except a rectangular prism. For example, a solid with a bottom row using 4 by 4, or 16 centimetre cubes, and a top row using 2 by 2, or 4 centimetre cubes. Students find the volumes are the same, but the length, width, and height of their solids may be different.
6. To estimate, I would find about how many centimetre cubes would fit along the length, width, and height of the book, and calculate the total. Then, I would use centimetre cubes to model the entire book, and count the total number. I might not have enough centimetre cubes to do this, so I will have to multiply.

REFLECT: If it is a rectangular prism, I could multiply the length by the width by the height to get the total volume. If it is not a rectangular prism, I would need to actually count the total number of centimetre cubes I used to make my solid.

Numbers Every Day

70 000 + 6000 + **30** + 2	**3 tens**
30 000 + 8000 + 500 + 40 + 5	**3 ten thousands**
90 000 + **300** + 6	**3 hundreds**
50 000 + **3000** + 100 + 10 + 4	**3 thousands**

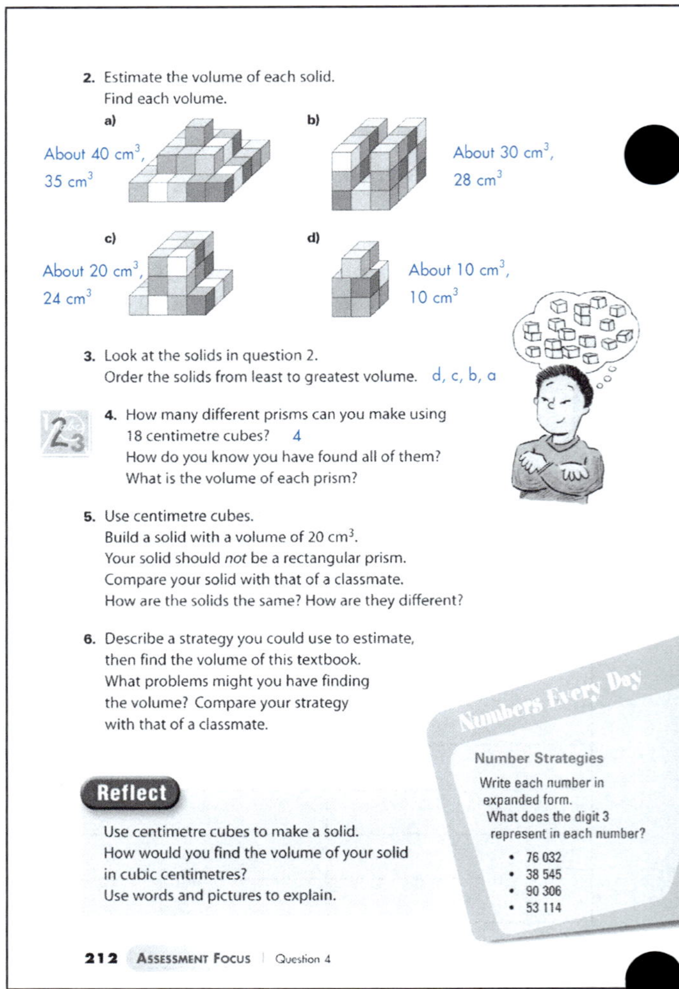

2. Estimate the volume of each solid.
Find each volume.
a) About 40 cm^3, 35 cm^3
b) About 30 cm^3, 28 cm^3
c) About 20 cm^3, 24 cm^3
d) About 10 cm^3, 10 cm^3

3. Look at the solids in question 2.
Order the solids from least to greatest volume. d, c, b, a

4. How many different prisms can you make using 18 centimetre cubes? 4
How do you know you have found all of them?
What is the volume of each prism?

5. Use centimetre cubes.
Build a solid with a volume of 20 cm^3.
Your solid should *not* be a rectangular prism.
Compare your solid with that of a classmate.
How are the solids the same? How are they different?

6. Describe a strategy you could use to estimate, then find the volume of this textbook.
What problems might you have finding the volume? Compare your strategy with that of a classmate.

Reflect

Use centimetre cubes to make a solid.
How would you find the volume of your solid in cubic centimetres?
Use words and pictures to explain.

Numbers Every Day

Number Strategies

Write each number in expanded form.
What does the digit 3 represent in each number?
- 76 032
- 38 545
- 90 306
- 53 114

212 ASSESSMENT FOCUS | Question 4

ASSESSMENT FOR LEARNING

What to Look For	What to Do
Understanding concepts ✔ Students understand the concept of volume as the amount of space an object takes up. ✔ Students understand cm^3 as a unit of volume. ***Applying procedures*** ✔ Students can estimate and determine volumes using centimetre cubes.	***Extra Support:*** Students can use Step-by-Step 7 (Master 6.16) to complete question 4. ***Extra Practice:*** Return to *Explore*. For each of the three solids, create another solid with the same volume but a different shape. Students can complete Extra Practice 3 (Master 6.24). ***Extension:*** Students build a solid using centimetre cubes. Then they write clues to describe it. At least one clue must involve the volume of the solid. Partners trade clues and try to build the solids.

Recording and Reporting
Master 6.2 Ongoing Observations: Measurement

LESSON

8

Relating Capacity and Volume

The capacity of a graduated cylinder is 500 mL.
This is how much liquid it can hold.
If we pour in 400 mL of water, we can say the volume of water is 400 mL.
That is, we can measure the volume of water in millilitres.

You will investigate how millilitres are related to cubic centimetres.

Explore

You will need centimetre cubes, a 500-mL graduated cylinder, and water.

- Pour 400 mL of water into a 500-mL graduated cylinder. Record the volume of water in a table. Place 10 cubes in the cylinder. Record the number of cubes added and the new volume, in millilitres. Calculate and record the change in volume.
- Add 10 more cubes. Record the new volume. Continue to add groups of 10 cubes. Each time, record the volume and the change in volume.
- Describe any patterns you see in the table.
- Look at your results. When you added 10 cubes, how did the volume in the cylinder change? How many millilitres equal 10 cm^3?

Number of Cubes Added	Volume (mL)	Change in Volume (mL)
0	400	–
10		

Show and Share

Share the patterns you found with another group of students.
How could you use water in a graduated cylinder to find the volume of a stone?

Relating Capacity and Volume

LESSON ORGANIZER 40-50 min

Curriculum Focus: Explore the relationship between millilitres and cubic centimetres. (5m60, 5m61, 5m62)

Teacher Materials
- 50 pennies
- 500-g mass
- ping-pong ball

Student Materials
- centimetre cubes
- small solid objects
- dimes
- modelling clay
- counters
- 3-column chart (PM 18)
- 500-mL graduated cylinders

Optional
- Step-by-Step 8 (Master 6.17)
- Extra Practice 4 (Master 6.25)

Vocabulary: cubic unit, displacement

Assessment: Master 6.2 Ongoing Observations: Measurement

Key Math Learnings

1. Capacity is measured in millilitres or litres.
2. The volume/capacity of an object can be measured in cubic centimetres or in millilitres (1 cm^3 = 1 mL).
3. Measuring the displacement of water is another method of finding the volume of an object.

BEFORE Get Started

Encourage students to think about what they know of volume and capacity. Ask questions, such as:

- How can you determine the volume of an object? (*By counting the number of centimetre cubes it takes to model the object*)
- How can you determine the capacity of an object? (*By filling the object with liquid, then measuring the amount of liquid it holds*)

Display three items that have similar volumes but different masses, for example: 50 pennies, a 500-g mass, and a ping-pong ball. Ask students to predict which has the greatest volume.

Put 300 mL of water into a 500-mL graduated cylinder. Place/hold each of the objects in the container and record the displacement of water. When holding the ping-pong ball down so it is totally submerged, be sure not to put your own fingers under water. Ask:

- Why do you think an object with very little mass (the ping-pong ball) may have a greater volume than an object with more mass (the pennies)? (*Volume refers to the amount of space an object takes up, not its mass. The air inside the ping-pong ball has no mass, but it takes up space.*)

Present *Explore*. Model the first step.

DURING Explore

Ongoing Assessment: Observe and Listen

Ensure students record their results accurately in table format. Ask:

- Why do you think we add 10 centimetre cubes at a time rather than just 1? (*The change in water level would be too small to measure if just 1 cube were added.*)

REACHING ALL LEARNERS

Alternative Explore

Materials: small milk cartons, 1-L graduated cylinder, water
Have students estimate, measure, and compare the volume of an empty small carton of milk in three conditions: normal, crushed into a ball, and flattened. Explain the differences in measurement that are observed.

Early Finishers/Extra Practice

Students estimate and compare the masses of a variety of different personal belongings. Students record the estimates and volumes of each object in a table.

Common Misconceptions

➤ After placing an object inside a graduated cylinder, some students may consider the volume of an object to be the measurement shown.

How to Help: Tell students that the difference in water level, or the displacement of the water, is the object's volume.

Sample Answers

1. Answers depend on the solids measured.
2. 250 cm^3 should have dimensions that are approximately 5 cm by 5 cm by 10 cm.
3. a) I selected the objects because they both appeared to be about the same size and shape.
4. b) Readings will be greater than 100 mL.
   c) The cylinder in part b includes spaces between the cubes, so the reading is greater.

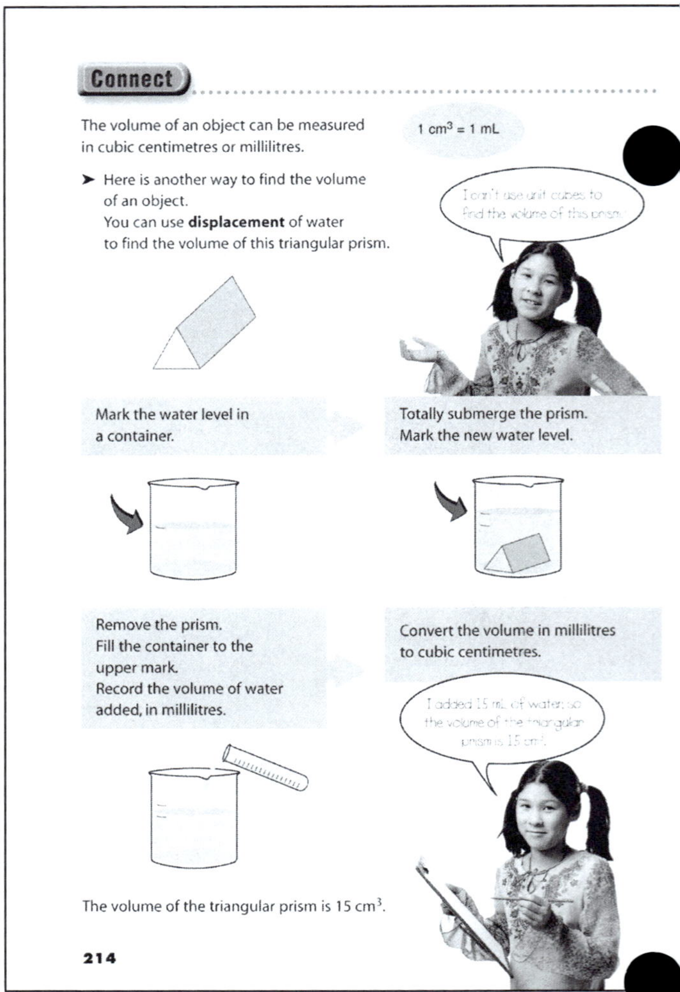
Connect

The volume of an object can be measured in cubic centimetres or millilitres.

$1\ cm^3 = 1\ mL$

➤ Here is another way to find the volume of an object.
You can use **displacement** of water to find the volume of this triangular prism.

Mark the water level in a container.

Totally submerge the prism. Mark the new water level.

Remove the prism.
Fill the container to the upper mark.
Record the volume of water added, in millilitres.

Convert the volume in millilitres to cubic centimetres.

The volume of the triangular prism is 15 cm^3.

214

- Can you see any patterns in the data? *(1 cm^3 = 1 mL)*
- If the centimetre cubes were made of lead, what effect would it have on the data? *(No effect; the cubes would be heavier, but their volume would be the same.)*

Watch for students who are not able to find patterns in the data. Focus students' attention on the *Change in Volume* column and have them make predictions before they measure.

AFTER Connect

Invite volunteers to share any patterns they found with the class. Students should be able to conclude that the smaller the object, the less space it occupies.

Use a triangular prism, or similar object, to model the process shown in *Connect*. Ask:

- How is this strategy similar to the way you measured volume before? *(It is similar because it measures the volume of an object.)*
- How is it different? *(It is different because it works for all shapes of objects, not just ones I can model with unit cubes.)*

Practice

Students will need access to: containers, graduated cylinders, water, various solid objects that can be submerged, modelling clay, dimes, centimetre cubes, and counters.

Assessment Focus: Question 3

Some students may have trouble seeing that objects have similar volumes when they have different shapes. Students with strong spatial abilities may select items that are close in volume, but quite different in shape. Students should pick objects that can be submerged and fit inside a graduated cylinder.

Practice

You will need a container, water, and a graduated cylinder.

Collect 4 small solid objects.
a) Estimate the volume of each object.
b) Find each volume.
c) Order the objects from least to greatest volume.

2. Use modelling clay to build a solid.
Try to make a solid with a volume of 250 cm^3.
a) Find the volume of your solid.
b) How close is the volume to 250 cm^3?

3. Choose two different solids from the classroom.
Look for solids with about the same volume.
a) Explain why you chose the solids you did.
b) Find the volume of each solid in cubic centimetres.

4. a) What is the volume of 100 centimetre cubes? 100 mL
b) Put 100 centimetre cubes into an empty graduated cylinder.
Read the number of millilitres from the scale.
c) Compare your answers to parts a and b.
Explain any differences.

5. You will need 50 counters.
a) Predict the volume of 50 counters in cubic centimetres.
b) Find the volume of 50 counters.
c) How does your estimate compare to the volume?

6. Describe how you could find each measure.
a) the volume of one dime in cubic centimetres
b) the volume of a toy car in millilitres

Numbers Every Day

Mental Math

Find the missing numbers.
Write each pattern rule.
- 625, 600, □, □, □, 500, 475
- 870, 940, □, □, □, 1220, 1290
- 1250, 1175, □, □, □, 875, 800
- 72, □, □, 108, □, 132

Reflect

Explain how you can use displacement of water to measure the volume of an object.

Assessment Focus | Question 3

215

5. a) An approximation can be made by multiplying the length, width, and height of a stack.
b) Students will use displacement to find the volume.
c) The estimate is greater than the actual volume because the estimate assumes a square counter, which is larger than the actual round counter.

6. a) Because a dime is very small, I will place 10 dimes in a 50-mL graduated cylinder filled with 20 mL of water. When I take the reading and calculate the displacement of water, I will divide by 10 to get the volume of 1 dime.
b) The volume of a toy car can be found by filling a graduated cylinder to 300 mL. Place the object in the cylinder and measure its displacement.

REFLECT: I mark the water level in a container. I then place the object into the container and carefully examine how much water is displaced. The amount of water displaced equals the volume of the object.

Numbers Every Day

Strategies	Answers
Start at 625. Subtract 25 each time.	575, 550, 525
Start at 870. Add 70 each time.	1010, 1080, 1150
Start at 1250. Subtract 75 each time.	1100, 1025, 950
Start at 72. Add 12 each time.	84, 96, 120

ASSESSMENT FOR LEARNING

What to Look For

Understanding concepts

✔ Students understand that the volume of objects is measured in cubic centimetres or millilitres.

✔ Students understand the relationship between millilitres and cubic centimetres.

Applying procedures

✔ Students can apply strategies to determine the relationship between capacity and volume by measuring the volume of various objects.

What to Do

Extra Support: Have students work with and measure lesser volumes using modelling clay and smaller graduated cylinders. Students can use Step-by-Step 8 (Master 6.17) to complete question 3.

Extra Practice: Have students use modelling clay to estimate volumes of 50, 100, 200, and 400 mL. Students then check their estimates by finding the volumes of their solids.
Students can complete Extra Practice 4 (Master 6.25).

Extension: Provide students with an empty film canister and some coins. Have students measure the volume of the canister, the coins, and then both together. Have students place the coins inside the film canister and measure the volume of the combined objects. Ask them to provide an explanation for what they have observed.

Recording and Reporting

Master 6.2 Ongoing Observations: Measurement

Measuring Mass

LESSON ORGANIZER

40–50 min

Curriculum Focus: Measure and compare mass in milligrams, grams, and kilograms. (5m64)

Student Materials
- balance scales
- standard masses

Optional
- Step-by-Step 9 (Master 6.18)
- Extra Practice 4 (Master 6.25)

Vocabulary: standard masses, milligrams

Assessment: Master 6.2 Ongoing Observations: Measurement

Key Math Learnings

1. Large masses are measured in kilograms, small masses are measured in grams, and very small masses are measured in milligrams.
2. 1000 mg = 1 g; 1000 g = 1 kg

Making Connections

Math Link: Some countries still use the Imperial system to record mass, capacity, and volume. One inch is about 2.54 cm; one fluid ounce is about 28.4 mL.

LESSON 9

Measuring Mass

Explore

You will need balance scales and a set of standard masses.

Find an object that has a mass:
- less than 1 g
- between 50 g and 100 g
- approximately 500 g
- approximately 1000 g, or 1 kg

Find:
- 3 objects with a total mass of about 2000 g, or 2 kg
- 2 objects whose masses differ by 500 g

Record your work in a table.

Object	Estimated Mass	Actual Mass
Chocolate milk	500 g	

Show and Share

Which masses was it easy to find objects for?
Which were difficult? Why?
How did you estimate the mass of each object?

Math Link

Social Studies

The next time you measure an object, look to see where it was made. Many countries use the metric system to record mass, capacity, and volume. One kilogram is the same in Canada, Singapore, or any other country.

216 LESSON FOCUS | Measure and compare mass in milligrams, grams, and kilograms

Math Note

It is common to say, "My weight is 50 kg." This is an error. Mass is measured in kg. Weight is a force, measured in Newtons. Model the correct language when talking with students—always use "mass," never "weight."

BEFORE Get Started

Discuss the meaning of the term "mass." Ask:
- What are grams, kilograms, and milligrams?
  (*Units for measuring mass in the metric system.*)
- What are pounds?
  (*Another unit for measuring mass, used in the United States. Most other countries use the metric system.*)
- What is the relationship between milligrams, grams, and kilograms?
  (*1000 mg = 1 g; 1000 g = 1 kg*)
- Why do we need different units of measurement for mass?
  (*Some masses are large while others are small.*)
- How do we measure mass?
  (*We use scales to measure mass.*)

Ask students to estimate the mass of a small item such as a chalk brush. Ask a volunteer to demonstrate how to use balance scales and standard masses to check the estimate. Repeat with a heavier object such as a textbook.

Present *Explore*. Provide each group with balance scales and a set of standard masses.

DURING Explore

Ongoing Assessment: Observe and Listen

While students investigate, ask questions, such as:
- Why do you think the object you selected will be close to 100 g? (*I compared its mass with the mass of the chalk brush.*)
- Is there a relationship between the size of an object and its mass? (*Not necessarily. A small object may have a greater mass than a larger object.*)

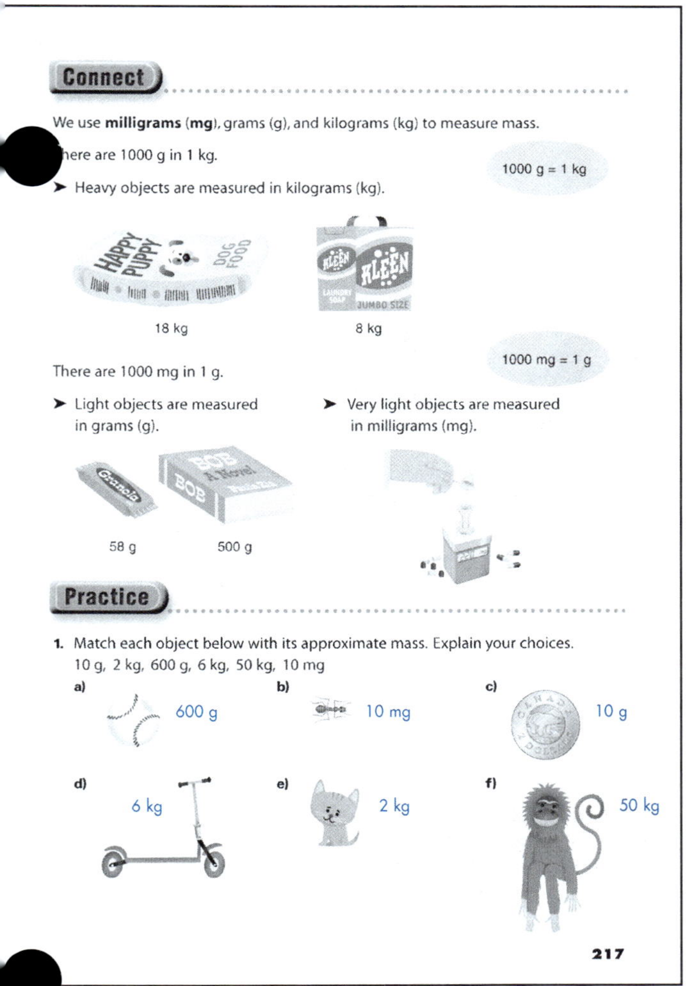

Connect

We use **milligrams (mg)**, grams (g), and kilograms (kg) to measure mass.

There are 1000 g in 1 kg.

1000 g = 1 kg

➤ Heavy objects are measured in kilograms (kg).

18 kg   8 kg

There are 1000 mg in 1 g.

1000 mg = 1 g

➤ Light objects are measured in grams (g).

➤ Very light objects are measured in milligrams (mg).

58 g   500 g

Practice

1. Match each object below with its approximate mass. Explain your choices.
   10 g, 2 kg, 600 g, 6 kg, 50 kg, 10 mg

a) 600 g
b) 10 mg
c) 10 g
d) 6 kg
e) 2 kg
f) 50 kg

217

REACHING ALL LEARNERS

Early Finishers

Students try to find 5 items from the classroom that have a combined mass of exactly 3 kg. Students may not break items or use 2 or more of the same item.

Extra Practice

Students try to find single classroom items that have one of the following masses: 1 g, 10 g, 100 g, and 1 kg

Common Misconceptions

➤ Students may have difficulty determining which unit of mass is appropriate for a given object.

How to Help: Encourage students to work through the *Extra Practice* above. Students can then draw upon their past experience with objects they have found to match specific benchmark values. For example, a student may recall that a paper clip has a mass of approximately 1 g or that an apple has a mass of approximately 100 g.

- Can you estimate the mass of an object without picking it up?
  (*Sometimes, but only if I'm familiar with the mass from previous experience.*)

AFTER Connect

Invite volunteers to share which masses were the easiest or most difficult to find.

Encourage students to explain their strategies for estimating the mass of an object. Ask:

- Will that strategy work for all objects?
  (*No. It will only work for things I can pick up.*)

Point to a piece of chalk, a student desk, and then a teacher desk. Ask students how they might estimate the mass of each.

Work through *Connect*. Highlight the relationship between milligrams, grams, and kilograms.

Emphasize that an object's mass can be shown in different ways: for example, 2 g 500 mg, or 2.5 g; 3 kg 700 g, or 3.7 kg.

Practice

Assessment Focus: Question 6

Students can assume that 1 week means 5 days of packed lunches. Most students will be able to calculate the total mass of peanut butter and jelly in grams. Some students will recognize that the units must match, and convert this mass to kilograms before calculating their answer.

Sample Answers

3. b) About 8 mice
   c) About 333 grasshoppers; 3 g × 333 = 999 g, which is about 1 kg.
4. 500 × 500 mg = 250 000 mg, or 250 g
6. 6 containers of jelly and 8 containers of peanut butter;
   40 × 5 days = 200 days;
   200 × 30 g = 6000 g, or 6 kg of jelly;
   200 × 40 g = 8000 g, or 8 kg of peanut butter

REFLECT: If the object has a very small mass, less than a dime for example, it would probably be measured in milligrams. If the object had a greater mass than a dime but less mass than this math textbook, it would be measured in grams. Anything with a greater mass would probably be measured in kilograms.

Numbers Every Day

Divide 48 700 by 2.
48 700 ÷ 2 = 24 350
Add: 10 000 + 24 350 = 34 350
Subtract: 24 350 − 10 000 = 14 350
14 350 + 34 350 = 48 700

2. Record the best estimate. Explain your choices.
   a) 100 g, 500 g, 1 kg, or 5 kg
   b) 300 mg, 3 g, 3 kg, or 30 kg

1 kg

3 g

3. a) One mouse has a mass of about 30 g.
   What is the mass of each animal?
   • 1 grasshopper About 3 g
   • 1 gerbil About 60 g
   • 1 yellow-collared macaw About 240 g
   b) About how many mice would balance the macaw?
   c) Suppose you had 1 kg of grasshoppers.
   About how many grasshoppers would you have?
   Explain.

4. The vitamin C tablets in a bottle have a mass of 250 g.
   Each tablet has a mass of 500 mg.
   How many tablets are in the bottle? 500 tablets
   Show your work.

5. Together, Sarah's two cats have the same mass as her dog, 11 kg.
   The mass of one cat is 1500 g greater than the mass of the other.
   What are the masses of the two cats?

6. Peter eats peanut butter and jelly sandwiches every day for lunch.
   He estimates that he uses 30 g of jelly and 40 g of peanut butter per sandwich. How many 1-kg containers of each would he need to make his lunches for 40 weeks?
   Use words and numbers to explain.

Reflect

How do you know when to use milligrams, grams, or kilograms to measure mass?
Give examples in your answer.

Numbers Every Day

Calculator Skills

Find two 5-digit numbers whose sum is 48 700 and whose difference is 20 000.
34 350, 14 350

ASSESSMENT FOR LEARNING

What to Look For	What to Do
Understanding concepts ✔ Students understand the concept of mass. ✔ Students understand the relationship between milligrams, grams, and kilograms. ***Applying procedures*** ✔ Students can select an appropriate unit to estimate and measure mass.	***Extra Support:*** Students can use Step-by-Step 9 (Master 6.18) to complete question 6. ***Extra Practice:*** Students can complete Extra Practice 4 (Master 6.25). ***Extension:*** Challenge students to create their own standard masses using modelling clay. Students may use their standard masses to find the mass of various objects.

Recording and Reporting
Master 6.2 Ongoing Observations: Measurement

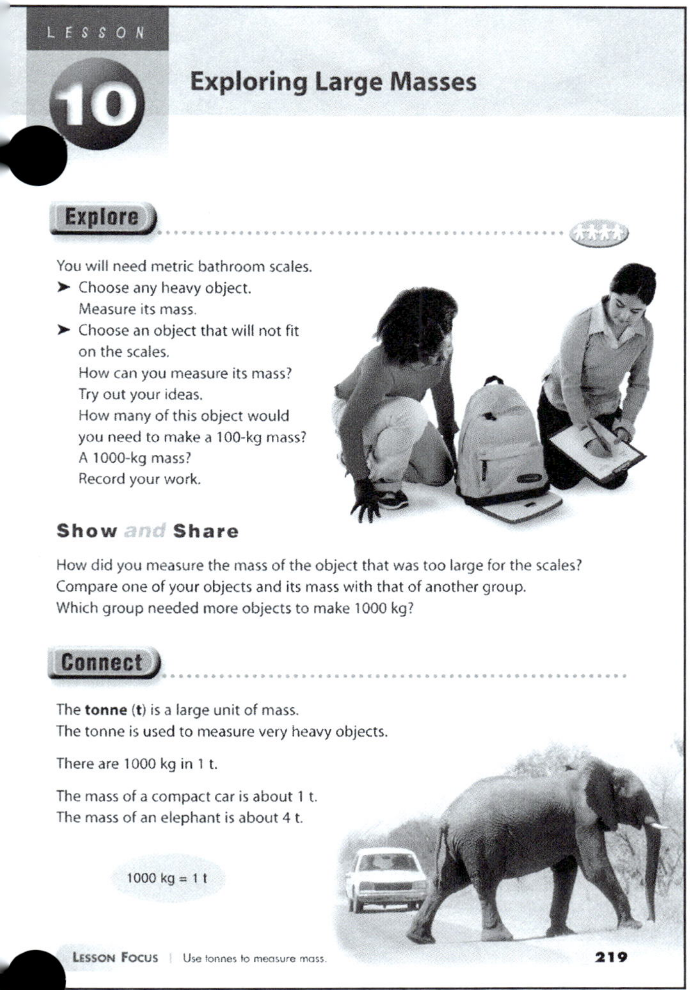

LESSON 10

Exploring Large Masses

Explore

You will need metric bathroom scales.

- Choose any heavy object.
  Measure its mass.
- Choose an object that will not fit on the scales.
  How can you measure its mass?
  Try out your ideas.
  How many of this object would you need to make a 100-kg mass?
  A 1000-kg mass?
  Record your work.

Show and Share

How did you measure the mass of the object that was too large for the scales?
Compare one of your objects and its mass with that of another group.
Which group needed more objects to make 1000 kg?

Connect

The **tonne** (**t**) is a large unit of mass.
The tonne is used to measure very heavy objects.

There are 1000 kg in 1 t.

The mass of a compact car is about 1 t.
The mass of an elephant is about 4 t.

1000 kg = 1 t

LESSON FOCUS | Use tonnes to measure mass.   219

Exploring Large Masses

LESSON ORGANIZER (40–50 min)

Curriculum Focus: Use tonnes to measure mass. (5m63, 5m64)

Student Materials
- metric bathroom scales

Optional
- Step-by-Step 10 (Master 6.19)
- Extra Practice 5 (Master 6.26)

Vocabulary: tonne

Assessment: Master 6.2 Ongoing Observations: Measurement

Key Math Learnings

1. The tonne is a large unit of mass, used to measure very heavy objects.
2. There are 1000 kg in 1 t.

BEFORE — Get Started

Review the relationships between milligrams, grams, and kilograms. Focus students' attention on the fact that 1000 mg = 1 g and 1000 g = 1 kg. Display these relationships in a table on the board.

Ask:

- If this pattern continued, what would come next in the table? (*1000 kg =* ____)
- Why might you need a larger unit of mass? (*To measure larger masses; to keep the numbers smaller and easier to work with so that errors are reduced*)

Ask if any student knows the proper unit for 1000 kg. Explain to students that 1000 kg = 1 t. Write the word *tonne* on the board, and add a line to your table: 1000 kg = 1 t.

Use examples to show when it might be better to measure in tonnes than in kilograms. (For example, an empty boxcar has a mass of approximately 70 t, or 70 000 kg.)

Tell students that in this lesson they will be exploring large masses, and will be examining the relationship between tonnes and kilograms.

Present *Explore*.

DURING — Explore

Ongoing Assessment: Observe and Listen

Ask students:

- How much mass do you think the bathroom scales will hold? (*About 150 kg*) Why? (*They are meant to measure the mass of a person.*)
- Suppose the average mass of a grade 5 student is 40 kg. About how many students would it take to make up 1 t? (*About 25 students*)

REACHING ALL LEARNERS

Alternative Explore

Materials: bathroom scales, calculators

Copy 8 numbers on the board: 10, 20, 50, 100, 200, 500, 1000, and 2000. Each group of 4–5 students has 20 min to find identical objects within the class that add up to 1 t when a number of the objects are measured. (For example, 500 of what object will have a mass of approximately 1 t? Each group records their answers. Results are shared and discussed.

Early Finishers

Students cut out and sort pictures of objects from magazines by the objects estimated mass. For each item, say which is the best estimate: 1 g, 10 g, 100 g, 1 kg, 10 kg, 100 kg, 1 t, or 10 t.

Extra Practice

Using a calculator, students can practise showing all values from questions 1–7 in both kilograms and tonnes.

Common Misconceptions

➤ Students may experience difficulty converting between kilograms and tonnes when there is a decimal involved.

How to Help: Have students estimate the answer before multiplying or dividing by 1000. When the conversion is complete have students check if their answer is reasonable.

ESL Strategies

Use visual cues. Have students physically manipulate 1- and 10-kg objects. Illustrate 10 groups of 10-kg objects to show 100 kg and 10 groups of 100-kg objects to show 1 t.

➤ The mass of an 18-wheel truck is about 44 t.
How many kilograms is that?

$$1\text{ t} = 1000\text{ kg}$$
$$\text{So, } 44\text{ t} = 44 \times 1000\text{ kg} = 44\,000\text{ kg}$$

The mass of the truck is about 44 000 kg.

➤ The mass of a walrus is about 1300 kg.
Find the mass of a walrus in tonnes.

$$1\text{ t} = 1000\text{ kg}$$
$$\text{So, } 1300\text{ kg} = \tfrac{1300}{1000}\text{ t} = 1.3\text{ t}$$

The mass of a walrus is about 1.3 t.

Practice

1. Match each object with its approximate mass.
Explain your choices.
30 kg, 2 t, 400 g, 20 t

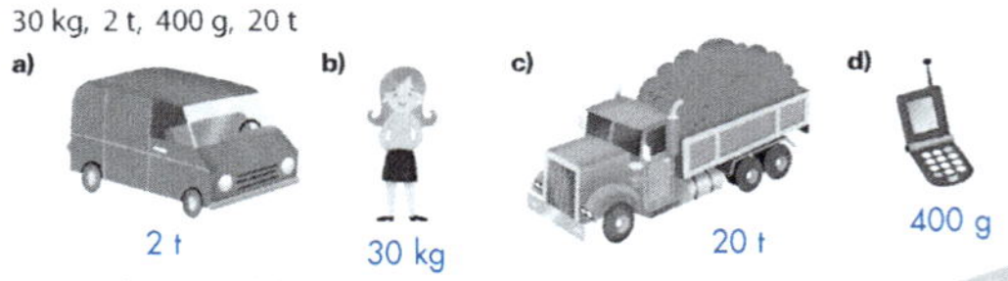

2. Find each mass in kilograms.
   a) The mass of a male giraffe is about 1.9 t. 1900 kg
   b) Debbie needs 0.75 t of concrete mix for her new patio. 750 kg
   c) A rhinoceros has a mass of about 2.3 t. 2300 kg

3. Find each mass in tonnes.
   a) A garbage truck has a mass of about 16 500 kg. 16.5 t
   b) The mass of a tent trailer is about 600 kg. 0.6 t
   c) The mass of a newborn blue whale is about 2500 kg. 2.5 t

Numbers Every Day

Number Strategies

Estimate the total amount.

$4.69
$1.89
$6.32
+ $4.98

About $18.00

220

AFTER Connect

Invite volunteers to share the strategies they used to measure the mass of an object that did not fit on the scales. Some groups will be able to find the precise mass of their object, while others will have to make an estimate. (For example, if the object is not too heavy, students may be able to stand on the scale while holding the object, then subtract their own mass. This will give them a precise result.)

Ask:

- Approximately how many of your object would you need to make a 100-kg mass? (*My object had a mass of about 30 kg. Approximately 3 of these objects would make a 100-kg mass.*) A 1000-kg mass? (*Approximately 33 of these objects would make a 1000-kg mass.*)
- Could you give an exact answer to this question? (*No, because 30 kg is only an estimate of the object's mass.*)

Work through the examples in *Connect* with students. Students can use these examples as references for future work.

Practice

Advise students to refer back to the examples in *Connect* when converting between kilograms and tonnes. Question 3 requires the use of a calculator.

Assessment Focus: Question 6

It may be necessary for some students to look carefully at the illustration provided. This will give students visual clues and may help them organize their thinking. Some students may figure out how many packages are required, then divide by 10 to find the number of boxes. Most students will need to find the mass of one box (25 kg) to solve the problem.

4. Record the best estimate. Explain your choice.

a) 200 g, 2 t, 50 kg, or 5 kg

50 kg

b) 15 g, 2 kg, 10 t, or 500 kg

500 kg

5. A small truck carrying computer parts has a mass of 8 t.
The computer parts have a mass of 3500 kg.
What is the mass of the empty truck? Show your work. 4500 kg or 4.5 t

6. One sheet of paper has a mass of about 5 g.
There are:
- 10 packages per box
- 500 sheets of paper per package

a) What is the mass of 1 package of paper? 2 packages? 2.5 kg, 5.0 kg

b) How many boxes of paper have a mass of 1 t? 40 boxes

Use words, numbers, or pictures to explain.

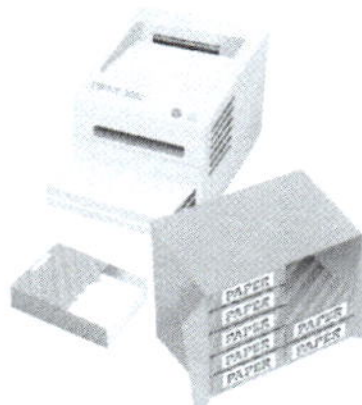

7. A transport truck carries stereo, computer, and television parts.
- The mass of the truck and the parts is 28 t.
- The mass of the empty truck is 6 t.
- The mass of computer parts is 2 t less than the mass of television parts.
- The mass of stereo parts is double the mass of television parts.

What is the mass of each type of parts?
Show your work.

Reflect

How are grams, kilograms, and tonnes related?
When is it better to record a mass in kilograms? In tonnes?

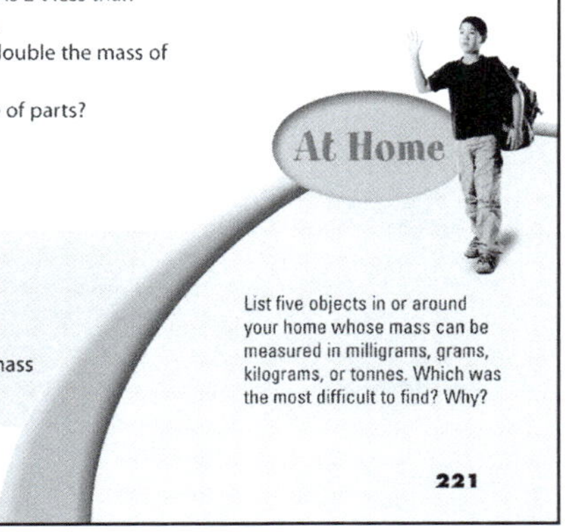

At Home

List five objects in or around your home whose mass can be measured in milligrams, grams, kilograms, or tonnes. Which was the most difficult to find? Why?

ASSESSMENT FOCUS | Question 6 221

Sample Answers

6. b) 1box = 10 × 2.5 kg
= 25 kg

$\frac{1000}{25}$ = 40 boxes

7. The mass of the parts is 28 t − 6 t = 22 t.
The masses are all expressed in relation to television parts. Use guess and check. Since there are 3 types of parts, start with 7 t of television parts. That does not work. Next try 6 t of television parts. That works.
12 t of stereo parts; 6 t of television parts; 4 t of computer parts

REFLECT: There are 1000 g in 1 kg and 1000 kg in 1 t. It is better to record a mass in tonnes when the mass in kilograms is too large. It is better to record a mass in kilograms when the mass in grams is too large. This keeps the numbers smaller and reduces the chance of errors in calculations.

At Home

Many household cooking ingredients are measured in grams. Spices are measured in milligrams. Most students will have a difficult time finding objects within their homes that measure 1 t.

Numbers Every Day

If you round the numbers to the nearest dollar, the estimate would be $18.

ASSESSMENT FOR LEARNING

What to Look For	What to Do
Understanding concepts ✔ Students understand the concept of mass. ✔ Students understand the relationships between grams, kilograms, and tonnes. ***Applying procedures*** ✔ Students can select an appropriate unit to estimate and measure mass.	***Extra Support:*** Students can use Step-by-Step 10 (Master 6.19) to complete question 6. ***Extra Practice:*** Students can complete the Additional Activity, *Muddling Through Mass* (Master 6.10). Students can complete Extra Practice 5 (Master 6.26). ***Extension:*** Students may look up and compare the masses of trains, planes, and automobiles using the Internet.

Recording and Reporting
Master 6.2 Ongoing Observations: Measurement

SHOW WHAT YOU KNOW

LESSON ORGANIZER (40–50 min)

Student Materials

Optional
- play money (PM 30)
- centimetre cubes
- calculators

Assessment: Master 6.1 Unit Rubric: Measurement
Master 6.4 Unit Summary: Measurement

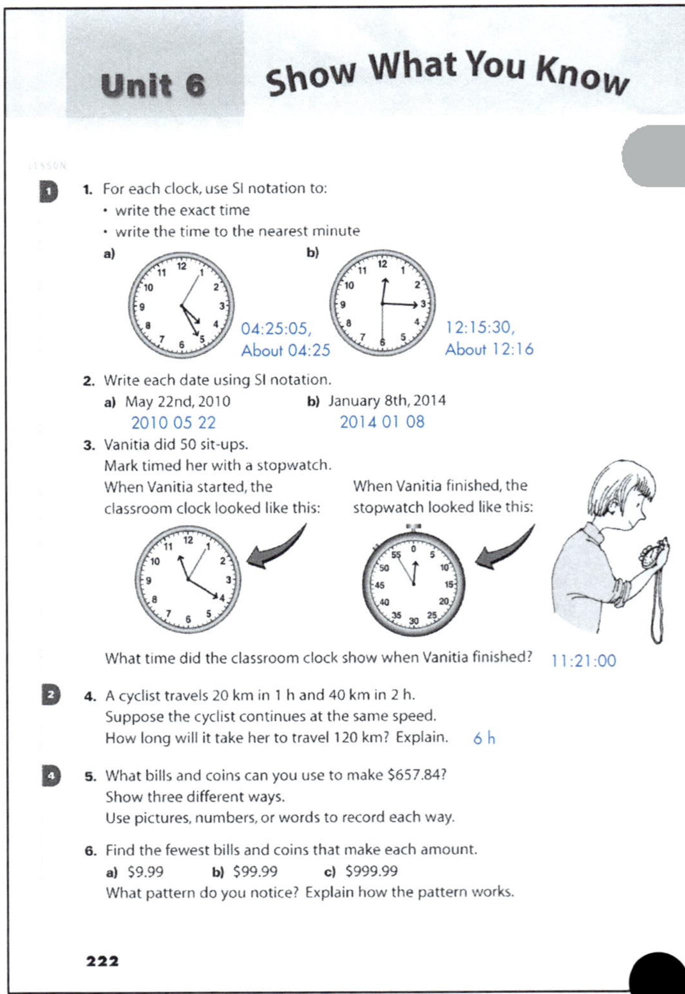

Unit 6 Show What You Know

1. For each clock, use SI notation to:
   - write the exact time
   - write the time to the nearest minute

   a) 04:25:05, About 04:25
   b) 12:15:30, About 12:16

2. Write each date using SI notation.
   a) May 22nd, 2010 — 2010 05 22
   b) January 8th, 2014 — 2014 01 08

3. Vanitia did 50 sit-ups.
   Mark timed her with a stopwatch.
   When Vanitia started, the classroom clock looked like this:
   When Vanitia finished, the stopwatch looked like this:
   What time did the classroom clock show when Vanitia finished? 11:21:00

4. A cyclist travels 20 km in 1 h and 40 km in 2 h.
   Suppose the cyclist continues at the same speed.
   How long will it take her to travel 120 km? Explain. 6 h

5. What bills and coins can you use to make \$657.84?
   Show three different ways.
   Use pictures, numbers, or words to record each way.

6. Find the fewest bills and coins that make each amount.
   a) \$9.99 b) \$99.99 c) \$999.99
   What pattern do you notice? Explain how the pattern works.

222

Sample Answers

4. To find the answer I followed the pattern: I h to go 20 km, 2 h to go 40 km, 3 h to go 60 km, ..., 6 h to go 120 km.
5. 6 hundred dollar bills, 1 fifty dollar bill, 1 five dollar bill, 1 toonie, 3 quarters, 1 nickel, 4 pennies; 5 hundred dollar bills, 2 fifty dollar bills, 2 twenty dollar bills, 3 five dollar bills, 2 loonies, 8 dimes, 4 pennies; 32 twenty dollar bills, 1 ten dollar bill, 1 five dollar bill, 1 toonie, 3 quarters, 1 nickel, 4 pennies
6. a) 1 five dollar bill, 2 toonies, 3 quarters, 2 dimes, 4 pennies
   b) 1 fifty dollar bill, 2 twenty dollar bills, 1 five dollar bill, 2 toonies, 3 quarters, 2 dimes, 4 pennies
   c) 9 hundred dollar bills, 1 fifty dollar bill, 2 twenty dollar bills, 1 five dollar bill, 2 toonies, 3 quarters, 2 dimes, 4 pennies

   The pattern is: Start with \$9.99. Each time add another 9 to the left of the decimal. In practical terms after the first value, you add \$90, then \$900, and so on, to the base amount of \$9.99.
7. Ray did not receive the correct change. He should have received \$5.73 but he received \$5.75 instead. (\$90.00 − 84.27 = \$5.73)
10. I could pour water into a graduated cylinder, and measure the water level. Then I could put the golf ball in the water, and measure the new level. The difference between the two levels is the volume of the golf ball.

Ray bought some clothes. The total bill was $84.27.
He paid with three $20 bills and three $10 bills.
He got a $5 bill and 3 quarters in change.
Did Ray get the correct change? How do you know? No.

6 **8.** Order these capacities from greatest to least.
2.5 L 2150 mL 4 L 1980 mL 4 L, 2.5 L, 2150 mL, 1980 mL

7 **9.** Each object is made with centimetre cubes.
Find the volume of each object.
Which object has the lesser volume? b

a)

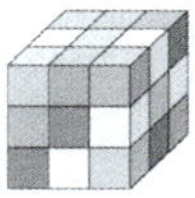

27 cm³

b)

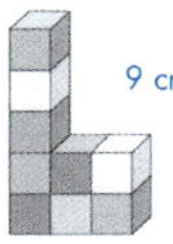

9 cm³

8 **10.** How could you find the volume of a golf ball?
Use pictures and words to explain.

9 10 **11.** Copy and complete.
a) 3200 kg = □ t 3.2 **b)** 21 kg = □ g 21 000
c) 8 t = □ kg 8000 **d)** 4000 mg = □ g 4
e) 12 500 kg = □ t 12.5 **f)** 2 t = □ kg 2000

10 **12.** An empty trailer has a mass of 850 kg.
When the trailer carries a load, its mass is 1.4 t.
What is the mass of the load? 550 kg

UNIT 6 **Learning Goals**

- ✓ tell time to the nearest second
- ✓ explore the relationship between time and distance
- ✓ count money and make change
- ✓ estimate, measure, and compare mass, volume, and capacity
- ✓ relate volume and capacity

223

ASSESSMENT FOR LEARNING

What to Look For

Understanding of concepts

✔ **Question 3:** Student can tell time and determine elapsed time.
✔ **Question 4:** Student understands the time and distance relationship.
✔ **Question 9:** Student understands how to determine volume, and compare objects with different volumes.

Applyication of mathematical procedures

✔ **Question 5:** Students can select an appropriate number of bills and/or coins to make a purchase.
✔ **Question 8:** Student can compare and order capacities with different units of measure.
✔ **Question 11:** Student can convert between different units of mass.

Problem solving

✔ **Question 6:** Student can show the least number of bills and coins needed to make an amount of money.
✔ **Question 7:** Student can interpret the problem, select an appropriate strategy, and show whether the correct change is provided.

Recording and Reporting

Master 6.1 Unit Rubric: Measurement
Master 6.4 Unit Summary: Measurement

All Aboard!

LESSON ORGANIZER 40–50 min

Student Grouping: Groups of 3 or 4
Student Materials
- drinking straws (rigid and flexible)
- scissors
- Bristol board
- pencil crayons or markers
- glue
- tape
- calculators
- centimetre cubes
- 4-column charts (PM 19)

Sample Response

Part 1 Students should use as close to $100 as possible.
Part 2

Length of Track (cm)	Cost of Track ($)	Extra Charges ($)	Total Cost ($)
6	0.60	0	95.65
7	0.70	0.40	96.75
10	1.00	1.25	99.00
6	0.60	0.20	99.80

I had $0.20 left as change.

Unit Problem All Aboard!

You will need:
- drinking straws
- flexible drinking straws
- scissors
- Bristol board
- pencil crayons or markers
- a glue stick
- tape
- a calculator
- centimetre cubes

Part 1

Design the track for a model railway.
Use drinking straws to build the track.
Cut the straws if you need to.

You have a budget of $100.
Straight sections of track cost $0.10 per centimetre.
There are extra charges of:
- $0.20 for each bend in the track
- $1.25 for each bridge or overpass

Part 2

As you place each section of track, record your work in a table.
How much change do you have from $100?

Length of Track (cm)	Cost of Track ($)	Extra Charges ($)	Total Cost ($)

224

Present the *Unit Problem.* Invite volunteers to read the instructions for each part of the problem. Answer any questions students may have.

Have one student read aloud the Check List to ensure all students understand what their work should include.

Before sketching the layout of their track, students should decide approximately how many bridges and overpasses they will use, and how much money they will have left for the track. They should estimate the length of straws they can purchase with this amount. They can then sketch the layout of the track. Students should be encouraged to make full use of the sheet of Bristol board. If time permits, students could create a three-dimensional layout using additional pieces of Bristol board for town buildings, farm structures, and bridges.

Note: The cost of the track depends on length only, not on the number of straws used. A student may cut straws to simulate railways ties and use two parallel straws to make "rails" without extra cost.

Part 3

Suppose the train travels these speeds:

- 3 cm every second on straight sections of track
- 2 cm every second on curved sections of track and bridges

Estimate how long it will take the train to travel once around your track.
Calculate the time.

Part 4

Use centimetre cubes to build a model boxcar.
Find the volume of your boxcar.

Suppose one real boxcar holds 70 000 kg of cargo.
How many real boxcars would you need to carry 120 t of cargo? Explain.

Part 5

Make up your own problem about your model railway.
Solve your problem.
Present your design and results to the class.

Check List

Your work should show

- ✓ a track design that costs less than $100
- ✓ how you decided which pieces of track to use
- ✓ your measurements and calculations recorded correctly, including units
- ✓ how you calculated your answers

Reflect on the Unit

Why do we measure?
Write about the different ways you have learned to measure objects.

225

Part 3 From my table, I used 660 cm of straight track and 150 cm of curved track or bridges. My train travels 3 cm every second on straight sections. It takes 660 ÷ 3 or 220 s to cover all the straight track. My train travels 2 cm every second on curved sections and bridges. This takes 150 ÷ 2 or 75 s.
It takes my train 220 + 75 = 295 s to travel once around the track. This is 4 min and 55 s.
Part 4 I used 36 centimetre cubes to build the boxcar, so it has a volume of 36 cm^3. 70 000 kg is 70 t. If 1 boxcar holds 70 t, 2 boxcars will hold 140 t. So, I would need 2 boxcars to carry 120 t of cargo, and I would have a little space left over.
Part 5 Suppose straight track cost $0.20 per cm.
How would the cost of this track change?
Answer: I used 660 cm of straight track, which cost me $66.
I spent $33.80 on bends and bridges. The $33.80 would not change, but the straight track would now cost me $132.
The total cost would be $132 + $33.80 = $165.80.

Reflect on the Unit

We measure to tell the difference between objects, and to compare or sort objects. By measuring the length, mass, or capacity of something we often learn other information as well.

I have learned how to measure time, mass, and volume.
I learned that there are 1000 g in 1 kg and 1000 kg in 1 t.
I learned objects can be different sizes, but can have the same volume. I learned to measure the volume of an object by finding how much water it displaced.

ASSESSMENT FOR LEARNING

What to Look For

Applying procedures

- ✔ Students can correctly calculate the total cost of railway track using a table.
- ✔ Students apply the relationship between time and distance to estimate and calculate time and distance values.

Understanding concepts

- ✔ Students understand the relationship between kilograms and tonnes.

Communicating

- ✔ Students describe measurement clearly and use mathematical terminology.

What to Do

Extra Support: Make the problem accessible.

Some students may have difficulty understanding how to begin the table from Parts 1 and 2. Copy a sample chart with different values on the board and guide students through the first few rows.

For Part 3, some students may need to visualize the relationship. Indicate a length of straw 3 cm long. Tell students that it takes the train 1 s to travel the distance. Repeat the above example using a curved section that is 2 cm long. Indicate that on a curve (or bridge) the train covers less distance in 1 s.

Recording and Reporting

Master 6.3 Performance Assessment Rubric: All Aboard!
Master 6.4 Unit Summary: Measurement

Evaluating Student Learning: Preparing to Report: Unit 6 Measurement

This unit provides an opportunity to report on the **Measurement** strand.
Master 6.4: Unit Summary: Measurement provides a comprehensive format for recording and summarizing evidence collected.

Here is an example of a completed summary chart for this Unit:

Strand: *Measurement*	**Problem solving**	**Understanding of concepts**	**Application of mathematical procedures**	**Communication**	***Overall***
Ongoing Observations	3	2	2	3	2/3
Strategies Toolkit (Lesson 3)			3		3
Work samples or portfolios; conferences	3	3	2	3	3
Show What You Know	3	3	3	3	3
Unit Test	3	2	2	3	2/3
Unit Problem All Aboard!	3	3	3	2	3
Achievement Level for reporting					3

Recording	**How to Report**
Ongoing Observations	Use *Master 6.2 Ongoing Observations: Measurement* to determine the most consistent level achieved in each category. Enter it in the chart. Choose to summarize by achievement category, or simply to enter an overall level. Observations from late in the Unit should be most heavily weighted.
Strategies Toolkit (problem solving)	Use *PM 1: Inquiry Process Check List* with the Strategies Toolkit (Lesson 3). Transfer results to the summary form. Teachers may choose to enter a level in the Problem solving column and/or Communication.
Portfolios or collections of work samples; conferences, or interviews	Use *Master 6.1 Unit Rubric: Measurement* to guide evaluation of collections of work and information gathered in conferences. Teachers may choose to focus particular attention on the *Assessment Focus* questions. Work from late in the unit should be most heavily weighted.
Show What You Know	Teachers may choose to assign some or all of these questions. *Master 6.1 Unit Rubric: Measurement* may be helpful in determining levels of achievement. #3, 4, and 9 provide evidence of Understanding of concepts; #5, 8, and 11 provide evidence of Application of mathematical procedures; #6 and 7 provide evidence of Problem solving; all questions provide evidence of Communication.
Unit Test	*Master 6.1 Unit Rubric: Measurement* may be helpful in determining levels of achievement. *Part A* provides evidence of Application of mathematical procedures; Part B provides evidence of Understanding of concepts; Part C provides evidence of Problem solving; all parts provide evidence of Communication.
Unit performance task	Use *Master 6.3 Performance Assessment Rubric: All Aboard!* The *Unit Problem* offers a snapshot of students' achievement. In particular, it shows their ability to synthesize and apply what they have learned.
Student Self-Assessment	Note students' perceptions of their own progress. This may take the form of an oral or written comment, or a self-rating.
Comments	Analyse the pattern of achievement to identify strengths and needs. In some cases, specific actions may be planned to support the learner.

Learning Skills	**Ongoing Records**
PM 4: Learning Skills Check List Use to record and report throughout a reporting period, rather than for each unit and/or strand.	*PM 10: Summary Class Records: Strands* *PM 11: Summary Class Records: Achievement Categories* *PM 12: Summary Record: Individual* Use to record and report evaluations of student achievement over several clusters, a reporting period, or a school year. These can also be used in place of the Unit Summary.

Name ____________________ Date ______________

Master 6.1

Unit Rubric: Measurement

	Level 1	Level 2	Level 3	Level 4
Problem solving • chooses and carries out a range of strategies to pose and solve measurement problems (estimation, diagrams, models, pictures, patterns, tables)	with assistance, chooses and carries out a limited range of appropriate strategies, rarely resulting in an accurate solution	with limited assistance, chooses and carries out appropriate strategies that frequently result in an accurate solution	chooses and carries out appropriate strategies to pose and solve problems with measurement that usually result in an accurate solution	chooses and carries out appropriate strategies to pose and solve problems with measurement accurately; may offer an innovative approach
Understanding of concepts • shows understanding by appropriately demonstrating and explaining: – relationships among measurement concepts (distance, time, money) – relationship between capacity and volume – justification of units and methods chosen – estimates of time intervals and of money	may be unable to demonstrate or explain: – relationships among measurement concepts (distance, time, money) – relationship between capacity and volume – justification of units and methods chosen – estimates of time intervals and of money	partially able to demonstrate and explain: – relationships among measurement concepts (distance, time, money) – relationship between capacity and volume – justification of units and methods chosen – estimates of time intervals and of money	demonstrates and explains: – relationships among measurement concepts (distance, time, money) – relationship between capacity and volume – justification of units and methods chosen – estimates of time intervals and of money	in various contexts, demonstrates and explains: – relationships among measurement concepts (distance, time, money) – relationship between capacity and volume – justification of units and methods chosen – estimates of time intervals and of money
Application of mathematical procedures • accurately: – uses metric prefixes – tells time to nearest second – counts and records money to $1000; makes change to $100 – uses SI notation for time and dates – measures volume, capacity, and mass in standard units – relates kg and tonnes	with limited accuracy and major errors: – uses metric prefixes – tells time to nearest second – counts and records money to $1000; makes change to $100 – uses SI notation for time and dates – measures volume, capacity, and mass in standard units – relates kg and tonnes	with some accuracy and several minor errors: – uses metric prefixes – tells time to nearest second – counts and records money to $1000; makes change to $100 – uses SI notation for time and dates – measures volume, capacity, and mass in standard units – relates kg and tonnes	with general accuracy and few minor errors: – uses metric prefixes – tells time to nearest second – counts and records money to $1000; makes change to $100 – uses SI notation for time and dates – measures volume, capacity, and mass in standard units – relates kg and tonnes	accurately, with very few or no errors: – uses metric prefixes – tells time to nearest second – counts and records money to $1000; makes change to $100 – uses SI notation for time and dates – measures volume, capacity, and mass in standard units – relates kg and tonnes
Communication • presents work clearly and precisely	work is often unclear and imprecise	work is presented with some clarity and precision	work is generally clear and precise	work is clear and precise
• describes procedures, and explains reasoning clearly	needs assistance to describe procedures and explain reasoning; often unclear and imprecise	describes procedures and explains reasoning with some clarity and precision	describes procedures and explains reasoning with general clarity and precision	describes procedures and explains reasoning clearly, precisely, and confidently

Name ____________________ Date ________________

Master 6.2

Ongoing Observations: Measurement

The behaviours described under each heading are examples; they are not intended to be an exhaustive list of all that might be observed. More detailed descriptions are provided in each lesson under *Assessment for Learning*.

STUDENT ACHIEVEMENT: Measurement				
Student	**Problem solving** ▪ Chooses and carries out a range of strategies to pose and solve measurement problems	**Understanding of concepts** ▪ Demonstrates and explains relationships among measurement concepts (distance, time, money)	**Application of mathematical procedures** ▪ Uses metric prefixes ▪ Measures volume, capacity, and mass in standard units ▪ Relates kg and tonnes	**Communication** ▪ Presents work, describes procedures, and explains reasoning clearly

Level 1 – very limited; Level 2 – somewhat or limited; Level 3 – satisfactory; Level 4 – thorough

Name ____________________ Date ______________

Master 6.3

Performance Assessment Rubric: All Aboard!

	Level 1	Level 2	Level 3	Level 4
Problem solving • chooses and carries out appropriate strategies, including estimation, to: – design a track that costs less than $100 (Part 1) – create and solve an original problem (Part 5)	chooses and carries out simple or inappropriate strategies that lead to inaccurate solutions, to: – design the required track route – create and solve an original problem	chooses and carries out some appropriate strategies, including estimation, with partial success to: – design the required track route – create and solve an original problem	chooses and carries out appropriate and effective strategies, including estimation, to: – design the required track route – create and solve an original problem	chooses innovative, appropriate, and effective strategies, including estimation, to: – design the required track route – create and solve an original problem
Understanding of concepts • shows understanding of measurement concepts by explaining track design and measurement results	shows very limited understanding by giving inappropriate explanations of track design and results	shows limited understanding by giving appropriate but incomplete explanations of track design and results	shows understanding by giving appropriate explanations of track design and results	shows thorough understanding by giving appropriate and complete explanations of track design and results
Application of mathematical procedures • completes table accurately (part 2)	completes table with major errors or omissions	completes table with several minor errors or omissions	completes table with few minor errors or omissions	completes table with very few or no minor errors or omissions
• calculates money, time, and mass correctly, including units: – change from $100 – time for one trip – volume of boxcar – number of boxcars for 120 t cargo – solution to own problem	limited accuracy; major errors or omissions in required calculations and recording of: – change from $100 – time for one trip – volume of boxcar – number of boxcars for 120 t cargo – solution to own problem	somewhat accurate; several minor errors in required calculations and recording of: – change from $100 – time for one trip – volume of boxcar – number of boxcars for 120 t cargo – solution to own problem	generally accurate; a few minor errors or omissions in required calculations and recording of: – change from $100 – time for one trip – volume of boxcar – number of boxcars for 120 t cargo – solution to own problem	accurate; very few or no minor errors in required calculations and recording of: – change from $100 – time for one trip – volume of boxcar – number of boxcars for 120 t cargo – solution to own problem
Communication • uses mathematical terminology, including units and symbols correctly (kg, t, speed, mass, km, h-min-s)	uses few appropriate mathematical terms and symbols	uses some appropriate mathematical terms and symbols	uses appropriate mathematical terms and symbols	uses a range of appropriate mathematical terminology and symbols clearly and precisely
• explains reasoning clearly	explains reasoning unclearly and imprecisely	explains reasoning with some clarity	explains reasoning clearly and precisely	explains reasoning clearly, precisely, and confidently

Name ____________________ Date ________________

Master 6.4

Unit Summary: Measurement

Review assessment records to determine the most consistent achievement levels for the assessments conducted. Some cells may be blank. *Overall* achievement levels may be recorded in each row, rather than identifying levels for each achievement category.

	Most Consistent Level of Achievement*				
Strand: *Measurement*	**Problem solving**	**Understanding of concepts**	**Application of mathematical procedures**	**Communication**	***Overall***
Ongoing Observations					
Strategies Toolkit (Lesson 3)					
Work samples or portfolios; conferences					
Show What You Know					
Unit Test					
Unit Problem All Aboard!					
Achievement Level for reporting					

*Use Ontario Achievement Levels 1, 2, 3, 4.

Self-Assessment:

Comments: (Strengths, Needs, Next Steps)

Name ____________________ Date _______________

Master 6.5

To Parents and Adults at Home …

Your child's class is starting a mathematics unit on measurement. Children will explore time, money, capacity, volume, and mass. Measurement is an essential part of how we interact with the world around us. As children increase their comfort and familiarity with these topics, they develop powerful tools they will use every day.

In this unit, your child will:

- Tell time to the nearest second.
- Explore the relationship between time and distance.
- Count money and make change.
- Estimate, measure, and compare masses, volumes, and capacities.
- Relate volume and capacity.

Your child will work with time to the nearest second, money amounts to $1000, capacity in millilitres and litres, volume in cubic centimetres, and mass in milligrams, grams, kilograms, and tonnes.

Classroom activities involving measurement build on the understanding children have developed in their daily lives.

Here are some activities you can try with your child:

- Have your child estimate, then measure, the seconds required to complete different activities.
- When travelling, have your child estimate how long it will take to get to your destination.
- When making a purchase, ask your child to count out the money given and count back the change received.
- Talk about the measurements found on various packages.

Name ____________________ Date _______________

Master 6.6

Auction Cards

Castle  Minimum bid: $7.50	Glittering Gem Cave  Minimum bid: $11.25	Treasure Chest  Minimum bid: $9.35
Plants  Minimum bid: $4.00	Sunken Ship  Minimum bid: $10.50	Mermaid Decoration  Minimum bid: $8.75
Tetras  Minimum bid: $5.50	Rainbow Shark 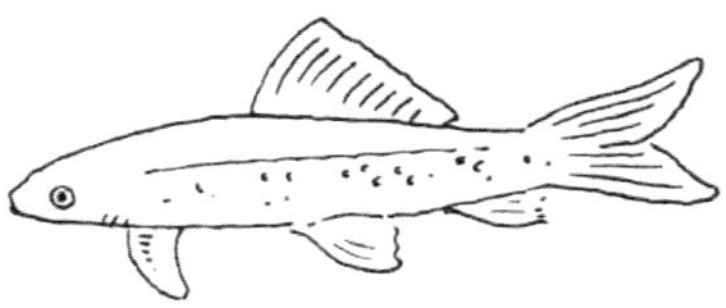 Minimum bid: $5.00	Fantail Goldfish  Minimum bid: $8.00
Angelfish  Minimum bid: $10.75	Snails  Minimum bid: $3.00	Algae Eater 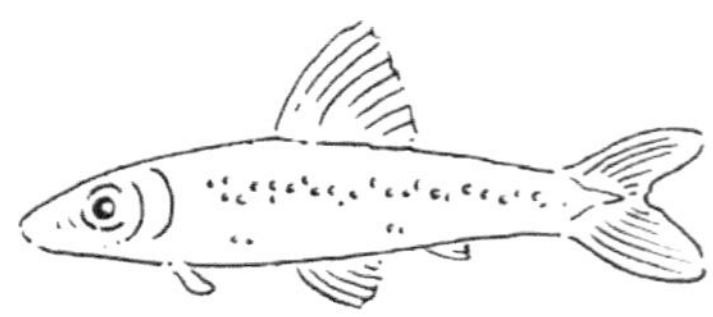 Minimum bid: $5.00

Name ____________________ Date ________________

Master 6.7

Additional Activity 1: Walk the Walk

Work with a partner.

You will need a metre stick and a stopwatch.

- Estimate how long it might take to walk 1 km.
- Use a metre stick to measure a distance of 10 m.
- Record the time it takes each partner to walk 10 m.
- Use the results to determine how long it would take to walk 1 km.
- Record the time in minutes and seconds.

Take It Further:
How long would it take to walk 10 km? 100 km?
Estimate the time it would take to run the same distances.
Repeat the activity, but run instead of walk.
Do you think that your results are accurate? Explain why or why not.

Name ____________________ Date ________________

Master 6.8a

Additional Activity 2: Money Matters

Work in groups of 3 or 4.

You will need play money, a calculator, and 1 set of Money Matters Price Cards (Master 6.8b).

The goal is to be the first person to finish counting the correct change for 2 purchases.

How to Play:

- Cut out and shuffle the price cards.
  Place the stack of cards face down in the centre of the table.
- Each player receives $100 in mixed coins and bills.
- One group member is the referee. The referee determines the winner of each round, and uses a calculator to check answers.
- For each round, 2 price cards are turned face up.
  Players find the total cost of the 2 items and count out how much change should be received from $100.
  The first student to count out the correct change wins the round.
- Play 5 rounds and then change referees and continue playing.
- The winner is the player who has won the most rounds when time is over.

Take It Further:
Start with $150 and draw 3 or more cards.

Name ____________________ Date _______________

Master 6.8b

Money Matters Price Cards

$32.44	$21.56	$45.98	$12.12	$41.76
$48.31	$1.09	$12.05	$3.75	$5.55
$7.98	$9.99	$49.97	$4.95	$1.98
$12.39	$32.09	$23.45	$7.20	$30.01
$50.00	$20.00	$10.00	$25.02	$29.99

Name ____________________ Date ______________

Master 6.9a

Additional Activity 3: Millilitre Mania

Work with a partner.

You will need an unmarked plastic container with capacity 500 mL or greater, some water, a measuring container, and 1 set of Millilitre Mania Capacity Cards (Master 6.9b).

The goal is to earn as many points as possible by estimating, then measuring, different amounts of water.

How to Play:

- Cut out and shuffle the capacity cards.
  Place the stack of cards face down in the centre of the table.
- Player 1 draws a capacity card from the stack and tries to pour the amount shown into an unmarked container.
- Player 2 pours the water from the unmarked container into a measuring container for scoring.
  Points are awarded as follows:
  15 points – within 5 mL
  5 points – within 25 mL
  3 points – within 50 mL
  0 points – out by 51 mL or more
- Players switch roles for the next turn.
  The player with the most points after 10 rounds wins the game.

Take It Further:
Work with greater capacities by adding 250 mL or 500 mL to each capacity card.

Name ____________________ Date ________________

Master 6.9b

Capacity Cards for Millilitre Mania

62 mL	183 mL	425 mL	98 mL	199 mL
50 mL	77 mL	125 mL	490 mL	300 mL
205 mL	351 mL	438 mL	175 mL	414 mL
323 mL	209 mL	275 mL	125 mL	355 mL
90 mL	471 mL	381 mL	304 mL	31 mL

Name ____________________ Date ________________

Master 6.10

Additional Activity 4: Muddling Through Mass

Work with a partner.

You will need a stack of paper, balance scales, a set of standard masses, a ruler, grid paper, and a calculator.

The goal is to find the height of a 100-kg stack of paper.

- Measure the height and mass of various stacks of paper. Record these measurements in a table.
- Draw a line graph showing these data. Put mass on the vertical axis and height on the horizontal axis.
- Use the measurements of the different stacks to estimate the height of a 100-kg stack.
- Use your graph to help explain why your estimate is reasonable.

Take It Further:
Estimate and then try to find the height of a 1-t stack of paper.
Explain how you can estimate the mass of 1 sheet of paper without directly measuring it.

Name ____________________ Date _______________

Master 6.11

Step-by-Step 1

Lesson 1, Question 5

Step 1 Here is Jack's watch when he left home:

What time is it? ___:___:___

Here is Jack's watch when he got to his friend's house:

What time is it? ___:___:___

Step 2 How long did it take Jack to get to his friend's house? ________

Step 3 What time did Jack get to his friend's house? ___:___:___

He left 30 s later. What time did Jack leave? ___:___:___

Step 4 Draw what Jack's watch looked like after the 30 s.

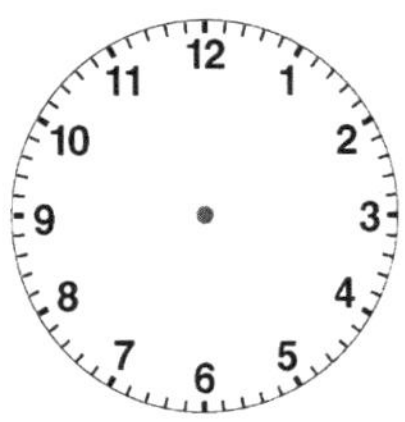

Step 5 How long do you think it took Jack to return home? Explain.

____

____

Name ____________________ Date ________________

Master 6.12

Step-by-Step 2

Lesson 2, Question 7

Step 1 Think about the roads the Cheung family might take.
On some roads, the family could drive 100 km in 1 h.
On other roads, the family could drive: 80 km in 1 h; or 60 km in 1 h; or even 50 km in 1 h.
Fill in the table with possible distances and times. The first line is done for you.

Distance	Time
100 km	1 h

Total: 500 km

Step 2 How much time would the Cheung family spend driving? ___________

Step 3 Think about some stops the Cheung family might make along the way. Record all of them in the table.

Stop	Time Spent
Rest stop	15 min
Lunch	1 h

Total:

Step 4 How much time would the Cheung family spend on these stops? ___________________________

Step 5 What would be the total time for the Cheung family to reach the vacation resort? ________________________

Name ________________ Date ______________

Master 6.13

Step-by-Step 4

Lesson 4, Question 8

Use play money if it helps.

Step 1 How much money does the man start with? ____________
How much money does he have when he gets to the mall? ____________

Step 2 Subtract to find the money he lost.

________ – ________ = ________

Step 3 How many ways can you make the amount in *Step 2* using exactly 4 bills? Fill in the table.

Number of Bills	$50	$20	$10	$5	Total Value
4					
4					
4					

Step 4 Think about some other bills and coins that would make up this amount.
Which of these ways uses exactly 4 bills?

____

Step 5 List 3 different sets of bills and coins the man might have lost.

____

____

____

Name ____________________ Date ______________

Master 6.14

Step-by-Step 5

Lesson 5, Question 5

Step 1 Start counting Michel's money. Fill in the table.

Bill	Number of Bills	Value
$20		
$10		

Step 2 How much money does Michel have with the $20 and $10 bills? __________

Step 3 The aquarium costs $82.27.
Does Michel have enough money? ______________________________

Did you need to count all the money to find out? ___________________

Explain. ____

Step 4 Which bills and coins could Michel use to pay for the aquarium?

____

What is the total value of these bills and coins? ____________________

Step 5 How much change would Michel get? ____________________________

Step 6 Pick another set of bills and coins Michel might use to pay. What is his change now?

____

Name ____________________ Date ________________

Master 6.15

Step-by-Step 6

Lesson 6, Question 4

Step 1 A benchmark is something you use as a reference.
Which container would make a good benchmark? ______________
Should you choose the smallest container? The largest?

____

Which will you pick as your benchmark? ______________________

Step 2 Choose another container. __________________________________
Do you think it would hold more or less water than your benchmark

container? _____________________________________

Would it hold the same amount? __________________________

How do you know? _______________________________________

Step 3 Repeat *Step 2* for each container.

Step 4 Sort the containers into these sets:
greater capacity than the benchmark container: _________________

lesser capacity than the benchmark container: __________________

capacity equal to the benchmark container: ____________________

Step 5 For each container:
Fill the container with water.
Do you think this water is more or less than the water your benchmark container will hold? How can you check?

____

____

____

Name ____________________ Date ______________

Master 6.16

Step-by-Step 7

Lesson 7, Question 4

Step 1 Use 18 centimetre cubes to build a rectangular prism.
Build a prism that is only 1 cube high.
How many different prisms can you make? Fill in the table.

Length	Width	Height
18	1	1
9		1
		1

Step 2 Build a prism that is 2 cubes high.
How many different prisms can you make? ____________________

Step 3 Build a prism that is 3 cubes high.
How is this the same as another prism you already made?

____

Step 4 How many different prisms can you make using all 18 cubes?

____

Step 5 Each prism you built has 18 centimetre cubes.
What is the volume of each prism?

____

Name ____________________ Date _______________

Master 6.17

Step-by-Step 8

Lesson 8, Question 3

Step 1 Look around the classroom. Find 2 different objects with about the same volume. Label the objects B and C.

Step 2 Partially fill a container with water.
Mark the water level as A.
Submerge object B. Mark the new water level as B.

Step 3 Remove object B.
Use a graduated cylinder.
Fill the container to the level marked B.

How much water have you added? __________________

What is the volume of object B? __________________

Step 4 Submerge object C in the container.
Mark the new water level as C.
Remove object C.
Use a graduated cylinder.
Fill the container to the level marked C.
How much water have you added? __________________

What is the volume of object C? __________________

Step 5 Do objects B and C have about the same volume? Explain.

____

____

Do objects need to have the same shape to have the same volume? Explain.

____

____

Name ____________________ Date ________________

Master 6.18

Step-by-Step 9

Lesson 9, Question 6

Step 1 Suppose Peter eats peanut butter and jelly sandwiches for lunch every school day for 40 weeks.
There are 5 school days each week.
How many lunches would Peter need?

____

Step 2 Peter uses 40 g of peanut butter per sandwich.
In 40 weeks, how many grams of peanut butter would Peter use?

____

What is this mass in kilograms? ______________________________

Step 3 Peter uses 30 g of jelly per sandwich.
In 40 weeks, how many grams of jelly would Peter use? ___________

What is this mass in kilograms? ______________________________

Step 4 How many 1-kg containers of peanut butter would Peter use

in 40 weeks? ____

How many 1-kg containers of jelly would Peter use in 40 weeks?

____

Name ____________________ Date ________________

Master 6.19

Step-by-Step 10

Lesson 10, Question 6

Step 1 One sheet of paper has a mass of about 5 g.
There are 500 sheets of paper in 1 package.
What is the mass of 1 package of paper in grams? ________________

What is the mass in kilograms? ________________________________

Step 2 What is the mass of 2 packages of paper? ______________________

Step 3 There are 10 packages of paper in a box.
What is the mass, in kilograms, of 1 box of paper? ________________

Step 4 How many kilograms are in 1 t?

1 t = ___ kg

Step 5 How many boxes of paper would it take to make 1 t? ______________

How do you know? ____

____

Name ______________ Date ______________

Master 6.20a

Unit Test: Unit 6 Measurement

Part A

1. Make each amount using the fewest bills and coins.
   a) $85.38 **b)** $632.89

   ______________ ______________

   ______________ ______________

   ______________ ______________

   ______________ ______________

2. A large bag of dog food costs $42.54.
   Ruth pays for the food with three $20 bills.
   Draw a picture to show how much change she receives.

3. Order these capacities from greatest to least.
   a) 5.21 L **b)** 521 mL **c)** 6 L **d)** 5215 mL **e)** 6001 mL

   ____

   ____

4. Order these masses from greatest to least.
   a) 0.42 t **b)** 450 kg **c)** 4199 g **d)** 4300 mg

   ____

   ____

Name ____________________ Date ______________

Master 6.20b

Unit Test continued

Part B

5. This rectangular prism is made with centimetre cubes.
What is the volume of this prism?

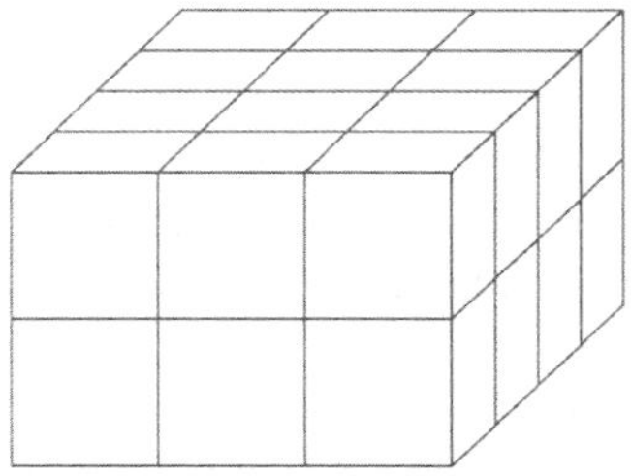

____

____

6. A motorcycle travels 80 km in 1 h.
Suppose the motorcycle continues at the same speed.

a) How far will it go in 5 h? ________________________________

b) How long will it take to travel 320 km? ______________________

7. Leigh ran for 50 s, walked for 5 min, ran for 60 s,
and walked for 4 min more.
Then she stopped.
When she left home the clock looked like this:

What time does the clock show? ___:___:___

At what time did Leigh stop? Show your thinking.

____

____

Name ____________________ Date ________________

Master 6.20c

Unit Test continued

Part C

8. There are 12 children on an elevator.
The maximum mass allowed on the elevator is 1 t.

Should the children be worried? ____________________________________

Give examples to support your answer.

____

____

____

____

9. Tony and Teena work at the museum.
The museum is 18 km away.
Tony leaves home and starts walking to work at 5:30.
He walks 4 km every hour.
Teena leaves home and starts riding her bike to work at 7:30.
She cycles 12 km every hour.

a) If the museum opens at 9:00, will Tony and Teena be on time? Explain.

____

____

b) When does Teena overtake Tony? How far have they travelled?

____

____

Name ____________________ Date ______________

Master 6.21

Sample Answers

Unit Test – Master 6.20

Part A

1. a)

Number	Bill/Coin ($)
1	50
1	20
1	10
1	5
1	0.25
1	0.10
3	0.01

b)

Number	Bill/Coin ($)
6	100
1	20
1	10
1	2
3	0.25
1	0.10
4	0.01

2. $17.46
3. e, c, d, a, b
4. b, a, c, d

Part B

5. The volume is 24 cm³.
Here are some possible solutions:

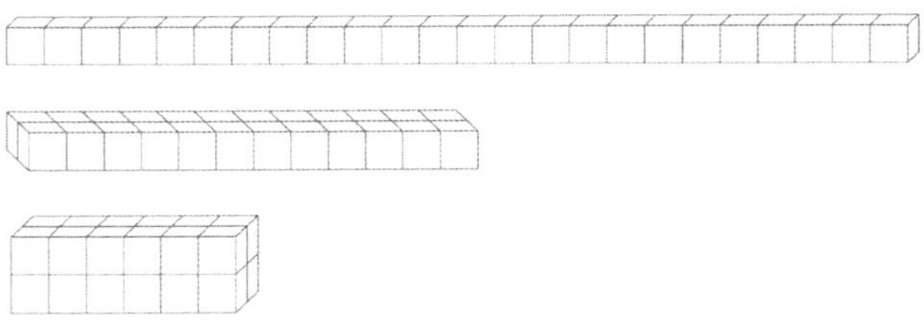

6. **a)** 400 km **b)** 4 h
7. 05:01:10. Leigh walked and ran for a total of 10 min 50 s

Part C

8. The children should be safe on the elevator. Since they are children, I assume their average mass is less than 50 kg. So 12 children would have a mass of less than 600 kg, which is much less than 1 t.
9. **a)** No. Teena will arrive on time but Tony will be 1 h late.
Teena travels 12 km in 1 h and 6 km in $\frac{1}{2}$ h.
It will take her 1.5 h to travel 18 km.
She arrives right at 9:00.
Tony travels 4 km every hour.
He travels 16 km in 4 h and 2 km in $\frac{1}{2}$ h.
It will take him 4.5 h to travel 18 km.
Since he leaves at 5:30, he does not arrive until 10:00. Tony will be 1 h late.

b)

Time	Tony's Distance	Teena's Distance
6:30	4 km	0 km
7:30	8 km	0 km
8:30	12 km	12 km

Teena will catch Tony at 8:30. She will have travelled 12 km in 1 h. Tony will have travelled 12 km in 3 h.

Extra Practice Masters 6.22–6.27

Go to the CD-ROM to access editable versions of these Extra Practice Masters.

Name ____________ Date ____________

Master 6.22 **Extra Practice 1**

Lesson 1: Measuring Time

1. Write each date in SI notation
   a) July 16, 1994   b) October 11, 1948   c) December 17, 1987
2. Write each date in words
   a) 1996 12 25 b) 2001 10 29   c) 1986 06 23   d) 2004 05 21
3. For each clock, write the exact time in SI notation to the nearest minute.
   a)   b)   c)   d)

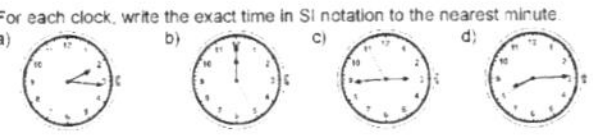

Lesson 2: Exploring Time and Distance

1. A jogger runs 15 km in 2 h.
   How many kilometres would the jogger travel in 4 h?
2. A go-cart goes around a track once every 12 s.
   How many times would it go around the track in 2 min?
   in 20 min?

Name ____________ Date ____________

Master 6.23 **Extra Practice 2**

Lesson 4: Estimating and Counting Money

1. Four people have $90 to share
   They share the money equally
   What is the greatest number of bills 1 person may have?
2. a) Show $786.23 using the least number of bills and coins.
   b) Show $786.23 using the greatest number of bills and coins
   c) Which method would be used the most? Why?

Lesson 5: Making Change

1. Mr. Singh pays for his cat to have a one-year membership at the grooming salon
   He gives the groomer four $20 bills, two $5 bills, and 2 toonies
   He is given 1 quarter, 6 dimes, and 3 pennies as change
   What was the price of his cat's membership?
2. Tell whether each customer was given the correct change
   a) Fifi
   Cost: $29.90
   Customer Paid: two $10 bills, two $ 5 bills
   Change: 2 nickels
   b) Grover
   Cost: $52.16
   Customer Paid: one $50 bill, 1 toonie, 1 quarter
   Change: 1 nickel, 3 pennies
   c) Magic
   Cost: $68.88
   Customer Paid: two $20 bills, two $10 bills, 4 toonies, 1 quarter, 6 dimes, 1 nickel
   Change: 1 penny
   d) Scarlet
   Cost: $83.59
   Customer Paid: one $50 bill, three $10 bills, 1 toonie, 2 loonies, 9 pennies
   Change: 2 quarters

Name ____________ Date ____________

Master 6.24 **Extra Practice 3**

Lesson 6: Capacity

1. Write each capacity in millilitres.
   a) 6.75 L   b) 2.05 L   c) 3.09 L   d) 0.91 L
2. Order these capacities from greatest to least
   a) 1840 mL   b) 1.8 L   c) 18.41 L   d) 18 400 mL
3. All the water in a large container is used to fill 4 smaller containers
   The capacities of the smaller containers are 250 mL, 500 mL, 2 L, 250 mL
   What is the capacity of the large container in litres?

Lesson 7: Volume

1. How many different prisms can you make using 16 centimetre cubes?
   How do you know you have found all of them?
2. Describe how you could find the volume of a brick in cubic centimetres

Name ____________ Date ____________

Master 6.25 **Extra Practice 4**

Lesson 8: Relating Capacity and Volume

1. Describe how you could find the volume of a basketball in cubic centimetres.
2. Shawn says that the volume of a rectangular prism is 32 cm^3.
   Maria says that the volume is 32 mL
   Who is correct? Explain

Lesson 9: Measuring Mass

1. Copy and complete
   a) 1000 g = ________ kg   b) 3 kg = ________ g
   c) 15 kg = ________ g   d) 5000 g = ________ kg
   e) 6 kg = ________ g   f) 25 000 g = ________ kg
2. Choose the best estimate

a) 4 pears	100 g	500 g	1 kg	5 kg
b) 2 dictionaries	100 g	200 g	2 kg	10 kg
c) 3 nickels	5 g	50 g	100 g	200 g
d) 5 boxes of cereal	10 g	50 g	2 kg	10 kg

3. A small box of chocolate bars has a mass of 3 kg.
   How many chocolate bars are in the box if each chocolate bar has a mass of 250 g? Show your work.

Name ____________ Date ____________

Master 6.26 **Extra Practice 5**

Lesson 10: Exploring Large Masses

1. Copy and complete
   a) 1000 kg = ______ t   b) 13 kg = ______ g   c) 15 t = ______ kg
   d) 3000 g = ______ kg   e) 6000 kg = ______ t   f) 25 t = ______ kg
   g) 1 t = ______ kg   h) 3000 kg = ______ t
2. Choose the best estimate

a) 2 alligators	100 kg	1 t	10 t	10 kg
b) 4 bananas	1 t	500 g	12 kg	50 g
c) 3 cowboys	15 000 g	150 kg	1.5 t	500 kg
d) 5 doorknobs	2 g	20 g	200 g	2000 g

3. A student in Ms. Matziuk's class asked her the following question
   "Why don't we just record the mass of all objects in grams?"
   If you were Ms. Matziuk, what mathematical response would you give?

Name ____________ Date ____________

Master 6.27 **Sample Answers**

Extra Practice 1 – Master 6.22

Lesson 1
1. a) 1994 07 16   b) 1948 10 11   c) 1987 12 17
2. a) December 25, 1996   b) October 29, 2001
   c) June 23, 1986   d) May 21, 2004
3. a) 02:16   b) 12:00   c) 03:45   d) 08:15

Lesson 2
1. 30 km
2. 10 times in 2 min; 100 times in 20 min
   The go-cart travels 5 times around the track every minute

Extra Practice 2 – Master 6.23

Lesson 4
1. 4 bills (all $5 bills)
   Each person would have $22.50
2. a) 7 $100 bills, 1 $50 bill, 1 $20 bill, 1 $10 bill, 1 $5 bill, 1 loonie, 2 dimes, 3 pennies
   b) 78 623 pennies
   c) The first method would be used the most because the second method would be very inconvenient.

Lesson 5
1. The membership is $93.12
2. a) Yes   b) No (1 more penny needed)
   c) No (1 more penny needed)   d) Yes

Extra Practice 3 – Master 6.24

Lesson 6
1. a) 6750 mL   b) 2050 mL
   c) 3090 mL   d) 910 mL
2. 18.41 L, 18 400 mL, 1840 mL, 1.8 L (c, d, a, b)
3. The capacity of the large container is 3 L

Lesson 7
1. 4: 1 × 1 × 16, 1 × 2 × 8, 1 × 4 × 4, 2 × 2 × 4
2. I could use centimetre cubes to make a solid that was close in size to the brick. Then I would count the number of centimetre cubes.

Extra Practice 4 – Master 6.25

Lesson 8
1. Fill water to the capacity of a large pail and then measure the amount of water. Completely submerge the basketball in the pail. Water will overflow the pail. Remove the basketball and measure the amount of water remaining in the pail. The difference between the first and last measurements is the volume of the basketball.
2. Both students are correct since 32 cm^3 = 32 mL. Volume can be recorded in millilitres or cubic centimetres.

Lesson 9
1. a) 1 kg   b) 3000 g   c) 15 000 g
   d) 5 kg   e) 6000 g   f) 25 kg
2. a) 500 g   b) 2 kg   c) 50 g   d) 2 kg
3. There would be 12 chocolate bars in the box (3000 g ÷ 250 g = 12)

Extra Practice 5 – Master 6.26

Lesson 10
1. a) 1 t   b) 13 000 g   c) 15 000 kg
   d) 3 kg   e) 6 t   f) 25 000 kg
   g) 1000 kg   h) 3 t
2. a) 1 t   b) 500 g   c) 150 kg   d) 2000 g
3. Some objects have large masses. If we used grams for all measures we would be forced to use very large numbers, when some objects could be easily described using tonnes or kilograms.

Addison Wesley
Mathematics
Makes Sense

Program Authors

Peggy Morrow
Ralph Connelly
Bryn Keyes
Jason Johnston
Steve Thomas
Jeananne Thomas
Angela D'Alessandro
Maggie Martin Connell
Don Jones
Michael Davis
Sharon Jeroski
Trevor Brown
Nora Alexander
Cynthia Pratt Nicolson

Printed and bound in Canada

8 9 MP 18 17

PEARSON
Education Canada

ADDISON WESLEY

Ontario

Math Makes Sense 5

Ontario

Teacher Guide

Unit 7: Transformational Geometry

PEARSON

Addison Wesley

UNIT 7

Transformational Geometry

"Geometric modeling and spatial reasoning offer ways to interpret and describe physical environments and can be important tools in problem solving."

NCTM, 2000

FOCUS STRAND
Geometry and Spatial Sense

SUPPORTING STRAND
Patterning and Algebra

Mathematics Background

What Are the Big Ideas?

- Coordinate systems can be used to describe the location of a figure.
- Translations (slides), reflections (flips), and rotations (turns) are transformations.
- Figures have attributes, such as parallel sides, right angles, and line symmetry, that allow us to sort and name them.

How Will the Concepts Develop?

Students begin by exploring two types of coordinate systems. This develops a system for describing transformations of figures.

Next, students explore transformations using concrete materials, such as grid paper, dot paper, Miras, geoboards, and Pattern Blocks. They are encouraged to predict the location and orientation of the final image.

Then, students explore congruent figures by hand and using a computer.

Next, students determine lines of symmetry for figures and construct a figure with one line of symmetry.

Finally, students explore tiling. Using a variety of congruent figures, they explore which figures can be used to tile a plane with no gaps or overlaps.

Why Are These Concepts Important?

Exploring transformational geometry helps students develop spatial awareness. Spatial visualization skills are important. Many everyday activities, such as map reading, giving directions, and following assembly instructions, rely on these skills. A study of geometry develops understanding of our natural and human-made world.

Curriculum Overview

Cluster 1: Exploring Coordinate Systems

Overall Expectations
- Use mathematical language effectively to describe … coordinate systems. (5m70)

Specific Expectations
- Demonstrate an understanding of coordinate systems on maps and grids. (5m90)

Launch
Geometry in Art

Lesson 1:
Coordinate Systems

Cluster 2: Transformational Geometry

Overall Expectations
- Explore transformations of geometric figures. (5m67)
- Understand key concepts in transformational geometry using concrete materials and drawings. (5m68)
- Identify congruent … figures using transformations. (5m69)
- Use mathematical language effectively to describe geometric concepts, reasoning, and investigations. (5m70)

Specific Expectations
- Describe the effect of a translation, reflection, and rotation. (5m86)
- Apply translations, reflections, and rotations to pose and solve problems. (5m87)
- Explore tiling patterns that cover a plane. (5m88)
- Construct two-dimensional shapes with one line of symmetry. (5m89)
- Demonstrate an understanding of congruent figures. (5m77)
- Demonstrate congruence of figures using paper folding, reflections in a transparent mirror, and various computer applications. (5m80)
- Use a computer application to explore and extend geometric concepts. (5m81)
- Recognize and explain the occurrence and application of geometric properties and principles in the everyday world. (5m83)
- Discuss geometric concepts with peers and use mathematical language to explain their understanding of the concepts. (5m84)

Lesson 2:
Transformations

Lesson 3:
Congruent Figures

Technology:
Using a Computer to Explore Congruent Figures

Lesson 4:
Line Symmetry

Lesson 5:
Strategies Toolkit

Lesson 6:
Exploring Tiling

Show What You Know

Unit Problem
Geometry in Art

Curriculum across the Grades

Grade 4	Grade 5	Grade 6
Students describe the characteristics of coordinate systems and apply them in simple games. Students perform translations, reflections, and rotations, and apply them using concrete materials and drawings to pose and solve problems. Students discover transformation patterns and solve geometric puzzles with and without the use of computer applications. Students use mathematical language to describe geometric ideas. Students recognize and describe the occurrence and application of geometric properties and principles in the everyday world, and discuss geometric concepts with peers and explain their thinking. Students discuss ideas, make connections, and articulate hypotheses about geometric properties and relationships. Students draw lines of symmetry on 2-D shapes.	Students describe and explain the coordinate systems on maps and grids. Students describe the effects of translations, reflections, and rotations, and apply them to pose and solve problems. Students explore tiling patterns that cover a plane. Students use a computer application to explore and extend geometric concepts. Students use mathematical language to describe geometric ideas and to recognize and explain the occurrence and application of geometric properties and principles in the everyday world. Students discuss geometric concepts with peers and use mathematical language to explain their understanding of the concepts. Students discuss ideas, make conjectures, and articulate hypotheses about geometric properties and relationships. Students construct 2-D shapes with one line of symmetry.	Students describe and explain coordinates in a Cartesian plane in the first quadrant, and plot points. Students visualize and describe the effect of translations, reflections, and rotations, and apply and analyse them in a variety of geometric contexts. Students use a computer application to explore and extend geometric concepts. Students construct tiling patterns to cover a plane. Students use mathematical language to describe geometric ideas and to recognize and describe the occurrence and application of geometric properties and principles in the everyday world. Students discuss geometric concepts with peers and use mathematical language to explain their understanding of the concepts. Students explain, make conjectures about, and articulate hypotheses about geometric properties and relationships. Students construct 2-D shapes with more than one line of symmetry.

Additional Activities

Hidden Pictures

For Extra Practice (Appropriate for use after Lesson 1)
Materials: *Hidden Pictures* (Master 7.10), 1-cm grid paper (PM 23), rulers

The work students do: Students work alone. They mark a point at each pair of coordinates, use a ruler to connect the points in order, and describe the hidden picture.

F7, G7, G5, J5, J4, P4, M1, E1, B4, F4, F7

Take It Further: Students create their own hidden pictures. They write instructions for their pictures, then trade instructions with a classmate. Students draw their classmate's picture.

Visual/Spatial
Individual Activity

Transformational Patterns

For Extra Practice (Appropriate for use after Lesson 2)
Materials: *Transformation Patterns* (Master 7.11), 1-cm grid paper (PM 23)

The work students do: Students work in pairs. They draw the next figure in patterns such as this and describe the transformations used to create each pattern.

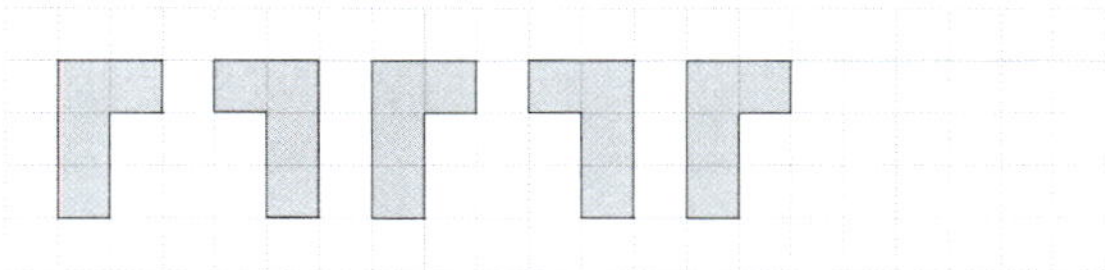

Take It Further: Students create their own patterns using transformations. They describe the transformations they used to create their patterns.

Visual/Spatial
Partner Activity

Folding Figures

For Extra Support (Appropriate for use after Lesson 4)
Materials: *Folding Figures* (Master 7.12), scissors

The work students do: Students work individually. They draw a broken line on each figure to make two congruent figures. They may be able to draw more than one line on some figures.

They may not be able to draw any lines on other figures.

Students cut out each figure and fold each figure along the line or lines they drew to check their work.

Take It Further: Students draw a figure for which they can draw each number of broken lines: 0, 1, 2

Kinesthetic
Individual Activity

Symmetry Patterns

For Extension (Appropriate for use after Lesson 6)
Materials: Symmetry Patterns (Master 7.13), 1-cm grid paper (PM 23), coloured pencils

The work students do: Students work in pairs. They draw the figure that is shown in the top left section in the other three sections to make a symmetrical pattern.

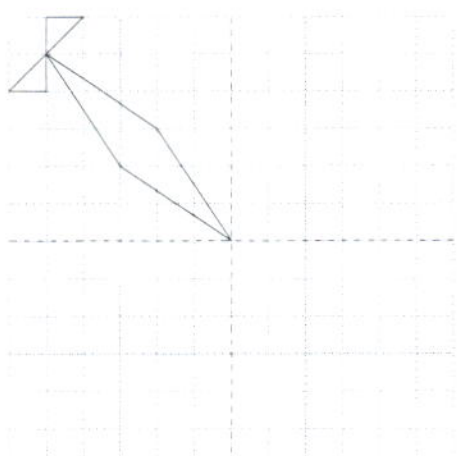

Take It Further: On grid paper, students draw a horizontal broken line and a vertical broken line. In the top left section, they draw a figure. They draw the figure in the other three sections to make a pattern with two lines of symmetry.

Visual/Spatial
Partner Activity

Planning for Unit 7

Planning for Instruction

Suggested Unit time: About 2 weeks

Lesson	Time	Materials	Program Support
Launch: Geometry in Art, page 2	15–20 min		
Lesson 1: Coordinate Systems, page 4 Use coordinates to find and describe locations on a grid.	40–50 min	grid paper rulers	PM 23: 1-cm Grid Paper Master 7.14: Step-by-Step 1 Master 7.21: Extra Practice 1
Lesson 2 Transformations, page 7 Rotate, reflect, and translate figures.	40–50 min	figures Miras grid paper tracing paper	Master 7.6 Figures for Lesson 2 Explore PM 23: 1-cm Grid Paper Master 7.15: Step-by-Step 2 Master 7.21: Extra Practice 1
Lesson 3 Congruent Figures, page 11 Identify and construct congruent figures.	40–50 min	geoboards geobands dot paper	PM 25: Square Dot Paper Master 7.16: Step-by-Step 3 Master 7.22: Extra Practice 2
Technology: Using a Computer to Explore Congruent Figures, page 14 Use a computer to create and identify congruent figures.	40–50 min	computer with *AppleWorks* or *The Geometer's Sketchpad*	
Lesson 4 Line Symmetry, page 17 Construct figures with line symmetry.	40–50 min	grid paper Pattern Blocks Miras scissors dot paper geoboards geobands	PM 23: 1-cm Grid Paper PM 25: Square Dot Paper PM 28: Pattern Blocks Master 7.17: Step-by-Step 4 Master 7.22: Extra Practice 2
Lesson 5 Strategies Toolkit, page 20 Interpret a problem and select an appropriate strategy.	40–50 min	Pattern Blocks Miras pentominoes 2-cm grid paper overhead projector overhead Pattern Blocks	PM 24: 2-cm Grid Paper PM 28: Pattern Blocks
Lesson 6 Exploring Tiling, page 23 Explore tiling patterns with congruent figures.	40–50 min	scissors dot paper quadrilaterals tracing paper grid paper congruent squares	PM 23: 1-cm Grid Paper PM 25: Square Dot Paper Master 7.18: Step by Step 6 Master 7.23: Extra Practice 3
Show What You Know, page 26 Assessment	40–50 min	grid paper dot paper figures tangrams triangular grid paper Pattern Blocks	PM 23: 1-cm Grid Paper PM 25: Square Dot Paper Master 7.9: Figures for Show What You Know PM 27: Triangular Grid Paper PM 28: Pattern Blocks PM 29: Tangram
Unit Problem: Geometry in Art, page 28 Assessment	40–50 min	Bristol board coloured paper 10-cm squares cut from 1-cm grid paper scissors	PM 23: 1-cm Grid Paper

Planning for Assessment

Purpose	Tools and Process	Recording and Reporting
Diagnostic	*Unit Launch* Question; conference; scaffold problems throughout the unit	PM 8: Conference Prompts
Formative	*Explore* — Ongoing Assessment: Observe and Listen	Master 7.2 Ongoing Observations: Transformational Geometry PM 1: Inquiry Process Check List PM 6: Observation Record 1 PM 7: Observation Record 2 PM 8: Conference Prompts
	Prompt student s self-assessment	PM 2: Self-Assessment PM 3: Self-Assessment: Problem Solving PM 9: Work Sample Records
	Practice — Assessment Focus Questions Review student work; provide feedback; scaffold as needed; select key pieces	
Summative	*Show What You Know* *Unit Problem* — Performance Assessment Unit Test	Master 7.1 Unit Rubric: Transformational Geometry Master 7.3 Performance Assessment Rubric: Geometry in Art Master 7.4 Unit Summary: Transformational Geometry
	Review assessment records; add unit results to ongoing records	PM 10: Summary Class Records: Strands PM 11: Summary Class Records: Achievement Categories PM 12: Summary Record: Individual
Learning Skills/Mathematical Disposition	Observe and record throughout unit	PM 4: Learning Skills Check List PM 5: Mathematical Dispositions and Learning Skills

Program Masters (PM) are in the *Grade 5 Planning and Program Masters* module.
Extra Practice Masters are on the CD-ROM.

Geometry in Art

LESSON ORGANIZER

15–20 min

Curriculum Focus: Activate prior knowledge about transformational geometry.
Vocabulary: translation, reflection, rotation, line of symmetry

ASSUMED PRIOR KNOWLEDGE

- ✓ Students recognize translations, reflections, and rotations.
- ✓ Students recognize congruent figures.

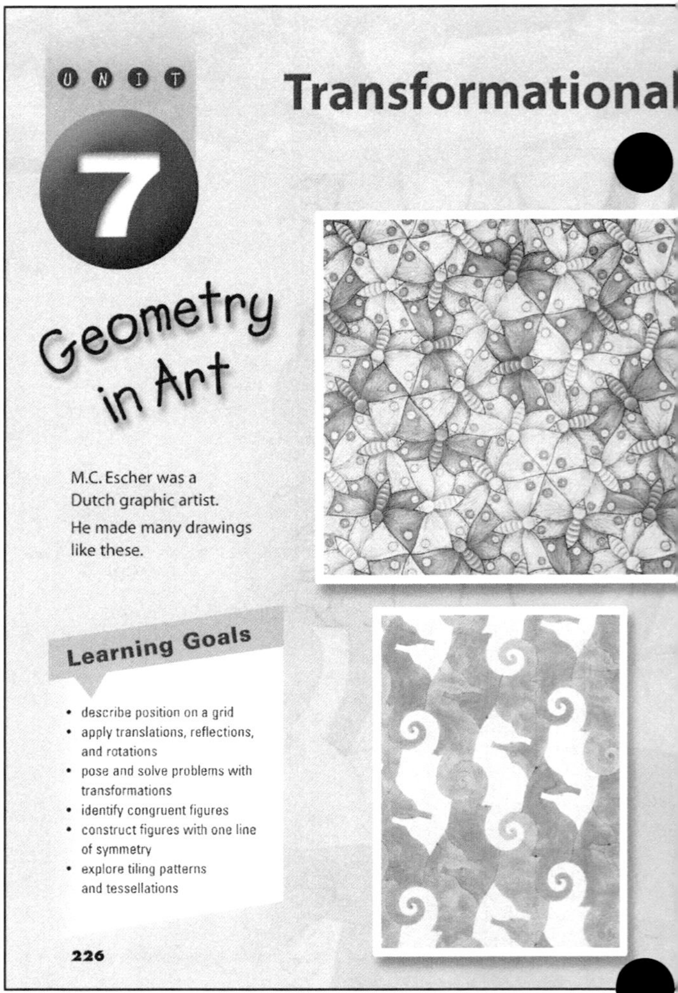

UNIT 7 Transformational

Geometry in Art

M.C. Escher was a Dutch graphic artist.
He made many drawings like these.

Learning Goals

- describe position on a grid
- apply translations, reflections, and rotations
- pose and solve problems with transformations
- identify congruent figures
- construct figures with one line of symmetry
- explore tiling patterns and tessellations

226

ACTIVATE PRIOR LEARNING

Have students examine the photos on pages 226 and 227 of the Student Book. Engage students in a discussion of transformations. Students should recognize that transformations affect the position and/or orientation of a figure.

Discuss the first question on page 227 of the Student Book. Record students' answers on chart paper.
(Sample answer: I see horses, seahorses, and moths. The figures have different positions and orientations.)

Discuss the second question in the Student Book and record students' answers.
(Sample answer: In all three pictures, the figures have been rotated and translated. It is possible that the seahorses and the horses were reflected in a vertical line, then reflected in a horizontal line.)

Ask:

- Look carefully at the picture of seahorses on page 226. What basic figure did Escher use to create this picture?
  (A parallelogram)
- Where could you draw a line of symmetry?
  (I can draw a line of symmetry through the body of the moth.)
- How can you find out where to draw a line of symmetry?
  (I can use a Mira, or I can trace a figure, cut out the tracing, and fold it so the edges align.)

Ensure students recognize that all the figures in each picture are congruent. They have different positions and orientations, but the same size.

Invite students to read the learning goals and key words. Tell students they will use what they have learned to create their own Escher-like diagram in the *Unit Problem*.

Geometry

Key Words

coordinate systems

symmetrical

tiling pattern

tessellation

tessellate

- Describe the figures you see.
- Which figures have been translated? Reflected? Rotated?

227

LITERATURE CONNECTIONS FOR THE UNIT

Further Adventures of Penrose the Mathematical Cat
by Theoni Pappas. Wide World Publishing/Tetra, 2004.
ISBN: 1884550320
Penrose, a cat who loves math, encounters amazing mathematical ideas in a sequence of adventure tales. Among other things, readers discover "rep-tiles"; and help Sorry Snowflake find its symmetry. Penrose will tickle your imagination and tease your brain with his exciting puzzles and games.

REACHING ALL LEARNERS

e-tools Some students may benefit from the virtual manipulatives on the e-Tools CD-ROM.
The e-Tools appropriate for this unit include Geometry Drawing. Students can use these tools to draw figures, then translate, reflect, and rotate them.

DIAGNOSTIC ASSESSMENT

What to Look For	What to Do
✔ Students recognize translations, reflections, and rotations.	***Extra Support:*** Have students use an irregular cardboard figure. They place the figure on grid paper, trace it, then transform it. Students record the attributes before and after the transformation. *Work on this skill during Lesson 2.*
✔ Students recognize congruent figures.	Have students trace figures and cut out the tracings. They then stack the figures one on the other to determine if the figures are congruent. *Work on this skill during Lesson 3.*

LESSON 1

Coordinate Systems

LESSON ORGANIZER

40–50 min

Curriculum Focus: Use coordinates to find and describe locations on a grid. (5m90)

Student Materials
- grid paper
- rulers

Optional
- Step-by-Step 1 (Master 7.14)
- Extra Practice 1 (Master 7.21)

Assessment: Master 7.2 Ongoing Observations: Transformational Geometry

Key Math Learnings

1. Coordinates can be used to describe locations on a grid.
2. On a map, coordinates refer to a square.
   On a grid, coordinates refer to a point.

LESSON 1

Coordinate Systems

Here is a map of an amusement park.
The roller coaster is at C1.
What are the coordinates of the water ride?
The swinging ship?

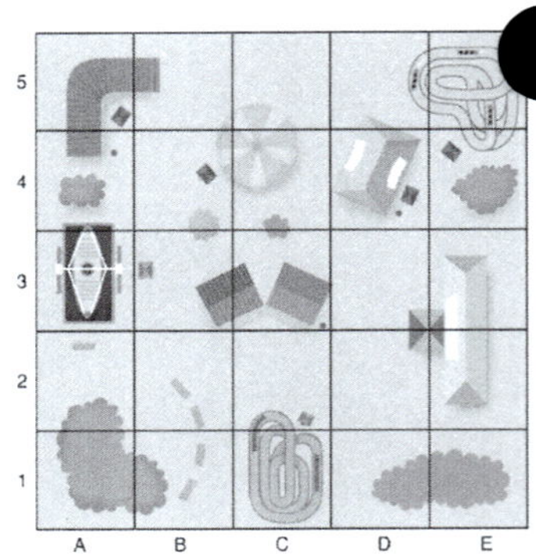

Explore

Each of you will need grid paper and a ruler.

➤ Copy this grid.
Mark a point at each pair of coordinates.
Use a ruler to connect the points in the order you draw them:
- B1 to A3
- A3 to D6
- D6 to G3
- G3 to F1
- F1 to B1

Which polygon did you draw? A pentagon

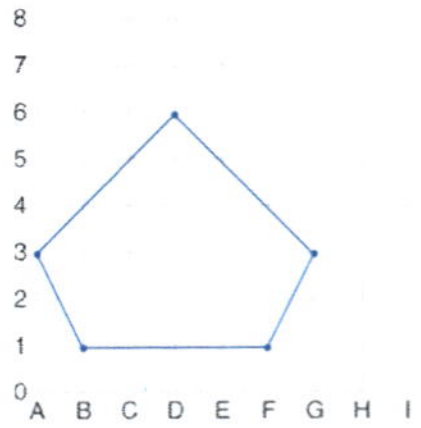

➤ Draw a polygon on a grid.
The vertices must be where the grid lines cross.
List the coordinates of the vertices.
Trade lists of coordinates with your partner.
Draw your partner's polygon.
How does the polygon you drew compare with your partner's?

228 LESSON FOCUS | Use coordinates to find and describe locations on a grid.

BEFORE Get Started

Have students look at the map of the amusement park on page 228 of the Student Book. Ask:

- How did you find the coordinates of the water slide? The swinging ship?
  (To find the coordinates of the water slide, I found the water slide on the map. From the water slide, I looked straight down at the horizontal axis to find the first coordinate. Again from the water slide, I looked directly across to the vertical axis to find the second coordinate. The water slide is at E5. I did the same thing for the swinging ship. It is at A3.)

Introduce *Explore*. Suggest that students connect each pair of points as they draw them.

DURING Explore

Ongoing Assessment: Observe and Listen

Ask questions, such as:

- How did you know where to mark the points?
  (I used the coordinates. For example, to mark the point at B1, I moved along the horizontal axis to line B, then I moved up line B to horizontal line 1. I marked a point at the intersection of line B and line 1.)
- Which polygon did you draw?
  (I drew a pentagon.)
- How did you write the coordinates of the vertices of the polygon you drew?
  (From each point, I looked down the vertical line and recorded the letter, then I looked across the horizontal line and recorded the number.)

Show and Share

Share your work with another pair of students.
ow did you know the coordinates of each vertex?
are these coordinates different from the coordinates
he map of the amusement park?

Connect

Here are 2 kinds of **coordinate systems**.

➤ On a map, a pair of coordinates refers to a square.

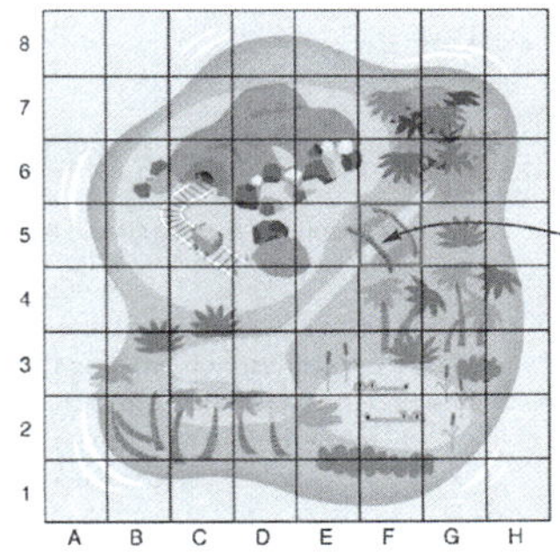

F5 is the square outlined in red.

The bridge is in F5.

➤ On a grid, a pair of coordinates refers to a point where the grid lines cross.

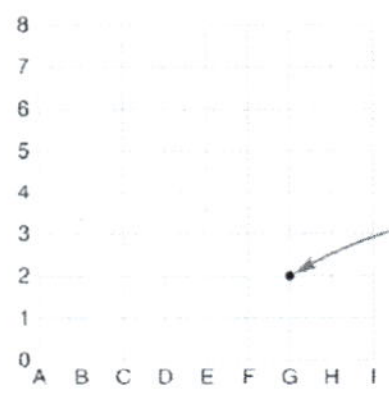

G2 is the point where the grid lines labelled "G" and "2" cross.

The dot is at G2.

229

REACHING ALL LEARNERS

Early Finishers

Have students identify the coordinates of the other rides and attractions on the amusement park map.

Common Misconceptions

➤ Students plot the coordinates in the wrong order. That is, they go up first, then across.

How to Help: Remind students to always go across first, then up. They can use this trick to help them remember: If across and up are in alphabetical order, across is first. The same is true for horizontal and vertical.

ESL Strategies

Have students underline the verbs that identify what they are to do in each set of instructions.

Numbers Every Day

Remind students that they are finding even numbers in this exercise. Have them do a mental estimate before using the calculator. Most students will use guess and check. Some students may recognize that they can find the 3 numbers by finding the quotient 42 ÷ 3 = 14. 14 is the middle number; 14 − 2 = 12 is the first number; 14 + 2 = 16 is the third number.

AFTER Connect

Invite students to share their polygons with the class. Ask other students to name each polygon. Ask:

- How do you write the coordinates of each vertex?
  (*The letter on the horizontal axis is written first, then the number from the vertical axis.*)
- How are these coordinates different from the coordinates on the map of the amusement park?
  (*The coordinates on the map of the amusement park name a square. These coordinates name a point.*)

Have students examine the coordinate systems presented in *Connect*. Ask:

- On the map, where are the letter coordinates? The number coordinates?
  (*On the map, the letter coordinates are between lines on the horizontal axis, the number coordinates are between lines on the vertical axis.*)
- On the grid, where are the letter coordinates? The number coordinates?
  (*On the grid, the letter coordinates are aligned with the vertical lines that meet the horizontal axis; the number coordinates are aligned with the horizontal lines that meet the vertical axis.*)

Practice

For question 1, direct students to start at the vertex closest to the vertical axis. Then work in a clockwise direction to name the coordinates of the vertices of the star.
Questions 2 and 3 require grid paper.

Assessment Focus: Question 3

When students draw their numbers, make certain they square off the round curves of numbers such as 2. Remind students that the vertices of their numbers must lie on the intersections of grid lines.

Sample Answers

3.

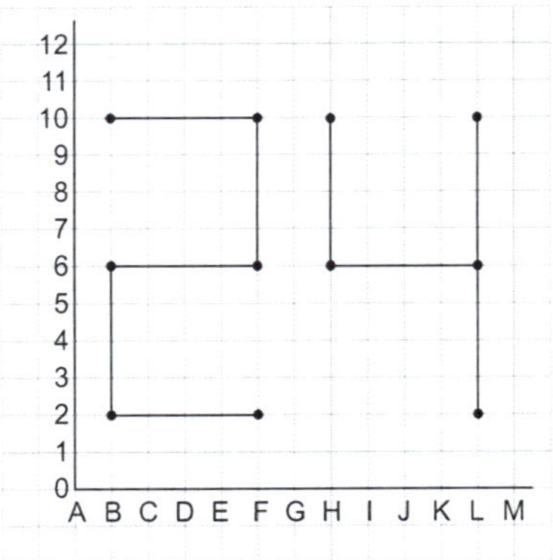

For each group of coordinates, mark a point at each set of coordinates, then connect the points in order.
- B10, F10, F6, B6, B2, F2
- H10, H6, L6
- L10, L2

REFLECT: One kind of coordinate system has coordinates that refer to the squares on the grid. This system is frequently used on maps. The coordinates D2 refer to the shaded square.

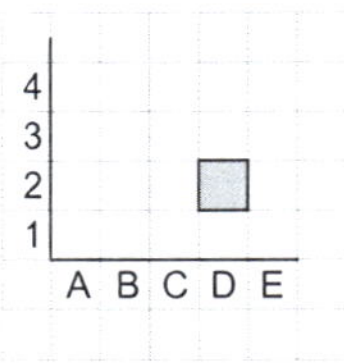

Another kind of coordinate system has coordinates that refer to the intersections of grid lines. On this grid, D2 refers to the point where line D and line 2 cross.

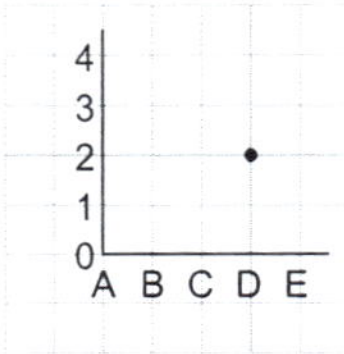

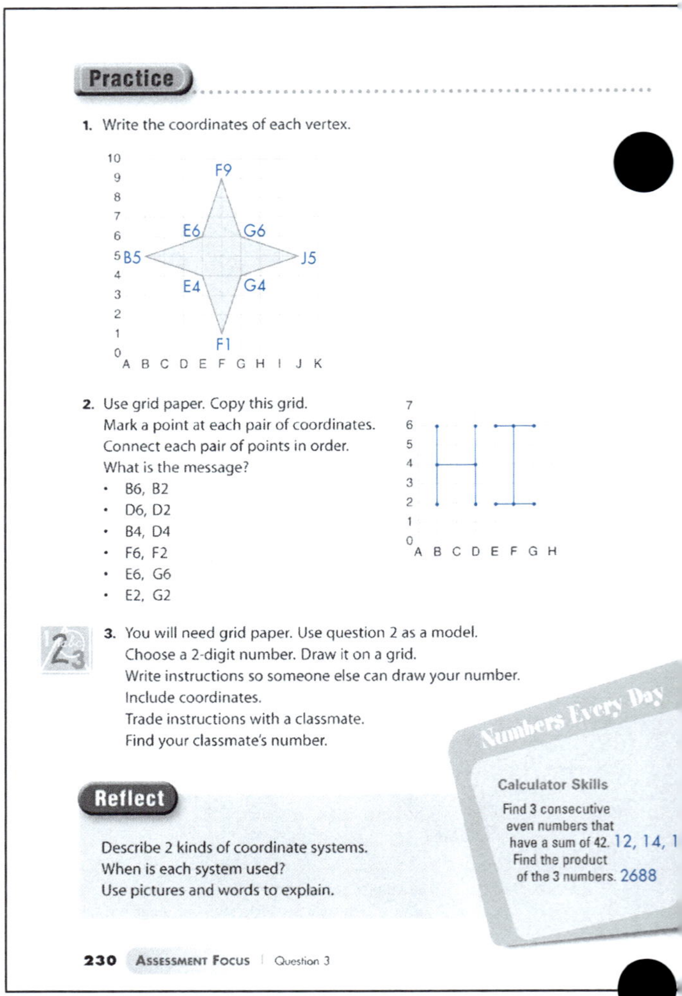

Practice

1. Write the coordinates of each vertex.

F9, E6, G6, B5, J5, E4, G4, F1

2. Use grid paper. Copy this grid.
Mark a point at each pair of coordinates.
Connect each pair of points in order.
What is the message?
- B6, B2
- D6, D2
- B4, D4
- F6, F2
- E6, G6
- E2, G2

3. You will need grid paper. Use question 2 as a model.
Choose a 2-digit number. Draw it on a grid.
Write instructions so someone else can draw your number.
Include coordinates.
Trade instructions with a classmate.
Find your classmate's number.

Reflect

Describe 2 kinds of coordinate systems.
When is each system used?
Use pictures and words to explain.

Numbers Every Day

Calculator Skills

Find 3 consecutive even numbers that have a sum of 42. 12, 14, 1
Find the product of the 3 numbers. 2688

230 ASSESSMENT FOCUS | Question 3

ASSESSMENT FOR LEARNING

What to Look For	What to Do
Understanding concepts ✔ Students understand that the first coordinate represents horizontal distance and the second coordinate represents vertical distance.	***Extra Support:*** Students can use Step-by-Step 1 (Master 7.14) to complete question 3.
Applying procedures ✔ Students name the coordinates of a point on a grid. ✔ Students plot points on a grid or find a location on a map given the coordinates.	***Extra Practice:*** Students can do the Additional Activity *Hidden Pictures* (Master 7.10). Students can complete Extra Practice 1 (Master 7.21). ***Extension:*** Have students draw an irregular polygon on a grid. They write a set of instructions and trade instructions with a classmate.

Recording and Reporting
Master 7.2 Ongoing Observations: Transformational Geometry

LESSON 2

Transformations

A translation, a reflection, and a rotation are transformations.

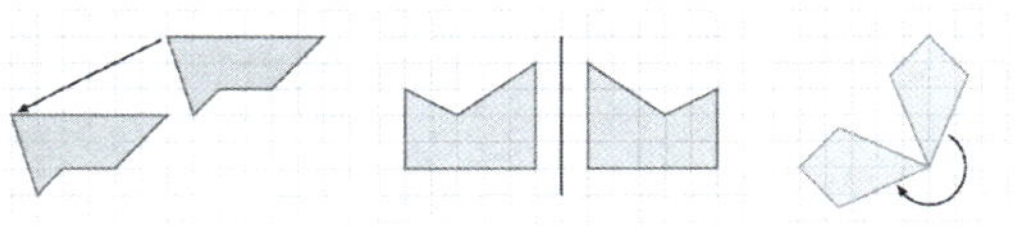

Explore

You will need a copy of this figure, a ruler, a Mira, grid paper, and tracing paper.

Work together.

➤ Draw and label the image of the hexagon after each transformation:
- a translation of 2 squares right, 3 squares up
- a reflection in the broken line
- a $\frac{1}{2}$ turn about the dot

➤ Compare the hexagon and its images. Look at size, shape, and the way each one faces.

➤ Predict the image after each transformation:
- a $\frac{1}{4}$ turn clockwise about the dot
- a translation of 1 square left, 7 squares down

Check your predictions.

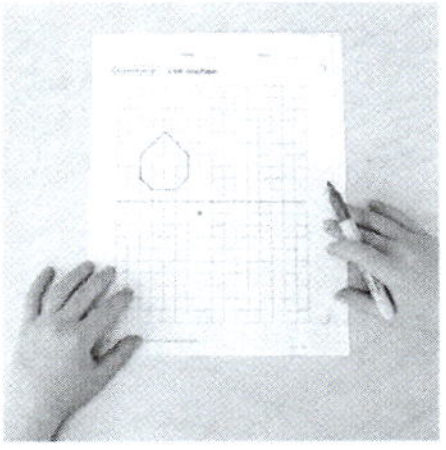

Show and Share

Share your work with another pair of students.
How is each image different from the figure?
How are a figure and its image the same?

LESSON 2

Transformations

LESSON ORGANIZER (40–50 min)

Curriculum Focus: Rotate, reflect, and translate figures. (5m86, 5m87)

Student Materials
- figures (Master 7.6)
- Miras
- tracing paper
- grid paper

Optional
- Step-by-Step 2 (Master 7.15)
- Extra Practice 1 (Master 7.21

Vocabulary: translation, reflection, rotation, congruent, Mira

Assessment: Master 7.2 Ongoing Observations: Transformational Geometry

Key Math Learnings

1. A figure and its image after a translation, a reflection, or a rotation are congruent.
2. A translation is a slide, a reflection is a flip, and a rotation is a turn.

Numbers Every Day

Encourage students to estimate each mean before using a calculator to calculate it. Students can redistribute from a greater number, such as 60, to a lesser number, such as 10.

BEFORE Get Started

Have students look at the transformations on page 231 of the Student Book. Ask:

- What transformation is shown in each picture? *(In the first picture, the figure is translated 6 squares left and 3 squares down. In the second picture, the figure is reflected in the vertical line. In the third picture, the figure is rotated a $\frac{3}{4}$ turn clockwise; the bottom vertex of the kite is the turn centre.)*
- How is each image different from the figure? How is it the same? *(For the translation, the image has a different position, but the same size, shape, and orientation. For the reflection, the image has a different position and orientation, but the same size and shape. For the rotation, the image has a different position and orientation, but the same size and shape.)*

Present *Explore*. Distribute copies of the figure (Master 7.6). Ensure students understand they are to apply each transformation to the original figure.

DURING Explore

Ongoing Assessment: Observe and Listen

Ask questions, such as:

- For each transformation, how do the size, shape, position, and orientation of the figure compare to those of its image? *(For the translation, the size, shape, and orientation are the same; the position is different. For the reflection, the size and shape are the same; the position and orientation are different. Each point on the figure is the same distance from the broken line as the corresponding point on the image. For the rotation, the size and shape are the same; the position and orientation are different.)*

REACHING ALL LEARNERS

Alternative Explore

Materials: tangrams, 1-cm grid paper
Have students complete *Explore* using the small triangle.

Early Finishers

Have students measure the side lengths and angles of each figure and its image. They describe any patterns.

Common Misconceptions

➤ Students have difficulty finding the image of a figure after a rotation.

How to Help: Have students trace the figure. They can begin with the tracing on top of the figure. They draw a horizontal or vertical line from the tracing to the turn centre. Then they place a pencil point on the turn centre and carefully turn the tracing the required distance.

Answers to Explore

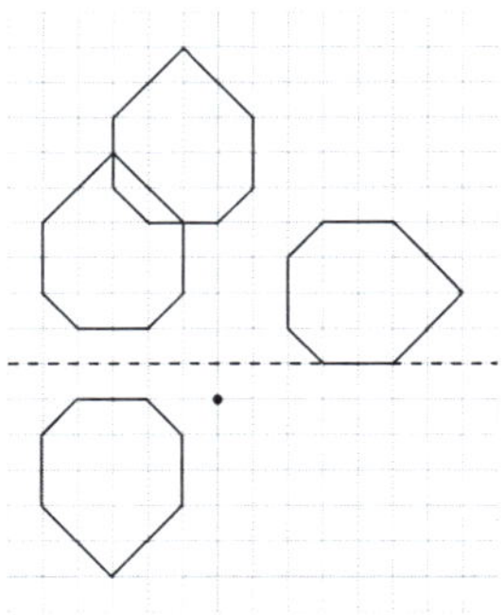

Connect

➤ A translation moves a figure along a straight line.
The figure and its image are congruent.

➤ A reflection is a flip.
The figure and its image face opposite ways.

➤ A rotation is a turn.
The figure and its image may face different ways.

When you translate, reflect, or rotate a figure, the figure and its image are congruent.

232

- Suppose the figure was rotated a $\frac{1}{4}$ turn clockwise about the dot. What effect would this transformation have on the size, shape, position, and orientation of the figure?
  (*The image after this rotation will have the same size and shape as the figure. The image would be turned on its side and "pointing" to the right.*)
- How would the image compare to the figure after a translation of 1 square left and 7 squares down?
  (*The figure and its translation image would have the same size and shape. Both the figure and its image would "point" up. The image would be below, and to the left of, the figure.*)

AFTER Connect

Invite students to share the strategies they used to predict the location of the image of a figure after a transformation. Ask:

- Which did you find easier to predict, the image after a rotation or the image after a translation? Why?
  (*I found it easier to predict the image after a translation. A translation only slides the figure to a new position, it does not change its orientation. For each vertex on the figure, it is easy to find the location of the corresponding vertex of the image. A translation is always a slide — up, down, left, or right. For a rotation, I have to think about the direction of the turn, the amount of turn, and the location of the turn centre.*)

Practice

Use tracing paper when it helps.

1. Describe the transformation that moves the figure to each image.
Can you describe any movements in more than one way? Explain.
   a) Image A
   b) Image B
   c) Image C
   d) Image D

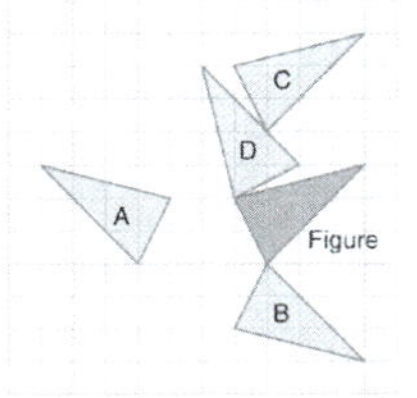

2. Copy this figure on 1-cm grid paper.
Draw the image after each transformation.
   a) a translation of 4 squares down and 1 square right
   b) a reflection in the broken line
   c) a $\frac{1}{4}$ turn counterclockwise about the dot

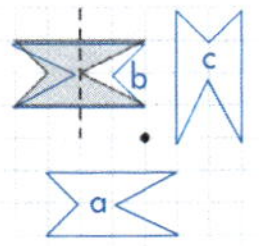

3. Use 1-cm grid paper.
   a) Draw a square.
      - Choose a translation.
      - Choose a mirror line.
      Reflect the square in the mirror line.
      - Choose a turn centre, a fraction of a turn, and the direction.
      Rotate the square about the turn centre.

   Draw and label the image of the square after each transformation.
   Compare the square to each image.
   b) Repeat part a.
   This time start with a rectangle.
   Compare the rectangle to each image.
   c) When you see a square and its image, can you always tell what the transformation was? Explain.
   Answer the same question for a rectangle and its image.

Numbers Every Day

Number Strategies

Find the mean of the numbers in each set.
- 15, 25, 5, 10, 45 20
- 30, 10, 60, 20, 40, 20 30
- 3, 8, 9, 12, 6, 5, 6 7

233

Sample Answers

1. a) A $\frac{1}{2}$ turn about a point halfway between the vertices that are closest together; a reflection in a mirror line that is halfway between the vertices that are closest together
   b) A reflection in a horizontal line; a half turn about the point where the 2 vertices meet
   c) A translation of 4 squares up
   d) A $\frac{1}{4}$ turn clockwise about one vertex
3. a) The image of the square after each transformation is congruent to the original square. Each square appears the same.
   b) The image of the rectangle after each transformation is congruent to the original rectangle. The orientation of the image of the rectangle after a $\frac{1}{4}$ rotation was different.
   c) No; it could be a translation, a rotation, or a reflection, because the image of the square after each transformation is congruent to the original square. For a rectangle, the image will have a different orientation if it is rotated a $\frac{1}{4}$ turn or a $\frac{3}{4}$ turn. A reflection can be the same as a translation, or as a $\frac{1}{2}$ turn.
4. a) These transformations would move Figure A to coincide with Figure B:
   - A translation of 4 squares right, 3 squares down
   - A rotation of Figure A one-half turn about a turn centre that is half way between the bottom right vertex of Figure A and the top left vertex of Figure B
   b) Figure A can be reflected in a vertical line halfway between the two figures, then this reflection image is translated 3 units down. Figure A could be reflected in a horizontal line halfway between the two figures, then this reflection image is translated 4 units right.

- Which attributes of a figure remain unchanged after each type of transformation? Explain.
(The size and shape of a figure and its image after a transformation are always the same. Transformations slide, flip, or turn a figure, but do not stretch, shrink, or distort it.)
- Is it possible for 2 figures with different orientations to be congruent? How do you know?
(Yes. If both figures have the same size and shape, they are congruent. One figure can be turned or flipped so it has the same orientation as the other figure.)

Discuss the examples presented in *Connect*. Ask:

- Look at the rotation of a $\frac{3}{4}$ turn counterclockwise. Describe another rotation that would result in the same image.
(If the figure was rotated a $\frac{1}{4}$ turn clockwise, the image would be the same as the image after a $\frac{3}{4}$ turn counterclockwise.)

Practice

Have tracing paper available for all questions. Questions 2, 3, 5, and 6 require grid paper.

Assessment Focus: Question 4

For part a, students should be able to describe a translation, a rotation, and a reflection that would move Figure A to coincide with Figure B. For part b, some students may describe two or more translations, or a combination of translations and rotations, translations and reflections, or rotations and reflections.

5. The figure may have been reflected in a horizontal line below it. The reflection image would be directly below the figure.
6. This figure was translated, then reflected. Where could the translation image be?

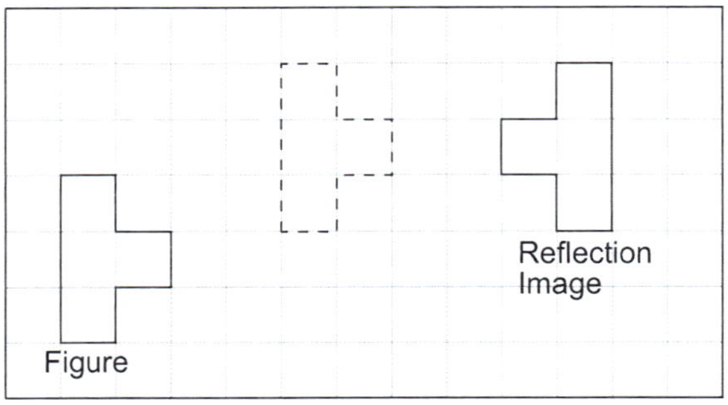

REFLECT: If the figure is a square or a rectangle, the translation image and the reflection image will appear the same. The images are actually different. You can mark one side of the rectangle with a dot to compare the images.

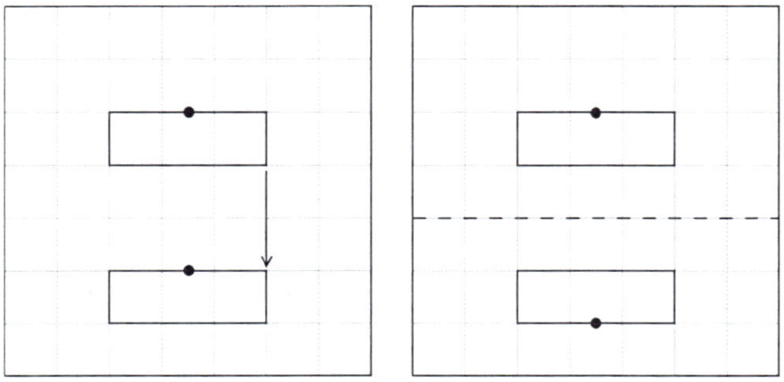

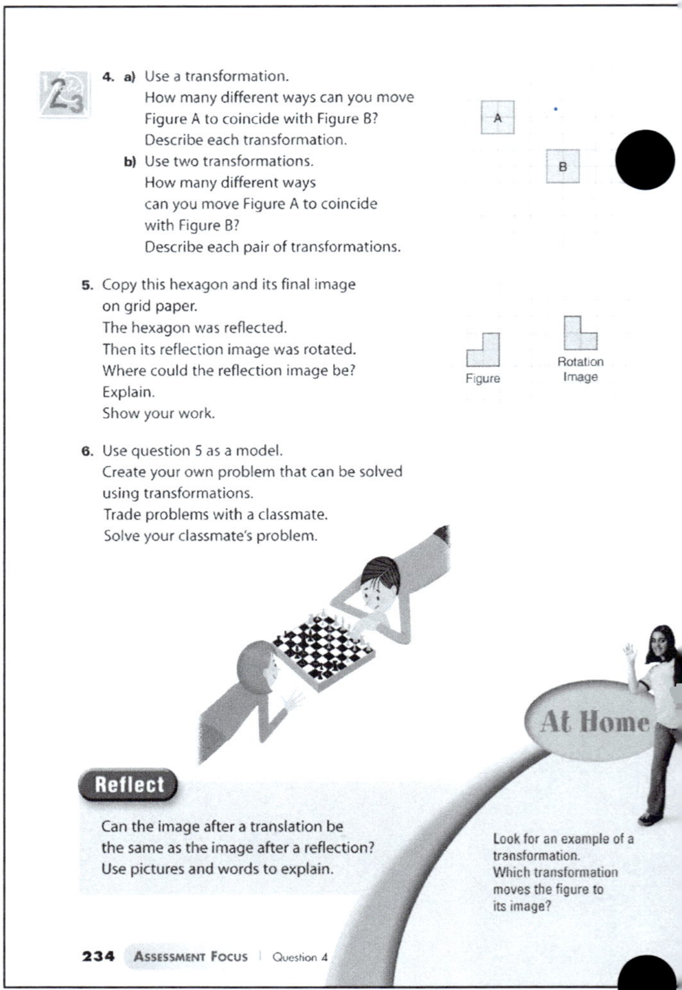
4. a) Use a transformation.
How many different ways can you move Figure A to coincide with Figure B?
Describe each transformation.
b) Use two transformations.
How many different ways can you move Figure A to coincide with Figure B?
Describe each pair of transformations.

5. Copy this hexagon and its final image on grid paper.
The hexagon was reflected.
Then its reflection image was rotated.
Where could the reflection image be?
Explain.
Show your work.

6. Use question 5 as a model.
Create your own problem that can be solved using transformations.
Trade problems with a classmate.
Solve your classmate's problem.

Reflect

Can the image after a translation be the same as the image after a reflection?
Use pictures and words to explain.

At Home

Look for an example of a transformation.
Which transformation moves the figure to its image?

234 ASSESSMENT FOCUS | Question 4

ASSESSMENT FOR LEARNING

What to Look For	What to Do
Understanding concepts ✔ Students can identify the transformation that would move a figure to coincide with another figure.	***Extra Support:*** Have students trace the original figure, then cut it out. They can take this figure through the transformations, then draw the final image. Students can use Step-by-Step 2 (Master 7.15) to complete question 4.
Applying procedures ✔ Students are able to transform a figure into a corresponding image using a translation, a reflection, or a rotation.	***Extra Practice:*** Students can do the Additional Activity *Transformation Patterns* (Master 7.11). Students can complete Extra Practice 1 (Master 7.21).
Communication ✔ Students use appropriate geometry terminology when discussing transformations.	***Extension:*** Encourage students to research applications of transformations in the world around them.

Recording and Reporting
Master 7.2 Ongoing Observations: Transformational Geometry

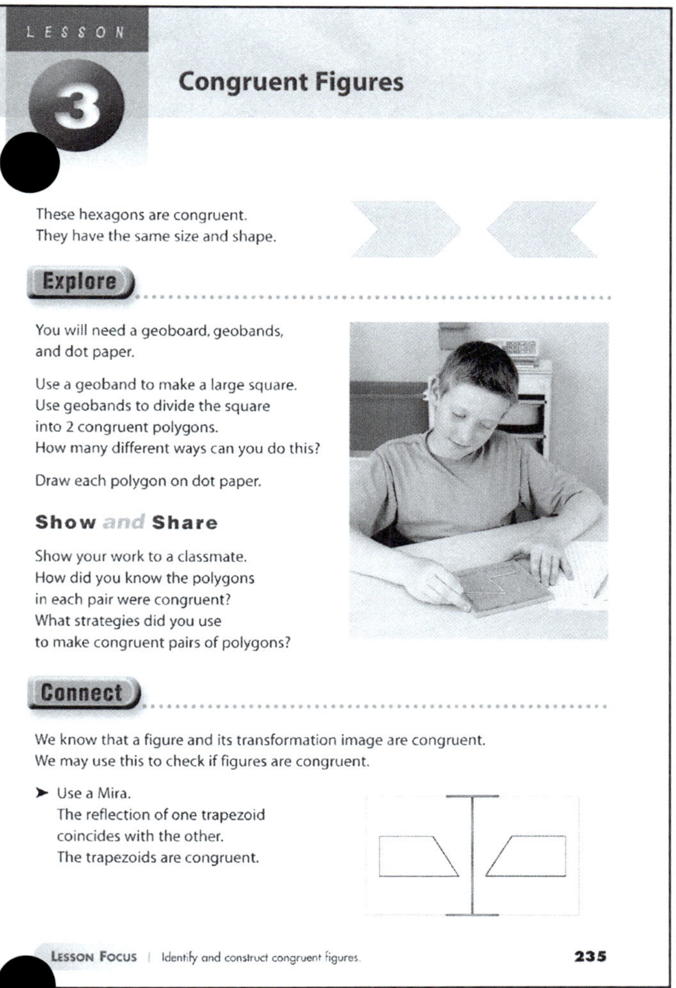
LESSON 3

Congruent Figures

These hexagons are congruent.
They have the same size and shape.

Explore

You will need a geoboard, geobands, and dot paper.

Use a geoband to make a large square.
Use geobands to divide the square into 2 congruent polygons.
How many different ways can you do this?

Draw each polygon on dot paper.

Show and Share

Show your work to a classmate.
How did you know the polygons in each pair were congruent?
What strategies did you use to make congruent pairs of polygons?

Connect

We know that a figure and its transformation image are congruent.
We may use this to check if figures are congruent.

➤ Use a Mira.
The reflection of one trapezoid coincides with the other.
The trapezoids are congruent.

LESSON FOCUS | Identify and construct congruent figures. 235

Congruent Figures

LESSON ORGANIZER (40–50 min)

Curriculum Focus: Identify and construct congruent figures. (5m77, 5m80)

Student Materials
- geoboards
- geobands
- dot paper (PM 25)

Optional
- Step-by-Step 3 (Master 7.16)
- Extra Practice 2 (Master 7.22)

Assessment: Master 7.2 Ongoing Observations: Transformational Geometry

Key Math Learnings

1. A figure and its transformation image are congruent.
2. Translations, reflections, and rotations produce congruent images.

BEFORE Get Started

Have students look at the hexagons at the top of page 235 in the Student Book. Ask:

- How can you show the hexagons are congruent?
  (*I could trace one of the hexagons, then lay the tracing over the other hexagon to see if they coincide.*)

Present *Explore*.

DURING Explore

Ongoing Assessment: Observe and Listen

Ask questions, such as:

- How do you know the polygons in each pair are congruent?
  (*They have the same size and the same shape.*)
- How can you tell if each way you divide the square is different from the other ways?
  (*I can compare the polygons on the geoboard with the polygons I recorded on dot paper. I would rotate the dot paper and compare the polygons with those on the geoboard each time.*)

Here are 6 possible solutions:

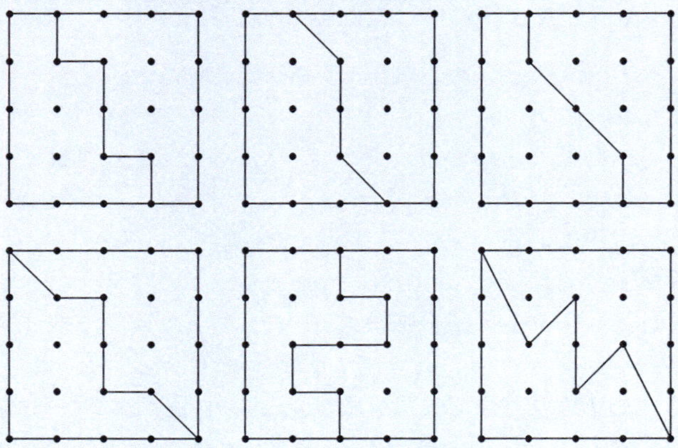

REACHING ALL LEARNERS

Alternative Explore

Materials: dot paper (PM 25)

Have students draw a figure on dot paper. Then they draw a figure that is congruent to the first figure. Students count the number of dots on each side of the figure and its image.

Early Finishers

Have students draw figures on dot paper. They trade figures with a classmate, apply a transformation to their classmate's figure, and explain why the figure and its transformation image are congruent.

Numbers Every Day

Most students will find pairs of numbers with a product of 36, then find the difference of the numbers in each pair.

Sample Answers

1. a) The figures never coincide; they have different shapes.
   b) Each figure is a rotation of the other.
   c) The figures never coincide; one is bigger than the other.
   d) Each figure is a reflection of the other.

➤ Fold the paper so one polygon coincides with the other.

The fold line is a mirror line.
The polygons coincide.
Each polygon is a reflection of the other.

➤ Use tracing paper.

Rotate then translate the tracing to see if it coincides with the other figure.

Practice

1. Which pairs of figures are congruent? How do you know?

a)

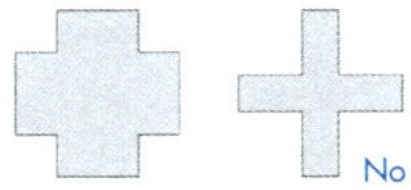

No

b)

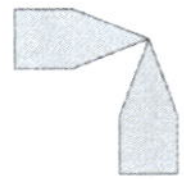

Yes

c)

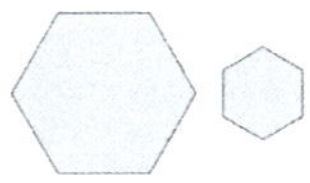

No

d)

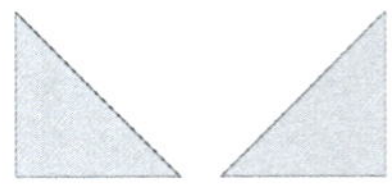

Yes

236

AFTER Connect

Share the diagrams the students have produced on the board. Encourage students to copy any congruent pairs they missed. Invite students to share the strategies they used to make congruent pairs of polygons.

Discuss the examples presented in *Connect*. Ask:

- When would you use a Mira or paper folding to check if figures are congruent?
  (If the figures are facing one another, that is, they appear to be mirror images of one another, I would use either a Mira or paper folding.)
- When would you use tracing paper to check if figures are congruent?
  (I would use tracing paper if the figures had the same orientation, but did not align horizontally or vertically, or did not appear to be mirror images of one another.)

Practice

Questions 3 and 4 require geoboards. Have green Pattern Blocks available for question 5. Students may either arrange 4 green Pattern Blocks or use a ruler to find and connect the midpoints of the sides.

Assessment Focus: Question 4

Students should begin by dividing the geoboard into 2 congruent parts, then dividing each part into 2 congruent parts, and so on.

Students should recognize that two solutions may look different when it is really just the orientation of the geoboard that is different.

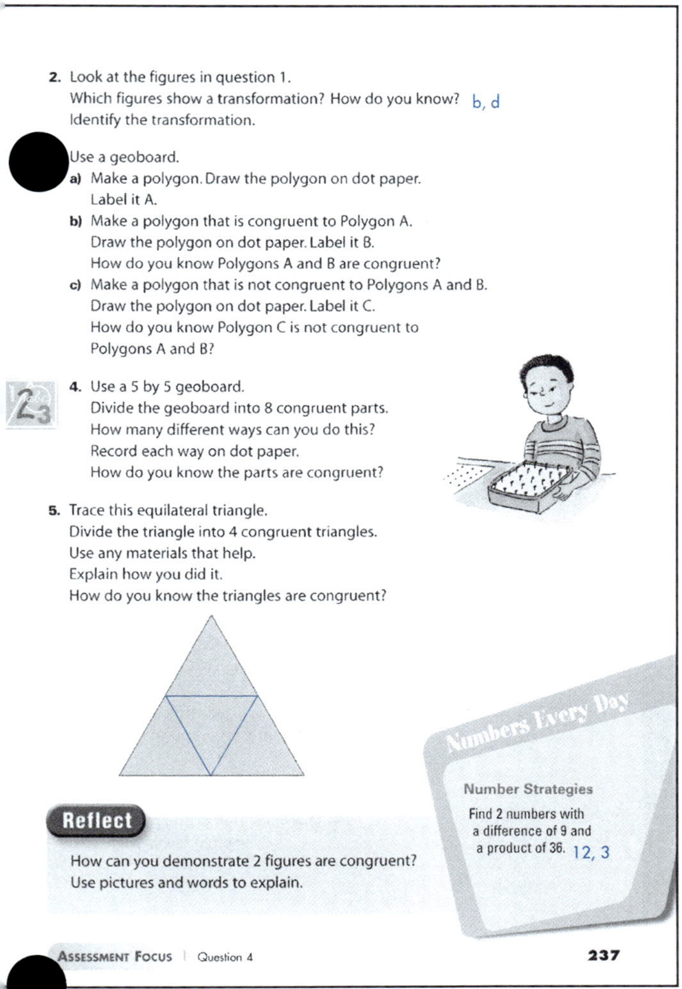
2. Look at the figures in question 1.
Which figures show a transformation? How do you know? b, d
Identify the transformation.

3. Use a geoboard.
a) Make a polygon. Draw the polygon on dot paper. Label it A.
b) Make a polygon that is congruent to Polygon A. Draw the polygon on dot paper. Label it B. How do you know Polygons A and B are congruent?
c) Make a polygon that is not congruent to Polygons A and B. Draw the polygon on dot paper. Label it C. How do you know Polygon C is not congruent to Polygons A and B?

4. Use a 5 by 5 geoboard.
Divide the geoboard into 8 congruent parts.
How many different ways can you do this?
Record each way on dot paper.
How do you know the parts are congruent?

5. Trace this equilateral triangle.
Divide the triangle into 4 congruent triangles.
Use any materials that help.
Explain how you did it.
How do you know the triangles are congruent?

Reflect

How can you demonstrate 2 figures are congruent?
Use pictures and words to explain.

Numbers Every Day

Number Strategies

Find 2 numbers with a difference of 9 and a product of 36. 12, 3

ASSESSMENT FOCUS | Question 4

237

2. In 1b, the figure was rotated a $\frac{1}{4}$ turn counterclockwise or a $\frac{3}{4}$ turn clockwise. In 1d, the figure was reflected in a vertical line halfway between the two closest vertices.

3. a) b) c)

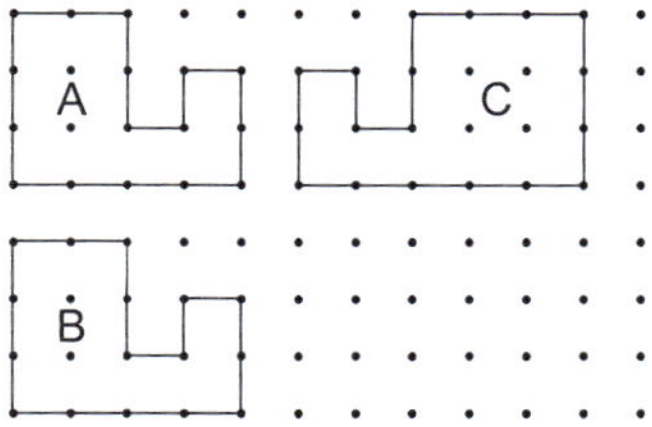

Polygons A and B have the same size and shape.
Polygon C has a different shape and size.

4. In each case, the parts have the same size and shape.

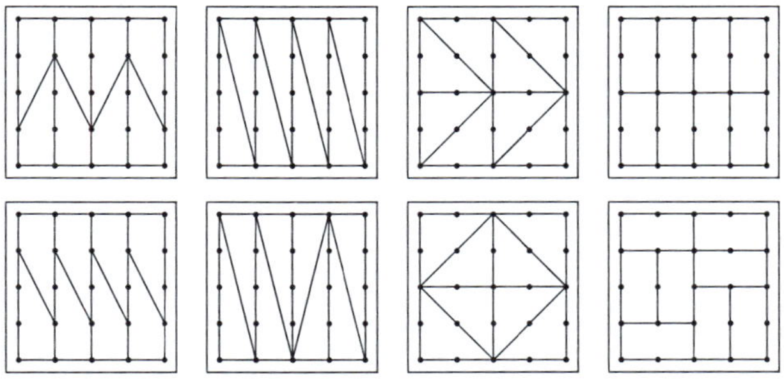

REFLECT: You can demonstrate that two figures are congruent by tracing one figure and placing the tracing on top of the second figure. You could also use a Mira. If the reflection of one figure coincides with the other figure, the figures are congruent.

ASSESSMENT FOR LEARNING

What to Look For	What to Do
Understanding concepts ✔ Students understand that a figure and its image after a transformation are congruent. ***Problem solving*** ✔ Students use a strategy such as guess and check to find solutions to problems with congruent figures.	***Extra Support:*** Students having difficulty should work with a partner and share ideas on identifying and constructing congruent figures. Students can use Step-by-Step 3 (Master 7.16) to complete question 4. ***Extra Practice:*** Students can complete Extra Practice 2 (Master 7.22). ***Extension:*** Have students measure and compare the side lengths and angle measures for each figure and its image after a transformation.

Recording and Reporting

Master 7.2 Ongoing Observations: Transformational Geometry

Using a Computer to Explore Congruent Figures

LESSON ORGANIZER

40–50 min

Curriculum Focus: Use a computer to create and identify congruent figures. (5m77, 5m80, 5m81)

Student Materials

- Computer with *AppleWorks* or *The Geometer's Sketchpad*

Key Math Learning

A computer can be used to create and identify congruent figures.

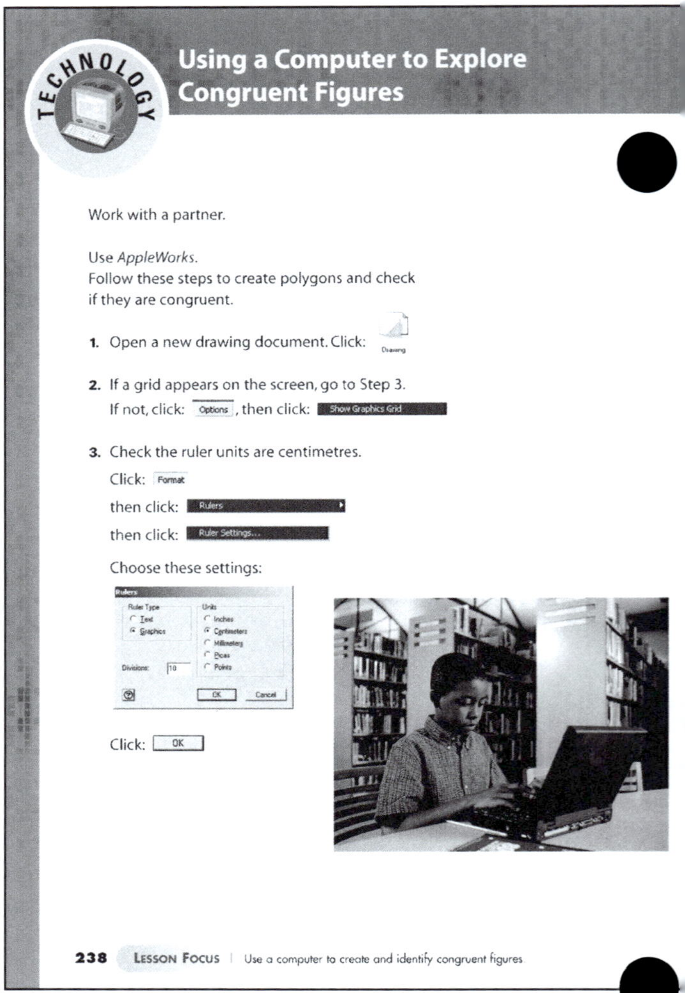

TECHNOLOGY

Using a Computer to Explore Congruent Figures

Work with a partner.

Use *AppleWorks*.
Follow these steps to create polygons and check if they are congruent.

1. Open a new drawing document. Click: Drawing
2. If a grid appears on the screen, go to Step 3.
   If not, click: Options, then click: Show Graphics Grid
3. Check the ruler units are centimetres.
   Click: Format
   then click: Rulers
   then click: Ruler Settings...
   Choose these settings:
   Rulers
   Ruler Type: Text, Graphics
   Units: Inches, Centimeters, Millimeters, Picas, Points
   Divisions: 10
   OK Cancel
   Click: OK

238 LESSON FOCUS | Use a computer to create and identify congruent figures

BEFORE Get Started

Explain to students they will be using a computer to create polygons and to check the polygons are congruent. Ask:

- How can you tell if two polygons are congruent?
  (*If two polygons have the same size and the same shape, they are congruent. If either polygon is placed on top of the other, it covers the polygon completely.*)

DURING Explore

Instructions for creating and identifying congruent polygons using *The Geometer's Sketchpad*:

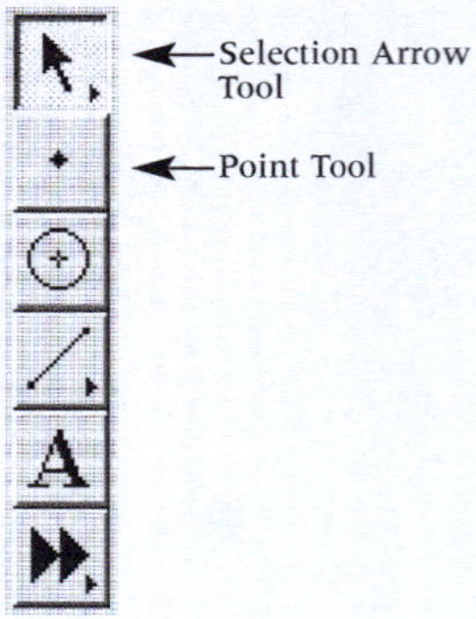

1. Open a new sketch in *The Geometer's Sketchpad*. Click: **File**, then click: **New Sketch**
2. Select the **Point Tool**. Click to draw a point. This will be one vertex of your polygon. Continue to draw points until you have as many vertices as you wish.

Use these tools to draw polygons:

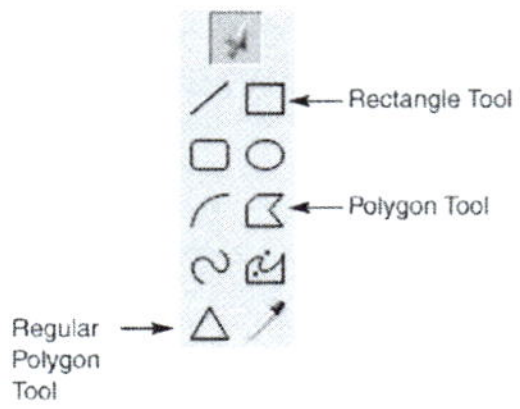

To make a **rectangle**, click the Rectangle Tool.
Click and hold down the mouse button.
Drag the cursor until the rectangle is the size and shape you want.
Release the mouse button.

To make a **square**, hold down the Shift key while you click and drag.

To make an **irregular polygon**, select the Polygon Tool.
Click and drag to make each side of the polygon.
Double-click when you have finished.

To make a **regular polygon**, select the Regular Polygon Tool.
Click: Edit, then click: Polygon Sides...
Type in the number of sides you want. Click: OK

5. To **colour a polygon**, click the polygon to select it.
Click the Fill formatting button:
Click the Color palette button: , then select a colour.

6. Use Steps 4 and 5 to create two polygons you think are congruent.
Colour one polygon red and the other one blue.

7. To **move a polygon**, put the cursor inside the polygon.
Click and hold down the mouse button.
Drag the polygon to where you want it.
Release the mouse button.

239

3. Select the **Selection Arrow Tool.**
Click to select the points in order.
Click: **Construct**, then click:
Polygon Interior
This forms a polygon with the points as vertices.

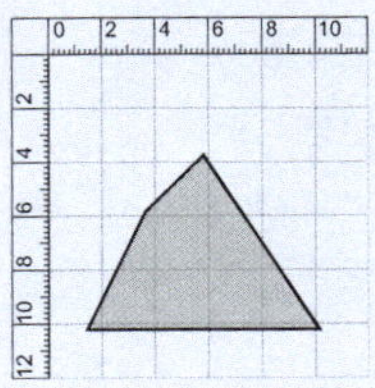

4. Click to select the polygon.
Click: **Display**, then click: **Color**
Select red.

5. Repeat Steps 2 to 4 to construct a second polygon.
Colour this polygon blue.

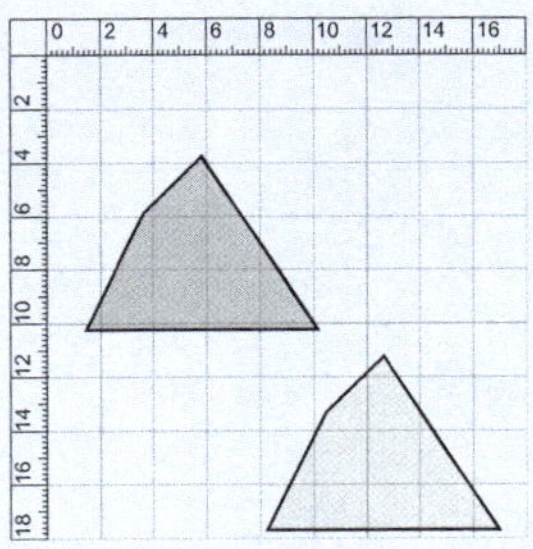

6. To change the size of a polygon:
Click one of the vertices.
Hold down the mouse button.
Drag the vertex until it is where you want it.
Release the mouse button.
Try to make your polygons congruent.

7. To check if your polygons are congruent:
Click one polygon.
Hold down the mouse button.
Drag the red polygon until it covers the blue polygon.
Release the mouse button.
If the edges of the two polygons align, they are congruent.

8. Save your polygons.
Click: **File**, then click: **Save As**
Give your file a name. Click: **Save**

9. Print your polygons.
Click: **File**, then click: **Print**
Click: **OK**

8. To **flip a polygon**, select the polygon.

Click: Arrange

then click: Flip Horizontally

or Flip Vertically

9. To check if the **polygons are congruent**:
If you need to, flip the polygons so they have the same orientation.
Select the red polygon.

Click: Arrange

Then click: Move To Front

Carefully drag the red polygon on top of the blue polygon.
If you see any of the blue polygon, the polygons are not congruent.

If you cannot see any of the blue polygon, select the red polygon.

Click: Arrange

Then click: Move To Back

If you see any of the red polygon, the polygons are not congruent.

10. Repeat Steps 6 to 9 several times.
Use a different pair of polygons each time.

11. Save your polygons.

Click: File, then click: Save As... Shift+Ctrl+S

Name your file. Click: Save

12. Print your polygons.

Click: File, then click: Print... Ctrl+P

Click: OK

Reflect

How can you use a computer to check if polygons are congruent?
Use pictures and words to explain.

240

REFLECT: I can drag one polygon on top of the other, then trade their positions. That is, I can then drag the second polygon on top of the first polygon. Each time, if none of the polygon on the bottom is visible, the polygons are congruent.

AFTER Connect

Invite volunteers to share their printouts and discuss how they created their polygons and checked they were congruent.

Ask:

- Why is it necessary to place the red polygon on top of the blue polygon *and* the blue polygon on top of the red polygon?
(If the red polygon is larger than the blue polygon, it will cover the blue polygon completely. But, when the blue polygon is placed on top of the red polygon, some of the red polygon will still be visible.)

Discuss using a computer to make nets. Elicit from students that using the copy and paste function makes congruent squares quickly.

LESSON

4 Line Symmetry

A line of symmetry is a mirror line.
It divides a figure into 2 congruent parts.
How many lines of symmetry does each Pattern Block have?

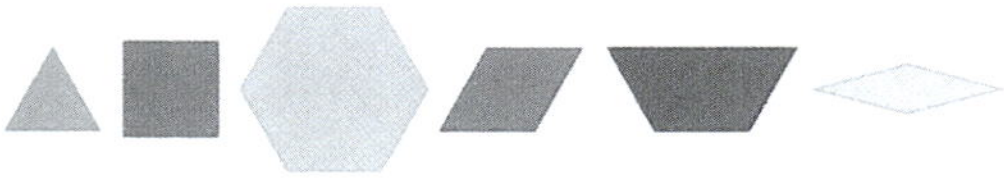

Explore

You will need grid paper, Pattern Blocks, and a Mira.

➤ Fold the grid paper in half.
Use Pattern Blocks.
Make a design on one side of the fold line.
Your design must touch the fold line.
Trace around your design.
Do not draw on the fold line.

➤ Open the paper.
Make a mirror image of the design on the other side of the fold line.
Trace around the mirror image.
Remove the Pattern Blocks.

➤ Find any lines of symmetry on the figure.

Show and Share

Show your work to another pair of students.
How did you find the lines of symmetry?
What did you notice about the fold line?

LESSON FOCUS | Construct figures with line symmetry. 241

Line Symmetry

LESSON ORGANIZER 40–50 min

Curriculum Focus: Construct figures with line symmetry. (5m89)

Student Materials
- grid paper (PM 23)
- dot paper (PM 25)
- Pattern Blocks (PM 28)
- Miras
- scissors
- geoboards
- geobands

Optional
- Step-by-Step 4 (Master 7.17)
- Extra Practice 2 (Master 7.22)

Vocabulary: line of symmetry, symmetrical

Assessment: Master 7.2 Ongoing Observations: Transformational Geometry

Key Math Learnings

1. A line of symmetry divides a figure into two congruent parts.
2. A symmetrical figure has one or more lines of symmetry.
3. A figure that is not symmetrical has no lines of symmetry.

BEFORE Get Started

Refer students to the images of Pattern Blocks at the top of page 241 in the Student Book. Ask:

- How can you tell how many lines of symmetry each Pattern Block has?
  (I can trace each Pattern Block, then cut out the tracing. The number of different ways I can fold the tracing so the parts on each side of the fold line are congruent tells me the number of lines of symmetry the block has.)
- How many lines of symmetry does each Pattern Block have?
  (The green triangle has 3 lines of symmetry. The orange square has 4 lines of symmetry. The yellow hexagon has 6 lines of symmetry. The blue and tan rhombuses each have 2 lines of symmetry. The red trapezoid has 1 line of symmetry.)

DURING Explore

Ongoing Assessment: Observe and Listen

Ask questions, such as:

- How did you find the lines of symmetry for your figure?
  (I used the fold line as a mirror to create the figure so I know it is as line of symmetry. To find other lines of symmetry, I used a Mira. I placed the Mira in different positions on the figure and checked if the reflection coincided with the lines on the paper.)

REACHING ALL LEARNERS

Early Finishers

Have students investigate the number of lines of symmetry on a five-armed starfish.

ESL Strategies

To help students learn the names of geometric figures, display labelled drawings of a variety of polygons around the classroom.

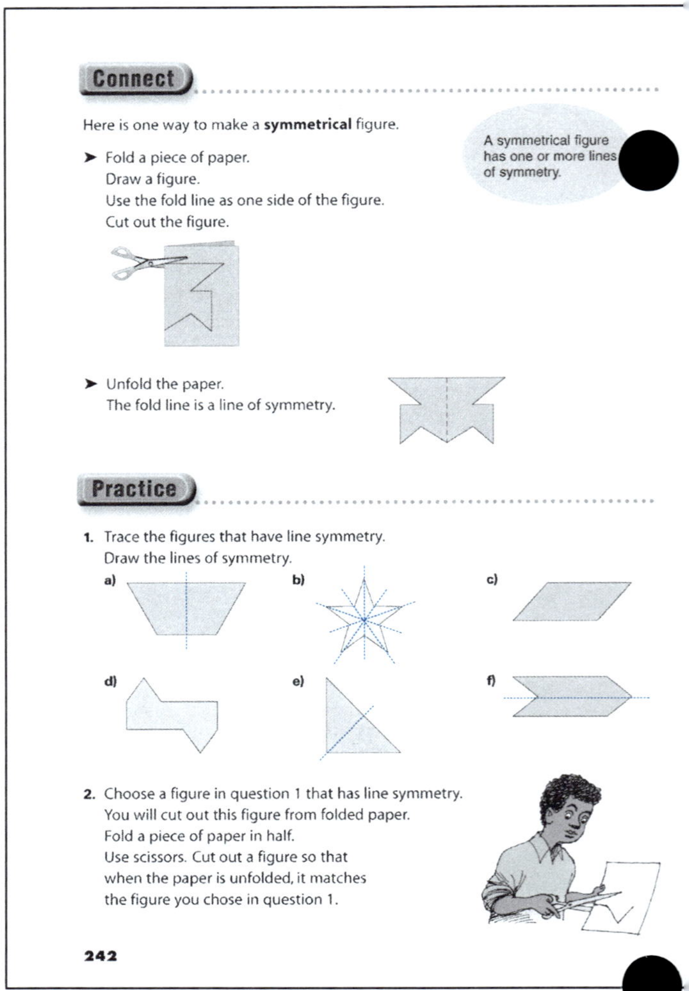

Connect

Here is one way to make a **symmetrical** figure.

A symmetrical figure has one or more lines of symmetry.

➤ Fold a piece of paper.
Draw a figure.
Use the fold line as one side of the figure.
Cut out the figure.

➤ Unfold the paper.
The fold line is a line of symmetry.

Practice

1. Trace the figures that have line symmetry.
Draw the lines of symmetry.
a) b) c) d) e) f)

2. Choose a figure in question 1 that has line symmetry.
You will cut out this figure from folded paper.
Fold a piece of paper in half.
Use scissors. Cut out a figure so that when the paper is unfolded, it matches the figure you chose in question 1.

242

AFTER — Connect

Invite student volunteers to share their designs and the strategies they used to find the lines of symmetry with the class.

Discuss the method used in *Connect* to construct a figure with one line of symmetry. Ask:

- Will paper folding always produce a figure with exactly one line of symmetry? How do you know?
  (No, if the figure I draw on the folded paper has symmetry, the figure that results when I unfold the cut-out will have more than one line of symmetry.)
- Describe another method you could use to construct a figure with line symmetry.
  (I could draw half a figure on paper, then place a Mira along the unfinished portion of the figure. To complete the figure, I would draw lines to coincide with the reflection in the Mira.)

Practice

Questions 2 and 6 require scissors, question 3 requires dot paper, question 4 requires geoboards, and question 5 requires grid paper.

Assessment Focus: Question 5

Ensure students understand they may add only one square to the figure. Students should draw lines in different positions, then see if they can add a square so the figures on each side of a given line are symmetrical.

3. One-half of a symmetrical figure is shown.
The broken line is a line of symmetry.
Copy the figure and the line of symmetry on dot paper.
Complete the figure.

a) b)

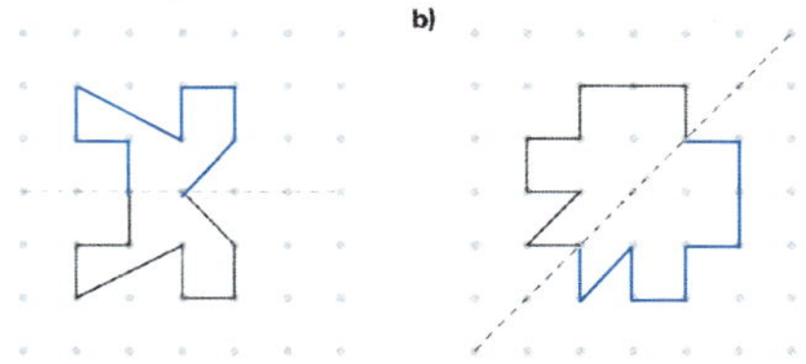

4. Use a geoboard and geobands.
Divide the geoboard in half with a mirror line.
Make a figure on one-half of the geoboard.
Make its mirror image on the other half,
so the two figures form a new figure.
Is the new figure symmetrical? How do you know? Yes

5. This figure does not have a line of symmetry.
Copy the figure on grid paper.
Add a square to it so it has a line of symmetry.
How many different ways can you do this?
Record each way on grid paper.

6. Fold a piece of paper in half.
Cut the paper to make each figure
when the paper is unfolded.
a) An isosceles triangle
b) A pentagon
Tell about the figures you created.

Reflect

How can you construct a figure that has line symmetry?
Use pictures, numbers, or words to explain.

Numbers Every Day

Number Strategies

Order the numbers in each set from least to greatest.

- 5.37, 7.35, 3.75, 5.73, 7.53
- 0.11, 0.51, 0.15, 0.09, 1.01
- 4.88, 3.98, 1.78, 8.14, 9.38

3.75, 5.37, 5.73, 7.35, 7.53
0.09, 0.11, 0.15, 0.51, 1.01
1.78, 3.98, 4.88, 8.14, 9.38

ASSESSMENT FOCUS | Question 5

243

Sample Answers

4. I know the figure is symmetrical because the two sides coincide when a Mira is placed on the mirror line.

5. There are two different places I could add a square to make a figure with line symmetry.

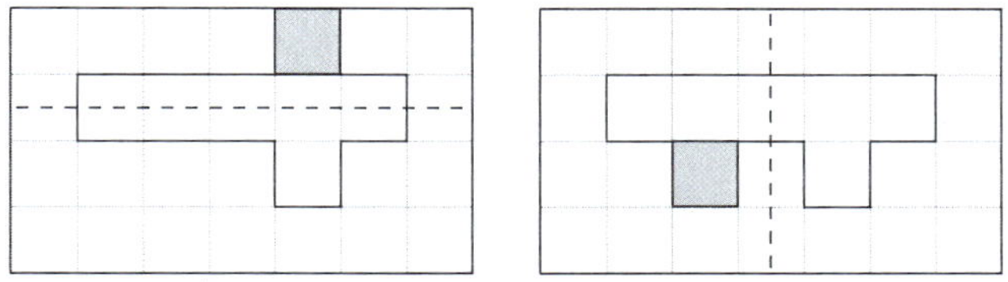

6. a) I cut out $\frac{1}{2}$ of an isosceles triangle (it looks like a right triangle). The fold is a line of symmetry.

b) I cut out $\frac{1}{2}$ of a pentagon (2 sides and $\frac{1}{2}$ of a third side). The fold is a line of symmetry.

REFLECT: I can construct a figure with line symmetry by folding a piece of paper, drawing a figure on one side of the fold line, then cutting out the figure. The fold line on the unfolded figure is a line of symmetry.

Numbers Every Day

Students should compare the ones digits, then the tenths digits, then the hundredths digits (if necessary).

ASSESSMENT FOR LEARNING

What to Look For	What to Do
Understanding concepts ✔ Students understand that a line of symmetry divides a figure into two congruent parts. ***Applying procedures*** ✔ Students can construct figures with one line of symmetry.	***Extra Support:*** Students can do the Additional Activity *Folding Figures* (Master 7.12). Students can use Step-by-Step 4 (Master 17) to complete question 5. ***Extra Practice:*** With a partner, have students design one-half of a figure on a geoboard. Students exchange geoboards and complete each other's figures. Students can complete Extra Practice 2 (Master 7.22). ***Extension:*** Students can do the Additional Activity *Symmetry Patterns* (Master 7.13).

Recording and Reporting
Master 7.2 Ongoing Observations: Transformational Geometry

Strategies Toolkit

LESSON ORGANIZER (40–50 min)

Curriculum Focus: Interpret a problem and select an appropriate strategy. (5m89, 5m84)

Teacher Materials

- overhead projector
- overhead Pattern Blocks

Student Materials

- Pattern Blocks (PM 28)
- 2-cm grid paper (PM 24)
- Miras
- pentominoes (Master 7.7)

Assessment: PM 3 Self-Assessment: Problem Solving
PM 1 Inquiry Process Check List

Key Math Learning

Guess and check is a good strategy to use when solving a problem with more than one possible solution.

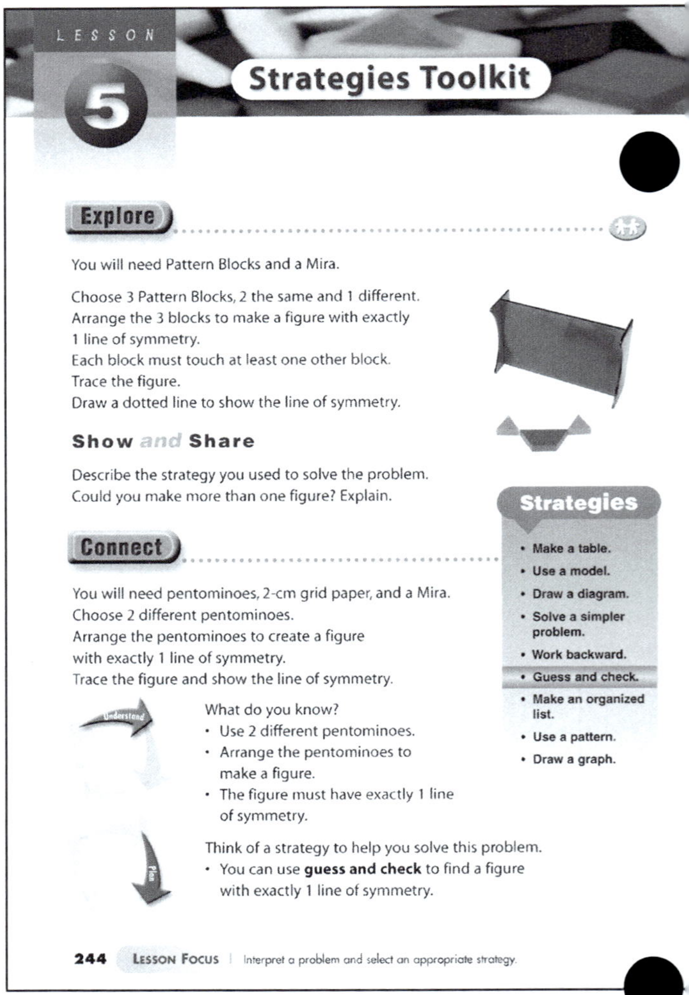

LESSON 5 Strategies Toolkit

Explore

You will need Pattern Blocks and a Mira.

Choose 3 Pattern Blocks, 2 the same and 1 different.
Arrange the 3 blocks to make a figure with exactly 1 line of symmetry.
Each block must touch at least one other block.
Trace the figure.
Draw a dotted line to show the line of symmetry.

Show and Share

Describe the strategy you used to solve the problem.
Could you make more than one figure? Explain.

Strategies

- Make a table.
- Use a model.
- Draw a diagram.
- Solve a simpler problem.
- Work backward.
- Guess and check.
- Make an organized list.
- Use a pattern.
- Draw a graph.

Connect

You will need pentominoes, 2-cm grid paper, and a Mira.
Choose 2 different pentominoes.
Arrange the pentominoes to create a figure with exactly 1 line of symmetry.
Trace the figure and show the line of symmetry.

Understand

What do you know?

- Use 2 different pentominoes.
- Arrange the pentominoes to make a figure.
- The figure must have exactly 1 line of symmetry.

Plan

Think of a strategy to help you solve this problem.

- You can use **guess and check** to find a figure with exactly 1 line of symmetry.

244 LESSON FOCUS | Interpret a problem and select an appropriate strategy.

BEFORE — Get Started

Present *Explore*. Ensure students understand they are to create a figure with *exactly* one line of symmetry.

If students choose blocks that fit on triangular grid paper, students could record their work on this paper instead of tracing.

DURING — Explore

Ongoing Assessment: Observe and Listen

Ask questions, such as:

- How did you decide which blocks to choose? (*I made sure are least one of the blocks I chose did not have many lines of symmetry.*)
- How do you know your figure has exactly one line of symmetry? (*I used a Mira. I placed the Mira in a variety of different positions and checked if the reflection of the blocks on one side of the figure coincide with the blocks on the other side of the figure.*)

Possible solutions:

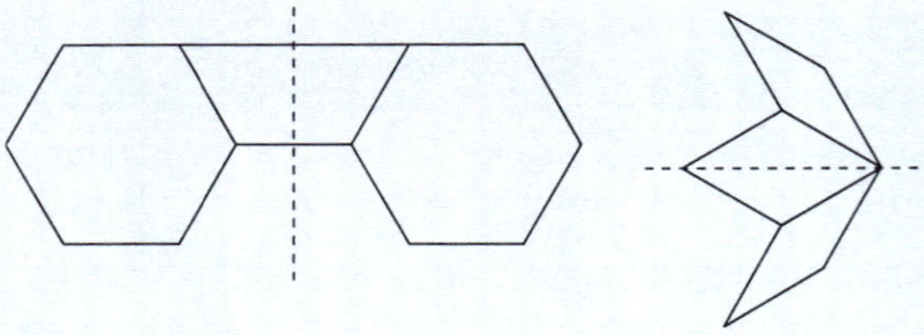

AFTER — Connect

Use an overhead projector and overhead Pattern Blocks. Invite students volunteers to share the figures they made.

Discuss the problem presented in *Connect*. You may wish to have students work in small groups to solve the problem, then discuss the results as a class.

Practice

Questions 1 and 2 require grid paper.

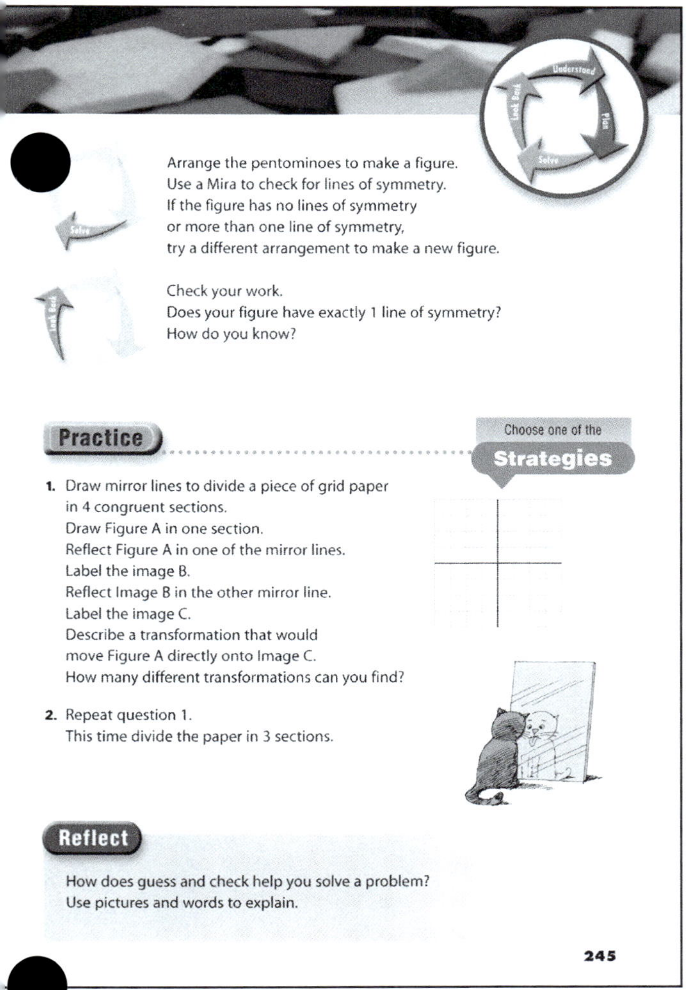

Arrange the pentominoes to make a figure.
Use a Mira to check for lines of symmetry.
If the figure has no lines of symmetry
or more than one line of symmetry,
try a different arrangement to make a new figure.

Check your work.
Does your figure have exactly 1 line of symmetry?
How do you know?

Practice

Choose one of the **Strategies**

1. Draw mirror lines to divide a piece of grid paper in 4 congruent sections.
   Draw Figure A in one section.
   Reflect Figure A in one of the mirror lines.
   Label the image B.
   Reflect Image B in the other mirror line.
   Label the image C.
   Describe a transformation that would move Figure A directly onto Image C.
   How many different transformations can you find?
2. Repeat question 1.
   This time divide the paper in 3 sections.

Reflect

How does guess and check help you solve a problem?
Use pictures and words to explain.

245

REACHING ALL LEARNERS

Early Finishers

Have students choose 3 different Pattern Blocks and arrange the blocks to make a figure with exactly one line of symmetry.

Common Misconceptions

➤ Students are not sure if the figure they made has exactly one line of symmetry.

How to Help: Have students trace the perimeter of the figure they made and cut out the tracing. Students can fold the tracing different ways to check for line symmetry.

Sample Answers

1.

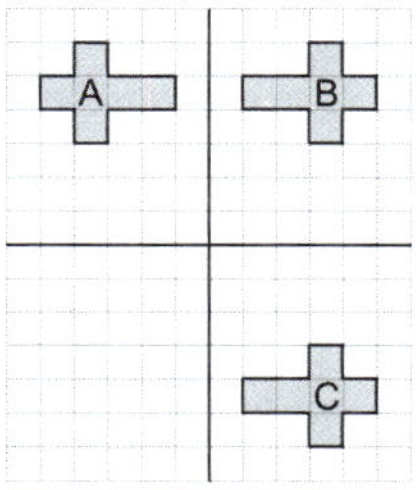

A rotation of a $\frac{1}{2}$ turn about a turn centre at the intersection of the mirror lines.

2.

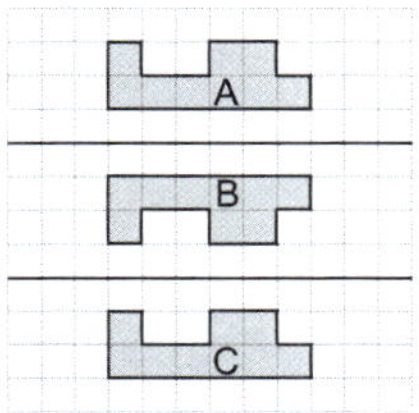

A translation of 8 squares down.

REFLECT: Guessing and checking lets you try different answers to see how they work. This gives you a place to start for your next guess.

ASSESSMENT FOR LEARNING

What to Look For	What to Do
Problem solving ✔ Students can use guess and check to solve problems involving transformational geometry. ***Communicating*** ✔ Students clearly explain the strategy they used to solve a problem.	***Extra Support:*** Have students draw a vertical line on paper and make their figure using the vertical line as a line of symmetry. ***Extra Practice:*** Have students choose 2 different pentominoes and arrange them to make a figure with exactly one line of symmetry. ***Extension:*** Challenge students to draw arrows on their answers to the *Practice* questions. The arrows should show the direction of any reflections, and any translations.

Recording and Reporting

PM 3 Self-Assessment: Problem Solving
PM 1 Inquiry Process Check List

Fashion Designer

Fashion Designer

Fashion designers create exclusive and ready-to-wear clothing, costumes, and accessories (handbags and scarves). Successful designers hold shows in cities like Toronto, Vancouver, Montreal, Paris, and Rome. Careers in fashion range from high-profile designers to illustrators, sewers, and pattern-drafters.

The fashion designer works in both two dimensions (drawings of concepts and designs and, later, patterns) and three dimensions (actual fabrics, models, and "forms"), and must convert between them. Reflections (left and right side), translations, rotations, and tiling, as well as symmetric and asymmetric designs, have all been used to make clothes more stylish and attractive.

When a ready-to-wear design is prepared for mass production, computerized pattern-making technology is used. Patterns are created for cutting the material so that the least amount of fabric is wasted and costs are kept down.

246

The study of geometry helps students develop spatial reasoning and visualization skills. These skills are useful in a wide variety of occupations, ranging from science to construction to the arts. In some occupations, the skills associated with symmetry, congruence, and transformational geometry are used directly.

Designers of fabrics and wallpaper, masons, and choreographers consider symmetry, balance, and transformations as they create their work.

In other occupations, although the skills associated with transformational geometry are not used directly, the ability to apply and extend spatial reasoning and flexible thinking is extremely useful.

Here are some occupations that use transformational geometry or spatial reasoning skills.

Composer: Many composers use symmetry and transformations in the structure of their music. A short melody is often repeated throughout a piece of music, with some minor changes. The melody may be repeated after the original has begun. This is what in mathematics we would call a translation. Alternatively, the melody may be played backwards or upside down. This is what in mathematics we would call a reflection.

Choreographer: A choreographer plans and coordinates the movements of a group of dancers. In classical ballet, all the steps are based on one of five basic positions. Several of these positions have line symmetry.

Carpenter: A carpenter requires good spatial awareness skills. She needs to visualize the finished product before she begins to build it.

Archaeologist: An archaeologist uses a grid to describe the location of objects found on a dig.

L E S S O N

6

Exploring Tiling

The design on this fabric is an area pattern. There are no gaps between the figures. None of the figures overlap.

Choose one figure to be the start figure. Describe each other figure as an image of the start figure after a transformation.

Explore

You will need scissors and dot paper. Your teacher will give you a large copy of these quadrilaterals.

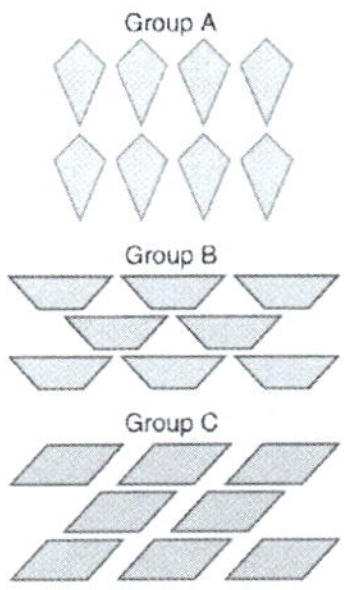

➤ Choose one group of quadrilaterals. Use scissors to cut out the quadrilaterals. Are the quadrilaterals in each group congruent? How do you know?

➤ Use the quadrilaterals you chose to create an area pattern with no gaps or overlaps. Record your pattern on dot paper. Describe your pattern.

➤ Repeat for a different group of quadrilaterals.

Show *and* Share

Share your patterns with another pair of students. How did you flip, turn, or slide the quadrilaterals to make each pattern? Explain.

LESSON FOCUS | Explore tiling patterns with congruent figures.

247

Exploring Tiling

LESSON ORGANIZER

40–50 min

Curriculum Focus: Explore tiling patterns with congruent figures. (5m88)

Student Materials
- grid paper (PM 23)
- dot paper (PM 25)
- quadrilaterals (Master 7.8)
- scissors
- tracing paper
- 4 congruent squares

Optional
- Step-by-Step 6 (Master 7.18)
- Extra Practice 3 (Master 7.23)

Vocabulary: tiling pattern, tessellation, tessellates

Assessment: Master 7.2 Ongoing Observations: Transformational Geometry

Key Math Learnings

1. A tiling pattern covers a surface with figures with no gaps or overlaps.
2. A tessellation is a tiling pattern with congruent figures.

BEFORE Get Started

Direct students' attention to the area pattern at the top of page 247. Ask:

- What is an area pattern?
  (*An area pattern is a pattern that covers a surface. There are no gaps between figures in the pattern and none of the figures overlaps.*)
- Describe the figures you see in this area pattern.
  (*I see red, orange, yellow, and blue triangles. Pairs of yellow and blue triangles form parallelograms as do pairs of red and orange triangles. Pairs of yellow and red triangles form kites as do pairs of orange and blue triangles. Groups of blue, yellow, red, and orange triangles form hexagons.*)
- How could you describe the figures in the pattern as transformations of the blue triangle at the top left?
  (*The orange triangle is a reflection of the blue triangle in a vertical line. The yellow triangle is a reflection of the blue triangle in a horizontal line that passes through the middle of the blue triangle. The red triangle is a reflection of the yellow triangle in a vertical line. Together, these four triangles form a hexagon. The hexagon is translated to the right and down to complete the pattern.*)

Present *Explore*. Distribute copies of the quadrilaterals. Tell students they will work with one group of quadrilaterals at a time.

DURING Explore

Ongoing Assessment: Observe and Listen

Ask questions, such as:

- How do you know whether the quadrilaterals in each group are congruent?
  (*The quadrilaterals in each group have the same size and the same shape.*)

REACHING ALL LEARNERS

Early Finishers

Have students use copies of one of the 12 pentominoes to create tiling patterns.

Common Misconceptions

➤ Students try to create tiling patterns with overlapped figures or gaps between figures.

How to Help: Provide students with many examples of area patterns that are tiling patterns and area patterns that are not tiling patterns. Ask students to describe the differences between the two kinds of patterns.

Sample Answers

1. I cannot arrange copies of the regular octagon to form a pattern with no gaps or overlaps. The regular octagon does not tessellate. I can arrange copies of the irregular octagon to form a pattern with no gaps or overlaps. This irregular octagon tessellates.

2. 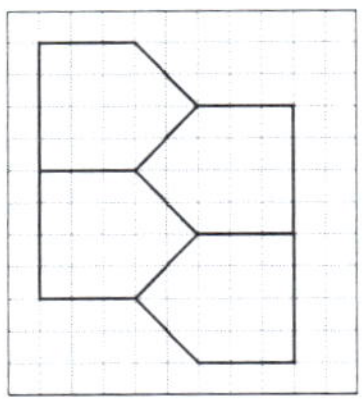

I can make 1 unique tiling pattern with this pentagon.

I used reflections in a vertical line and translations.

Numbers Every Day

Students should recognize the word "and" separates the whole number part of the number from the decimal part.

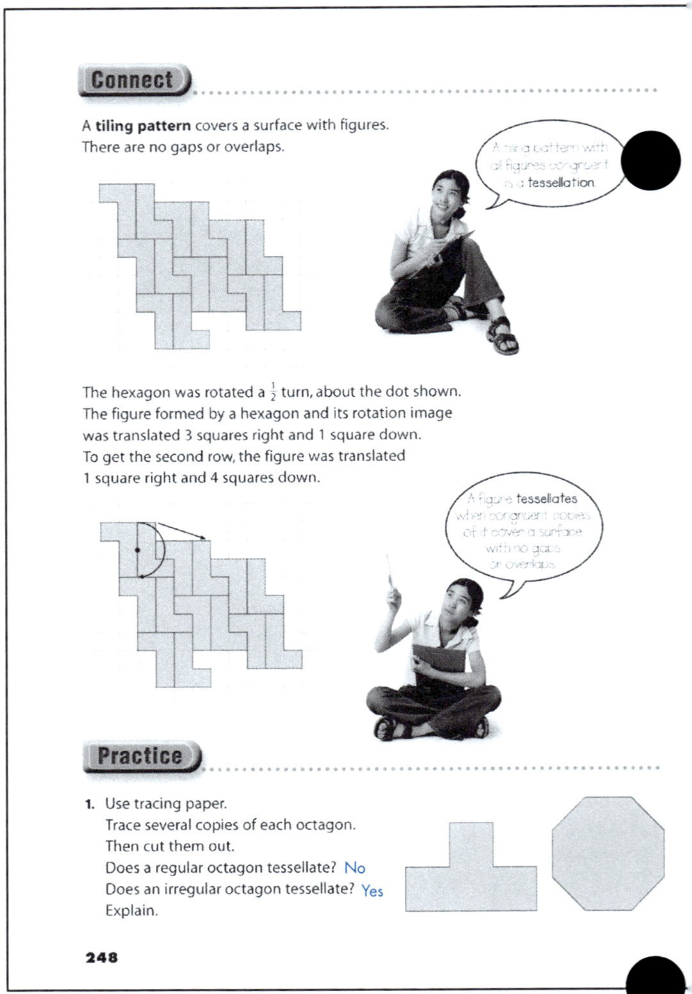

Connect

A **tiling pattern** covers a surface with figures.
There are no gaps or overlaps.

A tiling pattern with all figures congruent is a **tessellation**.

The hexagon was rotated a $\frac{1}{2}$ turn, about the dot shown.
The figure formed by a hexagon and its rotation image was translated 3 squares right and 1 square down.
To get the second row, the figure was translated 1 square right and 4 squares down.

A figure **tessellates** when congruent copies of it cover a surface with no gaps or overlaps.

Practice

1. Use tracing paper.
Trace several copies of each octagon.
Then cut them out.
Does a regular octagon tessellate? No
Does an irregular octagon tessellate? Yes
Explain.

248

- How did you use the quadrilaterals in one group to create an area pattern with no gaps or overlaps?
(For group B, I reflected some of the trapezoids vertically, then I alternated a trapezoid with a reflected trapezoid.)

AFTER — Connect

Invite students to display the patterns they created. Ask student volunteers to describe the transformations they used to create their patterns.

Discuss the example in *Connect*. Ask:

- How is a tiling pattern the same as an area pattern? How is it different?
(A tiling pattern is one kind of area pattern. Both tiling patterns and area patterns cover a surface with figures. A tiling pattern is an area pattern with no gaps or overlaps.)

- Is the hexagon on page 248 a regular hexagon? How do you know?
(No, a regular hexagon has all 6 sides equal and all 6 angles equal. This polygon has 6 sides, but they do not all have equal length.)

Practice

Questions 1 and 5 require tracing paper. Questions 2, 3, and 4 require grid paper. Students will need congruent squares for question 3.

Assessment Focus: Question 3

Students should recognize that two arrangements of squares may represent the same tetromino with different orientation.

2. Copy this pentagon on grid paper.
How many different tiling patterns can you make using this pentagon?
Describe the transformations you could use to make each pattern.

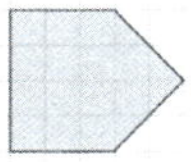

3. You will need grid paper and 4 congruent squares.
A tetromino is made with 4 congruent squares.
Each square must align with at least one other square along one edge.

This is a tetromino. This is not a tetromino.

a) How many different tetrominoes can you find?
Record each tetromino on grid paper.

b) Select one of your tetrominoes.
Does it tessellate? Explain.

4. Use grid paper.
Draw a figure.
Transform the figure to create a tiling pattern.
Describe the transformations you used.

5. Create a pentagon you think will tessellate.
Trace several copies of the figure.
Then cut them out.
Does the figure tessellate?
Tell why or why not.

Reflect

How can you use transformations to describe a tessellation?
Use pictures and words to explain.

Numbers Every Day

Number Strategies

Write each number as a decimal.

- thirty and fifty-three hundredths 30.53
- thirty-five and three-tenths 35.3
- twenty-two hundredths 0.22
- twenty and two-hundredths 20.02
- twenty-two and two-tenths 22.2

ASSESSMENT FOCUS | Question 3 249

3. a) There are 5 different tetrominoes.

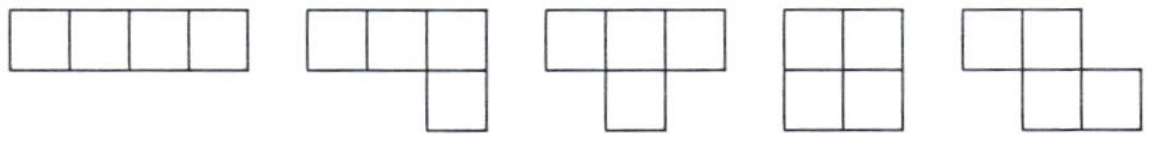

b) Each tetromino tessellates, because in each case congruent copies of it cover a surface with no gaps or overlaps. For example:

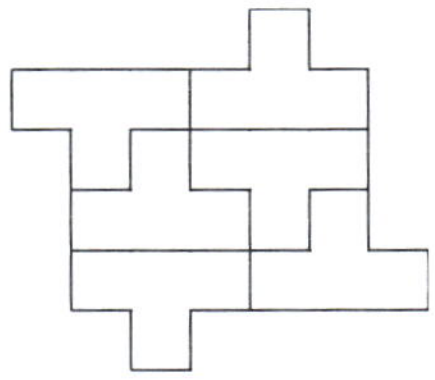

4.

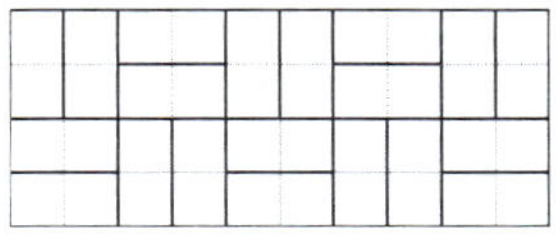

I used translations and rotations to create this tiling pattern.

5.

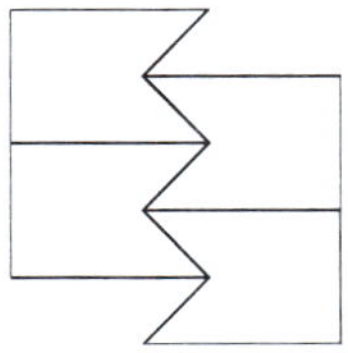

This irregular pentagon tessellates, because congruent copies of this pentagon can be arranged to cover a surface with no gaps or overlaps.

REFLECT: A tessellation can be thought of as a pattern created by images of figure after a variety of transformations. A single figure in the pattern can be identified, then the other figures can be described as images of the identified figure after transformations.

Making Connections

Language: Discuss the prefix on the stem "omino."
Ask for the name of 2 squares joined together (*domino*), 3 (*triomino*), 4 (*tetromino*), 5 (*pentomino*), 6 (*hexomino*).

ASSESSMENT FOR LEARNING

What to Look For	What to Do
Understanding concepts ✔ Students understand a tiling pattern is an area pattern with no gaps or overlaps between the figures.	***Extra Support:*** Students can use Step-by-Step 6 (Master 7.18) to complete question 3.
Applying procedures ✔ Students can create tessellations using a variety of figures.	***Extra Practice:*** Students can complete Extra Practice 3 (Master 7.23).
	Extension: Challenge students to discover which regular polygons tessellate and which do not.

Recording and Reporting
Master 7.2 Ongoing Observations: Transformational Geometry

LESSON ORGANIZER 40–50 min

Student Materials
- grid paper (PM 23)
- dot paper (PM 25)
- triangular grid paper (PM 27)
- Pattern Blocks (PM 28)
- tangrams (PM 29)
- figures (Master 7.9)

Assessment:
Master 7.1 Unit Rubric: Transformational Geometry
Master 7.4 Unit Summary: Transformational Geometry

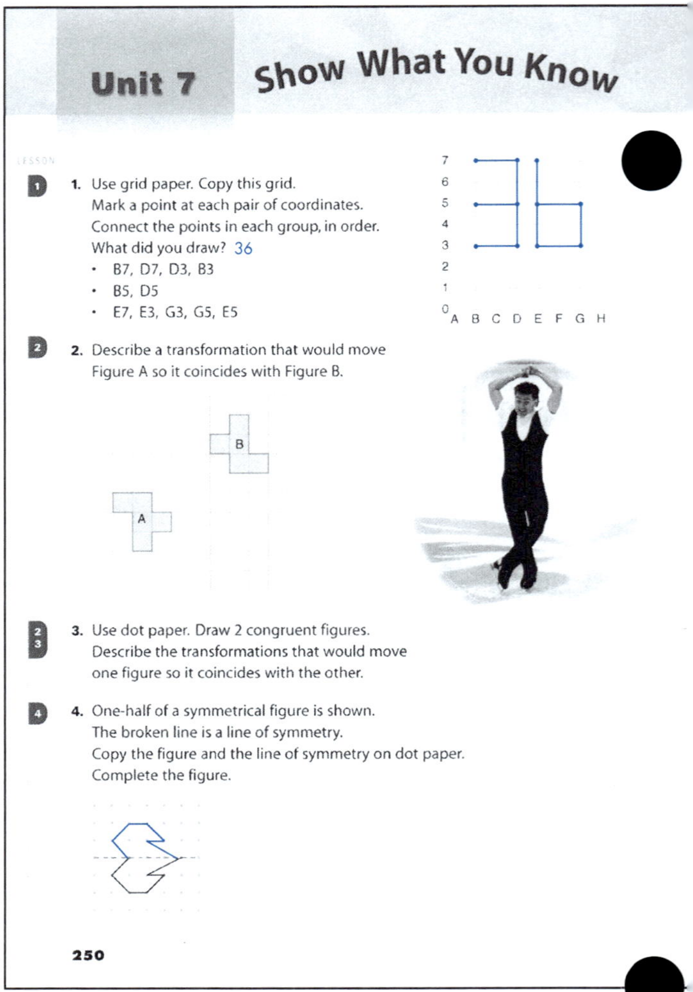

Unit 7 Show What You Know

1. Use grid paper. Copy this grid.
Mark a point at each pair of coordinates.
Connect the points in each group, in order.
What did you draw? 36
- B7, D7, D3, B3
- B5, D5
- E7, E3, G3, G5, E5

2. Describe a transformation that would move Figure A so it coincides with Figure B.

3. Use dot paper. Draw 2 congruent figures.
Describe the transformations that would move one figure so it coincides with the other.

4. One-half of a symmetrical figure is shown.
The broken line is a line of symmetry.
Copy the figure and the line of symmetry on dot paper.
Complete the figure.

250

Sample Answers

2. A $\frac{1}{2}$ turn rotation would move Figure A so it coincides with Figure B.

3. 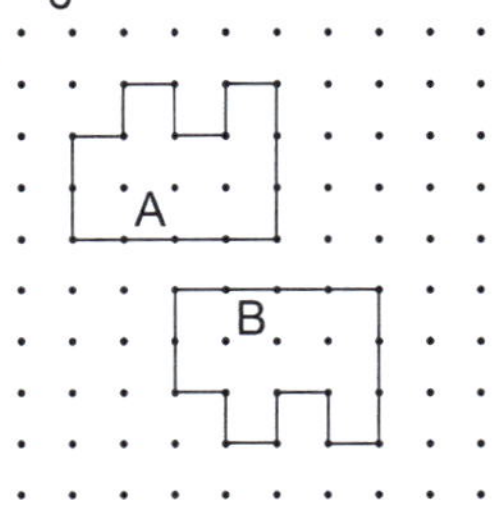

A translation of 2 spaces right followed by a reflection in a horizontal line moves Figure A so it coincides with Figure B.

5. a) Figures A, B, C, and D are congruent.
They all have the same size and shape.

b) 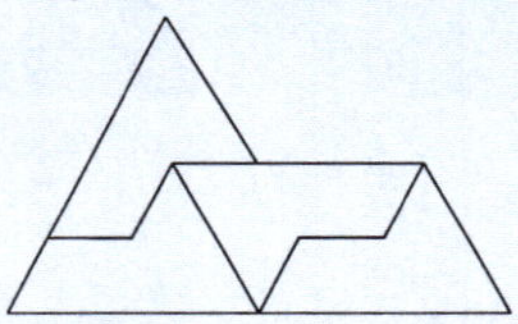

6. In a tangram set, the 2 small triangles are congruent and the 2 large triangles are congruent. Each pair of triangles has the same size and shape. They fit perfectly on top of each other.

7. I chose Figure A as the original figure.
The shortest side of Figure A is 1 unit.
Figure B is the image of Figure A after a $\frac{1}{4}$ turn counterclockwise about the vertex they have in common.
Figure C is the image of Figure A after a translation of 1 unit left and 1 unit down.
Figure D is the image of Figure A after a $\frac{1}{4}$ turn counterclockwise about the vertex they have in common.
Figure E is the image of Figure A after a $\frac{1}{4}$ turn counterclockwise about the midpoint of the right side of Figure D.
Figure F is the image of Figure A after a translation of 4 units down.
Figure G is the image of Figure A after a translation of 1 unit right and 3 units down.
Figure H is the image of Figure A after a $\frac{1}{4}$ turn counterclockwise about the top right vertex of Figure P.
Figure I is the image of Figure A after a $\frac{1}{4}$ turn counterclockwise about the midpoint of the top side of Figure N.
Figure J is the image of Figure A after a translation of 4 units right and 4 units down.
Figure K is the image of Figure A after a translation of 5 units right and 3 units down.
Figure L is the image of Figure A after a $\frac{1}{4}$ turn counterclockwise about a point that is 1 unit to the right of the top right vertex of Figure B.
Figure M is the image of Figure A after a $\frac{1}{4}$ turn counterclockwise about a point that is 1 unit right and 2 units up from the top right vertex of Figure B.
Figure N is the image of Figure A after a translation of 3 units right and 1 unit down.
Figure P is the image of Figure A after a translation of 2 units right and 2 units down.

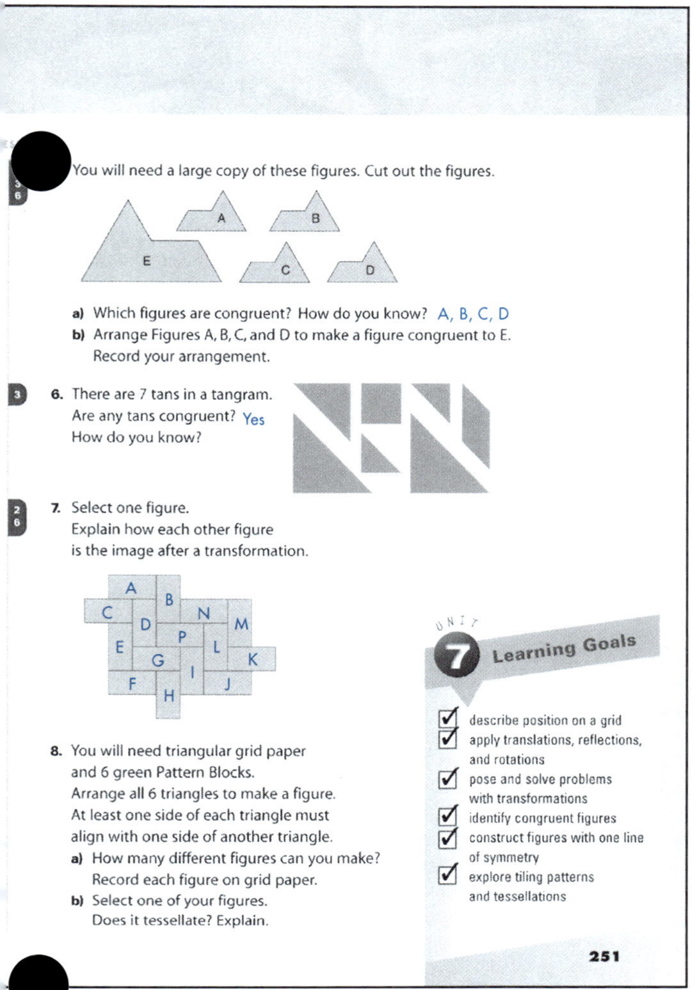

You will need a large copy of these figures. Cut out the figures.

a) Which figures are congruent? How do you know? A, B, C, D
b) Arrange Figures A, B, C, and D to make a figure congruent to E. Record your arrangement.

6. There are 7 tans in a tangram. Are any tans congruent? Yes How do you know?

7. Select one figure. Explain how each other figure is the image after a transformation.

8. You will need triangular grid paper and 6 green Pattern Blocks. Arrange all 6 triangles to make a figure. At least one side of each triangle must align with one side of another triangle.
a) How many different figures can you make? Record each figure on grid paper.
b) Select one of your figures. Does it tessellate? Explain.

UNIT 7 Learning Goals

- ✓ describe position on a grid
- ✓ apply translations, reflections, and rotations
- ✓ pose and solve problems with transformations
- ✓ identify congruent figures
- ✓ construct figures with one line of symmetry
- ✓ explore tiling patterns and tessellations

251

8. a) I can make 12 different figures.

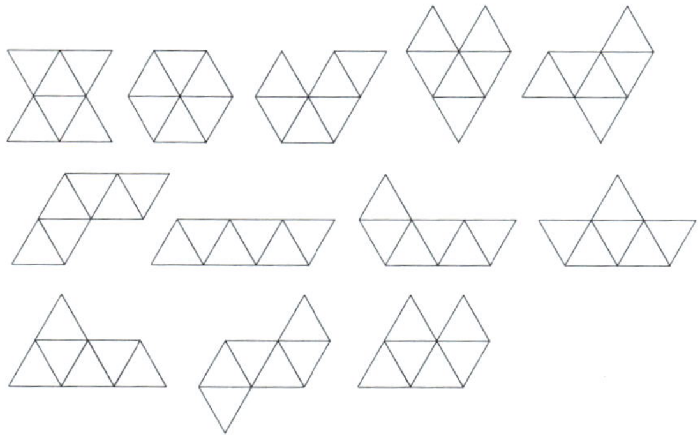

b) I chose the figure that looks like a butterfly. This figure covers a surface with no gaps or overlaps. It does tessellate.

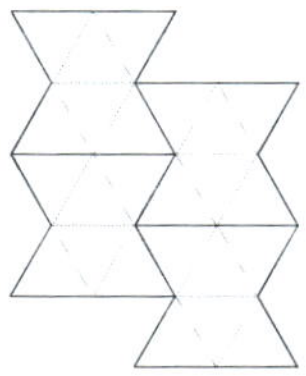

ASSESSMENT FOR LEARNING

What to Look For

Understanding of concepts

✔ **Questions 1, 2, 5, 6, and 7:** Student understands a grid coordinate system, recognizes transformations, and demonstrates an understanding of congruency.

Application of mathematical procedures

✔ **Question 3:** Student can identify congruent figures and apply a transformation to these figures.

✔ **Question 4:** Student can construct two-dimensional figures with one line of symmetry.

Problem solving

✔ **Question 8:** Student can create and explain a tiling pattern and use an appropriate problem-solving strategy to find more than one solution.

Recording and Reporting

Master 7.1 Unit Rubric: Transformational Geometry
Master 7.4 Unit Summary: Transformational Geometry

Geometry in Art

LESSON ORGANIZER 40–50 min

Student Grouping: individual

Student Materials

- Bristol board
- coloured paper
- 10-cm squares cut from 1-cm grid paper
- scissors

Assessment:

Master 7.3 Performance Assessment Rubric: Geometry in Art

Master 7.4 Unit Summary: Transformational Geometry

Unit Problem

Geometry in Art

You will need:

- Bristol board
- coloured paper
- a 10-cm square cut from 1-cm grid paper
- scissors

Part 1

Make a pattern for a tile that tessellates.

- Draw a figure on the grid paper square.
  One side of the figure must coincide with one side of the square.

252

Teaching notes for the Cross Strand Investigation, *Rep-Tiles*, are in the Additional Assessment Support module.

Have students turn to the *Unit Launch* on pages 226 and 227 of the Student Book.

Review the Learning Goals of the unit and discuss the meanings of the Key Words. Tell students they will use these skills and concepts as they complete the *Unit Problem.*

Distribute the materials.

Present the *Unit Problem.* Invite volunteers to read the guidelines and instructions for the problem aloud. Ensure students understand what they are expected to do.

Have one student read the Check List aloud. Remind students that they should use the Check List to assess their work before handing it in. You may also wish to provide students with copies of Master 7.3 Performance Assessment Rubric: Geometry in Art so they will know how their work will be assessed.

For Part 1, ensure students understand that one edge of the figure they draw must lie along one side of the square. After the figure is cut out, the piece must slide directly across the square and be aligned with the opposite side of the square. Some students may wish to experiment with rotations and reflections of the figures that are cut from the square. Encourage students to explore in this way and use their imagination to design their very own "Escher-like" tessellation.

Create a hall or display case presentation of completed designs.

- Cut out the figure.
- Slide the figure across the square and tape it to the opposite side. The edges must line up with no gaps or overlaps.
- Continue to cut figures and tape them to the opposite side until your pattern is the way you want it.

Check List

Your work should show
- ☑ a pattern for a tile that tessellates
- ☑ a tesselation of coloured tiles on Bristol board
- ☑ a description of whether or not your tessellation has line symmetry
- ☑ an explanation of how you could use transformations to make the tessellation

Part 2

Make a tessellation.
- Use your pattern to cut tiles from coloured paper.
- Glue the tiles onto Bristol board.

Part 3

Write about your tessellation.
- Does your tessellation have line symmetry? How do you know?
- How could you use transformations to make the tessellation? Describe as many ways as you can find.

Reflect on the Unit

What do you know about transformations and congruent figures?
Use pictures and words to explain.

253

Sample Answers

Part 1:

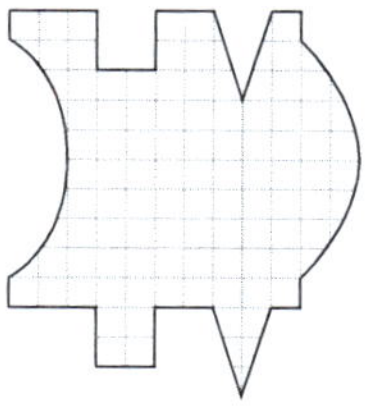

Part 2:

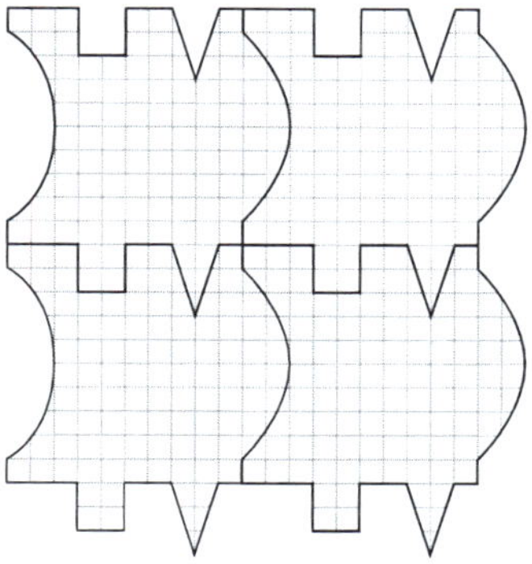

Part 3: My tessellation does not have line symmetry. There is no place I could fold the pattern so that the two parts would coincide. I used translations to make the tile pattern and to make the tessellation.

Reflect on the Unit

The image of a figure after a transformation is congruent to the figure. Transformations include reflections (flips), translations (slides), and rotations (turns). More than one transformation can be applied to a figure. The images of a figure after a variety of transformations can be used to create a tiling pattern.

ASSESSMENT FOR LEARNING

What to Look For	What to Do
Understanding concepts ✔ Students understand how to create a tiling pattern. ***Applying procedures*** ✔ Students design a tessellation with congruent figures without any gaps or overlaps. ***Communicating*** ✔ Students use appropriate language to describe their tessellation.	***Extra Support:*** Make the problem accessible. Have materials, such as tangram pieces, available for students to trace as a beginning for their design. Students having difficulty with Part 3 may benefit from making a list of vocabulary they can use to describe their tessellation.

Recording and Reporting

Master 7.3 Performance Assessment Rubric: Geometry in Art
Master 7.4 Unit Summary: Transformational Geometry

Evaluating Student Learning: Preparing to Report: Unit 7 Transformational Geometry

This unit provides an opportunity to report on the **Geometry and Spatial Sense** strand. *Master 7.4 Unit Summary: Transformational* provides a comprehensive format for recording and summarizing evidence collected.

Here is an example of a completed summary chart for this Unit:

Strand: *Geometry and Spatial Sense*	**Problem solving**	**Understanding of concepts**	**Application of mathematical procedures**	**Communication**	***Overall***
Ongoing Observations	3	4	2	4	3
Strategies Toolkit (Lesson 5)	3		3		3
Work samples or portfolios; conferences	3	3	3	4	3
Show What You Know	3	3	3	3	3
Unit Test	3	4	3	3	3
Unit Problem *Geometry in Art*	3	3	3	3	3
Achievement Level for reporting					3

Recording	How to Report
Ongoing Observations	Use *Master 7.2 Ongoing Observations: Transformational Geometry* to determine the most consistent level achieved in each category. Enter it in the chart. Choose to summarize by achievement category, or simply to enter an overall level. Observations from late in the Unit should be most heavily weighted.
Strategies Toolkit (problem solving)	Use *PM 1: Inquiry Process Check List* with the Strategies Toolkit (Lesson 5). Transfer results to the summary form. Teachers may choose to enter a level in the Problem solving column and/or Communication.
Portfolios or collections of work samples; conferences, or interviews	Use *Master 7.1 Unit Rubric: Transformational Geometry* to guide evaluation of collections of work and information gathered in conferences. Teachers may choose to focus particular attention on the *Assessment Focus* questions. Work from late in the unit should be most heavily weighted.
Show What You Know	Teachers may choose to assign some or all of these questions. *Master 7.1 Unit Rubric: Transformational Geometry* may be helpful in determining levels of achievement. #1, 2, 5, 6, and 7 provide evidence of Understanding of concepts; #3 and 4 provide evidence of Application of mathematical procedures; #8 provides evidence of Problem solving; all questions provide evidence of Communication
Unit Test	*Master 7.1 Unit Rubric: Transformational Geometry* may be helpful in determining levels of achievement. Part A provides evidence of Application of mathematical procedures; Part B provides evidence of Understanding of concepts; Part C provides evidence of Problem solving; all parts provide evidence of Communication.
Unit performance task	Use *Master 7.3 Performance Assessment Rubric: Geometry in Art*. The *Unit Problem* offers a snapshot of students' achievement. In particular, it shows their ability to synthesize and apply what they have learned.
Student Self-Assessment	Note students' perceptions of their own progress. This may take the form of an oral or written comment, or a self-rating.
Comments	Analyse the pattern of achievement to identify strengths and needs. In some cases, specific actions may be planned to support the learner.

Learning Skills	Ongoing Records
PM 4: Learning Skills Check List Use to record and report throughout a reporting period, rather than for each unit and/or strand.	*PM 10: Summary Class Records: Strands* *PM 11: Summary Class Records: Achievement Categories* *PM 12: Summary Record: Individual* Use to record and report evaluations of student achievement over several clusters, a reporting period, or a school year. These can also be used in place of the Unit Summary.

Name ____________________ Date ________________

Master 7.1

Unit Rubric: Transformational Geometry

	Level 1	Level 2	Level 3	Level 4
Problem solving • chooses and carries out appropriate strategies to identify and apply translations, rotations, and reflections to pose and solve problems	with assistance, chooses and carries out a limited range of appropriate strategies to pose and solve problems with transformations, rarely resulting in an accurate solution	with limited assistance, chooses and carries out some appropriate strategies to pose and solve problems with transformations, frequently resulting in an accurate solution	chooses and carries out appropriate strategies to pose and solve problems with transformations, usually resulting in an accurate solution	chooses and carries out appropriate strategies to accurately pose and solve problems with transformations; may be innovative
Understanding of concepts • shows understanding of concepts by explaining: – translations, reflections, and rotations – tiling patterns and tessellations	may be unable to apply/create or explain: – translations, reflections, and rotations – tiling patterns and tessellations	partially able to apply/create and explain: – translations, reflections, and rotations – tiling patterns and tessellations	appropriately applies/creates and explains: – translations, reflections, and rotations – tiling patterns and tessellations	in various contexts, consistently and appropriately applies/creates and explains: – translations, reflections, and rotations – tiling patterns and tessellations
Application of mathematical procedures • uses appropriate procedures to accurately: – describe location on a grid – apply translations, reflections, and rotations – identify congruent figures – construct figures with one line of symmetry	limited accuracy; major errors or omissions in: – describing location on a grid – applying translations, reflections, and rotations – identifying congruent figures – constructing figures with one line of symmetry	somewhat accurate; makes frequent minor errors/omissions in: – describing location on a grid – applying translations, reflections, and rotations – identifying congruent figures – constructing figures with one line of symmetry	generally accurate; makes few errors/omissions in: – describing location on a grid – applying translations, reflections, and rotations – identifying congruent figures – constructing figures with one line of symmetry	accurate; rarely makes errors/omissions in: – describing location on a grid – applying translations, reflections, and rotations – identifying congruent figures – constructing figures with one line of symmetry
Communication • presents work, describes procedures, and explains reasoning clearly, using appropriate mathematical terms	work is often unclear and imprecise; needs assistance to describe procedures and explain reasoning; often unclear and imprecise	work is presented with some clarity and precision; describes procedures and explains reasoning with some clarity, precision, and appropriate terminology	work is generally clear and precise; describes procedures and explains reasoning with general clarity and precision, and with appropriate terminology	work is clear and precise; describes procedures and explains reasoning clearly, precisely, and confidently, using the most appropriate terminology

Name ____________________ Date _______________

Master 7.2

Ongoing Observations: Transformational Geometry

The behaviours described under each heading are examples; they are not intended to be an exhaustive list of all that might be observed. More detailed descriptions are provided in each lesson under *Assessment for Learning.*

STUDENT ACHIEVEMENT: Transformational Geometry				
Student	**Problem solving**	**Understanding of concepts**	**Application of mathematical procedures**	**Communication**
	▪ Uses appropriate strategies to pose and solve problems with transformations	▪ Explains transformations, tiling patterns, and tessellations	▪ Describes location on a grid ▪ Applies transformations ▪ Identifies congruent figures ▪ Constructs figures with one line of symmetry	▪ Presents work, procedures, and reasoning clearly ▪ Uses appropraite geometric terminology

Level 1 – very limited; Level 2 – somewhat or limited; Level 3 – satisfactory; Level 4 – thorough

Name ____________________ Date ______________

Master 7.3

Performance Assessment Rubric: Geometry in Art

	Level 1	Level 2	Level 3	Level 4
Problem solving • chooses and carries out appropriate strategies to create a pattern for a tile that tessellates	chooses and carries out simple or inappropriate strategies; tile does not tessellate	chooses and carries out some appropriate strategies with partial success to create a tile that tessellates	chooses and carries out appropriate and effective strategies to create a tile that tessellates	chooses innovative, appropriate, and effective strategies to create a tile that tessellates
Understanding of concepts • shows understanding by explaining and describing: – whether or not the tessellation has line symmetry – ways to use transformations to create the tessellation	shows very limited understanding by giving inappropriate explanations and descriptions involving: – line symmetry – using transformations to create tessellations	shows limited understanding, giving appropriate but incomplete explanations and descriptions involving: – line symmetry – using transformations to create tessellations	shows understanding by giving appropriate explanations and descriptions involving: – line symmetry – using transformations to create tessellations	shows thorough understanding by giving appropriate and complete explanations and descriptions involving: – line symmetry – using transformations to create tessellations
Application of mathematical procedures • uses appropriate procedures to create a tessellation	limited accuracy; major errors or omissions in creating a tessellation	somewhat accurate; several minor errors or omissions in creating a tessellation	generally accurate; few errors or omissions in creating a tessellation	accurate; very few or no errors or omissions in creating a tessellation
Communication • provides clear explanations and descriptions • uses mathematical terminology	explanations and descriptions are unclear and imprecise; uses few appropriate mathematical terms	explanations and descriptions are partially clear and precise; uses some appropriate mathematical terms	explanations and descriptions are generally clear and precise; uses appropriate mathematical terms	explanations and descriptions are clear, precise, and confident; uses the most appropriate mathematical terms

Name ____________________ Date ________________

Master 7.4

Unit Summary: Transformational Geometry

Review assessment records to determine the most consistent achievement levels for the assessments conducted. Some cells may be blank. *Overall* achievement levels may be recorded in each row, rather than identifying levels for each achievement category.

	Most Consistent Level of Achievement*				
Strand: *Geometry and Spatial Sense*	**Problem solving**	**Understanding of concepts**	**Application of mathematical procedures**	**Communication**	***Overall***
Ongoing Observations					
Strategies Toolkit (Lesson 5)					
Work samples or portfolios; conferences					
Show What You Know					
Unit Test					
Unit Problem: Geometry in Art					
Achievement Level for reporting					

*Use Ontario Achievement Levels 1, 2, 3, 4.

Self-Assessment:

Comments: (Strengths, Needs, Next Steps)

Name ____________________ Date ________________

Master 7.5

To Parents and Adults at Home …

Your child's class is starting a mathematics unit on transformational geometry. Working with transformational geometry helps students develop spatial visualization skills. Many everyday activities, such as map reading, giving directions, and following assembly instructions, rely on these skills.

In this unit, your child will:

- Describe position on a grid.
- Apply translations, reflections, and rotations.
- Pose and solve problems with transformations.
- Identify congruent figures.
- Construct figures with one line of symmetry.
- Explore tiling patterns and tessellations.

As students explore the activities, they will be encouraged to visualize and predict outcomes.

Here are some activities you can do with your child at home:

- Draw a map of your neighbourhood on a grid.
  Identify the coordinates of 3 different locations.
- Play the game *Battleship*.
- Search your home and yard for objects with symmetry.
- Fold and cut paper to make paper snowflakes.
  Look for symmetry and holes with the same size and shape.

Name ____________________ Date ________________

Master 7.6

Figure for Lesson 2 *Explore*

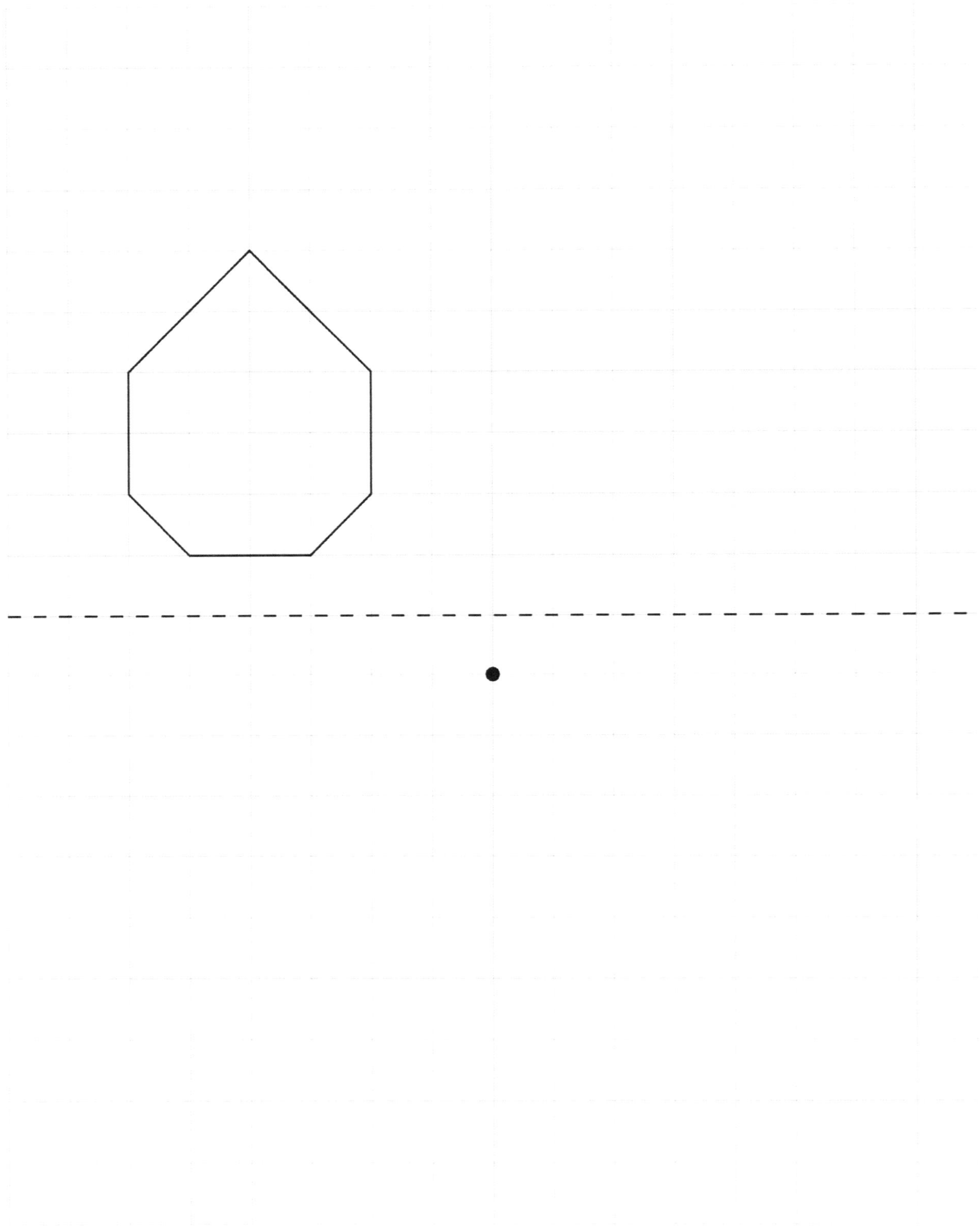

Name ____________________ Date ________________

Master 7.7

Pentominoes

Name ____________________ Date ________________

Master 7.8

Quadrilaterals for Lesson 6 *Explore*

Group A

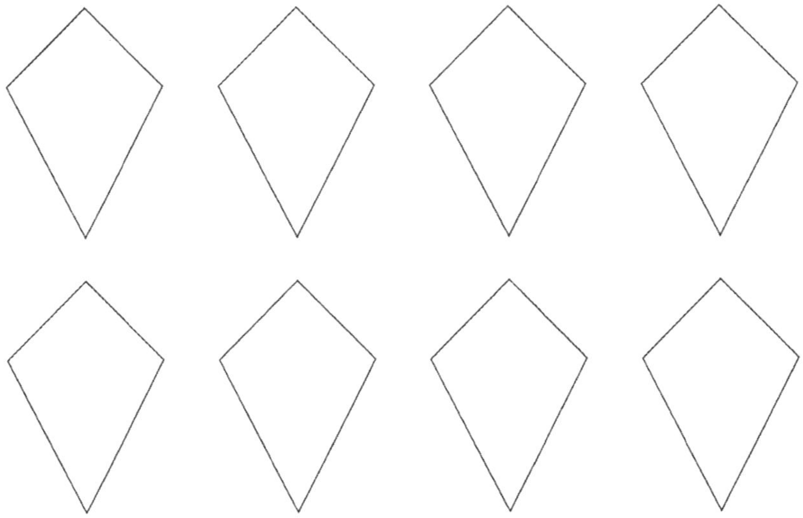

Group B

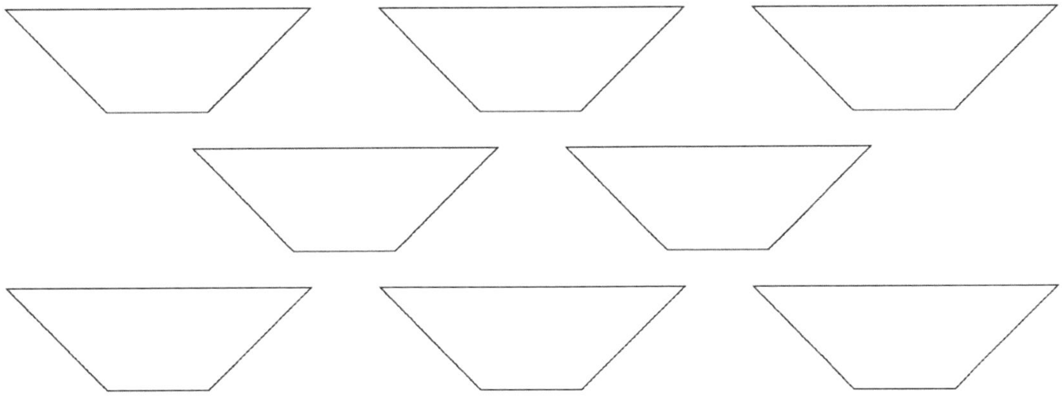

Group C

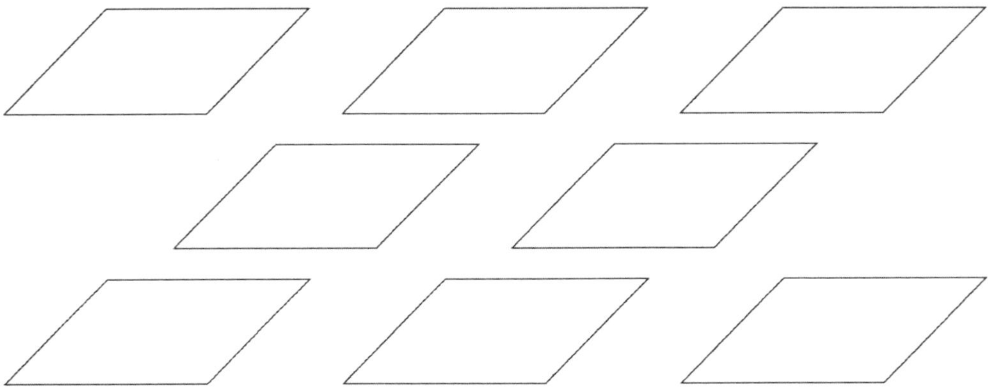

Name ____________________ Date ________________

Master 7.9

Figures for *Show What You Know*

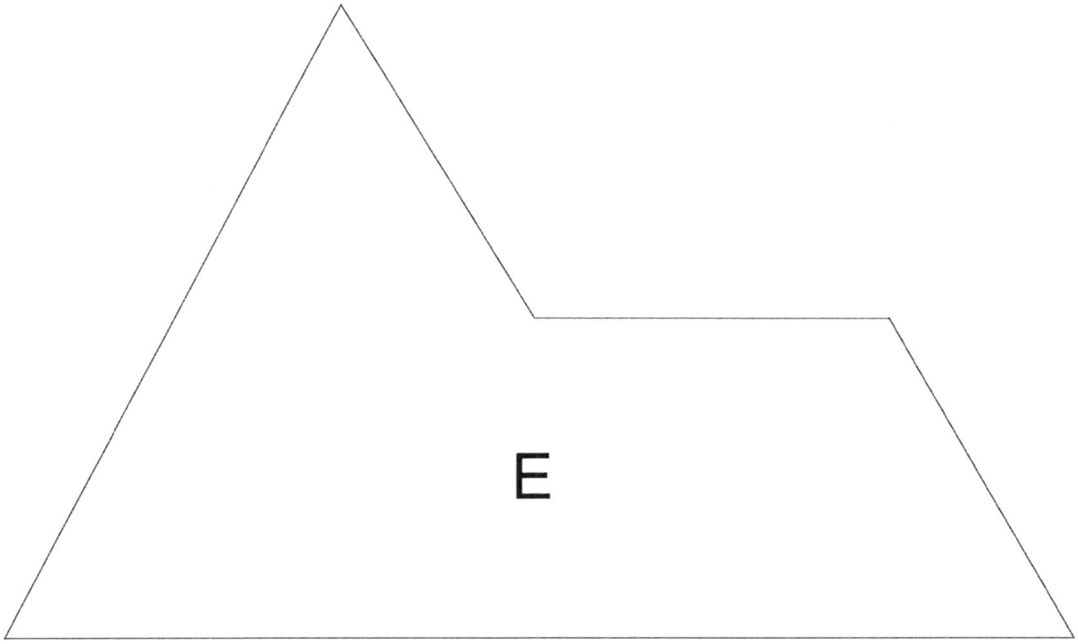

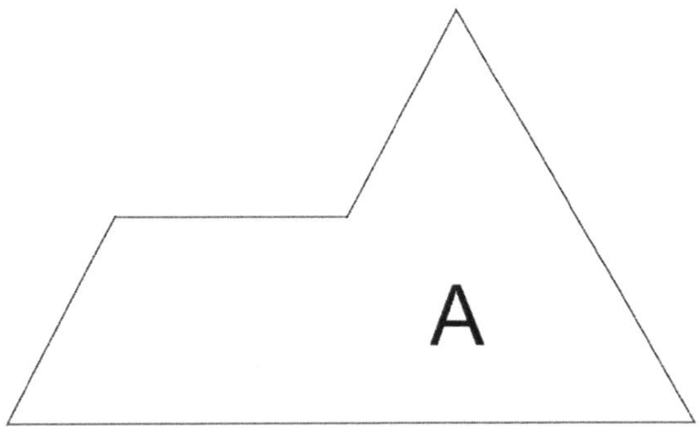

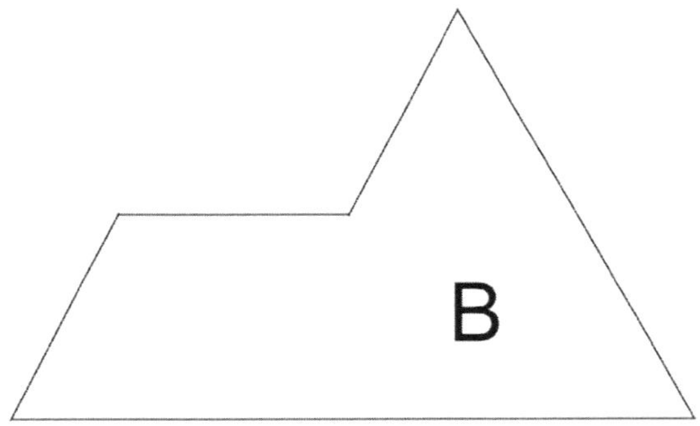

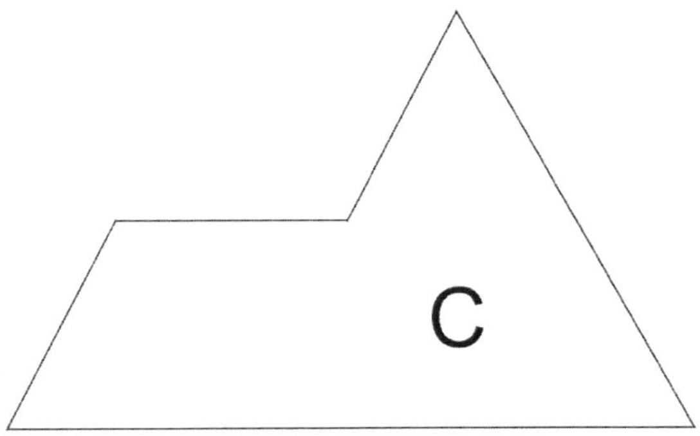

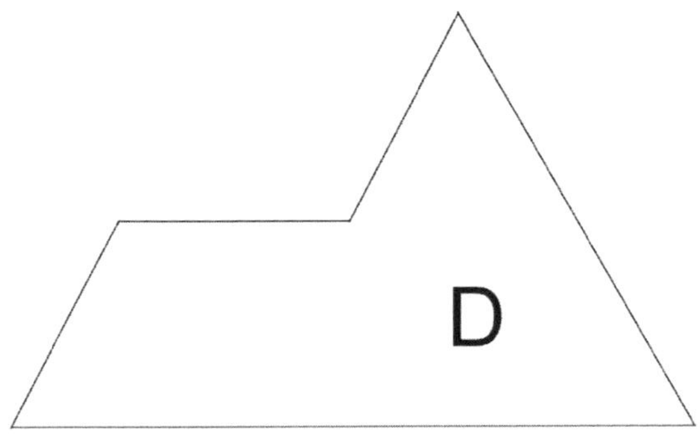

Name ____________ Date ____________

Master 7.10

Additional Activity 1: Hidden Pictures

Work on your own.
You will need grid paper and a ruler.

Mark a point at each pair of coordinates.
Use a ruler to connect the points in the order you draw them.

F7, G7, G5, J5, J4, P4, M1, E1, B4, F4, F7

What is the hidden picture?

Take It Further:
Create your own hidden picture.
Write instructions for your picture.
Trade instructions with a classmate.
Draw your classmate's picture.

Name ____________________ Date ________________

Master 7.11

Additional Activity 2: Transformation Patterns

Work with a partner.
You will need 1-cm grid paper.

Draw the next figure in each pattern.

Pattern A

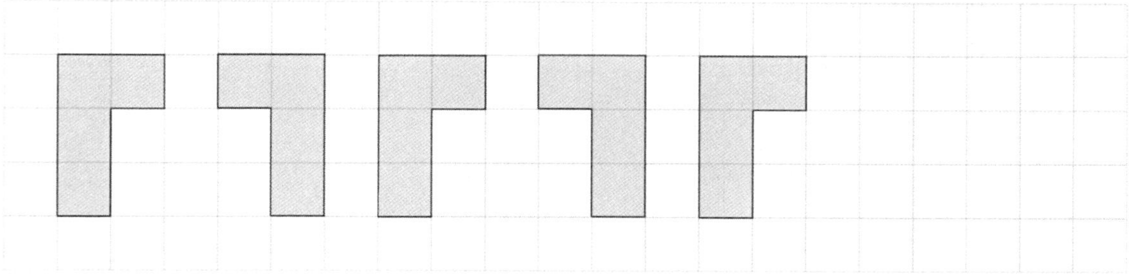

Pattern B

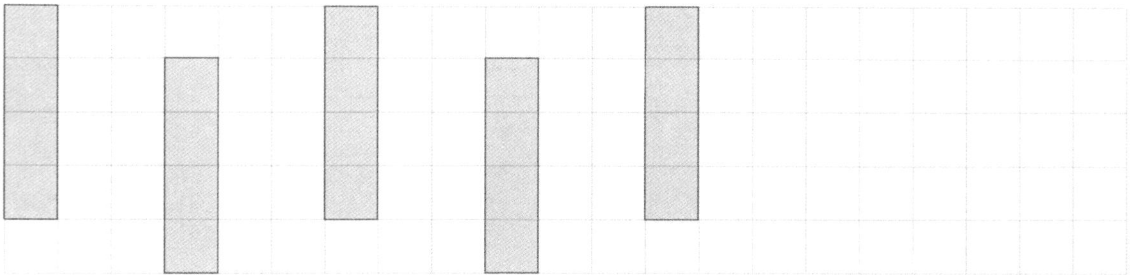

Pattern C

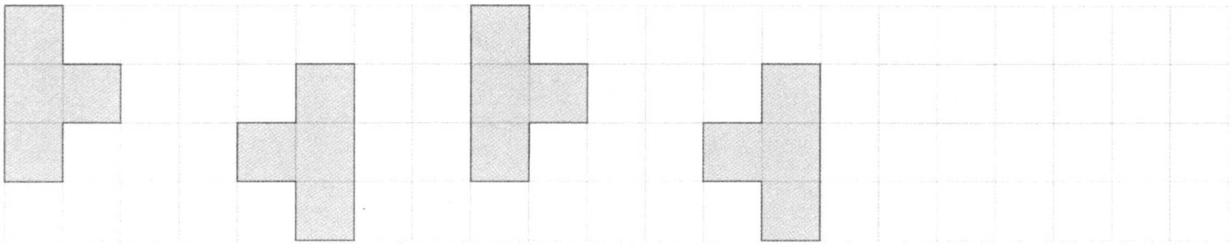

Describe the transformations used in each pattern.

Take It Further:
Create your own pattern using transformations.
Describe the transformations you used to create your pattern.

Name ____________________ Date ______________

Master 7.12

Additional Activity 3: Folding Figures

Work on your own.
You will need scissors.

Draw a broken line on each figure to make two congruent figures.
You may be able to draw more than one line on some figures.
You may not be able to draw any lines on other figures.

Cut out each figure.
Fold each figure along the line or lines you drew to check your work.

Take It Further:
Draw a figure for which you can draw each number
of broken lines: 0, 1, 2

Name ____________________ Date _______________

Master 7.13

Additional Activity 4: Symmetry Patterns

Work with a partner.
You will need grid paper and coloured pencils.

The broken lines are lines of symmetry.
Draw the figure that is shown in the top left section in the other three sections to make a symmetrical pattern.

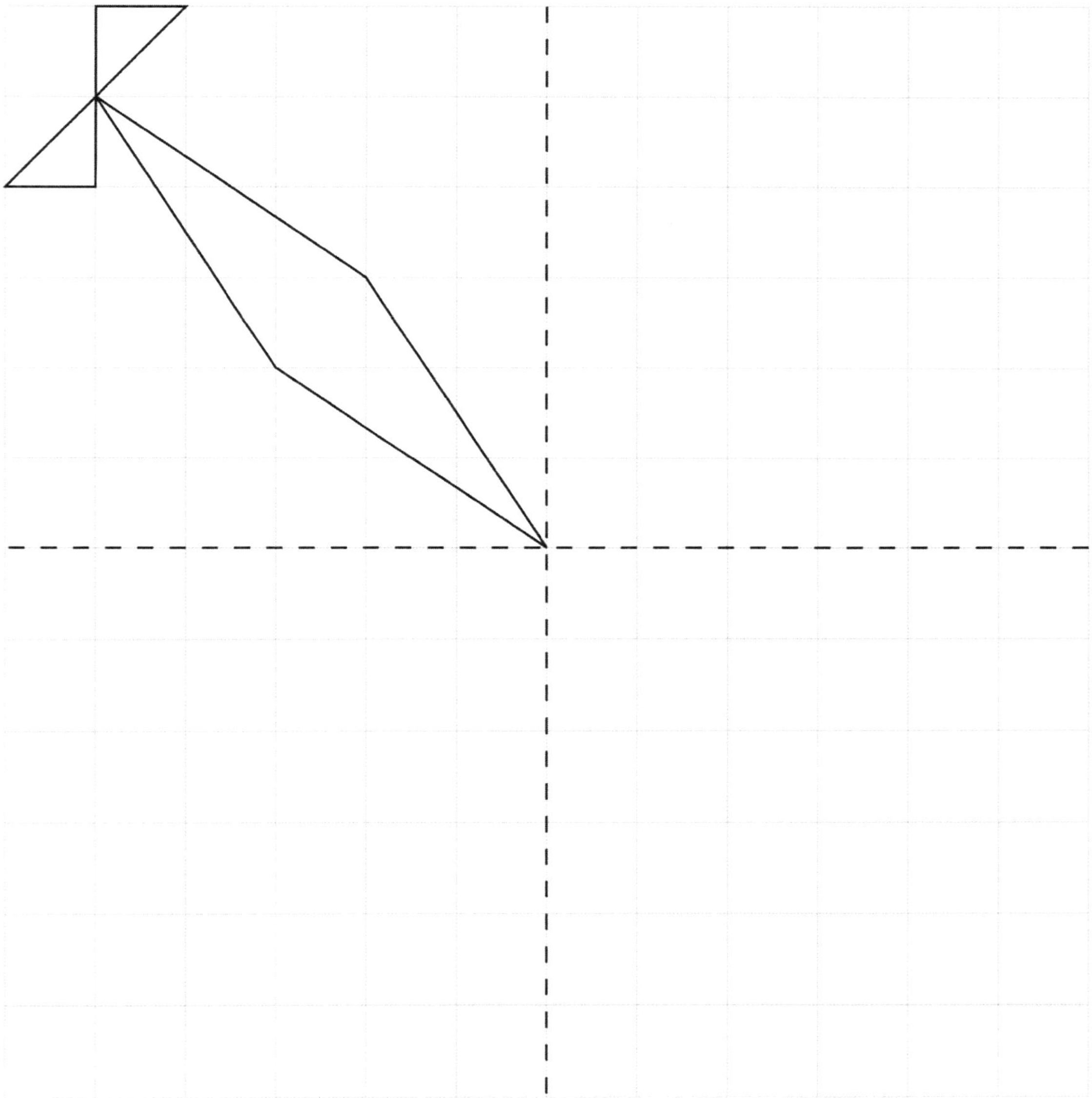

Take It Further: On grid paper, draw a horizontal broken line and a vertical broken line. In the top left section, draw a figure. Draw the figure in the other three sections to make a pattern with two lines of symmetry.

Name ____________________ Date ________________

Master 7.14

Step-by-Step 1

Lesson 1, Question 3

Step 1 Choose any 2-digit number. ______________

Write your number using only line segments.
For example, write the number 23 like this:

Step 2 Draw the number from *Step 1* on the grid below.
Make certain the line segments lie on grid lines.

Step 3 Record the coordinates of the corners of the digits.

____

____

Write instructions to draw your number.

____

____

Name ________________ Date ______________

Master 7.15

Step-by-Step 2

Lesson 2, Question 4

Use tracing paper.

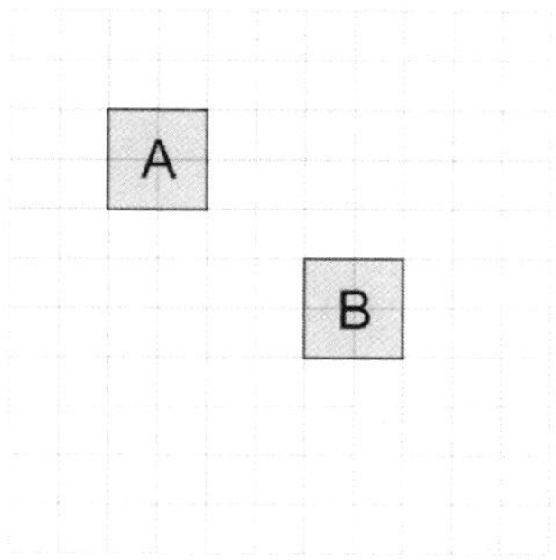

Step 1 Which translation would move Figure A to coincide with Figure B?

____

Step 2 Think of a rotation.
Mark a dot on the picture above to show the turn centre
that would turn Figure A to coincide with Figure B.
What fraction of a turn would Figure A move?

____

Step 3 Above, draw Figure C congruent to Figures A and B.
Describe a transformation that would move
Figure A to coincide with Figure C.

____

Describe a transformation that would move
Figure C to coincide with Figure B.

____

Name ____________________ Date ________________

Master 7.16

Step-by-Step 3

Lesson 3, Question 4

You will need a 5 by 5 geoboard, geobands, and dot paper.

Step 1 Divide the geoboard into 2 congruent parts.
How many different ways can you do this? ______________________
Record each way on dot paper.

Step 2 Use your results from *Step 1*.
Divide the geoboard into 4 congruent parts.
How many different ways can you do this?
Record each way on dot paper.

Step 3 Use your results from *Step 2*.
Divide the geoboard into 8 congruent parts.
How many different ways can you do this? ______________________
Record each way on dot paper.

Name ____________________ Date _______________

Master 7.17

Step-by-Step 4

Lesson 4, Question 5

Step 1 Add a square to this figure so the broken line is a line of symmetry.

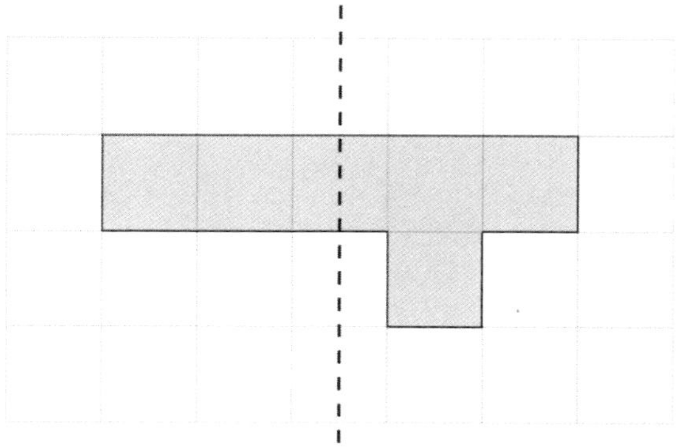

Step 2 Add a square to this figure so the broken line is a line of symmetry.

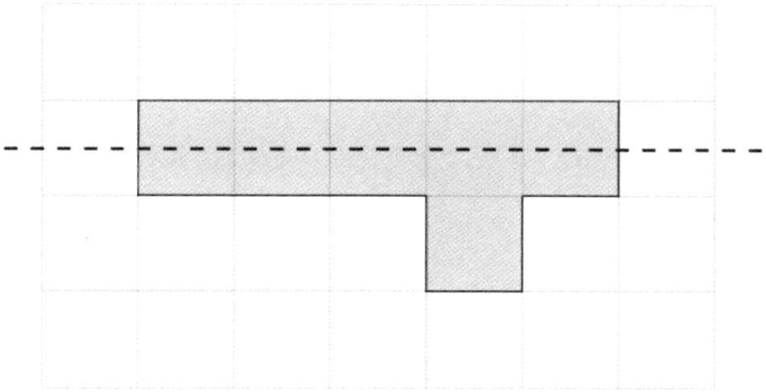

Step 3 Is it possible to add a square to this figure so the broken line is a line of symmetry? How do you know?

____

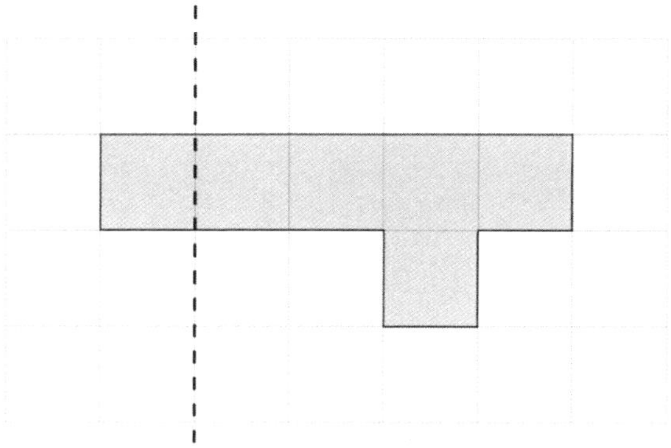

Name ____________________ Date ______________

Master 7.18

Step-by-Step 6

Lesson 6, Question 3

A tetromino is made with 4 congruent squares.

There are 5 different tetrominoes.

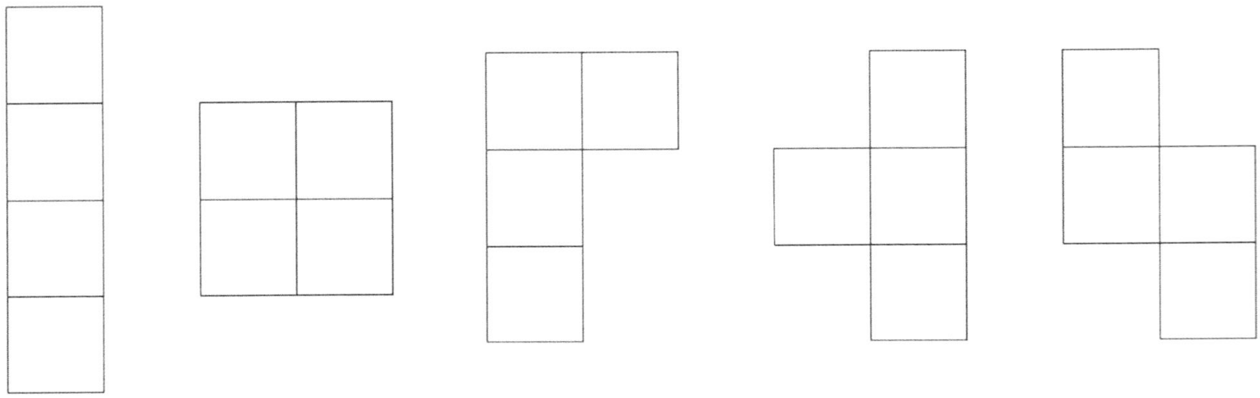

You will need 2-cm grid paper and scissors.

Step 1 Choose one of the tetrominoes.
Draw 8 copies of the tetromino on grid paper.
Use scissors. Cut out the copies.
Try to arrange the tetrominoes in a tiling pattern.

Step 2 Repeat *Step 1* four times.
Each time use a different tetromino.

Name ____________________ Date ________________

Master 7.19a

Unit Test: Unit 7 Transformational Geometry

Part A

1. On the grid, mark a point at each pair of coordinates.
   Connect the points in each group in order.
   B4, F8
   F8, J4
   C5, C1, I1, I5

   What did you draw? ____________________

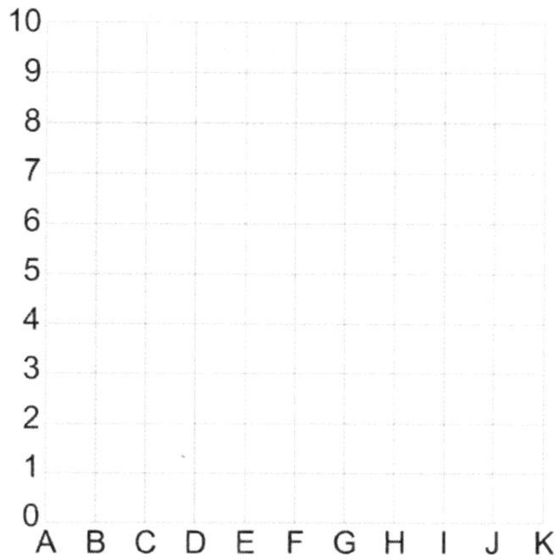

2. Draw the image of Figure A after each transformation.
   Label each image.

   a) A reflection in the broken line
   b) A translation of 5 squares left and 6 squares up
   c) A rotation of a $\frac{1}{2}$ turn clockwise about the dot

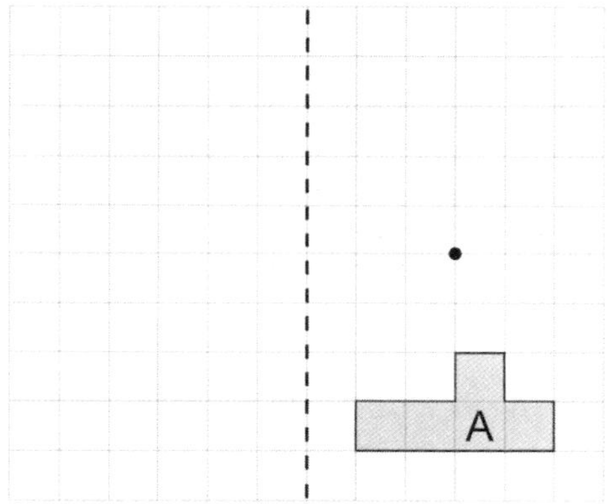

3. One-half of a symmetrical figure is shown.
   The broken line is a line of symmetry.
   Complete the figure.

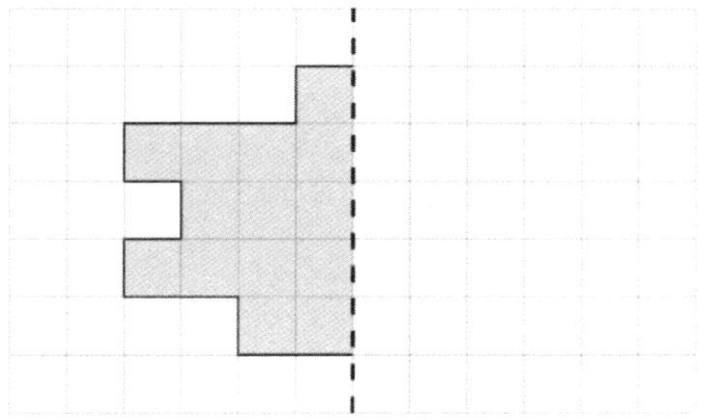

Name ____________________ Date ________________

Master 7.19b **Unit Test continued**

Part B

4. On the grid, draw 2 congruent figures.
Describe the transformations
that would move one figure so
it coincides with the other figure.

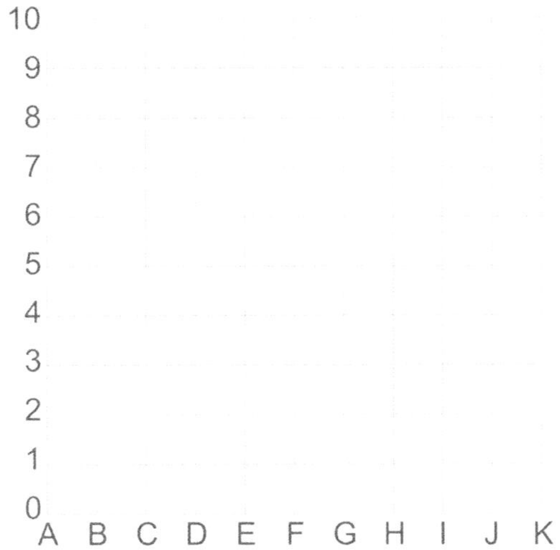

____

____

____

____

5. Draw a second polygon congruent to A. Label it B.
Draw a third polygon that is not congruent
to Polygons A and B. Label it C.
How do you know Polygon C is not congruent to Polygons A and B?

____

Name ____________________ Date ________________

Master 7.19c **Unit Test continued**

6. On the grid, draw a polygon.
Transform the polygon to make a tiling pattern.
Describe the transformations you used.

____

Part C

7. Draw a figure with exactly one line of symmetry.
How do you know your figure has only one line of symmetry?

____

Name ______________ Date ______________

Master 7.20

Unit Test Sample Answers

Unit Test – Master 7.19

Part A

1. House

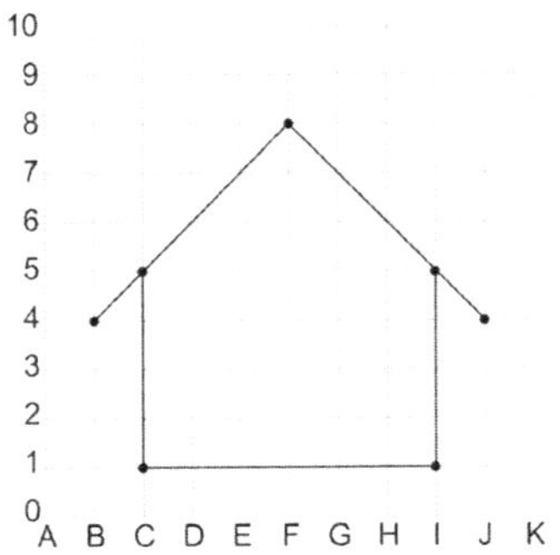

2.

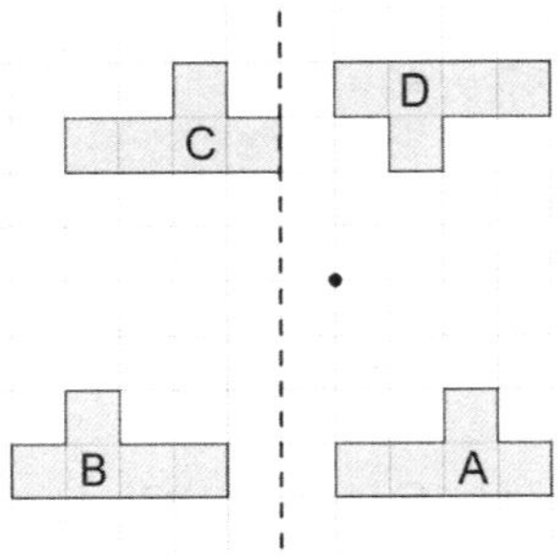

3.

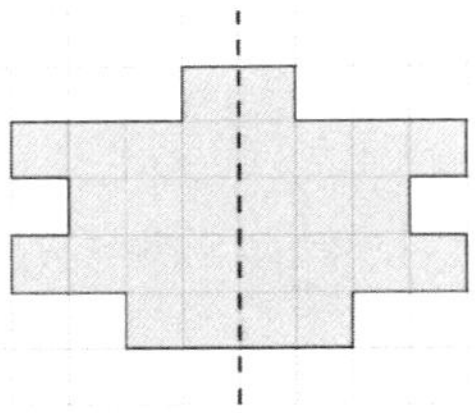

Part B

4.

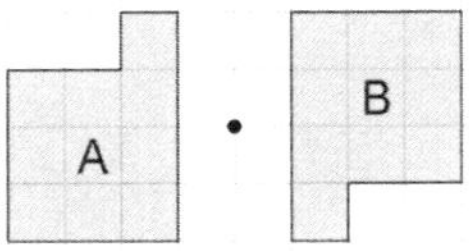

A rotation of a $\frac{1}{2}$ turn about the dot

5.

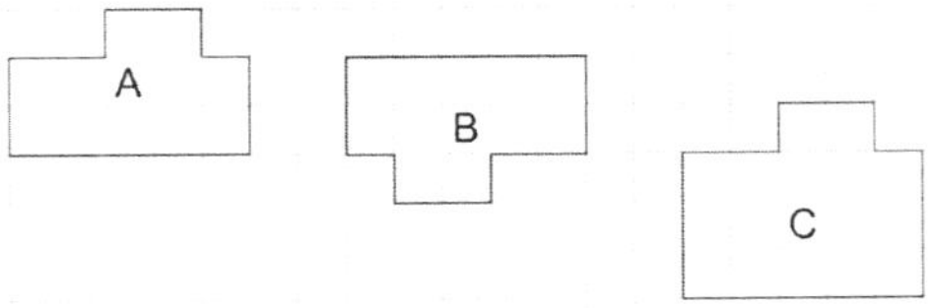

Polygons A and B have the same size and the same shape; they are congruent. Polygon C has greater height than Polygons A and B; it is not congruent to the other two polygons.

6.

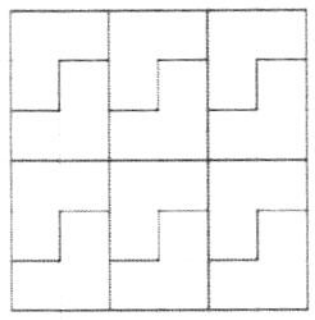

First I drew an L-shaped polygon. I rotated it a $\frac{1}{2}$ turn. The polygon and its rotation image form a rectangle. I translated the rectangle 2 squares right, then 3 squares down.

Part C

7.

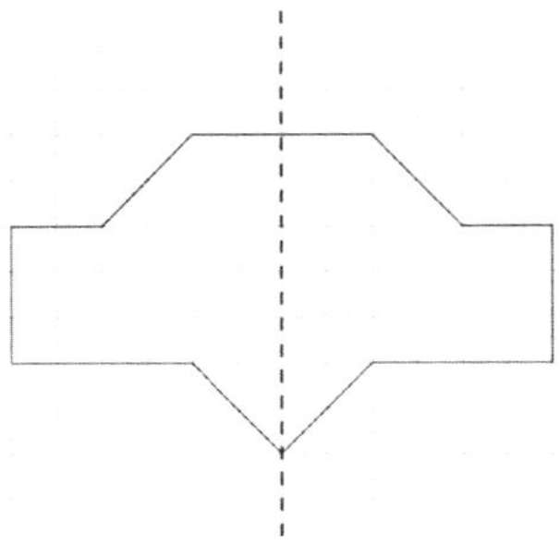

There is only one way I can fold the figure so the edges align, so it has only one line of symmetry.

Extra Practice Masters 7.21–7.24

Go to the CD-ROM to access editable versions of these Extra Practice Masters.

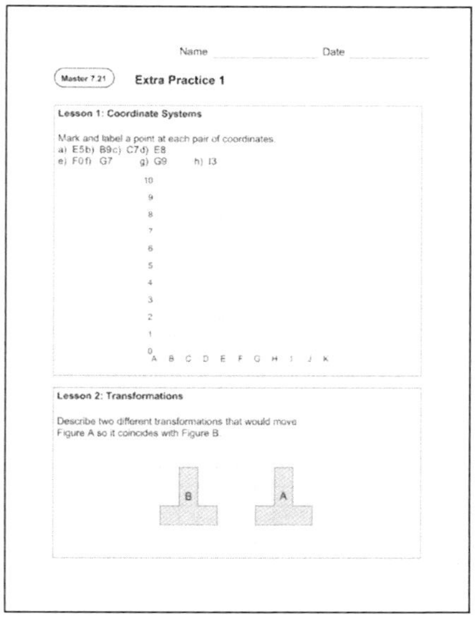

Name Date

Master 7.21 **Extra Practice 1**

Lesson 1: Coordinate Systems

Mark and label a point at each pair of coordinates.
a) E5b) B9c) C7d) E8
e) F0f) G7 g) G9 h) I3

Lesson 2: Transformations

Describe two different transformations that would move Figure A so it coincides with Figure B.

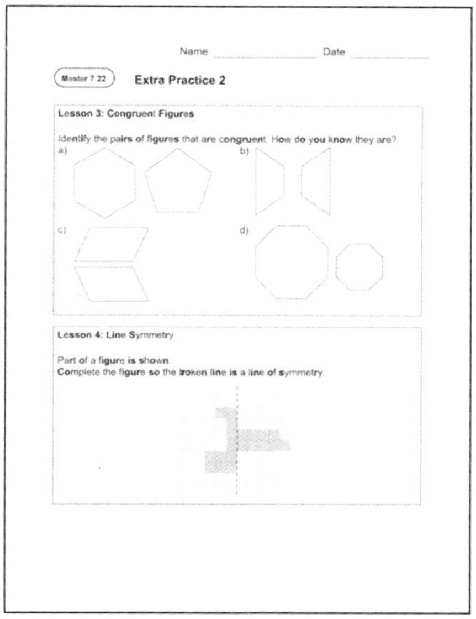

Name Date

Master 7.22 **Extra Practice 2**

Lesson 3: Congruent Figures

Identify the pairs of figures that are congruent. How do you know they are?

Lesson 4: Line Symmetry

Part of a figure is shown.
Complete the figure so the broken line is a line of symmetry.

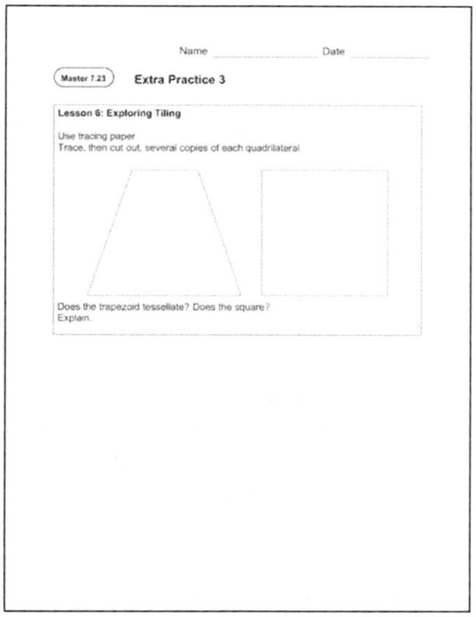

Name Date

Master 7.23 **Extra Practice 3**

Lesson 6: Exploring Tiling

Use tracing paper.
Trace, then cut out, several copies of each quadrilateral.

Does the trapezoid tessellate? Does the square?
Explain.

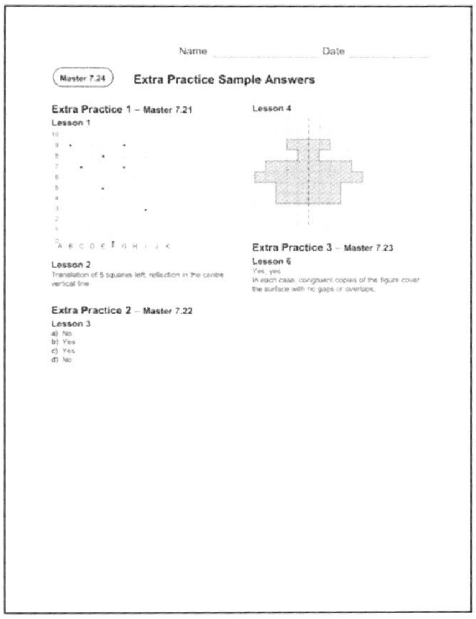

Name Date

Master 7.24 **Extra Practice Sample Answers**

Extra Practice 1 – Master 7.21

Lesson 1

Lesson 2

Translation of 5 squares left; reflection in the centre vertical line

Extra Practice 2 – Master 7.22

Lesson 3

a) No
b) Yes
c) Yes
d) No

Lesson 4

Extra Practice 3 – Master 7.23

Lesson 6

Yes; yes
In each case, congruent copies of the figure cover the surface with no gaps or overlaps.

Addison Wesley Mathematics Makes Sense

Program Authors

Peggy Morrow
Ralph Connelly
Bryn Keyes
Jason Johnston
Steve Thomas
Jeananne Thomas
Angela D'Alessandro
Maggie Martin Connell
Don Jones
Michael Davis
Sharon Jeroski
Trevor Brown
Nora Alexander
Cynthia Pratt Nicolson

Printed and bound in Canada

8 9 MP 18 17

PEARSON
Education Canada

ADDISON WESLEY

Ontario

Math Makes Sense 5

Ontario
Teacher Guide

Unit 8: Fractions and Decimals

PEARSON
Addison Wesley

UNIT 8

Fractions and Decimals

"When examining concepts related to fractions and decimals, two simple but powerful ideas — partitioning and equivalence — can help tie many of the concepts together. One idea related to equivalence is that decimals are another notation for fractions. Both common fractions and decimals can represent fractional parts, but decimals represent only partitions of tenths, hundredths, and powers of tenths while fractions can represent any partitioning."

Helping Children Learn Mathematics, Robert Reys, Mary Lindquist, et al., 2001

FOCUS STRAND
Number Sense and Numeration

SUPPORTING STRAND
Patterning and Algebra; Measurement

Mathematics Background

What Are the Big Ideas?

- Equivalent fractions are ways of describing the same amount using different-sized parts.
- Fractions that represent an amount greater than 1 can be written as either improper fractions or mixed numbers.
- Fractions with denominators of 10 or 100 can be written as decimals.
- Any fraction can also be thought of as a division statement (numerator ÷ denominator).
- Regardless of the positions of the decimal points, the multiplication or division of two numbers will produce the same digits. For example, $2 \times 3 = 6$ and $0.2 \times 3 = 0.6$ both have 6 in their answer, with the one difference being the placement of the decimal point. Thus, the computations can be performed as whole numbers, and the placement of the decimal point can be determined by estimation.

How Will the Concepts Develop?

Students build on their knowledge to explore patterns in the numerators and denominators of equivalent fractions; for example, $\frac{1}{2}, \frac{2}{4}, \frac{3}{6}, \frac{4}{8}, \frac{5}{10}, \frac{6}{12}$, and so on. Students realize they can continue to write as many equivalent fractions for $\frac{1}{2}$ as they wish by extending the pattern: numerators increase by 1, denominators increase by 2.

Students use models and their knowledge of equivalent fractions to compare and order fractions. They also use models to see the relationship between fractions and decimals. They expand their fraction benchmarks to include other fractions ($\frac{1}{4}, \frac{3}{4}$) and decimals (0, 0.25, 0.50, 0.75, 1.0).

Students connect the concept of division as sharing with the concept of fractions representing equal shares. They apply estimation skills developed for multiplication and division of whole numbers (front-end; rounding; compatible numbers) to estimate products and quotients with decimals, and to determine where the decimal point will go in multiplying and dividing with decimals.

Why Are These Concepts Important?

At the heart of flexibility in working with rational numbers is a solid understanding of different representations for, and a recognition of equivalent forms of, fractions and decimals.

A deep understanding of fractions and decimals is gained through experience with a variety of models (for example, fraction strips, number lines, 10 by 10 grids, area models, and concrete materials such as Base Ten Blocks).

Working with fractions and decimals contributes to students' understanding of, and facility with, proportionality.

Curriculum Overview

Cluster 1: Understanding Fractions

Overall Expectations:
- Compare, order, and represent whole numbers, decimals, and fractions using concrete materials and drawings. (5m2)
- Compare and order, and represent the relationship between, fractions, improper fractions, and mixed numbers using concrete materials and drawings. (5m6)
- Select and perform computation techniques appropriate to specific problems involving whole numbers, decimals, and equivalent fractions, and determine whether the results are reasonable. (5m7)

Specific Expectations:
- Order fractions on a number line. (5m13)
- Represent and compare mixed numbers and proper and improper fractions with simple denominators using concrete materials and drawings. (5m21)
- Investigate patterns involving fractions using concrete materials and drawings. (5m22)
- Demonstrate the equivalence of proper fractions using concrete materials, drawings, and symbols. (5m23)
- Explain their thinking when solving problems involving whole numbers, fractions, and decimals. (5m35)

Cluster 2: Relating Fractions and Decimals

Overall Expectations
- Represent, and explore relationships between, decimals, mixed numbers, and fractions using concrete materials and drawings. (5m1)

Specific Expectations
- Relate division to fractions. (5m17)
- Relate a fraction with a denominator of 10 or 100 to a decimal using concrete materials, drawings, and symbols. (5m24)
- Explore the relationships between fractions and decimals using a calculator, concrete materials, and drawings. (5m25)

Launch
In the Garden

Lesson 1:
Equivalent Fractions

Lesson 2:
Fractions and Mixed Numbers

Lesson 3:
Comparing and Ordering Fractions

Lesson 4:
Relating Fractions to Decimals

Lesson 5:
Fraction and Decimal Benchmarks

Lesson 6:
Relating Fractions to Division

Technology:
Fractions and Decimals on a Calculator

Cluster 3: Multiplying and Dividing with Decimals

Overall Expectations

- Understand and explain basic operations (multiplication and division) of decimals by modelling and discussing a variety of problem situations. (5m3)
- Develop proficiency in multiplying by tenths and hundredths and dividing by tenths. (5m4)
- Select and perform computation techniques appropriate to specific problems involving whole numbers, decimals, and equivalent fractions, and determine whether the results are reasonable. (5m7)
- Solve problems involving decimals and fractions, and describe and explain the variety of strategies used. (5m8)

Specific Expectations

- Explain processes and solutions with whole numbers and decimals using mathematical language. (5m18)
- Multiply and divide decimal numbers to hundredths by a one-digit whole number using concrete materials, drawings, and symbols. (5m32)
- Pose problems involving whole numbers and decimals and solve them using the appropriate calculation method: pencil and paper, or calculator or computer. (5m34)
- Explain their thinking when solving problems involving whole numbers, fractions, and decimals. (5m35)
- Use and explain estimation strategies to determine the reasonableness of solutions to problems, and justify the choice of strategies. (5m36)

Lesson 7:
Estimating Products and Quotients

Lesson 8:
Multiplying Decimals with Tenths

Lesson 9:
Multiplying Decimals with Hundredths

Lesson 10:
Strategies Toolkit

Lesson 11:
Dividing Decimals with Tenths

Lesson 12:
Dividing Decimals with Hundredths

Show What You Know

Unit Problem
In the Garden

Curriculum across the Grades

Grade 4	Grade 5	Grade 6
Students represent and explore the relationships among decimals, mixed numbers, and fractions. They compare and order fractions and mixed numbers with like denominators, and decimals to hundredths. Students connect proper fractions with decimals (tenths and hundredths). They demonstrate an understanding of the addition and subtraction of decimal numbers to hundredths and add and subtract decimal numbers to tenths using concrete materials, drawings, and symbols.	Students relate division to fractions. They order fractions on a number line, and read, write, compare, order, and represent the place value of decimals to hundredths. They multiply and divide decimal numbers to hundredths by a one-digit whole number using concrete materials, drawings, and symbols. Students explore equivalent decimals, and use relationships among addition, subtraction, multiplication, and division to develop strategies for multiplying and dividing decimal numbers. Students explore equivalent fractions and patterns involving fractions. They relate a fraction with a denominator of 10 or 100 to a decimal. They develop strategies to compare fractions and mixed numbers.	Students order fractions and decimals on any number line, and compare and order whole numbers and decimals from 0.001 to 1 000 000. Students relate fractions to decimals, percents, rates, and ratios using concrete materials, drawings, and symbols. They compare and order mixed numbers and improper fractions with unlike denominators. Students multiply and divide decimal numbers to thousandths by a one-digit whole number.

Materials for This Unit

Bring in seed catalogues for the *Unit Problem*.

Additional Activities

Great Fractions

For Extra Support (Appropriate for use after Lesson 3)
Materials: *Great Fractions* (Master 8.17), decks of cards with 10s and face cards removed

The work students do: Students play in pairs. Students use cards to make fractions whose numerators are less than or equal to their denominators. Players compare the fractions. The player with the greater fraction scores 1 point (if the fractions are equivalent, each player scores 1 point). The player with more points after all the cards have been played is the winner.

Take It Further: Students play the game again. This time students must also name an equivalent fraction for each fraction they make.

Social/Mathematical
Partner Activity

Box It In

For Extra Practice (Appropriate for use after Lesson 5)
Materials: *Box It In* (Master 8.18)

The work students do: Students use benchmarks to put the letters in the correct box. Students convert among improper fractions, mixed numbers, and decimals to estimate where to place the letters. Once students have compared and ordered the fractions and decimals correctly, the completed boxes will spell out a message.

Take It Further: Have students create their own "Box It In" challenges for other students to solve.

Linguistic/Mathematical
Individual Activity

Target 100

For Extra Practice (Appropriate for use after Lesson 7)
Materials: *Target 100* (Master 8.19), number cubes, calculators

The work students do: Students play in pairs. Each student rolls a number cube 3 times. Students use the digits, in the order rolled, as the ones digit, the tenths digit, and the hundredths digit of a number. Each student enters the number in a calculator, then estimates what number to multiply it by to get as close as possible to 100. Students calculate the products. The student with the estimate closer to 100 scores a point. The first student to score 10 points wins.

Take It Further: Students play again, with the target number being 200 or 500.

Kinesthetic/Logical
Partner Activity

Estimating Decimal Products

For Extra Practice (Appropriate for use after Lesson 8)
Materials: *Estimating Decimal Places* (Master 8.20); paper and pencils; calculators (optional)

The work students do: Students play in pairs. Students take turns to choose two numbers from the chart, one whole number and one decimal. Students cross off the numbers, then estimate their products. Students use calculators to find the actual products, then find the difference between the actual product and the estimate. Students find the range that contains their differences on the scoring chart to determine their scores for the round. Students record their scores. The student with the greater score after all numbers have been used wins.

Take it Further: Students play again. This time, players cannot use calculators to find the products.

Social/Mathematical
Partner Activity

Planning for Unit 8

Planning for Instruction

Suggested Unit time: About 3 weeks

Lesson	Time	Materials	Program Support
Launch: In the Garden, page 2	10–15 min		
Lesson 1: Equivalent Fractions, page 4 Find equivalent fractions and investigate patterns among them.	40–50 min	Colour Tiles 4 by 9 rectangle 1-cm grid paper 2-cm grid paper	Master 8.6: 4 by 9 Rectangle PM 24: 2-cm Grid Paper Master 8.21: Step-by-Step 1 Master 8.34: Extra Practice 1 PM 23: 1-cm Grid Paper
Lesson 2: Fractions and Mixed Numbers, page 8 Represent fractions and mixed numbers.	40–50 min	Cuisenaire rods or rulers fraction strips	Master 8.7: Fraction Strips Master 8.22: Step-by-Step 2 Master 8.34: Extra Practice 1
Lesson 3: Comparing and Ordering Fractions, page 11 Compare and order fractions.	40–50 min	fraction number lines and transparency paper strips number lines 1-cm grid paper rulers	PM 23: 1-cm Grid Paper Master 8.8: Fraction Number Lines Master 8.9: Paper Strips Master 8.10: Number Lines Master 8.23: Step-by-Step 3 Master 8.35: Extra Practice 2
Games: Order Up!, page 15	20 min	fraction cards game cards	Master 8.11: Fraction Cards Master 8.12: Game Cards
Lesson 4: Relating Fractions to Decimals, page 16 Relate fractions with denominators of 10 and 100 to decimals.	40–50 min	Base Ten Blocks overhead Base Ten Blocks hundredths grids and transparency	PM 15: Hundredths Grids Master 8.24: Step-by-Step 4 Master 8.35: Extra Practice 2
Lesson 5: Fraction and Decimal Benchmarks, page 20 Explore benchmarks for fractions and decimals.	40–50 min	circle graphs 10-cm number lines hundredths grids	Master 8.13: Circle Graph Master 8.14: 10-cm Number Lines Master 8.25: Step-by-Step 5 Master 8.36: Extra Practice 3 PM 15: Hundredths Grids
Lesson 6: Relating Fractions to Division, page 23 Relate fractions to division.	40–50 min	1-cm grid paper	PM 23: 1-cm Grid Paper Master 8.26: Step-by-Step 6 Master 8.36: Extra Practice 3
Technology: Fractions and Decimals on a Calculator, page 26 Use a calculator to convert fractions to decimals.	10–15 min	calculators	
Games: Fractions In-Between, page 27	20 min	fraction and decimal cards	Master 8.15: Fraction and Decimal Cards
Lesson 7: Estimating Products and Quotients, page 28 Estimate products and quotients with decimals.	40–50 min		Master 8.27: Step-by-Step 7 Master 8.37: Extra Practice 4
Lesson 8: Multiplying Decimals with Tenths, page 31 Multiply decimals with tenths by a 1-digit whole number.	40–50 min	Base Ten Blocks decimal place-value mats 0.5-cm grid paper	PM 22: 0.5-cm Grid Paper Master 8.16a: Decimal Place-Value Mats Master 8.28: Step-by-Step 8 Master 8.37: Extra Practice 4
Lesson 9: Multiplying Decimals with Hundredths, page 35 Multiply decimals with hundredths by a 1-digit whole number.	40–50 min	metre stick Base Ten Blocks decimal place-value mats	Master 8.16b: Decimal Place-Value Mats Master 8.29: Step-by-Step 9 Master 8.38: Extra Practice 5
Lesson 10: Strategies Toolkit, page 38 Interpret a problem and select an appropriate strategy.	40–50 min	Pattern Blocks overhead Pattern Blocks triangular grid paper	PM 28: Pattern Blocks PM 27: Triangular Grid Paper

Lesson	Time	Materials	Program Support
Lesson 11: Dividing Decimals with Tenths, page 40 Divide decimals with tenths by a 1-digit whole number.	40–50 min	Base Ten Blocks calculators	Master 8.30: Step-by-Step 11 Master 8.38: Extra Practice 5
Lesson 12: Dividing Decimals with Hundredths, page 43 Divide decimals with hundredths by a 1-digit whole number.	40–50 min	Base Ten Blocks play money	PM 30: Play Money Master 8.31: Step-by-Step 12 Master 8.39: Extra Practice 6
Show What You Know, page 46 Assessment	40–50 min	hundredths grids 0.5-cm grid paper	PM 15: Hundredths Grids PM 22: 0.5-cm Grid Paper
Unit Problem: In the Garden, page 48 Assessment	40–50 min	1-cm grid paper	PM 23: 1-cm Grid Paper

Planning for Assessment

Purpose	Tools and Process	Recording and Reporting
Diagnostic	*Unit Launch* Question; conference; scaffold problems throughout the unit	PM 8: Conference Prompts
Formative	*Explore* – Ongoing Assessment: Observe and Listen	Master 8.2 Ongoing Observations: Fractions and Decimals PM 1: Inquiry Process Check List PM 6: Observation Record 1 PM 7: Observation Record 2 PM 8: Conference Prompts
	Prompt student's self-assessment	PM 2: Self-Assessment PM 3: Self-Assessment: Problem Solving
	Practice – Assessment Focus Questions	PM 9: Work Sample Records
	Review student work; provide feedback; scaffold as needed; select key pieces	
Summative	*Show What You Know* *Unit Problem* – Performance Assessment Unit Test Review assessment records; add unit results to ongoing records	Master 8.1 Unit Rubric: Fractions and Decimals Master 8.3 Performance Assessment Rubric: In the Garden Master 8.4 Unit Summary: Fractions and Decimals PM 10: Summary Class Records: Strands PM 11: Summary Class Records: Achievement Categories PM 12: Summary Record: Individual
Learning Skills/ Mathematical Disposition	Observe and record throughout unit	PM 4: Learning Skills Check List PM 5: Mathematical Dispositions and Learning Skills

Program Masters (PM) are in the *Grade 5 Planning and Program Masters* module.
Extra Practice Masters are on the CD-ROM.

In the Garden

LESSON ORGANIZER

10–15 min

Curriculum Focus: Activate prior learning about fractions and decimals.

ASSUMED PRIOR KNOWLEDGE

- ✓ Students know that a fraction names equal parts of a whole.
- ✓ Students can multiply decimals (money amounts) by 10 and 100.
- ✓ Students can divide decimals (money amounts) by 10.

ACTIVATE PRIOR LEARNING

Discuss the illustration on page 257 in the Student Book. Ask questions, such as:

- How many small square plots are there in the garden? (*48*) How do you know? (*I counted them all. There are 6 squares in each row and there are 8 rows; 8 × 6 = 48, so there are 48 small squares.*)
- How many small squares will be planted with flowers? (*9 roses + 6 daisies = 15*) Vegetables? (*9 corn + 8 tomatoes + 10 zucchini + 6 pumpkins = 33*)

Discuss the question on page 256 of the Student Book to determine students' prior knowledge about writing fractions.

(*Flowers will be planted in 15 of the 48 small plots, or $\frac{15}{48}$ of the garden; vegetables in 33 of the 48 small plots, or $\frac{33}{48}$ of the garden.*)

Discuss the first question on page 257 of the Student Book to elicit student knowledge about multiplying and dividing decimals by 10 and 100. (*10 packages of zucchini will cost $10.90; 100 tomato plants will cost $85.00.*)

Discuss the second question on page 257. (*1 package of flower seeds would cost between 10 cents and 20 cents; to find the exact answer divide $1.50 by 10; $0.15.*)

Tell students they will learn how to write different fractions for the same amount, how fractions and decimals are related to one another, and how to multiply and divide with decimals.

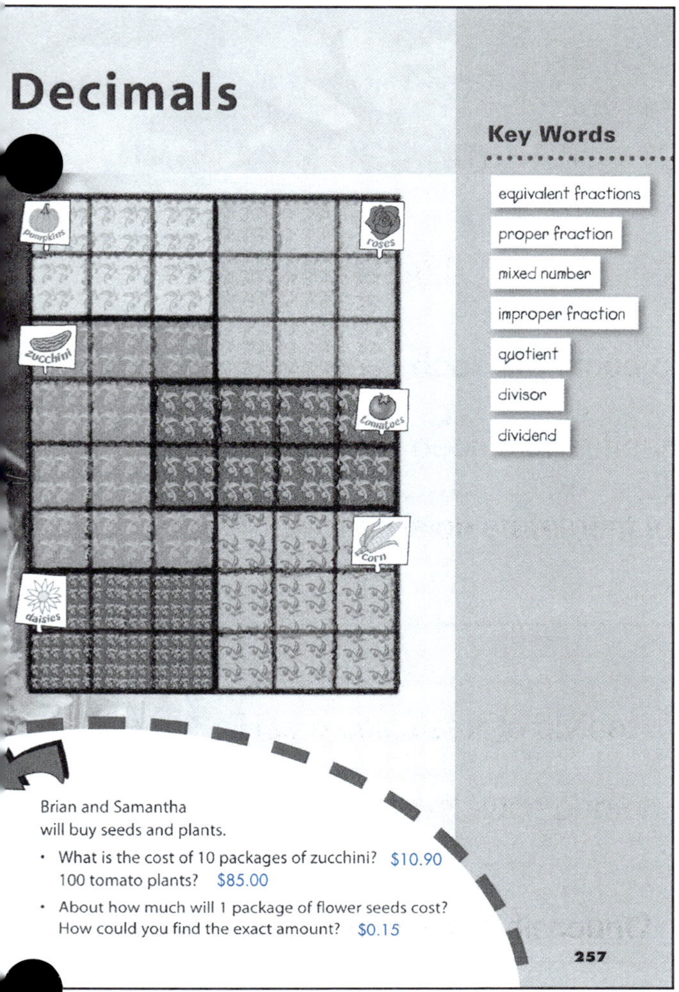
Decimals

Key Words

- equivalent fractions
- proper fraction
- mixed number
- improper fraction
- quotient
- divisor
- dividend

Brian and Samantha will buy seeds and plants.

- What is the cost of 10 packages of zucchini? $10.90
  100 tomato plants? $85.00
- About how much will 1 package of flower seeds cost? How could you find the exact amount? $0.15

257

LITERATURE CONNECTIONS FOR THE UNIT

The Best of Times by Greg Tang. Scholastic, Inc., 2002.
ISBN 0439210445
This book teaches readers simple but powerful techniques for multiplying numbers from 0 to 10. Readers are shown that smaller numbers are the key to multiplying larger numbers. There are challenging questions on every page.

REACHING ALL LEARNERS

Some students may benefit from using the virtual manipulatives on the e-Tools CD-ROM. The e-Tool appropriate for this unit is Fractions. Students can use this tool to investigate and create visual representations of fractions.

DIAGNOSTIC ASSESSMENT

What to Look For	What to Do
✔ Students know that a fraction names equal parts of a whole. ✔ Students can multiply decimals (money amounts) by 10 and 100. ✔ Students can divide decimals (money amounts) by 10.	***Extra Support:*** Some students may need to be reminded that the denominator represents the number of equal parts in 1 whole, and the numerator represents how many equal parts are counted. *Work on this skill during Lesson 1.* When multiplying by 10 and 100, some students may just “tack on” one zero or two zeros. You might want to use a place-value chart to show that this doesn’t change the place value of any of the digits, and that they need to shift the digits 1 or 2 place(s) to the left when multiplying by 10 and 100. *Work on this skill during Lessons 8 and 9.*

Equivalent Fractions

LESSON ORGANIZER

40–50 min

Curriculum Focus: Find equivalent fractions and investigate patterns among them. (5m22, 5m23)

Student Materials
- Colour Tiles, or congruent squares (make from PM 24)
- 4 by 9 rectangle (Master 8.6)
- 1-cm grid paper (PM 23)

Optional
- Step-by-Step 1 (Master 8.21)
- Extra Practice 1 (Master 8.34)

Vocabulary: equivalent fractions

Assessment: Master 8.2 Ongoing Observations: Fractions and Decimals

Key Math Learnings

1. Equivalent fractions name the same amount.
2. Patterns can be found in equivalent fractions.

LESSON 1

Equivalent Fractions

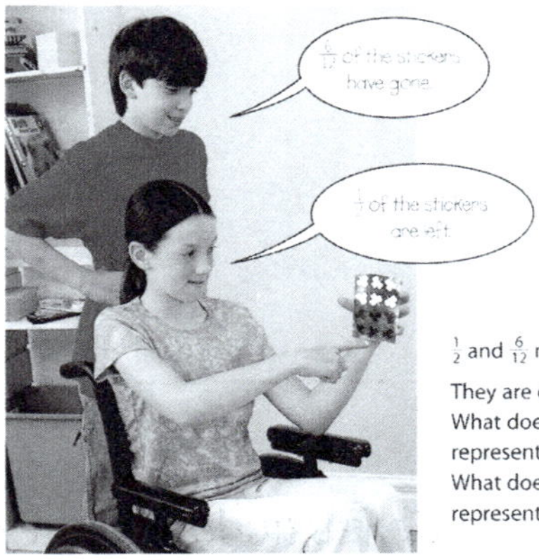

$\frac{1}{2}$ and $\frac{6}{12}$ name the same amount.

They are **equivalent fractions**.
What does each numerator represent?
What does each denominator represent?

Explore

You will need Colour Tiles or congruent squares.
Your teacher will give you a copy of this grid.

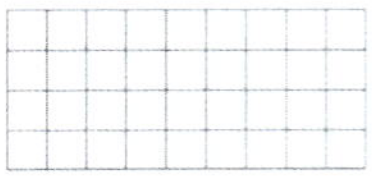

➤ Place the tiles on the rectangle so that:
- $\frac{1}{6}$ of the rectangle is red.
- $\frac{2}{3}$ of the rectangle is blue.
- $\frac{1}{9}$ of the rectangle is green.
- The rest of the rectangle is yellow.

Record your work on the grid.

➤ How many ways can you describe the fraction of the rectangle that is red? Blue? Green? Yellow?
Record each way.

258 LESSON FOCUS | Find equivalent fractions and investigate patterns among them.

BEFORE Get Started

Invite students to discuss and explain how two fractions can name the same amount. Ask:

- Why do both $\frac{6}{12}$ and $\frac{1}{2}$ name the same amount?
  (*There were 12 stickers and 6 of them are left, so* $\frac{6}{12}$ *are left. There were 2 groups of 6 stickers and 1 group of 6 is left, so* $\frac{1}{2}$ *is left.*)

Give pairs of students enough Colour Tiles to complete *Explore*. (If Colour Tiles are not available, students will have to colour and cut out congruent paper squares from PM 24. To ensure complete coverage of the squares on Master 8.6, teachers could enlarge PM 24 by 25%.) Give pairs of students a copy of Master 8.6.

DURING Explore

Ongoing Assessment: Observe and Listen

Ask questions, such as:

- How might you divide the rectangle into sixths? (*I can make six 2 by 3 rectangles, 3 on the top half of the rectangle and 3 on the bottom.*)
  Thirds? (*Three 4 by 3 rectangles going across*)
  Ninths? (*Nine 4 by 1 rectangles from left to right*)

This is a good opportunity to discuss the idea that "equal regions" do not have to be congruent, they just have to cover the same area.

Observe how many ways student pairs find to describe the fractions of the rectangle that are red, blue, green, and yellow. Do students only think of the given fraction (for example, $\frac{1}{6}$ for red) and the fraction using the total number of squares (for example, $\frac{6}{36}$ for red)? Do they recognize that $\frac{1}{6}$ of the rectangle could also be $\frac{2}{12}$?

Show and Share

Share your work with another pair of students.
Compare the fractions you wrote for each colour.
ow did you know which fractions to write?
escribe any patterns you see
in the fractions for each colour.

Connect

This rectangle was made with Colour Tiles.

What fraction of the rectangle is green?
How many different fractions can you write?

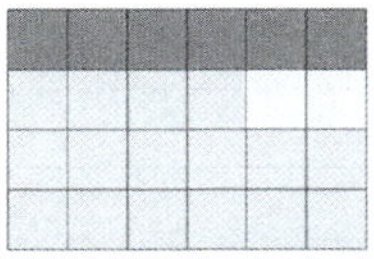

➤ There are 24 tiles in the rectangle.
12 tiles are green.
$\frac{12}{24}$ of the rectangle is green.

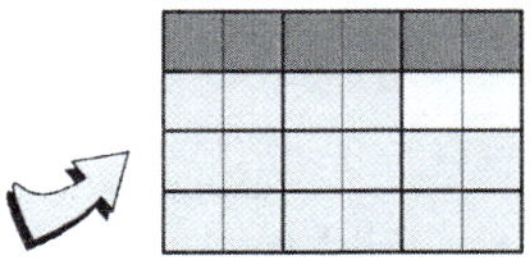

➤ There are 12 groups of 2 tiles.
6 groups are green.
$\frac{6}{12}$ of the rectangle is green.

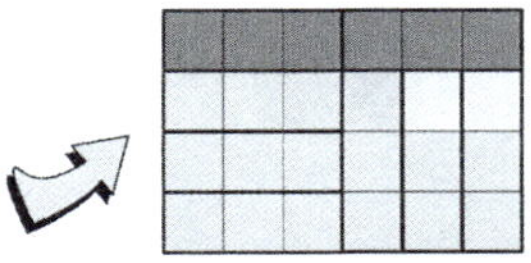

➤ There are 8 groups of 3 tiles.
4 groups are green.
$\frac{4}{8}$ of the rectangle is green.

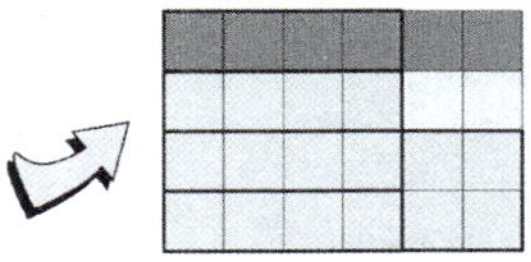

➤ There are 6 groups of 4 tiles.
3 groups are green.
$\frac{3}{6}$ of the rectangle is green.

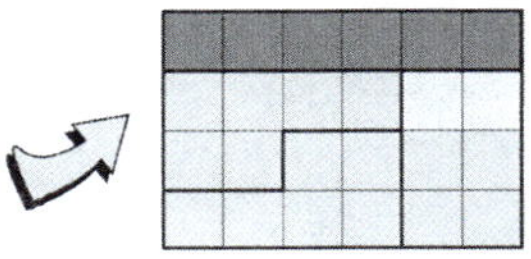

➤ There are 4 groups of 6 tiles.
2 groups are green.
$\frac{2}{4}$ of the rectangle is green.

259

REACHING ALL LEARNERS

Alternative Explore

Materials: 2-colour counters

Give pairs of students twenty-four 2-colour counters arranged in rows of 4, with the first two rows showing the red side up. Ask how many different fractions they can write to show the fraction of the counters that are red. ($\frac{12}{24}, \frac{6}{12}, \frac{4}{8}, \frac{3}{6}, \frac{2}{4}, \frac{1}{2}$)

Early Finishers

Have students explore other ways of placing Colour Tiles on the grid to make different fractions, and recall the ways of describing those fractions.

Common Misconceptions

➤ Some students think that when dividing a whole rectangular region into fractional parts, the parts have to be congruent.

How to Help: For example, suppose two of the regions are a 2 by 2 square and a 1 by 4 rectangle. Use a copy of the grid paper and cut up one of the shapes to place it on the other to show they cover the same amount of the whole rectangle.

Similarly, blue could be $\frac{2}{3}, \frac{4}{6}, \frac{6}{9}, \frac{8}{12}, \frac{12}{18}$, and $\frac{24}{36}$, but many students will only think of $\frac{2}{3}$ and $\frac{24}{36}$. Encourage students to find the patterns in the numerators and denominators of the fractions. Green is $\frac{1}{9}, \frac{2}{18}$, and $\frac{4}{36}$; yellow is $\frac{1}{18}$ and $\frac{2}{36}$.

AFTER Connect

Encourage students to discuss any patterns they notice in the fractions for each colour. Ask:

- What fractions did you write for blue? ($\frac{2}{3}, \frac{4}{6}, \frac{6}{9}, \frac{8}{12}, \frac{24}{36}$)
- What pattern do you see in the first 4 fractions?
  (The numerator starts at 2 and increases by 2 each time. The denominator starts at 3 and increases by 3 each time.)
- Why does the pattern not continue?
  (The first 4 denominators are all factors of 36 (the number of grid squares). The next possible denominator in the pattern, 15, is not a factor of 36.)
- What is another equivalent fraction for $\frac{2}{3}$? ($\frac{10}{15}$) How do you know? *(I took the fraction $\frac{8}{12}$, then added 2 to the numerator and 3 to the denominator.)*
- Did anyone find a different pattern?
  (The numerator and denominator are multiplied by the same number to get an equivalent fraction. For example, to get $\frac{8}{12}$, I multiply the numerator and denominator of $\frac{2}{3}$, by 4.)

Have students examine the rectangles in *Connect*. Ask:

- For 8 groups of 3 tiles, is a 1 by 3 rectangle an equal region to a 3 by 1 rectangle? Explain.
  (Yes; both regions are made with 3 colour tiles.)

Sample Answers

2. a) Blue: $\frac{1}{4}$, $\frac{2}{8}$; white: $\frac{3}{4}$, $\frac{6}{8}$
   b) Yellow: $\frac{1}{4}$, $\frac{3}{12}$; red: $\frac{3}{4}$, $\frac{9}{12}$
   c) Yellow: $\frac{1}{5}$, $\frac{2}{10}$, $\frac{4}{20}$; white: $\frac{4}{5}$, $\frac{8}{10}$, $\frac{16}{20}$
3. For a strip divided into 10 equal parts, I found that $\frac{2}{5}$ is equivalent to $\frac{4}{10}$. For a strip divided into 15 equal parts, I found that $\frac{2}{5}$ is equivalent to $\frac{6}{15}$. I divided each section of the strip with 10 parts in half, to get 20 equal parts, and found that $\frac{2}{5}$ is equivalent to $\frac{8}{20}$.
4. a)

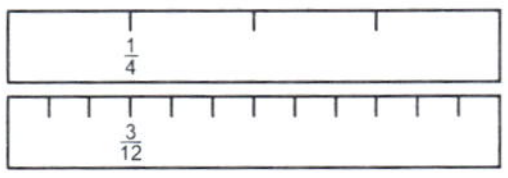

   b)

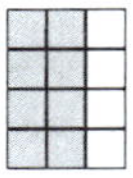

   c)

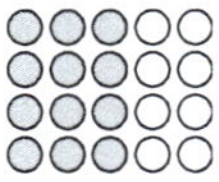

5.

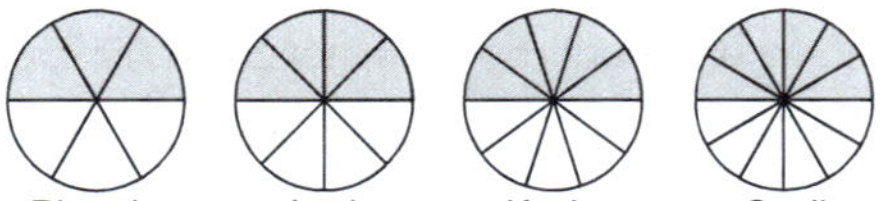

Rhonda Apak Kayla Sunil

Rhonda is correct. From my drawings, I see that each person ate half of their pizza. $\frac{3}{6}$, $\frac{4}{8}$, $\frac{5}{10}$, and $\frac{6}{12}$ are all equivalent fractions.

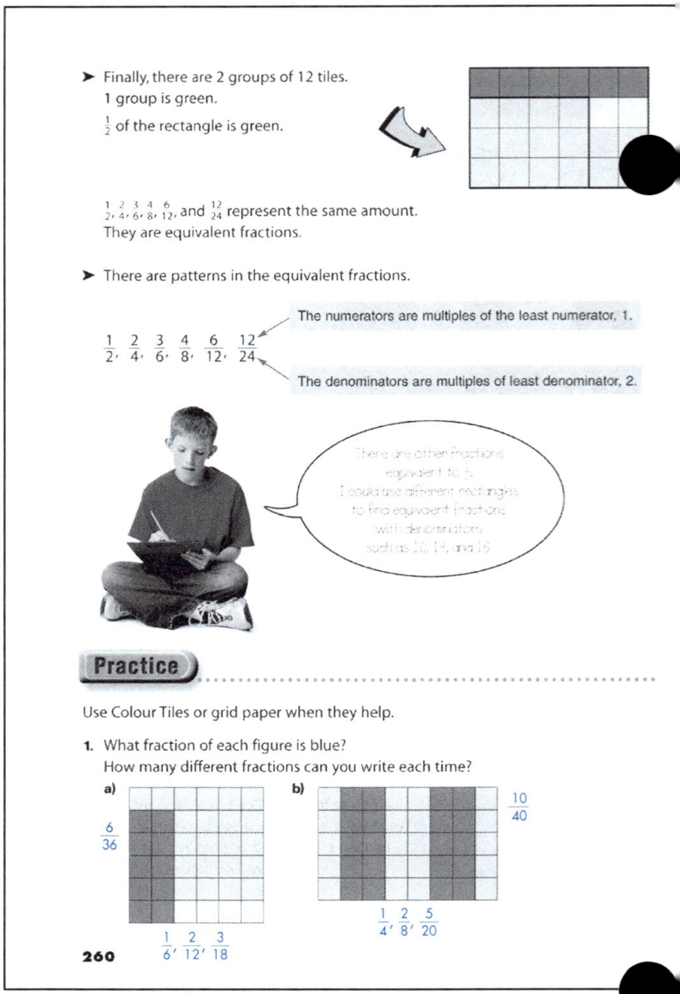

➤ Finally, there are 2 groups of 12 tiles.
1 group is green.
$\frac{1}{2}$ of the rectangle is green.

$\frac{1}{2}$, $\frac{2}{4}$, $\frac{3}{6}$, $\frac{4}{8}$, $\frac{6}{12}$, and $\frac{12}{24}$ represent the same amount.
They are equivalent fractions.

➤ There are patterns in the equivalent fractions.

$\frac{1}{2}$, $\frac{2}{4}$, $\frac{3}{6}$, $\frac{4}{8}$, $\frac{6}{12}$, $\frac{12}{24}$

The numerators are multiples of the least numerator, 1.
The denominators are multiples of least denominator, 2.

Practice

Use Colour Tiles or grid paper when they help.

1. What fraction of each figure is blue?
How many different fractions can you write each time?
a) $\frac{6}{36}$; $\frac{1}{6}$, $\frac{2}{12}$, $\frac{3}{18}$
b) $\frac{10}{40}$; $\frac{1}{4}$, $\frac{2}{8}$, $\frac{5}{20}$

260

- Describe the pattern you see in the list of equivalent fractions for $\frac{1}{2}$. What equivalent fractions might you add to the list?
  (*Equivalent fractions include* $\frac{1}{2}$, $\frac{2}{4}$, $\frac{3}{6}$, $\frac{4}{8}$, $\frac{5}{10}$, $\frac{6}{12}$, $\frac{7}{14}$, $\frac{8}{16}$, *and so on. The numerators increase by 1; the denominators increase by 2.*)

Practice

For question 2, students may find equivalent fractions for both the shaded (coloured) parts and the white parts of each picture.

Assessment Focus: Question 5

Students should draw four rectangular regions on grid paper that they can divide equally into sixths, eighths, tenths, and twelfths. Students colour the number of squares that represent the amount eaten by each person. Some students may work wih circles, but they will be more difficult to divide into equal parts.

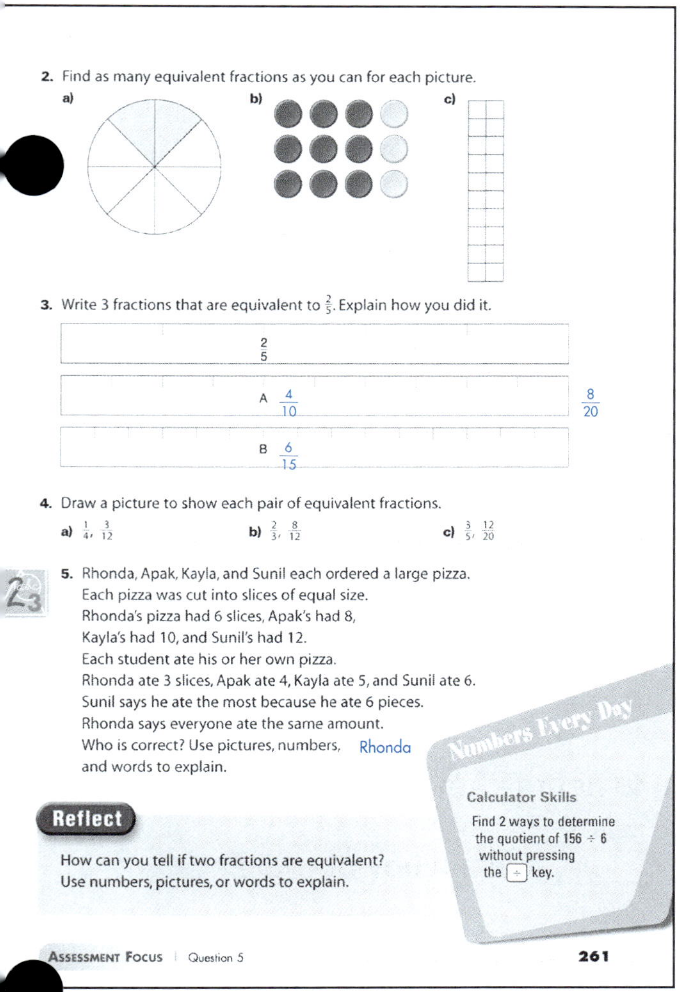

2. Find as many equivalent fractions as you can for each picture.
a) b) c)

3. Write 3 fractions that are equivalent to $\frac{2}{5}$. Explain how you did it.

$\frac{2}{5}$

A $\frac{4}{10}$ $\frac{8}{20}$

B $\frac{6}{15}$

4. Draw a picture to show each pair of equivalent fractions.
a) $\frac{1}{4}, \frac{3}{12}$ b) $\frac{2}{3}, \frac{8}{12}$ c) $\frac{3}{5}, \frac{12}{20}$

5. Rhonda, Apak, Kayla, and Sunil each ordered a large pizza. Each pizza was cut into slices of equal size. Rhonda's pizza had 6 slices, Apak's had 8, Kayla's had 10, and Sunil's had 12. Each student ate his or her own pizza. Rhonda ate 3 slices, Apak ate 4, Kayla ate 5, and Sunil ate 6. Sunil says he ate the most because he ate 6 pieces. Rhonda says everyone ate the same amount. Who is correct? Use pictures, numbers, and words to explain. Rhonda

Reflect

How can you tell if two fractions are equivalent? Use numbers, pictures, or words to explain.

Numbers Every Day

Calculator Skills

Find 2 ways to determine the quotient of 156 ÷ 6 without pressing the ÷ key.

Assessment Focus | Question 5 261

REFLECT: To find out if two fractions are equivalent, you have to see if they are an equal amount of the whole or group. For example, when I colour $\frac{1}{2}$ of a 2 by 2 grid red, I see that 2 of the 4 grid squares have been coloured. So, $\frac{1}{2}$ is equivalent to $\frac{2}{4}$.

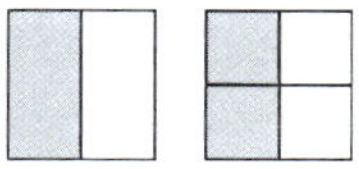

Numbers Every Day

Students could use guess and check and the inverse operation:
$6 \times \_\_\_ = 156$.
Students could do 156 – 6 = = =, and so on, to count how many 6s they subtract from 156 to reach 0.

ASSESSMENT FOR LEARNING

What to Look For	What to Do
Understanding concepts ✔ Students understand that equivalent fractions name the same amount. ***Applying procedures*** ✔ Students are able to represent equivalent fractions in various ways. ✔ Students can generate sets of equivalent fractions.	***Extra Support:*** Students may benefit from using a variety of different materials to model equivalent fractions. Ensure that Colour Tiles, fraction strips, grid paper, and counters are available for students to use. Students can use Step-by-Step 1 (Master 8.21) to complete question 5. ***Extra Practice:*** Have students use patterns to generate lists of equivalent fractions. For example, $\frac{1}{3}, \frac{2}{6}, \frac{3}{9}$, —, —, — ($\frac{4}{12}, \frac{5}{15}, \frac{6}{18}$); $\frac{2}{5}, \frac{4}{10}, \frac{6}{15}$, —, —, — ($\frac{8}{20}, \frac{10}{25}, \frac{12}{30}$) Students can complete Extra Practice 1 (Master 8.34). ***Extension:*** Students can make up "rectangular grid" questions showing different equivalent fractions for other students to solve.

Recording and Reporting
Master 8.2: Ongoing Observations: Fractions and Decimals

Fractions and Mixed Numbers

LESSON ORGANIZER

40–50 min

Curriculum Focus: Represent fractions and mixed numbers. (5m21)

Student Materials
- Cuisenaire rods or rulers
- Fraction Strips (Master 8.7)

Optional
- paper strips
- centimetre cubes
- Step-by-Step 2 (Master 8.22)
- Extra Practice 1 (Master 8.34)

Vocabulary: proper fraction, improper fraction, mixed number

Assessment: Master 8.2 Ongoing Observations: Fractions and Decimals

Key Math Learning

Fractions representing more than one whole can be shown using either an improper fraction or a mixed number.

Making Connections

At Home Have students ask their families when they've used fractions or mixed numbers (for example, in recipes; measuring material, or measuring wood).

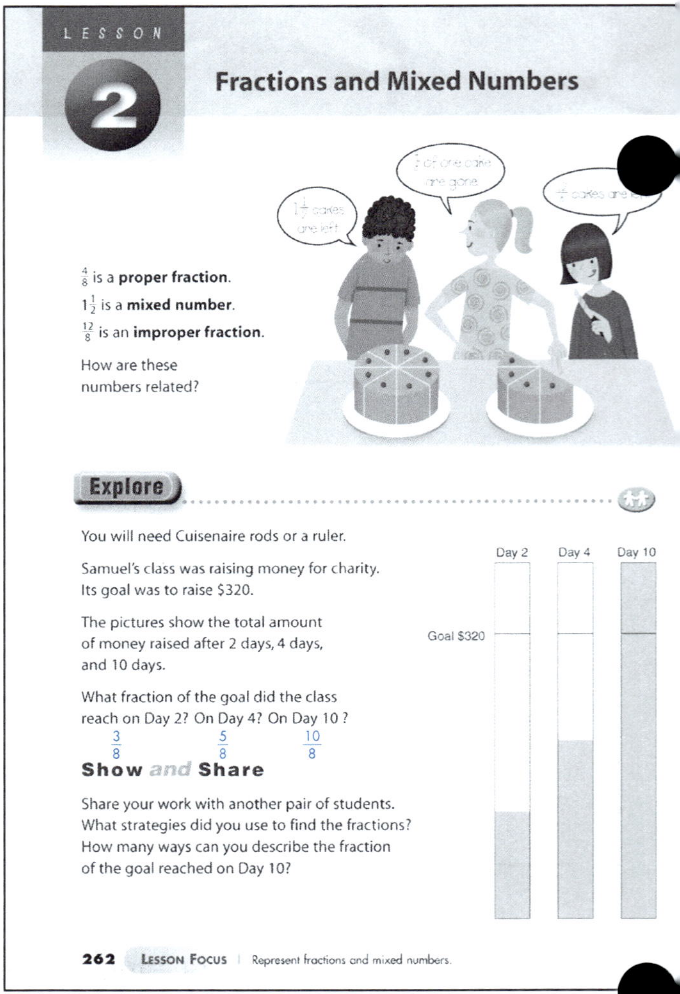
LESSON 2

Fractions and Mixed Numbers

$\frac{4}{8}$ is a **proper fraction**.

$1\frac{1}{2}$ is a **mixed number**.

$\frac{12}{8}$ is an **improper fraction**.

How are these numbers related?

Explore

You will need Cuisenaire rods or a ruler.

Samuel's class was raising money for charity. Its goal was to raise $320.

The pictures show the total amount of money raised after 2 days, 4 days, and 10 days.

What fraction of the goal did the class reach on Day 2? On Day 4? On Day 10 ?
$\frac{3}{8}$ $\frac{5}{8}$ $\frac{10}{8}$

Show and Share

Share your work with another pair of students. What strategies did you use to find the fractions? How many ways can you describe the fraction of the goal reached on Day 10?

262 LESSON FOCUS | Represent fractions and mixed numbers.

BEFORE Get Started

Have students look at the cake illustration on page 262 of the Student Book. Ask:

- What fraction do the parts of the whole cake represent? (*Eighths*)
- How might you describe all 12 remaining pieces of the cake as a fraction? ($\frac{12}{8}$)
- How might you describe the total amount of cake that is left as a mixed number? ($1\frac{4}{8}$ *or* $1\frac{1}{2}$)
- How are a mixed number, such as $1\frac{1}{2}$, and an improper fraction, such as $\frac{12}{8}$, alike? (*They represent the same amount.*) Different? (*A mixed number is made up of a whole number part and a fraction part. An improper fraction has its numerator greater than its denominator.*)

Present *Explore*. Student pairs will need Cuisenaire rods or rulers. Hand out Fraction Strips (Master 8.7). Ensure students recognize that the black line on each drawing represents the class goal.

DURING Explore

Ongoing Assessment: Observe and Listen

Ask questions, such as:

- What length on the strip represents the class goal? (*8 cm or 1 brown rod*)
- What length shows the amount Samuel's class raised after 2 days? (*3 cm or 1 light green rod*) 4 days? (*5 cm or 1 yellow rod*) 10 days? (*10 cm or 1 orange rod*)
- What denominator will you use to record the fractions of the goal? (*8*) Explain. (*I thought of the class goal as a number line broken into 8 equal 1-cm pieces.*)
- What do you notice about the fraction for Day 10? (*It is greater than 1; it is the whole goal and then some more.*)

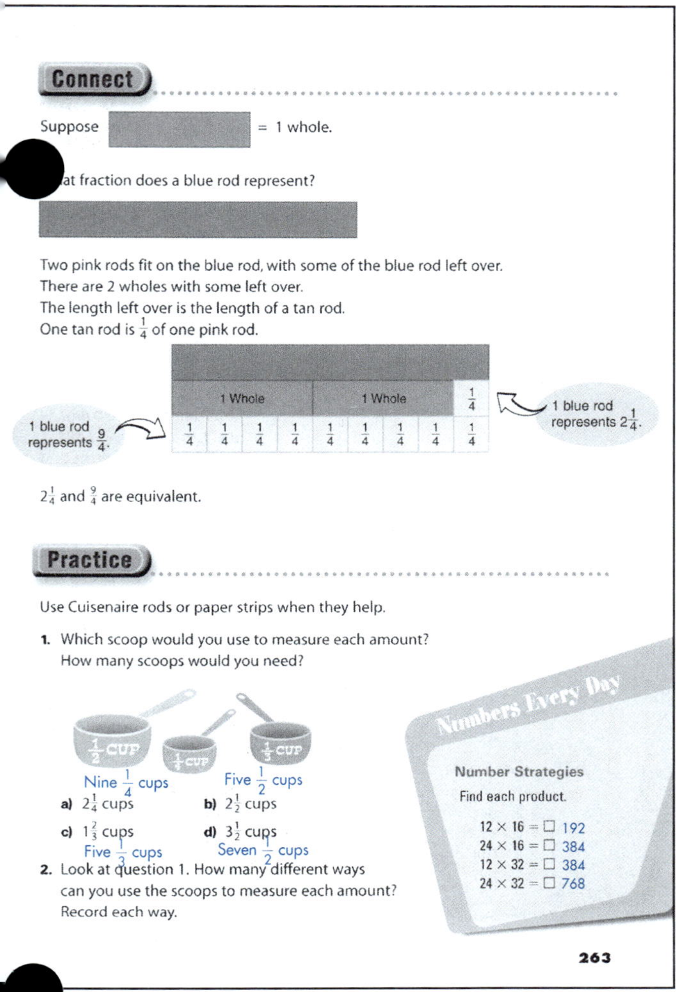

Connect

Suppose [rod] = 1 whole.

at fraction does a blue rod represent?

Two pink rods fit on the blue rod, with some of the blue rod left over.
There are 2 wholes with some left over.
The length left over is the length of a tan rod.
One tan rod is $\frac{1}{4}$ of one pink rod.

$2\frac{1}{4}$ and $\frac{9}{4}$ are equivalent.

Practice

Use Cuisenaire rods or paper strips when they help.

1. Which scoop would you use to measure each amount? How many scoops would you need?

a) $2\frac{1}{4}$ cups — Nine $\frac{1}{4}$ cups
b) $2\frac{1}{2}$ cups — Five $\frac{1}{2}$ cups
c) $1\frac{2}{3}$ cups — Five $\frac{1}{3}$ cups
d) $3\frac{1}{2}$ cups — Seven $\frac{1}{2}$ cups

2. Look at question 1. How many different ways can you use the scoops to measure each amount? Record each way.

Numbers Every Day

Number Strategies

Find each product.

12 × 16 = □ 192
24 × 16 = □ 384
12 × 32 = □ 384
24 × 32 = □ 768

263

REACHING ALL LEARNERS

Alternative Explore

Materials: Pattern Blocks

Students work in pairs, using the yellow Pattern Block as 1 whole, to answer the following questions: What fraction is shown with 3 red Pattern Blocks? 4 blue Pattern Blocks? Write each fraction two different ways. ($1\frac{1}{2}$, $\frac{3}{2}$; $1\frac{1}{3}$, $\frac{4}{3}$)

Common Misconceptions

➤ Students have difficulty converting measurements on paper strips to fractions in *Explore*.

How to Help: Have students draw lines dividing the strips into 1-cm squares, then count the number of squares to the goal line. This represents 1 whole.

Early Finishers

Challenge early finishers to find the dollar amounts that were reached on Day 2, Day 4, and Day 10 in *Explore*.

Numbers Every Day

For 12 × 16, students could find 10 × 16 = 160, and 2 × 16 = 32, then add to get 12 × 16 = 192.
For 24 × 16, students could see that 24 × 16 is double 12 × 16, since 2 × 12 = 24.
For 12 × 32, students could see that 12 × 32 is also double 12 × 16, since 2 × 16 = 32.
For 24 × 32, students could see that 24 × 32 is double 12 × 32, since 12 × 2 = 24.

AFTER Connect

Invite pairs of students to show their work. In particular, have students who recorded their fractions for Day 10 differently show their answers. Encourage discussion to make students aware that different fractions can be written to express the same amount. For example, the fraction for Day 10 can be written as: $\frac{10}{8}$, $\frac{5}{4}$, $1\frac{2}{8}$, and $1\frac{1}{4}$.

Have students read the question in *Connect*. Ask questions, such as:

- Is the blue rod more than 1 whole? (*Yes*) How do you know?
  (*It is longer than the pink rod, which is 1 whole.*)
- How do we know the tan rod shows $\frac{1}{4}$?
  (*It takes 4 tan rods to make 1 pink rod, which is the whole, so each tan rod shows* $\frac{1}{4}$.)
- How do we know $2\frac{1}{4}$ and $\frac{9}{4}$ are equivalent?
  (*We can break up each pink rod, or 1 whole, into 4 tan rods, or fourths, and count all the fourths. There are 9 fourths in all, which is equivalent to* $2\frac{1}{4}$.)

Practice

Have Cuisenaire rods or paper strips available.

Assessment Focus: Question 6

Students will likely consider the pies separately. If more than $2\frac{1}{2}$ but less than three 8-piece pies were left, students would determine which fractions with eighths are greater than $2\frac{1}{2}$, but less than 3. They would treat the 6-piece pies in a similar manner.

Sample Answers

2. For example:
   a) Four $\frac{1}{2}$ cups and one $\frac{1}{4}$ cup; or six $\frac{1}{3}$ cups and one $\frac{1}{4}$ cup
   b) Four $\frac{1}{2}$ cups and two $\frac{1}{4}$ cups; or six $\frac{1}{3}$ cups and one $\frac{1}{2}$ cup
   c) Two $\frac{1}{2}$ cups and two $\frac{1}{3}$ cups; or four $\frac{1}{4}$ cups and two $\frac{1}{3}$ cups; or one $\frac{1}{2}$ cup, two $\frac{1}{4}$ cups, and two $\frac{1}{3}$ cups
   d) Six $\frac{1}{2}$ cups and two $\frac{1}{4}$ cups; or nine $\frac{1}{3}$ cups and one $\frac{1}{2}$ cup; or nine $\frac{1}{3}$ cups and two $\frac{1}{4}$ cups
4. a) They name the same amount.
   b) They name the same amount.
   c) $2\frac{3}{4}$ is the same as $\frac{11}{4}$, not $\frac{9}{4}$.
5. Mario mowed for $\frac{7}{4}$h, which is less than 2 h.
6. For an 8-piece pie: $2\frac{5}{8}$, $2\frac{6}{8}$, or $2\frac{7}{8}$ could be left. For a 6-piece pie: $2\frac{4}{6}$ or $2\frac{5}{6}$ could be left.

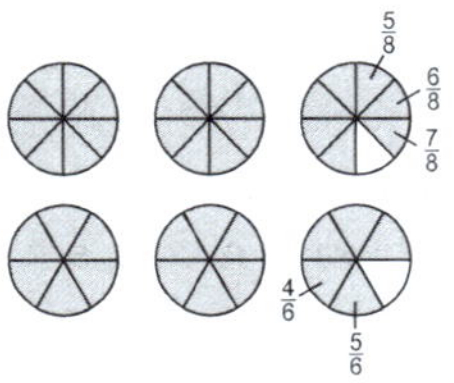

7. Draw three 4 by 1 rectangles on grid paper. Colour 2 whole rectangles and $\frac{1}{2}$ of the third rectangle. Count the total number of coloured squares. Each rectangle is divided into quarters, so $\frac{10}{4}$ were coloured. $2\frac{1}{2}$ is equivalent to $\frac{10}{4}$.

REFLECT: For example, consider $\frac{7}{4}$. One whole is the same as $\frac{4}{4}$, so $\frac{7}{4}$ is 1 whole and $\frac{3}{4}$ left over. $\frac{7}{4} = 1\frac{3}{4}$

3. What fraction does each picture represent? Write an equivalent fraction for each.

a) b) c)

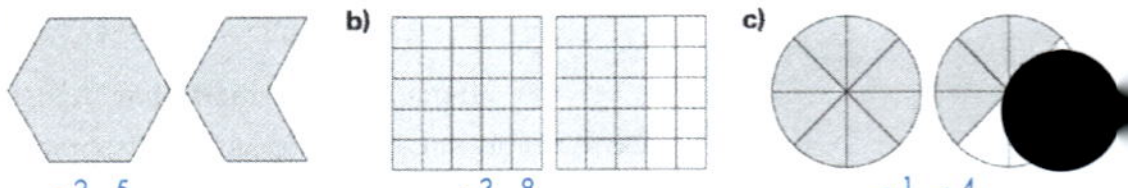

a) $1\frac{2}{3}, \frac{5}{3}$ b) $1\frac{3}{5}, \frac{8}{5}$ c) $1\frac{1}{2}, 1\frac{4}{8}$

4. Are the fractions in each pair equivalent? How do you know?
   a) $3\frac{2}{3}$ and $\frac{11}{3}$ Yes b) $\frac{13}{8}$ and $1\frac{5}{8}$ Yes c) $2\frac{3}{4}$ and $\frac{9}{4}$ No
5. Kendra mowed her lawn in $2\frac{1}{2}$ h. Mario mowed his lawn for $\frac{1}{4}$ h, then stopped. He did this 7 times. Who spent the most time mowing the lawn? Kendra How do you know?
6. Carlo baked pies for a party. He cut some pies into 6 pieces and some into 8 pieces. After the party, more than $2\frac{1}{2}$ but less than 3 pies were left. How much pie might have been left? Show how you know.

7. How can you find out if $2\frac{1}{2}$ and $\frac{10}{4}$ name the same amount? Use words, numbers, and pictures to explain.

Reflect

When you see an improper fraction, how can you write it as a mixed number?

When do you use fractions and mixed numbers at home? Explain.

264 ASSESSMENT FOCUS | Question 6

ASSESSMENT FOR LEARNING

What to Look For

Understanding concepts

✔ Students recognize that an improper fraction represents more than one whole, and that its numerator is greater than its denominator.

Applying procedures

✔ Students can rewrite an improper fraction as a mixed number.

✔ Students can rewrite a mixed number as an improper fraction.

Communicating

✔ Students can explain how improper fractions or mixed numbers represent a given drawing.

What to Do

Extra Support: Students can use paper strips to model mixed numbers. For example, for $1\frac{3}{4}$, they can fold paper strips into fourths (in half, then in half again), then count the parts. In $1\frac{3}{4}$, there are 4 parts in 1 whole, and 3 more, so 7 altogether. Each piece is $\frac{1}{4}$, so $1\frac{3}{4}$ is the same as $\frac{7}{4}$.
Students can use Step-by-Step 2 (Master 8.22) to complete question 6.

Extra Practice: Have students draw pictures to represent the fractions in question 4.
Students can complete Extra Practice 1 (Master 8.34).

Extension: Have students work in small groups. One student selects a Cuisenaire rod to represent 1 whole. The group then works together to find what fraction of the whole each of the other rods represents.

Recording and Reporting

Master 8.2: Ongoing Observations: Fractions and Decimals

LESSON

3

Comparing and Ordering Fractions

Explore

Your teacher will give you a large copy of these number lines.

The first number line shows halves. The second shows thirds, and so on.

➤ The number lines are incomplete. Mark and label the lines with the missing fractions. Use any materials that help.

➤ Describe any patterns in the completed lines.

➤ Which fraction in each pair is greater? How do you know?

- $\frac{2}{3}$ or $\frac{2}{5}$
- $\frac{3}{8}$ or $\frac{4}{10}$

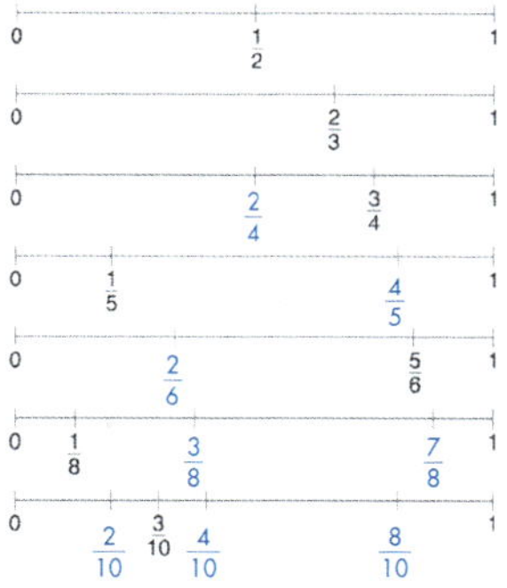

Show and Share

Show your work to another pair of students.
How did you know where to place the fractions on the number lines?
Share the patterns you found.
How did you decide which fraction was greater?

Numbers Every Day

Mental Math

Estimate each quotient.

$5453 \div 5 = \square$ About 1100
$2425 \div 6 = \square$ About 400
$1047 \div 9 = \square$ About 110
$2104 \div 7 = \square$ About 300

LESSON FOCUS | Compare and order fractions. 265

Comparing and Ordering Fractions

LESSON ORGANIZER

40–50 min

Curriculum Focus: Compare and order fractions. (5m13, 5m21)

Teacher Materials:
- transparency of fraction number lines (Master 8.8)

Student Materials
- fraction number lines (Master 8.8)
- paper strips (Master 8.9)
- number lines (Master 8.10)
- 1-cm grid paper (PM 23)
- rulers

Optional
- Step-by-Step 3 (Master 8.23)
- Extra Practice 2 (Master 8.35)

Vocabulary: numerator, denominator

Assessment: Master 8.2 Ongoing Observations: Fractions and Decimals

Key Math Learnings

1. Fractions can be compared or ordered by locating them on same-size number lines.
2. Fractions can be compared or ordered if they have the same numerator, or the same denominator.

BEFORE Get Started

Have students think about the relative size of fractions with the same denominator. Invite volunteers to explain their answers, perhaps using a drawing. Ask questions, such as:

- Which is more, $\frac{1}{3}$ of a pie or $\frac{2}{3}$ of the same pie? How do you know?
(*Thirds means the pie is cut into 3 equal parts; $\frac{1}{3}$ means you have 1 of those parts; $\frac{2}{3}$ means you have 2 of those parts, so $\frac{2}{3}$ is greater than $\frac{1}{3}$.*)

Present *Explore*. Give student pairs copies of the fraction number lines on Master 8.8 to complete. Ensure they have rulers available.

DURING Explore

Ongoing Assessment: Observe and Listen

As students work, ask questions, such as:

- How many equal parts would the thirds number line have? How do you know?
(*3; the denominator tells you the whole has 3 equal parts.*)

Students should discover that $\frac{2}{5}$ has not been marked on their number lines. Ask:

- On which number line does $\frac{2}{5}$ belong?
(*On the number line that shows fifths.*)
- How could we decide where to place $\frac{2}{5}$ on the line? (*We could measure the distance between 0 and $\frac{1}{5}$ with a ruler, then mark an equal distance to the right of $\frac{1}{5}$.*)
- Is there another strategy we could use to place the fraction? (*The number line is 10 cm long. If the line is divided into 5 equal parts, each part will be 2 cm long. I can mark a point 2 cm to the right of $\frac{1}{5}$.*)

REACHING ALL LEARNERS

Alternative Explore

Materials: Pattern Blocks

Using the yellow hexagon as 1 whole, students put the following fractions in order from least to greatest: $\frac{2}{3}$, $\frac{1}{2}$, and $\frac{5}{6}$, and explain how they have done this. ($\frac{1}{2}$, $\frac{2}{3}$, $\frac{5}{6}$)

Early Finishers

Have early finishers complete the fraction number lines on Master 8.8.

Common Misconceptions

➤ When comparing fractions with the same numerator but different denominators, some students believe that the fraction with the greater denominator is the greater fraction.

How to Help: Have students think about sharing a whole, such as a pizza, by dividing it into equal parts. Ask, "In which pizza would the parts be larger, one cut into 3 equal parts, or one cut into 5 equal parts?" Have students draw the picture to see that "third" parts are bigger than "fifth" parts, so $\frac{2}{3}$ is greater than $\frac{2}{5}$.

Numbers Every Day

Students could round the larger number (the dividend) to a number that is easily divisible by the lesser number (the divisor).
5453 ÷ 5 is about 5500 ÷ 5; 2425 ÷ 6 is about 2400 ÷ 6; 1047 ÷ 9 is about 990 ÷ 9; 2104 ÷ 7 is about 2100 ÷ 7.

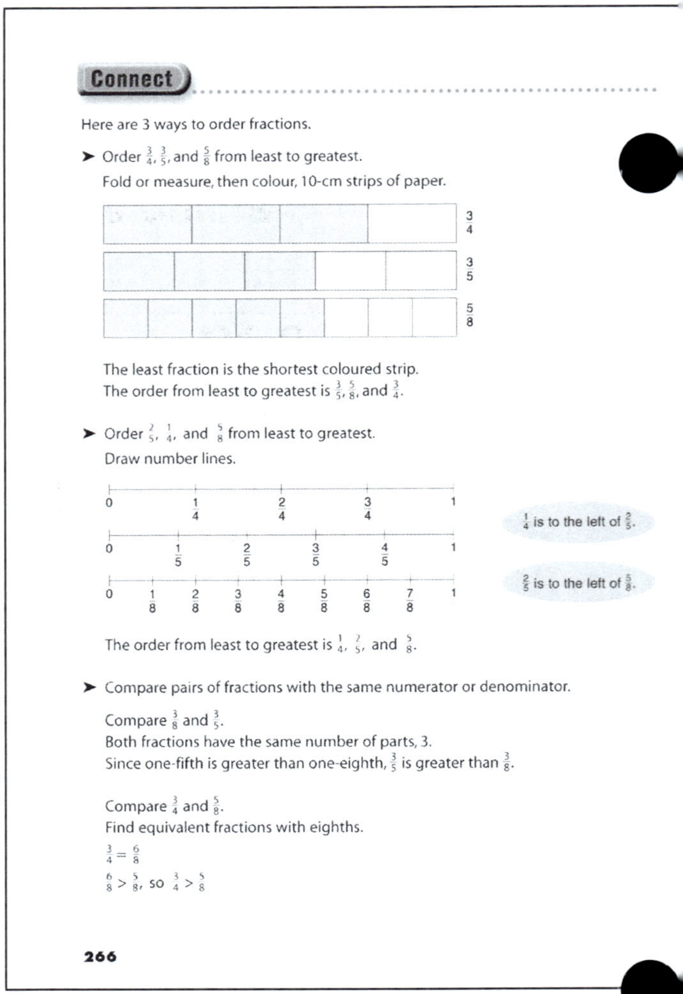

Connect

Here are 3 ways to order fractions.

➤ Order $\frac{3}{4}$, $\frac{3}{5}$, and $\frac{5}{8}$ from least to greatest.

Fold or measure, then colour, 10-cm strips of paper.

The least fraction is the shortest coloured strip.
The order from least to greatest is $\frac{3}{5}$, $\frac{5}{8}$, and $\frac{3}{4}$.

➤ Order $\frac{2}{5}$, $\frac{1}{4}$, and $\frac{5}{8}$ from least to greatest.

Draw number lines.

The order from least to greatest is $\frac{1}{4}$, $\frac{2}{5}$, and $\frac{5}{8}$.

➤ Compare pairs of fractions with the same numerator or denominator.

Compare $\frac{3}{8}$ and $\frac{3}{5}$.
Both fractions have the same number of parts, 3.
Since one-fifth is greater than one-eighth, $\frac{3}{5}$ is greater than $\frac{3}{8}$.

Compare $\frac{3}{4}$ and $\frac{5}{8}$.
Find equivalent fractions with eighths.
$\frac{3}{4} = \frac{6}{8}$
$\frac{6}{8} > \frac{5}{8}$, so $\frac{3}{4} > \frac{5}{8}$

266

Once students have marked $\frac{2}{5}$ on their number lines, ask:

- What patterns do you see in the line that shows tenths? (*For the fractions $\frac{2}{10}$, $\frac{3}{10}$, and $\frac{4}{10}$, the numerator increases by 1 each time and the denominator remains the same.*)
- What do you notice about the number lines? (*All the lines are the same length. As I move down the page, the number lines are divided into smaller and smaller parts. As the parts decrease in length, the denominators of the fractions increase.*)
- How do you know which fraction in each pair is greater? (*Thirds are larger parts than fifths, so $\frac{2}{3}$ is greater than $\frac{2}{5}$; $\frac{4}{10}$ is a little farther to the right of $\frac{3}{8}$ on the number line, and fractions get larger as you go to the right on the number line, so $\frac{4}{10}$ is greater than $\frac{3}{8}$.*)

Invite pairs to explain how they compared pairs of fractions. Ask:

- How do you know which fraction in each pair is greater? (*Thirds are larger parts than fifths, so $\frac{2}{3}$ is greater than $\frac{2}{5}$; $\frac{4}{10}$ is a little farther to the right of $\frac{3}{8}$ on the number line, and fractions get larger as you go to the right on the number line, so $\frac{4}{10}$ is greater than $\frac{3}{8}$.*)

AFTER Connect

Display the fraction number lines completed in *Explore* on the overhead projector. Ask:

- What do you notice about the marks for $\frac{1}{2}$ and $\frac{2}{4}$? $\frac{1}{5}$ and $\frac{2}{10}$? $\frac{4}{5}$ and $\frac{8}{10}$? Explain. (*The marks for each pair of fractions are the same distance on the number line. That is because each pair names the same amount—they are pairs of equivalent fractions.*)
- How did you know what the first missing fraction on the line showing tenths was? (*I knew it had to be $\frac{1}{10}$ or $\frac{2}{10}$ so, since the mark is closer to $\frac{3}{10}$ than to 0, the fraction must be $\frac{2}{10}$.*)

Practice

1. Use three 12-cm strips of paper.
   Show thirds on one strip.
   Show halves on another strip.
   Show quarters on the third strip.
   Use the strips to order these fractions from least to greatest.
   $\frac{1}{3}, \frac{1}{2}, \frac{1}{4}$ $\frac{1}{4}, \frac{1}{3}, \frac{1}{2}$
2. Use three 10-cm strips of paper.
   Show halves on one strip.
   Show tenths on another strip.
   Show fifths on the third strip.
   Use the strips to order these fractions from least to greatest.
   $\frac{1}{2}, \frac{7}{10}, \frac{4}{5}$ $\frac{1}{2}, \frac{7}{10}, \frac{4}{5}$
3. Use three 12-cm strips of paper.
   Mark each strip with appropriate fractions.
   Use the strips to order these fractions from least to greatest.
   $\frac{5}{6}, \frac{2}{3}, \frac{7}{12}$ $\frac{7}{12}, \frac{2}{3}, \frac{5}{6}$
4. Use 3 copies of a12-cm number line like the one below.

   0 ——— 1

   Show eighths on one line.
   Show sixths on another line.
   Show quarters on the third line.
   Use the number lines to order these fractions from least to greatest.
   $\frac{7}{8}, \frac{4}{6}, \frac{3}{4}$ $\frac{4}{6}, \frac{3}{4}, \frac{7}{8}$

267

Sample Answers

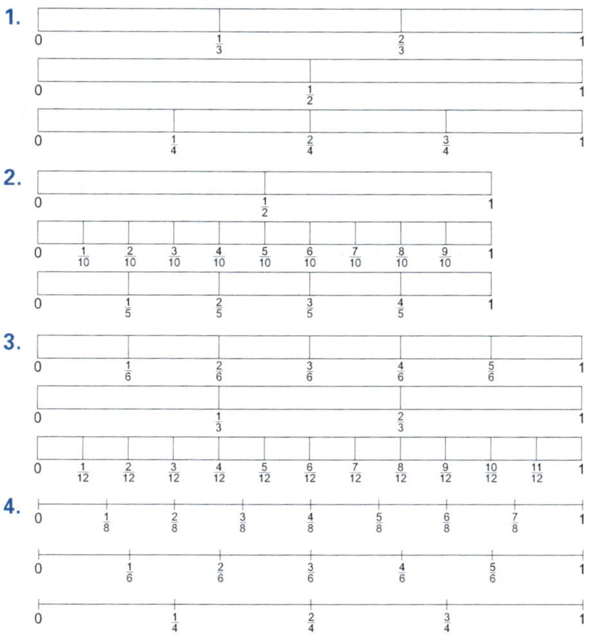

Review *Connect*. Ask:

- How is using paper strips to order fractions similar to using number lines?
  (*You treat the right-hand edge of the coloured parts of the paper strip as the dot/point on an ordinary number line. Then just order the fractions as usual.*)

Ensure students understand a quick way to compare fractions with the same numerator. When two or more fractions have the same numerator, the fraction with the greatest denominator is the least fraction, and the fraction with the least denominator is the greatest fraction. For example, for the fractions $\frac{3}{5}, \frac{3}{8}$, and $\frac{3}{10}$, $\frac{3}{10}$ is the least fraction and $\frac{3}{5}$ is the greatest fraction.

To compare fractions with the same denominator, the fraction with the greatest numerator is always the greatest fraction. For example, for the fractions $\frac{3}{8}, \frac{7}{8}$, and $\frac{6}{8}$, $\frac{7}{8}$ is the greatest fraction. Remind students that if two or more fractions with different denominators can be written with the same denominator, it becomes easy to compare and order the fractions.

Practice

Provide students with paper strips (Master 8.9), number lines (Master 8.10), and grid paper.

Ensure students understand that when a fraction has the same numerator and denominator, it represents 1 whole.

Assessment Focus: Question 7

Students should find equivalent fractions with twentieths and use this information to determine how many patches there would be for each colour.

Students could represent the quilt on grid paper and colour the squares as required.

5.

6.

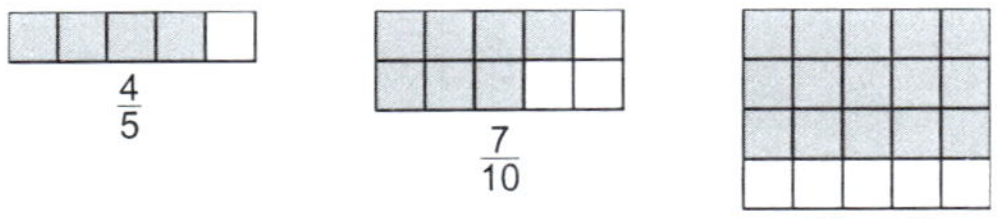

$\frac{4}{5}$ $\frac{7}{10}$ $\frac{15}{20} = \frac{3}{4}$

7.

Y	G	G	G
Y	G	G	G
Y	G	G	G
Y	G	G	G
Y	R	R	R

$\frac{1}{4}$ is equivalent to $\frac{5}{20}$; $\frac{3}{5}$ is equivalent to $\frac{12}{20}$. The number of red patches is $\frac{3}{20}$. The greatest number of patches is green $(\frac{12}{20})$. The least number of patches is red $(\frac{3}{20})$.

8. Jessica sold $\frac{6}{8}$ of her ribbon; Ramon sold $\frac{8}{12}$. Using a number line, I can see that $\frac{6}{8}$ is greater than $\frac{8}{12}$.

9. Thirds are larger parts than fifths, so $\frac{2}{3}$ is greater than $\frac{2}{5}$.

10. **a)** Fifths are larger parts than tenths.

b) The denominators are the same size in both fractions, so having 3 pieces $(\frac{3}{8})$ is more than having 2 pieces $(\frac{2}{8})$.

c) They are equivalent fractions; they name the same amount.

d) Fourths are smaller pieces than thirds.

REFLECT: An equivalent fraction for $\frac{3}{4}$ is $\frac{6}{8}$. Since $\frac{7}{8}$ is greater than $\frac{6}{8}$, $\frac{7}{8}$ is greater than $\frac{3}{4}$.

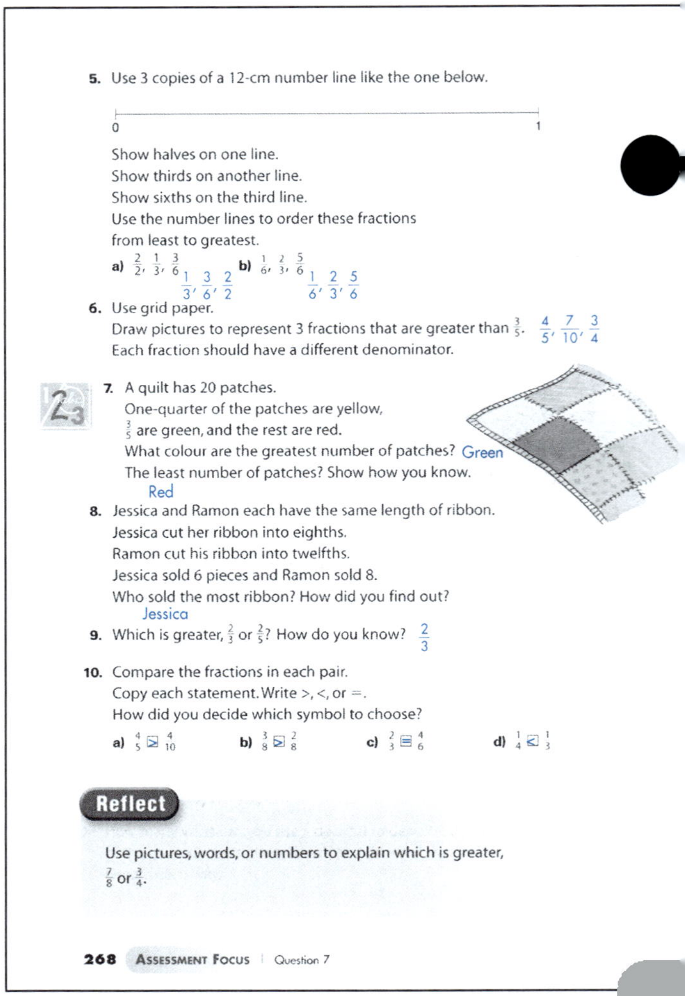

5. Use 3 copies of a 12-cm number line like the one below.

0 1

Show halves on one line.
Show thirds on another line.
Show sixths on the third line.
Use the number lines to order these fractions from least to greatest.

a) $\frac{2}{2}, \frac{1}{3}, \frac{3}{6}$ $\frac{1}{3}, \frac{3}{6}, \frac{2}{2}$ **b)** $\frac{1}{6}, \frac{2}{3}, \frac{5}{6}$ $\frac{1}{6}, \frac{2}{3}, \frac{5}{6}$

6. Use grid paper.
Draw pictures to represent 3 fractions that are greater than $\frac{3}{5}$. $\frac{4}{5}, \frac{7}{10}, \frac{3}{4}$
Each fraction should have a different denominator.

7. A quilt has 20 patches.
One-quarter of the patches are yellow,
$\frac{3}{5}$ are green, and the rest are red.
What colour are the greatest number of patches? Green
The least number of patches? Show how you know.
Red

8. Jessica and Ramon each have the same length of ribbon.
Jessica cut her ribbon into eighths.
Ramon cut his ribbon into twelfths.
Jessica sold 6 pieces and Ramon sold 8.
Who sold the most ribbon? How did you find out?
Jessica

9. Which is greater, $\frac{2}{3}$ or $\frac{2}{5}$? How do you know? $\frac{2}{3}$

10. Compare the fractions in each pair.
Copy each statement. Write >, <, or =.
How did you decide which symbol to choose?

a) $\frac{4}{5} > \frac{4}{10}$ **b)** $\frac{3}{8} > \frac{2}{8}$ **c)** $\frac{2}{3} = \frac{4}{6}$ **d)** $\frac{1}{4} < \frac{1}{3}$

Reflect

Use pictures, words, or numbers to explain which is greater, $\frac{7}{8}$ or $\frac{3}{4}$.

268 ASSESSMENT FOCUS | Question 7

ASSESSMENT FOR LEARNING

What to Look For	What to Do
Understanding concepts ✔ Students realize that a greater denominator means more (and hence smaller) equal parts in the whole.	***Extra Support:*** Students can do the Additional Activity, *Great Fractions* (Master 8.17). Students can use Step-by-Step 3 (Master 8.23) to complete question 7.
Applying procedures ✔ Students can use paper strips and number lines to compare and order fractions. ✔ Students can compare and order fractions with the same numerators and with the same denominators.	***Extra Practice:*** Students could write a problem similar to question 8. Then have them trade problems with a partner and solve the partner's problem. Students can complete Extra Practice 2 (Master 8.35).
Problem solving ✔ Students can use a variety of strategies to compare and order fractions.	***Extension:*** Challenge students to order the improper fractions $\frac{11}{5}$, $\frac{13}{6}$, and $\frac{9}{4}$.

Recording and Reporting
Master 8.2: Ongoing Observations: Fractions and Decimals

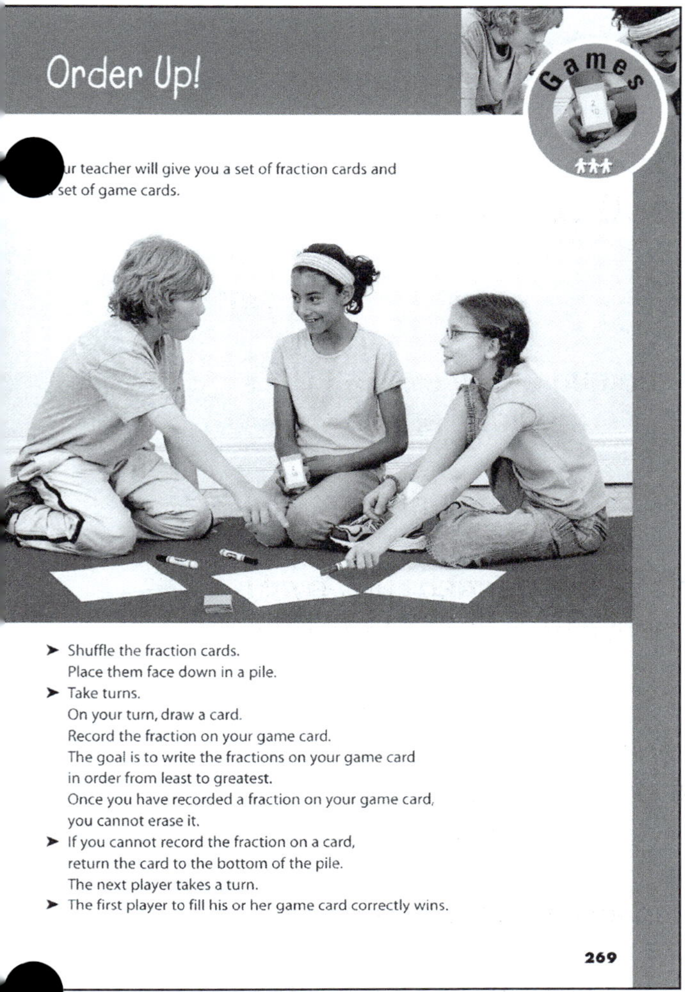

Order Up!

Games

...ur teacher will give you a set of fraction cards and
... set of game cards.

- ➤ Shuffle the fraction cards.
  Place them face down in a pile.
- ➤ Take turns.
  On your turn, draw a card.
  Record the fraction on your game card.
  The goal is to write the fractions on your game card
  in order from least to greatest.
  Once you have recorded a fraction on your game card,
  you cannot erase it.
- ➤ If you cannot record the fraction on a card,
  return the card to the bottom of the pile.
  The next player takes a turn.
- ➤ The first player to fill his or her game card correctly wins.

269

Order Up!

LESSON ORGANIZER — 20 min

Student Materials
- Fraction cards (Master 8.11)
- Game cards (Master 8.12)

YOUR NOTES

Relating Fractions to Decimals

LESSON ORGANIZER

40–50 min

Curriculum Focus: Relate fractions with denominators of 10 and 100 to decimals. (5m24)

Teacher Materials:
- overhead Base Ten Blocks
- hundredths grid transparency (PM 15)

Student Materials
- Base Ten Blocks
- hundredths grids (PM 15)

Optional
- Step-by-Step 4 (Master 8.24)
- Extra Practice 2 (Master 8.35)

Assessment: Master 8.2 Ongoing Observations: Fractions and Decimals

Key Math Learnings

1. Fractions with denominators of 10 and 100 can be written as decimals.
2. Fractions that do not have a denominator of 10 or 100 can be written as decimals if an equivalent fraction can be found that has a denominator of 10 or 100.

LESSON 4

Relating Fractions to Decimals

Many vegetable gardens have similar vegetables planted in the same area.

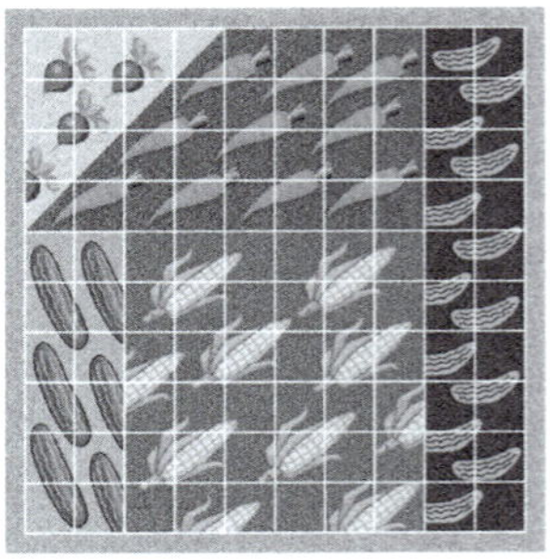

Explore

You will need Base Ten Blocks and grid paper.

Use rods and unit cubes to design a vegetable garden.
Use a flat to represent the whole garden.
Each vegetable is to occupy a separate region of the garden.
The garden must have:
- more carrots than corn
- more onions than zucchini
- all of the land planted with one of these vegetables

Record your vegetable garden design on grid paper.

➤ Write the fraction of your garden planted with each vegetable in as many ways as you can.

➤ How many ways can you use a decimal to describe the fraction of the garden that is planted with each kind of vegetable? Record each way.

270 LESSON FOCUS | Relate fractions with denominators of 10 and 100 to decimals.

BEFORE Get Started

Have students examine the vegetable garden on page 270 of the Student Book. Ask questions, such as:

- How many small squares are there in the garden? (*100*) How did you find out? (*There are 10 rows of squares and 10 squares in each row; 10 × 10 = 100*)
- How many small squares are planted with zucchini? (*20*) What fraction of the garden is that? ($\frac{20}{100}$, *or* $\frac{2}{10}$) How would you write a decimal showing what part of the garden is planted in zucchini? (*0.20, or 0.2*)

Depending on how well students answer the questions, you may want to repeat the questions for other vegetables.

Present *Explore*. Be sure students understand that the garden can be any shape.

DURING Explore

Ongoing Assessment: Observe and Listen

As students work on *Explore*, ask questions, such as:

- How many different vegetables have to be planted? (*4*)
- Can you plant $\frac{1}{4}$ of the garden with each vegetable? (*No; there must be more carrots than corn and more onions than zucchini.*)

Remind students they are to use both fractions and decimals in describing the part of their garden that is planted with each vegetable. Ask:

- Is there more than one way to describe the fraction of the garden planted with each vegetable? Explain. (*Yes; for example,* $\frac{20}{100}$ *of the garden is planted with corn. This is equivalent to* $\frac{2}{10}$, *or* $\frac{4}{20}$.)

Show and Share

Share your results with another pair of students.
How did you find the fractions and decimals?
hich fractions and decimals name the same amount?
w do you know?

Connect

This is Jake and Willa's design of a flower garden.

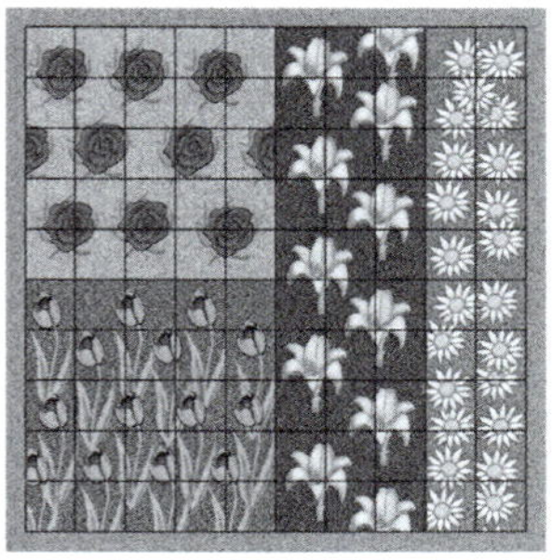

$\frac{1}{4}$, or $\frac{25}{100}$, of the garden is planted with roses.

$\frac{1}{4}$, or $\frac{25}{100}$, of the garden is planted with tulips.

$\frac{3}{10}$, or $\frac{30}{100}$, of the garden is planted with lilies.

$\frac{2}{10}$, or $\frac{20}{100}$, of the garden is planted with daisies.

➤ You can write fractions with denominators of 10 and 100 as decimals.

$\frac{3}{10}$ is 3 tenths, or 0.3.
$\frac{15}{100}$ is 15 hundredths, or 0.15.
$\frac{125}{100}$ is 125 hundredths, or 1.25.

271

REACHING ALL LEARNERS

Early Finishers

Students can explore questions such as: Is it possible to have $\frac{8}{10}$ of the garden planted in carrots and still meet all the conditions? $\frac{9}{10}$? Explain.

Common Misconceptions

➤ Students believe that fractions such as $\frac{1}{4}$ and $\frac{3}{4}$ cannot be written as a decimal because they do not have a denominator of 10 or 100.

How to Help: Use the hundredths grid to show students that $\frac{1}{4}$ and $\frac{25}{100}$, $\frac{3}{4}$ and $\frac{75}{100}$ name the same amounts.

- Can you write a decimal to describe your fraction in more than one way?
  (*Yes; 0.20, or 0.2*)

AFTER Connect

Invite pairs of students to share their designs, and to explain how they found the fractions and decimals to describe the parts of their garden. Pay particular attention to fractions and decimals that can be written in many different ways (for example, $\frac{2}{5}$, $\frac{4}{10}$, $\frac{40}{100}$, 0.4, 0.40, and so on). Ask questions, such as:

- How did you know you could write this fraction as $\frac{4}{10}$? $\frac{2}{5}$? $\frac{40}{100}$?
  (*Of the 10 rows in the garden, I planted 4 rows of carrots, so that is $\frac{4}{10}$. I thought of 2 rows together as a section, so out of 5 sections, 2 of them were corn and that is $\frac{2}{5}$. $\frac{40}{100}$ was easy; there are 100 small squares and 40 of them are corn.*)
- How did you know which decimals and fractions name the same amount?
  (*You read $\frac{4}{10}$ and 0.4 as four-tenths. You read $\frac{40}{100}$ and 0.40 as forty-hundredths.*)

Have students look at the fractions describing the flower garden in *Connect*.

Ask questions, such as:

- How do you know that $\frac{2}{10}$ and $\frac{20}{100}$ name the same amount?
  (*Of the 10 columns, 2 columns are daisies. So $\frac{2}{10}$ of the 100 squares are daisies. $\frac{2}{10} = \frac{20}{100}$*)
- Why is it easy to write fractions with denominators of 10 and 100 as decimals?
  (*We read them the same way; $\frac{3}{10}$ and 0.3 are both three-tenths.*)
- How do we know that $\frac{1}{4}$ can be written as a decimal?
  (*Since $\frac{1}{4}$ of the garden is the same as $\frac{25}{100}$ of the garden, and $\frac{25}{100}$ is the same as 0.25, we know that $\frac{1}{4}$ and 0.25 name the same amount.*)

Sample Answers

5. a) 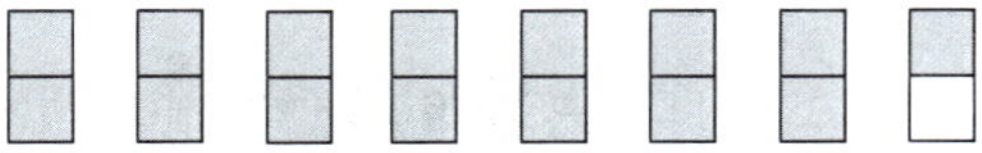

b) 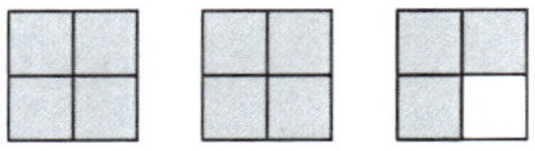

c) 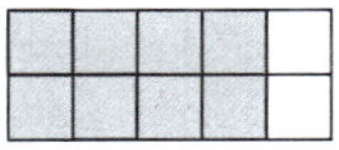

d) 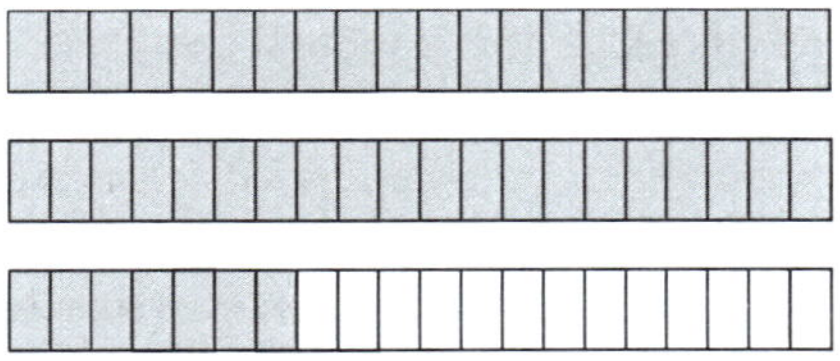

8. a) 0.20 + 0.25 = 0.45

b) 0.20 is the same as $\frac{20}{100}$, or $\frac{2}{10}$, or $\frac{1}{5}$.

0.25 is the same as $\frac{25}{100}$, or $\frac{1}{4}$.

9. No. $2\frac{3}{5}$ is the same amount as $2\frac{6}{10}$; when written as a decimal, this is 2.6, not 2.35.

REFLECT: Any fraction with a denominator of 10 or 100, such as $\frac{3}{10}$ (0.3) or $\frac{67}{100}$ (0.67), can easily be written as a decimal.

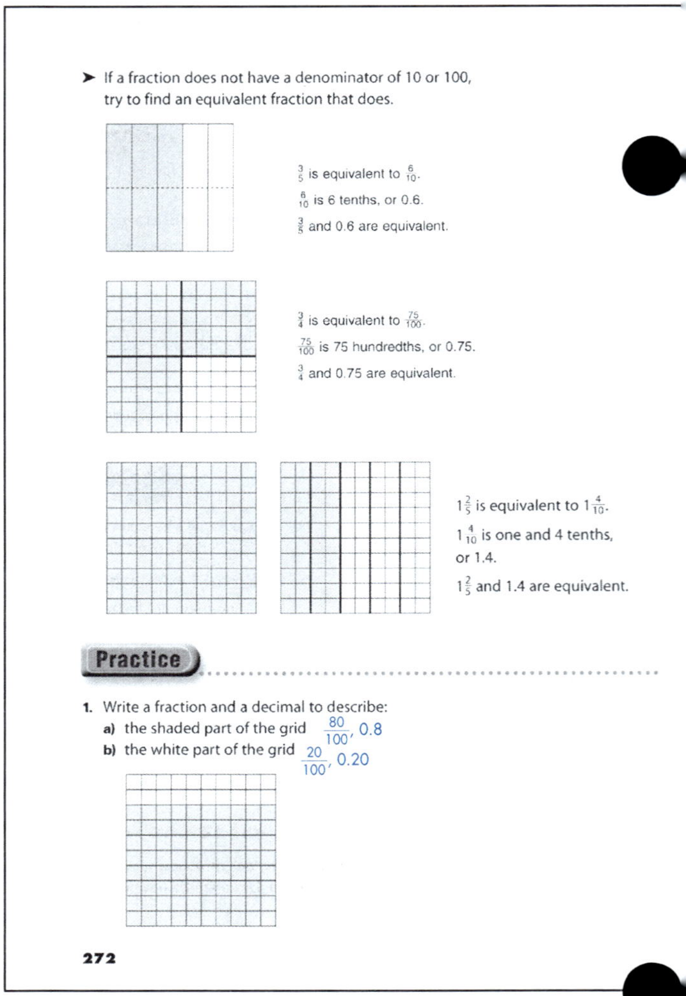

➤ If a fraction does not have a denominator of 10 or 100, try to find an equivalent fraction that does.

$\frac{3}{5}$ is equivalent to $\frac{6}{10}$.
$\frac{6}{10}$ is 6 tenths, or 0.6.
$\frac{3}{5}$ and 0.6 are equivalent.

$\frac{3}{4}$ is equivalent to $\frac{75}{100}$.
$\frac{75}{100}$ is 75 hundredths, or 0.75.
$\frac{3}{4}$ and 0.75 are equivalent.

$1\frac{2}{5}$ is equivalent to $1\frac{4}{10}$.
$1\frac{4}{10}$ is one and 4 tenths, or 1.4.
$1\frac{2}{5}$ and 1.4 are equivalent.

Practice

1. Write a fraction and a decimal to describe:
   a) the shaded part of the grid $\frac{80}{100}$, 0.8
   b) the white part of the grid $\frac{20}{100}$, 0.20

272

Practice

Ensure that students have Base Ten Blocks and hundredths grids available.

Assessment Focus: Question 8

Some students will write fractions with denominators of 10 or 100, such as $\frac{15}{100}$ and $\frac{30}{100}$. Others will be able to recognize that there is a simpler form of the fractions, such as $\frac{3}{20}$ and $\frac{3}{10}$.

Some students may represent the fractions or decimals on a grid to show that their sum is correct.

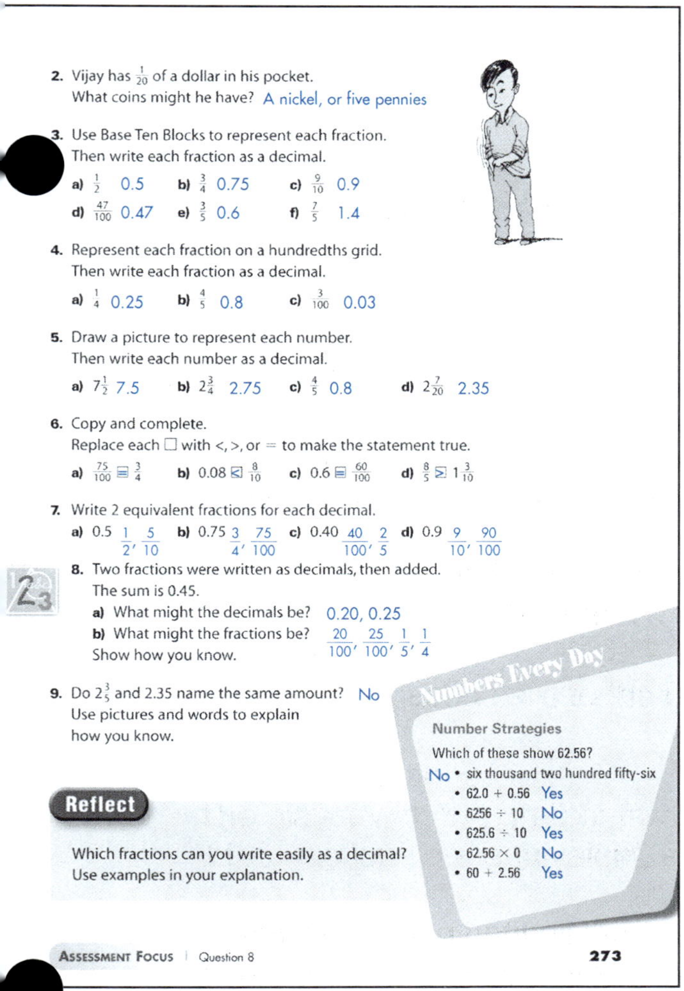

2. Vijay has $\frac{1}{20}$ of a dollar in his pocket.
What coins might he have? A nickel, or five pennies

3. Use Base Ten Blocks to represent each fraction.
Then write each fraction as a decimal.
a) $\frac{1}{2}$ 0.5 b) $\frac{3}{4}$ 0.75 c) $\frac{9}{10}$ 0.9
d) $\frac{47}{100}$ 0.47 e) $\frac{3}{5}$ 0.6 f) $\frac{7}{5}$ 1.4

4. Represent each fraction on a hundredths grid.
Then write each fraction as a decimal.
a) $\frac{1}{4}$ 0.25 b) $\frac{4}{5}$ 0.8 c) $\frac{3}{100}$ 0.03

5. Draw a picture to represent each number.
Then write each number as a decimal.
a) $7\frac{1}{2}$ 7.5 b) $2\frac{3}{4}$ 2.75 c) $\frac{4}{5}$ 0.8 d) $2\frac{7}{20}$ 2.35

6. Copy and complete.
Replace each □ with <, >, or = to make the statement true.
a) $\frac{75}{100} = \frac{3}{4}$ b) $0.08 < \frac{8}{10}$ c) $0.6 = \frac{60}{100}$ d) $\frac{8}{5} > 1\frac{3}{10}$

7. Write 2 equivalent fractions for each decimal.
a) 0.5 $\frac{1}{2}, \frac{5}{10}$ b) 0.75 $\frac{3}{4}, \frac{75}{100}$ c) 0.40 $\frac{40}{100}, \frac{2}{5}$ d) 0.9 $\frac{9}{10}, \frac{90}{100}$

8. Two fractions were written as decimals, then added.
The sum is 0.45.
a) What might the decimals be? 0.20, 0.25
b) What might the fractions be? $\frac{20}{100}, \frac{25}{100}, \frac{1}{5}, \frac{1}{4}$
Show how you know.

9. Do $2\frac{3}{5}$ and 2.35 name the same amount? No
Use pictures and words to explain how you know.

Numbers Every Day

Number Strategies

Which of these show 62.56?
- six thousand two hundred fifty-six No
- 62.0 + 0.56 Yes
- 6256 ÷ 10 No
- 625.6 ÷ 10 Yes
- 62.56 × 0 No
- 60 + 2.56 Yes

Reflect

Which fractions can you write easily as a decimal?
Use examples in your explanation.

Assessment Focus | Question 8

273

Numbers Every Day

Students could use place value to find which statements equal 62.56.

ASSESSMENT FOR LEARNING

What to Look For	What to Do
Applying procedures ✔ Students can write decimals for fractions with denominators of 10 and 100, and for fractions that have equivalent fractions with denominators of 10 and 100.	***Extra Support:*** Provide students with hundredths grids divided into fourths, fifths, and twentieths using bold lines to make it easier to see equivalent fractions. Students can use Step-by-Step 4 (Master 8.24) to complete question 8.
Understanding concepts ✔ Students recognize that decimals are another way of representing fractions with denominators of 10 and 100.	***Extra Practice:*** Students can prepare a chart showing fractions and their decimal equivalents (for example, for $\frac{1}{4}, \frac{1}{2}, \frac{3}{4}, \frac{1}{5}, \frac{2}{5}, \frac{3}{5}, \frac{4}{5}$). Students can complete Extra Practice 2 (Master 8.35).
	Extension: Have students list the denominators of fractions that can be written as equivalent fractions with denominators of 10 or 100. (*Answer: 2, 4, 5, 10, 20, 25, 50, 100*) Students describe their findings. (*Answer: They are factors of 100.)*

Recording and Reporting

Master 8.2: Ongoing Observations: Fractions and Decimals

Fraction and Decimal Benchmarks

LESSON ORGANIZER

40–50 min

Curriculum Focus: Explore benchmarks for fractions and decimals. (5m23, 5m24)

Student Materials
- circle graphs (Master 8.13)
- 10-cm number lines (Master 8.14)
- hundredths grids (PM15)

Optional
- Step-by-Step 5 (Master 8.25)
- Extra Practice 3 (Master 8.36)

Vocabulary: benchmark

Assessment: Master 8.2 Ongoing Observations: Fractions and Decimals

Key Math Learnings

1. The relative size of a fraction can be determined by comparing the fraction to 0, $\frac{1}{4}$, $\frac{1}{2}$, $\frac{3}{4}$, and 1.
2. The relative size of a decimal can be determined by comparing the decimal to 0, 0.25, 0.5, 0.75 , and 1.

LESSON 5 **Fraction and Decimal Benchmarks**

You have used fraction benchmarks to estimate with fractions.

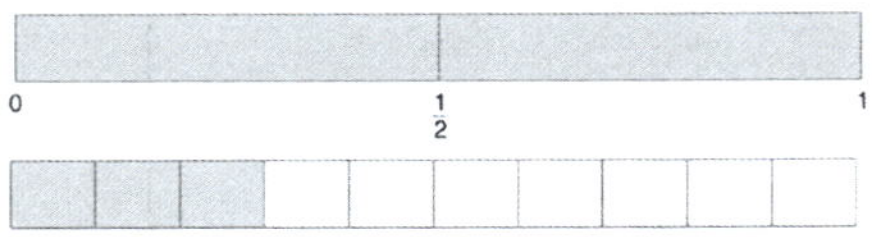

Is $\frac{3}{10}$ closer to 0, $\frac{1}{2}$, or 1? How do you know? $\frac{1}{2}$

In this lesson, you will explore decimal benchmarks.

Explore

You will need a large copy of this circle graph.

Jamal surveyed 100 people.

He asked this question:
What kind of animal would you most like to have as a pet?
The circle graph shows his results.

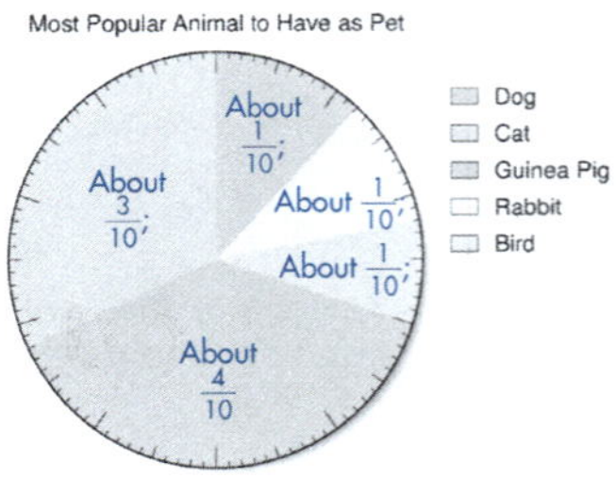

➤ About what fraction of the people surveyed would like to have each animal as a pet?

➤ Write each fraction as a decimal. Estimate when you need to.
0.4; 0.3; 0.1; 0.1; 0.1

Show and Share

Share your work with another pair of students.
How did you estimate each fraction? Each decimal?

274 LESSON FOCUS | Explore benchmarks for fractions and decimals.

BEFORE Get Started

Discuss the illustration at the top of page 274 in the Student Book.

Ask questions, such as:
- Why do you think 0, $\frac{1}{2}$, and 1 are used as benchmarks?
  (They are easy to locate on a number line or fraction strip.)
- Which benchmark is $\frac{3}{10}$ closest to? ($\frac{1}{2}$)
  How do you know?
  (It is between 0 and $\frac{1}{2}$, but closer to $\frac{1}{2}$.)

Present *Explore*. Distribute copies of Master 8.13.

DURING Explore

Ongoing Assessment: Observe and Listen

Ask questions, such as:
- How many people were surveyed? (*100*)
- Using the longest marks around the circle, what fraction of the circle would the distance between the marks represent? ($\frac{1}{10}$) How do you know?
  (There are 10 evenly spaced long marks around the circle, so each represents $\frac{1}{10}$.)

As students work, observe the strategies they use to estimate the fractions and decimals involved.

AFTER Connect

Invite volunteers to explain how they estimated the fraction for each pet type. Ask questions, such as:
- Were any pets preferred by more than half of those surveyed? (*No*)
- Which pet type was closest to $\frac{1}{2}$?
  (Dogs were preferred by about $\frac{4}{10}$.)

Connect

You can use benchmarks to compare fractions and decimals by estimating.

tend the fraction benchmarks to include quarters.
e can rename the benchmarks as decimals.

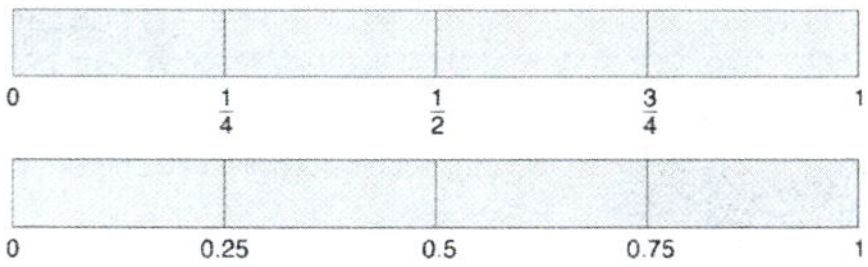

➤ Which benchmark is $\frac{5}{12}$ closest to?

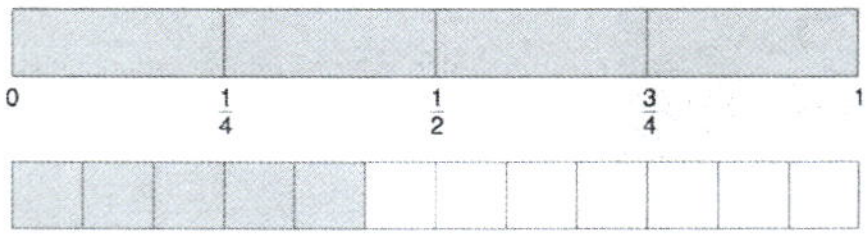

$\frac{5}{12}$ is greater than $\frac{1}{4}$ and less than $\frac{1}{2}$.
It is closer to $\frac{1}{2}$.

➤ Which benchmark is 0.6 closest to?

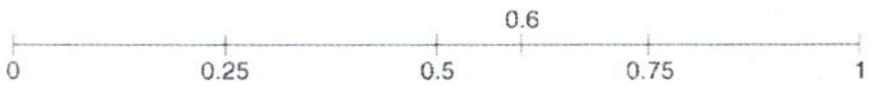

0.6 is greater than 0.5 and less than 0.75.
It is closer to 0.5.

Practice

1. Which benchmark is each fraction closest to? How do you know?

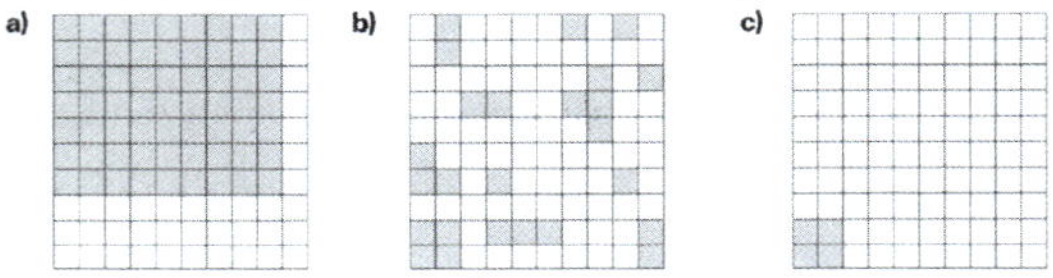

$\frac{3}{4}$ or 0.75 | $\frac{1}{4}$ or 0.25 | 0

275

REACHING ALL LEARNERS

Early Finishers

Students can answer questions, such as: About what fraction of the people surveyed did not choose the rabbit as the most popular pet?

ESL Strategies

Some students may not understand the term "benchmark." Explain that a benchmark is a reference used for comparing two things. Use a metre stick as a benchmark. Have students find and sort objects in the classroom into 2 groups: the first group consists of objects that are shorter than the benchmark, and the second group consists of objects that are longer than the benchmark.

Sample Answers

1. a) $\frac{63}{100}$ squares are shaded. This is just over halfway between $\frac{1}{2}$ and $\frac{3}{4}$ (or 0.5 and 0.75).

b) $\frac{25}{100}$ squares are shaded; this is equivalent to $\frac{1}{4}$ (or 0.25).

c) $\frac{4}{100}$ squares are shaded; this is closest to 0.

- What did you notice about the fraction of people that chose guinea pig, rabbit, or bird? (*The fraction for each of these animals is about the same, about $\frac{1}{10}$.*)
- How did you write the fractions as decimals? (*Each fraction had a denominator of 10, so it was easy to write it as a decimal.*)

Point out to students that the fraction strip in *Connect* uses 0, $\frac{1}{4}$, $\frac{1}{2}$, $\frac{3}{4}$, and 1 as reference points, and similarly the decimal number line uses 0, 0.25, 0.5, 0.75, and 1 as reference points. Explain that these fractions or decimals are easy to identify on a fraction strip or number line.

Practice

A number line marked in tenths (Master 8.14) and a hundredths grid (PM15) are needed for question 4.

Assessment Focus: Question 4

Students will likely answer "no" to part b because there are no marks between $\frac{7}{10}$ and $\frac{4}{5}$, but using the hundredths grid they will realize that 0.71, 0.72 , 0.73 , …, 0.79 are all between $\frac{7}{10}$ and $\frac{4}{5}$. It is possible that a few strong math students will put their own marks on the number line and label decimals. This would be a Level 4 response.

2. a) b) c) d)

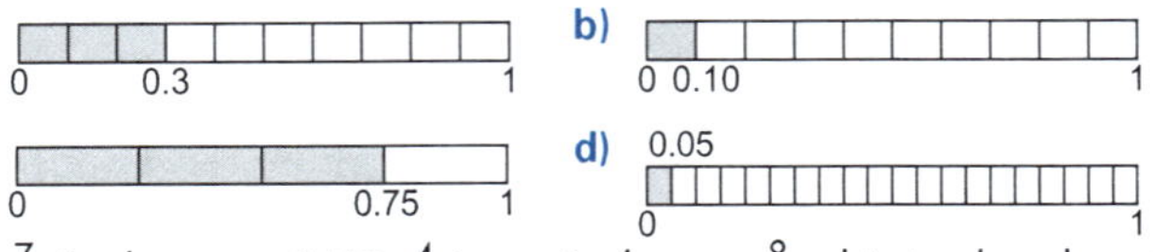

4. a) $\frac{7}{10}$ is closest to 0.75. $\frac{4}{5}$ is equivalent to $\frac{8}{10}$; this is also closest to 0.75.

b) Yes; they are 0.71, 0.72, 0.73, 0.74, 0.75. No; there are no marks between $\frac{7}{10}$ and $\frac{4}{5}$.

c) 0.71, 0.72, 0.73, …, 0.78, 0.79

5. $\frac{4}{5}$ is equivalent to $\frac{8}{10}$, or 0.8. This is closer to 0.75. 0.9 is closer to 1. So, 0.9 is greater than $\frac{4}{5}$.

REFLECT: Benchmarks help you get a quick idea how large a fraction or a decimal is. For example, if you are comparing $\frac{4}{10}$ and $\frac{2}{3}$, you know that $\frac{2}{3}$ is greater than $\frac{4}{10}$, because $\frac{4}{10}$ is close to $\frac{1}{2}$ while $\frac{2}{3}$ is close to $\frac{3}{4}$.

2. Draw a picture for each decimal.
What is the closest benchmark for each decimal?
a) 0.3 0.25 b) 0.10 0 c) 0.75 0.75 d) 0.05 0

3. Write each fraction as a decimal.
a) $\frac{2}{4}$ 0.5 b) $\frac{9}{10}$ 0.9 c) $\frac{37}{100}$ 0.37 d) $\frac{3}{5}$ 0.6
Which decimal benchmark is each fraction closest to?
a) 0.5 b) 1 c) 0.25 d) 0.5

4. Use a copy of this number line.

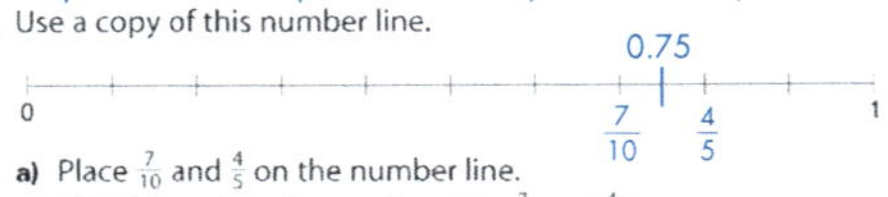

a) Place $\frac{7}{10}$ and $\frac{4}{5}$ on the number line.
Which benchmarks are closest to $\frac{7}{10}$ and $\frac{4}{5}$?

b) Can you place 5 decimals between the fractions on the number line?
If so, mark and label each decimal. If not, explain why not.

c) Use a hundredths grid to write 5 decimals between $\frac{7}{10}$ and $\frac{4}{5}$.

5. Use benchmarks to compare $\frac{4}{5}$ and 0.9.

6. Copy and complete the table.

Decimal	Lower Benchmark	Upper Benchmark	Nearest Benchmark
0.21	0	0.25	0.25
0.09	0	0.25	0
0.37	0.25	0.5	0.25
0.63	0.5	0.75	0.75
0.80	0.75	1	0.75
0.99	0.75	1	1

Reflect

Describe how using benchmarks can help you to compare and order fractions and decimals.

Numbers Every Day

Number Strategies

Find each difference.

17.5 − 8.3 9.2
0.85 − 0.07 0.78
21.2 − 10.3 10.9
10.01 − 6.51 3.5

276 Assessment Focus | Question 4

Numbers Every Day

Encourage students to think of mental math strategies they can use to find the differences.

ASSESSMENT FOR LEARNING

What to Look For

Applying procedures

✔ Students can use the benchmarks 0, $\frac{1}{4}$, $\frac{1}{2}$, $\frac{3}{4}$, and 1 to compare a fraction.

✔ Students can use the benchmarks 0, 0.25, 0.5, 0.75, and 1 to compare a decimal.

Communicating

✔ Students can describe how using benchmarks can help to compare and order fractions and decimals.

What to Do

Extra Support: Students having difficulty with question 6 could plot the numbers on a 0 to 1 number line.

Students can use Step-by-Step 5 (Master 8.25) to complete question 4.

Extra Practice: Students can do the Additional Activity, *Box It In* (Master 8.18).

Students can complete Extra Practice 3 (Master 8.36).

Extension: Students make a 0 to 1 number line marked in tenths. They then use these new benchmarks to complete question 6.

Recording and Reporting

Master 8.2: Ongoing Observations: Fractions and Decimals

LESSON
6
Relating Fractions to Division

Explore

Javier has 11 apples to share with a friend.
How many apples will each person get? $\frac{11}{2}$ or $5\frac{1}{2}$
Try to do this 2 different ways.
How will you record your answer?

Show and Share

Share your answer with another pair of classmates. Did you get the same answer? How do you know?

Connect

Helena has 8 doughnuts to share among 5 people.
How much will each person get?

Here are 2 ways to solve the problem.

➤ Use pictures.

Each person has 1 doughnut. There are 3 left over.
Divide each leftover doughnut in fifths.

There are $\frac{15}{5}$.
Each person gets $\frac{3}{5}$ of the leftover doughnuts.

LESSON FOCUS | Relate fractions to division. 277

LESSON 6

Relating Fractions to Division

LESSON ORGANIZER 40–50 min

Curriculum Focus: Relate fractions to division. (5m17)

Student Materials
- 1-cm grid paper (PM 23)

Optional
- Step-by-Step 6 (Master 8.26)
- Extra Practice 3 (Master 8.36)

Assessment: Master 8.2 Ongoing Observations: Fractions and Decimals

Key Math Learnings

1. Fractions can be thought of as "equal shares," and division can be thought of as "sharing."
2. A fraction can be represented as a division statement.

Numbers Every Day

Ensure students recall decimal place values (tenths, hundredths).

BEFORE Get Started

Draw 10 full circles and $\frac{1}{2}$ of another circle on the board, or on the overhead projector. Divide each full circle in half and shade one side of each circle. Ask:

- If you had ten $\frac{1}{2}$-pies left from a bake sale, how many whole pies could you make? (5)

We could write that $\frac{10}{2}$ is the same as 5. Ask:

- If 10 pies were to be shared between 2 people, how many pies would each person get? (5)

We would write $10 \div 2 = 5$.
Note that $\frac{10}{2}$ and $10 \div 2$ both equal 5.

Present *Explore*.

DURING Explore

Ongoing Assessment: Observe and Listen

As students work, ask questions, such as:

- If we share 11 whole apples between 2 people, how many whole apples will each person get? (5)
- Will there be any apples left over? (*Yes; 1*)
- What can we do with the leftover apple? (*Cut it in half and give half to each person.*)

AFTER Connect

Invite volunteers to show how they got their answers. Ask:

- What are two different ways of solving the problem? Explain each way.
(*Each person gets 5 whole apples. There is 1 apple left over. Cut the apple in half and give half to each, so that is $5\frac{1}{2}$ apples. Cut all the apples in half. Each person gets 11 pieces, so each person gets $\frac{11}{2}$ apples.*)

REACHING ALL LEARNERS

Alternative Explore

Materials: fraction strips marked in thirds

Students use the fraction strips to answer the question, "If it takes $\frac{1}{3}$ m of ribbon to make a bow, how much ribbon is needed for 10 bows?" (*$\frac{10}{3}$ m*)

Early Finishers

Have students determine how many apples each person would get if 11 apples were shared among 3 people, 4 people, and so on, to 11 people.

Sample Answers

1. a) 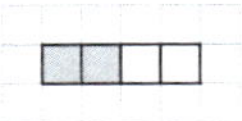

b) 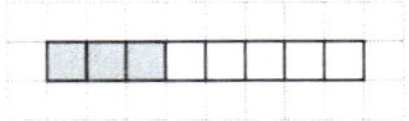

c) 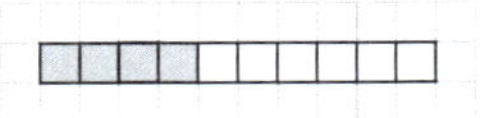

d) 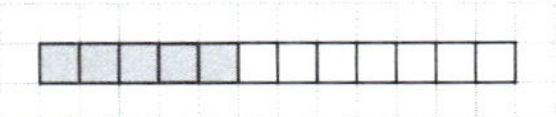

2. a) 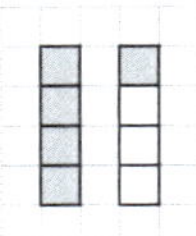

b) 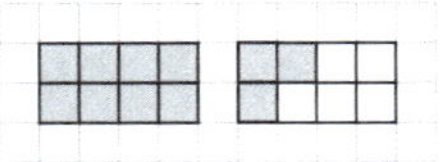

c) 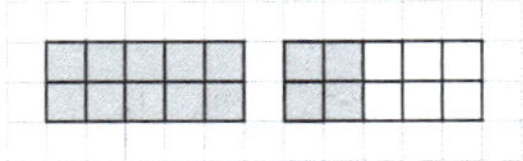

d) 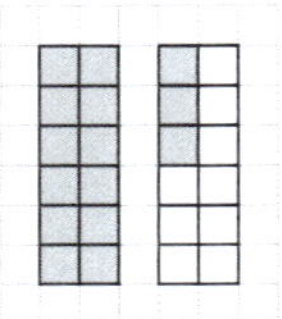

➤ Divide.
Eight doughnuts shared among 5 people is written as $8 \div 5$, or $\frac{8}{5}$.

$$5\overline{)8}$$
1 R3

The 3 left over are shared among 5 people.
This is written as $3 \div 5$, or $\frac{3}{5}$.

We write 1 R3 as $1\frac{3}{5}$.

Any division statement can be written as a fraction.

$8 \div 5 = \frac{8}{5}$

If the quotient is greater than 1, it can be written as a mixed number.

$8 \div 5 = \frac{8}{5} = 1\frac{3}{5}$

Practice

1. Write each division statement as a fraction.
Use grid paper. Draw a picture for each fraction.
a) $2 \div 4$ $\frac{2}{4}$ or $\frac{1}{2}$ b) $3 \div 8$ $\frac{3}{8}$ c) $4 \div 10$ $\frac{4}{10}$ d) $5 \div 12$ $\frac{5}{12}$

2. Write each division statement as a fraction.
Use grid paper. Draw a picture for each fraction.
a) $5 \div 4$ $\frac{5}{4}$ or $1\frac{1}{4}$ b) $11 \div 8$ $\frac{11}{8}$ or $1\frac{3}{8}$ c) $14 \div 10$ $\frac{14}{10}$ or $1\frac{4}{10}$ d) $15 \div 12$ $\frac{15}{12}$ or $1\frac{1}{4}$

3. Write each division statement as an improper fraction and as a mixed number.
Draw a picture to show each fraction.
a) $35 \div 6$ $\frac{35}{6}$, $5\frac{5}{6}$ b) $66 \div 5$ $\frac{66}{5}$, $13\frac{1}{5}$ c) $29 \div 3$ $\frac{29}{3}$, $9\frac{2}{3}$ d) $121 \div 10$ $\frac{121}{10}$, 12-

4. Write each fraction as a division statement.
a) $\frac{2}{3}$ $2 \div 3$ b) $\frac{14}{9}$ $14 \div 9$ c) $\frac{1}{8}$ $1 \div 8$ d) $\frac{47}{4}$ $47 \div 4$

5. Write a fraction and a division statement for this picture.

$\frac{2}{5}$, $2 \div 5$ or $\frac{3}{5}$, $3 \div 5$

278

Have students examine the doughnut diagram in *Connect*. Ask:

- Why were the leftover doughnuts divided into fifths?
(5 people are sharing them.)
- How many pieces of the leftover doughnuts will each person get? (*3*) Why do we write $\frac{3}{5}$ as each person's share of the leftover doughnuts?
(The pieces of the doughnut are fifths and each person will get 3 of them, so each person gets $\frac{3}{5}$.)
- How do we write the total amount each person gets? Explain in words. (*$1\frac{3}{5}$; 1 whole doughnut and $\frac{3}{5}$ of another one*)

Use *Connect* to show that any division statement can also be written as a fraction.

Practice

Students require grid paper for questions 1 and 2.

For question 7, students may choose the shaded or the unshaded part of the picture.

Assessment Focus: Question 6

Students recognize that the fractions represent whole numbers and they can draw a picture to illustrate this. Students should realize that the numerators of special fractions for twelfths will be multiples of 12.

6. These are special fractions for eighths:

$\frac{48}{8}, \frac{56}{8}, \frac{64}{8}, \frac{72}{8}$

a) Why do you think these fractions are special?
Use numbers, pictures, and words to explain.

b) Find 4 special fractions for twelfths. Show your work.
$\frac{12}{12}, \frac{24}{12}, \frac{36}{12}, \frac{48}{12}$

7. Write an improper fraction and a division statement for this picture.

$\frac{7}{4}$, $7 \div 4$; $\frac{1}{4}$, $1 \div 4$

8. Draw pictures.
Write $2\frac{2}{3}$ as an improper fraction and as a division statement. $\frac{8}{3}$, $8 \div 3$

9. Wenchun can make 4 origami swans from one sheet of paper.
How many sheets of paper will she need to make 45 swans? $11\frac{1}{4}$ sheets, or 12 sheets

10. Jimmy has 10 rolls of string. He plans to make 7 kites.
How much string is available for each kite? $\frac{10}{7}$ or $1\frac{3}{7}$ rolls

11. Six people share a gift of $900 equally.
How much do they each receive? $150

12. Mario cycled 17 km from his home to visit a friend.
He left home at 9 a.m. and arrived at his friend's home at 11 a.m.
He cycled the same distance each hour. How far was this? $\frac{17}{2}$ or $8\frac{1}{2}$ km

13. Janine made 5 pizzas for her party.
She invited 7 friends.
How much pizza did Janine think each person would eat? Explain. $\frac{5}{7}$

Numbers Every Day

Number Strategies

Write each number in expanded form.

- 20.25 $20 + 0.20 + 0.05$
- 202.5 $200 + 2 + 0.5$
- 2.02 $2 + 0.02$
- 2.52 $2 + 0.50 + 0.02$

Reflect

How are $\frac{13}{5}$ and $13 \div 5$ the same?
Use pictures, numbers, or words to explain.

ASSESSMENT FOCUS | Question 6 279

3. a)

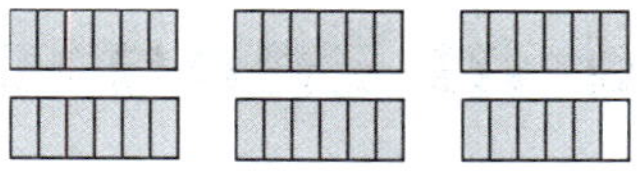

b)

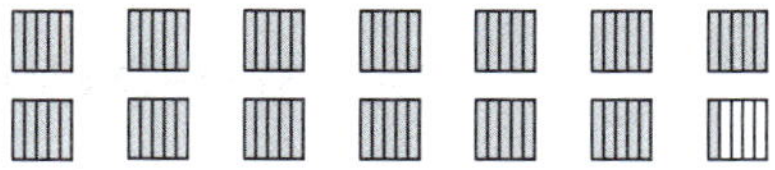

c)

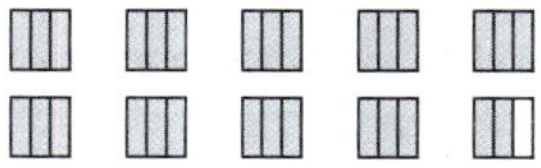

d)

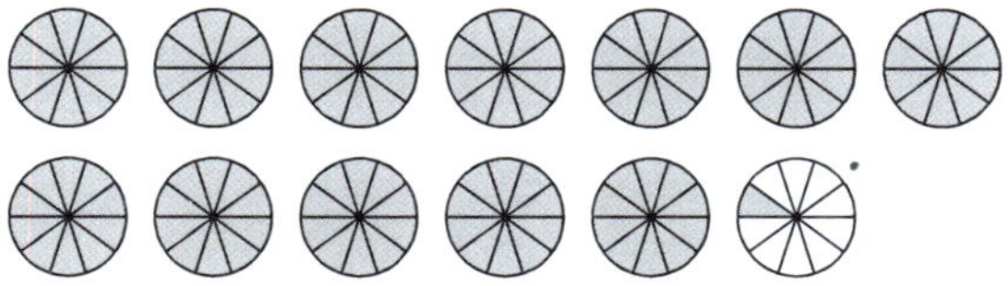

6. a) These fractions represent whole numbers.
For example, $48 \div 8 = 6$

b) $12 \times 1 = 12$, so $\frac{12}{12} = 1$; $12 \times 2 = 24$, so $\frac{24}{12} = 2$;
$12 \times 3 = 36$, so $\frac{36}{12} = 3$; $12 \times 4 = 48$, so $\frac{48}{12} = 4$

8.

13. If each pizza is cut into 7 pieces, each person will get 5 pieces, or $\frac{5}{7}$ of a pizza.

REFLECT: If you have 13 things to share among 5 people, that's $13 \div 5$. Each person would get $\frac{13}{5}$ of whatever was being shared.

ASSESSMENT FOR LEARNING

What to Look For	What to Do
Applying procedures ✔ Students can write a division statement as a fraction. ✔ Students can write a fraction as a division statement. ***Communicating*** ✔ Students can explain how fractions are related to division.	***Extra Support:*** Provide students with manipulatives to help them relate division statements to fractions. Students can use Step-by-Step 6 (Master 8.26) to complete question 6. ***Extra Practice:*** Have students write a division problem similar to questions 9 to 13. Then have students trade their problem with a partner and solve the partner's problem. Students can complete Extra Practice 3 (Master 8.36). ***Extension:*** Students draw 3 copies of a regular geometric figure, then divide them into equal parts. Students shade parts of each figure, then add to find the total number of shaded parts. Students write an improper fraction and a division statement for their drawing.

Recording and Reporting

Master 8.2: Ongoing Observations: Fractions and Decimals

Fractions and Decimals on a Calculator

LESSON ORGANIZER 10–15 min

Curriculum Focus: Use a calculator to convert fractions to decimals. (5m25)
Student Materials
- calculators

Assessment: Master 8.2: Ongoing Observations: Fractions and Decimals

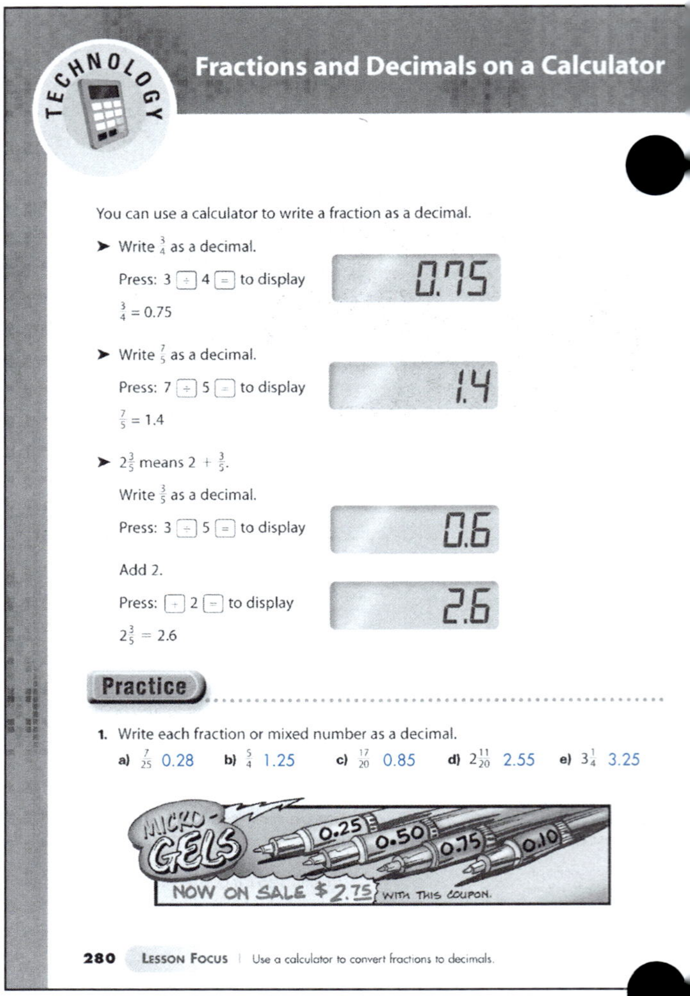
TECHNOLOGY

Fractions and Decimals on a Calculator

You can use a calculator to write a fraction as a decimal.

➤ Write $\frac{3}{4}$ as a decimal.
Press: 3 [÷] 4 [=] to display 0.75
$\frac{3}{4} = 0.75$

➤ Write $\frac{7}{5}$ as a decimal.
Press: 7 [÷] 5 [=] to display 1.4
$\frac{7}{5} = 1.4$

➤ $2\frac{3}{5}$ means $2 + \frac{3}{5}$.
Write $\frac{3}{5}$ as a decimal.
Press: 3 [÷] 5 [=] to display 0.6
Add 2.
Press: [+] 2 [=] to display 2.6
$2\frac{3}{5} = 2.6$

Practice

1. Write each fraction or mixed number as a decimal.
a) $\frac{7}{25}$ 0.28 b) $\frac{5}{4}$ 1.25 c) $\frac{17}{20}$ 0.85 d) $2\frac{11}{20}$ 2.55 e) $3\frac{1}{4}$ 3.25

280 LESSON FOCUS | Use a calculator to convert fractions to decimals.

BEFORE Get Started

Invite a volunteer to read the instructions.

Remind students to press [ON/C] before working with the next fraction or mixed number.

Have students convert some additional mixed numbers to decimals, such as $3\frac{2}{8}$, $5\frac{6}{7}$, and $8\frac{9}{10}$.

Remind students to record the numbers displayed by the calculator.

For students using a calculator other than a TI-108, consult the instruction manual.

DURING

Ask questions, such as:

- What are the easiest calculations to perform?
  (*Those involving proper fractions and improper fractions because they require only one step*)
- Why are mixed numbers more difficult to convert?
  (*There are two steps. I first use the calculator to convert the fraction part to a decimal. Then I have to remember to add the whole number part.*)
- How else could you convert a mixed number to a decimal?
  (*I could rewrite the mixed number as an improper fraction, then perform the division on a calculator.*)

AFTER

Have students discuss the use of decimals in the illustration at the bottom of page 280 of the Student Book.

Fractions In-Between

LESSON ORGANIZER — 20 min

Student Materials
- Fraction and decimal cards (Master 8.15)

Fractions In-Between

Games

ur teacher will give you a set of fraction and decimal cards.

- Place the decimal cards on the table in order from least to greatest.
  There should be space for 4 more cards between
  each pair of decimal cards.
- Shuffle the fraction cards.
  Deal 6 cards to each player.
- Take turns to place a card.
  The goal is to place the fraction cards so the fractions
  and decimals are in order from least to greatest.
  Place each fraction card so it touches another card.
  Fraction cards may be placed on either side of a card
  already on the table.
  If the fraction on the card is equivalent to one of the decimals,
  place the fraction directly below the decimal card.
  Cards may not be placed between two cards that are touching.
- As you place the card, name the fraction and its decimal equivalent.
- Place as many of your cards as you can.
  Once neither player can place any more cards, the round is over.
  Each player receives a strike for each card left in her or his hand.
- Play 5 rounds.
  Record the strikes for each round.
  The player with the fewest strikes wins.

281

YOUR NOTES

Estimating Products and Quotients

LESSON ORGANIZER

40–50 min

Curriculum Focus: Estimate products and quotients with decimals. (5m36)

Student Materials *Optional*
- Step-by-Step 7 (Master 8.27)
- Extra Practice 4 (Master 8.37)

Vocabulary: product, quotient, divisor, dividend, compatible numbers, decimal benchmarks

Assessment: Master 8.2 Ongoing Observations: Fractions and Decimals

Key Math Learning

Rounding, doubles, and compatible numbers can be used to estimate products and quotients with decimals.

Numbers Every Day

Students should round $3.47 up to $3.50, then find the difference between $5.00 and $3.50. Divide the difference by 25 to get the greatest number of quarters. To get the least number of quarters, students should realize that the change can be made up of other coins, such as 15 dimes and 3 pennies.

LESSON 7

Estimating Products and Quotients

Look at this division sentence: 63 ÷ 7 = 9
Which number is the divisor? The dividend? The quotient?
7; 63; 9

Explore

- A nickel has a mass of 3.95 g.
  What is the approximate mass of 7 nickels? About 28g
- Nine bags of dog food have a mass of 134.55 kg.
  What is the approximate mass of one bag? About 14 kg

Estimate each result.
Record your strategies and your estimates.
Show your work.

Show and Share

Share your estimates with another pair of students.
Discuss the strategies you used to estimate.
How can you use decimal benchmarks to estimate?

Numbers Every Day

Mental Math

A veggie burger costs $3.47. Suppose you pay with a $5 bill.
What is the greatest number of quarters you could get for change? The least number? 0

282 LESSON FOCUS | Estimate products and quotients with decimals.

BEFORE — Get Started

Ask students for examples of situations in which they might estimate the product of a decimal and a whole number (for example, finding the total cost of three items that cost $3.99 each), or the quotient of a decimal divided by a whole number (for example, sharing $5.50 among 3 people).

Present *Explore*. Ensure students understand they are to estimate the product and quotient, not to calculate them.

DURING — Explore

Ongoing Assessment: Observe and Listen

Ask questions, such as:

- Which operation did you use to estimate the mass of nickels? (*Multiplication*) The mass of 1 bag of dog food? (*Division*)
- How did you decide which strategy to use to estimate?
  (*I looked for ways of changing the numbers to those which I could calculate mentally.*)
- Do you think your estimate is high or low?
  (*I think my estimate is a little bit higher than the exact answer, because I rounded the decimal up.*)

AFTER — Connect

Invite volunteers to share their estimates and their estimation strategies. Ask:

- How did you estimate the mass of 7 nickels?
  (*I rounded 3.95 to 4, then multiplied by 7.*)
  What was your answer? (*28 g*)
- How did you estimate the mass of one bag of dog food?
  (*I used compatible numbers. I rounded 134.55 to 140, and divided by 10 instead of 9. My estimate was 14 kg.*)

Connect

➤ A ping-pong ball has a mass of 2.39 g.
Estimate the mass of 8 ping-pong balls.

Estimate: 2.39 × 8

2.39 is about 2.5.
Use doubles.
2 × 2.5 is 5.
Double 2 is 4: 4 × 2.5 is 10.
Double 4 is 8: 8 × 2.5 is 20.
The mass of 8 ping-pong balls is about 20 g.

> Another way to estimate is to use rounding.
> Round 2.39 to the nearest whole number, 2.
> 2 × 8 = 16
> The mass of 8 ping-pong balls is about 16 g.

➤ Four baseballs have a total mass of 575.94 g.
Estimate the mass of 1 baseball.

Estimate: 575.94 ÷ 4

Look for compatible numbers.
These are pairs of numbers you can divide mentally.
575.94 is close to 600.

600 is 60 tens.
60 tens ÷ 4 = 15 tens
= 150

The mass of 1 baseball is about 150 g.

> You can also estimate by rounding.
> Round 575.94 to the nearest ten, 580.
> 580 ÷ 4 = 145
> The mass of 1 baseball is about 145 g.

Practice

1. Estimate each product.
For which questions did you use decimal benchmarks?
   a) 7.01 × 9 About 63
   b) 3.8 × 7 About 28
   c) 11.85 × 5 About 60
   d) 19.9 × 4 About 80
   e) 25.78 × 2 About 52
   f) 9.4 × 6 About 57
   g) 2.84 × 8 About 24
   h) 3.61 × 12 About 42
2. Estimate each quotient.
   a) 9.8 ÷ 5 About 2
   b) 12.31 ÷ 2 About 6
   c) 44.69 ÷ 9 About 5
   d) 56.09 ÷ 7 About 8
   e) 225.3 ÷ 5 About 45
   f) 44.23 ÷ 4 About 11
   g) 255.2 ÷ 5 About 51
   h) 18.29 ÷ 6 About 3
3. One football costs $14.89.
About how much will 6 footballs cost?
About $90

283

REACHING ALL LEARNERS

Early Finishers

Have students explain whether their estimates for questions 1 and 2 are greater or less than the actual products and quotients, then use a calculator to check their predictions.

Common Misconceptions

➤ Some students may always use rounding to the nearest whole number as their estimation strategy.

How to Help: Lead students to see that rounding does not always result in the best estimate. The first example in *Connect* demonstrates this. Encourage students to try other estimation strategies, such as doubles and compatible numbers, to see which strategy will give an estimate that is as close to the actual product or quotient as possible.

Sample Answers

1. f) I used the decimal benchmark of 9.5
   h) I used the decimal benchmark of 3.5.

- Who used a different strategy?
(I rounded 134.55 to 135 and divided by 9. My estimate was 15 kg.)
- Which strategy do you think resulted in an estimate closer to the actual quotient?
(Rounding to 135 and dividing by 9 gives a closer estimate; the answer is just slightly greater than the actual quotient, because 135 is very close to 134.55.)
- How did you use decimal benchmarks to estimate the product in the first part of *Explore*?
(I put 3.95 on a 3 to 4 decimal number line and noticed that it is much closer to 4 than to 3.75, so I rounded 3.95 to 4, then multiplied by 7.)
- Why did you not use decimal benchmarks to estimate the quotient in the second part of *Explore*? *(Because 134.55 is closest to 134.5, but I do not know how to divide decimals at this point. So, I rounded to a whole number.)*

Review the strategies in *Connect*, then ask:

- When might you use doubles to estimate?
(When I am multiplying by an even number, such as 4, 6, or 8.)
- When might you round up to estimate? Explain.
(When shopping, I would round the cost of the items up to make sure I had enough money to pay for them.)

Practice

Assessment Focus: Question 8

In part a, students should change the decimal to a whole number that gives a product of 45. Students should realize that when you round down one of the factors in a multiplication statement, the estimated product will be less than the actual product.

In part b, students should round the decimal to a whole number that gives a quotient of 6. Students should realize that when they round the dividend up, the estimated quotient will be greater than the actual quotient.

8. a) I know 9 × 5 = 45. 9.47 is greater than 9.
So, 9.47 × 5 is greater than 45.
b) I know 24 ÷ 4 = 6. 23.86 is less than 24.
So, 23.86 ÷ 4 is less than 6.

9. a) 5.6 × 2 is about 6 × 2, which is 12.
1.4 × 4 is about 1 × 4, which is 4. 12 > 4
b) 6.8 ÷ 2 is about 7 ÷ 2, which is 3.5.
15.5 ÷ 5 is about 15 ÷ 5, which is 3. 3.5 > 3

REFLECT: To estimate 30.15 × 6, round 30.15 to the nearest whole number, then multiply: 30 × 6 = 180
So, 30.15 × 6 is about 180.
To estimate 49.32 ÷ 6, use the compatible numbers 48 and 6: 48 ÷ 6 = 8
So, 49.32 ÷ 6 is about 8.

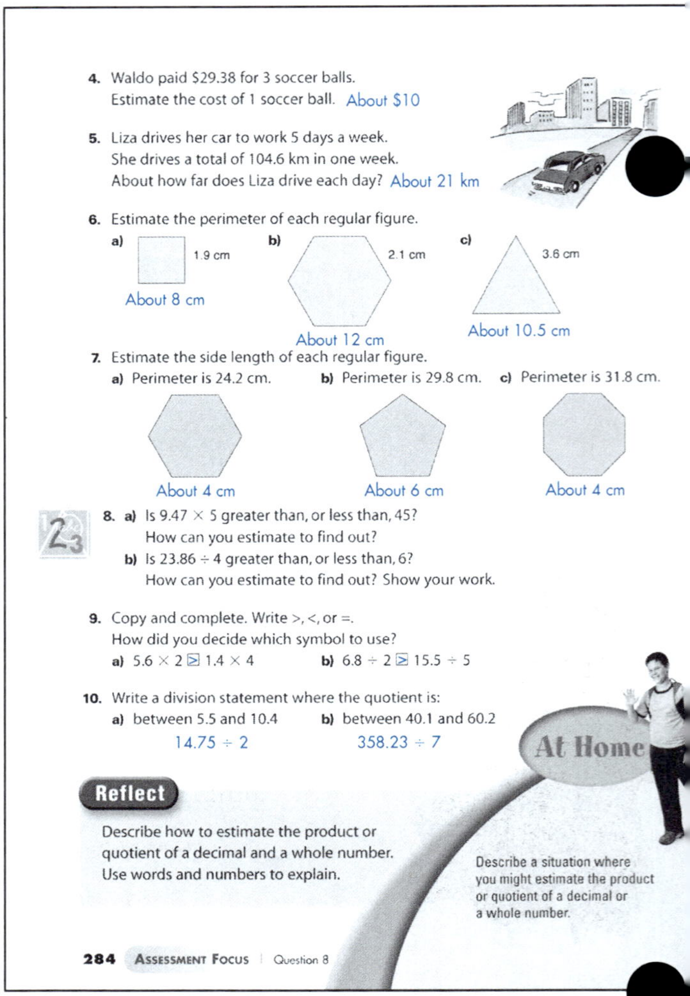

4. Waldo paid $29.38 for 3 soccer balls.
Estimate the cost of 1 soccer ball. About $10

5. Liza drives her car to work 5 days a week.
She drives a total of 104.6 km in one week.
About how far does Liza drive each day? About 21 km

6. Estimate the perimeter of each regular figure.
a) 1.9 cm — About 8 cm
b) 2.1 cm — About 12 cm
c) 3.6 cm — About 10.5 cm

7. Estimate the side length of each regular figure.
a) Perimeter is 24.2 cm. About 4 cm
b) Perimeter is 29.8 cm. About 6 cm
c) Perimeter is 31.8 cm. About 4 cm

8. a) Is 9.47 × 5 greater than, or less than, 45?
How can you estimate to find out?
b) Is 23.86 ÷ 4 greater than, or less than, 6?
How can you estimate to find out? Show your work.

9. Copy and complete. Write >, <, or =.
How did you decide which symbol to use?
a) 5.6 × 2 ☐ 1.4 × 4 (>)
b) 6.8 ÷ 2 ☐ 15.5 ÷ 5 (>)

10. Write a division statement where the quotient is:
a) between 5.5 and 10.4 — 14.75 ÷ 2
b) between 40.1 and 60.2 — 358.23 ÷ 7

Reflect

Describe how to estimate the product or quotient of a decimal and a whole number. Use words and numbers to explain.

At Home

Describe a situation where you might estimate the product or quotient of a decimal or a whole number.

284 ASSESSMENT FOCUS | Question 8

ASSESSMENT FOR LEARNING

What to Look For	What to Do
Applying procedures ✔ Students are able to use different strategies (rounding, doubles, compatible numbers) to estimate products and quotients with decimals. ***Communicating*** ✔ Students describe and justify the estimation strategies they use.	***Extra Support:*** Provide students with practice in finding compatible numbers, first for two whole numbers (such as 26 ÷ 5, 18 × 7) and then for a decimal and a whole number (such as 135.2 ÷ 7, 21.3 × 9). Students can use Step-by-Step 7 (Master 8.27) to complete question 8. ***Extra Practice:*** Have students complete Additional Activity 3, *Target 100* (Master 8.19). Students can complete Extra Practice 4 (Master 8.37). ***Extension:*** Have students cut out three priced items from a catalogue, then estimate how much it would cost to buy 7 of each item. Students then find the total cost.

Recording and Reporting
Master 8.2: Ongoing Observations: Fractions and Decimals

LESSON 8

Multiplying Decimals with Tenths

Explore

Denise drove around the track 3 times.
About how far did Denise travel? About 4.5 km
Find the exact distance. 4.8 km
Use any materials that help.
Show your work.

Show and Share

Share your work with another pair of students.
How did you estimate? Calculate?
Describe the strategies you used.
How do you know your answer is correct?

Connect

Another day, Denise drove around the track 4 times.
Find how far she travelled.

Multiply: 1.6 × 4
Here are 3 ways to find 1.6 × 4.

➤ Use Base Ten Blocks on a place-value mat.
Model 4 groups of 1.6.
Then regroup 20 tenths as 2 ones.

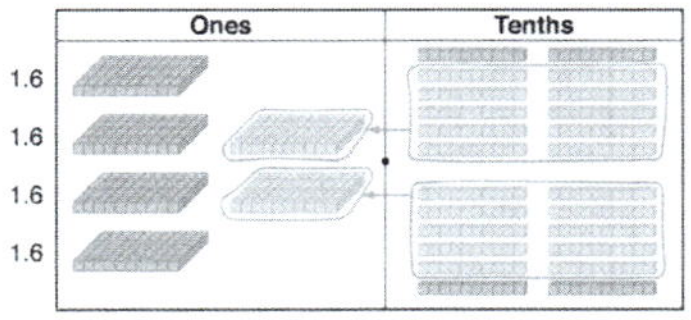

LESSON FOCUS | Multiply decimals with tenths by a 1-digit whole number. 285

Multiplying Decimals with Tenths

LESSON ORGANIZER 40–50 min

Curriculum Focus: Multiply decimals with tenths by a 1-digit whole number. (5m15, 5m26, 5m32)

Student Materials
- Base Ten Blocks
- decimal place-value mats (Master 8.16a)
- 0.5-cm grid paper (PM 22)

Optional
- Step-by-Step 8 (Master 8.28)
- Extra Practice 4 (Master 8.37)

Assessment: Master 8.2 Ongoing Observations: Fractions and Decimals

Key Math Learnings

1. Decimals can be multiplied using Base Ten Blocks, grid paper, or place value.
2. Multiplying a decimal by a whole number is similar to multiplying two whole numbers.

BEFORE Get Started

Write the decimal 2.5 on the board. Ask:
- How many ones are there? (2) How many tenths are there? (5)

Have students find 2.5 × 5 using mental math. First, they should try rounding down: 2 × 5 = 10. Then, they should try rounding up: 3 × 5 = 15. Ask:
- What do you think the product of 2.5 × 5 is? Explain.
(2.5 is halfway between 2 and 3. 2.5 × 5 is halfway between 10 and 15, or 12.5).

Tell students that, in this Lesson, they will learn different strategies to multiply decimals with tenths.

Present and discuss the problem in *Explore*.

Make Base Ten Blocks and decimal place-value mats available for students.
Establish that 1 flat = 1 and 1 rod = 0.1.

DURING Explore

Ongoing Assessment: Observe and Listen

Ensure students understand they should find an estimate of the distance Denise travelled before finding the exact distance.

Ask questions, such as:
- What materials could you use to solve the problem? How would you use them?
(I could use Base Ten Blocks to model 3 groups of 1.6.)
- How did you estimate how far Denise travelled? *(I rounded 1.6 down to 1 and multiplied by 3 to get a low estimate of about 3. I rounded 1.6 up to 2 and multiplied by 3 to get a high estimate of about 6. The product is between 3 and 6 but closer to 6, so I estimated Denise travelled about 5 km.)*
- How did you model 1.6 with Base Ten Blocks? *(I used 1 flat to represent 1, and 6 rods to represent 6 tenths.)*
- Why did you model 1.6 three times? *(Denise went around the track 3 times.)*

REACHING ALL LEARNERS

Alternative Explore

Materials: Cutouts of regular figures whose side lengths are not whole numbers.

Have students measure one side length of each figure to the nearest tenth of a centimetre. Students multiply to find the perimeter of each figure.

Early Finishers

Have students work in pairs. In turn, students roll 3 number cubes. They use the numbers rolled on the first 2 cubes to make a decimal number with tenths. They multiply the decimal by the number rolled on the third cube. The player with the greater product wins.

Common Misconceptions

➤ Students are unsure of how to multiply a decimal less than 1 by a whole number (for example, 0.8×5).

How to Help: Have students model the problem with Base Ten Blocks and regroup as needed:

0.8×5 = 8 tenths $\times$ 5 = 40 tenths = 4 ones = 4

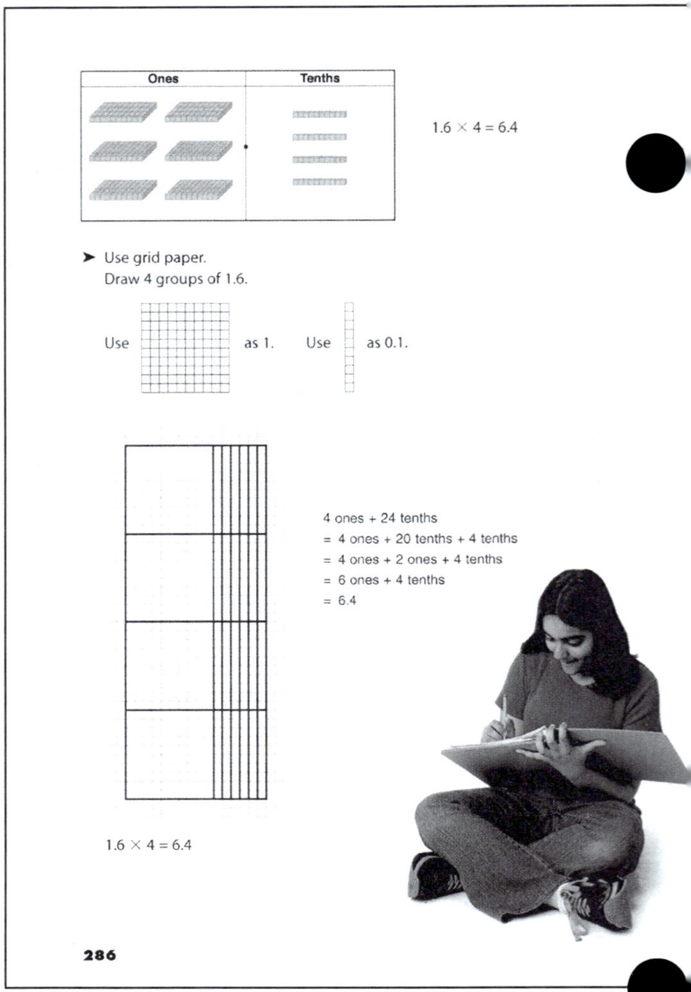
Ones | Tenths

$1.6 \times 4 = 6.4$

➤ Use grid paper.
Draw 4 groups of 1.6.

Use [grid] as 1. Use [strip] as 0.1.

4 ones + 24 tenths
= 4 ones + 20 tenths + 4 tenths
= 4 ones + 2 ones + 4 tenths
= 6 ones + 4 tenths
= 6.4

$1.6 \times 4 = 6.4$

286

- How many tenths are there on your mat? (*Three groups of 6 tenths equals 18 tenths.*) How many ones? (*Three groups of 1 equals 3 ones.*)
- What must you do with the tenths? (*Regroup 10 tenths as 1 one.*)
- How many ones are there now? (*4 ones*) Tenths? (*8 tenths*)
- How far did Denise travel? (*4.8 km*)

Watch for students who develop a strategy for multiplying 1.6 by 3 without using Base Ten Blocks. Make a note to have them explain their strategies to the class.

AFTER Connect

Invite students to share their estimates and solutions, and to explain the strategies and procedures they used. Some students may have used Base Ten Blocks or drawn pictures of Base Ten Blocks. Some may have used paper and pencil to add 1.6 + 1.6 + 1.6. Other students may have broken 1.6 into partial products and multiplied by 3. As volunteers demonstrate and/or describe their strategies, encourage the class to ask questions for clarification.

Review the strategies presented in *Connect*. If time allows, you may wish to have students model each strategy with another problem, such as 2.9×2.

➤ Use what you know about multiplying whole numbers.

```
  1.6
×   4
  2.4  ←—— 4 × 6 tenths = 24 tenths or 2.4
+ 4.0  ←—— 4 × 1 = 4, or 4.0
  6.4  ←—— 2.4 + 4.0 = 6.4
```

4 ones, 0 tenths is the same as 4 ones. So write 4 as 4.0.

➤ Estimate to check your work.
1.6 is close to 1.5.
2 × 1.5 is 3.
4 × 1.5 is 6.
The answer will be close to 6.

Denise travelled 6.4 km.

Practice

Use grid paper or Base Ten Blocks when they help.

1. Find only the products that are greater than 40.
   a) 4.3 × 2
   b) 7.5 × 4
   c) 6.8 × 7 47.6
   d) 10.7 × 8 85.6
   e) 0.8 × 5
   f) 24.1 × 9 216.9
   g) 36.3 × 6 217.8
   h) 15.8 × 3 47.4
   i) 8.6 × 4
   j) 50.7 × 7 354.9
2. Find only the products that are less than 40.
   a) 12.2 × 8
   b) 7.9 × 5 39.5
   c) 0.6 × 9 5.4
   d) 13.1 × 2 26.2
   e) 3.6 × 7 25.2
   f) 0.9 × 9 8.1
   g) 80.4 × 6
   h) 62.3 × 7
3. Choose the number that is closest to the product.
   How did you choose the number?
   a) 5.9 × 8 — 40, 46, (47)
   b) 15.7 × 3 — 45, (47), 50
   c) 40.2 × 5 — (200), 205, 210
   d) 8.1 × 4 — 31, (32), 33

287

Sample Answers

3. I rounded the decimal to the nearest whole number and multiplied. Then I chose the number closest to the product.

Practice

Have Base Ten Blocks and grid paper available for all questions.

Assessment Focus: Question 8

Students should be able to multiply 1.4 × 6 and compare the product with 8. Some students may subtract 8 from the product to determine how much ribbon Jakob is short.

Level 4 students will point out that in fact Jakob may need more ribbon to allow for overlap or cutting losses.

YOUR NOTES

6. Jeanette walked 2.2 km each day for 4 days. How far did she walk in all?
2.2 × 4 = 8.8; Jeanette walked 8.8 km in all.

7. a) The answer is incorrect because it is less than 25.4, one of the factors in the multiplication statement, and the other factor is greater than 1.
b) If Marija had estimated the product, she would have known that it would be greater than 25 × 6 = 150.

8. 1.4 × 6 = 8.4; Jakob needs 8.4 m of ribbon. 8.4 m is greater than 8 m.
So, Jakob will not have enough ribbon.

9. 1.4 × 2 = 2.8
1.4 × 4 = 5.6
1.4 × 6 = 8.4
The other factor is 6.

10. I know 1 × 8 = 8 and 2 × 8 = 16. 1.23 is greater than 1 and less than 2, so the product of 1.23 × 8 will be greater than 8 and less than 16. So, 1.23 × 8 must be 9.84.

REFLECT: It is important to estimate the product when you multiply a decimal by a whole number to make sure your answer is reasonable. I can also use an estimate to help me place the decimal point.

Numbers Every Day

Students can use guess and check.

---

4. The Jonestown go-kart track is 0.9 km long.
Suppose you went around the track 5 times.
How far would you travel? 4.5 km

5. Suppose you completed 5 laps at Kendall's Kartway and 4 laps at the Jonestown track.
How far would you travel in all? 11.6 km

6. Write a story problem you can solve by multiplying a decimal with tenths by a whole number.
Solve your problem.

7. Marija multiplied 25.4 × 6.
Her answer was 15.24.
a) Why is this answer incorrect?
b) If Marija had estimated the product, what would she have known?

8. Jakob has 6 gifts.
He needs 1.4 m of ribbon to wrap each gift.
Jakob buys 8 m of ribbon.
Will Jakob have enough ribbon? Explain.
No

9. The product of two factors is 8.4.
One factor is 1.4.
The other factor is a 1-digit whole number.
Find the other factor. 6
Show your work.

10. Is the product of 1.23 × 8 equal to 0.984, 9.84, or 98.4? 9.84
Without calculating, explain how you know.

Reflect

Explain why it is important to estimate the product when you multiply a decimal by a whole number.

Numbers Every Day

Calculator Skills

Find 3 numbers with a product of 30 and a sum of 9.5.
3, 4, 2.5

288 ASSESSMENT FOCUS | Question 8

ASSESSMENT FOR LEARNING

What to Look For	What to Do
Applying procedures ✔ Students can use more than one strategy to multiply a decimal with tenths by a 1-digit whole number.	***Extra Support:*** Encourage students to model each multiplication problem with Base Ten Blocks, then use a different strategy to check. Students can use Step-by-Step 8 (Master 8.28) to complete question 8.
Problem solving ✔ Students can pose and solve problems involving the multiplication of a decimal with tenths by a 1-digit whole number.	***Extra Practice:*** Have students complete Additional Activity 4, *Estimating Decimal Products* (Master 8.20). Students can complete Extra Practice 4 (Master 8.37).
Communicating ✔ Students can explain their estimation and calculation strategies clearly and concisely.	***Extension:*** Challenge students to find a decimal with tenths and a 1-digit whole number whose product is 15.6. Encourage students to find as many answers as they can. (*15.6 × 1, 7.8 × 2, 5.2 × 3, 3.9 × 4, 2.6 × 6*)

Recording and Reporting
Master 8.2: Ongoing Observations: Fractions and Decimals

LESSON 9

Multiplying Decimals with Hundredths

Explore

The fastest growing plant in the world is a species of bamboo.
It grows at an amazing rate of 0.91 m per day.
How much does this species of bamboo grow in one week?
6.37 m

First estimate.
Then find ways to check your estimate.
Show your work.

Show and Share

Share your work with another pair of students.
Describe the strategies you used.
How do you know your answer is correct?

Connect

Some varieties of cactus grow only 2.54 cm per year!
How much would one of these cacti grow in 3 years?

Multiply: 2.54 × 3

Here are 2 ways to find 2.54 × 3.

➤ Use Base Ten Blocks.
Model 3 groups of 2.54.

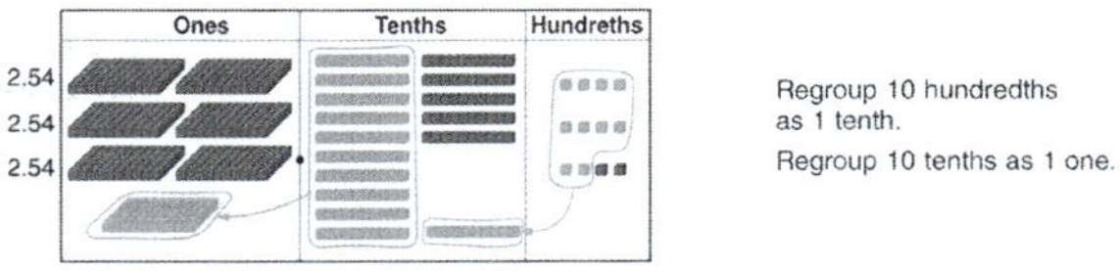

LESSON FOCUS | Multiply decimals with hundredths by a 1-digit whole number. 289

Multiplying Decimals with Hundredths

LESSON ORGANIZER 40–50 min

Curriculum Focus: Multiply decimals with hundredths by a 1-digit whole number. (5m26, 5m32)

Teacher Materials
- metre stick

Student Materials
- Base Ten Blocks
- decimal place-value mats (Master 8.16b)

Optional
- Step-by-Step 9 (Master 8.29)
- Extra Practice 5 (Master 8.38)

Assessment: Master 8.2 Ongoing Observations: Fractions and Decimals

Key Math Learnings

1. Multiplying a decimal with hundredths by a whole number is similar to multiplying a 3-digit number by a 1-digit whole number.
2. Estimation can be used to place the decimal in the product.

BEFORE Get Started

Display a metre stick and have students recall that 1 m = 100 cm. Ask:
- What fraction of 1 m is 1 cm? (*$\frac{1}{100}$*)
- How would you write $\frac{1}{100}$ as a decimal? (*0.01*)

Present the problem in *Explore*. Ask:
- How many centimetres is 0.91 m? (*91 cm*)

Have a volunteer find 0.91 on the metre stick. Ask:
- How will you find how much the bamboo grows in one week? (*Multiply 0.91 × 7, since there are 7 days in 1 week.*)
- Suppose you use Base Ten Blocks to multiply 0.91 × 7. What blocks will you use to represent ones? (*Flats*) Tenths? (*Rods*) Hundredths? (*Unit cubes*)

Have Base Ten Blocks available for student use.

DURING Explore

Ongoing Assessment: Observe and Listen

Ask questions, such as:
- How did you model 0.91 with Base Ten Blocks?
  (*I used 9 rods and 1 unit cube.*)
- How many groups of 9 rods and 1 unit cube did you make? (7) Why? (*There are 7 days in a week.*)
- How many hundredths do you have? (*7 hundredths*) How many tenths? (*7 groups of 9 tenths is 63 tenths.*)
- What will you do with the tenths? (*Regroup them as 6 ones and 3 tenths.*)
- What do you see on your mat now? (*6 ones, 3 tenths, and 7 hundredths*)
- How much will the bamboo grow in 1 week? (*6.37 m*)

REACHING ALL LEARNERS

Alternative Explore

Materials: play money (loonies, dimes, and pennies)
Corrina walked 5 km in the charity walk-a-thon. Her aunt sponsored Corrina at $0.75 a km. Estimate, then find how much money Corrina's aunt pledged. (*About $4, $3.75*)

Early Finishers

Have students choose 2 multiplications from question 2 and write a story problem for each one.

Common Misconceptions

➤ Students fail to align the digits properly when using partial products to multiply.

How to Help: Have students work on lined paper turned sideways. This may help them to position the digits correctly.

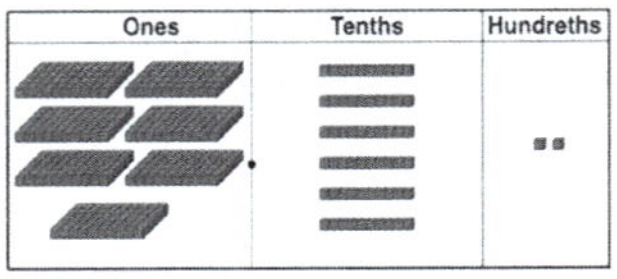

7 ones + 6 tenths + 2 hundredths = 7.62
2.54 × 3 = 7.62

➤ Use what you know about multiplying whole numbers.

Step 1: Record the numbers without the decimal point.
Multiply as you would with whole numbers.

```
 254
×  3
  12
 150
 600
 762
```

Step 2: Estimate to place the decimal point in the product.
Use front-end estimation: 2.54 is about 2.
3 × 2 = 6, so place the decimal point after 7.
2.54 × 3 = 7.62

The cactus would grow 7.62 cm in 3 years.

Practice

Use Base Ten Blocks when they help.

1. Estimate. Then multiply.

a) 2.34 × 2 = 4.68 About 4
b) 6.08 × 6 = 36.48 About 36
c) 3.79 × 4 = 15.16 About 16
d) 5.25 × 3 = 15.75 About 15
e) 7.88 × 5 = 39.4 About 40
f) $4.85 × 7 = $33.95 About $35

290

Watch for students who use a different strategy to multiply 0.91 × 7. Have them explain the strategy.

AFTER Connect

Invite students to share their estimation and computation strategies with the class. Ask questions, such as:

- How do you know your answer is reasonable? (*My estimate was about 7 m. 6.37 m is close to 7 m.*)
- How can you check your answer to make sure it is correct? (*I can add 0.91 seven times or I can use a calculator to check.*)

Review the strategies presented in *Connect*. When using multiplication, emphasize that multiplying with decimals involves the same process as multiplying with whole numbers. The difference lies in the need for a decimal point in the product when multiplying with decimals. Stress as well the strategy of estimating to place the decimal point in the product.

Practice

Have Base Ten Blocks available for all questions.

Assessment Focus: Question 6

Students should be able to provide an estimate for each question, compare the estimate with 15, and explain their strategy.

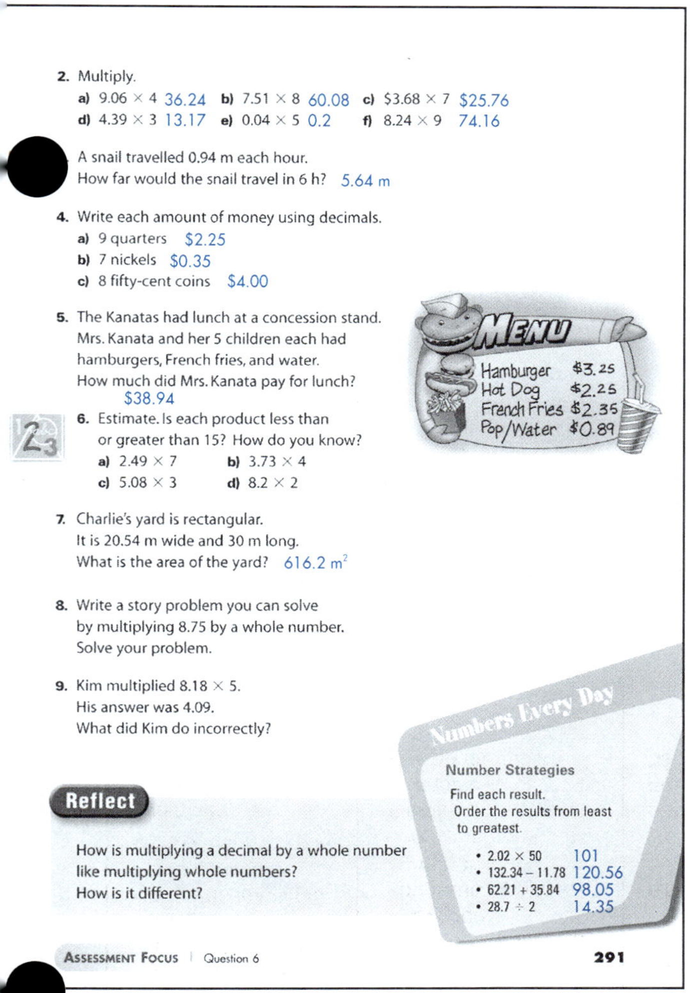

2. Multiply.
   a) 9.06 × 4 36.24 b) 7.51 × 8 60.08 c) $3.68 × 7 $25.76
   d) 4.39 × 3 13.17 e) 0.04 × 5 0.2 f) 8.24 × 9 74.16

A snail travelled 0.94 m each hour.
How far would the snail travel in 6 h? 5.64 m

4. Write each amount of money using decimals.
   a) 9 quarters $2.25
   b) 7 nickels $0.35
   c) 8 fifty-cent coins $4.00

5. The Kanatas had lunch at a concession stand. Mrs. Kanata and her 5 children each had hamburgers, French fries, and water. How much did Mrs. Kanata pay for lunch? $38.94

6. Estimate. Is each product less than or greater than 15? How do you know?
   a) 2.49 × 7 b) 3.73 × 4
   c) 5.08 × 3 d) 8.2 × 2

7. Charlie's yard is rectangular. It is 20.54 m wide and 30 m long. What is the area of the yard? 616.2 m^2

8. Write a story problem you can solve by multiplying 8.75 by a whole number. Solve your problem.

9. Kim multiplied 8.18 × 5. His answer was 4.09. What did Kim do incorrectly?

Reflect

How is multiplying a decimal by a whole number like multiplying whole numbers? How is it different?

Numbers Every Day

Number Strategies

Find each result. Order the results from least to greatest.
- 2.02 × 50 101
- 132.34 − 11.78 120.56
- 62.21 + 35.84 98.05
- 28.7 ÷ 2 14.35

ASSESSMENT FOCUS | Question 6 291

Sample Answers

6. a) 2.49 is close to 2.5. 2.5 × 7 = 17.5; so, 2.49 × 7 is greater than 15.
   b) 3.73 is close to 3.75. 3.75 × 4 = 15; so, 3.73 × 4 is less than 15.
   c) 5.08 is close to 5. 5 × 3 = 15; so, 5.08 × 3 is greater than 15.
   d) 8.2 is close to 8. 8 × 2 = 16; so, 8.2 × 2 is greater than 15.
8. Perry's garden is 8.75 m long and 4 m wide.
   What is the area of Perry's garden?
   8.75 × 4 = 35; the area of Perry's garden is 35 m^2.
9. Kim put the decimal point in the wrong place.
   If he had estimated to place the decimal point, he would have put it after the 0, because 8.18 × 5 is about 8 × 5, which is 40.

REFLECT: Multiplying a decimal by a whole number is like multiplying two whole numbers because you use exactly the same steps. It's different because you need to put a decimal point in the product, unless the product is a whole number.

Numbers Every Day

Students can use Base Ten Blocks or paper and pencil to find each result.
From least to greatest: 14.35, 98.05, 101, 120.56

ASSESSMENT FOR LEARNING

What to Look For	What to Do
Applying procedures ✔ Students can multiply a decimal with hundredths by a 1-digit whole number. ✔ Students can check their products for reasonableness by estimating. ***Understanding concepts*** ✔ Students understand that the process of multiplying a decimal by a whole number is the same as multiplying two whole numbers. With decimals, a decimal point is needed in the product.	***Extra Support:*** Have students model each question with Base Ten Blocks. Students can use Step-by Step 9 (Master 8.29) to complete question 6. ***Extra Practice:*** Have students use the menu on page 291. They find the cost of 8 of each item on the menu, then find the total cost. Students can complete Extra Practice 5 (Master 8.38). ***Extension:*** Challenge students to solve this problem: Ballpoint pens cost $0.35. Gel pens cost $1.25. Elsie spent exactly $13 on 14 pens, How many of each kind of pen did Elsie buy? (*9 gel pens and 5 ballpoint pens*)

Recording and Reporting

Master 8.2: Ongoing Observations: Fractions and Decimals

Strategies Toolkit

LESSON ORGANIZER — 40–50 min

Curriculum Focus: Interpret a problem and select an appropriate strategy. (5m8, 5m35)

Teacher Materials

- Pattern Blocks (PM28) or overhead Pattern Blocks

Student Materials

- Pattern Blocks (PM 28)
- triangular grid paper (PM27)

Assessment: PM1 Inquiry Process Check List, PM 3 Self-Assessment: Problem Solving

Key Math Learning

A model can be used to help solve problems with fractions and decimals.

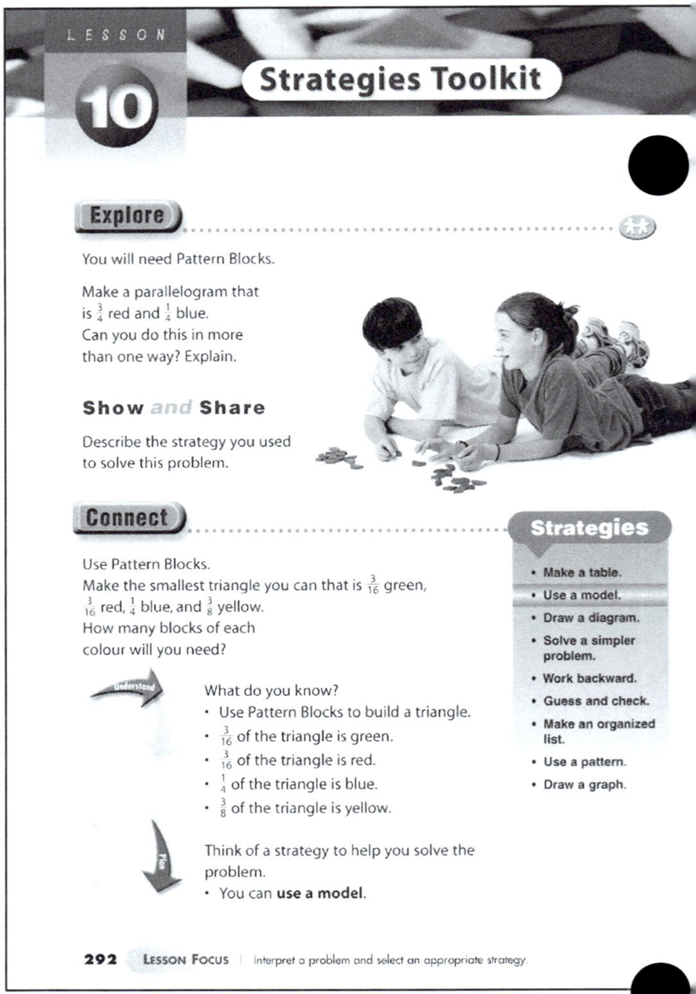
LESSON 10 Strategies Toolkit

Explore

You will need Pattern Blocks.

Make a parallelogram that is $\frac{3}{4}$ red and $\frac{1}{4}$ blue.
Can you do this in more than one way? Explain.

Show and Share

Describe the strategy you used to solve this problem.

Connect

Use Pattern Blocks.
Make the smallest triangle you can that is $\frac{3}{16}$ green, $\frac{3}{16}$ red, $\frac{1}{4}$ blue, and $\frac{3}{8}$ yellow.
How many blocks of each colour will you need?

Understand

What do you know?

- Use Pattern Blocks to build a triangle.
- $\frac{3}{16}$ of the triangle is green.
- $\frac{3}{16}$ of the triangle is red.
- $\frac{1}{4}$ of the triangle is blue.
- $\frac{3}{8}$ of the triangle is yellow.

Plan

Think of a strategy to help you solve the problem.

- You can **use a model.**

Strategies

- Make a table.
- Use a model.
- Draw a diagram.
- Solve a simpler problem.
- Work backward.
- Guess and check.
- Make an organized list.
- Use a pattern.
- Draw a graph.

292 LESSON FOCUS | Interpret a problem and select an appropriate strategy.

BEFORE — Get Started

Display a green triangle, a blue rhombus, and a red trapezoid Pattern Block in a hexagon shape on the overhead projector. Ask:

- What fraction of the figure is the triangle? ($\frac{1}{6}$) How do you know? (*6 triangles make 1 hexagon, so each triangle is* $\frac{1}{6}$.)
- What fraction of the figure is the rhombus? ($\frac{1}{3}$ *or* $\frac{2}{6}$) The trapezoid? ($\frac{1}{2}$ *or* $\frac{3}{6}$)

Present *Explore*. Encourage students to record all the ways to make a parallelogram.

DURING — Explore

Ongoing Assessment: Observe and Listen

As students work, ask questions, such as:

- Can you make a parallelogram with 1 red trapezoid and 1 blue rhombus? (*No*) Why? (*Because I cannot make the short sides of the trapezoid parallel by adding a blue rhombus.*)

AFTER — Connect

Invite volunteers to share their solutions and the strategies they used. Ask:

- How did you make a parallelogram? (*I used 1 trapezoid, 1 blue rhombus, and 1 trapezoid turned half a turn or, I used 6 trapezoids and 3 blue rhombuses. I also turned half the rhombuses half a turn to make parallel sides.*)

Work through *Connect* together, having students build the triangle as they check and verify that all the conditions have been met.

Ask questions, such as:

- How many parts is the triangle divided into? (*16*) What is the basic part? (*The green triangle*)
- How many parts are in 1 red trapezoid? (*3 green triangles, or* $\frac{3}{16}$) 1 yellow hexagon? (*6 green triangles or* $\frac{6}{16}$*, which is* $\frac{3}{8}$) 2 blue rhombuses? (*4 green triangles or* $\frac{4}{16}$*, which equals* $\frac{1}{4}$)

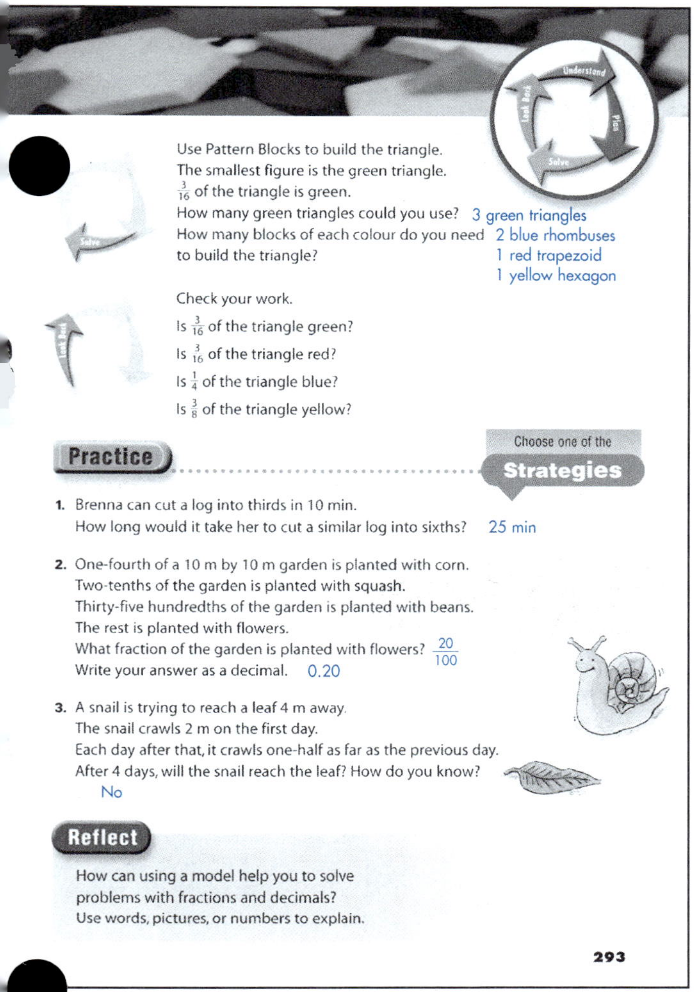
Use Pattern Blocks to build the triangle.
The smallest figure is the green triangle.
$\frac{3}{16}$ of the triangle is green.
How many green triangles could you use? 3 green triangles
How many blocks of each colour do you need to build the triangle? 2 blue rhombuses, 1 red trapezoid, 1 yellow hexagon

Check your work.
Is $\frac{3}{16}$ of the triangle green?
Is $\frac{3}{16}$ of the triangle red?
Is $\frac{1}{4}$ of the triangle blue?
Is $\frac{3}{8}$ of the triangle yellow?

Practice

Choose one of the **Strategies**

1. Brenna can cut a log into thirds in 10 min.
   How long would it take her to cut a similar log into sixths? 25 min
2. One-fourth of a 10 m by 10 m garden is planted with corn.
   Two-tenths of the garden is planted with squash.
   Thirty-five hundredths of the garden is planted with beans.
   The rest is planted with flowers.
   What fraction of the garden is planted with flowers? $\frac{20}{100}$
   Write your answer as a decimal. 0.20
3. A snail is trying to reach a leaf 4 m away.
   The snail crawls 2 m on the first day.
   Each day after that, it crawls one-half as far as the previous day.
   After 4 days, will the snail reach the leaf? How do you know?
   No

Reflect

How can using a model help you to solve problems with fractions and decimals?
Use words, pictures, or numbers to explain.

293

REACHING ALL LEARNERS

Early Finishers

Challenge students to use Pattern Blocks to make a figure that is $\frac{1}{2}$ red, $\frac{1}{2}$ blue (or $\frac{2}{3}$ blue, $\frac{1}{3}$ red; and so on).

Sample Answers

1. Five cuts are required.
2.

C	C	C	C	C	C	C	C	C	C
C	C	C	C	C	C	C	C	C	C
C	C	C	C	C	S	S	S	S	S
S	S	S	S	S	S	S	S	S	S
S	S	S	S	S	B	B	B	B	B
B	B	B	B	B	B	B	B	B	B
B	B	B	B	B	B	B	B	B	B
B	B	B	B	B	B	B	B	B	B
F	F	F	F	F	F	F	F	F	F
F	F	F	F	F	F	F	F	F	F

3. 1st day: the snail will have travelled 2 m.
   2nd day: the snail will have travelled 2 m + 1 m = 3 m.
   3rd day: the snail will have travelled 3 m + 0.5 m = 3.5 m.
   4th day: the snail will have travelled 3.5 m + 0.25 m = 3. 75 m.
   The snail will not reach the leaf after 4 days. It will only have travelled 3.75 m, not 4 m.

REFLECT: It is easier to solve problems with fractions and decimals if I have a model. For example, for question 2, I can count the squares that are left in the garden to figure out the fraction planted with flowers.

ASSESSMENT FOR LEARNING

What to Look For

Understanding concepts

✔ Students can interpret problems involving fractions and decimals.

Problem solving

✔ Students can select appropriate strategies to solve a problem.
✔ Students can verify that their answers are correct.

What to Do

Extra Support: Provide students with triangular grid paper to help them draw and count the parts of the figures they are modelling with Pattern Blocks.

Extra Practice: Have students try to make Pattern Block figures such as:
A rhombus that is $\frac{3}{4}$ blue and $\frac{1}{4}$ green
A hexagon that is $\frac{1}{2}$ red, $\frac{1}{4}$ yellow, and $\frac{1}{4}$ blue

Extension: Students create fraction Pattern Block questions and give them to other students to solve.

Recording and Reporting
PM 1 Inquiry Process Check List
PM 3 Self-Assessment: Problem Solving

Dividing Decimals by Tenths

LESSON ORGANIZER 40–50 min

Curriculum Focus: Divide decimals with tenths by a 1-digit number. (5m32)

Student Materials
- Base Ten Blocks
- calculators

Optional
- Step-by-Step 11 (Master 8.30)
- Extra Practice 5 (Master 8.38)

Assessment: Master 8.2 Ongoing Observations: Fractions and Decimals

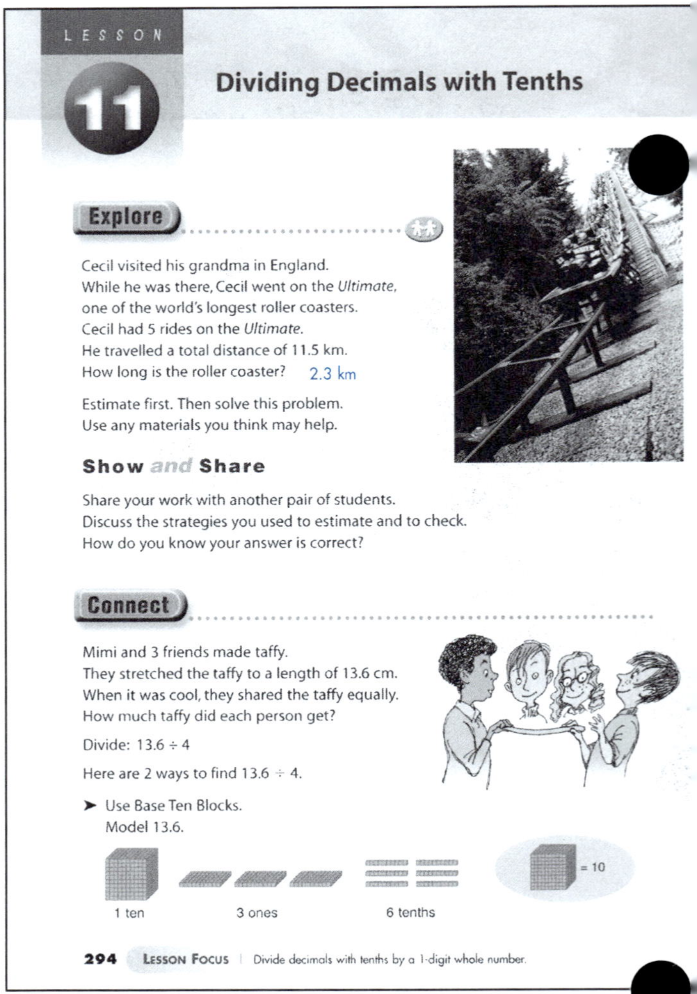

LESSON 11

Dividing Decimals with Tenths

Explore

Cecil visited his grandma in England.
While he was there, Cecil went on the *Ultimate*, one of the world's longest roller coasters.
Cecil had 5 rides on the *Ultimate*.
He travelled a total distance of 11.5 km.
How long is the roller coaster? 2.3 km

Estimate first. Then solve this problem.
Use any materials you think may help.

Show and Share

Share your work with another pair of students.
Discuss the strategies you used to estimate and to check.
How do you know your answer is correct?

Connect

Mimi and 3 friends made taffy.
They stretched the taffy to a length of 13.6 cm.
When it was cool, they shared the taffy equally.
How much taffy did each person get?

Divide: 13.6 ÷ 4

Here are 2 ways to find 13.6 ÷ 4.

➤ Use Base Ten Blocks.
Model 13.6.

1 ten 3 ones 6 tenths = 10

294 LESSON FOCUS | Divide decimals with tenths by a 1-digit whole number.

Key Math Learnings

1. Dividing a decimal by a whole number involves the same process as dividing a whole number by another whole number.
2. Estimation can be used to place the decimal point in the quotient.
3. The inverse operation (multiplication) can be used to check division.

BEFORE Get Started

Make students aware that they should first estimate, then divide a decimal, to make sure their answer is reasonable. Ask:

- How would you estimate 6.5 ÷ 2?
  (*I would choose a compatible number, such as 6; I know 6 ÷ 2 = 3.*)
- Is your estimate high or low?
  (*Since 6 is less than 6.5, my estimate is low.*)

Present the problem in *Explore*. Ask:

- How will you find the length of the roller coaster?
  (*I would divide 11.5 km by 5.*)
- What materials could you use?
  (*I could use Base Ten Blocks. The large cube could represent tens, the flat could represent ones, and the rod could represent tenths.*)

Remind students to estimate before they find the actual length of the roller coaster.

Make Base Ten Blocks available for student use.

DURING Explore

Ongoing Assessment: Observe and Listen

Ask questions such as:

- What strategy did you use to estimate?
  (*I looked for compatible numbers. I divided 10 by 5 and got 2.*)
- Is you estimate high or low?
  (*My estimate is low because 10 is less than 11.5.*)
- How will you model 11.5 with Base Ten Blocks?
  (*11.5 = 1 ten + 1 one + 5 tenths, so I will use 1 large cube, 1 flat, and 5 rods.*)
- How will you divide the blocks into 5 equal groups? (*I will trade 1 ten for 10 ones and put 2 ones in each group. I will trade the remaining 1 one for 10 tenths. Then I will have 15 tenths. I will put 3 tenths in each group.*)
- How much will you have in each group?
  (*2 ones and 3 tenths*)
- How much is 11.5 ÷ 5? (*2.3*)

Trade 1 ten for 10 ones.

13 ones   6 tenths

Share 13 ones among 4 equal groups.

There are 3 ones in each group, with 1 one and 6 tenths left over.
Trade 1 one for 10 tenths. There are now 16 tenths.

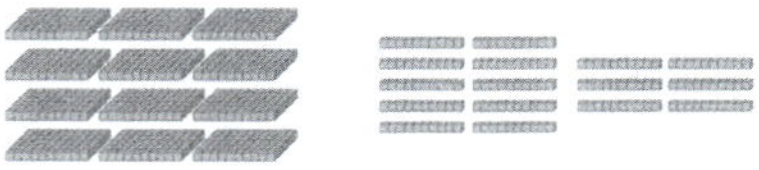

Arrange the 16 tenths among the 4 equal groups.

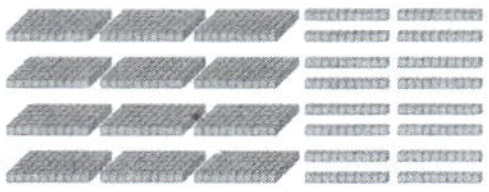

There are 3 ones and 4 tenths in each group.

$13.6 \div 4 = 3.4$

➤ Use what you know about dividing whole numbers.

Step 1: Record the numbers without the decimal point. Divide as you would with whole numbers.

$$4\overline{)1\,3\,{}^{1}6}$$
$$\;\;3\;4$$

Step 2: Estimate to place the decimal point.

$13.6 \div 4 = 3.4$

Check by multiplying: $3.4 \times 4 = 13.6$
Each person gets 3.4 cm of taffy.

295

REACHING ALL LEARNERS

Early Finishers

Have students solve this problem. Miguel's sunflower grew 4.4 m in 7 weeks. About how much did the sunflower grow each week? (*Answer: About 0.6 m*)

Common Misconceptions

➤ Students have difficulty with division because they do not know their basic division facts.

How to Help: Review division facts with students on a regular basis. Have students keep a list of facts they have trouble remembering.

AFTER Connect

Ask students to share their estimates and solutions. Invite volunteers to demonstrate the strategies they used to divide 11.5 by 5.

Ask:

- How do you know your solution is reasonable? (*I estimated a little more than 2. 2.3 is a little more than 2.*)
- What strategy could you use to check your answer? (*I could start at 11.5 and subtract 2.3 five times. If I end up at 0, then I know my answer is correct.*)
- How else could you check your answer? (*I could multiply 2.3 by 5. The product should be 11.5. I could also use a calculator to divide 11.5 by 5.*)

Review the division strategies presented in *Connect*. With the second strategy, stress the importance of using estimation to place the decimal point.

Practice

Have Base Ten Blocks available for all questions and calculators available for question 5.

Students should use estimation to complete question 3.

Assessment Focus: Question 6

Students should understand that this problem can be solved by dividing. Some students may divide 20.5 by 5 to get the distance walked each day, then divide the quotient by 2 to find how far it is one way. Other students may skip one step and simply divide 20.5 by 10.

Sample Answers

3. a) I rounded down; 12 ÷ 3 = 4, so the answer is a little greater than 4.
   b) I rounded up; 36 ÷ 6 = 6, so the answer is slightly less than 6.
   c) I rounded up; 80 ÷ 8 = 10, so the answer is slightly less than 10.

6. There are 5 days in a week. 20.5 ÷ 5 = 4.1; Olav walks 4.1 km a day.
   4.1 ÷ 2 = 2.05; Olav walks 2.05 km each way, so he lives 2.05 km from his workplace.

7. $\frac{1}{2}$ of a lap is the same as dividing by 2; 2.7 ÷ 2 = 1.35
   $\frac{1}{3}$ of a lap is the same as dividing by 3; 2.7 ÷ 3 = 0.9

REFLECT: Here is how I found the quotient of 9.3 ÷ 3. First, I divided 9 ones into 3 equal groups. There are 3 ones in a group. Then, I divided 3 tenths into 3 equal groups. There is 1 tenth in each group. So, 9.3 ÷ 3 = 3.1

Practice

Use Base Ten Blocks when they help.

1. Estimate each quotient.
   a) 18.7 ÷ 2 About 9 b) 28.9 ÷ 7 About 4 c) 1.9 ÷ 2 About 1 d) 150.4 ÷ 3 About 50
2. Divide.
   a) 7.4 ÷ 2 3.7 b) 9.3 ÷ 3 3.1 c) 25.6 ÷ 8 3.2 d) 85.8 ÷ 6 14.3
   e) 8.4 ÷ 6 1.4 f) 45.5 ÷ 7 6.5 g) 623.4 ÷ 3 207.8 h) 375.4 ÷ 2 187.7
3. Which number is the quotient?
   How did you choose the number?
   a) 13.5 ÷ 3 45, (4.5), 0.45
   b) 34.2 ÷ 6 (5.7), 7.5, 57
   c) 78.4 ÷ 8 8.8, 98, (9.8)
4. A box of 6 individual servings of oatmeal has a mass of 170.4 g.
   What is the mass of 1 serving? 28.4 g
5. A photo in Chelsey's book shows an insect magnified 25 times its actual size.
   In the book, the insect is 9.5 cm long.
   What is the actual length of the insect? 0.38 cm
6. Olav walks to and from work every day from Monday to Friday.
   This is a total of 20.5 km a week.
   How far does Olav live from his workplace? 2.05 km
   Show your work.
7. One lap around the track is 2.7 km.
   How long is one-half of a lap around the track? 1.35 km
   How long is one-third of a lap? 0.9 km
   How do you know?

Numbers Every Day

Number Strategies

Is 31 × 42 greater than 1200? Greater than
How do you know without multiplying?

Reflect

Choose one of the questions from *Practice*.
Explain how you found the quotient.

296 ASSESSMENT FOCUS | Question 6

Numbers Every Day

Students should use estimation to find that 30 × 40 = 1200. Since 31 × 42 is greater than 30 × 40, the product of 31 × 42 will be greater than 1200.

ASSESSMENT FOR LEARNING

What to Look For	What to Do
Understanding concepts ✔ Students understand that dividing a decimal by a whole number involves the same process as dividing a whole number by a whole number.	***Extra Support:*** Encourage students to use Base Ten Blocks to model each problem. Students can use Step-by-Step 11 (Master 8.30) to complete question 6.
Applying procedures ✔ Students can divide a decimal by a 1-digit whole number. ✔ Students can use estimation to place the decimal point in the quotient. ✔ Students can check their answers to division problems by multiplying, by using repeated subtraction, or with a calculator.	***Extra Support:*** Have students choose 2 divisions from question 2 and write a story problem for each. Students can complete Extra Practice 5 (Master 8.38). ***Extension:*** Challenge students to write a story problem similar to question 6 that can be solved by dividing. Students trade problems and solve their partner's problem.

Recording and Reporting

Master 8.2: Ongoing Observations: Fractions and Decimals

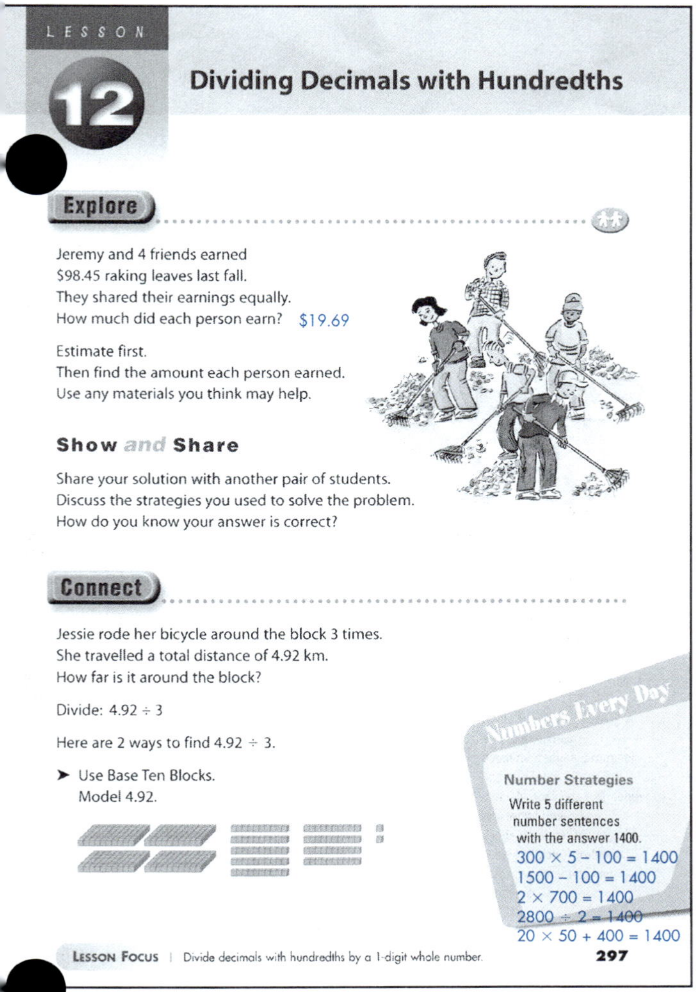

LESSON 12 Dividing Decimals with Hundredths

Explore

Jeremy and 4 friends earned
$98.45 raking leaves last fall.
They shared their earnings equally.
How much did each person earn? $19.69

Estimate first.
Then find the amount each person earned.
Use any materials you think may help.

Show and Share

Share your solution with another pair of students.
Discuss the strategies you used to solve the problem.
How do you know your answer is correct?

Connect

Jessie rode her bicycle around the block 3 times.
She travelled a total distance of 4.92 km.
How far is it around the block?

Divide: 4.92 ÷ 3

Here are 2 ways to find 4.92 ÷ 3.

➤ Use Base Ten Blocks.
Model 4.92.

Numbers Every Day

Number Strategies

Write 5 different number sentences with the answer 1400.
300 × 5 − 100 = 1400
1500 − 100 = 1400
2 × 700 = 1400
2800 ÷ 2 = 1400
20 × 50 + 400 = 1400

LESSON FOCUS | Divide decimals with hundredths by a 1-digit whole number. 297

Dividing Decimals with Hundredths

LESSON ORGANIZER 40–50 min

Curriculum Focus: Divide decimals with hundredths by a 1-digit whole number. (5m32, 5m36)

Student Materials
- Base Ten Blocks
- play money (PM 30)

Optional
- Step-by-Step 12 (Master 8.31)
- Extra Practice 6 (Master 8.39)

Assessment: Master 8.2 Ongoing Observations: Fractions and Decimals

Key Math Learning

The strategies used to divide decimals with hundredths are the same as those used to divide decimals with tenths.

Numbers Every Day

Students could use one operation or a combination of operations.

BEFORE Get Started

Record the amount $25.48 on the board. Remind students that money can be written using decimal notation.

Ask:

- What does each digit in $25.48 represent? *(2 tens, 5 ones, 4 tenths, and 8 hundredths)*
- Which coin represents $\frac{1}{10}$ of one dollar? (*A dime*) $\frac{1}{100}$ of one dollar? (*A penny*)

Present *Explore*. Ask:

- How many friends shared the money? *(5 friends)*
- How can you find how much each person earned? *(Divide $98.45 by 5)*
- What materials could you use to model the problem? *(Play money or Base Ten Blocks)*

Have Base Ten Blocks and play money available for student use. Remind students to estimate first.

DURING Explore

Ongoing Assessment: Observe and Listen

Ask questions, such as:

- How did you estimate how much money each person got? *($98.45 is close to $100. I divided $100 by 5. Each person gets a little less than $20.)*
- Which bills and coins could you use to model $98.45? *(ten dollar bills, 8 loonies, 4 dimes, and 5 pennies)*
- Which Base Ten Blocks could you use? *(9 large cubes, 8 flats, 4 rods, and 5 unit cubes)*
- How many equal groups will you make? *(5: 1 for Jeremy and 4 for his friends)*

REACHING ALL LEARNERS

Early Finishers

Have students solve the problem of sharing $18.12 among 2, 3, 4, and 6 friends.

Common Misconceptions

➤ Students have difficulty using money to model decimal numbers because of the bills and coins that do not fit into the base-ten system.

How to Help: Encourage students to use pennies, dimes, loonies, $10 bills, and $100 bills so they can easily relate money to Base Ten Blocks.

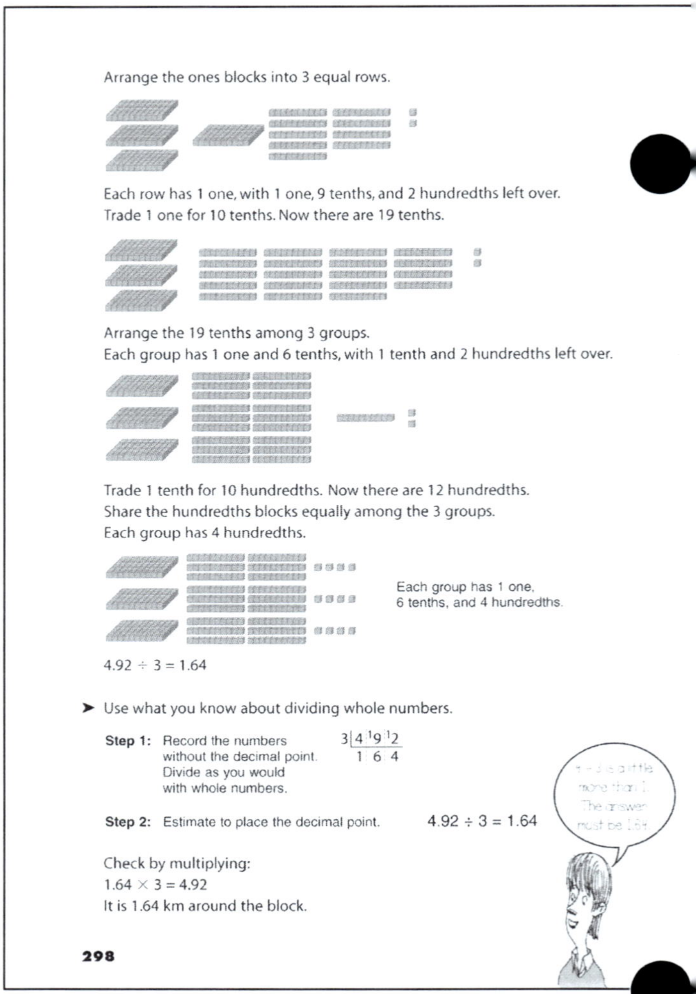
Arrange the ones blocks into 3 equal rows.

Each row has 1 one, with 1 one, 9 tenths, and 2 hundredths left over.
Trade 1 one for 10 tenths. Now there are 19 tenths.

Arrange the 19 tenths among 3 groups.
Each group has 1 one and 6 tenths, with 1 tenth and 2 hundredths left over.

Trade 1 tenth for 10 hundredths. Now there are 12 hundredths.
Share the hundredths blocks equally among the 3 groups.
Each group has 4 hundredths.

Each group has 1 one, 6 tenths, and 4 hundredths.

$4.92 \div 3 = 1.64$

➤ Use what you know about dividing whole numbers.

Step 1: Record the numbers without the decimal point. Divide as you would with whole numbers.

$3\overline{)4\,{}^{1}9\,{}^{1}2}$
$\;\;1\;6\;4$

Step 2: Estimate to place the decimal point. $4.92 \div 3 = 1.64$

Check by multiplying:
$1.64 \times 3 = 4.92$
It is 1.64 km around the block.

298

AFTER Connect

Invite volunteers to demonstrate and describe the strategies they used to divide $98.45 by 5. Ask:

- How do you know $19.69 is reasonable?
  (*My estimate was $20. $19.69 is close to $20.*)
- How did you check your answer?
  (*I multiplied $19.69 by 5 and got $98.45.*)
- How else might you have checked your answer?
  (*I could have used repeated subtraction. I could also have used a calculator.*)

Review the examples in *Connect*. Emphasize the strategy of estimating to place the decimal point. You may wish to give students another problem to ensure they are comfortable with short division procedures (for example, 83.76 ÷ 2).

Practice

Have Base Ten Blocks and play money available for student use.

Note: In the first edition of the Student Book, in question 3b, the perimeter should read 18.48 m instead of 18.42 m.

Assessment Focus: Question 5

Students should understand that part a of this problem can be solved by dividing the cost of the item by the number of people paying for it. Part b requires students to subtract the discount from the original price before they divide.

Practice

Use Base Ten Blocks when they help.

1. Divide.
   a) 4.62 ÷ 2 2.31 b) 7.65 ÷ 9 0.85 c) 2.04 ÷ 6 0.34 d) 8.32 ÷ 4 2.08
   e) 26.35 ÷ 5 5.27 f) 17.16 ÷ 6 2.86 g) 19.14 ÷ 3 6.38 h) 0.08 ÷ 2 0.04

2. Find only the quotients that are greater than 1.5.
   a) 7.56 ÷ 3 2.52 b) 2.16 ÷ 9 c) 4.38 ÷ 6 d) 5.88 ÷ 4
   e) 8.75 ÷ 5 1.75 f) 24.84 ÷ 2 12.42 g) 60.32 ÷ 8 7.54 h) 10.64 ÷ 7 1.52

3. Find the length of one side of each regular polygon.
   a) Perimeter = 11.64 m b) Perimeter = 18.42 m

2.91 m

2.31 m

4. A 6-pack of bottled water costs $3.54.
   What is the cost of one bottle? $0.59

5. a) A new tripod costs $89.46.
   Fourteen people will share the cost equally.
   How much will each person pay? $6.39
   b) The camera shop gave a $9.10 discount.
   How much did each person pay? $5.74
   Show your work.

6. Write a story problem that can be solved by dividing a decimal by a whole number.
   Solve your problem. Show your work.

7. Carl divided 4.76 by 4 and got 119.
   How was Carl incorrect?

Reflect

Why can you divide decimals the same way you divide whole numbers?
Use words and numbers to explain.

ASSESSMENT FOCUS | Question 5 **299**

Sample Answers

5. a) $89.46 ÷ 14 = $6.39; each person will pay $6.39.
   b) $89.46 − $9.10 = 80.36
   $80.36 ÷ 14 = $5.74
   Each person paid $5.74.
6. Peggy's square garden has a perimeter of 33.44 m.
   How long are the sides?
   33.44 ÷ 4 = 8.36; each side is 8.36 m.
7. Carl forgot to put a decimal point in the quotient.
   4 ÷ 4 = 1; so, 4.76 ÷ 4 will be a little more than 1.
   Carl should have put a decimal between the two 1s:
   4.76 ÷ 4 = 1.19

REFLECT: I can divide decimals the same way I divide whole numbers, because the steps are exactly the same. I divide the dividend into equal groups and trade when needed. Then I estimate to place the decimal point. When I divide 955 by 5, the quotient is 191.
Dividing 9.55 by 5 is exactly the same, but instead of dividing 9 hundreds, 5 tens, and 5 ones into 5 groups, I divide 9 ones, 5 tenths, and 5 hundredths into 5 groups. Each group gets about 2. So, I put the decimal point after the first 1. Each group gets 1.91.

ASSESSMENT FOR LEARNING

What to Look For	What to Do
Applying procedures ✔ Students can divide a decimal with hundredths by a 1-digit whole number. ✔ Students can estimate to check for reasonableness. ✔ Students can verify quotients by multiplying. ***Problem solving*** ✔ Students can pose and solve problems involving the division of a decimal by a whole number.	***Extra Support:*** Provide students with play money: $100 bills, $10 bills, loonies, dimes, and pennies, to model problems involving the division of money. Students can use Step-by-Step 12 (Master 8.31) to complete question 5. ***Extra Practice:*** Tell students that 5 workbooks cost $29.75. Have them calculate the cost of 1 book. Students can complete Extra Practice 6 (Master 8.39). ***Extension:*** Challenge students to find how many different numbers of people could share $25.40 equally with no money left over.

Recording and Reporting
Master 8.2: Ongoing Observations: Fractions and Decimals

LESSON ORGANIZER 40–50 min

Student Materials
- hundredths grids (PM 15)
- 0.5-cm grid paper (PM 22)

Assessment: Masters 8.1 Unit Rubric: Fractions and Decimals, 8.4 Unit Summary: Fractions and Decimals

Unit 8 Show What You Know

LESSON

1 **1.** How many ways can you describe the fraction of the figure that is shaded?
Record each way.

a) $\frac{6}{9}, \frac{2}{3}$

b) $\frac{8}{12}, \frac{4}{6}, \frac{2}{3}$

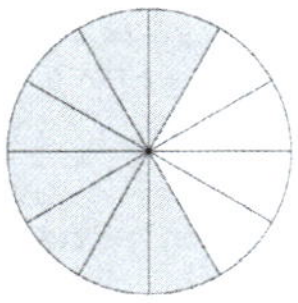

2 **2.** Are the fractions in each pair equivalent?
How do you know?

a) $1\frac{2}{5}$ and $\frac{7}{3}$ No **b)** $\frac{25}{8}$ and $2\frac{5}{8}$ No **c)** $2\frac{1}{4}$ and $\frac{10}{4}$ No

3 **3.** Order the fractions in each set from least to greatest.

a) $\frac{12}{5}, \frac{13}{6}, \frac{14}{7}$ $\frac{14}{7}, \frac{13}{6}, \frac{12}{5}$

b) $3\frac{4}{9}, 2\frac{5}{8}, 3\frac{5}{12}$ $2\frac{5}{8}, 3\frac{5}{12}, 3\frac{4}{9}$

4. A mosaic has 36 tiles.
One-sixth of the tiles are blue,
$\frac{5}{12}$ are green, and $\frac{2}{9}$ are tan.
The rest are white.
Which colour are the greatest number of tiles? Green

5. Which dot on the number line represents each number?
2.3, $\frac{12}{4}$, $\frac{16}{10}$, 1.8

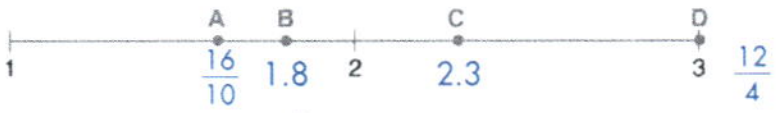

4 **6.** Draw a picture to represent each fraction.
Then write each fraction as a decimal.

a) $\frac{3}{5}$ 0.6 **b)** $\frac{9}{100}$ 0.09 **c)** $3\frac{3}{4}$ 3.75 **d)** $1\frac{11}{25}$ 1.44

300

Sample Answers

2. a) $\frac{7}{3}$ is $2\frac{1}{3}$, which is greater than $1\frac{2}{5}$.

b) $2\frac{5}{8}$ is $\frac{21}{8}$, not $\frac{25}{8}$.

c) $2\frac{1}{4}$ is $\frac{9}{4}$, not $\frac{10}{4}$.

6. a)

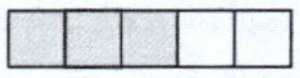

b)

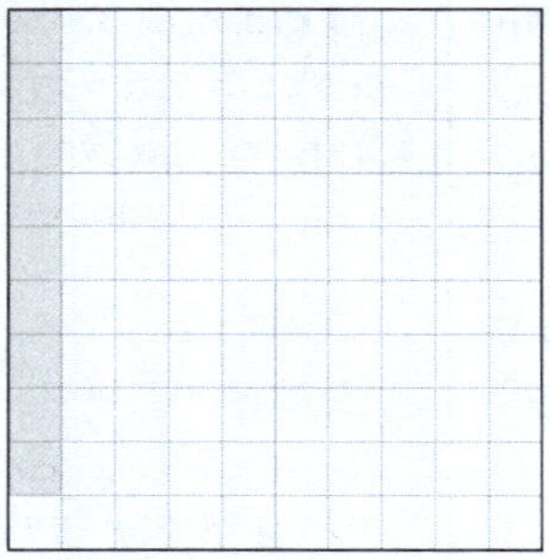

c)

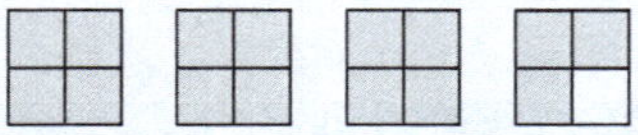

d)

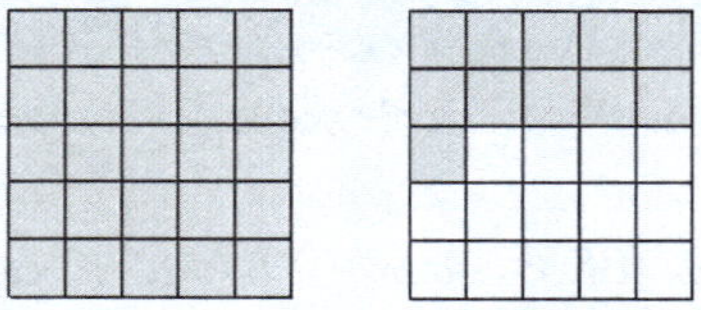

7. a)

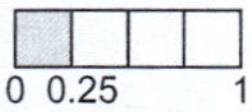

b)

c)

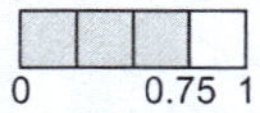

d)

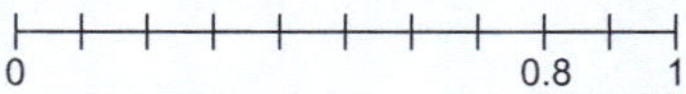

13. I can check by estimating: 14 ÷ 7 = 2, so the answer is slightly greater than 2.
The correct answer is 2.09.

7. Draw a picture to represent each decimal.
Then write each decimal as a fraction.
a) 0.25 $\frac{1}{4}$ b) 0.6 $\frac{6}{10}$ c) 0.75 $\frac{3}{4}$ d) 0.8 $\frac{8}{10}$

6 8. Write each improper fraction as a mixed number.
a) $\frac{81}{4}$ $20\frac{1}{4}$ b) $\frac{111}{3}$ 37 c) $\frac{77}{5}$ $15\frac{2}{5}$ d) $\frac{135}{10}$ $13\frac{5}{10}$ or $13\frac{1}{2}$

7 9. Estimate each product or quotient.
a) 4.89×6 About 30 b) $19.5 \div 4$ About 5 c) 2.04×7 About 14 d) $17.6 \div 3$ About 6

10. How much would you pay for 5 snow cones? $5.00

8 9 11. Multiply.
a) 45.6×2 91.2 b) 0.76×9 6.84
c) 5.09×6 30.54 d) 8.4×8 67.2

11 12 12. Divide.
a) $14.8 \div 4$ 3.7 b) $7.35 \div 5$ 1.47
c) $12.96 \div 8$ 1.62 d) $5.39 \div 7$ 0.77

13. Janine divided $14.63 \div 7$ and got 20.9.
Check Janine's answer. Is she correct? No
How do you know?

UNIT 8 Learning Goals

- ✓ model, compare, and order fractions, improper fractions, and mixed numbers
- ✓ explore equivalent fractions and decimals
- ✓ explore patterns involving fractions
- ✓ relate fractions to division and to decimals
- ✓ estimate decimal products and quotients
- ✓ multiply decimals with tenths and with hundredths
- ✓ divide decimals with tenths
- ✓ pose and solve problems involving decimals and fractions

301

ASSESSMENT FOR LEARNING

What to Look For

Understanding of concepts

✔ **Question 1:** Student recognizes equivalent fractions.
✔ **Questions 6 and 7:** Student can write fractions as decimals and decimals as fractions.

Application of mathematical procedures

✔ **Questions 2 and 3:** Student can compare and order improper fractions and mixed numbers.
✔ **Question 5:** Student can use benchmarks to locate fractions/decimals on a number line.
✔ **Question 8:** Student can rewrite improper fractions as mixed numbers.
✔ **Question 9:** Student can estimate products and quotients involving decimal tenths and hundredths.
✔ **Questions 10–13:** Student can multiply/divide with decimal tenths and hundredths.

Problem solving

✔ **Question 4:** Student can compare fractions to solve problems.

Recording and Reporting

Master 8.1 Unit Rubric: Fractions and Decimals
Master 8.4 Unit Summary: Fractions and Decimals

In the Garden

LESSON ORGANIZER 40–50 min

Student Grouping: 2
Student Materials
- 1-cm grid paper (PM 23)

Assessment: Masters 8.3 Performance Assessment Rubric: In the Garden, 8.4 Unit Summary: Fractions and Decimals

Sample Response

Part 1

Flowers	F	F	F	F	F	F	F	F	F	F
	F	F	F	F	F	F	F	F	F	F
Radishes	R	R	R	R	R	R	R	R	R	R
	R	R	R	R	R	R	R	R	R	R
	R	R	R	R	R	R	R	R	R	R
Tomatoes	T	T	T	T	T	T	T	T	T	T
	T	T	T	T	T	T	T	T	T	T
Corn	C	C	C	C	C	C	C	C	C	C
Onions	O	O	O	O	O	O	O	O	O	O
Zucchini	Z	Z	Z	Z	Z	S	S	S	S	S
							Squash			

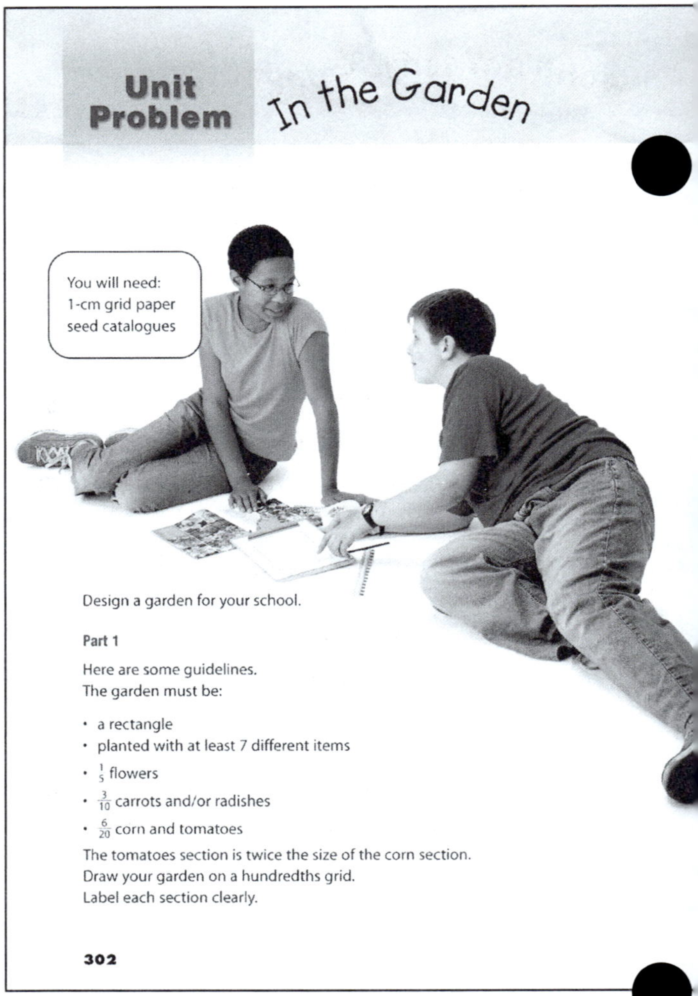
Unit Problem In the Garden

You will need:
1-cm grid paper
seed catalogues

Design a garden for your school.

Part 1

Here are some guidelines.
The garden must be:

- a rectangle
- planted with at least 7 different items
- $\frac{1}{5}$ flowers
- $\frac{3}{10}$ carrots and/or radishes
- $\frac{6}{20}$ corn and tomatoes

The tomatoes section is twice the size of the corn section.
Draw your garden on a hundredths grid.
Label each section clearly.

302

Have students turn to the *Unit Launch* on pages 256 and 257 of the Student Book.

Review the Learning Goals for the Unit with the students. Initiate a brief discussion about each goal.

If the responses to the first question on p. 256 of the Launch were recorded, display them to help students picture a garden layout.

Present the *Unit Problem*. Have a volunteer read Parts 1 through 3. Ensure students understand what they are to do in each part, and that some parts have more than one task to complete or question to answer. Have another volunteer read through the Check List to ensure students are clear on what is required in the more open-ended parts.

Mention that an illustration on grid paper will help students think about multiplication and division with decimals.

What fraction of the garden does each section represent?
What decimal does each section represent?

Part 2

Make up your own guidelines for designing a garden.
Exchange guidelines with another pair of classmates.
Follow the guidelines to design your classmate's garden.

Part 3

Write 2 story problems about your garden:

- One problem involves multiplication with decimals.
- The other problem involves division with decimals.

Exchange problems with another pair of classmates.
Solve your classmates' problems.
Check each other's work.

Check List

Your work should show

- ☑ a plan of the garden on grid paper, with each section clearly labelled
- ☑ the fraction or decimal each section represents
- ☑ how you calculated how to represent each section on the grid
- ☑ how you multiplied and divided decimals

Reflect on the Unit

How are fractions and decimals the same?
How are they different?

$\frac{1}{5}$, or $\frac{20}{100}$ flowers; 0.20. $\frac{3}{10}$, or $\frac{30}{100}$ radishes; 0.30.
$\frac{4}{20}$, or $\frac{20}{100}$ tomatoes; 0.20. $\frac{2}{20}$, or $\frac{10}{100}$ corn; 0.10.
I added 3 other items, to make 7 different items.
$\frac{1}{10}$, or $\frac{10}{100}$ onions; 0.10. $\frac{1}{20}$, or $\frac{5}{100}$ zucchini; 0.05.
$\frac{1}{20}$, or $\frac{5}{100}$ squash; 0.05.

Part 2

Student guidelines should be clear and possible to design. The required fractions must total to 1 or less; for example, $\frac{1}{4}$ roses, $\frac{3}{10}$ daisies, $\frac{7}{20}$ peppers, and $\frac{1}{10}$ for the rest of their choices.

Part 3

The story problems should involve multiplying and dividing with decimal tenths or hundredths. For example: My neighbour planted an identical garden to mine. In decimal form, what amount of roses and daisies do we have together?
$0.25 + 0.30 = 0.55$; $0.55 \times 2 = 1.1$
I shared my peppers equally with 4 other neighbours.
How many peppers did we each get?
$0.35 \div 5 = 0.07$; from my grid, I see that we each got 7 peppers.

Reflect on the Unit

Fractions and decimals are the same, because both are numbers. Both a decimal and a fraction can be used to represent parts of one whole. They are different because a fraction has a numerator and a denominator, while a decimal has a decimal point followed by digits in the tenths and hundredths places.

ASSESSMENT FOR LEARNING

What to Look For	What to Do
Understanding concepts ✔ Students can relate a fraction with denominator 10 or 100 to a decimal. ***Applying procedures*** ✔ Students can explore the relationship between fractions and decimals ***Problem solving*** ✔ Students can pose problems involving decimals and solve them. ***Communicating*** ✔ Students can explain their thinking when solving problems involving fractions and decimals.	***Extra Support:*** Make the problem accessible. For Parts 2 and 3, you may wish to brainstorm with the class about different problems that could be written about the garden.

Recording and Reporting

Master 8.3 Performance Assessment Rubric: In the Garden,
Master 8.4 Unit Summary: Fractions and Decimals

Cumulative Review

LESSON ORGANIZER

40–50 min

Student Materials
- rulers
- protractors
- square dot paper (PM 25)
- 1-cm grid paper (PM 23)
- tracing paper

Assessment: PM 9 Work Sample Records

Units 1–8 Cumulative Review

UNIT

1 **1.** Write the first 6 terms of each pattern.
- **a)** Start at 65. Alternately subtract 8, then add 2. 65, 57, 59, 51, 53, 45
- **b)** Start at 2. Alternately add 3, then multiply by 2. 2, 5, 10, 13, 26, 29

2 **2.** Estimate first. Find each result greater than 2000.
- **a)** 1007 + 1088 = 2095
- **b)** 92 × 87 = 8004
- **c)** 7764 − 5948
- **d)** 3)6496 = 2165 R 1

3. Aidan plans to plant 12 rows of trees.
There will be 11 trees in each row.
How many trees will Aidan plant? 132

3 **4.** Use a ruler and a protractor.
- **a)** Construct triangle MNP. The length of MN is 6.7 cm. The measure of ∠M is 50°. The measure of ∠N is 65°.
- **b)** What are the lengths of MP and NP? MP = 6.7 cm, NP = 5.6 cm
What is the measure of ∠P? 65°

5. Which of these shows a net for a cube?

a) 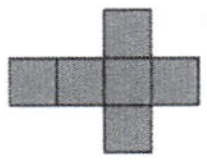 Yes

b) 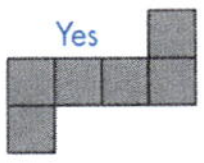 Yes

c) 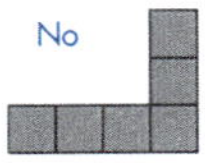 No

4 **6.** Estimate first. Find each sum or difference less than 3.5.
- **a)** 9.4 − 3.7
- **b)** 5.65 − 4.91 0.74
- **c)** 1.02 + 1.29 2.31
- **d)** 6.3 − 5.18 1.12
- **e)** 4.4 + 1.72
- **f)** 2.04 + 1.17 3.21
- **g)** 2.22 + 1.44
- **h)** 8.67 − 3.54 5.13

7. One book cost $5.79. Kim had $62.48.
She bought 10 books. How much money does Kim have left? $4.58

5 **8.** Here are the masses, to the nearest kilogram, of a group of dogs:
34, 9, 27, 7, 22, 31, 31, 9, 27, 8, 14, 31, 14, 29, 24, 7, 8, 12
- **a)** Find the mean and the mode of the masses. Mean: about 19.1, Mode: 31
- **b)** Arrange the data into intervals.
- **c)** Display the data in a bar graph.
- **d)** What information can you get from the graph?

304

Students can use this review to evaluate their progress in the mathematical content of Units 1–8.

Remind students that the unit containing the content required to answer each question is listed beside the question.

Encourage students to refer to the *Connect* sections of the relevant units.

Encourage students to draw on each other's skills as they work through the review.

Students who have identified areas in which they are strong may wish to act as volunteer tutors for students who require assistance.

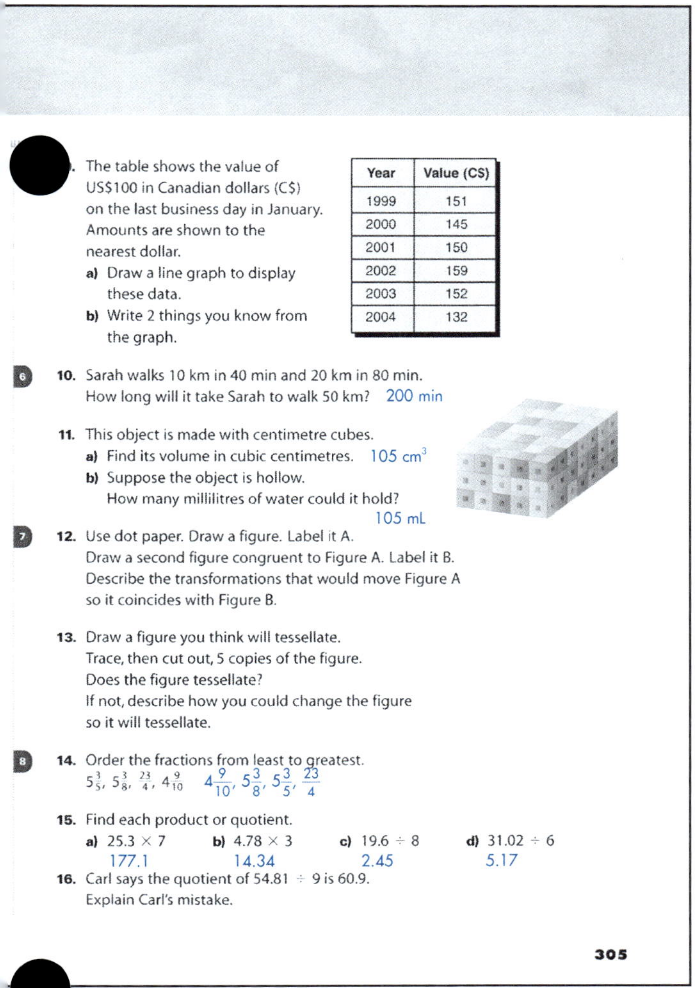

The table shows the value of US$100 in Canadian dollars (C$) on the last business day in January. Amounts are shown to the nearest dollar.

a) Draw a line graph to display these data.

b) Write 2 things you know from the graph.

Year	Value (C$)
1999	151
2000	145
2001	150
2002	159
2003	152
2004	132

6

10. Sarah walks 10 km in 40 min and 20 km in 80 min. How long will it take Sarah to walk 50 km? 200 min

11. This object is made with centimetre cubes.

a) Find its volume in cubic centimetres. 105 cm^3

b) Suppose the object is hollow. How many millilitres of water could it hold? 105 mL

7

12. Use dot paper. Draw a figure. Label it A. Draw a second figure congruent to Figure A. Label it B. Describe the transformations that would move Figure A so it coincides with Figure B.

13. Draw a figure you think will tessellate. Trace, then cut out, 5 copies of the figure. Does the figure tessellate? If not, describe how you could change the figure so it will tessellate.

8

14. Order the fractions from least to greatest.
$5\frac{3}{5}$, $5\frac{3}{8}$, $\frac{23}{4}$, $4\frac{9}{10}$ $4\frac{9}{10}$, $5\frac{3}{8}$, $5\frac{3}{5}$, $\frac{23}{4}$

15. Find each product or quotient.

a) 25.3×7 177.1 b) 4.78×3 14.34 c) $19.6 \div 8$ 2.45 d) $31.02 \div 6$ 5.17

16. Carl says the quotient of $54.81 \div 9$ is 60.9. Explain Carl's mistake.

305

Sample Answers

2. a) About 2100 b) About 8100
   c) About 1800 d) About 2000

4. a)

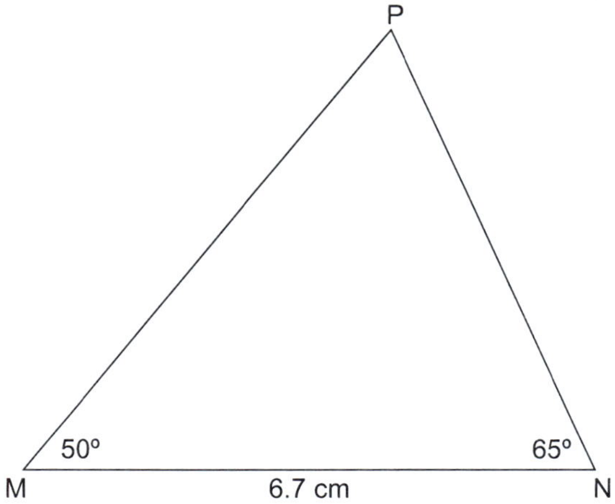

6. a) About 5 b) About 1 c) About 2
   d) About 1 e) About 6 f) About 3
   g) About 3.5 h) About 5

8. b)

Weight (kg)	Number of Dogs
1–10	6
11–20	3
21–30	5
31–40	4

c)

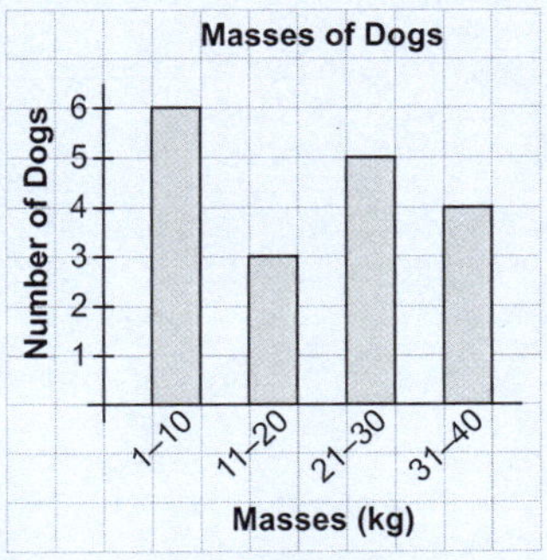

d) The graph shows that the greatest number of dogs weigh between 1 and 10 kg. The least number of dogs weigh between 11 and 20 kg.

9. a)

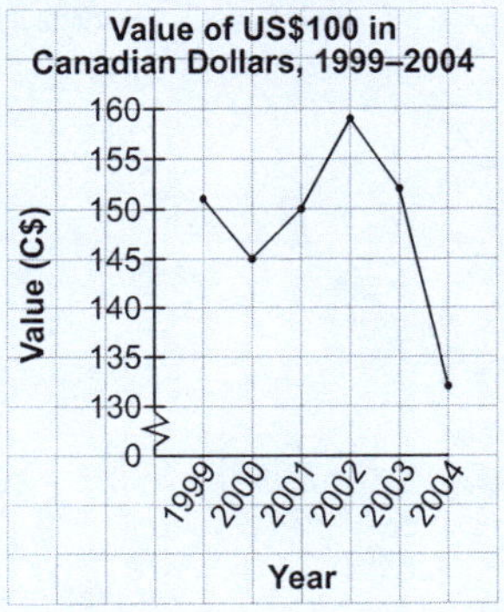

b) The value of the US dollar increased between 2000 and 2002, and decreased between 2002 and 2004.

12.

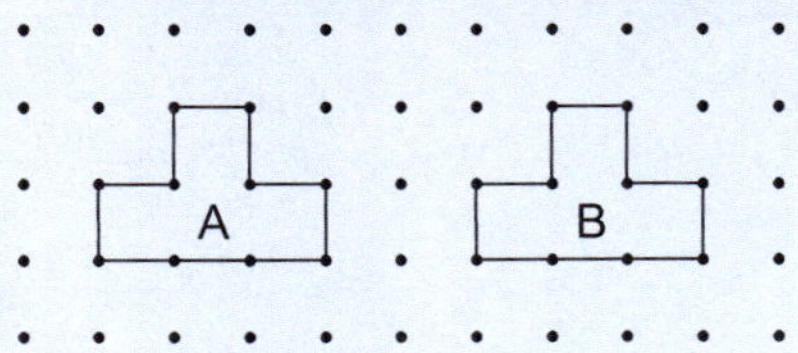

Reflect Figure A in a vertical mirror line running directly between Figures A and B.
Translate Figure A 5 squares to the right.

13. I drew an isosceles triangle. My figure tessellates.

16. Carl placed the decimal point incorrectly; $54.81 \div 9$ is about $54 \div 9 = 6$, so the correct answer is 6.09.

Evaluating Student Learning: Preparing to Report: Unit 8 Fractions and Decimals

This unit provides an opportunity to report on the **Number Sense and Numeration** strand. *Master 8.4: Unit Summary: Fractions and Decimals* provides a comprehensive format for recording and summarizing evidence collected.

Here is an example of a completed summary chart for this Unit:

Strand: *Number Sense and Numeration*	**Reasoning; Applying concepts**	**Accuracy of procedures**	**Problem solving**	**Communication**	***Overall***
Ongoing Observations	2	3	2	3	**2/3**
Strategies Toolkit (Lesson 10)	3				**3**
Work samples or portfolios; conferences	2	3	3	3	**3**
Show What You Know	3	3	3	3	**3**
Unit Test	2	3	2	3	**2/3**
Unit Problem In the Garden	3	3	2	3	**3**
Achievement Level for reporting					**3**

Recording	**How to Report**
Ongoing Observations	Use *Master 8.2 Ongoing Observations: Fractions and Decimals* to determine the most consistent level achieved in each category. Enter it in the chart. Choose to summarize by achievement category, or simply to enter an overall level. Observations from late in the unit should be most heavily weighted.
Strategies Toolkit (problem solving)	Use *PM 1: Inquiry Process Check List* with the Strategies Toolkit (Lesson 10). Transfer results to the summary form. Teachers may choose to enter a level in the Problem solving column and/or Communication.
Portfolios or collections of work samples; conferences, or interviews	Use *Master 8.1 Unit Rubric: Fractions and Decimals* to guide evaluation of collections of work and information gathered in conferences. Teachers may choose to focus particular attention on the Assessment Focus questions. Work from late in the unit should be most heavily weighted.
Show What You Know	*Master 8.1 Unit Rubric: Fractions and Decimals* may be helpful in determining levels of achievement. #1, 6, and 7 provide evidence of Understanding of concepts; #2, 3, 5, 8–13 provide evidence of Application of mathematical procedures; #4 provides evidence of Problem solving; all questions provide evidence of Communication.
Unit Test	*Master 8.1 Unit Rubric: Fractions and Decimals* may be helpful in determining levels of achievement. Part A provides evidence of Understanding of concepts; Part B provides evidence of Application of mathematical procedures; Part C provides evidence of Problem solving; all parts provide evidence of Communication.
Unit performance task	Use *Master 8.3 Performance Assessment Rubric: In the Garden*. The *Unit Problem* offers a snapshot of students' achievement. In particular, it shows their ability to synthesize and apply what they have learned.
Student Self-Assessment	Note students' perceptions of their own progress. This may take the form of an oral or written comment, or a self-rating.
Comments	Analyse the pattern of achievement to identify strengths and needs. In some cases, specific actions may need to be planned to support the learner.

Learning Skills	**Ongoing Records**
PM 4: Learning Skills Check List Use to record and report throughout a reporting period, rather than for each unit and/or strand.	*PM 10: Summary Class Records: Strands* *PM 11: Summary Class Records: Achievement Categories* *PM 12: Summary Record: Individual* Use to record and report evaluations of student achievement over several clusters, a reporting period, or a school year. These can also be used in place of the Unit Summary.

Name ____________________ Date ________________

Master 8.1

Unit Rubric: Fractions and Decimals

	Level 1	Level 2	Level 3	Level 4
Problem solving • chooses and carries out a range of strategies to pose and solve problems involving decimals and fractions (e.g., estimation, calculators, concrete materials, drawings, using a model, tables)	with assistance, chooses and carries out a limited range of appropriate strategies to pose and solve problems with decimals and fractions, rarely results in an accurate solution	with limited assistance, chooses and carries out appropriate strategies to pose and solve problems with decimals and fractions; usually results in a partially accurate solution	chooses and carries out appropriate strategies to pose and solve problems with decimals and fractions; usually results in an accurate solution	chooses and carries out appropriate strategies to pose and solve problems with decimals and fractions accurately; may offer an innovative approach
Understanding of concepts • appropriately demonstrates and explains: – equivalent fractions and decimals – patterns involving fractions – fractions, improper fractions, mixed numbers, and their relationships – relationships of fractions to division and to decimals – estimation of decimal products and quotients – justification for chosen strategies	may be unable to demonstrate or explain: – equivalent fractions and decimals – patterns involving fractions – fractions, improper fractions, mixed numbers, and their relationships – relationship of fractions to division and to decimals – estimation of decimal products and quotients – justification of methods chosen	partially able to demonstrate and explain: – equivalent fractions and decimals – patterns involving fractions – fractions, improper fractions, mixed numbers, and their relationships – relationship of fractions to division and to decimals – estimation of decimal products and quotients – justification of methods chosen	demonstrates and explains: – equivalent fractions and decimals – patterns involving fractions – fractions, improper fractions, mixed numbers, and their relationships – relationship of fractions to division and to decimals – estimation of decimal products and quotients – justification of methods chosen	in various contexts, demonstrates and explains: – equivalent fractions and decimals – patterns involving fractions – fractions, improper fractions, mixed numbers, and their relationships – relationship of fractions to division and to decimals – estimation of decimal products and quotients – justification of methods chosen
Application of mathematical procedures • accurately: – compares and orders fractions, improper fractions, and mixed numbers – multiplies decimals by 10 and 100; divides decimals by 10 and 100	limited accuracy; major errors in: – comparing and ordering – multiplying decimals by 10 and 100 – dividing decimals by 10 and 100	somewhat accurate; makes several minor errors in: – comparing and ordering – multiplying decimals by 10 and 100 – dividing decimals by 10 and 100	generally accurate; makes few minor errors in: – comparing and ordering – multiplying decimals by 10 and 100 – dividing decimals by 10 and 100	accurate; makes very few or no errors in: – comparing and ordering – multiplying decimals by 10 and 100 – dividing decimals by 10 and 100
Communication • presents work, describes procedures, and explains reasoning clearly, using appropriate mathematical language	needs assistance to present work, describes procedures, and explain reasoning; often unclear and imprecise with little mathematical language	presents work, describes procedures, and explains reasoning with some clarity, precision, and mathematical language	presents work, describes procedures, and explains reasoning with general clarity and precision, usually using appropriate mathematical language	presents work, describes procedures, and explains reasoning clearly, precisely, and confidently, using appropriate mathematical language

Name ____________________ Date ______________

Master 8.2

Ongoing Observations: Fractions and Decimals

The behaviours described under each heading are examples; they are not intended to be an exhaustive list of all that might be observed. More detailed descriptions are provided in each lesson under *Assessment for Learning*.

STUDENT ACHIEVEMENT: Fractions and Decimals

Student	Problem solving	Understanding of concepts	Application of mathematical procedures	Communication
	▪ Chooses and carries out a range of strategies to pose and solve problems involving decimals and fractions	▪ Demonstrates and explains: – equivalent fractions and decimals – relationships (e.g., fractions and decimals; improper fractions and mixed numbers)	▪ Compares and orders fractions, improper fractions, and mixed numbers ▪ Multiplies decimals by 10 and 100; divides decimals by 10 and 100	▪ Explains procedures and reasoning clearly, using appropriate terminology ▪ Presents work clearly

Level 1 – very limited; Level 2 – somewhat or limited; Level 3 – satisfactory; Level 4 – thorough

Name ____________________ Date ________________

Master 8.3

Performance Assessment Rubric: In the Garden

	Level 1	Level 2	Level 3	Level 4
Problem solving • uses appropriate strategies to successfully: – create plans that satisfy guidelines for a garden – solve problems posed by classmates – pose story problems involving multiplication and division with decimals	uses few simple strategies to solve and create problems involving fractions and decimals; limited success	uses some appropriate strategies to solve and create problems involving fractions and decimals; some success	uses appropriate strategies to solve and create problems involving fractions and decimals; successful	uses innovative and appropriate strategies to solve and create problems involving fractions and decimals; successful and effective
Understanding of concepts • shows understanding of fractions and decimals by using concepts related to fractions, decimals, and their relationships, and recognizing when results are reasonable	shows very limited understanding; uses few concepts related to fractions and decimals	shows limited understanding by using some concepts related to fractions and decimals	shows understanding by using relevant concepts related to fractions and decimals	shows thorough understanding by using all relevant concepts related to fractions and decimals
Application of mathematical procedures • accurately: – represents fractions as regions of a rectangle (using grid paper) – describes regions of a rectangle (on grid paper) as decimals – relates fractions and decimals – multiplies and divides decimals	makes few accurate calculations; major errors or omissions in: – adding, subtracting, multiplying, and dividing fractions and decimals – reading and writing fractions and decimals and money values	makes some accurate calculations, with several minor errors or omissions in: – adding, subtracting, multiplying, and dividing fractions and decimals – reading and writing fractions and decimals and money values	makes accurate calculations, with few minor errors or omissions in: – adding, subtracting, multiplying, and dividing fractions and decimals – reading and writing fractions and decimals and money values	makes accurate calculations, with practically no minor errors or omissions in: – adding, subtracting, multiplying, and dividing fractions and decimals – reading and writing fractions and decimals and money values
Communication • presents work clearly, using appropriate mathematical terminology, numbers, and symbols (e.g., decimal point)	presents work unclearly and imprecisely; uses few appropriate mathematical terms and symbols	presents work with some clarity; uses some appropriate mathematical terms and symbols	presents work clearly and precisely; uses appropriate mathematical terms and symbols	presents work clearly, precisely, and confidently; uses a range of appropriate mathematical terms and symbols with precision

Name ____________________ Date ________________

Master 8.4

Unit Summary: Fractions and Decimals

Review assessment records to determine the most consistent achievement levels for the assessments conducted. Some cells may be blank. *Overall* achievement levels may be recorded in each row, rather than identifying levels for each achievement category.

	Most Consistent Level of Achievement*				
Strand: *Number Sense and Numeration*	**Problem solving**	**Understanding of concepts**	**Application of mathematical procedures**	**Communication**	***Overall***
Ongoing Observations					
Strategies Toolkit (Lesson 10)					
Work samples or portfolios; conferences					
Show What You Know					
Unit Test					
Unit Problem: In the Garden					
Achievement Level for reporting					

*Use Ontario Achievement Levels 1, 2, 3, 4.

Self-Assessment:

Comments: (Strengths; Needs, Next Steps)

Name ____________________ Date ________________

Master 8.5

To Parents and Adults at Home …

Your child's class is starting a mathematics unit on fractions and decimals.

In this unit, your child will:

- Model, compare, and order fractions, improper fractions, and mixed numbers
- Explore equivalent fractions and decimals
- Relate fractions to division and to decimals
- Estimate decimal products and quotients
- Multiply decimals with tenths and with hundredths
- Divide decimals with tenths and with hundredths
- Pose and solve problems involving decimals and fractions

Fractions and decimals are common in our world. For example, prices on a grocery store flyer will have decimals; store sale announcements may have fractions. Encourage your child to look for and use fractions and decimals at home.

If you are dividing something into equal pieces, such as an orange, have your child name fractions that describe the pieces. For example, if the orange is divided into 8 equal pieces, each person receives one-eighth of the orange.

While shopping, encourage your child to look for decimals on price tags and labels. Have your child help you estimate the total amount of your items, and how much change you will receive.

Master 8.6

4 by 9 Rectangle

Name ____________________ Date _______________

Master 8.7

Fraction Strips

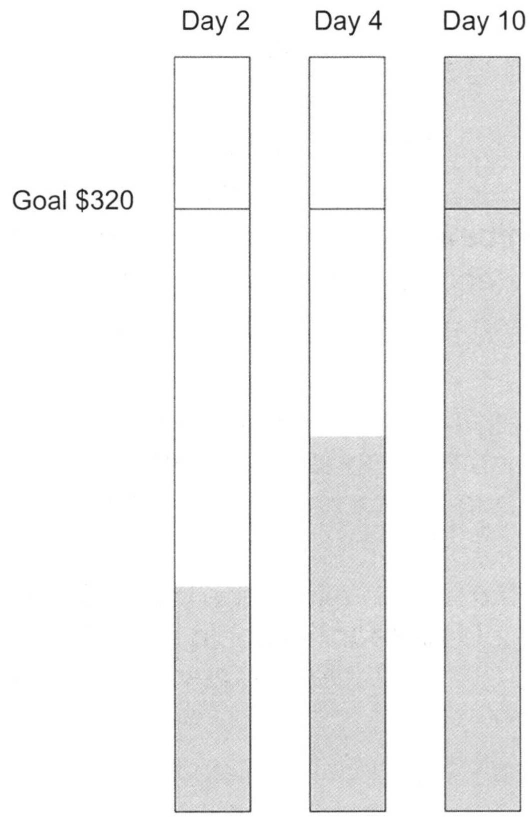

Name ____________________ Date ________________

Master 8.8

Fraction Number Lines

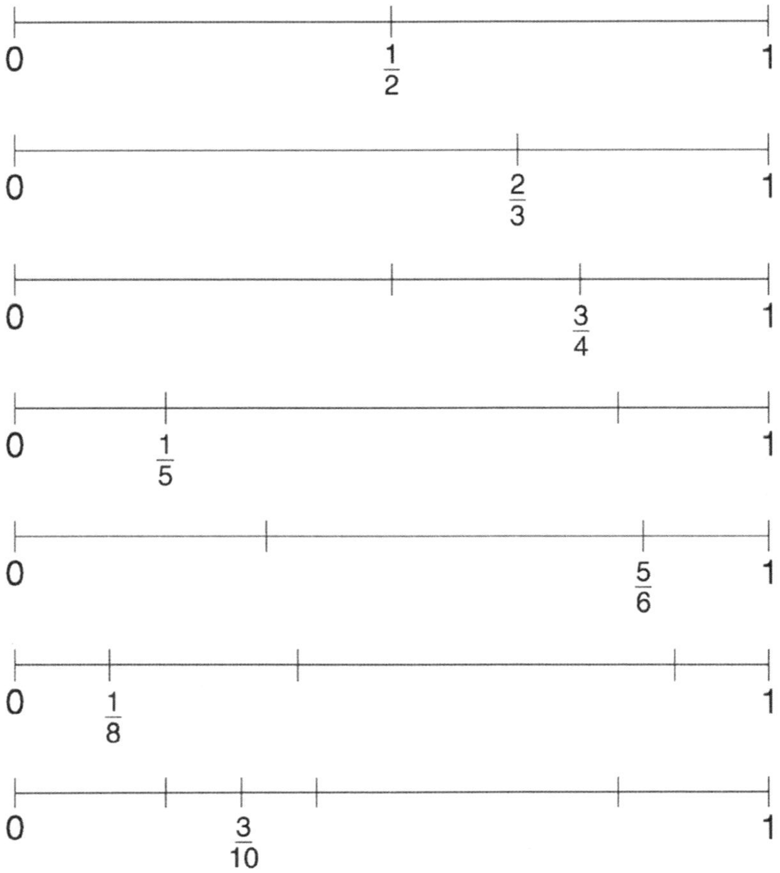

Name ____________________ Date ________________

Master 8.9

Paper Strips

Question 1, page 267

Question 2, page 267

Question 3, page 267

Name ____________ Date ____________

Master 8.10

Number Lines

Question 4, page 267

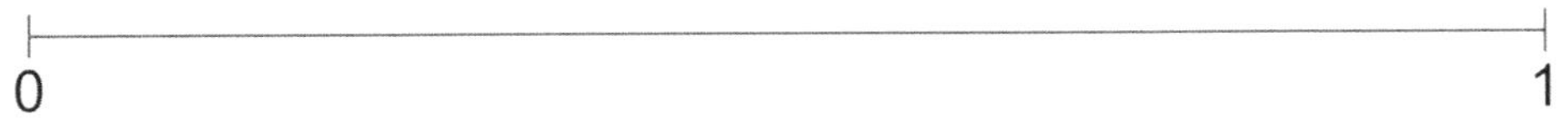

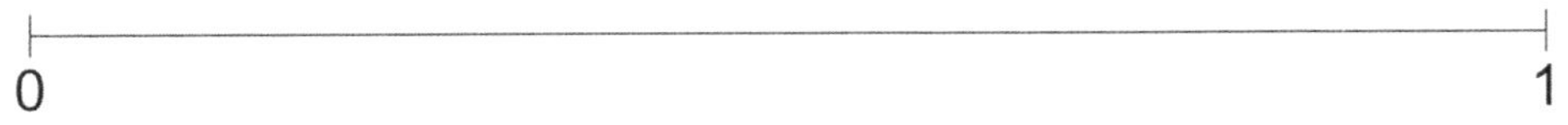

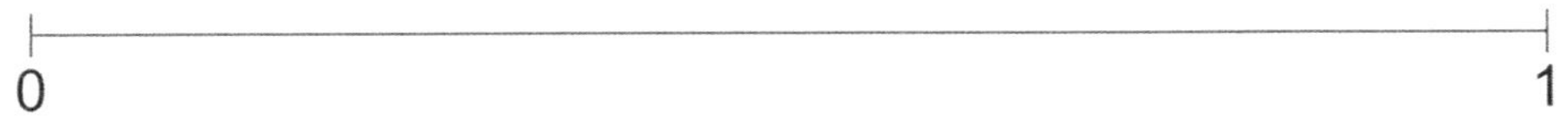

Question 5, page 267

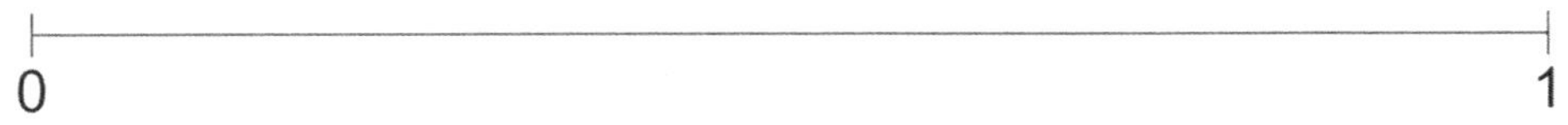

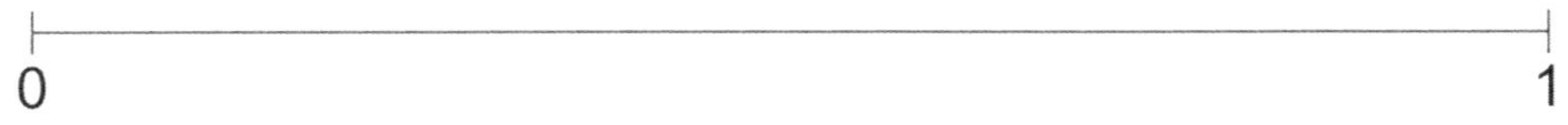

Name ____________________ Date ________________

Master 8.11a

Fraction Cards 1

$\frac{1}{10}$	$\frac{1}{8}$	$\frac{1}{6}$
$\frac{1}{4}$	$\frac{1}{2}$	$\frac{1}{3}$
$\frac{1}{5}$	$\frac{2}{10}$	$\frac{2}{8}$
$\frac{55}{100}$	$\frac{3}{4}$	$\frac{2}{5}$

Name ____________________ Date ________________

Master 8.11b

Fraction Cards 2

$\frac{5}{2}$	$\frac{7}{4}$	$\frac{8}{6}$
$\frac{40}{100}$	$\frac{6}{2}$	$\frac{4}{3}$
$\frac{4}{5}$	$\frac{9}{10}$	$\frac{8}{2}$
$\frac{9}{4}$	$\frac{5}{6}$	$\frac{7}{5}$

Name ____________________ Date ________________

Master 8.12

Game Cards

Name ______________________ Date ________________

Master 8.13

Circle Graph

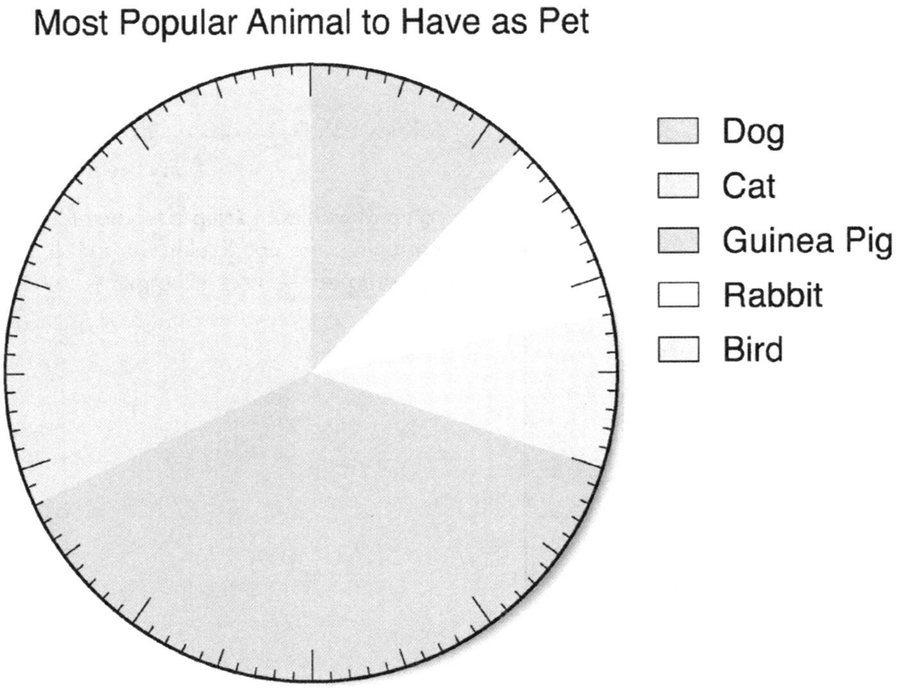

Name ____________________ Date _______________

Master 8.14

10-cm Number Lines

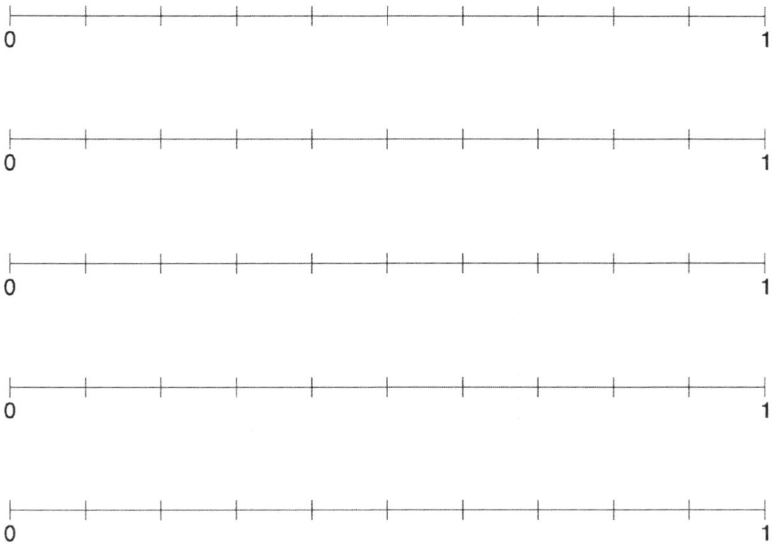

Name ____________________ Date ______________

Master 8.15

Fraction and Decimal Cards

$\frac{6}{6}$	$\frac{2}{5}$	$\frac{9}{10}$
$\frac{4}{8}$	$\frac{6}{8}$	$\frac{3}{5}$
$\frac{4}{5}$	$\frac{3}{10}$	$\frac{1}{4}$
$\frac{7}{10}$	$\frac{9}{6}$	$\frac{7}{5}$
0.1	0.5	0.9

Name ________________ Date ______________

Master 8.16a

Decimal Place-Value Mats

Tenths	
Ones	

Name ____________________ Date _______________

Master 8.16b

Decimal Place-Value Mats

Hundredths	
Tenths	
Ones	

Name ____________________ Date ______________

Master 8.17

Additional Activity 1: Great Fractions

Work with a partner.

You will need a deck of cards with 10s and face cards removed. An ace equals 1.

- One player shuffles and deals the all the cards face down.
  Players put their cards in a pile.

- Each player takes 3 cards from the top of her or his pile.
  Using 2 of the 3 cards, make a fraction whose numerator is less than or equal to its denominator.
  Return the unused card to the bottom of the pile.

- Compare fractions.
  The player with the greater fraction scores 1 point.
  If the fractions are equivalent, each player scores 1 point.

- Continue playing until all the cards have been used.
  The player with more points wins.

Take it Further:
Play the game again.
This time players must also name an equivalent fraction for each fraction they make.

Name ____________________ Date ______________

Master 8.18a

Additional Activity 2: Box It In

Work on your own.

You will need a copy of *Box It In Game Boards* (Master 8.18b).

- Look at the fractions below the first strip.
  The letters below each strip belong to the strip above them.
- Use the benchmarks on each fraction strip.
  Write the letter for each fraction or mixed number in the box between the two benchmarks that it is closest to. You may want to write the improper fractions as mixed numbers to help you place the letters.
- The completed strip will spell out a message.
- Repeat with the second strip. You may want to write the improper fraction as a mixed number to help you place the letter.
- Repeat with the third strip. You may want to write all the fractions as decimals to help you place the letters.

Take it Further:
Create your own "Box It In" challenge for other students to solve.

Name ____________________ Date ________________

Master 8.18b

Additional Activity 2: Box It In Game Boards

Put the letters in the correct box.

1.

0 $\frac{1}{2}$ 1 $1\frac{1}{2}$ 2 $2\frac{1}{2}$ 3 $3\frac{1}{2}$ 4 $4\frac{1}{2}$

L $\frac{5}{8}$ **G** $\frac{10}{3}$ **I** $2\frac{2}{3}$ **A** $\frac{3}{7}$

L $\frac{10}{7}$ **T** $4\frac{9}{20}$ **H** $3\frac{2}{3}$ **R** $\frac{9}{4}$

2.

0 $\frac{1}{4}$ $\frac{1}{2}$ $\frac{3}{4}$ 1 $1\frac{1}{4}$ $1\frac{1}{2}$ $1\frac{3}{4}$ 2 $2\frac{1}{4}$

D $2\frac{1}{8}$ **Y** $\frac{7}{8}$ **O** $1\frac{2}{3}$ **O** $\frac{15}{8}$

E $\frac{3}{8}$ **V** $\frac{1}{5}$ **R** $\frac{7}{10}$ **G** $1\frac{3}{8}$

3.

0 0.1 0.2 0.3 0.4 0.5 0.6 0.7 0.8 0.9 1.0 1.1

R $\frac{3}{4}$ **T** $\frac{21}{20}$ **O** $\frac{53}{100}$ **A** $\frac{7}{100}$

L $\frac{1}{4}$ **R** $\frac{31}{50}$ **E** $\frac{17}{20}$ **C** $\frac{19}{20}$

C $\frac{11}{25}$ **L** $\frac{7}{50}$

Name ____________________ Date _______________

Master 8.19

Additional Activity 3: Target 100

Work with a partner.

You will need a number cube and calculators.

- Each player rolls the number cube 3 times to make a decimal.
  The first number rolled is the ones digit, the second number is the tenths digit, and the third number is the hundredths digit.
- Enter the decimal in your calculator.
  Estimate what number to multiply the decimal by to get a product as close to 100 as possible.
  Calculate the product.
- The player with the product closer to 100 scores 1 point.
- Continue to play. The first player to score 10 points wins.

Take it Further:
Play the game again, with a target number of 200 or 500.

Name ____________________ Date _______________

Master 8.20a

Additional Activity 4: Estimating Decimal Products

Take turns:

- Choose one whole number and one decimal from the chart.
  Cross off the numbers.
- Estimate the product.
- Have your partner use a calculator to find the actual product.
  Find the difference between the actual product and the estimate.
- Use the scoring chart.
  Find the range that contains this difference.
  Score the number of points indicated.
  Record your score.
- Continue to play until all numbers have been used.
- Total your scores. The player with the greater score wins.

Take it Further:
Play the game again. This time, players cannot use calculators to find the products.

Name ____________________ Date ________________

Master 8.20b

Additional Activity 4: Estimating Decimal Products Charts

3.9	2.6	21.8
2	5	8
32.4	15.7	3
48.6	6	4.3
4	10	1.4
19.2	7	9

Scoring Chart

Range	Points
0–4.9	3
5–9.9	2
10–15.9	1
16 and over	0

Name ____________________ Date ________________

Master 8.21

Step-by-Step 1

Lesson 1, Question 5

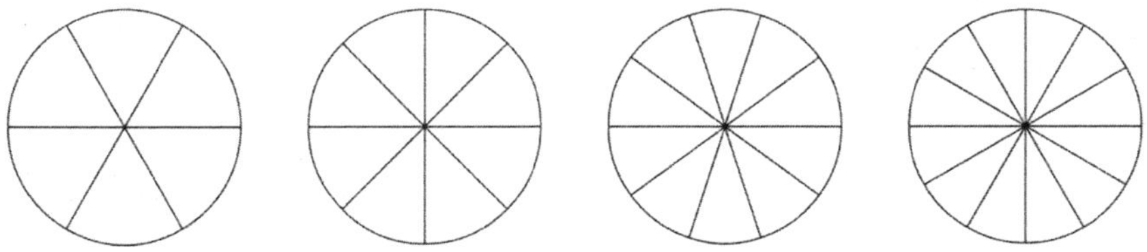

Step 1 In each pizza above, shade the amount that each person ate:
Rhonda: 3 pieces
Apak: 4 pieces
Kayla: 5 pieces
Sunil: 6 pieces

Step 2 What fraction of each pizza is shaded?

Rhonda: ______________________________

Apak: ________________________________

Kayla: _______________________________

Sunil: _______________________________

Step 3 How do the fractions in *Step 2* compare? How do you know?

____

____

Step 4 Who's correct—Sunil, who says he ate the most, or Rhonda, who says everyone ate the same amount? Explain.

____

____

____

Name ____________________ Date ________________

Master 8.22

Step-by-Step 2

Lesson 2, Question 6

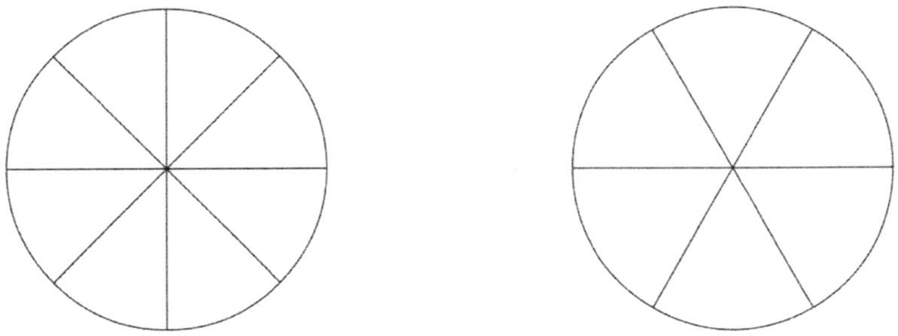

Step 1 How many eighths are in $\frac{1}{2}$ a pie? ____________

In a whole pie? ____________

Write 3 fractions, with denominator 8, that are greater than $\frac{1}{2}$ but less than 1. __________________________

Step 2 How many sixths are in $\frac{1}{2}$ a pie? ____________

In a whole pie? ____________

Write 2 fractions, with denominator 6, that are greater than $\frac{1}{2}$ but less than 1. ___________________________

Step 3 After the party, more than $2\frac{1}{2}$ but less than 3 pies were left.

Look at your answers to *Steps 1* and *2*.

How much pie might have been left? ____________________

Name ____________________ Date _______________

Master 8.23

Step-by-Step 3

Lesson 3, Question 7

Step 1 A quilt has 20 patches. $\frac{1}{4}$ of the patches are yellow.

Use patterns to find equivalent fractions:

$$\frac{1}{4} = \frac{2}{8} = \frac{\square}{12} = \frac{\square}{16} = \frac{\square}{20}$$

How many patches out of 20 are yellow? _______________

Step 2 $\frac{3}{5}$ of the patches are green.

Use patterns to find equivalent fractions:

$$\frac{3}{5} = \frac{\square}{10} = \frac{\square}{15} = \frac{\square}{20}$$

How many patches out of 20 are green? _______________

Step 3 Colour the patches on the quilt.

Step 4 Colour the rest of the patches red.

How many patches are red? _______________

Step 5 What colour are the greatest number of patches? _______________

What colour are the least number of patches? _______________

Name ____________________ Date _______________

Master 8.24 **Step-by-Step 4**

Lesson 4, Question 8

Step 1 Choose a decimal less than 0.45. ________________________

Step 2 Think subtraction.

Subtract your decimal from 0.45 to get the missing number.

0.45 – _____ = _____

Step 3 Write each decimal from *Steps 1* and *2* as a fraction.

____

Step 4 Repeat *Steps 1* to *3*, choosing a different decimal in *Step 1*.

____

Name ____________________ Date ________________

Master 8.25

Step-by-Step 5

Lesson 5, Question 4

Step 1 How many equal parts are there on the number line above? ____________

Label $\frac{7}{10}$ on the number line.

Step 2 What is $\frac{4}{5}$ equivalent to? $\frac{4}{5} = \frac{\square}{10}$

Step 3 Label $\frac{4}{5}$ on the number line above.

Step 4 Mark the benchmarks 0.25, 0.5, and 0.75 on the number line.

Which benchmark is closest to $\frac{7}{10}$ and $\frac{4}{5}$? ______________

Step 5 Shade $\frac{7}{10}$ on a hundredths grid. How many more squares do you need to shade to cover $\frac{4}{5}$ of your grid? Colour these squares with a different colour.

$\frac{7}{10} = \frac{\square}{100}$ and $\frac{4}{5} = \frac{\square}{100}$

Write 5 fractions with denominator 100 that fall between $\frac{7}{10}$ and $\frac{4}{5}$.

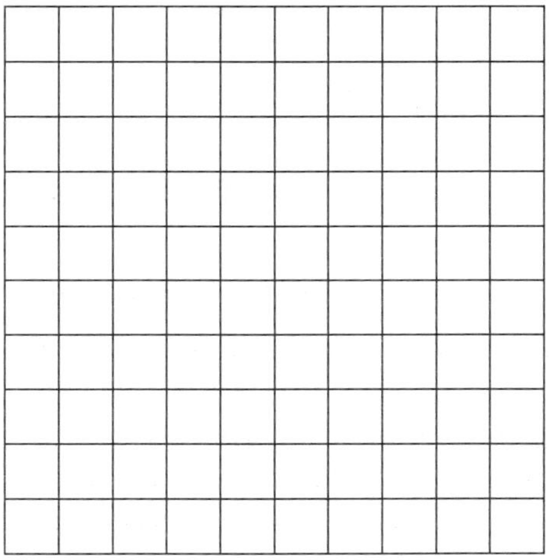

Step 6 Write each of these fractions as a decimal.

____

Name ________________ Date ______________

Master 8.26

Step-by-Step 6

Lesson 6, Question 6

These are special fractions for eighths: $\frac{48}{8}$, $\frac{56}{8}$, $\frac{64}{8}$, $\frac{72}{8}$

Step 1 Write each of the fractions above as a division statement.

$\frac{48}{8}$ = _____ ÷ _____ $\frac{56}{8}$ = _____ ÷ _____

$\frac{64}{8}$ = _____ ÷ _____ $\frac{72}{8}$ = _____ ÷ _____

Step 2 Find the quotient for each division statement in *Step 1*.

____

Step 3 What do you notice about all the answers in *Step 2*?

____

Step 4 Explain why you think the fractions are special.

____

Step 5 Now look at the special fractions for twelfths. Think of the multiplication facts for 12. Fill in the missing boxes.

☐ ÷ 12 = 1; this special fraction is $\frac{\square}{12}$.

☐ ÷ 12 = 2; this special fraction is $\frac{\square}{12}$.

Step 6 Find 2 more special fractions for twelfths.

____

Name ____________________ Date ________________

Master 8.27

Step-by-Step 7

Lesson 7, Question 8

Step 1 Estimate 9.47×5.

Round 9.47 to the nearest whole number. ____________

Step 2 Multiply your answer for *Step 1* by 5. ____________

Step 3 Is 9.47 greater than or less than its rounded number? ____________

Step 4 Is 9.47×5 greater than or less than 45? ____________

How do you know? ____

____

Step 5 Estimate $23.86 \div 4$.

Round 23.86 to a number compatible with 4. ____________

Step 6 Divide your answer for *Step 5* by 4. ____________

Step 7 Is 23.86 greater than or less than its rounded number? ____________

Step 8 Is $23.86 \div 4$ greater than or less than 6? ____________

How do you know? ____

Name ______________ Date ______________

Master 8.28

Step-by-Step 8

Lesson 7, Question 8

Step 1 How many gifts does Jakob have? ____________

How much ribbon does he need for each gift? ____________

Step 2 Write a multiplication sentence to show how much ribbon Jakob needs.

____

Step 3 Use Base Ten Blocks on a place-value mat.
Model the multiplication.

Step 4 How many ones are on the mat? ____________

How many tenths? ____________

Step 5 Trade 20 tenths for 2 ones.

How many ones are there now____________

How many tenths? ____________

How much ribbon does Jakob need? ____________

Step 6 How much ribbon did Jakob buy? ____________

Step 7 Compare the amount of ribbon Jakob bought with your answer in *Step 5*.

Does Jakob have enough ribbon? ____________

How do you know? ______________________________________

____

Name ____________________ Date ________________

Master 8.29

Step-by-Step 9

Lesson 9, Question 6

Step 1 To estimate 2.49×7:

Find 2×7. __________ Find 3×7. __________

What is a good estimate for 2.49×7? ______________

Step 2 Estimate each product.
Show how you made the estimate.

3.73×4 ____

____

5.08×3 ____

____

8.2×2 ____

____

Step 3 Show whether each product is greater than (>) or less than (<) 15.

2.49×7 ☐ 15 5.08×3 ☐ 15

3.73×4 ☐ 15 8.2×2 ☐ 15

Name ________________ Date ____________

Master 8.30

Step-by-Step 11

Lesson 11, Question 6

Step 1 How many days in a week does Olav walk to work? __________

How many one-way trips does Olav make each day? __________

Step 2 Use your answers in *Step 1*.
Write a multiplication sentence to show how many one-way trips Olav makes each week.

____

Step 3 How many kilometres does Olav walk a week? __________

Divide this number by the number of one-way trips Olav makes each week.

____

Step 4 How far is 1 one-way trip? __________

How far does Olav live from his workplace? __________

Name ________________ Date ______________

Master 8.31

Step-by-Step 12

Lesson 12, Question 5

Step 1 How much does the tripod cost? ______________

How many people are sharing the cost? ______________

Write a division statement to find how much each person will pay.

____

Step 2 Use a calculator to divide.

How much will each person pay? ______________

Step 3 How much is the discount? ______________

Subtract the discount from the original cost.

$89.46 – _________ = _________

What is the new cost of the tripod? ______________

Step 4 Use your answer from *Step 3.*
Write a new division statement to show how much each person will pay.

____

Use a calculator to divide.

How much did each person pay? ______________

Name ____________________ Date ________________

Master 8.32a

Unit Test: Unit 8 Fractions and Decimals

Part A

1. Use this list of numbers.

$\frac{3}{4}$ $2\frac{3}{5}$ $\frac{23}{20}$ 2.35 1.3 0.9

a) Write each fraction or mixed number as a decimal.

____

____

____

b) Write each decimal as a fraction or mixed number.

____

____

____

c) Order the original list of numbers from least to greatest.

____

2. Are the numbers in each pair equivalent? How do you know?

a) 0.45 and $\frac{9}{20}$ b) $3\frac{1}{5}$ and $\frac{17}{5}$ c) $\frac{12}{3}$ and $\frac{48}{12}$

Name ____________________ Date ______________

Master 8.32b

Unit Test continued

3. Julia says that $\frac{13}{4}$ is greater than $\frac{11}{3}$, because 13 is greater than 11, and 4 is greater than 3. Is this correct? Explain.

____

____

Part B

4. Find 3 different ways to use the digits 3, 4, 5, and 6 in fractions to make a true statement. Use the digits once each time.

$\frac{\square}{\square} > \frac{\square}{\square}$ $\frac{\square}{\square} > \frac{\square}{\square}$ $\frac{\square}{\square} > \frac{\square}{\square}$

5. Estimate each product or quotient.

a) 29.8×4 **b)** 2.93×7 **c)** 7.09×12

d) $8.7 \div 3$ **e)** $25.14 \div 5$ **f)** $79.99 \div 8$

Name ________________ Date ______________

Master 8.32c **Unit Test continued**

6. Multiply or divide.

a) 58.4×6 **b)** 8.07×9 **c)** $\$25.45 \times 4$

d) $26.25 \div 5$ **e)** $9.36 \div 3$ **f)** $8.76 \div 2$

Part C

7. a) Seven students get together to buy a video game for Josh's birthday.
The game costs $98.91, including tax.
How much will each student pay, assuming they share the cost equally?

b) One of the students has a coupon for $10.50 off the cost of the game.
If they use the coupon, how much will each person pay?

8. An octagonal card table (regular octagon) has a side length of 0.67 m.
What is the perimeter of the table?

____

Name ____________________ Date ______________

Master 8.33

Sample Answers

Unit Test – Master 8.32

Part A

1. a) $\frac{3}{4} = 0.75$; $2\frac{3}{5} = 2.6$
   $\frac{23}{20} = 1.15$

   b) $2.35 = \frac{235}{100}$ or $2\frac{35}{100}$ or $2\frac{7}{20}$;
   $1.3 = \frac{13}{10}$ or $1\frac{3}{10}$; $0.9 = \frac{9}{10}$

   c) $\frac{3}{4}$, 0.9, $\frac{23}{20}$, 1.3, 2.35, $2\frac{3}{5}$

2. a) Yes; $0.45 = \frac{45}{100} = \frac{9}{20}$

   b) No; $3\frac{1}{5} = \frac{16}{5}$, not $\frac{17}{5}$

   c) Yes; $\frac{12}{3} = 4$ and $\frac{48}{12} = 4$

3. No. An equivalent fraction for $\frac{13}{4}$ is $3\frac{1}{4}$; an equivalent fraction for $\frac{11}{3}$ is $3\frac{2}{3}$. Since both fractions have 3 wholes and a fractional part, compare the fractional parts: $\frac{1}{4}$ is less than $\frac{2}{3}$, so $3\frac{1}{4} < 3\frac{2}{3}$, or $\frac{13}{4} < \frac{11}{3}$.

Part B

4. For example: $\frac{4}{3} > \frac{5}{6}$; $\frac{5}{4} > \frac{3}{6}$; $\frac{5}{3} > \frac{6}{4}$

5. a) About 120 b) About 21
   c) About 84 d) About 3
   e) About 5 f) About 10
6. a) 350.4 b) 72.63
   c) $101.80 d) 5.25
   e) 3.12 f) 4.38

Part C

7. a) $14.13 b) $12.63
8. The length of each side of the table is 5.36 m.

Extra Practice Masters 8.34–8.40

Go to the CD-ROM to access editable versions of these Extra Practice Masters.

Name ________ Date ________

Master 8.34 **Extra Practice 1**

Lesson 1: Equivalent Fractions

1. Write two equivalent fractions for the shaded part of each picture.
   a) b)
2. Draw a picture to show that $\frac{1}{2} = \frac{3}{6}$.
3. Write three more equivalent fractions.
   a) $\frac{1}{5}$, $\frac{2}{10}$, ___, ___, ___ b) $\frac{3}{4}$, $\frac{6}{8}$, ___, ___, ___

Lesson 2: Fractions and Mixed Numbers

1. Write a mixed number and an improper fraction for each picture.
   a)
   b)
   c)
2. Write an improper fraction for each mixed number.
   a) $3\frac{5}{8}$ b) $5\frac{1}{3}$ c) $6\frac{1}{4}$ d) $3\frac{1}{8}$

Name ________ Date ________

Master 8.35 **Extra Practice 2**

Lesson 3: Comparing and Ordering Fractions

1. 0 ———— 1
   0 ———— 1
   Show thirds on one line. Show twelfths on the other line.
   Use the number lines. Which fraction is greater? $\frac{2}{3}$ or $\frac{7}{12}$
2. Order the fractions from least to greatest.
   a) $\frac{1}{3}$, $\frac{1}{2}$, $\frac{1}{4}$ b) $1\frac{3}{8}$, $\frac{7}{8}$, 1 c) $\frac{5}{2}$, $\frac{9}{3}$, $\frac{13}{6}$
3. Use >, <, or = to make each of the following a true statement.
   a) $\frac{9}{10}$ □ $\frac{13}{10}$ b) $\frac{11}{5}$ □ $1\frac{9}{10}$ c) $\frac{3}{4}$ □ $\frac{9}{12}$

Lesson 4: Relating Fractions to Decimals

1. Write each fraction as a decimal.
   a) $\frac{7}{10}$ b) $\frac{21}{100}$ c) $4\frac{3}{4}$
2. Complete the equivalent fraction. Then write each fraction as a decimal.
   a) $\frac{7}{20} = \frac{\square}{100}$ = ___ b) $3\frac{3}{4} = 3\frac{\square}{100}$ = ___
3. Tamara jumped $2\frac{3}{4}$ m in the long jump. Write how far she jumped as a decimal.

Name ________ Date ________

Master 8.36 **Extra Practice 3**

Lesson 5: Fraction and Decimal Benchmarks

1. Complete the table.

Decimal	Lower Benchmark	Upper Benchmark	Nearest Benchmark
0.95			
0.54			
0.02			
0.7			

2. Describe how you could use benchmarks to compare $\frac{5}{8}$ and 0.48.

Lesson 6: Relating Fractions to Division

1. Write each division statement as a fraction.
   a) 7 ÷ 9 b) 3 ÷ 8 c) 14 ÷ 8 d) 11 ÷ 4
2. Write each fraction as a division statement.
   a) $\frac{17}{3}$ b) $\frac{1}{5}$ c) $\frac{7}{12}$ d) $\frac{24}{6}$
3. Brenna has 15 m of ribbon to make awards for 9 children.
   How much ribbon can she use for each award, assuming she uses the same amount of material for each one?

Name ________ Date ________

Master 8.37 **Extra Practice 4**

Lesson 7: Estimating Products and Quotients

1. Estimate each product or quotient.
   a) 2.9 × 8 b) 6.04 × 9 c) 9.58 × 7 d) 16.7 × 4
   e) 4.27 × 4 f) 24.12 × 5 g) 0.94 × 6 h) 3.98 × 12
   i) 59.89 ÷ 6 j) 23.19 ÷ 3 k) 17.91 ÷ 6 l) 9.64 ÷ 5
2. Alex rode around the block 4 times for a total distance of 15.64 km.
   About how far is it around the block?

Lesson 8: Multiplying Decimals with Tenths

1. Estimate first. Then multiply.
   a) 7.2 × 4 b) 6.8 × 3 c) 11.9 × 8 d) 0.9 × 7
   e) 10.6 × 9 f) 44.9 × 3 g) 24.1 × 3 h) 99.9 × 8
2. Jasmine travels on her bike to and from school every day.
   She lives 1.3 km from the school.
   a) How far does Jasmine travel each day?
   b) How far does she travel each week?

Name ________ Date ________

Master 8.38 **Extra Practice 5**

Lesson 9: Multiplying Decimals with Hundredths

1. Multiply.
   a) 3.09 × 5 b) 7.42 × 8 c) 9.86 × 7
   d) 12.25 × 3 e) 0.78 × 4 f) 1.01 × 9
2. Estimate. Then multiply.
   a) 5.14 × 8 b) 3.72 × 6 c) $2.51 × 5 d) 0.68 × 9

Lesson 11: Dividing Decimals with Tenths

1. Estimate each quotient.
   a) 45.7 ÷ 9 b) 27.9 ÷ 7 c) 13.1 ÷ 4
2. Divide. Use multiplication to check.
   a) 8.1 ÷ 3 b) 12.6 ÷ 2 c) 189.6 ÷ 6
   d) 37.6 ÷ 4 e) 0.8 ÷ 2 f) 123.5 ÷ 5

Name ________ Date ________

Master 8.39 **Extra Practice 6**

Lesson 12: Dividing Decimals with Hundredths

1. Estimate.
   a) 3.98 ÷ 4 b) 0.76 ÷ 3 c) 25.08 ÷ 5
   d) 4.72 ÷ 5 e) 15.94 ÷ 4 f) $48.31 ÷ 7
2. Divide. Multiply to check.
   a) 9.76 ÷ 2 b) $18.74 ÷ 2 c) 32.58 ÷ 6
   d) 6.04 ÷ 4 e) 12.42 ÷ 6 f) 0.08 ÷ 2
3. Harry earned $15.95.
   He had exactly enough money to buy 5 glow pens.
   How much did Harry pay for each pen?

Name ________ Date ________

Master 8.40 **Sample Answers**

Extra Practice 1 – Master 8.34
Lesson 1
1. a) [illegible] or [illegible] b) [illegible] or [illegible]
2.
3. a) [illegible]
   b) [illegible]

Lesson 2
1. a) [illegible] b) [illegible] c) [illegible]
2. a) [illegible] b) [illegible]
   c) [illegible] d) [illegible]

Extra Practice 2 – Master 8.35
Lesson 3
1. [illegible]
2. a) [illegible] b) [illegible]
   c) [illegible]
3. a) < b) > c) =

Lesson 4
1. a) 0.7 b) 0.21 c) 4.75
2. a) $\frac{35}{100}$ = 0.35 b) $3\frac{75}{100}$ = 3.75
3. 2.75 m

Extra Practice 3 – Master 8.36
Lesson 5
1.

Lower Benchmark	Upper Benchmark	Nearest Benchmark
0.75	1	1
0.5	0.75	0.5
0	0.25	0
0.5	0.75	0.75

2. $\frac{5}{8}$ is greater than $\frac{1}{2}$, which is 0.5.
   0.5 is greater than 0.48, so $\frac{5}{8}$ is greater than 0.48.

Lesson 6
1. a) [illegible] b) [illegible]
   c) [illegible] d) [illegible]
2. a) 17 ÷ 3 b) 1 ÷ 5
   c) 7 ÷ 12 d) 24 ÷ 6
3. $\frac{15}{9}$ m or $1\frac{6}{9}$ m or $1\frac{2}{3}$ m

Extra Practice 4 – Master 8.37
Lesson 7
1. a) About 24 b) About 54
   c) About 70 d) About 68
   e) About 16 f) About 96
   g) About 6 h) About 48
   i) About 10 j) About 8
   k) About 3 l) About 2
2. About 4 km

Lesson 8
1. a) About 28; 28.8
   b) About 21; 20.4
   c) About 96; 95.2
   d) About 7; 6.3
   e) About 99; 95.4
   f) About 135; 134.7
   g) About 72; 72.3
   h) About 800; 799.2
2. a) 2.6 km b) 13 km

Extra Practice 5 – Master 8.38
Lesson 9
1. a) 15.45 b) 59.36 c) 69.02
   d) 36.75 e) 3.12 f) 9.09
2. a) About 40; 41.12
   b) About 24; 22.32
   c) About 15; 12.55
   d) About 9; 6.12

Lesson 11
1. a) About 5 b) About 4 c) About 3
2. a) 2.7 b) 6.3 c) 31.6
   d) 9.4 e) 0.4 f) 24.7

Extra Practice 6 – Master 8.39
Lesson 12
1. a) About 1 b) About 0.3 c) About 5
   d) About 1 e) About 4 f) About 7
2. a) 4.88 b) 9.37 c) 5.43
   d) 1.51 e) 2.07 f) 0.04
3. $3.19

Addison Wesley Mathematics Makes Sense

Program Authors

Peggy Morrow
Ralph Connelly
Bryn Keyes
Jason Johnston
Steve Thomas
Jeananne Thomas
Angela D'Alessandro
Maggie Martin Connell
Don Jones
Michael Davis
Sharon Jeroski
Trevor Brown
Nora Alexander
Cynthia Pratt Nicolson

Printed and bound in Canada

8 9 MP 18 17

PEARSON
Education Canada

ADDISON WESLEY

Ontario

Math Makes Sense 5

Ontario

Teacher Guide

Unit 9: Length, Perimeter, and Area

PEARSON

Addison Wesley

UNIT 9

Length, Perimeter, and Area

"Area and perimeter are continually a source of confusion for students. Perhaps it is because both involve regions to be measured or because students are taught formulas for both concepts and tend to get formulas confused. Children should never use formulas without participating in the development of those formulas .... Developing the formulas and seeing how they are connected and interrelated is significantly more important than blindly plugging numbers into formulas, which is primarily computational tedium."

John A. Van de Walle

FOCUS STRAND
Measurement

SUPPORTING STRANDS
Number Sense and Numeration, Geometry and Spatial Sense, Patterning and Algebra

Mathematics Background

What Are the Big Ideas?

- There are relationships among the units used to measure length.
- Perimeter and circumference are measured using units of length.
- Perimeter and area formulas provide a method of measuring these attributes by using only measures of length.
- Area and perimeter are related.

How Will the Concepts Develop?

Students choose an appropriate unit and measure the linear dimensions of various objects. They explore the relationships among the different units of length and use decimals to report part units. They develop strategies for finding the circumference of a circular object.

Students use geoboards, grid paper, and counting strategies to track and measure the perimeters and areas of polygons, and the areas of figures other than polygons. They use rulers to measure the perimeters of irregular polygons.

Students build rectangles with Colour Tiles, then develop rules for calculating perimeter by using the length and width measures. Similarly, students develop rules for calculating the area of a rectangle, by determining the number of 1-cm squares that fit along the length of a rectangle and the number of rows of 1-cm squares that fit inside the rectangle. From these rules, formulas are developed.

Why Are These Concepts Important?

The development of formulas for calculating perimeter and area forms the foundation for the development of other measurement formulas in later grades. Understanding the relationships among units of measure and being able to readily convert from one unit to another have many real-world applications.

Curriculum Overview

Cluster 1: Measuring Length

Overall Expectations
- Demonstrate an understanding of and ability to apply appropriate metric prefixes in measurement and estimation activities. (5m37)
- Identify relationships between and among measurement concepts. (5m38)

Specific Expectations
- Use prefixes in the metric system correctly. (5m41)
- Draw items using a wide variety of SI units of length. (5m42)
- Select the most appropriate standard unit to measure linear dimensions. (5m43)
- Determine the relationship between linear units. (5m44)
- Estimate long lengths using non-standard units. (5m45)
- Investigate measures of circumference using concrete materials. (5m46)

Launch
At the Zoo

Lesson 1:
Measuring Linear Dimensions

Lesson 2:
Relating Units of Measure

Lesson 3:
Using Non-Standard Units to Estimate Lengths

Lesson 4:
Measuring Distance Around a Circular Object

Cluster 2: Measuring Perimeter and Area

Overall Expectations
- Solve problems related to the calculation of the perimeter and the area of regular and irregular two-dimensional shapes. (5m39)

Specific Expectations
- Select the most appropriate standard unit to measure … the perimeter of irregular polygons. (5m43)
- Develop rules for calculating the perimeter and area of rectangles, generalize rules, and develop formulas. (5m54)
- Estimate and calculate the perimeter and area of rectangles and squares. (5m55)
- Explain the rules used in calculating the perimeter and area of rectangles and squares. (5m56)
- Estimate the area of irregular polygons and measure the area by dividing the polygons into parts, using grid paper. (5m57)
- Develop methods of using grid paper to track and measure the perimeter and area of polygons and irregular two-dimensional shapes. (5m58)

Lesson 5:
Using Grids to Find Perimeter and Area

Lesson 6:
Measuring to Find Perimeter

Lesson 7:
Calculating the Perimeter of a Rectangle

Lesson 8:
Calculating the Area of a Rectangle

Lesson 9:
Finding the Area of an Irregular Polygon

Lesson 10:
Estimating Area

Lesson 11:
Strategies Toolkit

Show What You Know

Unit Problem
At the Zoo

Curriculum across the Grades

Grade 4	Grade 5	Grade 6
Students estimate and measure linear dimensions and perimeter of polygons using millimetres, centimetres, metres, and kilometres. They draw items of specific lengths. Students measure area in square centimetres and square metres. Students explore the relationship between perimeter and area.	Students estimate and measure linear dimensions and perimeter of irregular polygons using millimetres, centimetres, decimetres, metres, and kilometres. They investigate measures of circumference using concrete materials. Students determine the relationships among linear units. Students develop rules and formulas for calculating the perimeter and area of rectangles. Students use grid paper to measure the area of irregular polygons, and to track and measure the perimeter and area of irregular figures.	Students determine the relationship between linear and square units. Students relate dimensions of rectangles and area to factors and products. Students explore relationships between the area of a parallelogram and that of a rectangle, and between the area of a triangle and those of a rectangle and a parallelogram. Students use a formula to calculate the area of a parallelogram and of a triangle. Students sketch various figures given their area and/or perimeter.

Materials for This Unit

Gather a collection of circular objects for Lesson 4 (for example, tin cans, thread spools, film containers, jar lids).

Prepare these materials:

- 15-cm by 15-cm light cardboard squares for Lesson 6 (1 square per pair)
- construction paper rectangles (6 cm by 3 cm, 8 cm by 7 cm, 9 cm by 4 cm, and 5 cm by 5 cm) for Lesson 8 (1 set per pair)
- 1-cm cardboard squares for Lesson 8 (1 per pair)
- 5 different cardboard rectangles labelled A to E, with whole-number sides or one whole-number dimension and one decimal-number dimension (for example, 8 cm by 5.4 cm) for Additional Activity 3 (1 set per pair)
- 20-cm pieces of string for the Unit Test (1 per student)

Additional Activities

A Kilometre of Dental Floss

For Enrichment (Appropriate for use after Lesson 1)
Materials: *A Kilometre of Dental Floss* (Master 9.6), a package of dental floss, paper, pencils

The work students do: Working under the assumption that each family member flosses her or his teeth once a day, students determine whether their families use more or less than 1 km of dental floss in a year.

Take It Further: Students calculate approximately how many packages of dental floss equal 1 km.

Logical/Mathematical
Individual Activity

Tangram Perimeters

For Extra Support (Appropriate for use after Lesson 6)
Materials: *Tangram Perimeters* (Master 9.7), tangrams, paper, pencils, rulers

The work students do: Students use tangram pieces to create a figure or a design. They trace the outline of the figure onto paper. Students estimate, then measure to find, the perimeter of the figure to the nearest tenth of a centimetre.

Take It Further: Students trade tracings with a classmate, estimate, and then measure to find the perimeter.

Kinesthetic
Individual Activity

Calculating Perimeter and Area

For Extra Support (Appropriate for use after Lesson 8)
Materials: *Calculating Perimeter and Area* (Master 9.8), 5 cardboard rectangles labelled A to E, with whole-number sides or one whole-number dimension and one decimal-number dimension (e.g., 8 cm by 5.4 cm), rulers, paper, pencils

The work students do: Students work in pairs. They choose a rectangle and estimate its perimeter and its area. One student measures the length and width while the other student records the measures in a chart. Students then work together to calculate the perimeter and the area. They record the results in the chart. Students repeat the activity with the other rectangles.

Take It Further: Students order the rectangles from least to greatest perimeter and from least to greatest area.

Logical/Mathematical
Partner Activity

Investigating Hands

For Extra Practice (Appropriate for use after Lesson 10)
Materials: *Investigating Hands* (Master 9.9), 1-cm grid paper, string, measuring tape

The work students do: Students work in groups of 4. They examine their hands and estimate to order them from least to greatest area. Each student traces a hand onto 1-cm grid paper and finds its approximate area. Students compare their results and their estimates.

Take It Further: Students estimate to order the hands from least to greatest perimeter. They use any strategy they like to find the approximate perimeters of the hands.

Naturalistic/Social
Group Activity

Planning for Unit 9

Planning for Instruction

Suggested Unit time: 3 weeks

Lesson	Time	Materials	Program Support
Launch: At the Zoo, page 2	10–15 min		
Lesson 1: Measuring Linear Dimensions, page 4 Select an appropriate unit to measure linear dimensions.	40–50 min	rulers metre sticks or measuring tapes 1-cm grid paper	PM 23: 1-cm Grid Paper Master 9.10: Step-by-Step 1 Master 9.22: Extra Practice 1
Lesson 2: Relating Units of Measure, page 7 Describe the length of an object in different units.	40–50 min	string scissors rulers metre sticks or measuring tapes	Master 9.11: Step-by-Step 2 Master 9.22: Extra Practice 1
Lesson 3: Using Non-Standard Units to Estimate Lengths, page 10 Estimate long lengths using non-standard units.	40–50 min	hockey sticks, brooms, or similar objects string	Master 9.12: Step-by-Step 3 Master 9.23: Extra Practice 2
Lesson 4: Measuring Distance Around a Circular Object, page 12 Measure circumference.	40–50 min	string scissors metre sticks rulers circular objects (e.g., tin cans, spools, jar lids) 3-column charts	PM 18: 3-Column Chart Master 9.13: Step-by-Step 4 Master 9.23: Extra Practice 2
Lesson 5: Using Grids to Find Perimeter and Area, page 15 Use grid paper to measure perimeter and area.	40–50 min	11 by 11 geoboards geobands square dot paper 1-cm grid paper	PM 25: Square Dot Paper PM 23: 1-cm Grid Paper Master 9.14: Step-by-Step 5 Master 9.24: Extra Practice 3
Lesson 6: Measuring to Find Perimeter, page 19 Measure the perimeter of a polygon.	40–50 min	15 cm by 15 cm cardboard squares rulers scissors calculators	Master 9.15: Step-by-Step 6 Master 9.24: Extra Practice 3
Lesson 7: Calculating the Perimeter of a Rectangle, page 23 Develop rules for calculating the perimeter of a rectangle.	40–50 min	Colour Tiles or congruent paper squares 2-cm grid paper 1-cm grid paper calculators 3-column charts	PM 24: 2-cm Grid Paper PM 23: 1-cm Grid Paper PM 18: 3-Column Chart Master 9.16: Step-by-Step 7 Master 9.25: Extra Practice 4
Lesson 8: Calculating the Area of a Rectangle, page 27 Develop a rule for calculating the area of a rectangle.	40–50 min	paper rectangles (6 cm by 3 cm, 8 cm by 7 cm, 9 cm by 4 cm, 5 cm by 5 cm) 1-cm cardboard squares rulers transparent 1-cm grids calculators	PM 23: 1-cm Grid Paper Master 9.17: Step-by-Step 8 Master 9.25: Extra Practice 4
Lesson 9: Finding the Area of an Irregular Polygon, page 31 Find the area of an irregular polygon using square dot paper.	40–50 min	11 by 11 geoboards geobands square dot paper and transparency	PM 25: Square Dot Paper Master 9.18: Step-by-Step 9 Master 9.26: Extra Practice 5

Lesson	Time	Materials	Program Support
Lesson 10: Estimating Area, page 35 Estimate the area of a figure that is not a polygon.	40–50 min	1-cm grid paper and transparency paper towels pencil crayons water circular objects string rulers	PM 23: 1-cm Grid Paper Master 9.19: Step-by-Step 10 Master 9.26: Extra Practice 5
Lesson 11: Strategies Toolkit, page 38 Interpret a problem and select an appropriate strategy.	40–50 min	1-cm grid paper calculators Colour Tiles or congruent paper squares	PM 23: 1-cm Grid Paper
Show What You Know, page 40 Assessment	40–50 min	rulers metre sticks or measuring tapes brooms, hockey sticks, or similar objects cylindrical objects string scissors Colour Tiles or congruent paper squares 1-cm grid paper	PM 23: 1-cm Grid Paper
Unit Problem: At the Zoo, page 42 Assessment	40–50 min	1-cm grid paper 0.5-cm grid paper rulers pencil crayons calculators	PM 23: 1-cm Grid Paper PM 22: 0.5-cm Grid Paper

Planning for Assessment

Purpose	Tools and Process	Recording and Reporting
Diagnostic	*Unit Launch* Question; conference; scaffold problems throughout the unit	PM 8: Conference Prompts
Formative	*Explore* – Ongoing Assessment: Observe and Listen	Master 9.2 Ongoing Observations: Length, Perimeter, and Area PM 1: Inquiry Process Check List PM 6: Observation Record 1 PM 7: Observation Record 2 PM 8: Conference Prompts
	Prompt student's self-assessment	PM 2: Self-Assessment PM 3: Self-Assessment: Problem Solving
	Practice – Assessment Focus Questions	PM 9: Work Sample Records
	Review student work; provide feedback; scaffold as needed; select key pieces	
Summative	*Show What You Know*	Master 9.1 Unit Rubric: Length, Perimeter, and Area
	Unit Problem – Performance Assessment	Master 9.3 Performance Assessment Rubric: At the Zoo
	Unit Test	Master 9.4 Unit Summary: Length, Perimeter, and Area
	Review assessment records; add unit results to ongoing records	PM 10: Summary Class Records: Strands PM 11: Summary Class Records: Achievement Categories PM 12: Summary Record: Individual
Learning Skills/Mathematical Disposition	Observe and record throughout the unit	PM 4: Learning Skills Check List PM 5: Mathematical Dispositions and Learning Skills

Program Masters (PM) are in the *Grade 5 Planning and Program Masters* module.
Extra Practice Masters are on the CD-ROM.

At the Zoo

LESSON ORGANIZER

10–15 min

Curriculum Focus: Activate prior learning about length, perimeter, and area.
Vocabulary: length, width, height, depth, perimeter, area

ASSUMED PRIOR KNOWLEDGE

- ✓ Students are familiar with the approximate lengths of various linear units.
- ✓ Students choose an appropriate unit to measure length.
- ✓ Students use personal benchmarks to estimate linear dimensions.
- ✓ Students can measure the perimeter and area of a polygon.

ACTIVATE PRIOR LEARNING

Invite students to examine the scene on pages 306 and 307 in the Student Book.

Ask questions, such as:

- Suppose you were travelling on the highway heading toward the zoo. How fast might you be travelling? Explain.
  (*I could be travelling 100 km/h on the highway, and then I would slow down to 50 km/h on the local roads.*)

Discuss the first question in the Student Book. Record students' answers on the board.
(*Property for sale, 500 m by 300 m; overpass clearance, 8.4 m; water depth, 2.6 m; Africa Loop, 2.2 km; Asia Loop, 1.3 km; 2 km*^{2} *of adventure; 8 km of trails; Zoo, turn right, 1km; Bitown, 20; Ulville, 55*)

Discuss the second question in the Student Book.
(*Length: Africa Loop, 2.2 km; Asia Loop, 1.3 km; 8 km of trails to explore; turn right, 1 km; height: overpass clearance, 8.4 m; water depth, 2.6 m; area: 2 km*^{2} *of adventure; length and width: property for sale, 500 m by 300 m*)

Discuss the third question in the Student Book.
(*500 m by 300 m describes the length and the width of the property.*)

Discuss the fourth question in the Student Book.
(*I think the property is larger than the school's property.*)

Discuss the fifth question in the Student Book.
(*I would add all the sides together to find the perimeter.*)

Discuss the sixth question in the Student Book.
(*2 km*^{2} *is the area of the zoo.*)

Discuss the last question in the Student Book.
(*Metres; kilometres; metres*)

Tell students that, in this unit, they will learn more about measuring length, perimeter, and area. At the end of the unit, they will use what they learned to design a children's petting zoo in the *Unit Problem*.

and Area

Key Words

- linear dimensions
- standard units
- non-standard units
- circumference
- scale
- formula

- Which measurements can you find in this picture?
- Which measurements describe length? Height? Width? Area?
- What does "500 m by 300 m" on the property for sale sign mean?
- Do you think this property is larger or smaller than your school's property?
- How would you find the perimeter of the property for sale?
- What does 2 km^2 on the "Welcome" sign mean?
- Which unit would you use to measure the perimeter of the apple orchard? The perimeter of the zoo grounds? The length of the rhinoceros?

307

LITERATURE CONNECTIONS FOR THE UNIT

Spaghetti and Meatballs for All by Marilyn Burns. New York: Scholastic Press, 1997.
ISBN 0590944392
Mr. and Mrs. Comfort are having a family reunion. They will need to seat and feed 32 people, including themselves.
Mrs. Comfort rents 8 small square tables. She plans to seat 4 people at each table. However, the guests arrive with seating plans of their own and the fun begins.

REACHING ALL LEARNERS

e-tools Some students may benefit from using the virtual manipulatives on the e-Tools CD-ROM. The e-Tool appropriate for this unit is Geometry Drawing.

DIAGNOSTIC ASSESSMENT

What to Look For	What to Do
✔ Students are familiar with the approximate lengths of various linear units.	***Extra Support:*** Students who are unsure of the approximate lengths of linear units may benefit from practice in using their fingers/hands to show an estimate for 1 mm, 5 mm, 1 cm, 15 cm, 1 dm, 2 dm, 1 m, and so on. *Work on this skill during Lesson 1.*
✔ Students choose an appropriate unit to measure length.	Students who have difficulty choosing an appropriate unit to measure length may benefit from working with a partner who explains how she decides which unit to use. *Work on this skill during Lesson 1.*
✔ Students use personal benchmarks to estimate linear dimensions.	Students who do not use benchmarks when estimating lengths may benefit from developing a chart of benchmarks to use as a reference. *Work on this skill during Lesson 1.*
✔ Students can measure perimeter using a ruler, and area using a grid.	Students who have difficulty measuring perimeter accurately may benefit from using a calculator. Students who have difficulty using a grid to find area may benefit from covering a surface with congruent squares, then counting. *Work on these skills during Lessons 5 and 6.*

Measuring Linear Dimensions

LESSON ORGANIZER

40–50 min

Curriculum Focus: Select an appropriate unit to measure linear dimensions. (5m41, 5m43)

Student Materials
- rulers
- metre sticks or measuring tapes
- 1-cm grid paper (PM 23)

Optional
- packages of dental floss
- Step-by-Step 1 (Master 9.10)
- Extra Practice 1 (Master 9.22)

Vocabulary: linear dimension

Assessment: Master 9.2 Ongoing Observations: Length, Perimeter, and Area

LESSON 1

Measuring Linear Dimensions

What units could you use to measure the length of this book?

Explore

You will need a ruler and a metre stick or measuring tape.

➤ Choose an object.
Find another object that is about twice as high.
Estimate. Then measure to the nearest unit to check.

➤ Choose a different object.
Find another object that is about one-half as wide.
Estimate. Then measure to check.

➤ Choose a different object.
Find another object that is about three times as long.
Estimate. Then measure to check.

Record your work.

Show and Share

Share your work with another pair of students.
Explain how you decided on the units to use to measure.
What strategies did you use to estimate?

Try to choose objects so you measure:
- in millimetres (mm)
- in centimetres (cm)
- in decimetres (dm)
- in metres (m)

308 LESSON FOCUS | Select an appropriate unit to measure linear dimensions.

Key Math Learnings

1. Length, width, height, thickness, and depth are linear dimensions.
2. Units of length are used to measure linear dimensions.
3. Millimetres, centimetres, decimetres, metres, and kilometres are units of length.

BEFORE — Get Started

Initiate a class discussion to describe which units could be used to measure the length of the book on page 308 of the Student Book.

Ask:
- Which unit did you use to estimate and measure the book? (*Centimetres*)
  How did you choose the unit to use?
  (*I can measure the length of my math book in centimetres, with my ruler. I can measure the length of most books in centimetres.*)
- What strategy did you use to estimate?
  (*I compared it to the length of my math book, which is about 28 cm. I estimated the length of the book would be shorter than that, about 15 cm.*)

Present *Explore*. Ensure students realize they should estimate and measure both objects in each part of the activity. Discuss possible methods of recording their work.

DURING — Explore

Ongoing Assessment: Observe and Listen

Ask questions, such as:
- Why did you choose metres to measure that object?
  (*It's very long, so it's easier to measure in metres than in centimetres.*)
- Which unit will you use to measure the height of your eraser? (*Millimetres*) Why?
  (*I think the eraser is less than 1 cm tall.*)
- How did you estimate the width of the table?
  (*I know a Base Ten rod is 1 dm long. I think 8 rods would fit along the width.*)

Watch for students who are using only one unit to measure. Encourage them to look for objects that could be measured in other units.

Connect

When you measure the length, width, height, thickness, or depth of an object, you are measuring a **linear dimension**.

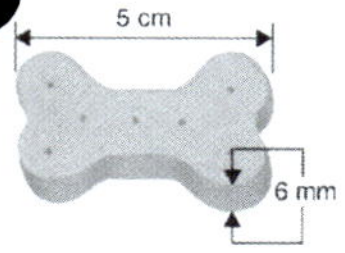

This dog biscuit is 5 cm long and 6 mm thick.

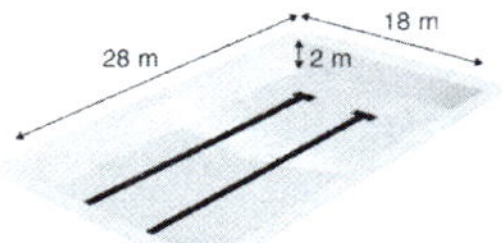

This pool is 28 m long and 18 m wide. The depth of the water in the pool is 2 m.

This dog is 4 dm tall.

The Hillsborough River on Prince Edward Island is 45 km long.

Practice

1. Name:
   a) an object that is about 2 mm thick A loonie
   b) an animal that is about 6 m high A giraffe
   c) an object that is about 1 dm long A calculator
   d) an animal that is about 8 cm long A hamster
   e) a natural object that is about 7 m high A tree

2. Choose the most appropriate unit for measuring each item. Explain your choice.
   a) the length of a driveway Metre
   b) the height of a mountain Metre
   c) the depth of a footprint in the sand Millimetre
   d) the distance from Calgary to Regina Kilometre
   e) the width of a baby's finger Millimetre

309

REACHING ALL LEARNERS

Alternative Explore

Materials: rulers, measuring tapes, or metre sticks

Post a list of items and dimensions, such as the following:

- the height of the blackboard
- the width of an eraser
- the length of a bookshelf
- the thickness of a book

Have students work in pairs to choose an appropriate unit, then estimate and measure each object.

Early Finishers

Have students go on a scavenger hunt to find items of specific dimensions (for example, 7 mm long, 4 m wide, 75 cm tall).

Common Misconceptions

➤Students omit the unit when recording a measurement.

How to Help: Point out that omitting the unit after a number such as 5 makes it impossible for the reader to know whether it means 5 mm, 5 cm, 5 dm, 5 m, or 5 km.

ESL Strategies

Work with ESL students to develop a vocabulary chart of related word forms used in the lesson.

Nouns	Adjectives
length	long
width	wide
height	high, tall
depth	deep
thickness	thick

AFTER

Connect

Invite volunteers to share their results. Ask:

- When do you use millimetres? (*When the length is very small*)
- When do you use centimetres? (*When the length is more than 1 cm and less than 1 m*)
- Which unit can you use instead of centimetres? (*Decimetres*)
- Which unit would you use to measure very long distances? (*Kilometres*)

Use *Connect* to review the term **linear dimension.**

Conclude by having students use their eyes to find an object in the room that is:

- about 4 m long
- between 2 dm and 3 dm high
- about 7 mm thick

Practice

Students will need rulers and metre sticks or measuring tapes to complete the questions. Have 1-cm grid paper available for question 4.

Assessment Focus: Question 6

Students' decisions illustrate whether they have a good sense of the approximate lengths of 15 dm, 25 cm, and 5 km. Some students may use a personal benchmark to explain their thinking (for example, 15 dm is ten and one-half Base Ten rods long). Others may express the length in a more familiar unit (for example, 15 dm is 150 cm). Some students may use personal experience (for example, it takes me 20 min to walk to school and I live a little more than 1 km away).

Making Connections

Language: Have students use a dictionary to find the meanings of the metre prefixes: *milli-*, *centi-*, *deci-*, and *kilo-*.

Sample Answers

5. a) The height of the pole is greater than one metre stick. I would use a metre stick.
   b) A ladybug can be smaller than 1 cm. I would use a ruler.
   c) A province is many kilometres wide. I would measure it in kilometres.
6. a) Unreasonable; 15 dm is 150 cm. That's $1\frac{1}{2}$ metre sticks wide. A sun parakeet is a small bird. Its wingspan would not be that wide.
   b) Reasonable; 25 cm is almost the length of my ruler. I think a fish that long is enough to feed 4 people.
   c) Unreasonable; it takes about 15 min for me to walk 1 km. Nobody can walk 5 km in less than 5 min.
   d) Reasonable; one shoelace is about the length of my arm, so the length of two shoelaces is probably about the height of a small child.

REFLECT: I would use millimetres to measure the fingernail on my baby finger because I think my nail is less than 1 cm long or wide.

Numbers Every Day

21 352: Twenty-one thousand three hundred fifty-two
20 000 + 1000 + 300 + 50 + 2
210 001: Two hundred ten thousand one
200 000 + 10 000 + 1

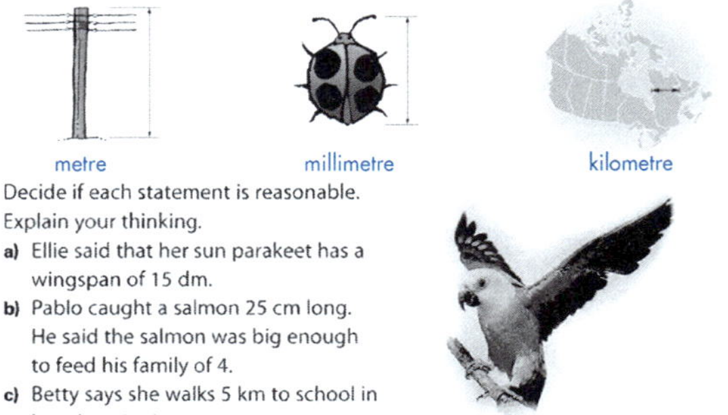

3. Estimate each linear dimension.
Then measure to the nearest whole unit.
Which tool did you use to measure? Why?
a) the height of your desk 1 m; 70 cm
b) the width of the hallway 2 m; 3 m
c) the thickness of a counter 1 mm; 2 mm
d) the length of a new piece of chalk 10 cm; 9 cm

4. Draw a picture of each object. Use grid paper when it helps.
a) a pencil 15 cm long
b) an insect 14 mm long
c) a book 6 cm long and 4 cm wide
d) a flower 1 dm tall

5. Choose the better unit of length for measuring each object.
Why is it better?
Which tool would you use to measure each object?
a) centimetre or metre
b) millimetre or centimetre
c) metre or kilometre

metre millimetre kilometre

6. Decide if each statement is reasonable.
Explain your thinking.
a) Ellie said that her sun parakeet has a wingspan of 15 dm.
b) Pablo caught a salmon 25 cm long. He said the salmon was big enough to feed his family of 4.
c) Betty says she walks 5 km to school in less than 5 minutes.
d) The length of two shoelaces tied together equals the height of a small child.

Reflect

Choose an object.
Explain how you decide which unit and which tool to use for measuring its linear dimensions.

Numbers Every Day

Number Strategies
Write each number in words, and in expanded form.
21 352
210 001

310 ASSESSMENT FOCUS | Question 6

ASSESSMENT FOR LEARNING

What to Look For	What to Do
Understanding concepts ✔ Students have a good sense of the relative lengths of standard linear units. ✔ Students understand that linear dimensions are measured in units of length. ***Applying procedures*** ✔ Students estimate and measure linear dimensions of objects using appropriate units. ***Communication*** ✔ Students use appropriate language and symbols associated with linear measurement.	***Extra Support:*** Have students make a decimetre ruler by marking a 1-m length of string in 10-cm lengths with a marker. Students can use this ruler to measure the lengths of objects to the nearest decimetre. Students can use Step-by-Step 1 (Master 9.10) to complete question 6. ***Extra Practice:*** Have students work in pairs to estimate and measure each other (length of a finger, thumb, arm, leg, face, and so on). Students can complete Extra Practice 1 (Master 9.22). ***Extension:*** Students can do the Additional Activity, *A Kilometre of Dental Floss* (Master 9.6).

Recording and Reporting
Master 9.2 Ongoing Observations: Length, Perimeter, and Area

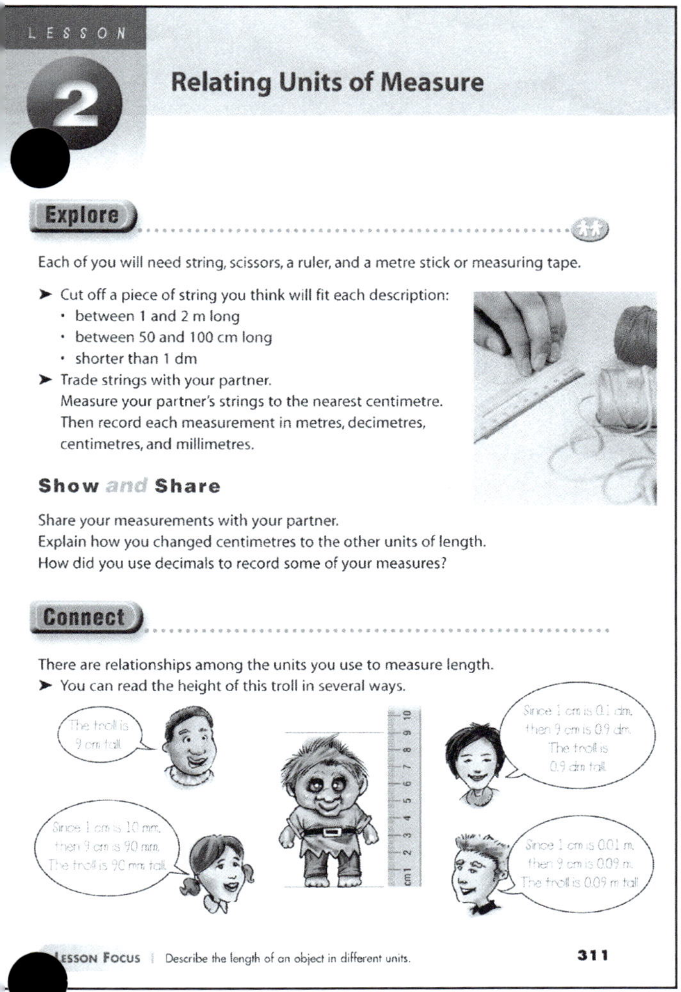
LESSON 2

Relating Units of Measure

Explore

Each of you will need string, scissors, a ruler, and a metre stick or measuring tape.

➤ Cut off a piece of string you think will fit each description:
- between 1 and 2 m long
- between 50 and 100 cm long
- shorter than 1 dm

➤ Trade strings with your partner.
Measure your partner's strings to the nearest centimetre.
Then record each measurement in metres, decimetres, centimetres, and millimetres.

Show and Share

Share your measurements with your partner.
Explain how you changed centimetres to the other units of length.
How did you use decimals to record some of your measures?

Connect

There are relationships among the units you use to measure length.

➤ You can read the height of this troll in several ways.

LESSON FOCUS | Describe the length of an object in different units. 311

LESSON 2

Relating Units of Measure

LESSON ORGANIZER (40–50 min)

Curriculum Focus: Describe the length of an object in different units. (5m41, 5m42, 5m43, 5m44)

Student Materials
- string
- scissors
- rulers
- metre sticks or measuring tapes

Optional
- Step-by-Step 2 (Master 9.11)
- Extra Practice 1 (Master 9.22)
- strips of paper of various lengths

Assessment: Master 9.2 Ongoing Observations: Length, Perimeter, and Area

Key Math Learnings

1. There are relationships among the units you use to measure length.
2. Measurements can be changed from one unit to another by using the relationships among the units.
3. Decimals are used to record fractional parts of linear units.

Numbers Every Day

To divide by 10, students should move one decimal place to the left. To multiply by 10, students should move one decimal place to the right. To multiply by 100, students should move two decimal places to the right.

BEFORE Get Started

Have students use their arms, hands, or fingers to show an estimate for each length:
1 m, 1 dm, 1 cm, 1 mm

Explain that the metre is the basic unit for measuring length and that the other units are related to the metre and to each other.

Present *Explore*. Ensure students realize they should use estimation to cut off the 3 pieces of string for their partners.

DURING Explore

Ongoing Assessment: Observe and Listen

As students are cutting the lengths of string, ask questions, such as:

- How did you estimate to get a length between 1 m and 2 m?
  (I estimated it would be longer than my arm span, because 1 m is about the length of my arm span.)
- Do you think that piece of string is closer to 1 m or 2 m? Explain.
  (Closer to 1 m; I didn't make it much longer than my arm span, which is about the length of a metre stick.)

Watch as students record their measurements. Are they mentally multiplying or dividing to change centimetres to the other units? Are they using decimals to record fractional parts of units?

AFTER Connect

Invite volunteers to share their measurements and to explain how they changed centimetres to the other units. Ask questions, such as:

- Why did you divide by 100 to change centimetres to metres? *($1\ cm = \frac{1}{100}\ m$)*
- What did you divide by to change centimetres to decimetres? *(10)*
  Why? *($1\ cm = \frac{1}{10}\ dm$)*

REACHING ALL LEARNERS

Alternative Explore

Materials: metre sticks or measuring tapes, rulers
Have students find the length, to the nearest unit, of one object in the classroom in metres, one in decimetres, one in centimetres, and one in millimetres. Students then express each measurement in as many units as they can.

Early Finishers

Have students measure the length of one of their shoes to the nearest centimetre, then express the measurement in millimetres, decimetres, and metres.

Common Misconceptions

➤ Students use the wrong operation to change between measurement units.

How to Help: Have students determine whether they are changing from a longer to a shorter unit, or from a shorter to a longer unit. Help them to see that the former requires multiplication and the latter division. Provide students with this visual:

metre decimetre centimetre millimetre

⟶ Multiply

⟵ Divide

Making Connections

Math Link: Ask students to determine what we can divide by to change millimetres to decimetres, and centimetres to metres, and to explain why.

1 mm = 0.1 cm	1 dm = 100 mm	1 m = 1000 mm
1 mm = 0.01 dm	1 dm = 10 cm	1 m = 100 cm
	1 dm = 0.1 m	1 m = 10 dm
1 cm = 10 mm		
1 cm = 0.1 dm		1 km = 1000 m
1 cm = 0.01 m		

➤ Change 0.28 dm to millimetres.
1 dm = 100 mm
So, 0.28 dm = 0.28 × 100 mm
= 28 mm

➤ Change 3.8 dm to centimetres.
1 dm = 10 cm
So, 3.8 dm = 3.8 × 10 cm
= 38 cm

➤ Change 12 mm to centimetres.
10 mm = 1 cm
So, 12 mm = $\frac{12}{10}$ cm
= 1.2 cm

➤ Change 23 cm to metres.
100 cm = 1 m
So, 23 cm = $\frac{23}{100}$ m
= 0.23 m

Practice

Use a metre stick when it helps.

1. The Komodo dragon is the world's largest lizard.
It can grow to a length of 3 m.
Write this length in decimetres and in centimetres. 30 dm, 300 cm

2. Copy and complete.
a) 9.6 dm = ☐ cm 96 cm b) 15 mm = ☐ cm 1.5 cm
c) 5.3 dm = ☐ mm 530 mm d) 17 cm = ☐ dm 1.7 dm
e) 0.45 m = ☐ cm 45 cm f) 45 cm = ☐ m 0.45 m

3. How many centimetre cubes do you need to make a line of each length?
a) 50 mm 5 b) 1.2 m 120 c) 21.6 dm 216 d) 70 mm 7

4. Record each measure in millimetres, decimetres, and metres.
a) 24 cm b) 17 cm c) 80 cm d) 145 cm

5. Record each measure in millimetres, centimetres, and decimetres.
a) 3 m b) 2.5 m c) 1.4 m d) 0.9 m

312

- Why did you multiply by 10 to change centimetres to millimetres?
(1 cm = 10 mm)
- How would you change decimetres to centimetres?
(Multiply by 10.)
- How would you change centimetres to decimetres?
(Divide by 10.)
- When do you multiply?
(To change a longer unit to a shorter unit)
- When do you divide?
(To change a shorter unit to a longer unit)

Conclude by recording the following expressions on the board. Have students complete each expression in as many ways as they can.

1 m = 1 dm = 1 cm = 1 mm =

Practice

Assessment Focus: Question 10

Students should realize that to order the students from shortest to tallest, they must express the three measurements using the same unit. Some students may change the first two measurements to centimetres, then compare them to 131 cm. To find which boy is taller, students subtract the second-tallest height from the tallest height.

6. Draw a feather of each length.
Then write each length in 3 different units.
a) 50 mm b) 3 cm
c) 1.1 dm d) 0.07 m

7. Copy and complete. Use =, <, or >.
Explain how you know.
a) 5.56 m < 70 dm b) 250 cm > 1.46 m
c) 16 mm = 1.6 cm d) 3000 mm > 2.8 m
e) 5.3 dm = 53 cm f) 2.90 m > 227 cm

Math Link

Number Sense

Since $0.1 = \frac{1}{10}$, we can multiply by 0.1 to change millimetres to centimetres, and decimetres to metres.

12 mm = 12 × 0.1 cm = 1.2 cm

8. The great white shark can grow to a length of 4.9 m.
The mako shark can grow to a length of 40 dm.
Which shark can grow to the greater length? Explain. The great white shark.

9. Jackie is 123 cm tall. 1.23 m
Suppose she wants to know her height in metres.
How will the number that represents her height in metres compare to the number that represents her height in centimetres? Explain.

10. Rico is 1.21 m tall, Jeremy is 10.3 dm tall, and Sasha is 131 cm tall. Jeremy, Rico, Sasha
Order the students from shortest to tallest.
Who is tallest? By how much? Explain. Sasha; 10 cm

11. Hannah-Li plans to measure the width of the classroom door in millimetres and decimetres. Which will be greater: the number that represents the width in millimetres or the number that represents the width in decimetres? How do you know?

Reflect

Explain how to change a measurement from one unit to another.
Give examples to support your answer.

Numbers Every Day

Mental Math

Multiply or divide.

27.2 ÷ 10 2.72
3.08 × 100 308
41.2 ÷ 10 4.12
1.82 × 10 18.2
0.95 × 100 95

ASSESSMENT FOCUS | Question 10

313

Sample Answers

4. a) 240 mm, 2.4 dm, 0.24 m b) 170 mm, 1.7 dm, 0.17 m
c) 800 mm, 8 dm, 0.8 m d) 1450 mm, 14.5 dm, 1.45 m
5. a) 3000 mm, 300 cm, 30 dm b) 2500 mm, 250 cm, 25 dm
c) 1400 mm, 140 cm, 14 dm d) 900 mm, 90 cm, 9 dm
6. a) 5 cm, 0.5 dm, 0.05 m b) 30 mm, 0.3 dm, 0.03 m
c) 110 mm, 11 cm, 0.11 m d) 0.7 dm, 7 cm, 70 mm
Check drawings for accuracy of dimensions.
7. a) 70 dm = 7 m; 5.56 m is less than 7 m.
b) 1.46 m = 146 cm; 250 cm is greater than 146 cm.
c) 1.6 cm is the same length as 16 mm.
d) 3000 mm = 3 m; 3 m is greater than 2.8 m.
e) 5.3 dm is the same length as 53 cm.
f) 2.90 m = 290 cm; 290 cm is greater than 227 cm.
8. 40 dm = 4 m, and 4.9 m is greater than 4 m.
9. Jackie must divide by 100 to get her height in metres from her height in centimetres. The number that represents her height in metres is smaller than the number that represents her height in centimetres.
11. The number that represents the width in millimetres will be the greater number, because you have to divide that number by 100 to get the width in decimetres.

REFLECT: To change a longer unit to a shorter unit, multiply by 10, 100, or 1000. Example: To change 5 m to centimetres, multiply: 5 × 100 = 500; 5 m = 500 cm
To change a shorter unit to a longer unit, divide by 10, 100, or 1000. Example: To change 50 cm to decimetres, divide: 50 ÷ 10 = 5; 50 cm = 5 dm

ASSESSMENT FOR LEARNING

What to Look For

Understanding concepts

✔ Students understand the relationships among the standard units of length.

Applying procedures

✔ Students can express linear measurements in various units.

✔ Students use decimal notation to record fractional parts of units.

Communication

✔ Students record linear measurements using unit symbols appropriately.

What to Do

Extra Support: Provide students with a 1-m measuring tape marked in centimetres and millimetres. Have them mark 60 cm on the tape. Have students: count by 10s as they point to each 1-cm mark to rename the length in millimetres; count by 1s as they point to the 10-cm markings to rename the length in decimetres, and name 60 cm as a fraction of 100 cm to express the length in metres.
Students can use Step-by-Step 2 (Master 9.11) to complete question 10.

Extra Practice: Students can complete Extra Practice 1 (Master 9.22).

Extension: Have students write and solve problems similar to those in questions 8–10.

Recording and Reporting

Master 9.2 Ongoing Observations: Length, Perimeter, and Area

Using Non-Standard Units to Estimate Lengths

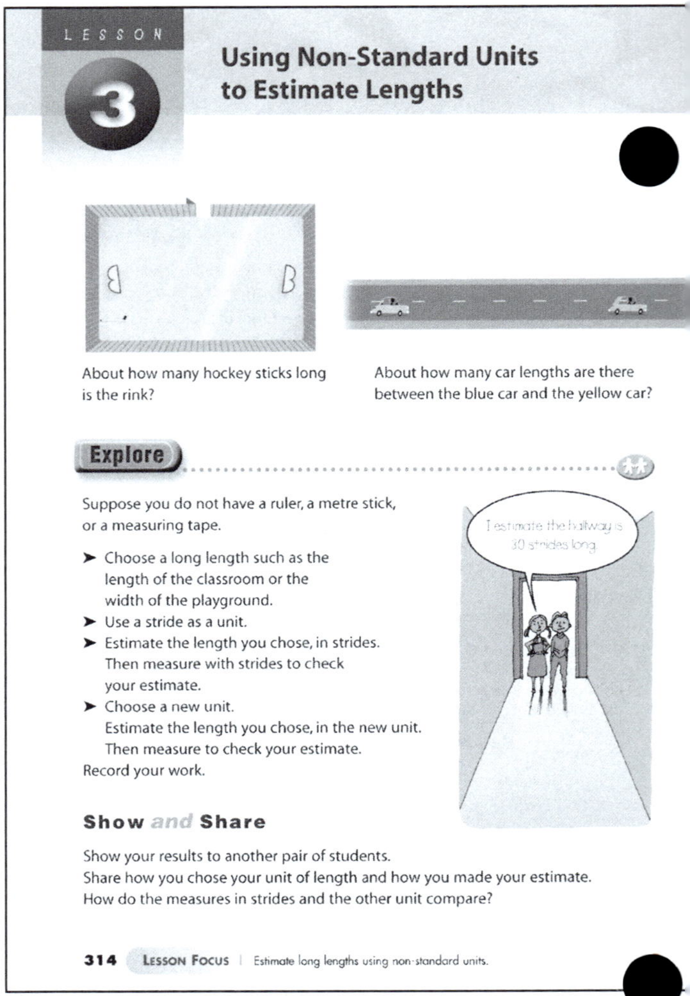
LESSON 3

Using Non-Standard Units to Estimate Lengths

About how many hockey sticks long is the rink?

About how many car lengths are there between the blue car and the yellow car?

Explore

Suppose you do not have a ruler, a metre stick, or a measuring tape.

➤ Choose a long length such as the length of the classroom or the width of the playground.
➤ Use a stride as a unit.
➤ Estimate the length you chose, in strides. Then measure with strides to check your estimate.
➤ Choose a new unit. Estimate the length you chose, in the new unit. Then measure to check your estimate.

Record your work.

Show and Share

Show your results to another pair of students.
Share how you chose your unit of length and how you made your estimate.
How do the measures in strides and the other unit compare?

314 LESSON FOCUS | Estimate long lengths using non-standard units.

LESSON ORGANIZER 40–50 min

Curriculum Focus: Estimate long lengths using non-standard units. (5m45)

Student Materials
- hockey sticks, brooms, or similar objects
- string

Optional
- Step-by-Step 3 (Master 9.12)
- Extra Practice 2 (Master 9.23)

Vocabulary: standard units, non-standard units

Assessment: Master 9.2 Ongoing Observations: Length, Perimeter, and Area

Key Math Learnings

1. Units, such as hockey sticks and car lengths, are non-standard units.
2. Non-standard units are sometimes used to estimate long lengths.
3. Metres and kilometres are standard units.

Numbers Every Day

Students find the sum using a calculator.

BEFORE Get Started

Present *Explore*. Invite a volunteer to demonstrate what a stride is.

DURING Explore

Ongoing Assessment: Observe and Listen

Ask questions, such as:
- How did you estimate the length in strides? *(I think my stride is about 1 m long, so I estimated the length of the classroom is about 20 strides.)*
- Why is it important to try to measure in a straight line? *(If we don't measure in a straight line, the measurement will be longer.)*

Watch to ensure students are attempting to make their strides equal in length.

AFTER Connect

Invite volunteers to share their estimates and their measurements. Ask:
- Why did different students get different results in strides? (*Different stride lengths*)

Use *Connect* to introduce the terms **standard** and **non-standard units.**

Practice

Assessment Focus: Question 4

Some students may suggest using a portable object that is approximately as long as the table. Other students may suggest using a piece of string equal in length to the table.

Connect

- Metres and kilometres are **standard units.** You use them to estimate and measure long lengths.
- Units such as floor tiles, car lengths, and strides are **non-standard units.** They can also be used to estimate and measure long lengths.
- A car length is longer than a stride. The measure of a distance in car lengths will be less than the measure of the same distance in strides.

Practice

1. Estimate each distance in strides. Then measure to check your estimates.
   a) the distance from the teacher's desk to the classroom door 5 strides; 4 m
   b) the distance from your classroom door to the principal's office 25 strides; 20 m
2. Compare your measurements from question 1 with those of two other classmates. Why are the results different?
3. Explain how you could use the height of a classmate to measure the length of the playground.
4. Suppose you want to find out how many tables could be lined up in the hallway. How could you do this without moving the tables? Are you and a classmate likely to get the same result? Explain.

Numbers Every Day

Calculator Skills

Add.

4356
2722
+ 5006
12 084

Reflect

Describe a situation when you might want to estimate a long length using a non-standard unit.

ASSESSMENT FOCUS | Question 4

315

REACHING ALL LEARNERS

Common Misconceptions

➤Students do not understand the relationship between the size of the unit used to measure length and the resulting numerical value. (For example, students may think that, since hockey sticks are longer than baseball bats, the measurement in hockey sticks will be greater.)

How to Help: Have students use large paper clips and then small paper clips to measure the width of a book, and note which measurement took more paper clips. The longer the size of the unit, the fewer of that unit that are needed to measure a length.

Sample Answers

1. Estimates and measurements will vary.
2. The results are different because my strides are shorter than Humsa's strides.
3. Cut a piece of string equal to the classmate's height, then use the string to measure.
4. I would cut a piece of string as long as the table. I would use the string to measure the length of the hallway. I'm not likely to get the same result as my classmate, because I may have cut my string a different length.

REFLECT: If I wanted to know if a piece of carpeting would fit in my bedroom, I could use strides to measure my bedroom, then use strides to measure the carpeting.

ASSESSMENT FOR LEARNING

What to Look For	What to Do
Understanding concepts ✔ Students understand what a non-standard unit is. ***Applying procedures*** ✔ Students can estimate and measure a long length using a non-standard unit.	***Extra Support:*** Have students estimate and measure the width of the gym in strides, then use their results to estimate the length. They can then measure the length to check. Students can use Step-by-Step 3 (Master 9.12) to complete question 4. ***Extra Practice:*** Have students select a non-standard unit on their own and use it to measure a long length. Students can complete Extra Practice 2 (Master 9.23). ***Extension:*** Invite students to interview adults to find out how estimation of length is used while driving a vehicle.

Recording and Reporting

Master 9.2 Ongoing Observations: Length, Perimeter, and Area

Measuring Distance Around a Circular Object

LESSON ORGANIZER 40–50 min

Curriculum Focus: Measure circumference. (5m46)

Student Materials
- circular objects
- string
- scissors
- metre sticks
- rulers
- 3-column charts (PM 18)

Optional
- Step-by-Step 4 (Master 9.13)
- Extra Practice 2 (Master 9.23)

Vocabulary: circumference

Assessment: Master 9.2 Ongoing Observations: Length, Perimeter, and Area

Key Math Learning

The distance around a cylinder or a circle is its circumference.

Numbers Every Day

- Start at 190. Subtract 11 each time: 146, 135, 124, 113, 102
- Start at 190. Add 2. Increase the number you add by 2 each time: 210, 220, 232, 246, 262

LESSON 4

Measuring Distance Around a Circular Object

Explore

You will need a collection of circular objects, string, scissors, and a metre stick.

➤ Predict the order of the objects from the object with the greatest distance around to the object with the least distance around.
➤ Choose an object from the collection.
Estimate the distance around the object.
Use any materials you like to measure the distance.
➤ Record the estimate and the measurement.
➤ Repeat the activity with other objects.
➤ Order the objects from the object with the greatest distance around to the object with the least distance around.

Show and Share

Share your results with another pair of students.
Discuss the strategies you used to measure the distance around an object.
How did you use one measurement to help estimate the next?

316 LESSON FOCUS | Measure circumference.

Math Note

An object is circular if it has a circular cross section, but students do not need to know the term "cross section" at this time.

BEFORE Get Started

Display a collection of circular objects such as tin cans, thread spools, jar lids, and plates. Ask:

- What do all these objects have in common? (*They are all circular or round.*)
- Suppose you traced one of these objects on paper. What figure would it make? (*A circle*)

Present *Explore*. Establish what is meant by "distance around."

Provide each pair of students with 4 or 5 objects.

DURING Explore

Ongoing Assessment: Observe and Listen

- Which unit will you use to estimate and measure the distance around that object? Why? (*Centimetres; the distance around the object is not very big.*)
- How did you estimate the distance around? (*Based on a previous measurement*)
- How can you use the measure of the distance around that object to estimate the distance around this object? (*The objects look to be about the same size, so the measure of the distance around each object is about the same.*)

Watch for students who develop a strategy other than wrapping string around the object (for example, marking a starting point on the rim of the object, rolling it along a piece of paper, then measuring the distance it travels).

Connect

The distance around a circular object or figure is its **circumference**.

e is one way to find the circumference of a circular object.
e string and a ruler.

Cut a length of string equal to the circumference of the object.

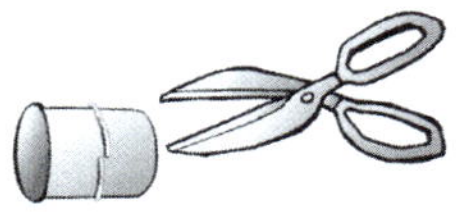

Measure the string.

The circumference of this film canister is 11 cm.

Practice

1. Which unit and which tool would you use to measure the circumference of each item? Explain your choice.
   a) a bicycle wheel b) a garbage can
   c) a diamond ring d) Earth
   e) a circus ring f) a lollipop stick

2. Estimate first. Then find the circumference of each object in the classroom.
   a) the leg of your chair 10 cm; 13 cm
   b) a piece of chalk 5 cm; 2 cm
   c) a globe 30 cm; 40 cm

3. Work with a partner. Estimate, then measure, the distance around your partner's:
   a) wrist b) baby finger c) ankle
   Why might you want to know these measurements?

4. Find an object with each circumference. Measure to check.
   a) about 1 m a garbage can
   b) about 5 cm a marker

Numbers Every Day

Number Strategies

Find each pattern rule. Write the next 5 terms in each pattern.

- 190, 179, 168, 157, ...
- 190, 192, 196, 202, ...

317

REACHING ALL LEARNERS

Early Finishers

Have students rename their measurements from *Explore* using other units.

Common Misconceptions

➤ Students produce an inaccurate measurement of circumference because they overlap the string before cutting.

How to Help: Suggest students check by wrapping the length of string around the can again after cutting it. Explain that the ends of the string must meet, but not overlap.

Sample Answers

1. a) Centimetre or metre; I would use string or measuring tape. The circumference is probably about 1 m.
   b) Centimetre; I would use string or measuring tape. I can wrap my arms around the circumference, and that's about 1 m.
   c) Centimetre; I would use string. I can measure the circumference of the ring in centimetres.
   d) Kilometre; I do not have a way to measure this.
   e) Metre; I would use strides. The circumference is greater than 1 m, but less than 1 km.
   f) Millimetre; I would use string. The circumference is very small.
2. a), b), and c); answers will vary.
3. Answers will vary.
   a) 10 cm; 15 cm b) 2 cm; 3 cm c) 15 cm; 20 cm
   Someone buying a watch, a ring, or an ankle bracelet might want to know these measurements.

AFTER Connect

Invite volunteers to describe and/or demonstrate the strategies they used. Ask:

- Do you think your measurements are exact or approximate? (*Approximate*) Explain. (*It's hard to cut the string so its length is equal to the exact distance around the object; we measured to the nearest centimetre.*)
- How could you get a more precise measurement? (*Measure to tenths of a centimetre.*)

Explain that the distance around a circular object is called its **circumference**. Ask:

- What do we call the distance around a polygon? (*Perimeter*)
- How are circumference and perimeter alike? Different? (*Both circumference and perimeter measure the distance around. Circumference applies only to circular objects. Perimeter can apply to polygons as well as circles.*)

Practice

Students will need string, metre sticks, and rulers to complete some of the questions.

Assessment Focus: Question 7

Students use a piece of string to measure the circumference of their wrists. Students will then measure the length of the string. Students compare their wrist measurement with the bracelet's circumference to determine if the bracelet will fit.

7. I measured the circumference of my wrist with a piece of string. The circumference of my wrist is about 14 cm. I think I could wear the bracelet.
8. My estimate is 5 cm. I could check my estimate by laying string along the circle, then measuring the string; or by wrapping string around the object, then measuring the string.
9. The circumference in metres will be the lesser number, because you will have to multiply by 100 to get the circumference in centimetres, and this will be a greater number.
10. Answers will vary. The circumference seems to be about 3 times the width.

REFLECT:

Dear Jonathon,

Here's how to find the circumference of a telephone pole: Get some string or rope. Wrap it around the pole. Cut off the string or rope to fit exactly around the pole. Make sure the ends don't overlap. Take the string or rope home. Measure it with a measuring tape. That's the circumference of the telephone pole.

Your friend,
Bettina

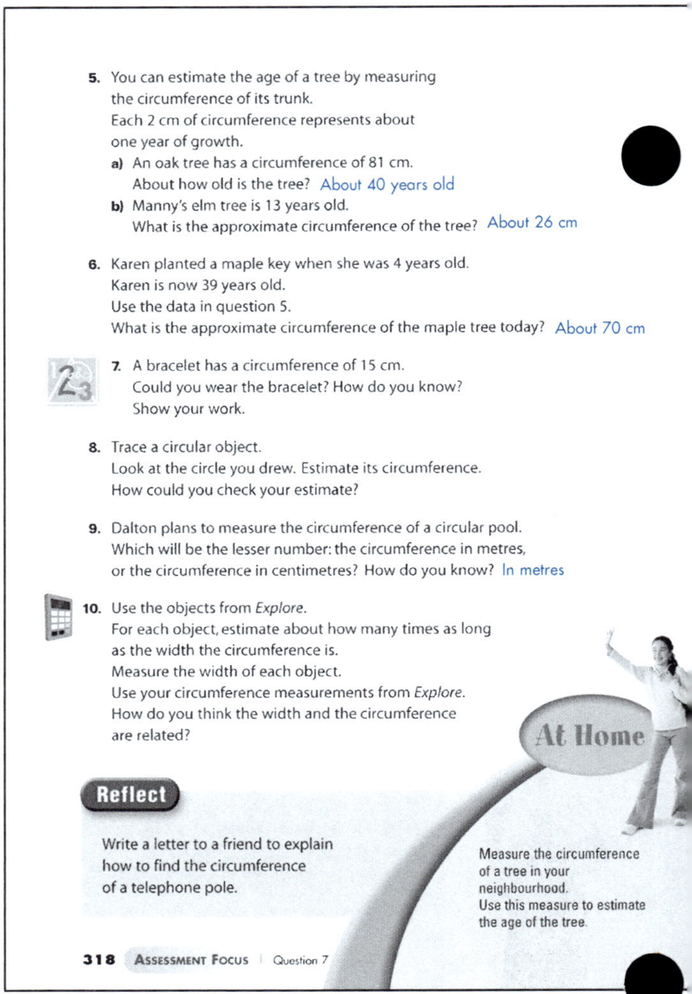

5. You can estimate the age of a tree by measuring the circumference of its trunk.
Each 2 cm of circumference represents about one year of growth.
a) An oak tree has a circumference of 81 cm.
About how old is the tree? About 40 years old
b) Manny's elm tree is 13 years old.
What is the approximate circumference of the tree? About 26 cm

6. Karen planted a maple key when she was 4 years old.
Karen is now 39 years old.
Use the data in question 5.
What is the approximate circumference of the maple tree today? About 70 cm

7. A bracelet has a circumference of 15 cm.
Could you wear the bracelet? How do you know?
Show your work.

8. Trace a circular object.
Look at the circle you drew. Estimate its circumference.
How could you check your estimate?

9. Dalton plans to measure the circumference of a circular pool.
Which will be the lesser number: the circumference in metres, or the circumference in centimetres? How do you know? In metres

10. Use the objects from *Explore*.
For each object, estimate about how many times as long as the width the circumference is.
Measure the width of each object.
Use your circumference measurements from *Explore*.
How do you think the width and the circumference are related?

Reflect

Write a letter to a friend to explain how to find the circumference of a telephone pole.

At Home

Measure the circumference of a tree in your neighbourhood.
Use this measure to estimate the age of the tree.

318 ASSESSMENT FOCUS | Question 7

ASSESSMENT FOR LEARNING

What to Look For	What to Do
Understanding concepts ✔ Students understand that the circumference is the measure of the distance around a circular figure. ***Applying procedures*** ✔ Students choose an appropriate unit, then estimate and measure circumference.	***Extra Support:*** Students who have difficulty working with string to measure circumference may have more success with dental floss. Students can use Step-by-Step 4 (Master 9.13) to complete question 6. ***Extra Practice:*** Have students find objects with approximate circumferences of 1 dm, 2 dm, and 3 dm. Students can complete Extra Practice 2 (Master 9.23). ***Extension:*** Students use a calculator to divide circumference by diameter after completing question 10. They look for a pattern in the results.

Recording and Reporting
Master 9.2 Ongoing Observations: Length, Perimeter, and Area

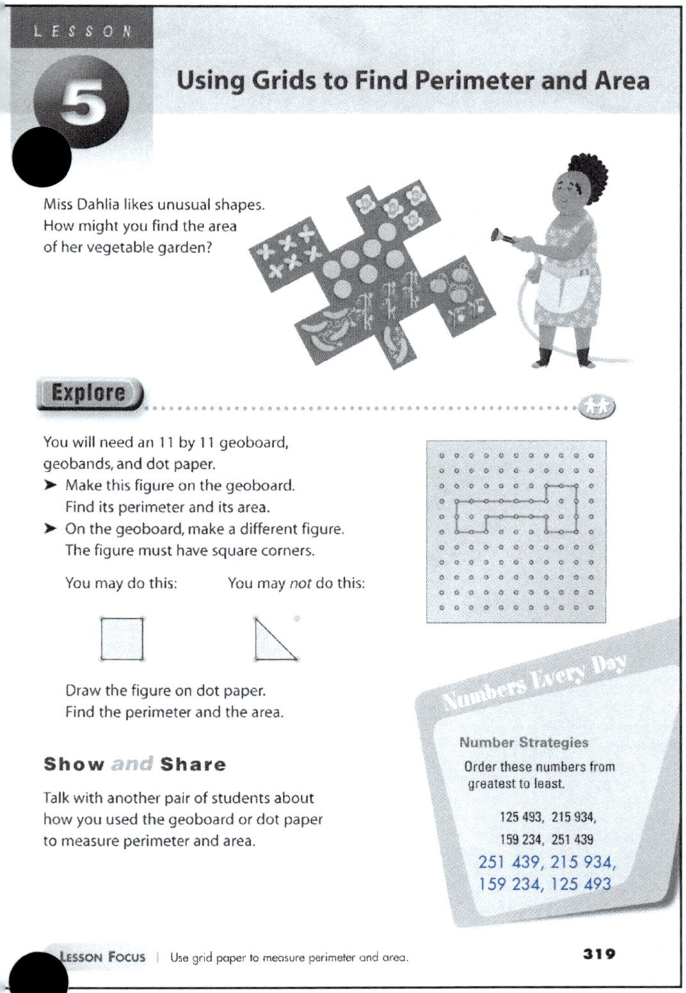
LESSON 5

Using Grids to Find Perimeter and Area

Miss Dahlia likes unusual shapes.
How might you find the area
of her vegetable garden?

Explore

You will need an 11 by 11 geoboard, geobands, and dot paper.

➤ Make this figure on the geoboard. Find its perimeter and its area.

➤ On the geoboard, make a different figure. The figure must have square corners.

You may do this: You may *not* do this:

Draw the figure on dot paper. Find the perimeter and the area.

Show *and* Share

Talk with another pair of students about how you used the geoboard or dot paper to measure perimeter and area.

Numbers Every Day

Number Strategies

Order these numbers from greatest to least.

125 493, 215 934, 159 234, 251 439

251 439, 215 934, 159 234, 125 493

LESSON FOCUS | Use grid paper to measure perimeter and area.

319

Using Grids to Find Perimeter and Area

LESSON ORGANIZER — 40–50 min

Curriculum Focus: Use grid paper to measure perimeter and area. (5m43, 5m55, 5m57)

Teacher Materials:
- dot paper transparency (PM 25)

Student Materials
- 11 by 11 geoboards
- geobands
- dot paper (PM 25)
- 1-cm grid paper (PM 23)

Optional
- Step-by-Step 5 (Master 9.14)
- Extra Practice 3 (Master 9.24)
- Cuisenaire rod
- Colour Tiles or congruent paper squares

Assessment: Master 9.2 Ongoing Observations: Length, Perimeter, and Area

Key Math Learnings

1. The perimeter of a figure on a grid can be found by counting the units along the outside of the figure.
2. The area of a figure on a grid can be found by counting the square units inside the figure.

Numbers Every Day

Students should compare hundreds of thousands, tens of thousands, and thousands.

BEFORE — Get Started

Invite students to examine the illustration of the garden in the Student Book.

Ask questions, such as:

- What do you notice about the garden? (*Unusual shape; many sides*)
- Why can we call the garden a polygon? (*It is a closed figure. It has straight sides.*)
- Suppose a model of the garden was drawn on grid paper. How could you find the perimeter of the garden? (*Count the units along the outside.*) The area? (*Count the squares inside the figure.*)

Present *Explore*.

DURING — Explore

Watch for students who are not making square corners on their figures. Remind them that all geobands must be horizontal or vertical.

Ongoing Assessment: Observe and Listen

Ask questions, such as:

- How did you find the perimeter of your figure? (*I drew the figure on 1-cm grid paper. Then I counted the squares along the outside of the figure to find the perimeter in centimetres.*)
- How did you find the area? (*I counted the number of squares inside the figure to find the area in square centimetres.*)

For those students for whom it is appropriate, ask:

- What kind of number was your perimeter? (*An even number*)

REACHING ALL LEARNERS

Alternative Explore

Materials: 1-cm grid paper, Cuisenaire rods

Have students take a handful of rods. They arrange the rods on the grid paper to form a figure, then trace around the arrangement. Students trade figures with their partners. They estimate, then find and record the perimeter and area of their partner's figure.

Early Finishers

Have students use geoboards to find as many figures as they can with area 5 square units and perimeter 12 units.

Common Misconceptions

➤Students count units and square units incorrectly.

How to Help: Encourage students to mark units as they count to find perimeter. Have them colour or cross off square units as they count to find area. This will help students avoid counting the same unit twice or missing units.

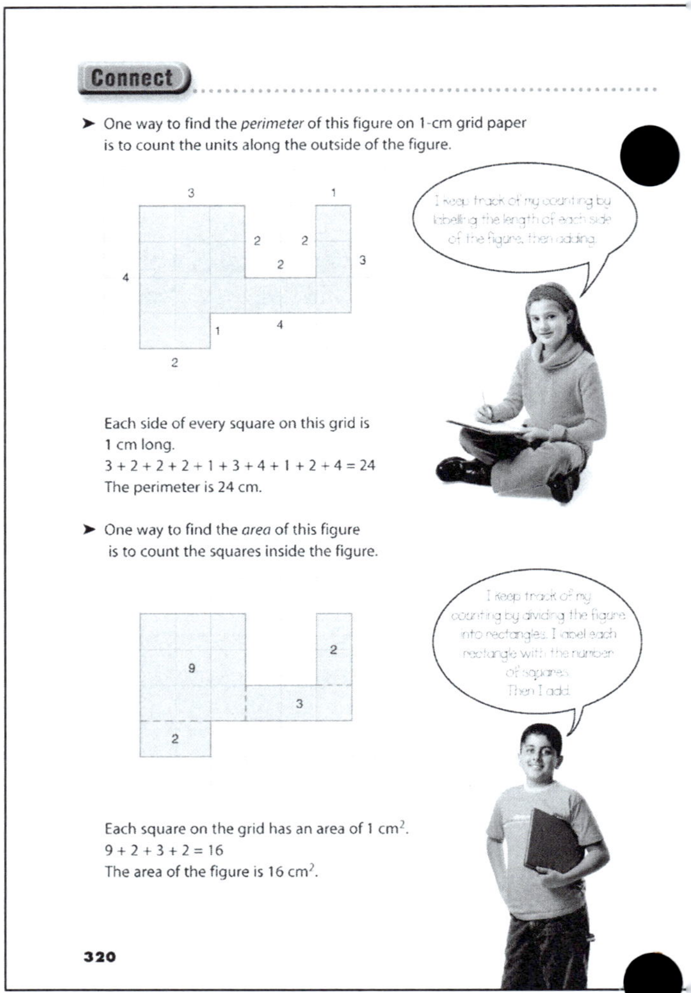

Connect

➤ One way to find the *perimeter* of this figure on 1-cm grid paper is to count the units along the outside of the figure.

Each side of every square on this grid is 1 cm long.

3 + 2 + 2 + 2 + 1 + 3 + 4 + 1 + 2 + 4 = 24

The perimeter is 24 cm.

➤ One way to find the *area* of this figure is to count the squares inside the figure.

Each square on the grid has an area of 1 cm^2.

9 + 2 + 3 + 2 = 16

The area of the figure is 16 cm^2.

320

Encourage these students to use their geoboards to investigate this result for different polygons. Have them share their findings with other students. Once they have discovered that the result is true for all the polygons with square corners, encourage them to explain why this is so. Ask questions such as:

- Why do you think the perimeter of a figure with square corners is an even number?
  (I can draw a rectangle along the outermost sides. Because the polygon is closed, any indents from this rectangle always go in and come out again an equal number of units. The perimeter of a rectangle is always an even number and the indents always add an even number of units so the answer will always be an even number.)
- How could you make a different figure with the same perimeter as your figure?
  (I could draw a rectangle. I would divide the perimeter by 2 to find the sum of the length and width. For example, if the perimeter of my figure is 24 cm, I can draw a rectangle with length 8 cm and width 4 cm. I can create other figures by indenting the corners of the rectangle.)
- How can you make a figure with the same area?
  (I can draw a rectangle with width 1 cm. For example, if the area is 5 cm^2, I would draw a rectangle with length 5 cm, width 1 cm.)

Practice

1. a) Estimate first. Then find the perimeter and area of each figure on this 1-cm grid.

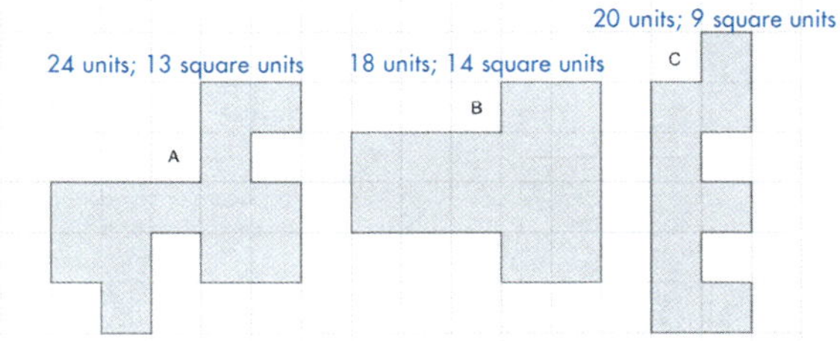

b) Order the figures from least to greatest perimeter. B, C, A
Then order them from least to greatest area. C, A, B

2. Use 1-cm grid paper. Draw only on the lines.
Draw 3 figures.
Find and record the perimeter and area of each figure.

3. Use a geoboard. Make a figure with perimeter 16 units.
The figure must have square corners.
Draw your figure on grid paper.
a) Explain how you know the perimeter is 16 units.
b) What is the area of your figure?
c) Make a different figure with perimeter 16 units.
What is the area of this figure?

4. Use a geoboard.
Make a figure to fit each description.
Each figure should have only square corners.
a) a perimeter of 12 units and an area of 5 square units
b) a perimeter of 14 units and an area of 6 square units
c) a perimeter of 10 units and an area of 5 square units
Record your work on grid paper.
Describe each figure you made.

321

Sample Answers

2. Figures will vary. Perimeters should be recorded in centimetres and areas in square centimetres.

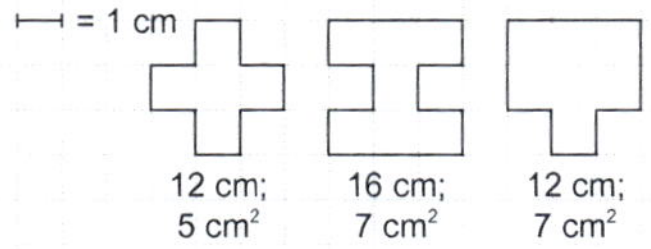

3. Figure should be drawn along the lines of the grid paper.
a)

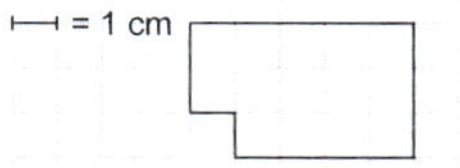

I know the perimeter is 16 units because I drew the sides of the figure along 16 side lengths of the grid.

b) Answers will vary. 14 cm^2

c)

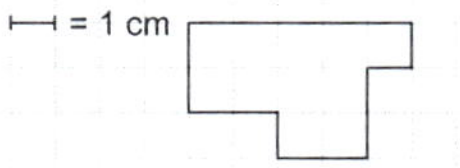

Answers will vary. 11 cm^2

4. Figures should be drawn along the lines of the grid. Answers will vary.

a)

b)

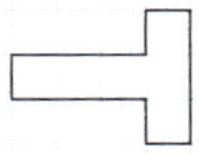

c)

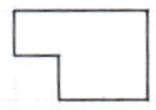

5. All 3 figures should have perimeter 24, 28, or 18 units. These figures have perimeter 18 cm.

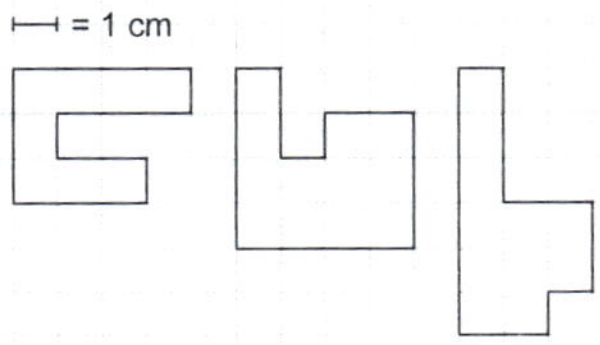

AFTER Connect

Invite a volunteer to give the perimeter (*24 units*) and area (*14 square units*) of the original figure in *Explore*. Invite other students to draw the figure they made with perimeter 24 units on a transparency on the overhead projector. For each example, ask a volunteer to verify the perimeter by counting the units along the outside of the figure.

Ask:

- What can you do to keep track of your counting?
  (*Mark the first unit I count. Label the length of each side, then add.*)

Follow a similar procedure for figures with area 14 square units.

Practice

Students will need 1-cm grid paper, geoboards, and geobands.

Assessment Focus: Question 6

a) Students should understand that the figures they draw should not be rectangles. They realize that, to count units to find perimeter, the sides of the figures must be drawn on the lines of the grid paper. Students draw 3 figures, each with perimeter 28 units. Some may include the key ⊢⊣ = 1 m on their grids.

b) Students should identify the figure with the greatest area as the one that will provide the greatest amount of space for flowers. They record the area in square metres.

6. a)

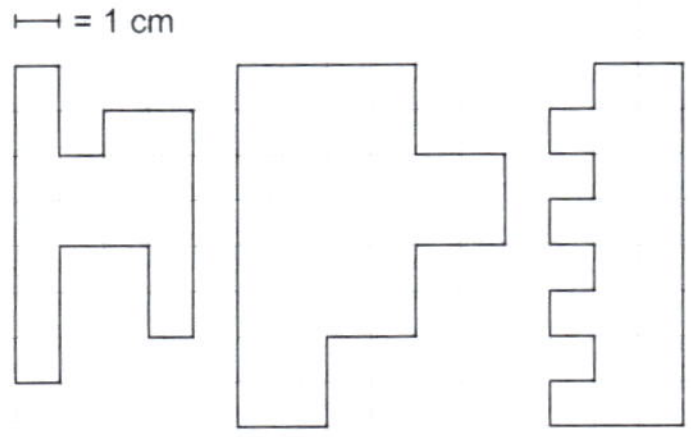

b) The figure with the greatest area; the second figure

7.

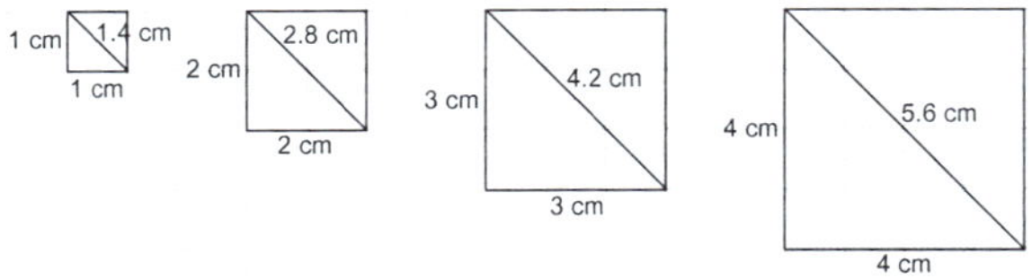

a) I notice that the length of the diagonal on each square is longer than the side length of the square.

b) The perimeter is more than 10 cm because three of the figure's sides are drawn on the diagonals of the squares. The diagonal of a square is longer than the side length.

REFLECT: The figure should be drawn on grid paper. I count the square units inside the figure to find the area, and the units along the outside of the figure to find the perimeter.

5. These 3 figures have different perimeters.

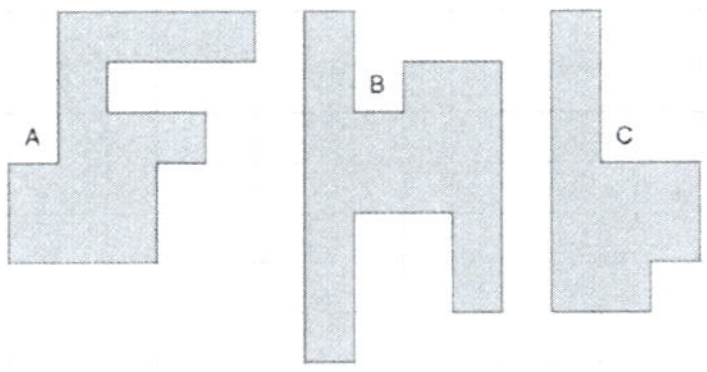

Copy the figures onto 1-cm grid paper.
Change 2 of the figures so that all 3 figures have equal perimeters.

6. Miss Dahlia wants to make a flower garden with an unusual shape. She has 28 m of fencing to enclose the garden.

a) Draw 3 different figures on 1-cm grid paper for Miss Dahlia to choose from. Let the length of each square on the grid represent 1 m.

b) Which one of your 3 figures will give Miss Dahlia the greatest amount of space for planting flowers? Show your work.

7. a) Use 1-cm grid paper. Draw a 1-cm, a 2-cm, a 3-cm, and a 4-cm square. Use a ruler to draw a diagonal on each square. Measure and record the length of each diagonal. Compare the side length of each square to the length of its diagonal. What do you notice?

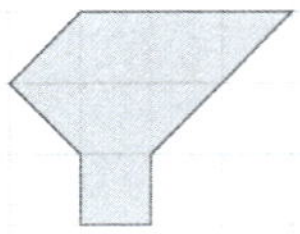

b) Danny said the perimeter of this figure is 10 cm. Do you agree? Explain.

Reflect

Describe how to find the perimeter and area of a figure drawn on the lines of grid paper. Use pictures and words to explain.

322 ASSESSMENT FOCUS | Question 6

ASSESSMENT FOR LEARNING

What to Look For	What to Do
Applying procedures ✔ Students count units along the outside of a figure to find perimeter. ✔ Students count square units inside a figure to find area. ***Problem solving*** ✔ Students develop and use appropriate strategies for tracking and measuring the perimeter and area of a figure on a grid.	***Extra Support:*** Have students use Colour Tiles or congruent paper squares to build figures. Students count units and square units to find perimeter and area. Students can use Step-by-Step 5 (Master 9.14) to complete question 6. ***Extra Practice:*** Students make a figure with square corners on a geoboard. They trade geoboards with a partner, then find the area and the perimeter of their partner's figure. Students can complete Extra Practice 3 (Master 9.24). ***Extension:*** Challenge students to use Colour Tiles or congruent paper squares to find as many figures as they can with area 6 square units.

Recording and Reporting

Master 9.2 Ongoing Observations: Length, Perimeter, and Area

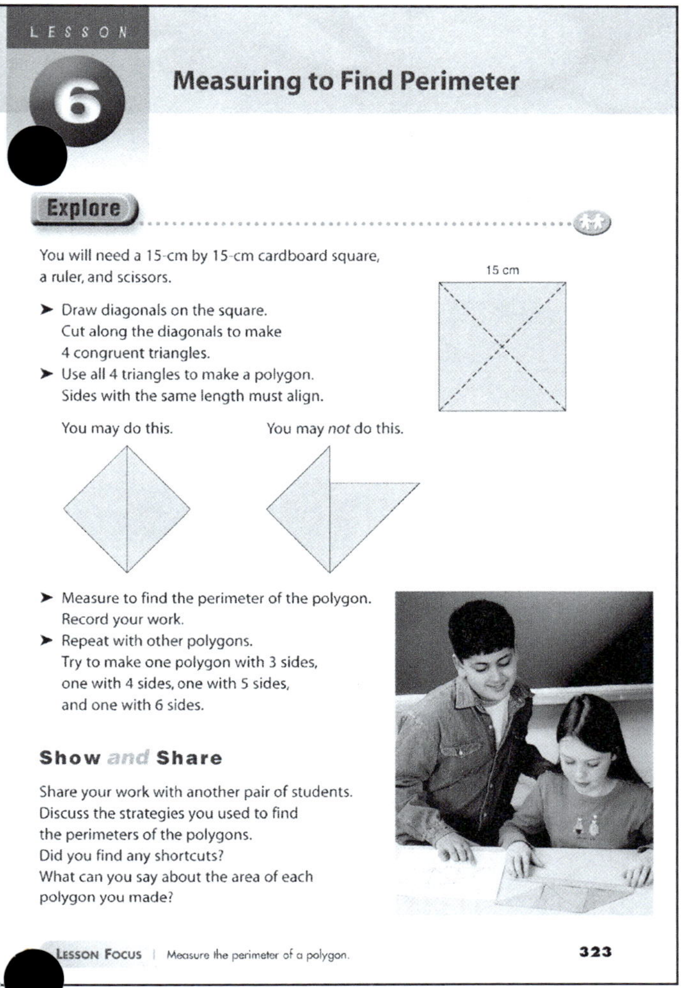
LESSON 6

Measuring to Find Perimeter

Explore

You will need a 15-cm by 15-cm cardboard square, a ruler, and scissors.

➤ Draw diagonals on the square.
Cut along the diagonals to make 4 congruent triangles.

➤ Use all 4 triangles to make a polygon.
Sides with the same length must align.

15 cm

You may do this. You may *not* do this.

➤ Measure to find the perimeter of the polygon.
Record your work.

➤ Repeat with other polygons.
Try to make one polygon with 3 sides, one with 4 sides, one with 5 sides, and one with 6 sides.

Show and Share

Share your work with another pair of students.
Discuss the strategies you used to find the perimeters of the polygons.
Did you find any shortcuts?
What can you say about the area of each polygon you made?

LESSON FOCUS | Measure the perimeter of a polygon.

323

Measuring to Find Perimeter

LESSON ORGANIZER (40–50 min)

Curriculum Focus: Measure the perimeter of a polygon. (5m43)

Student Materials
- 15-cm by 15-cm cardboard squares
- rulers
- scissors
- calculators

Optional
- Step-by-Step 6 (Master 9.15)
- Extra Practice 3 (Master 9.24)
- tangrams

Vocabulary: scale

Assessment: Master 9.2 Ongoing Observations: Length, Perimeter, and Area

Key Math Learnings

1. The perimeter of a polygon can be found by measuring the side lengths, then adding.
2. The perimeter of a polygon, drawn to scale with side lengths given, can be found by adding the lengths of its sides.

BEFORE Get Started

Sketch a large square on the board. Draw a dotted diagonal on the square.

Ask:
- What is the dotted line called? (*A diagonal*) How do you know? (*It joins opposite vertices of the square.*)
- How does the length of the diagonal compare to the length of a side of the square? (*The diagonal is longer than the side.*)

Invite a student to draw the second diagonal on the square.

Ask:
- What can you say about the lengths of the 2 diagonals? (*They are equal.*) About the 4 triangles that have been formed? (*They are congruent isosceles triangles.*)

Present *Explore*. Caution students to draw the diagonals carefully with a ruler, and to cut along the diagonals as accurately as they can. Establish that students should sketch each figure and record its perimeter.

DURING Explore

Ongoing Assessment: Observe and Listen

Watch to see how students find the side lengths of their figures. Are they measuring each side? Or have they found shortcuts, such as adding 15 and 15 to find the length of a side composed of 2 side lengths of the original square?

Watch to ensure students are aligning sides with the same length.

REACHING ALL LEARNERS

Alternative Explore

Materials: rulers, calculators

Have students find the perimeters of various classroom objects, and record the length, width, and perimeter of each object in a chart.

Early Finishers

Have students use the 4 triangles from *Explore* to make as many quadrilaterals as they can, then find the perimeter of each quadrilateral.

Common Misconceptions

- Given the length and width of a rectangle, as in question 5a, students add the two measurements to find perimeter.

How to Help: Remind students that a rectangle has 2 pairs of equal sides. Sketch a rectangle and tell students to suppose it is 4 dm long and 2 dm wide. Have students label the lengths of all sides, then explain how to find the perimeter. When students are to complete a question for which measurements are given, but no figure is given, suggest students sketch and label the figure with the length of each side.

Connect

- To find the perimeter of a polygon, measure the lengths of its sides, then add.

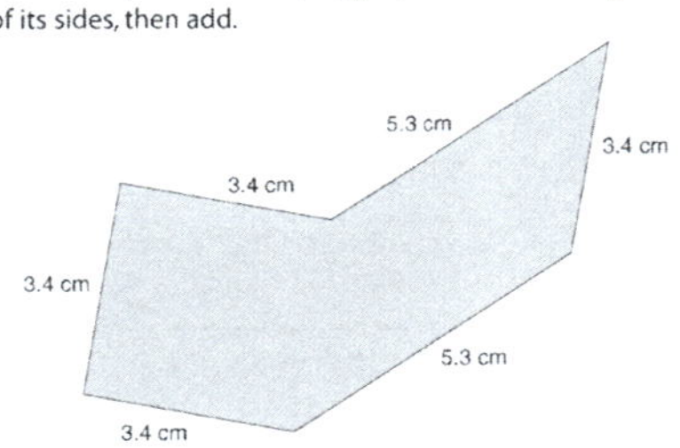

Perimeter = 5.3 cm + 3.4 cm + 5.3 cm + 3.4 cm + 3.4 cm + 3.4 cm
Perimeter = 24.2 cm

- Some polygons are too large to draw on a page.
  A polygon like this is drawn to **scale**.
  The drawing is similar to the polygon.
  It has the same shape as the polygon, but it is smaller.
  The length of each side is given.
  To find the perimeter of the polygon, add the lengths of its sides.

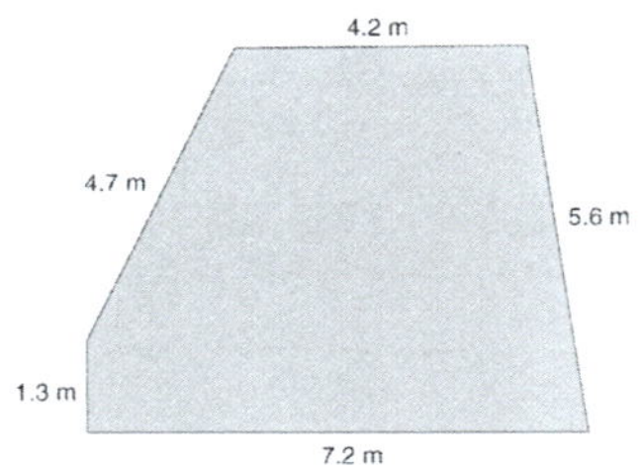

Perimeter = 4.2 m + 5.6 m + 7.2 m + 1.3 m + 4.7 m
Perimeter = 23.0 m

Numbers Every Day

Number Strategies

Estimate each sum. About

1356 + 2478 3900

5020 + 2891 7900

4522 + 3005 7500

Which strategies did you use?

324

Ask questions, such as:

- How did you find the perimeter of that rhombus?
  (*I added all the side lengths together.*)
- Is there a faster way to find the side lengths of that triangle?
  (*Yes, I know that the length of a side of the triangle is the side length of the original square, which is 15 cm, so I don't have to measure it again.*)
- What figure have you made? (*A pentagon*)
  How do you know it is a pentagon?
  (*It has 5 sides.*)

AFTER Connect

Invite volunteers to share some of the figures they made.

Ask:

- What is this figure called? (*A hexagon*)
  How do you know it is a hexagon?
  (*It has 6 sides.*)
- How did you find the perimeter?
  (*I measured the side lengths, then added.*)
- How could you find the perimeter in a different way?
  (*I know that each short side of the triangle is 10.6 cm and the long side is 15 cm. To find the perimeter of the hexagon, I multiply 15 × 4, then add 10.6 × 2.*)
- Did anyone make a different hexagon? A different figure with the same perimeter as the hexagon? A shorter perimeter? A longer perimeter?
- What is the perimeter of the original square?
  (*60 cm*)
- What is the area of the original square?
  (*225* cm^2)
- What can you say about the area of each figure you made?
  (*It is 225* cm^2*; the same as the area of the square.*)
  How do you know?
  (*I didn't add or take away any area. I just rearranged it.*)

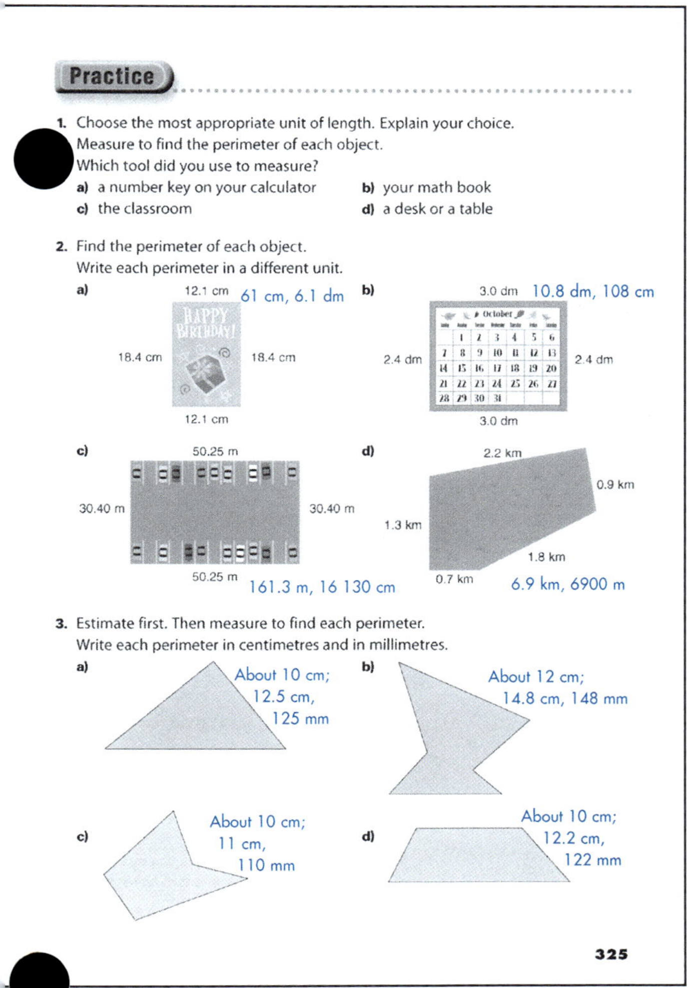

Practice

1. Choose the most appropriate unit of length. Explain your choice.
Measure to find the perimeter of each object.
Which tool did you use to measure?
   a) a number key on your calculator
   b) your math book
   c) the classroom
   d) a desk or a table

2. Find the perimeter of each object.
Write each perimeter in a different unit.

3. Estimate first. Then measure to find each perimeter.
Write each perimeter in centimetres and in millimetres.

325

Numbers Every Day

Estimates may vary. Students can round to the nearest ten, hundred, or thousand.
1356 + 2478 is about 1400 + 2500, or 3900.
5020 + 2891 is about 5000 + 2900, or 7900.
4522 + 3005 is about 4500 + 3000, or 7500.

Sample Answers

1. Answers will vary, but should be given in:
   a) Millimetres; measured with a ruler
   b) Centimetres; measured with a ruler
   c) Metres; measured with a metre stick
   d) Centimetres or metres; measured with a metre stick

Use *Connect* to introduce the term **scale.** Review how to find the perimeter of a figure when its side lengths are given.

Practice

Students will need rulers to complete some of the exercises. Have calculators available for those who wish to use them.

Assessment Focus: Question 7

Students should understand they must find the lengths and widths of gardens with perimeter 55 m. They will choose a number between 12.0 and 12.8 (for example, 12.1), double the number to get the sum of one pair of equal sides (that is, 24.2), subtract the total from 55 (that is, 55 – 24.2 = 30.8), then divide the difference by 2 to get the lengths of the other pair of equal sides (that is, 30.8 ÷ 2 = 15.4).

Some students may approach the search in an organized fashion (for example, 12.0 by 15.5, 12.1 by 15.4, 12.2 by 15.3, and so on), then use the emerging pattern to find the remaining dimensions. Other students may approach the task randomly. Some students might consider adjacent sides each to be between 12.0 m and 12.8 m, but will quickly realize that the sum of the four sides will be less than 55 m, and they will discard this option.

7. a) 12.0 m by 15.5 m; 12.1 m by 15.4 m; 12.2 m by 15.3 m; 12.3 m by 15.2 m; 12.4 m by 15.1 m; 12.5 m by 15.0 m; 12.6 m by 14.9 m; 12.7 m by 14.8 m; 12.8 m by 14.7 m. I have found 9 answers.
   b) Because not all four sides are equal
8. a) Kilometre, because I would drive around it
   b) Metre, because I could use a metre stick to measure
   c) Centimetre, because I could use a ruler to measure
   d) Metre, because I could use a metre stick to measure
   e) Centimetre, because I can hold it in my hand and use a ruler to measure
   f) Kilometre, because it is much greater than a metre stick

REFLECT:

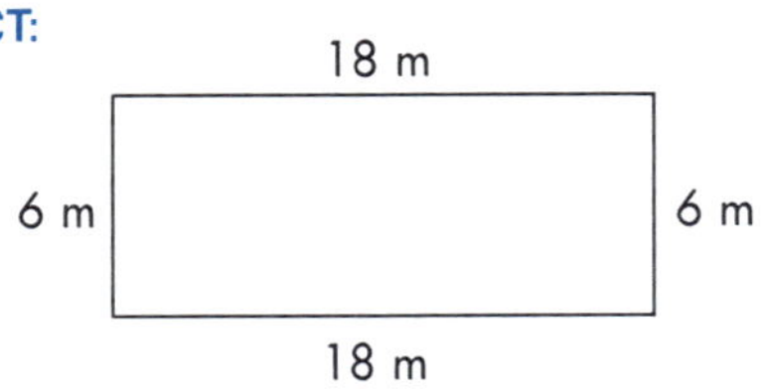

This is a rectangle. To find its perimeter, you add all the side lengths.
18 m + 6 m + 18 m + 6 m = 48 m

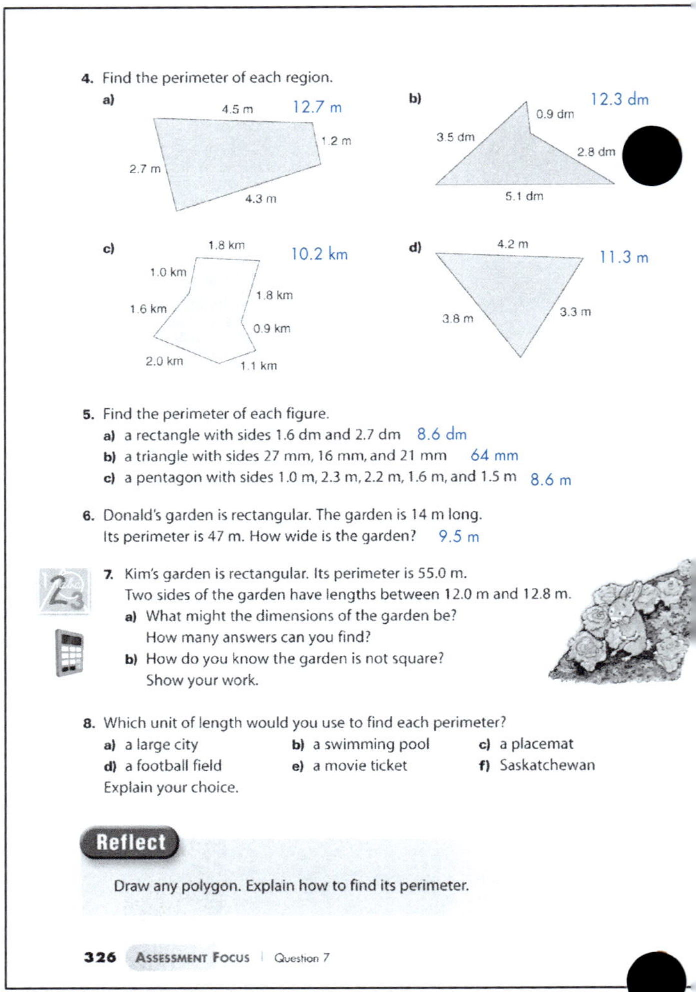

4. Find the perimeter of each region.
a) 4.5 m, 1.2 m, 4.3 m, 2.7 m — 12.7 m
b) 0.9 dm, 3.5 dm, 2.8 dm, 5.1 dm — 12.3 dm
c) 1.8 km, 1.0 km, 1.8 km, 1.6 km, 0.9 km, 2.0 km, 1.1 km — 10.2 km
d) 4.2 m, 3.8 m, 3.3 m — 11.3 m

5. Find the perimeter of each figure.
a) a rectangle with sides 1.6 dm and 2.7 dm 8.6 dm
b) a triangle with sides 27 mm, 16 mm, and 21 mm 64 mm
c) a pentagon with sides 1.0 m, 2.3 m, 2.2 m, 1.6 m, and 1.5 m 8.6 m

6. Donald's garden is rectangular. The garden is 14 m long. Its perimeter is 47 m. How wide is the garden? 9.5 m

7. Kim's garden is rectangular. Its perimeter is 55.0 m. Two sides of the garden have lengths between 12.0 m and 12.8 m.
a) What might the dimensions of the garden be? How many answers can you find?
b) How do you know the garden is not square? Show your work.

8. Which unit of length would you use to find each perimeter?
a) a large city b) a swimming pool c) a placemat
d) a football field e) a movie ticket f) Saskatchewan
Explain your choice.

Reflect

Draw any polygon. Explain how to find its perimeter.

326 ASSESSMENT FOCUS | Question 7

ASSESSMENT FOR LEARNING

What to Look For	What to Do
Understanding concepts ✔ Students understand that perimeter can be found by measuring side lengths, then adding.	***Extra Support:*** Have students complete the Additional Activity, *Tangram Perimeters* (Master 9.7). Students can use Step-by-Step 6 (Master 9.15) to complete question 7.
Applying procedures ✔ Students can measure the side lengths of a polygon, then add to find the perimeter.	***Extra Practice:*** Have students measure the dimensions of a large region, such as the gym, then find its perimeter. Students can complete Extra Practice 3 (Master 9.24).
Problem solving ✔ Students choose an appropriate strategy to solve problems involving perimeter.	***Extension:*** Challenge students to determine whether the perimeter of $\frac{1}{2}$ of a sheet of paper is $\frac{1}{2}$ the perimeter of the whole sheet of paper.

Recording and Reporting
Master 9.2 Ongoing Observations: Length, Perimeter, and Area

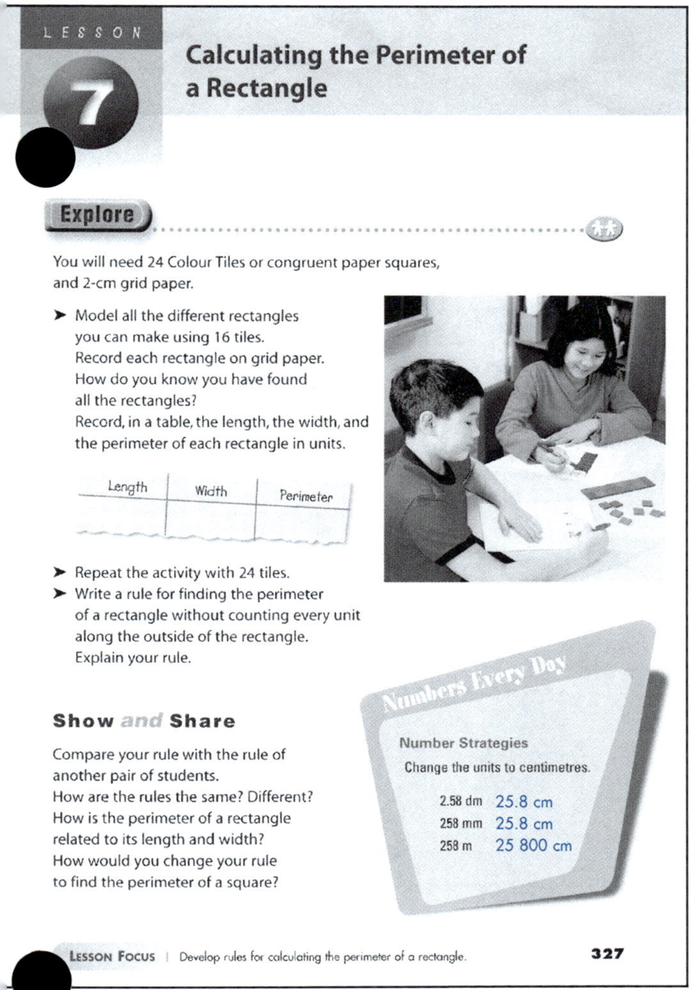

LESSON 7

Calculating the Perimeter of a Rectangle

Explore

You will need 24 Colour Tiles or congruent paper squares, and 2-cm grid paper.

➤ Model all the different rectangles you can make using 16 tiles.
Record each rectangle on grid paper.
How do you know you have found all the rectangles?
Record, in a table, the length, the width, and the perimeter of each rectangle in units.

Length	Width	Perimeter

➤ Repeat the activity with 24 tiles.

➤ Write a rule for finding the perimeter of a rectangle without counting every unit along the outside of the rectangle.
Explain your rule.

Show *and* Share

Compare your rule with the rule of another pair of students.
How are the rules the same? Different?
How is the perimeter of a rectangle related to its length and width?
How would you change your rule to find the perimeter of a square?

Numbers Every Day

Number Strategies

Change the units to centimetres.

2.58 dm 25.8 cm
258 mm 25.8 cm
258 m 25 800 cm

LESSON FOCUS | Develop rules for calculating the perimeter of a rectangle. 327

Calculating the Perimeter of a Rectangle

LESSON ORGANIZER (40–50 min)

Curriculum Focus: Develop rules for calculating the perimeter of a rectangle. (5m54, 5m55, 5m56)

Teacher Materials
- transparent Colour Tiles (optional)

Student Materials
- Colour Tiles or congruent paper squares
- 2-cm grid paper (PM 24)
- 1-cm grid paper (PM 23)
- calculators
- 3-column charts (PM 18)

Optional
- Step-by-Step 7 (Master 9.16)
- Extra Practice 4 (Master 9.25)
- metre sticks

Vocabulary: formula

Assessment: Master 9.2 Ongoing Observations: Length, Perimeter, and Area

Key Math Learnings

1. The perimeter of a rectangle can be found using a formula.
2. A formula is a short way to state a rule.

Math Note

The two versions of the formula for the perimeter of a rectangle produce the same results. This is an example of the distributive property of numbers.

$2 \times \text{length} + 2 \times \text{width} = 2(\text{length} + \text{width})$

BEFORE Get Started

Use 4 Colour Tiles to display a 1 by 4 rectangle on the overhead projector. Ask:

- What is the length of this rectangle? (*4 units*) The width? (*1 unit*)
- What is the perimeter? (*10 units*) How do you know? (*I counted the units along the outside.*)

Invite a volunteer to make a different rectangle (it will be a square) with the 4 tiles, describe its dimensions, then find its perimeter.

Present *Explore*. Remind students to record the dimensions and perimeter of each rectangle in units.

DURING Explore

Ongoing Assessment: Observe and Listen

Watch to ensure students are building only rectangles and using the specified number of tiles. Ask questions, such as:

- How can you describe that rectangle? (*It is 8 units long and 2 units wide.*)
- Can you use 16 tiles to make a rectangle 5 units long? (*No*) Why not? (*A tile would be left over.*)
- How do you know you have found all the rectangles? (*1, 2, 4, 8, and 16 are all the factors of 16. No other number divides evenly into 16.*)
- How can you find the perimeter without counting all the units? (*I know the rectangle has 2 sides of 8 units and 2 sides of 2 units, so I can multiply 8 by 2 and 2 by 2, then add.*)

REACHING ALL LEARNERS

Alternative Explore

Materials: 1-cm grid paper

Have students draw on the grid paper to show all the possible rectangles with area 16 cm^2 and 24 cm^2. Students find the dimensions and perimeter of each rectangle, and record them in a chart. They write a rule for finding the perimeter of a rectangle.

Early Finishers

Have students measure the length and width of a door or bulletin board, and use their rule to find its perimeter.

Common Misconceptions

➤ When building rectangles with Colour Tiles, students believe that a rectangle built vertically is different from the same rectangle built horizontally. For example, students build a 1 by 16 and a 16 by 1 rectangle, and consider them to be different rectangles.

How to Help: Explain that the rectangles only seem different because they are in different positions. Rotate one rectangle to match the other to demonstrate that the rectangles are congruent.

ESL Strategies

ESL students may have difficulty writing a rule for finding the perimeter of a rectangle. Have these students sketch and label a rectangle, then use symbols to record how to find its perimeter.

Connect

➤ Here are two different rules for finding the perimeter of a rectangle.
Each rule can be expressed by a **formula**.

A formula is a short wa
to state a rule.

To find the perimeter of a rectangle:
Multiply the length by 2.
Multiply the width by 2.
Then add.

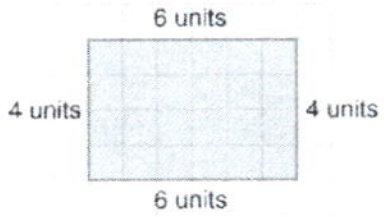

$2 \times 6 = 12$
$2 \times 4 = 8$
$12 + 8 = 20$
Perimeter = 20 units

Formula
Perimeter = 2 × length + 2 × width

To find the perimeter of a rectangle:
Add the length and width.
Then multiply by 2.

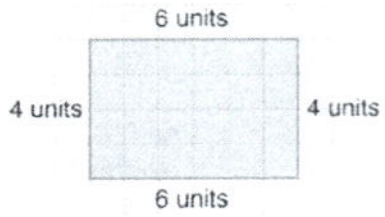

$6 + 4 = 10$
$10 \times 2 = 20$
Perimeter = 20 units

Formula
Perimeter = (length + width) × 2

The brackets show that you add the length and width, then multiply the sum by 2.

➤ Here is a shortcut to find the perimeter of a square.

To find the perimeter of a square, I multiply the side length by 4.

$5 \times 4 = 20$
Perimeter = 20 units

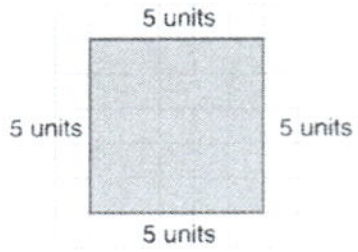

Formula
Perimeter = side length × 4

328

AFTER Connect

Invite volunteers to describe the rectangles they found with 16 tiles. Record the dimensions and the perimeter of each rectangle in a chart. Repeat for rectangles with 24 tiles.

Ask:

- What rule did you write to find the perimeter of a rectangle?
  (*Multiply the width by 2 and multiply the length by 2, then add.*)
- Who wrote a different rule?
  (*I can add the length and the width, then multiply the sum by 2.*)

As each rule is given, record it on the board. For example, the rule may be "Multiply the length by 2. Multiply the width by 2. Then add." Have students use the rule with each rectangle in the chart to verify that it works (for example, $16 \times 2 = 32$; $1 \times 2 = 2$; $32 + 2 = 34$).

Use *Connect* to introduce the term **formula**, and the formulas for finding the perimeter of a rectangle and a square.

Draw a rectangle on the board. Label the length 8 cm and the width 6 cm. Have volunteers use each formula to calculate the perimeter. Repeat with other rectangles, including some with one or two side lengths given in decimals (for example, 7 m by 2.4 m).

Demonstrate the equivalence of the two versions of the formula to students using 2 pencils and 2 rulers. Show them that rearranging the groups of 2 pencils and 2 rulers to produce 2 groups each consisting of a pencil and a ruler does not change the total items.

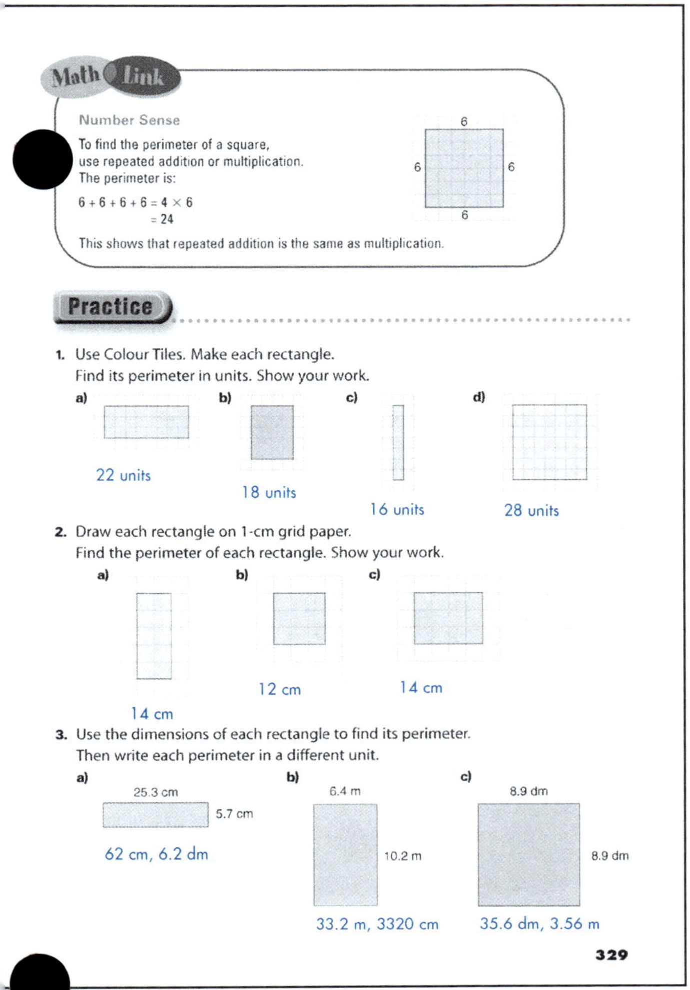

Math Link

Number Sense

To find the perimeter of a square, use repeated addition or multiplication.
The perimeter is:

$6 + 6 + 6 + 6 = 4 \times 6$
$= 24$

This shows that repeated addition is the same as multiplication.

Practice

1. Use Colour Tiles. Make each rectangle.
Find its perimeter in units. Show your work.
a) 22 units b) 18 units c) 16 units d) 28 units

2. Draw each rectangle on 1-cm grid paper.
Find the perimeter of each rectangle. Show your work.
a) 14 cm b) 12 cm c) 14 cm

3. Use the dimensions of each rectangle to find its perimeter.
Then write each perimeter in a different unit.
a) 25.3 cm, 5.7 cm — 62 cm, 6.2 dm
b) 6.4 m, 10.2 m — 33.2 m, 3320 cm
c) 8.9 dm, 8.9 dm — 35.6 dm, 3.56 m

329

Sample Answers

1. a) $(8 + 3) \times 2 = 22$
   b) $(4 + 5) \times 2 = 18$
   c) $(1 + 7) \times 2 = 16$
   d) $(7 + 7) \times 2 = 28$
2. a) $(2 + 5) \times 2 = 14$
   b) $(3 + 3) \times 2 = 12$
   c) $(4 + 3) \times 2 = 14$

Making Connections

Math Link: Have students find the perimeter of a 7.4-cm square using repeated addition, then multiplication.

Numbers Every Day

To change from decimetres to centimetres, students should multiply by 10. To change from millimetres to centimetres, students should divide by 10. To change from metres to centimetres, students should multiply by 100.

Practice

Colour Tiles are needed for question 1. Questions 2 and 9, and *Reflect* require 1-cm grid paper. Have calculators available for students who wish to use them.

Assessment Focus: Question 9

Students will draw all the possible gardens with side lengths that are whole numbers of metres, and with perimeter 28 m. Some students may find the dimensions in an organized fashion (for example, 1 m by 13 m, 2 m by 12 m, 3 m by 11 m, and so on). Other students may approach the task in a random fashion. Students will then verify the side lengths using a formula for finding the perimeter of the rectangle, which must equal 28 m. Some students will realize that the garden with the most growing space also has the greatest area, and the garden with the least growing space has the least area.

4. Answers will vary. Length = 2 m, width = 1 m
$(2 + 1) \times 2 = 6$; the perimeter is 6 m.
5. Perimeters – A: 151.6 m, B: 123 m, C: 202.4 m
Garden C has the greatest perimeter, so it needs the most fencing.
8. Since the patio is a square, all sides are equal.
$12.8 \div 4 = 3.2$; each side is 3.2 m.
9. Possible gardens: 13 m by 1 m; 12 m by 2 m; 11 m by 3 m; 10 m by 4 m; 9 m by 5 m; 8 m by 6 m; 7 m by 7 m
Most growing space: 7 m by 7 m garden
Least growing space: 13 m by 1 m garden
10. Perimeter of playground is 250 m: $2 \times 90 = 180$; $2 \times 35 = 70$; $180 + 70 = 250$
It will take Royanna 4 laps to jog 1 km.
1 km = 1000 m; $250 + 250 + 250 + 250 = 250 \times 4 = 1000$

REFLECT:

Perimeter = $(5 + 5) \times 2 = 20$
Perimeter = 5×4
= 20
Perimeter is 20 cm.

I prefer the second formula because it is faster to calculate.

4. Measure the length and width of a rectangular table to the nearest unit. Use these dimensions to find the perimeter of the table. Show your work.

5. Which garden needs the most fencing to enclose it? C
Explain how you know.

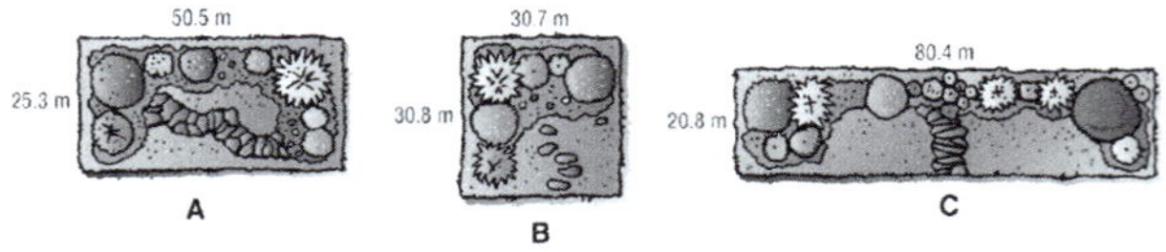

6. The playground at the Community Centre is rectangular. Its length is 60 m. The perimeter is 180 m. What is the width of the playground? 30 m

7. The perimeter of Tony's rectangular apple orchard is 1 km. How long might each side be? 250 m by 250 m; 400 m by 100 m; 300 m by 200 m; 350 m by 150 m, and so on

8. The perimeter of a square patio is 12.8 m. How long is each side? Explain how you know. 3.2 m

9. The Grade 5 students at Potter Avenue School are planting a rectangular garden. The side lengths will be whole numbers of metres. Twenty-eight metres of fencing will be used for the border. Use grid paper to draw all the possible gardens. Which garden would provide the most growing space? The least growing space? Show your work.

10. Royanna jogs laps around a park playground. The playground is 90 m long and 35 m wide. How many laps will it take her to jog 1 km?

Reflect

Draw a square on 1-cm grid paper. Label it with its side length. Use two different formulas to find the perimeter of the square. Which formula do you prefer? Explain.

330 ASSESSMENT FOCUS | Question 9

ASSESSMENT FOR LEARNING

What to Look For

Understanding concepts

✔ Students develop a rule for finding the perimeter of a rectangle and explain why the rule works.

✔ Students understand the function of a formula.

Applying procedures

✔ Students use a formula to calculate the perimeter of a rectangle.

What to Do

Extra Support: Have students use 12 Colour Tiles or congruent paper squares to find all the possible rectangles. Students use a formula to find the perimeter of each rectangle. Students can use Step-by-Step 7 (Master 9.16) to complete question 9.

Extra Practice: Have students choose 3 books of different sizes. Students measure the length and the width of each book, then use a formula to find its perimeter.
Students can complete Extra Practice 4 (Master 9.25).

Extension: Have students find the possible dimensions of 2 rectangular sheets of paper whose perimeters differ by 10 cm.

Recording and Reporting
Master 9.2 Ongoing Observations: Length, Perimeter, and Area

LESSON

8

Calculating the Area of a Rectangle

Explore

You will need paper rectangles, a 1-cm cardboard square, a ruler, and a transparent 1-cm grid.

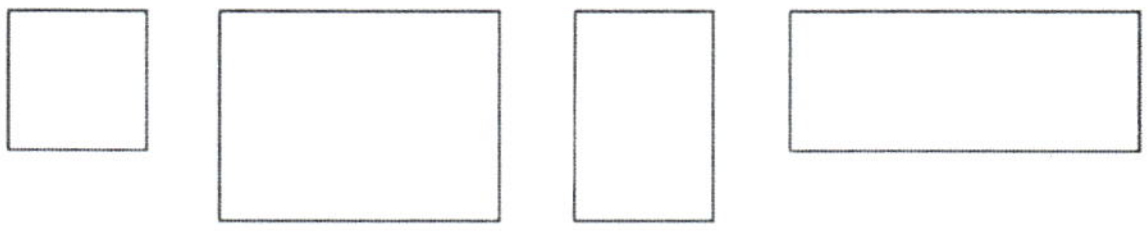

- ➤ Choose a rectangle.
  Use only the 1-cm square and a ruler.
  Find the area of the rectangle.
  Verify the area by using the transparent grid.
- ➤ Repeat this activity to find the areas of the other rectangles.
- ➤ Write a rule for finding the area of a rectangle without counting every square.

Show *and* Share

Share your results with another pair of students. Discuss the strategy you used to find the area of a rectangle without a grid. Explain the thinking behind your strategy.

Calculating the Area of a Rectangle

LESSON ORGANIZER

40–50 min

Curriculum Focus: Develop a rule for calculating the area of a rectangle. (5m54, 5m55, 5m56)

Teacher Materials

- transparency of 1-cm grid paper (PM 23)

Student Materials

- paper rectangles (6 cm by 3 cm, 8 cm by 7 cm, 9 cm by 4 cm, 5 cm by 5 cm)
- 1-cm cardboard squares
- rulers
- transparencies of 1-cm grid paper (PM 23)
- calculators

Optional

- Step-by-Step 8 (Master 9.17)
- Extra Practice 4 (Master 9.25)
- 5 cardboard rectangles labelled A, B, C, D, E
- Colour Tiles or congruent paper squares

Assessment: Master 9.2 Ongoing Observations: Length, Perimeter, and Area

Key Math Learning

The area of a rectangle can be found by using a formula.

BEFORE Get Started

On the overhead projector, display a 1-cm by 6-cm rectangle drawn on a 1-cm grid. Ask:

- What is the area of this rectangle? (*6 cm*^{2})
  How do you know?
  (*It has six 1-cm squares inside.*)

Invite a student to draw a rectangle with area 8 cm^2. Ask:

- How do you know the area is 8 cm^2?
  (*It has eight 1-cm squares inside.*)

Show students a paper rectangle. Ask:

- How could you find the area of this rectangle?
  (*Place a transparent grid on it and count the squares. Or, cover it with small squares, then count.*)

Present *Explore*. Emphasize that students are to find a way to determine the area of each rectangle using just one 1-cm square and a ruler, and that the transparent grid is to be used only to verify their answers.

DURING Explore

Ongoing Assessment: Observe and Listen

Watch for students who are trying to find the area by moving the 1-cm square from place to place on the rectangle. Point out that it is unlikely they will get an accurate answer. Remind them to use the ruler along with the 1-cm square.

Ask questions, such as:

- What is the side length of the small square?
  (*1 cm*)
- How can you use your ruler to figure out how many of the squares will fit along the length of the rectangle? (*Measure the length of the rectangle.*)
- How can you find out how many rows of squares will fit in the rectangle?
  (*Measure the width of the rectangle.*)

REACHING ALL LEARNERS

Alternative Explore

Materials: Colour Tiles or congruent paper squares
Have each student build a rectangle with Colour Tiles. Invite volunteers to name the length, the width, and the area of their rectangles. Record these measurements in a chart. Have students look for a pattern in the chart. Record **Area = length** × **width** on the board. Have students explain why this formula works. *(Length is the number of square units in a row. Width is the number of rows. Multiplying length by width tells how many square units there are in all.)*

Early Finishers

Have students measure the length and width of a desk or table, then use the dimensions to find the area.

Common Misconceptions

➤ Students use the formula to find the area of a rectangle but are unable to explain why it works.

How to Help: Remind students of their work with arrays to model products. Outline a rectangle on 1-cm grid paper. Have students think of the rectangle as an array of squares. Have them describe the array (for example, 6 rows of 4 = 24). Repeat with other rectangles.

Making Connections

Literacy: Read the story *Spaghetti and Meatballs for All.* Have students model the different table arrangements with Colour Tiles, then find the perimeter and area of each arrangement.

Connect

➤ Here is one way to find the area of a rectangle.

Measure the length of the rectangle.

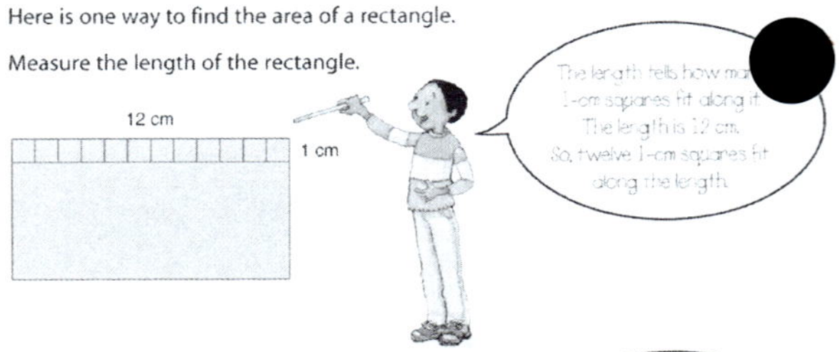

Measure the width of the rectangle.

Multiply the length by the width.
12 × 6 = 72
So, the area of the rectangle is 72 cm^2.

We can write this rule:
To find the area of a rectangle, multiply the length by the width.

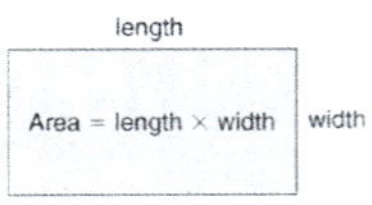

This rule can be expressed as a formula.

Area = length × width

332

AFTER Connect

Call on volunteers to describe the length, the width, and the area of each rectangle. Record these measurements in a chart.

Ask:

- How did you find the area using just your ruler and one 1-cm square?
  (I measured the length and the width of the rectangle with my ruler. The length is 6 cm. I know 6 squares fit along the length. The width is 3 cm. I know 3 squares fit along the width. The area is 18 cm^2.)
- What rule did you write?
  (Multiply the length by the width.)

Record the formula **Area = length** × **width** on the board. Have students explain what it means. Students can practise their mental math by multiplying different lengths and widths. They can take this opportunity to reinforce their multiplication skills.

Remind students that the order in which we multiply 2 numbers does not matter; that is, 5 × 6 = 6 × 5. So, when evaluating products mentally you can use the order you find easiest. Reinforce the idea that the orientation of the rectangle does not matter.

Summarize by asking:

- What does the length of the rectangle tell you?
  (How many 1-cm squares fit along it)
- What does the width tell you?
  (How many rows of 1-cm squares fit in the rectangle)
- Why do we multiply the length by the width to find the area?
  (That tells how many 1-cm squares fit in the rectangle)

➤ We can use the same method when the dimensions are not whole numbers.

4.5 cm; 3 cm

The rectangle is drawn on a 1-cm grid.
4.5 squares fit along the length.
There are 3 rows.
The area is $4.5 \times 3 = 13.5$.
The area is $13.5\ cm^2$.

Practice

1. Find the area of each rectangle.
   a) 3 cm; 5 cm — $15\ cm^2$
   b) 18 mm; 10 mm — $180\ mm^2$
   c) 15 m; 7 m — $105\ m^2$
   d) 9.2 cm; 5 cm — $46\ cm^2$
   e) 7 m; 7 m — $49\ m^2$
   f) 18 cm; 2.7 cm — $48.6\ cm^2$

2. Find the area of each rectangle.
   a) 0.8 km; 1 km — $0.8\ km^2$
   b) 2 km; 0.5 km — $1\ km^2$
   c) 0.7 km; 1 km — $0.7\ km^2$

3. Order the areas in question 2 from least to greatest.
   $0.7\ km^2$, $0.8\ km^2$, $1\ km^2$

333

Sample Answers

4. Answers may vary. Width = 21 cm; length = 28 cm; area = $21 \times 28 = 588$. The area is $588\ cm^2$.
7. Possible rectangles: 1 by 18, 2 by 9, 3 by 6

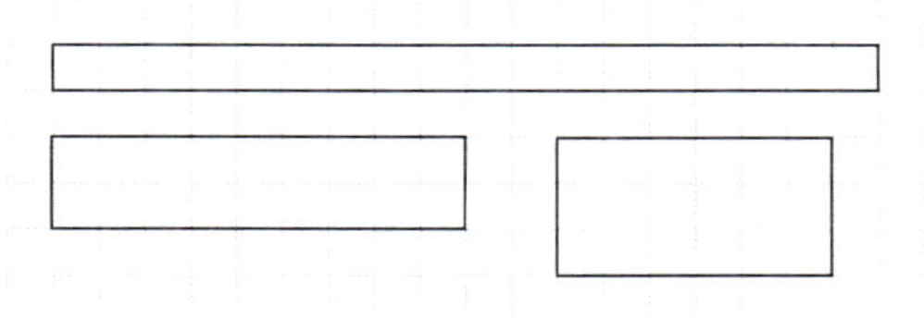

Perimeters: 38 units, 22 units, 18 units
Greatest perimeter: 1 by 18 rectangle
Least perimeter: 3 by 6 rectangle

Present *Connect.* Review the fact that the formula also works when one side length is measured in tenths of a unit. Ensure students understand they must always write the correct unit of measurement with their answer. Area is written in square units.

Practice

Have calculators available for students who wish to use them. Question 7 requires Colour Tiles and grid paper. Question 10 requires grid paper.

Assessment Focus: Question 10

Students should multiply length by width to find the area of the rectangle. In part a, they double the length and find the new area. Students should realize that the area doubles when the length is doubled. In part b, students double both the length and width, then find the area. They should realize that the area is four times as great when both length and width are doubled.

Students who can use the properties of multiplication of numbers to explain why the area will always be four times greater are showing a performance that exceeds expectations.

10. $4 \times 3 = 12$; area is 12 m^2

a) Area when length is doubled: $8 \times 3 = 24$
The area doubles when the length is doubled.

b) Area when length and width are doubled: $8 \times 6 = 48$
The area is 4 times as great when the length and width are doubled.

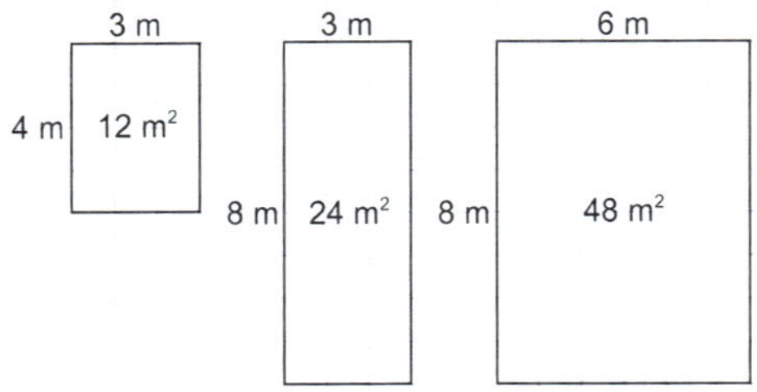

REFLECT: I can find the length by dividing the area by the width. For example, if the width is 3 m and the area is 15 m^2, I can divide: $15 \div 3 = 5$. The length is 5 m. I can check by multiplying length by width to make sure the product does equal the area.

Numbers Every Day

Students convert each fraction to a decimal using a calculator, and order them from least to greatest. Students then show the equivalent fractions in the same order on a number line.

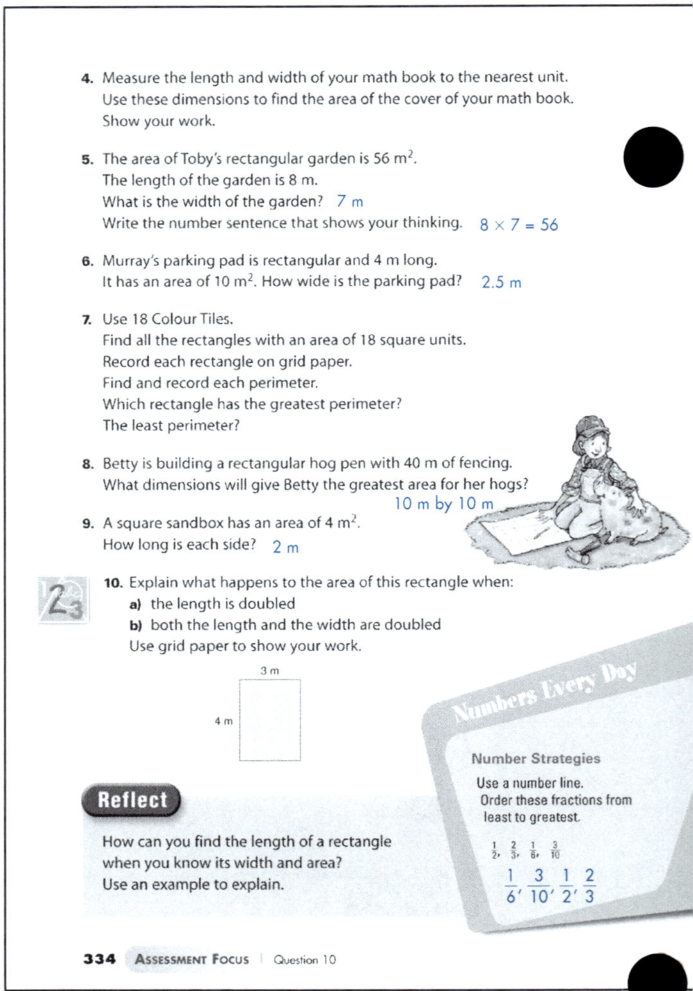

4. Measure the length and width of your math book to the nearest unit.
Use these dimensions to find the area of the cover of your math book.
Show your work.

5. The area of Toby's rectangular garden is 56 m^2.
The length of the garden is 8 m.
What is the width of the garden? 7 m
Write the number sentence that shows your thinking. $8 \times 7 = 56$

6. Murray's parking pad is rectangular and 4 m long.
It has an area of 10 m^2. How wide is the parking pad? 2.5 m

7. Use 18 Colour Tiles.
Find all the rectangles with an area of 18 square units.
Record each rectangle on grid paper.
Find and record each perimeter.
Which rectangle has the greatest perimeter?
The least perimeter?

8. Betty is building a rectangular hog pen with 40 m of fencing.
What dimensions will give Betty the greatest area for her hogs?
10 m by 10 m

9. A square sandbox has an area of 4 m^2.
How long is each side? 2 m

10. Explain what happens to the area of this rectangle when:
a) the length is doubled
b) both the length and the width are doubled
Use grid paper to show your work.

3 m
4 m

Reflect

How can you find the length of a rectangle when you know its width and area?
Use an example to explain.

Numbers Every Day

Number Strategies
Use a number line.
Order these fractions from least to greatest.

$\frac{1}{2}$, $\frac{2}{3}$, $\frac{1}{6}$, $\frac{3}{10}$

$\frac{1}{6}$, $\frac{3}{10}$, $\frac{1}{2}$, $\frac{2}{3}$

334 ASSESSMENT FOCUS | Question 10

ASSESSMENT FOR LEARNING

What to Look For	What to Do
Understanding concepts ✔ Students develop and explain a rule for finding the area of a rectangle.	***Extra Support:*** Students can complete the Additional Activity, *Calculating Perimeter and Area* (Master 9.8). Students can use Step-by-Step 8 (Master 9.17) to complete question 10.
Applying procedures ✔ Students use a formula to find the area of a rectangle.	***Extra Practice:*** Have students measure, to the nearest metre, the dimensions of a large area, such as a hallway or classroom, then use the dimensions to calculate the area. Students can complete Extra Practice 4 (Master 9.25).
	Extension: Challenge students to find the dimensions of a room that has perimeter 60 m and area 200 m^2.

Recording and Reporting

Master 9.2 Ongoing Observations: Length, Perimeter, and Area

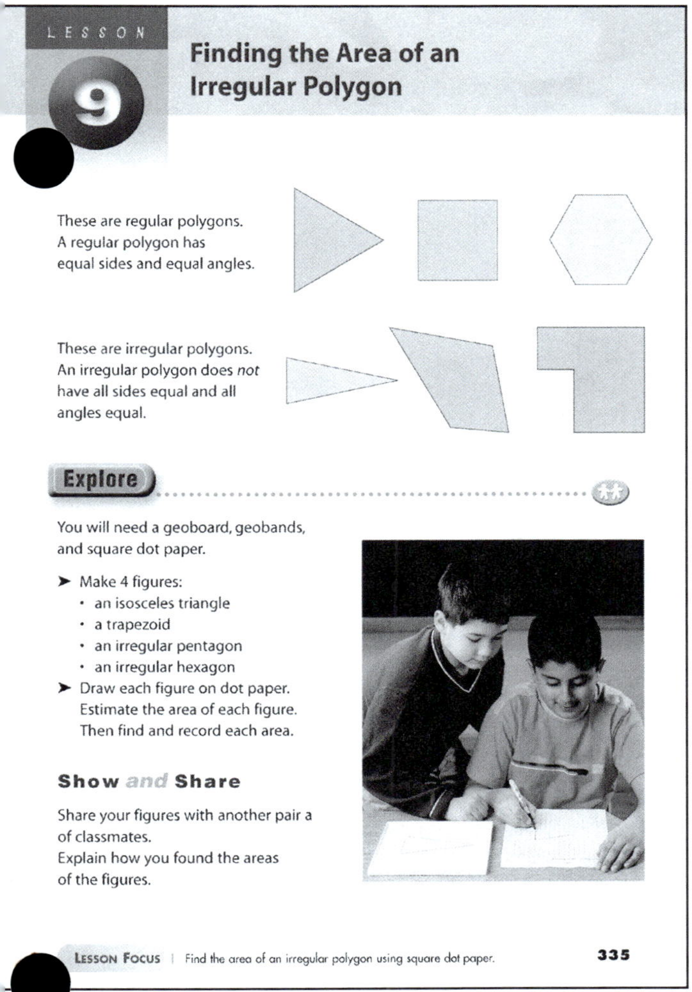

LESSON 9

Finding the Area of an Irregular Polygon

These are regular polygons. A regular polygon has equal sides and equal angles.

These are irregular polygons. An irregular polygon does *not* have all sides equal and all angles equal.

Explore

You will need a geoboard, geobands, and square dot paper.

➤ Make 4 figures:
- an isosceles triangle
- a trapezoid
- an irregular pentagon
- an irregular hexagon

➤ Draw each figure on dot paper. Estimate the area of each figure. Then find and record each area.

Show and Share

Share your figures with another pair of classmates. Explain how you found the areas of the figures.

LESSON FOCUS | Find the area of an irregular polygon using square dot paper.

335

Finding the Area of an Irregular Polygon

LESSON ORGANIZER 40–50 min

Curriculum Focus: Find the area of an irregular polygon using square dot paper. (5m57)

Teacher Materials
- transparency of square dot paper (PM 25)

Student Materials
- 11 by 11 geoboards
- geobands
- square dot paper (PM 25)

Optional
- Step-by-Step 9 (Master 9.18)
- Extra Practice 5 (Master 9.26)

Vocabulary: regular polygons, irregular polygons

Assessment: Master 9.2 Ongoing Observations: Length, Perimeter, and Area

Key Math Learning

The area of a polygon on dot paper or grid paper can be found by dividing the polygon into parts.

BEFORE Get Started

Have students examine and name the polygons illustrated in the Student Book.

Ask:
- For which regular polygons could you find the area? (*The square*)
- What can you see in the classroom or out the window that has the shape of a regular polygon?
(*Square bulletin board, octagonal table, stop sign*)
An irregular polygon?
(*Desktop, book, door frame*)

Present *Explore*. Explain to students that they will make irregular polygons and find their areas in square units.

DURING Explore

Ongoing Assessment: Observe and Listen

Ask questions, such as:
- How do you know you have made an isosceles triangle? (*It has 2 equal sides.*)
- How do you know your trapezoid is an irregular polygon? (*It does not have all sides equal and all angles equal.*)
- How will you find the area of an irregular hexagon? (*I will break it up into smaller sections.*)
- Can you think of another way to find the area of your figure? (*I could enclose the figure within a rectangle. Then I could find the area of the rectangle. I can find the areas of the figures inside the rectangle and subtract these from the area of the rectangle to find the area of my figure.*)

REACHING ALL LEARNERS

Alternative Explore

Provide students with a sheet of irregular polygons drawn on dot paper. Have students find the area of each polygon.

Early Finishers

Have students draw an irregular polygon on dot paper. Students trade papers, then find the area of one another's polygon.

Common Misconceptions

➤ Students have difficulty finding the area of a figure that does not have perpendicular sides.

How to Help: Suggest students colour whole units to enable them to better examine the remaining parts of units. Have them look for part units that are triangles, then draw a rectangle around each part unit.

ESL Strategies

ESL students may not realize that some common words (such as regular and irregular) have different meanings in a math context. Clarify the meanings of such words for them.

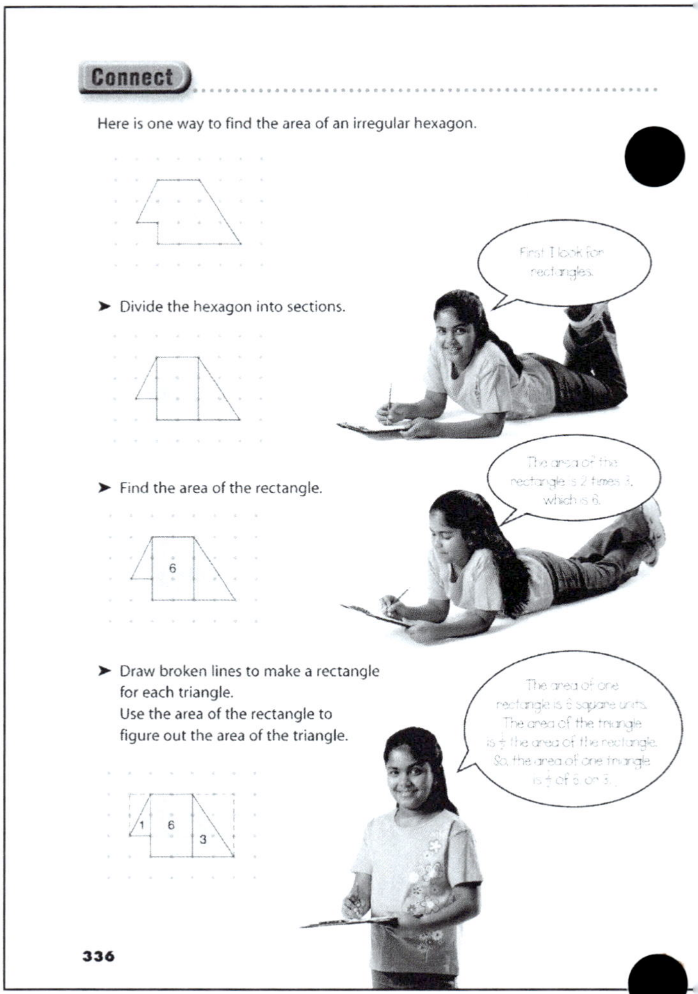
Connect

Here is one way to find the area of an irregular hexagon.

➤ Divide the hexagon into sections.

➤ Find the area of the rectangle.

➤ Draw broken lines to make a rectangle for each triangle.
Use the area of the rectangle to figure out the area of the triangle.

336

Watch for students who have made polygons whose areas are difficult to find. Offer suggestions, such as:

- Would enclosing the hexagon in a rectangle help?
- Could you divide the figure into sections?
- Could you enclose the triangular parts of your figure with rectangles?

AFTER Connect

Invite a volunteer to draw one of his figures on a dot paper transparency, then demonstrate and describe the strategy he used to find the area.

Ask:

- Do you think your area is exact or an estimate? Explain.
  (I think it's an estimate because I counted parts of squares greater than $\frac{1}{2}$ a square as 1 square, and I ignored parts less than $\frac{1}{2}$ a square.)
- How does dividing a figure into parts help you find its area?
  (I can find the area of each rectangular part using a formula. Then, I can find the area of each triangular part by drawing a rectangle around it, then finding one-half the area of the rectangle.)

Use *Connect* to explain how to calculate the exact area of a triangular part of a figure. Draw a rectangle whose area is double the area of the triangle.

➤ Add the areas of the sections to find the area of the hexagon.
1 + 6 + 3 = 10
The area of the hexagon is 10 square units.

Practice

1. Make each polygon on a geoboard. Estimate first.
Then find the area of each figure in square units.

a)

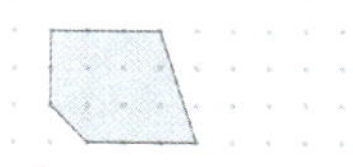

About 8 square units;
10 square units

b)

About 5 square units;
6 square units

c)

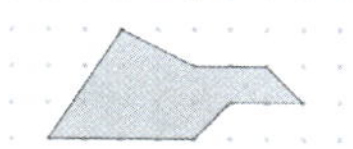

About 10 square units;
11 square units

d)

About 5 square units;
6 square units

2. Order the polygons in question 1 from least to greatest area. b and d, a, c

3. Use a geoboard.
Make an irregular polygon with each area.
Draw the polygon on dot paper.
a) 5 square units
b) 13 square units
c) $3\frac{1}{2}$ square units
d) 12 square units
e) 8.5 square units
f) 20 square units

Numbers Every Day

Number Strategies

Estimate each difference.

6048 − 3972 About 2000
5856 − 4724 About 1200
9147 − 6315 About 2800

Which strategies did you use?
Round to the nearest hundreds

Sample Answers

3. Answers may vary. Check each figure is an irregular polygon.

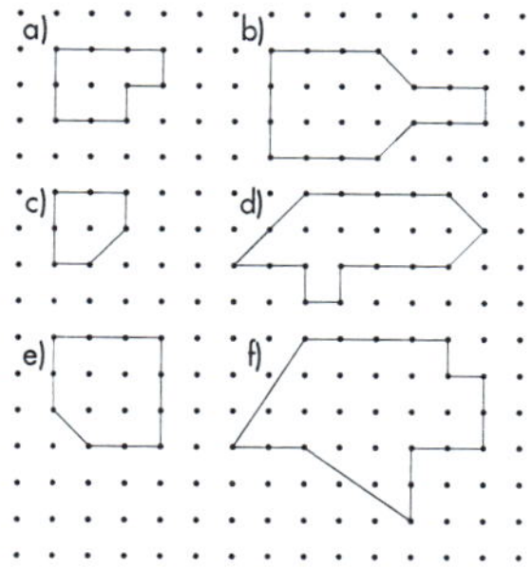

4. Answers may vary. Check each figure has an area of 16 square units.

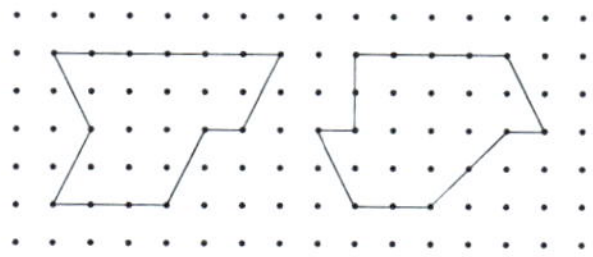

Numbers Every Day

Estimates may vary. Students can round to the nearest ten, hundred, or thousand to estimate each difference.

Practice

Geoboards, geobands, and dot paper are required.

Assessment Focus: Question 5

Students can copy each figure onto dot paper. They should understand the term **congruent** and that congruent figures can be oriented differently. Students divide each figure into 2 congruent parts. They find the area of each figure and of each congruent part. Students could use tracing paper to check for congruency. Students should know that a figure may be flipped to show it is congruent to another figure.

Students find other ways to divide each figure into congruent parts. Some students may divide each figure into whole or half squares. Others may find ways to combine whole and half squares to make congruent parts.

5. a) A: 7 square units, $3\frac{1}{2}$ square units
B: 6 square units, 3 square units
C: 14 square units, 7 square units

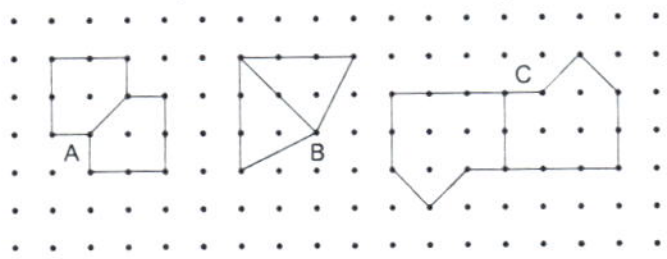

b) A: 7 congruent parts, 1 square unit
B: 6 congruent parts, 1 square unit
C: 28 congruent parts, $\frac{1}{2}$ square unit

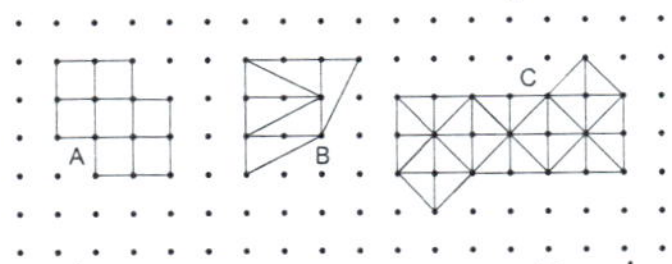

6. From least to greatest area: Doghouse, Bench, Composter, Cabana, Trampoline, Garden, Pool, Deck

REFLECT: Dot paper or grid paper helps because I can divide it into rectangles and triangles. I use a formula to find the area of each rectangle (length × width = area). I draw a rectangle around each triangle, so the area of the triangle is $\frac{1}{2}$ the area of the rectangle. I then add the areas of the parts to find the area of the polygon.

4. Use dot paper.
Draw 2 different polygons, each with an area of 16 square units.

5. Use a geoboard. Make each figure below.

a) Use a geoband to divide each figure into 2 congruent parts.
What is the area of each figure? Each congruent part?
Record your work on dot paper.

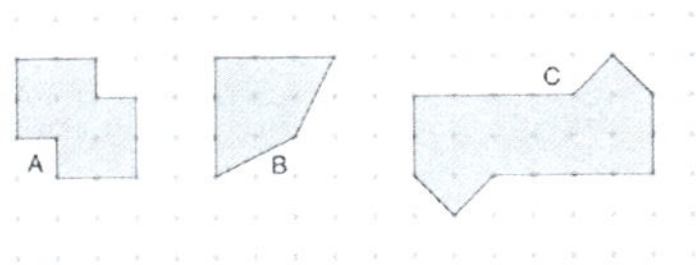

b) Find other ways to divide each figure into different numbers of congruent parts.
Find the area of each congruent part.
Record your work on dot paper.

6. Here is a map of Gail's backyard.
Find the area of each section of the yard in square units.
Order the sections from least to greatest area.

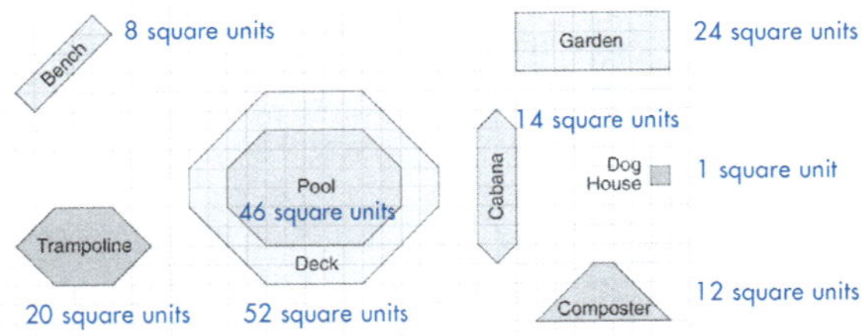

Reflect

How does using dot paper or grid paper help you to find the area of an irregular polygon? Use an example to explain.

338 ASSESSMENT FOCUS | Question 5

ASSESSMENT FOR LEARNING

What to Look For	What to Do
Understanding concepts ✔ Students understand what an irregular polygon is. ***Applying procedures*** ✔ Students can use grid paper or dot paper to find the area of an irregular polygon.	***Extra Support:*** Provide students with several irregular polygons drawn on grid paper. Have them use pencil crayons to divide each figure into parts. Have them count the squares and part squares to find the area. Students can use Step-by-Step 9 (Master 9.18) to complete question 5. ***Extra Practice:*** Have students work with a partner. One student makes an irregular figure on a geoboard. The other student finds its area. Students switch roles and repeat the activity. Students can complete Extra Practice 5 (Master 9.26). ***Extension:*** Challenge students to draw, on dot paper, an irregular hexagon with area $27\frac{1}{2}$ square units.

Recording and Reporting
Master 9.2 Ongoing Observations: Length, Perimeter, and Area

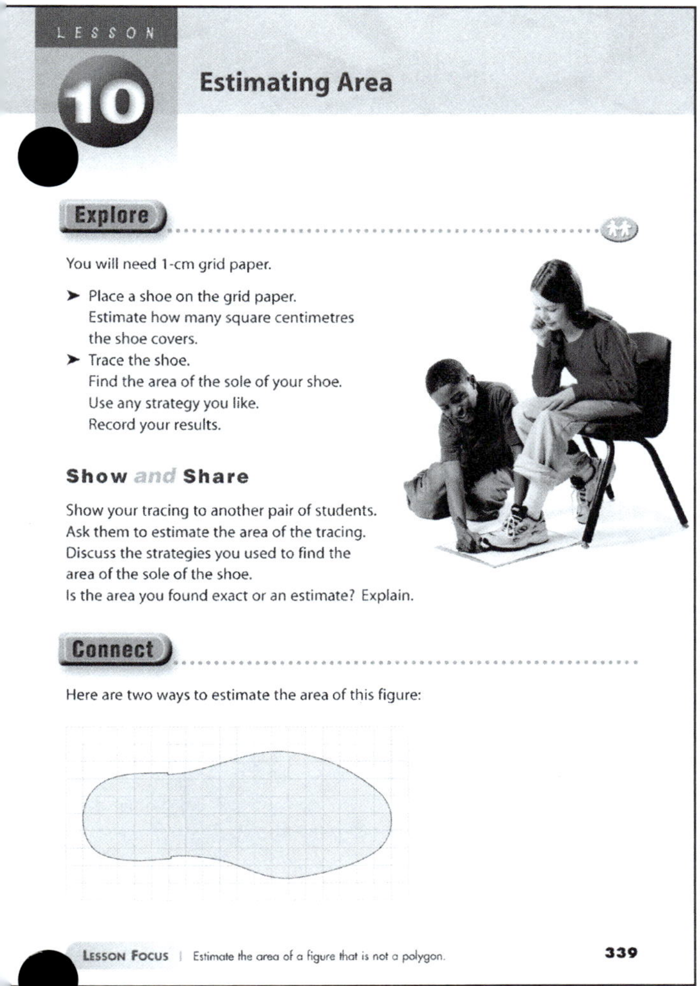
LESSON 10 Estimating Area

Explore

You will need 1-cm grid paper.

➤ Place a shoe on the grid paper.
Estimate how many square centimetres the shoe covers.

➤ Trace the shoe.
Find the area of the sole of your shoe.
Use any strategy you like.
Record your results.

Show and Share

Show your tracing to another pair of students.
Ask them to estimate the area of the tracing.
Discuss the strategies you used to find the area of the sole of the shoe.
Is the area you found exact or an estimate? Explain.

Connect

Here are two ways to estimate the area of this figure:

LESSON FOCUS | Estimate the area of a figure that is not a polygon.

339

Estimating Area

LESSON ORGANIZER (40–50 min)

Curriculum Focus: Estimate the area of a figure that is not a polygon. (5m58)

Teacher Materials
- transparency of 1-cm grid paper (PM 23)

Student Materials
- 1-cm grid paper (PM 23)
- pencil crayons
- paper towels
- water
- circular objects
- string
- rulers

Optional
- Step-by-Step 10 (Master 9.19)
- Extra Practice 5 (Master 9.26)
- 2-cm grid paper (PM 24)
- measuring tapes

Assessment: Master 9.2 Ongoing Observations: Length, Perimeter, and Area

Key Math Learning

The area of a figure that is not a polygon can be found by tracing the figure on grid paper, then counting square units.

BEFORE Get Started

Have students examine one of their shoes.

Ask:
- Suppose you wanted to describe your shoe to a friend. Which attributes could you use? (*Colour, type of shoe, size, kind of material*)
- How could you describe your shoe size? (*Using length, width, height*)
- Which unit would you use to describe the shoe's dimensions? (*Centimetres*) Why? (*My shoe is shorter than my ruler, so centimetres would be a good unit.*)
- Suppose you wanted to describe the area of the sole of your shoe. Which unit would you use? (*Square centimetres*)

Present *Explore*. Have students record their estimates in square centimetres.

DURING Explore

Ongoing Assessment: Observe and Listen

Ask questions, such as:
- What is your plan for finding the area of your tracing? (*I can count all the whole squares on my grid.*)
- How will you keep track of your counting? (*I will mark each square I count.*)
- What will you do with part squares? (*If the part square is smaller than $\frac{1}{2}$ a square, I will ignore it. If it is larger than $\frac{1}{2}$ a square, I will count it.*)
- Will your results be an exact measure or an approximation? Explain. (*An approximation, because it is an estimate*)

Watch for students who are using a method other than counting every square. Have them explain their method to the class.

REACHING ALL LEARNERS

Alternative Explore

Have students draw a "blob" shape on 1-cm grid paper. Students choose a strategy to find the area of the blob.

Early Finishers

Have students find the dimensions of as many rectangles as they can with approximately the same area as their shoe tracing.

Common Misconceptions

➤ Students ignore all part squares when finding the area of their tracing.

How to Help: Point out the importance of including part squares in the count to arrive at a more accurate measurement.

Sample Answers

1. a) Answers will vary.
For an area of 100 cm^2:
a 10-cm by 10-cm rectangle

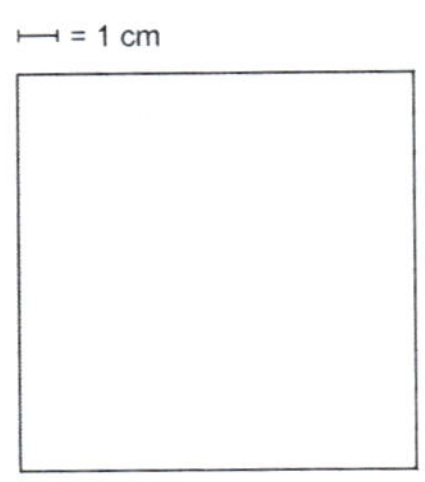

➤ Draw a rectangle along grid lines inside the figure.
Make it as big as you can. Find the area of the rectangle.
Count the whole squares and part squares outside the rectangle.
Add to find the total area.

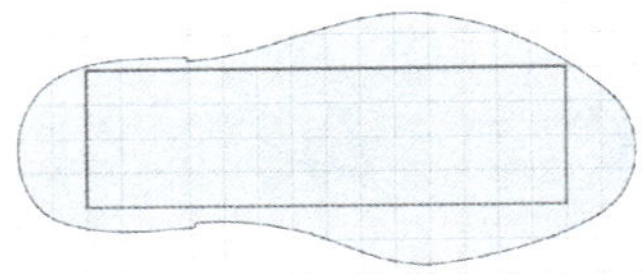

Area of rectangle: $14 \times 4 = 56$
Area outside rectangle: about 40
$56 + 40 = 96$
The area of the figure is about 96 square units.

➤ Draw a rectangle along grid lines around the figure.
Find the area of the rectangle.
Count the whole squares and part squares outside the figure, and inside the rectangle.
Subtract this number from the area of the rectangle.

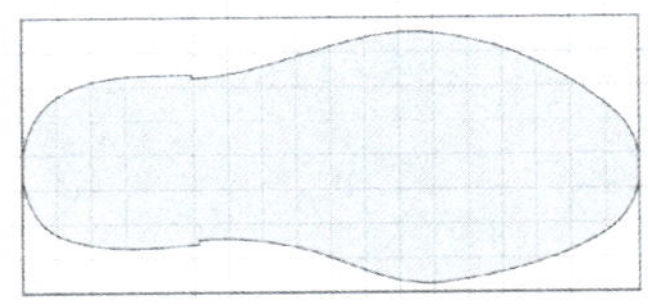

Area of rectangle: $8 \times 18 = 144$
Area outside the figure: about 45
$144 - 45 = 99$
The area of the figure is about 99 square units.

340

AFTER Connect

Invite volunteers to share their estimates and their measurements. Call on students to describe the strategies they used.

Ask:

- How does Erica's strategy compare with the strategy you used?
(Erica's strategy was faster because she did not count squares smaller than half a square.)
- Which strategy do you think produces the most accurate results?
(I think the strategy where all part squares are counted is more accurate.)

If no one used the strategies in *Connect*, review them with students and invite comments.

Practice

Have 1-cm grid paper available for all questions. Students need a circular object and string to complete question 3. Paper towels and water are needed for *Reflect*.

Assessment Focus: Question 3

Students trace an object on grid paper. They choose a strategy to find the area of the tracing, and report the results in square centimetres. Some students may use strategies similar to those presented in *Connect*. Others may choose to count every square and part square. Students measure the perimeter and report the measurement in centimetres. Some students may wrap string around the circular object to find its perimeter. Others may attempt to lay string along the tracing.

Practice

1. Use 1-cm grid paper.
   a) Draw a rectangle that has about the same area as the tracing of the shoe you made in *Explore*.
   b) Draw a rectangle that has about one-half the area of the shoe tracing.

2. This is a map of several lakes.
   Each square on the map represents 1 km^2.

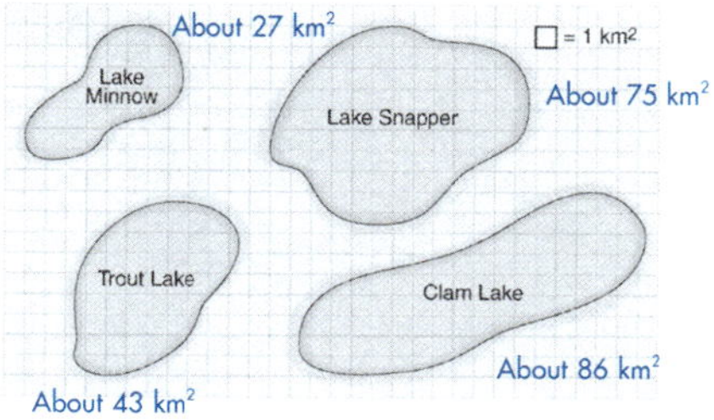

   a) Find the approximate area of each lake.
   b) Order the lakes from least to greatest area. Minnow, Trout, Snapper, Clam
   c) Use grid paper. Draw a lake with an area greater than Trout Lake but less than Clam Lake. Find and record the area of your lake.

3. Trace a circular object on 1-cm grid paper. Find and record the circumference of the object and the area of its tracing. Explain how you found the circumference and the area. Show your work.

Reflect

Drip a few drops of water onto a paper towel. Describe how you could measure the area of the wet spot on the towel.

Numbers Every Day

Number Strategies

Order these decimals from least to greatest.

1.28, 0.37, 1.8, 0.09

0.09, 0.37, 1.28, 1.8

ASSESSMENT FOCUS | Question 3

341

b) A 10-cm by 5-cm rectangle

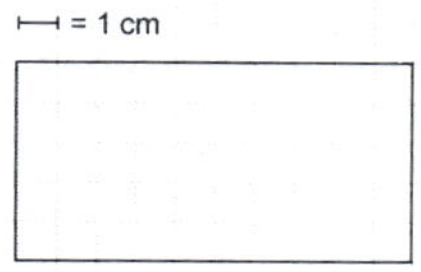

2. c) Area: about 60 km^2

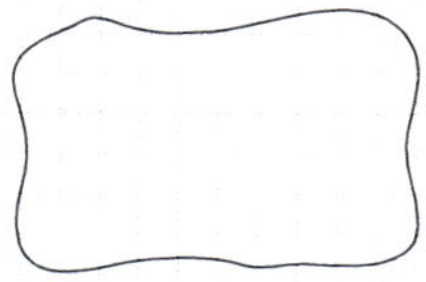

3. Answers will vary.
Circumference: about 10 cm
Area: about 15 cm^2
I found the circumference using a piece of string. I found the area by counting the squares and part squares on the grid.

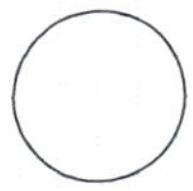

REFLECT: I cut out the wet spot and traced it onto 1-cm grid paper. Then I counted the squares and part squares to find the area.

Numbers Every Day

To order the decimals from least to greatest, students should compare ones digits, then tenths, then hundredths.

ASSESSMENT FOR LEARNING

What to Look For	What to Do
Understanding concepts ✔ Students can use grid paper to estimate and find the approximate area of a figure that is not a polygon. ***Applying procedures*** ✔ Students develop and use an appropriate strategy for finding the area of a figure that is not a polygon. ***Communication*** ✔ Students explain their strategy with clarity and precision.	***Extra Support:*** Some students may be unable to keep track of the large number of 1-cm squares that represent the area of their shoes. Provide these students with 2-cm grid paper. Students can use Step-by-Step 10 (Master 9.19) to complete question 3. ***Extra Practice:*** Students can do the Additional Activity, *Investigating Hands* (Master 9.9). Students can complete Extra Practice 5 (Master 9.26). ***Extension:*** Have students estimate the difference between the area of their shoe tracing and the area of their hand. Students trace their hand on 1-cm grid paper and find its area to check their estimates.

Recording and Reporting

Master 9.2 Ongoing Observations: Length, Perimeter, and Area

Strategies Toolkit

LESSON ORGANIZER — 40–50 min

Curriculum Focus: Interpret a problem and select an appropriate strategy. (5m54, 5m55)

Teacher Materials
- transparent Colour Tiles (optional)

Student Materials
- Colour Tiles or congruent paper squares
- 1-cm grid paper (PM 23)
- calculators

Assessment:
PM 3: Self-Assessment: Problem Solving
PM 1: Inquiry Process Check List

Key Math Learnings

1. Interpret a problem involving perimeter and area.
2. Solve a problem involving perimeter and area by using the strategy "use a pattern."

LESSON 11

Strategies Toolkit

Explore

Ernesto made a 1-m square garden this year. He plans to enlarge the garden by increasing the side lengths by 2 m each year. What will the perimeter and area of Ernesto's garden be in 6 years? 52 m; 169 m²

Show and Share

Describe the strategy you used to solve the problem.

Connect

Helen raises Angora goats. When Helen got her first pair of goats, she built a 2-m by 1-m pen for them. As Helen's goat population grew, she increased the size of the pen by doubling the length and the width. What were the perimeter and area of Helen's pen after she increased its size 5 times? 192 m; 2048 m²

Strategies
- Make a table.
- Use a model.
- Draw a diagram.
- Solve a simpler problem.
- Work backward.
- Guess and check.
- Make an organized list.
- Use a pattern.
- Draw a graph.

Understand

What do you know?
- Helen's first pen measured 2 m by 1 m.
- She increased the size of the pen by doubling the length and width.
- She did this 5 times.

Plan

Think of a strategy to help you solve the problem.
- You can **use a pattern**.
- Use Colour Tiles to model each pen.
- List the dimensions, the perimeter, and the area of each pen.

342 LESSON FOCUS | Interpret a problem and select an appropriate strategy.

BEFORE — Get Started

Present the problem in *Explore*. Ask questions to ensure students understand the problem. Review the key steps in problem solving. Have Colour Tiles and grid paper available for students who wish to use them.

DURING — Explore

Ongoing Assessment: Observe and Listen

Ask questions, such as:
- What are the dimensions of Ernesto's garden this year? (*1 m by 1 m*)
  The perimeter? (*4 m*) The area? (*1 m²*)
- What will you do next? (*I will make a table and find the dimensions, the perimeter, and the area of the garden for the next 6 years.*)
- What patterns do you see in your table? (*The perimeter increases by 8 each time, the area increases by 8, 16, 24, ….*)

AFTER — Connect

Work through the problem in *Connect*. Highlight each step of the problem-solving process as you proceed. In the *Plan* stage, have students refer to the Strategies list to select possible strategies to try.

Ask:
- How did using the pattern in the table help us solve the problem?
  (*Once we modelled several pens, we could figure out the perimeters and areas of the rest by using the patterns. We didn't have to model all the pens.*)
- How could you find the perimeter of the pen after the next increase?
  (*Multiply the last perimeter by 2.*)
  The area? (*Multiply the last area by 4.*)

Practice

Remind students to refer to the Strategies list. Students will need grid paper to solve the problems.

Record your list in a table.

	Length	Width	Perimeter	Area
Original Pen	2 m	1 m	6 m	2 m^2
First Increase	4 m	2 m	12 m	8 m^2
Second Increase				

Look for patterns.
Continue the patterns to find
the perimeter and area after 5 increases.

Check your work.
What pattern rules created the patterns in your table?

Practice

Choose one of the **Strategies**

1. Harold is designing a patio with congruent square concrete tiles. He has 36 tiles.
Use grid paper to model all the possible rectangular patios Harold could build. Label the dimensions in units. 1 by 36, 2 by 18, 3 by 12, 4 by 9, 6 by 6
Which patio has the greatest perimeter? The least perimeter? 1 by 36; 6 by 6

2. Suppose you have a 7-cm by 5-cm rectangle.
You increase the length by 1 cm and decrease the width by 1 cm.
You continue to do this.
What happens to the perimeter of the rectangle? The area?
Explain why this happens.

Reflect

How does using a pattern help you solve a problem?
Use pictures, words, or numbers to explain.

343

REACHING ALL LEARNERS

Common Misconceptions

➤Students have difficulty identifying a growing pattern.

How to Help: Present a simple pattern such as 2, 4, 8, 14, 22, 32, and help students identify the pattern rule. (Start at 2. Add 2. Increase the number you add by 2 each time.) Allow students to use calculators to subtract consecutive terms to find what is added each time. Point out that the sequence of numbers added forms the counting pattern 2, 4, 6, 8, ...

Sample Answer

2. The perimeter of the rectangle stays the same because when you increase the length by 1 cm, you add 2 cm of perimeter, and when you decrease the width by 1 cm, you remove 2 cm of perimeter.
At the start, when you decrease the width by 1 cm, from 5 cm to 4 cm, you take away 7 cm^2. When you increase the length by 1 cm, from 7 cm to 8 cm, you add 4 cm^2. The net effect is a decrease of 3 cm^2. As the length continues to increase and the width continues to decrease, the net effect is a greater decrease in area. Students' explanations should include successive rectangles drawn on grid paper.

REFLECT: When I find a pattern in the numbers, I can extend it to solve the problem. For example, if I see 4, 8, 12, 16, ..., I know the 8th number will be 32 because the pattern is the numbers you say when you count by 4s.

ASSESSMENT FOR LEARNING

What to Look For

Problem solving

✔ Students use the steps of the problem-solving process to solve a problem.

✔ Students can use the strategy use a pattern to solve a problem involving perimeter and area.

What to Do

Extra Support: Students may benefit from further work with growing patterns. Have students write the next 3 terms for patterns such as: 7, 10, 16, 25, ...; 14, 18, 26, 38, ...

Extra Practice: Have students repeat question 1, using 48 tiles.

Extension: Challenge students to write and solve a problem similar to the one in *Explore*.

Recording and Reporting

PM 3: Self-Assessment: Problem Solving
PM 1: Inquiry Process Check List

Show What You Know

LESSON ORGANIZER 40–50 min

Student Materials
- rulers, measuring tapes, or metre sticks
- brooms, hockey sticks, or similar objects
- cylindrical objects
- string
- scissors
- Colour Tiles or congruent paper squares
- 1-cm grid paper (PM 23)

Assessment: Masters 9.1 Unit Rubric: Length, Perimeter, and Area, 9.4 Unit Summary: Length, Perimeter, and Area

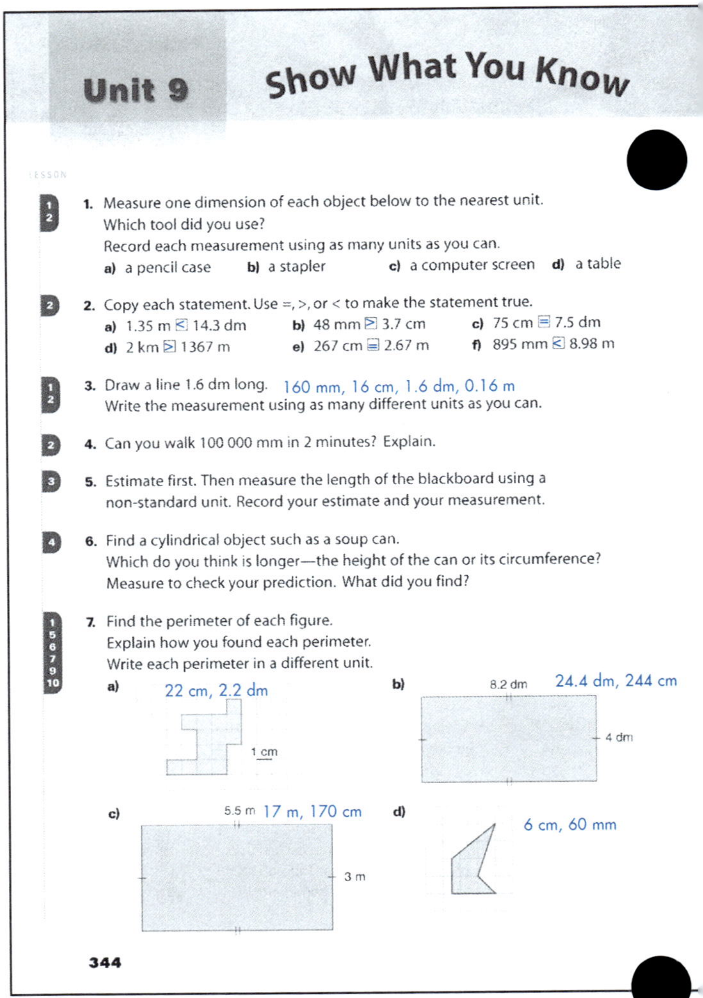

Unit 9 Show What You Know

LESSON

1 2 — 1. Measure one dimension of each object below to the nearest unit.
Which tool did you use?
Record each measurement using as many units as you can.
a) a pencil case b) a stapler c) a computer screen d) a table

2 — 2. Copy each statement. Use =, >, or < to make the statement true.
a) 1.35 m < 14.3 dm b) 48 mm > 3.7 cm c) 75 cm = 7.5 dm
d) 2 km > 1367 m e) 267 cm = 2.67 m f) 895 mm < 8.98 m

1 2 — 3. Draw a line 1.6 dm long. 160 mm, 16 cm, 1.6 dm, 0.16 m
Write the measurement using as many different units as you can.

2 — 4. Can you walk 100 000 mm in 2 minutes? Explain.

3 — 5. Estimate first. Then measure the length of the blackboard using a non-standard unit. Record your estimate and your measurement.

4 — 6. Find a cylindrical object such as a soup can.
Which do you think is longer—the height of the can or its circumference?
Measure to check your prediction. What did you find?

1 5 6 7 9 10 — 7. Find the perimeter of each figure.
Explain how you found each perimeter.
Write each perimeter in a different unit.

a) 22 cm, 2.2 dm

b) 24.4 dm, 244 cm

c) 17 m, 170 cm

d) 6 cm, 60 mm

344

Sample Answers

1. Answers may vary.
   a) 20 cm, 200 mm, 2 dm, 0.20 m; I used a ruler.
   b) 17 cm, 170 mm, 1.7 dm, 0.17 m; I used a ruler.
   c) 30 cm, 300 mm, 3 dm, 0.30 m; I used a ruler.
   d) 2 m, 200 cm, 20 dm, 2000 mm; I used a metre stick.
4. Yes. 100 000 mm is 10 000 cm, which is 100 m. 100 m is $\frac{1}{10}$ of a kilometre. It takes about 15 min to walk 1 km. So it would take about 1.5 min to walk $\frac{1}{10}$ of a kilometre.
5. I used a broom. I estimated 2 broom sticks; the blackboard was 3 broomsticks long.
6. I think the circumference is longer.
   I measured the can. The circumference is 21 cm and the height is 9.6 cm. My prediction was correct.
7. a) I counted the units along the outside of the figure.
   b) I added 8.2 and 4, then multiplied by 2.
   c) I added 5.5 and 3, then multiplied by 2.
   d) I measured the side lengths with a ruler, then added.
8. 14 cm^2; I counted the 1-cm squares.
   32.8 dm^2; I multiplied the length by the width.
   16.5 m^2; I multiplied the length by the width.
   About 5 cm^2; I counted the whole squares and the part squares.
   My measure of the area of the last figure is an estimate because I put several part squares together to count as 1.
9. a)

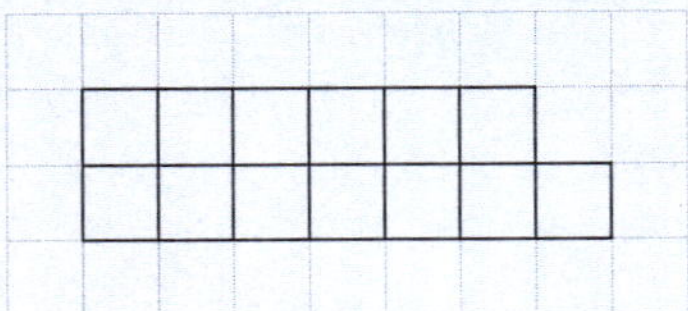

b)

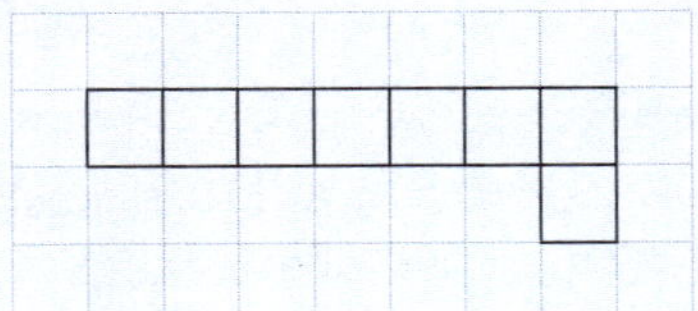

c)

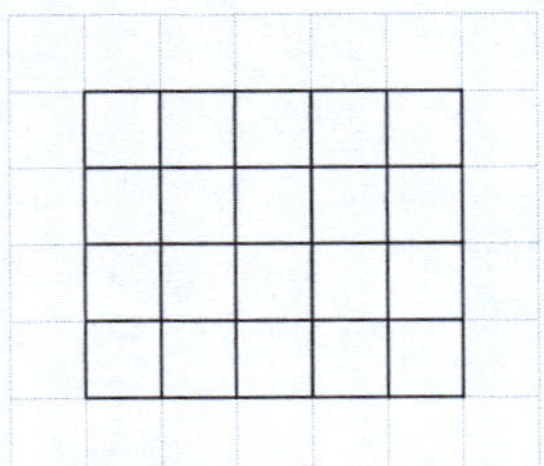

Find the area of each figure in question 7.
Explain how you did this.
For which figures is your measure of area an estimate? Explain.

9. Use Colour Tiles. Make this pentomino:

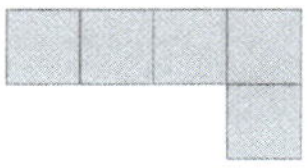

a) Add tiles to the pentomino to make a figure with perimeter 18 units. Draw your figure on grid paper.

b) What are the fewest tiles you can add to the pentomino to make a figure with perimeter 18 units? Draw your figure. 3 tiles

c) What are the most tiles you can add to the pentomino to make a figure with perimeter 18 units? Draw your figure. 15 tiles

d) Find the area of each figure you drew in parts a, b, and c.
13 square units; 8 square units; 20 square units

10. Choose the most appropriate unit to measure:

a) the length of the school parking lot Metre

b) the perimeter of a province Kilometre

c) the circumference of a birthday cake Centimetre

d) the width of a honeybee's leg Millimetre

e) the area of Lake Superior square Kilometre

11. Darlene built a rectangular dog pen with area 24.5 m^2. The length of the pen is 5 m. What is the width of the pen? 4.9 m

12. The building is one storey and rectangular.

What might the dimensions of the floor be? Give 3 different answers.
60 m by 20 m; 30 m by 40 m; 120 m by 10 m

UNIT 9 Learning Goals

- ✓ estimate and measure linear dimensions
- ✓ relate units of linear measure
- ✓ use decimals to report linear measures
- ✓ explore circumference
- ✓ estimate and measure perimeter and area
- ✓ develop and use rules for calculating perimeter and area of a rectangle
- ✓ solve problems related to length, perimeter, and area

345

ASSESSMENT FOR LEARNING

What to Look For

Understanding of concepts

✓ **Questions 1–4, and 7:** Student understands the relationships among linear units.

✓ **Question 6:** Student understands the meaning of circumference.

Application of mathematical procedures

✓ **Questions 1, 2, 3, 4, and 7:** Student can convert among linear units.

✓ **Questions 8 and 9:** Student can use various strategies to measure area.

✓ **Questions 1, 2, 7, and 8:** Student can use decimals to record measurements.

Problem solving

✓ **Questions 4, 9, 11, and 12:** Student can select an appropriate strategy and solve problems involving length, perimeter, and area.

Recording and Reporting

Master 9.1 Unit Rubric: Length, Perimeter, and Area
Master 9.4 Unit Summary: Length, Perimeter, and Area

At the Zoo

LESSON ORGANIZER

40–50 min

Student Grouping: Groups of 2 or 3
Student Materials
- 1-cm grid paper (PM 23)
- 0.5-cm grid paper (PM 22)
- rulers
- pencil crayons
- calculators

Assessment: Masters 9.3 Performance Assessment Rubric: At the Zoo, 9.4 Unit Summary: Length, Perimeter, and Area

Sample Response

	Area	Perimeter
Pigs	207 m^2	56.53 m
Sheep	225 m^2	60 m
Goats	252 m^2	77.06 m
Rabbits	108 m^2	47.36 m
Ponies	324 m^2	90 m

Rabbits: To find the perimeter, I measured the side lengths, then added: 18 + 14.68 + 14.68 = 47.36
To find the area, I drew a rectangle around the triangle, and used the formula for the area:
18 × 12 = 216.

Have students turn to the *Unit Launch* on pages 306 and 307 to review the context of the *Unit Problem*. Use the lists of Learning Goals and Key Words to remind students of some of the skills and concepts they learned throughout the unit. Tell students they will use these skills and concepts as they complete the *Unit Problem*.

Present the *Unit Problem*. Invite students to take turns reading the instructions and guidelines for designing a petting zoo. Explain that students may use either size of grid paper to draw their maps. (Students will need to tape pieces of 1-cm grid paper together.) Remind students that each square on the grid represents 1 m^2.

Have a volunteer read aloud the Check List to ensure all students understand the criteria to be used in assessing their work. Encourage students to make their maps as interesting and attractive as they can.

Check List

Your work should show

- ✓ a map of the petting zoo on grid paper, with each section outlined and labelled
- ✓ the dimensions, perimeter, and area of each section and how you found them
- ✓ a different shape for each region
- ✓ that the size of a region reflects the size of the animal

Reflect on the Unit

How are linear dimensions, perimeter, and area related? Write what you know about them.

347

Then I divided by 2 to get the area of the triangle:
216 ÷ 2 = 108

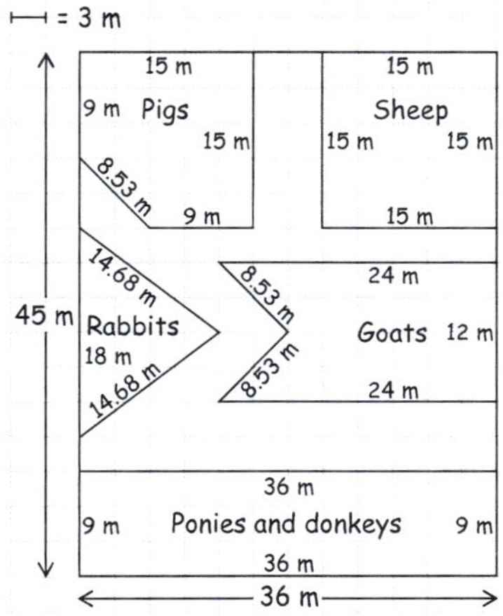

Reflect on the Unit

A linear dimension of an object is a measure of its length, width, height, thickness, or depth. Perimeter is the distance around a figure.
To find the perimeter of a figure, you measure its side lengths, then add them. If you want to find the perimeter of a rectangle, you can use a formula, such as (length + width) × 2.
Area tells how much space is inside a figure. Area is measured in square units. A fast way to find the area of a rectangle is to multiply its length times its width.

So, to find area and perimeter, we use the linear dimensions of the figure.

ASSESSMENT FOR LEARNING

What to Look For

Understanding concepts

✔ Students design a map that reflects an understanding of linear dimensions, perimeter, and area.

Applying procedures

✔ Students accurately find the side lengths and the area of each section they draw.

Communication

✔ Students use mathematical symbols appropriately to record the measurements on their maps.

What to Do

Extra Support: Make the problem accessible.

Some students may not know how to get started. Point out that they could start by outlining the perimeter of the petting zoo. Have them locate the dimensions in the instructions.

Some students may have difficulty judging how big to make each area. Have them indicate a section of the classroom that would be a suitable size for a particular animal, then measure to find the dimensions of the section.

Recording and Reporting

Master 9.3 Performance Assessment Rubric: At the Zoo
Master 9.4 Unit Summary: Length, Perimeter, and Area

Evaluating Student Learning: Preparing to Report: Unit 9 Length, Perimeter, and Area

This unit provides an opportunity to report on the **Measurement** strand. *Master 9.4 Unit Summary: Length, Perimeter, and Area* provides a comprehensive format for recording and summarizing evidence collected.

Here is an example of a completed summary chart for this Unit:

Strand: *Measurement*	**Problem solving**	**Understanding of concepts**	**Application of mathematical procedures**	**Communication**	***Overall***
Ongoing Observations	3	2	2	3	**2/3**
Strategies Toolkit (Lesson 11)			3		**3**
Work samples or portfolios; conferences	3	3	2	3	**3**
Show What You Know	3	3	3	3	**3**
Unit Test	3	2	2	3	**2/3**
Unit Problem At the Zoo	3	3	3	2	**3**
Achievement Level for reporting					**3**

Recording	How to Report
Ongoing Observations	Use *Master 9.2 Ongoing Observations: Length, Perimeter, and Area* to determine the most consistent level achieved in each category. Enter it in the chart. Choose to summarize by achievement category, or simply to enter an overall level. Observations from late in the unit should be most heavily weighted.
Strategies Toolkit (problem solving)	Use *PM 1: Inquiry Process Check List* with the Strategies Toolkit (Lesson 11). Transfer results to the summary form. Teachers may choose to enter a level in the Problem solving column and/or Communication.
Portfolios or collections of work samples; conferences, or interviews	Use *Master 9.1 Unit Rubric: Length, Perimeter, and Area* to guide evaluation of collections of work and information gathered in conferences. Teachers may choose to focus particular attention on the *Assessment Focus* questions. Work from late in the unit should be most heavily weighted.
Show What You Know	Teachers may choose to assign some or all of these questions. *Master 9.1 Unit Rubric: Length, Perimeter, and Area* may be helpful in determining levels of achievement. #1–4, 6, and 7 provide evidence of Understanding of concepts; #1–4 and 7–9 provide evidence of Application of mathematical procedures; #4, 9, 11, and 12 provide evidence of Problem solving; all questions provide evidence of Communication.
Unit Test	*Master 9.1 Unit Rubric: Length, Perimeter, and Area* may be helpful in determining levels of achievement. Part A provides evidence of Application of mathematical procedures; Part B provides evidence of Understanding of concepts; Part C provides evidence of Problem solving; all parts provide evidence of Communication.
Unit performance task	Use *Master 9.3 Performance Assessment Rubric: At the Zoo.* The *Unit Problem* offers a snapshot of students' achievement. In particular, it shows their ability to synthesize and apply what they have learned.
Student Self-Assessment	Note students' perceptions of their own progress. This may take the form of an oral or written comment, or a self-rating.
Comments	Analyse the pattern of achievement to identify strengths and needs. In some cases, specific actions may be planned to support the learner.

Learning Skills	**Ongoing Records**
PM 4: Learning Skills Check List Use to record and report throughout a reporting period, rather than for each unit and/or strand.	*PM 10: Summary Class Records: Strands* *PM 11: Summary Class Records: Achievement Categories* *PM 12: Summary Record: Individual* Use to record and report evaluations of student achievement over several clusters, a reporting period, or a school year. These can also be used in place of the Unit Summary.

Name ____________________ Date ______________

Master 9.1

Unit Rubric: Length, Perimeter, and Area

	Level 1	Level 2	Level 3	Level 4
Problem solving • chooses and carries out a range of strategies (e.g., estimation, diagrams, models, pictures, grid paper) to solve problems involving length, perimeter, and area	with assistance, chooses and carries out a limited range of appropriate strategies, rarely resulting in an accurate solution	with limited assistance, chooses and carries out appropriate strategies that frequently result in an accurate solution	chooses and carries out appropriate strategies to pose and solve problems involving length, perimeter, and area that usually result in accurate solution	chooses and carries out appropriate strategies to pose and solve problems involving length, perimeter, and area accurately; may offer an innovative approach
Understanding of concepts • shows understanding by appropriately demonstrating and explaining: – justification of units and methods chosen – rules for calculating perimeter and area of rectangles – estimates of perimeter and area of rectangles – estimates of area of irregular polygons (dividing in parts and using grid paper) – equivalence in investigations of circumference	may be unable to demonstrate or explain: – justification of units and methods chosen – rules used in calculating perimeter and area of rectangles – estimates of perimeter and area of rectangles – estimates of area of irregular polygons – investigations of circumference	partially able to demonstrate and explain: – justification of units and methods chosen – rules used in calculating perimeter and area of rectangles – estimates of perimeter and area of rectangles – estimates of area of irregular polygons – investigations of circumference	demonstrates and explains: – justification of units and methods chosen – rules used in calculating perimeter and area of rectangles – estimates of perimeter and area of rectangles – estimates of area of irregular polygons – investigations of circumference	in various contexts, demonstrates and explains: – justification of units and methods chosen – rules used in calculating perimeter and area of rectangles – estimates of perimeter and area of rectangles – estimates of area of irregular polygons – investigations of circumference
Application of mathematical procedures • accurately: – measures linear dimensions – relates units of linear measure – uses decimals to record and report linear measures – measures perimeter and area – uses rules for calculating perimeter and area of a rectangle	limited accuracy; major errors in: – measuring linear dimensions – relating units of linear measure – using decimals to report linear measures – measuring perimeter and area – using rules for calculating perimeter and area of a rectangle	somewhat accurate; makes several minor errors: – measuring linear dimensions – relating units of linear measure – using decimals to report linear measures – measuring perimeter and area – using rules for calculating perimeter and area of a rectangle	generally accurate; makes few minor errors in: – measuring linear dimensions – relating units of linear measure – using decimals to report linear measures – measuring perimeter and area – using rules for calculating perimeter and area of a rectangle	accurate; makes very few or no errors in: – measuring linear dimensions – relating units of linear measure – using decimals to report linear measures – measuring perimeter and area – using rules for calculating perimeter and area of a rectangle
Communication • presents work, describes procedures and explains reasoning clearly, using appropriate terminology	work is often unclear and imprecise needs assistance to describe procedures and to explain reasoning; often unclear and imprecise	work is presented with some clarity and precision describes procedures and explains reasoning with some clarity and precision	work is generally clear and precise describes procedures and explains reasoning with general clarity and precision	work is clear and precise describes procedures and explains reasoning clearly, precisely, and confidently

Name ____________________ Date ________________

Master 9.2

Ongoing Observations: Length, Perimeter, and Area

The behaviours described under each heading are examples; they are not intended to be an exhaustive list of all that might be observed. More detailed descriptions are provided in each lesson under *Assessment for Learning.*

STUDENT ACHIEVEMENT: Length, Perimeter, and Area				
Student	**Problem solving** ▪ Uses appropriate strategies to solve problems	**Understanding of concepts** ▪ Demonstrates and explains units and methods chosen, and estimates ▪ Explains rules for calculating perimeter and area	**Application of mathematical procedures** ▪ Measures linear dimensions, perimeter, and area of rectangles ▪ Uses rules for calculating perimeter and area	**Communication** ▪ Presents work, procedures, and reasoning clearly

Level 1 – very limited; Level 2 – somewhat or limited; Level 3 – satisfactory; Level 4 – thorough

Name ____________________ Date ______________

Master 9.3

Performance Assessment Rubric: At the Zoo

	Level 1	Level 2	Level 3	Level 4
Problem solving • chooses and carries out appropriate strategies, including estimation, to design a petting zoo that provides appropriate sections, varied by size and shape, for each animal within the given perimeter and area	chooses and carries out simple or inappropriate strategies to develop a map that meets requirements; may be unrealistic	chooses and carries out some appropriate strategies, including estimation, to develop a map that meets most requirements; may be somewhat unrealistic	chooses and carries out appropriate and effective strategies, including estimation, to develop a reasonable map that meets requirements	chooses innovative, appropriate, and effective strategies, including estimation, to develop a reasonable map that meets all requirements effectively
Understanding of concepts • shows understanding of linear dimensions, perimeter, and area by creating a reasonable area for each animal within the specified perimeter and using concepts of perimeter and area in their explanation	shows very limited understanding by: – creating inappropriate areas for many animals – giving a partial explanation of the map	shows limited understanding by: – creating inappropriate areas for some animals – giving appropriate but incomplete explanations of the map	shows understanding by: – creating appropriate areas for most animals – giving appropriate explanations of the map	shows thorough understanding by: – creating appropriate areas for all animals – giving appropriate and complete explanations of the map
Application of mathematical procedures • measures and records the linear dimensions of each region accurately, including units	measures and records linear dimensions with major errors or omissions	measures and records linear dimensions with several minor errors or omissions	measures and records linear dimensions with few minor errors or omissions	measures and records linear dimensions with practically no minor errors or omissions
• applies appropriate procedures to calculate and record the perimeter and area of each region accurately, including units	calculates and records perimeter and area with major errors or omissions	calculates and records perimeter and area with several minor errors or omissions	calculates and records perimeter and area with few errors or omissions	calculates and records perimeter and area with practically no errors or omissions
Communication • uses mathematical terminology, including units and symbols, correctly (metre, square metre, area, linear dimensions)	uses few appropriate mathematical terms and symbols	uses some appropriate mathematical terms and symbols	uses appropriate mathematical terms and symbols	uses a range of appropriate mathematical terminology and symbols clearly and precisely
• explains reasoning clearly	explains reasoning with little clarity	explains reasoning with some clarity	explains reasoning clearly and precisely	explains reasoning clearly, precisely, and confidently

Name ____________________ Date ______________

Master 9.4

Unit Summary: Length, Perimeter, and Area

Review assessment records to determine the most consistent achievement levels for the assessments conducted. Some cells may be blank. *Overall* achievement levels may be recorded in each row, rather than identifying levels for each achievement category.

	Most Consistent Level of Achievement*				
Strand: *Measurement*	**Problem solving**	**Understanding of concepts**	**Application of mathematical procedures**	**Communication**	***Overall***
Ongoing Observations					
Strategies Toolkit (Lesson 11)					
Work samples or portfolios; conferences					
Show What You Know					
Unit Test					
Unit Problem: At the Zoo					
Achievement Level for reporting					

*Use Ontario Achievement Levels 1, 2, 3, 4.

Self-Assessment:

Comments: (Strengths, Needs, Next Steps)

Name ____________________ Date _______________

Master 9.5

To Parents and Adults at Home …

Your child's class is starting a mathematics unit on length, perimeter, and area.

In this unit, your child will:

- Estimate and measure in millimetres, centimetres, decimetres, metres, and estimate in kilometres.
- Investigate the relationship among the units used to measure length.
- Measure the distance around circular objects.
- Estimate and measure the perimeter and area of irregular figures.
- Develop rules for calculating the perimeter and area of rectangles.
- Recognize and demonstrate that figures with equal perimeters can have different areas, and figures with equal areas can have different perimeters.

Measurement provides a strong connection between what students learn in mathematics, and their life experiences. Measurement is a skill that one uses in everyday life: in building, designing, and constructing any kind of project.

Here are some suggestions for activities that you can do at home.

Ask your child to help you measure things around the home. For example, if you are re-arranging a room, have your child draw a new floor plan for the room that includes the measurements of each piece of furniture. If you are hanging a mirror, your child can help you measure the mirror to find a place for it on the wall.

When you are driving or are on a bus, have your child estimate how many kilometres you travel.

Name ____________________ Date ________________

Master 9.6

Additional Activity 1: A Kilometre of Dental Floss

Work on your own.

You will need a package of dental floss, and paper and pencil.

- Suppose each member of your family flosses her or his teeth once a day.
  Do you think your family would use more or less than 1 km of dental floss in a year?

- Explain how you got your answer.

Take It Further:

Calculate about how many packages of dental floss equal 1 km.

Name ____________________ Date ______________

Master 9.7

Additional Activity 2: Tangram Perimeters

Work on your own.

You will need a tangram, paper and pencil, and a ruler.

- Use the tangram pieces.
  Create a figure or a design.

- Trace the outline of your figure onto paper.
  You may need to have a classmate help you hold the pieces in place while you trace.

- Estimate first.
  Then measure to find the perimeter of your figure to the nearest tenth of a centimetre.

Take It Further:

Trade tracings with a classmate.
Measure to find the perimeter of your classmate's figure.

Name ____________________ Date ________________

Master 9.8

Additional Activity 3: Calculating Perimeter and Area

Work with a partner.

You will need 5 cardboard rectangles of various sizes, labelled A, B, C, D, and E, a ruler, and paper and pencil.

- Choose a rectangle.
  One of you estimates the perimeter of the rectangle.
  The other estimates its area.
  Record your estimates.

- Measure the length and the width of the rectangle.
  Record these measurements.

- Use the measurements to calculate the perimeter, then the area of the rectangle.
  Record these measurements.

- Repeat with the other rectangles.

Take It Further:

Order the rectangles from least to greatest perimeter.
Then order them from least to greatest area.

Name ____________________ Date ______________

Master 9.9

Additional Activity 4: Investigating Hands

Work in a group of 4.

You will need a pencil, 1-cm grid paper, string, and measuring tape.

- Hold out your right hands so they are near.
  Examine the 4 hands.
  Estimate to order them from least to greatest area.

- Each of you trace your right hand onto 1-cm grid paper.
  Find the approximate area of your hand.

- Order the hands from least to greatest area.
  Compare the results with your estimate.

Take It Further:

Estimate to order the hands from least to greatest perimeter.
Use the string to find the perimeter of each hand.
Compare the results with your estimate.

Name ____________________ Date ________________

Master 9.10 **Step-by-Step 1**

Lesson 1, Question 6

Step 1 How many centimetres is 15 dm? __________

Can you draw a length of 15 dm on this page? ______________________

Step 2 Do you think a wingspan of 15 dm is reasonable for a pet bird?

Explain.

____

Step 3 25 cm is about 24 cm.

Divide 24 cm into 4 equal lengths.

Each length is ______ cm.

Step 4 Is each length of salmon large enough to feed one person? _______

Is Pablo's statement reasonable? Explain.

____

Step 5 About how long does it take you to walk 1 km? ______________________

About how long would it take you to walk 5 km? ______________________

Is Betty's statement reasonable? Explain.

____

____

Step 6 The length of one shoelace is about 30 cm.

How long would 2 shoelaces tied together be? ______________________

Do you think this would equal the height of a small child? Explain.

____

____

Name ____________________ Date _______________

Master 9.11 **Step-by-Step 2**

Lesson 2, Question 10

Step 1 How tall is Rico? ________________________________

What is Rico's height in centimetres? ______________________

Step 2 How tall is Jeremy? ________________________________

What is Jeremy's height in centimetres? ____________________

Step 3 How tall is Sasha? ________________________________

Step 4 Order the students from shortest to tallest, using their heights in centimetres. ________________________________

Step 5 Who is tallest? ________________________________

Step 6 Subtract the height of the second-tallest student from the height of the tallest student.

____

Step 7 How much taller is the tallest student?

____

Name ____________________ Date ________________

Master 9.12 **Step-by-Step 3**

Lesson 3, Question 4

Step 1 Find a table in your classroom.
Cut a piece of string as long as the table.

Step 2 How many times does the length of string fit along the length of the hallway?

____

Step 3 Assume your classmates used a broom.
Do you think your classmates will get the same result as you?
Explain.

____

____

Name ____________________ Date ________________

Master 9.13

Step-by-Step 4

Lesson 4, Question 7

Step 1 What is the circumference of the bracelet? ____________________

Step 2 Cut a length of string equal to the circumference of your wrist.
Measure the string with a ruler.
What is the circumference of your wrist? ____________________

Step 3 Is the circumference of your wrist greater than or less than the circumference of the bracelet? ____________________

Step 4 Could you wear the bracelet? ____________________
How do you know? ____________________
____

Name ____________________ Date ______________

Master 9.14

Step-by-Step 5

Lesson 5, Question 6

Step 1 What is the perimeter of Miss Dahlia's flower garden? ________________

Step 2 Use1-cm grid paper. Let the length of 1 grid square represent 1 m.
Draw a figure that is not a rectangle, with perimeter 28 m.
The sides of the figure must be drawn on the lines of the grid paper.

Step 3 Draw 2 other figures that are not rectangles, each with perimeter 28 m.

Step 4 Count the squares in each of your 3 figures.
How many squares are in the first figure? ______________________
What is the area of the first figure? ______________________
How many squares are in the second figure? ______________________
What is the area of the second figure?______________________
How many squares are in the third figure? ______________________
What is the area of the third figure? ______________________

Step 5 Which figure has the greatest area? ______________________

Step 6 Which figure will give Miss Dahlia the greatest amount of space for planting flowers?

____

Name ____________________ Date _______________

Master 9.15

Step-by-Step 6

Lesson 6, Question 7

Step 1 Draw a rectangle.

Label the lengths of two opposite sides 12.0 m.

Add these lengths: ____

Step 2 The perimeter is 55.0 m.

Subtract to find the sum of the other two sides.

55.0 m – _______ m = _______ m

Step 3 We know the other two sides of the rectangle are of equal length.

Divide your answer to *Step 2* by 2 to find the length of each side.

_______ m ÷ 2 = _______ m

The dimensions of the garden are _______ m by _______ m.

Step 4 Repeat the above calculations for side lengths of 12.1 m to 12.8 m.

____

____

____

____

____

____

____

____

How many rectangles did you find? ________________________________

Step 5 Were you able to draw a rectangle with all 4 sides equal? _____________

Name ____________________ Date _______________

Master 9.16

Step-by-Step 7

Lesson 7, Question 9

Step 1 What is the perimeter of the rectangular garden? ____________________

Step 2 Start with a pair of sides on the rectangle being equal to 1 m.
All the side lengths will be whole numbers of metres.
What will the length of the other two sides be?

____

Step 3 Draw the rectangle on grip paper.
Label all the dimensions.
Check to make sure the perimeter is the same as in *Step 1*.

Step 4 Increase the length of a pair of sides on the rectangle to 2 m.
What will the lengths of the other two sides be?

____

Draw the rectangle on grid paper.

Step 5 Continue to increase the length of a pair of sides on the rectangle.
Keep the same perimeter as in *Step 1*.
Draw all your rectangles on grid paper.

Step 6 Count the number of squares in each of the rectangles.
What is the greatest number of squares you can count? _______________
What is the area of that rectangle? ____________________

Step 7 Which garden would provide the most growing space? _______________
The least growing space? ____________________

Name ________________ Date ____________

Master 9.17

Step-by-Step 8

Lesson 8, Question 10

Step 1 Look at the rectangle.

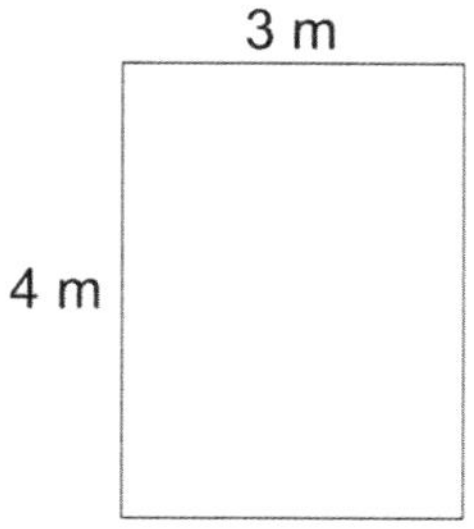

Step 2 What is its length? ______________ What is its width? ___________

What is the area of this rectangle? ___________________________

Step 3 Double the length of the rectangle.
What is the new length? ________________________________

What is the area of the rectangle now? ________________________
On grid paper, draw the rectangle with its length doubled.

Step 4 Compare the area in *Step 2* with the area in *Step 3*.
What do you have to do to the area in *Step 2* to get the area in *Step 3*?

____

Step 5 Use the rectangle from *Step 1*.
Double the length and double the width.
What is the new length? ________________________________

What is the new width? _________________________________

What is the area of this rectangle? ___________________________
On grid paper, draw the rectangle with its length and width doubled.

Step 6 Compare the area in *Step 2* with the area in *Step 5*.
What do you have to do to the area in *Step 2* to get the area in *Step 5*?

____

Name ____________________ Date ________________

Master 9.18 **Step-by-Step 9**

Lesson 9, Question 5

You will need square dot paper, a geoboard, and geobands.

Step 1 On a geoboard, make each figure below.

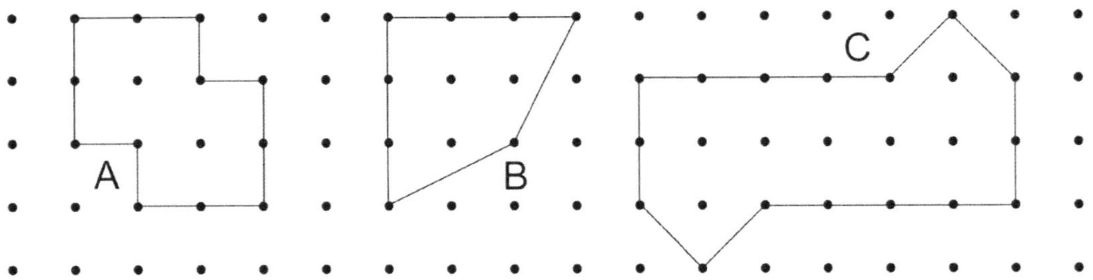

Step 2 Count the number of whole squares and half squares.
What is the area of each figure?

Figure A: ______________________________

Figure B: ______________________________

Figure C: ______________________________

Step 3 Use a geoband to divide each figure into 2 congruent parts.
Count the number of whole squares and half squares.
What is the area of each congruent part?

Figure A: ______________________________

Figure B: ______________________________

Figure C: ______________________________

Record your work on dot paper.
For each figure, check that the sum of the areas of the congruent parts is equal to the area of the whole figure in *Step 2*.

Step 4 Divide each figure into as many congruent parts as you can.
You can use whole squares or half squares or a combination of both.
Check that each congruent part of a figure has the same area.
Record your work on dot paper.

Name ____________________ Date _______________

Master 9.19

Step-by-Step 10

Lesson 10, Question 3

Step 1 Trace a circular object on the grid below.

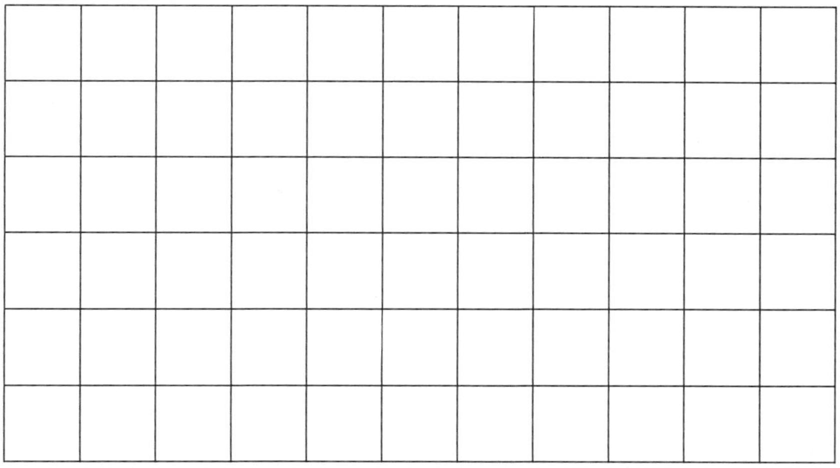

Step 2 Cut a length of string equal to the circumference of the object.

Measure the string with a ruler.

What is the circumference of the object?

____

Step 3 Draw a rectangle along grid lines around the tracing of the object.

Count squares to find the area of the rectangle. ______________________

Count the whole squares and part squares outside the tracing of the object, but inside the rectangle. ____

Subtract this number from the area of the rectangle.

_______ – _______ = ________

What is the area of the tracing of the object? ________________________

Name ____________________ Date _______________

Master 9.20a

Unit Test: Unit 9 Length, Perimeter, and Area

Part A

1. Choose the most appropriate unit. Estimate, then measure.
Use any materials you need to help you.

	What to Measure	**Estimate**	**Measurement**
a)	The height of the classroom door		
b)	The thickness of a paper clip		
c)	The circumference of your ankle		
d)	The perimeter of your math book		
e)	The area of this paper		

2. Complete. Use >, <, or =.

a) 0.7 m ☐ 7 dm **b)** 75 mm ☐ 6 cm **c)** 500 m ☐ 1 km

3. Complete.

a) 75 mm = ______ cm **b)** 0.24 m = ______ cm **c)** 8 m = ______ dm

4. Record each measure in millimetres, in centimetres, and in decimetres.

a) 0.8 m ______________________ **b)** 1.5 m ______________________

5. a) Find the perimeter and the area of each figure.
Use any materials you need.

b) For which figure are the answers approximate? _______________

Figure	**Perimeter**	**Area**
A		
B		
C		

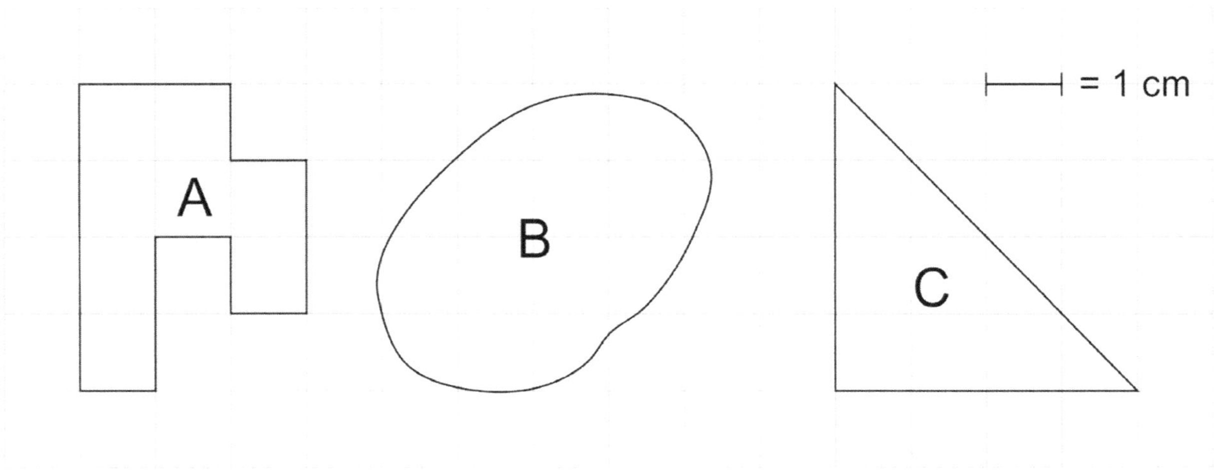

c) For which figures did you have to use a ruler? _________________________

Name ____________ Date ____________

Master 9.20b

Unit Test continued

Part B

6. Suppose you want to find how many benches lined up end to end will fit across the width of the gym floor. How could you do this without moving any benches?

____

____

____

____

____

7. a) Willa's rectangular patio has area 64 m^2, and whole-number side lengths. What might the length and width of the patio be? Give as many answers as you can.

   b) Willa enclosed her patio with 40 m of fence. What are the length and width of her patio? Explain how you know.

8. Use the data in the table.

Tropical Fish	
Name	**Length**
Guppy	2.5 cm
Paradise fish	75 mm
Red platy	0.4 dm
Ruby barb	65 mm
Neon tetra	4.0 cm
Swordtail	8.2 cm

   a) Which 2 fish are the same length?

   ____

   b) Which fish is shortest?

   ____

   c) Which fish is longest?

   ____

   d) Which fish is longer than the ruby barb but shorter than the swordtail?

   ____

Name ____________________ Date ________________

Master 9.20c **Unit Test continued**

9. Pablo speed walks around the school playground every evening.
The playground is 80 m long and 45 m wide.
How many times would Pablo have to speed walk around the playground to walk 2 km?
Use a diagram, words, or numbers to explain your answer.

Part C

10. Albert has a rectangular garden with perimeter 48 m.
The length and width of the garden are whole numbers of metres.
What might the dimensions and area of Albert's garden be?
Find all the possible answers.

Name ____________________ Date ______________

Master 9.21

Sample Answers

Unit Test – Master 9.20

Part A

1. Estimates and measurements will vary.
2. a) 0.7 m = 7 dm
   b) 75 mm > 6 cm
   c) 500 m < 1 km
3. a) 7.5 cm
   b) 24 cm
   c) 80 dm
4. a) 800 mm, 80 cm, 8 dm
   b) 1500 mm, 150 cm, 15 dm
5. a)

Figure	Perimeter	Area
A	16 cm	8 cm^2
B	About 11 cm	About 12 cm^2
C	13.7 cm	8 cm^2

   b) Figure B
   c) Figures B and C

Part B

6. Sample answer:
   I would measure the length of one bench, then measure the width of the gym floor. Then I would divide the width of the floor by the length of a bench. This gives me the number of benches.
7. a) Possible answers: 1 m by 64 m; 2 m by 32 m, 4 m by 16 m, 8 m by 8 m
   b) Length: 16 m; width: 4 m
   Sample answer: If the length is 16 m and the width is 4 m, the perimeter is 40 m: $(16 + 4) \times 2 = 40$.
8. a) Red platy and neon tetra
   b) Guppy
   c) Swordtail
   d) Paradise fish

9. Sample answer:
   Perimeter: $(80\text{ m} + 45\text{ m}) \times 2 = 250\text{ m}$
   2 km = 2000 m
   $250\text{ m} \times 4 = 1000\text{ m}$
   So, $250\text{ m} \times 8 = 2000\text{ m}$
   Pablo would have to walk around the playground 8 times.

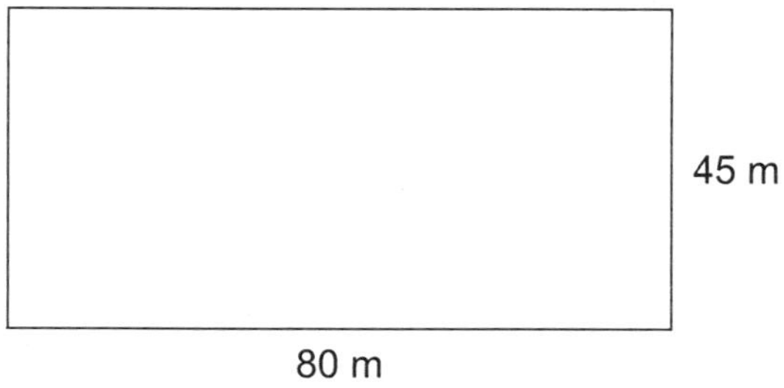

Part C

10. Possible answers:

Length	Width	Area
23 m	1 m	23 m^2
22 m	2 m	44 m^2
21 m	3 m	63 m^2
20 m	4 m	80 m^2
19 m	5 m	95 m^2
18 m	6 m	108 m^2
17 m	7 m	119 m^2
16 m	8 m	128 m^2
15 m	9 m	135 m^2
14 m	10 m	140 m^2
13 m	11 m	143 m^2
12 m	12 m	144 m^2

Extra Practice Masters 9.22–9.27

Go to the CD-ROM to access editable versions of these Extra Practice Masters.

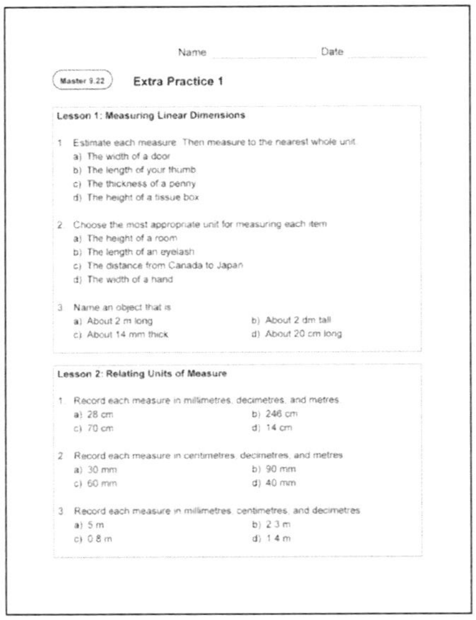

Name ______ Date ______

Master 9.22 **Extra Practice 1**

Lesson 1: Measuring Linear Dimensions

1. Estimate each measure. Then measure to the nearest whole unit.
   a) The width of a door
   b) The length of your thumb
   c) The thickness of a penny
   d) The height of a tissue box
2. Choose the most appropriate unit for measuring each item.
   a) The height of a room
   b) The length of an eyelash
   c) The distance from Canada to Japan
   d) The width of a hand
3. Name an object that is:
   a) About 2 m long b) About 2 dm tall
   c) About 14 mm thick d) About 20 cm long

Lesson 2: Relating Units of Measure

1. Record each measure in millimetres, decimetres, and metres.
   a) 28 cm b) 246 cm
   c) 70 cm d) 14 cm
2. Record each measure in centimetres, decimetres, and metres.
   a) 30 mm b) 90 mm
   c) 60 mm d) 40 mm
3. Record each measure in millimetres, centimetres, and decimetres.
   a) 5 m b) 2.3 m
   c) 0.8 m d) 1.4 m

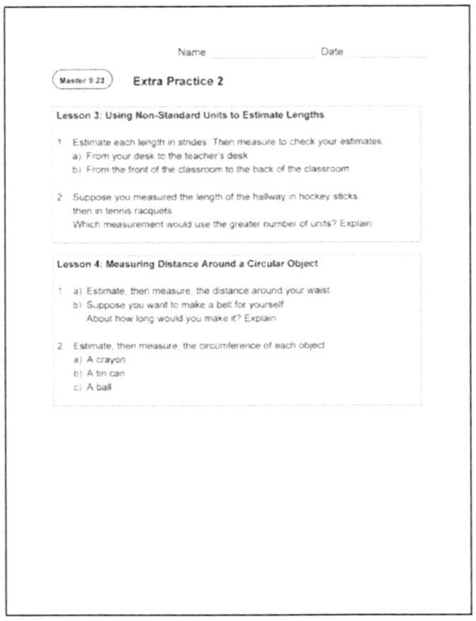

Name ______ Date ______

Master 9.23 **Extra Practice 2**

Lesson 3: Using Non-Standard Units to Estimate Lengths

1. Estimate each length in strides. Then measure to check your estimates.
   a) From your desk to the teacher's desk
   b) From the front of the classroom to the back of the classroom
2. Suppose you measured the length of the hallway in hockey sticks, then in tennis racquets.
   Which measurement would use the greater number of units? Explain.

Lesson 4: Measuring Distance Around a Circular Object

1. a) Estimate, then measure, the distance around your waist.
   b) Suppose you want to make a belt for yourself.
   About how long would you make it? Explain.
2. Estimate, then measure, the circumference of each object.
   a) A crayon
   b) A tin can
   c) A ball

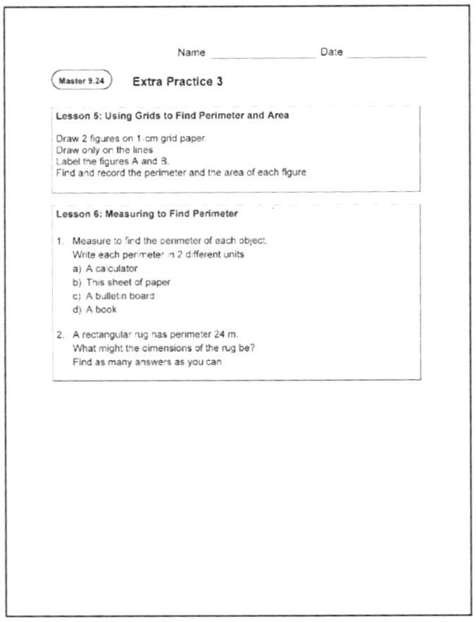

Name ______ Date ______

Master 9.24 **Extra Practice 3**

Lesson 5: Using Grids to Find Perimeter and Area

Draw 2 figures on 1-cm grid paper.
Draw only on the lines.
Label the figures A and B.
Find and record the perimeter and the area of each figure.

Lesson 6: Measuring to Find Perimeter

1. Measure to find the perimeter of each object.
   Write each perimeter in 2 different units.
   a) A calculator
   b) This sheet of paper
   c) A bulletin board
   d) A book
2. A rectangular rug has perimeter 24 m.
   What might the dimensions of the rug be?
   Find as many answers as you can.

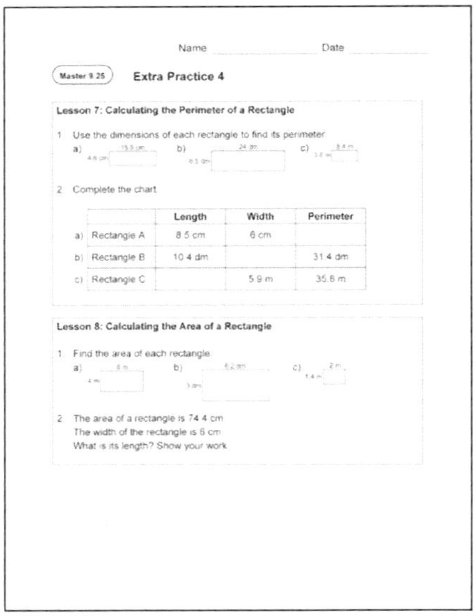

Name ______ Date ______

Master 9.25 **Extra Practice 4**

Lesson 7: Calculating the Perimeter of a Rectangle

1. Use the dimensions of each rectangle to find its perimeter.
   a) b) c)
2. Complete the chart.

		Length	Width	Perimeter
a)	Rectangle A	8.5 cm	6 cm	
b)	Rectangle B	10.4 dm		31.4 dm
c)	Rectangle C		5.9 m	35.8 m

Lesson 8: Calculating the Area of a Rectangle

1. Find the area of each rectangle.
   a) b) c)
2. The area of a rectangle is 74.4 cm.
   The width of the rectangle is 6 cm.
   What is its length? Show your work.

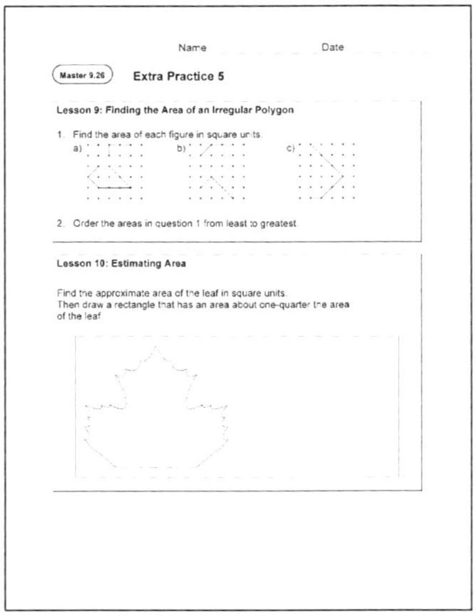

Name ______ Date ______

Master 9.26 **Extra Practice 5**

Lesson 9: Finding the Area of an Irregular Polygon

1. Find the area of each figure in square units.
   a) b) c)
2. Order the areas in question 1 from least to greatest.

Lesson 10: Estimating Area

Find the approximate area of the leaf in square units.
Then draw a rectangle that has an area about one-quarter the area of the leaf.

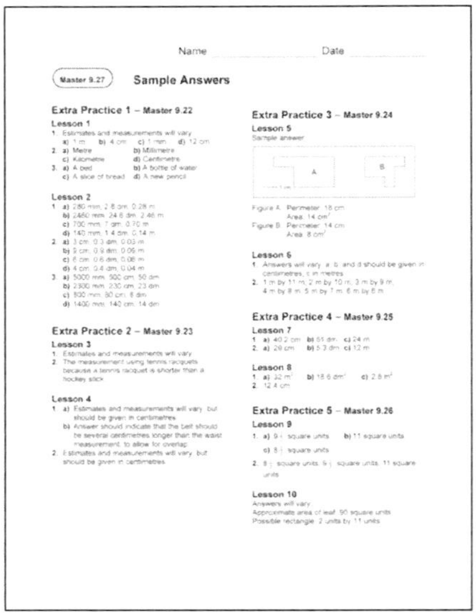

Name ______ Date ______

Master 9.27 **Sample Answers**

Extra Practice 1 – Master 9.22

Lesson 1
1. Estimates and measurements will vary.
   a) 1 m b) 4 cm c) 1 mm d) 12 cm
2. a) Metre b) Millimetre
   c) Kilometre d) Centimetre
3. a) A bed b) A bottle of water
   c) A slice of bread d) A new pencil

Lesson 2
1. a) 280 mm, 2.8 dm, 0.28 m
   b) 2460 mm, 24.6 dm, 2.46 m
   c) 700 mm, 7 dm, 0.70 m
   d) 140 mm, 1.4 dm, 0.14 m
2. a) 3 cm, 0.3 dm, 0.03 m
   b) 9 cm, 0.9 dm, 0.09 m
   c) 6 cm, 0.6 dm, 0.06 m
   d) 4 cm, 0.4 dm, 0.04 m
3. a) 5000 mm, 500 cm, 50 dm
   b) 2300 mm, 230 cm, 23 dm
   c) 800 mm, 80 cm, 8 dm
   d) 1400 mm, 140 cm, 14 dm

Extra Practice 2 – Master 9.23

Lesson 3
1. Estimates and measurements will vary.
2. The measurement using tennis racquets because a tennis racquet is shorter than a hockey stick.

Lesson 4
1. a) Estimates and measurements will vary, but should be given in centimetres.
   b) Answer should indicate that the belt should be several centimetres longer than the waist measurement, to allow for overlap.
2. Estimates and measurements will vary, but should be given in centimetres.

Extra Practice 3 – Master 9.24

Lesson 5
Sample answer:

Figure A: Perimeter: 18 cm
Area: 14 cm^2
Figure B: Perimeter: 14 cm
Area: 8 cm^2

Lesson 6
1. Answers will vary; a, b, and d should be given in centimetres, c in metres.
2. 1 m by 11 m, 2 m by 10 m, 3 m by 9 m, 4 m by 8 m, 5 m by 7 m, 6 m by 6 m

Extra Practice 4 – Master 9.25

Lesson 7
1. a) 40.2 cm b) 61 dm c) 24 m
2. a) 29 cm b) 5.3 dm c) 12 m

Lesson 8
1. a) 32 m^2 b) 18.6 dm^2 c) 2.8 m^2
2. 12.4 cm

Extra Practice 5 – Master 9.26

Lesson 9
1. a) 9 [illegible] square units b) 11 square units
   c) 8 [illegible] square units
2. 8 [illegible] square units, 9 [illegible] square units, 11 square units

Lesson 10
Answers will vary.
Approximate area of leaf: 90 square units
Possible rectangle: 2 units by 11 units

Addison Wesley
Mathematics
Makes Sense

Program Authors

Peggy Morrow
Ralph Connelly
Bryn Keyes
Jason Johnston
Steve Thomas
Jeananne Thomas
Angela D'Alessandro
Maggie Martin Connell
Don Jones
Michael Davis
Sharon Jeroski
Trevor Brown
Nora Alexander
Cynthia Pratt Nicolson

Printed and bound in Canada.

8 9 MP 18 17

PEARSON
Education Canada

ADDISON WESLEY

Ontario

Math Makes Sense 5

Ontario

Teacher Guide

Unit 10: Patterns in Number and Geometry

PEARSON
Addison Wesley

UNIT 10

Patterns in Number and Geometry

"Mathematicians continue to search and discover new patterns and relationships. Applications of mathematical patterns have led to solutions of real-world problems that were once thought to be unsolvable. Patterns are powerful ideas."

John A. Van de Walle, *Elementary and Middle School Mathematics* Fifth Edition

FOCUS STRAND
Patterning and Algebra

SUPPORTING STRANDS
Number Sense and Numeration
Geometry and Spatial Sense

Mathematics Background

What Are the Big Ideas?

- Tables and graphs can be used to make predictions.
- Patterns can be represented by concrete models, in tables, and by graphs.
- Patterns exist throughout mathematics and nature.

How Will the Concepts Develop?

Students investigate numerical and geometric patterns, and express them mathematically in words, pictures, and/or symbols.

Students are introduced to the idea that looking for patterns and rearranging factors can make multiplying easier. Students further explore patterns in multiplication, fractions, and decimals using a calculator.

Students analyse patterns and create models of them. They represent patterns with tables and extend patterns. Students graph patterns and analyse the graphs.

Students work with Fibonacci numbers and discover the prevalence of the Fibonacci sequence.

Students model and extend tiling patterns with manipulatives and using a computer.

Why Are These Concepts Important?

Looking for patterns in fractions and their decimal equivalents improves understanding and computational proficiency. Recognizing different representations of a pattern allows the student to make mathematical connections and strengthen algebraic reasoning.

Working with Fibonacci numbers and the Fibonacci sequence illustrates patterns found in nature.

Giving opportunities to discover patterns lays the foundation for the understanding of advanced geometric properties and theorems in the later grades. The ability to recognize and apply patterns is a vital skill in many careers.

Curriculum Overview

Cluster 1: Investigating Number Patterns

Overall Expectations

- Solve problems involving decimals and fractions, and describe and explain the variety of strategies used. (5m8)
- Recognize and discuss the mathematical relationships between and among patterns. (5m91)
- Identify, extend, and create patterns in a variety of contexts. (5m92)
- Analyse and discuss patterning rules. (5m93)
- Create tables to display patterns. (5m94)
- Apply patterning strategies to problem-solving situations. (5m95)

Specific Expectations

- Use a calculator and computer applications to explore patterns. (5m100)
- Pose and solve problems by applying a patterning strategy. (5m101)
- Analyse number patterns and state the rule for any relationships. (5m102)
- Discuss and defend the choice of a pattern rule. (5m103)
- Given a rule expressed in informal mathematical language, extend a pattern. (5m104)
- Use patterns in a table of values to make predictions. (5m105)
- Determine the value of a missing factor in equations involving multiplication, with and without the use of calculator. (5m106)

Launch
Squares Everywhere!

Lesson 1:
Patterns in Multiplication

Lesson 2:
Exploring Patterns in Decimals with a Calculator

Cluster 2: Representing Patterns

Overall Expectations

- Recognize and discuss the mathematical relationships between and among patterns. (5m91)
- Identify, extend, and create patterns in a variety of contexts. (5m92)
- Analyse and discuss patterning rules. (5m93)
- Create tables to display patterns. (5m94)
- Apply patterning strategies to problem-solving situations. (5m95)

Specific Expectations

- Describe patterns encountered in any context, make models of the patterns, and create charts to display the patterns. (5m98)
- Identify and extend patterns to solve problems in meaningful contexts. (5m99)
- Use a calculator ... to explore patterns. (5m100)
- Pose and solve problems by applying a patterning strategy. (5m101)
- Analyse number patterns and state the rule for any relationships. (5m102)
- Discuss and defend the choice of a pattern rule. (5m103)
- Given a rule expressed in informal mathematical language, extend a pattern. (5m104)
- Use patterns in a table of values to make predictions. (5m105)

Lesson 3:
Graphing Patterns

Lesson 4:
Another Number Pattern

Lesson 5:
Strategies Toolkit

Cluster 3: Exploring Tiling

Overall Expectations
- Identify, extend, and create patterns in a variety of contexts. (5m92)
- Analyse and discuss patterning rules. (5m93)

Specific Expectations
- Use ... computer applications to explore patterns. (5m100)
- Pose and solve problems by applying a patterning strategy. (5m101)
- Given a rule expressed in informal mathematical language, extend a pattern. (5m104)
- Explore tiling patterns that cover a plane. (5m88)

Lesson 6:
Tiling Patterns

Technology:
Using a Computer to Explore Tiling Patterns

Show What You Know

Unit Problem
Squares Everywhere!

Curriculum across the Grades

Grade 4	Grade 5	Grade 6
Students analyse number patterns and state the rule for any relationships. Students continue to identify and extend patterns, given a pattern rule. They defend the choice of pattern rule. Students create charts to display patterns. They pose and solve problems by applying a patterning strategy.	Students describe patterns encountered in context, make models of the patterns, and create charts to display the patterns. Students identify and extend patterns to solve problems in meaningful contexts. Students use a calculator and computer applications to explore patterns. Students pose and solve problems by applying a patterning strategy. Students use patterns in a table of values to make predictions.	Students recognize relationships and use them to summarize and generalize patterns. Students continue to analyse number patterns and state the rule for relationships. Students state a rule for a relationship between terms in a given data table of values and graph the relationship in the first quadrant. Students pose and solve problems by recognizing a pattern.

Materials for This Unit

For Lesson 6, bring in a variety of examples of tiling patterns, such as quilts, wallpaper, flags, tiles, and rugs, for students to look at. You may find examples of such patterns in books or magazines.

Additional Activities

Cover Up

For Extra Practice (Appropriate for use after Lesson 1)
Materials: *Cover Up* (Master 10.7), hundred charts (PM 13), counters

The work students do: With a partner, students use a hundred chart to play a game that involves factors and multiples. They look for patterns and apply patterning strategies to win the game. Many games will end when one player chooses a prime number greater than 50. This challenges students to improve their multiplication and division skills and to gain a better understanding of factors and multiples.

Take It Further: Students extend the game board to a 200 chart.

Logical/Mathematical
Partner Activity

Graph It

For Extension (Appropriate for use after Lesson 3)
Materials: *Graph It* (Master 10.8), Colour Tiles, 1-cm grid paper (PM 23), pencil crayons

The work students do: Students work with a partner to extend a growing pattern. In a table, students record the frame number and the area of the figure. They extend the table of values and use the table to graph the pattern on grid paper. Students describe the pattern rule and use it to predict larger areas that follow the pattern.

Take It Further: Students use congruent squares to make and record a different area pattern.

Logical/Mathematical/ Kinesthetic
Partner Activity

Win with Less

For Enrichment (Appropriate for use after Lesson 4)
Materials: *Win with Less* (Master 10.9), Pattern Blocks (PM 28), paper bags, pencil and paper

The work students do: Students play a game trying to create Pattern Block figures with a minimum perimeter. They place several Pattern Blocks in a paper bag and, without looking, draw 3 figures from the bag. The object of the game is use all three shapes to make a figure that has the least perimeter. Students look for patterns in the figures and apply patterning strategies to win the game.

Take It Further: Challenge students to play the game drawing 4, 5, or 6 Pattern Blocks from the bag.

Kinesthetic/Social/ Visual/Spatial
Partner Activity

Painted Patterns

For Extension (Appropriate for use after Lesson 6)
Materials: *Painted Patterns* (Master 10.10), 4 colours of Snap Cubes, paper and pencil

The work students do: Students work in pairs. They build cube structures using Snap Cubes. They begin with a 2 by 2 by 2 cube structure. Students imagine that the cubes are dipped in paint and they have to figure out how many Snap Cubes would have: 3 painted faces, 2 painted faces, 1 painted face, and no painted faces. Students look for patterns in a 3 by 3 by 3 cube, and then a 4 by 4 by 4 cube. They may use different colours to represent the Snap Cubes with each number of faces painted.
Students record the data in a chart and look for patterns.

Take It Further: Have students extend the activity for single-layer prisms (for example, a 1 by 1 by 2 rectangular prism).

Kinesthetic/Social/ Visual/Spatial
Partner Activity

Planning for Unit 10

Planning for Instruction

Suggested Unit time: About 2 weeks

Lesson	Time	Materials	Program Support
Launch: Squares Everywhere!, page 2	10–15 min		
Lesson 1: Patterns in Multiplication, page 4 Use patterns to solve multiplication problems.	40–50 min	calculators	Master 10.11: Step-by-Step 1 Master 10.18: Extra Practice 1
Lesson 2: Exploring Patterns in Decimals with a Calculator, page 8 Use a calculator to explore patterns in decimals.	40–50 min	overhead calculator calculators	Master 10.12: Step-by-Step 2 Master 10.18: Extra Practice 1
Lesson 3: Graphing Patterns, page 12 Use models, tables, and graphs to represent patterns.	80–100 min	Colour Tiles 1-cm grid paper and transparency pencil crayons rulers	PM 23: 1-cm Grid Paper Master 10.13: Step-by-Step 3 Master 10.19: Extra Practice 2 Master 10.6: Perimeter of a Square
Lesson 4: Another Number Pattern, page 16 Explore number patterns in context.	40–50 min	calculators dominoes	Master 10.14: Step-by-Step 4 Master 10.19: Extra Practice 2
Lesson 5: Strategies Toolkit, page 20 Interpret a problem and select an appropriate strategy.	40–50 min	counters (optional)	
Lesson 6: Tiling Patterns, page 22 Model and extend tiling patterns.	40–50 min	Pattern Blocks triangular dot paper 1-cm grid paper square dot paper	Master 10.15: Step-by-Step 6 Master 10.20: Extra Practice 3 PM 28: Pattern Blocks PM 23: 1-cm Grid Paper PM 25: Square Dot Paper PM 26: Triangular Dot Paper
Technology: Using a Computer to Explore Tiling Patterns, page 25 Use a computer to explore tiling patterns.	40–50 min	computers with *AppleWorks* or *The Geometer's Sketchpad*	
Show What You Know, page 28 Assessment	40–50 min	calculators Pattern Blocks	PM 28: Pattern Blocks
Unit Problem: Squares Everywhere!, page 30 Assessment	40–50 min	1-cm grid paper coloured pencils 2-column charts	PM 23: 1-cm Grid Paper PM 17: 2-Column Chart

Planning for Assessment

Purpose	Tools and Process	Recording and Reporting
Diagnostic	*Unit Launch* Question; conference; scaffold problems throughout the unit	PM 8: Conference Prompts
Formative	*Explore* – Ongoing Assessment: Observe and Listen	Master 10.2 Ongoing Observations: Patterns in Number and Geometry PM 1: Inquiry Process Check List PM 6: Observation Record 1 PM 7: Observation Record 2 PM 8: Conference Prompts
	Prompt student's self-assessment	PM 2: Self-Assessment PM 3: Self-Assessment: Problem Solving
	Practice – Assessment Focus Questions	PM 9: Work Sample Records
	Review student work; provide feedback; scaffold as needed; select key pieces	
Summative	*Show What You Know*	Master 10.1 Unit Rubric: Patterns in Number and Geometry
	Unit Problem – Performance Assessment	Master 10.3 Performance Assessment Rubric: Squares Everywhere!
	Unit Test	Master 10.4 Unit Summary: Patterns in Number and Geometry
	Review assessment records; add unit results to ongoing records	PM 10: Summary Class Records: Strands PM 11: Summary Class Records: Achievement Categories PM 12: Summary Record: Individual
Learning Skills/ Mathematical Disposition	Observe and record throughout unit	PM 4: Learning Skills Check List PM 5: Mathematical Dispositions and Learning Skills

Program Masters (PM) are in the *Grade 5 Planning and Program Masters* module.
Extra Practice Masters are on the CD-ROM.

Squares Everywhere!

LESSON ORGANIZER

10–15 min

Curriculum Focus: Activate prior knowledge about patterns in number and geometry.

ASSUMED PRIOR KNOWLEDGE

- ✓ Students can recognize an area pattern and can describe it in informal language.
- ✓ Students can recognize a pattern in geometry and extend the pattern.

ACTIVATE PRIOR LEARNING

Have students examine the patterns in the Student Book.

Ask the first question in the *Launch*.
(*I see geometric patterns.*)

Discuss the second and third questions posed in the Student Book. Have students share their answers with a partner and the class. Record the answers on the board.
(*The patterns are the same because they all use figures that give the impression of squares; they are different because one pattern uses shaded rhombuses to give the impression of squares and another uses alternating shaded squares.*)

Ask:

- What other figures do you see commonly used in area patterns?
  (*Cross, hexagon, L-shape, T-shape*)
- Why do you think many area patterns use squares?
  (*Because squares leave no gaps in an area pattern*)
- Are other quadrilaterals commonly used in area patterns? Why do you think so?
  (*Yes. Quadrilaterals form area patterns with no gaps.*)

Tell students that, in this unit, they will investigate number patterns and patterns in geometry. They will use number patterns to make predictions and use Input/Output tables to look for relationships. Graphing a pattern enriches students' understanding of it. They will also learn that number patterns can have geometric representations. At the end of this unit, students will continue to look for patterns in squares and create a design using squares.

and Geometry

What patterns do you see?
How are the patterns the same?
How are they different?
How could you extend any of the patterns?

Key Words

Fibonacci sequence

Fibonacci number

349

LITERATURE CONNECTIONS FOR THE UNIT

Math Wizardry for Kids by Margaret Elizabeth Kenda, Tim Robinson (Illustrator), and Phyllis S. Williams. Barron's Educational Series, Incorporated, 1995.
ISBN 0812018095
In this book, there are activities for finding math in nature, art, music, dance, poetry, gamesmanship, magic, and espionage. There is enough diversity here to ensure that at least some activities will appeal to even the most die-hard math adversary.

Math-Terpieces: The Art of Problem-Solving by Greg Tang. Scholastic, Inc., 2003.
ISBN 0439443881
In *Math-Terpieces*, Greg Tang continues to challenge kids with his innovative approach to math, and uses art history to expand his vision for creative problem-solving.

Fibonacci Fun: Fascinating Activities with Intriguing Numbers by Trudi Hammel Garland. Dale Seymour Publications, 1997.
ISBN 1572322659
From "Raising Rabbits" to "Prickly Pinecones," 24 easy-to-use, reproducible activities and projects help introduce students to Fibonacci numbers.

REACHING ALL LEARNERS

Some students may benefit from using the virtual manipulatives on the e-Tools CD-ROM. The e-Tools appropriate for this unit include Geometry Shapes and Place-Value Blocks.

DIAGNOSTIC ASSESSMENT

What to Look For	What to Do
✔ Students can recognize an area pattern and describe it in informal language. ✔ Students can recognize a pattern in geometry and extend the pattern.	***Extra Support:*** Students who have difficulty finding patterns may benefit from more specific questions, such as: • How is the chess game board the same as the other game boards? • How would you describe the pattern in terms of colour and shape? *Work on this skill during Lessons 3, 4, 6, and Technology.* Students who cannot describe a pattern may benefit from modelling or preparing an illustration. Bring in a chess board or checker board to show to the class. To find the number of squares in a chess board or checker board, students could start by counting single squares, or 1 by 1 squares, then 2 by 2 squares, and so on. *Work on this skill during Lessons 3, 4, 6, and Technology.*

Patterns in Multiplication

LESSON ORGANIZER 40–50 min

Curriculum Focus: Use patterns to solve multiplication problems. (5m106)

Student Materials
- calculators

Optional
- Step-by-Step 1 (Master 10.11)
- Extra Practice 1 (Master 10.18)

Vocabulary: product, factor

Assessment: Master 10.2 Ongoing Observations: Patterns in Number and Geometry

Key Math Learnings

1. When multiplying numbers, the factors can be reordered or regrouped to facilitate finding the product.
2. Factors in a product can be further broken down to facilitate the calculation.
3. Multiplication and division are inverse operations. That is, each undoes the other.

LESSON 1

Patterns in Multiplication

Explore

You will need a calculator.

➤ Predict each product.

$4 \times 5 \times 18$ 360
$4 \times 18 \times 5$ 360
$2 \times 36 \times 5$ 360
$18 \times 5 \times 4$ 360
$18 \times 10 \times 2$ 360
$9 \times 10 \times 4$ 360
$9 \times 10 \times 2 \times 2$ 360

Use a calculator. Find each product.
What do you notice about the products?
Compare the factors in the questions.
How are they related?

➤ Choose 3 different 1- or 2-digit numbers.
Multiply the 3 numbers in as many orders as you can.
How many arrangements can you make?
Which order makes multiplication easiest?

➤ Predict each product.

$5 \times 21 \times 10$ 1050
$2 \times 12 \times 30$ 720
$4 \times 5 \times 20$ 400

Use a calculator. Find each product.
How do the products compare to your predictions?

➤ Use a calculator.
Find each missing factor.

16 $\square \times 15 = 240$
20 $12 \times \square = 240$

What strategies did you use?

350 LESSON FOCUS | Use patterns to solve multiplication problems.

BEFORE Get Started

Remind students of patterns in multiplication they have seen in earlier grades.

Display these products:

439×10 439×100 439×1000

Invite a volunteer to provide the answers. (4390, 43 900, 439 000)

Ask:

- Why is it easy to find these products without using a calculator?
(*We use a base 10 number system. So, multiplying by 10 moves the digits 1 place to the left, and we add a zero as a place-value holder. 100 = 10 × 10, so multiplying by 100 moves the digits 2 places to the left, and we add 2 zeroes as place-value holders. 1000 = 10 × 10 × 10, so multiplying by 1000 moves the digits 3 places to the left, and we add 3 zeroes as place-value holders.*)
- How can you find 439×20 without a calculator?
(*20 = 10 × 2. Use the previous result. 439 × 20 = 439 × 10 × 2 = 4390 × 2 = 8780*)
- How can you use mental math to find 15×9?
(*I think of an array for 9 × 15. It would have 9 rows of 10, and 9 rows of 5, which can be written as 9 × 10 + 9 × 5. This gives me 90 + 45, which is 135.*)

Present *Explore*. Tell students they should write down their prediction before using a calculator. Remind students that it will be easier to notice patterns if their work is presented in an orderly manner; for example, they could write their predictions and calculations in a 2-column chart.

Show *and* Share

Share your answers with another pair of students.
How did you predict each product?
...cribe any patterns.
...e your strategies for finding the missing factor.

Connect

The order in which you multiply factors does not matter.
You can rearrange factors to make multiplication easier.

- Multiply: $3 \times 200 \times 14$

  The product $3 \times 200 \times 14$ is the same as the product $3 \times 14 \times 200$.

  Multiply: $3 \times 14 = 42$
  Use place value to multiply 42×200.
  42×2 hundreds = 84 hundreds
  $42 \times 200 = 8400$

  $3 \times 200 \times 14 = 8400$

- Multiply: $5 \times 12 \times 3$

  Rewrite 12 as 2×6.
  $5 \times 2 \times 6 \times 3$
  Multiply: $5 \times 2 = 10$
  Multiply: $6 \times 3 = 18$

  Then multiply: $10 \times 18 = 180$

  $5 \times 12 \times 3 = 180$

- Multiply 12×29.

  The product 12×29 is 12 less than the product 12×30.
  Use mental math to find the product 12×30.
  12×3 tens = 36 tens
  $12 \times 30 = 360$

  $360 - 12 = 348$

  $12 \times 29 = 348$

351

REACHING ALL LEARNERS

Alternative Explore

Materials: index cards

Students work in pairs. They choose 3 different 1- or 2-digit numbers and write these numbers on separate cards. Have them trade cards with a partner. The partner arranges the cards in as many ways as he or she can and describes which order makes multiplication the easiest. Have students predict each product, as in *Explore*. Continue the rest of *Explore* as outlined in the Student Book.

Early Finishers

Students can use patterns to create and solve problems with four 1- or 2-digit factors.

Common Misconceptions

➤ Students may not know their basic multiplication facts and thus have difficulty multiplying.

How to Help: Have a 10×10 multiplication chart available for students to use. Encourage students to practise multiplication facts daily by playing simple games, such as multiplication bingo.

ESL Strategies

Model the use of different multiplication words by displaying them on a word wall. Include a multiplication sentence with the words "factors" and "product" underneath the sentence.

DURING Explore

Ongoing Assessment: Observe and Listen

As pairs of students work on the first part in *Explore*, ask:

- How are the products similar?
  (*All the products are the same: 360*)
- How are the factors in the questions related?
  (*9, 18, and 36 are multiples of 9; 2, 4, 5, and 10 are factors of 20.*)
- Does the order in which you multiply the factors affect the product?
  (*No, the product is always the same, no matter in which order you multiply the factors.*)

For the second part, ensure students find all the different arrangements that can be made. Ask:

- How do you know you have found all the different possible arrangements?
  (*I made a list, and found that I can arrange the 3 numbers in 6 different ways. I know I have found all the different arrangements because I cannot reorder the numbers without repeating a row in my list.*)
- What is an example of an order that makes multiplication easiest?
  (*An order that produces a pair with a product that is a multiple of 10*)

As students work on the third part, ask:

- Did you break any of the numbers apart to make it easier to multiply mentally? Explain.
  (*Yes, I broke down the multiples of 10 and tried to regroup. For example,* $20 = 2 \times 10$*, so* $4 \times 5 \times 20 = 4 \times 5 \times 2 \times 10 = 4 \times 10 \times 10 = 400$)
- How did you find the other products?
  (*To multiply* 5×21*, I used* $21 = 20 + 1$*, so* $5 \times 21 = 5 \times 20 + 5 \times 1 = 100 + 5 = 105$*. So,* $5 \times 21 \times 10 = 105 \times 10 = 1050$)

Sample Answers

1. Possible strategies: Use numbers that are easy to multiply. Multiply by multiples of 10.
2. a) $15 \times 19 = 15 \times 20 - 15$
   $= 300 - 15$
   $= 285$
   $15 \times 21 = 15 \times 20 + 15$
   $= 300 + 15$
   $= 315$

   b)

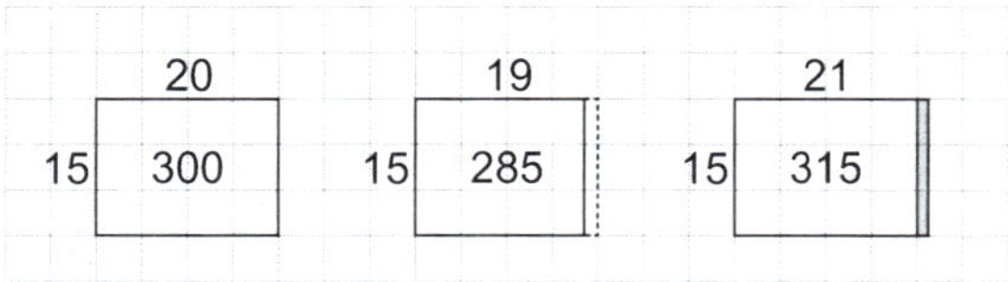

   c) 14×20, 16×20; since the product of 15×20 is 300, 14×20 would be 20 less and 16×20 would be 20 more.

6. $45 \times \square = 2475$; 55
8. 33×30 is the same as $33 \times 10 \times 3$. I can multiply 33×10 first to get 330, then 330×3 to get 990. The area of the gym floor is 990 m^2.
9. b) $\square \times 56 = 4200$
10. First multiply 2×5 to get 10, and then multiply 7×8 to get 56. Then multiply 10×56.

➤ Here are 2 ways to find a missing factor.

- $\square \times 5 = 45$
  If the numbers are small, think about the facts you know.
  $9 \times 5 = 45$
  So, the missing factor is 9.

- $285 = 15 \times \square$
  When the numbers are large, use a calculator.
  Think: Which number do we multiply 15 by to get 285?
  This is the same number we get if we divide:
  $285 \div 15$
  Use a calculator.
  $285 \div 15 = 19$

  So, $285 = 15 \times 19$
  The missing factor is 19.

Practice

1. Use mental math to multiply. What strategies did you use?
   a) $2 \times 16 \times 5$ 160 b) $25 \times 5 \times 2$ 250 c) $2 \times 125 \times 5$ 1250
   d) $2 \times 34 \times 50$ 3400 e) $3 \times 15 \times 10$ 450 f) $4 \times 40 \times 6$ 960
2. a) Use mental math to multiply 15×20.
   Use this product to find:
   15×19 15×21
   b) Draw diagrams to show why the results in part a are correct.
   c) What other products could you find when you know 15×20? Explain.
3. Multiply 10×25. 250
   Use the product 10×25 to find the missing factors.
   a) $\square \times 25 = 275$ b) $25 \times \square = 225$
   c) $200 = \square \times 25$ d) $300 = 25 \times \square$
   3. a) 11 b) 9 c) 8 d) 12
4. Find each missing factor.
   a) $\square \times 9 = 72$ b) $56 = 8 \times \square$
   c) $11 \times \square = 121$ d) $108 = \square \times 12$
   4. a) 8 b) 7 c) 11 d) 9

352

As students try to find the missing factors in the fourth part, they may decide to use guess and check or to divide. Ask them how they decided on the initial value to check and how they knew to refine the value by comparing the resulting product with the required value. Ask the students if they can think of an alternate strategy that would produce the result immediately. If necessary, remind the students of related facts, such as $4 \times 6 = 24$, so $24 \div 4 = 6$, and $24 \div 6 = 4$. Remind them that multiplication and division undo each other.

AFTER Connect

Invite various students to share their answers and strategies. *Connect* demonstrates that finding factors that are easy to multiply and regrouping factors can help with mental math.

Practice

Have calculators available.

Assessment Focus: Question 8

Students should demonstrate they are able to break numbers apart into factors that are easier to multiply. Some students might need to draw an array, and then try different ways of breaking the array into 2, until they are able to find a way to break the numbers apart and regroup the factors.

5. Find each missing factor.
a) □ × 50 = 1250 b) 40 × □ = 600
c) 672 = 28 × □ d) 882 = □ × 21

5. a) 25 **b)** 15 **c)** 24 **d)** 42

Make up your own missing factor problem.
Trade problems with a classmate.
Solve your classmate's problem.

7. Use a calculator to explore the pattern.
Copy and complete the pattern to find the missing factors.
99 × 9 = 891
99 × 99 = 9801
99 × 999 = 98 901
99 × □ = 989 901 9999
99 × □ = 9 899 901 99999

8. Abdi wants to find the area of the gym floor.
The dimensions are 33 m by 30 m.
How can Abdi use patterns and mental math to find the area?
Use words and numbers to explain.

9. Emma raised $4200 for charity.
She cycled in a bike-a-thon.
Emma's sponsors paid her $56 per kilometre.
a) Find how far Emma cycled. 75 km
b) How can you write this problem as a missing factor problem?

10. How could you use mental math to multiply 2 × 7 × 5 × 8?

Reflect

How can using patterns help you to multiply?
Use words and numbers to explain.

Numbers Every Day

Calculator Skills

Copy and complete each number pattern. Write each pattern rule.

3.75, 7.50, 11.25, □, □, □ 15, 18.75, 22.5
2.4, 7.2, 21.6, 64.8, □, □, □ 194.4, 583.2, 1749.6
2.25, □, 9.25, 12.75, □, □ 5.75, 16.25, 19.75

ASSESSMENT FOCUS | Question 8

353

REFLECT: I can use patterns to multiply by looking for numbers that make multiplication easy, such as 2, 5, or 10. For example, in 2 × 17 × 5, I would first multiply 2 × 5 to get 10, and then multiply 10 × 17 to get 170.

Numbers Every Day

Pattern rules: Start at 3.75, add 3.75 each time.
Start at 2.4, multiply by 3 each time.
Start at 2.25, add 3.5 each time.

ASSESSMENT FOR LEARNING

What to Look For	What to Do
Understanding concepts ✔ Students can use more than one strategy to solve multiplication problems. ✔ Students look for multiplication patterns to predict products.	***Extra Support:*** Have students model *Practice* questions with Base Ten Blocks. Students can use Step-by-Step 1 (Master 10.11) to complete question 8. ***Extra Practice:*** Students can complete the Additional Activity, *Cover Up* (Master 10.7). Students can complete Extra Practice 1 (Master 10.18).
Applying procedures ✔ Students use mental math to multiply. ✔ Students use multiplication facts to determine the missing factors.	***Extension:*** Have students use a set of digit cards from 1 to 10, or a deck of cards with the face cards removed. The Ace will be used as 1. Challenge students to create and solve multiplication sentences using 5 cards as the factors.

Recording and Reporting
Master 10.2 Ongoing Observations: Patterns in Number and Geometry

Exploring Patterns in Decimals with a Calculator

LESSON ORGANIZER 40–50 min

Curriculum Focus: Use a calculator to explore patterns in decimals. (5m8, 5m105)

Teacher Materials
- overhead calculator

Student Materials
- calculators

Optional
- Step-by-Step 2 (Master 10.12)
- Extra Practice 1 (Master 10.18)

Vocabulary: decimal, fraction, equivalent, core, numerator, denominator

Assessment: Master 10.2 Ongoing Observations: Patterns in Number and Geometry

Key Math Learnings

1. To change a fraction to a decimal, divide the numerator by the denominator.
2. Patterns exist in fractions and in their decimal equivalents, allowing us to extend the pattern and make predictions.

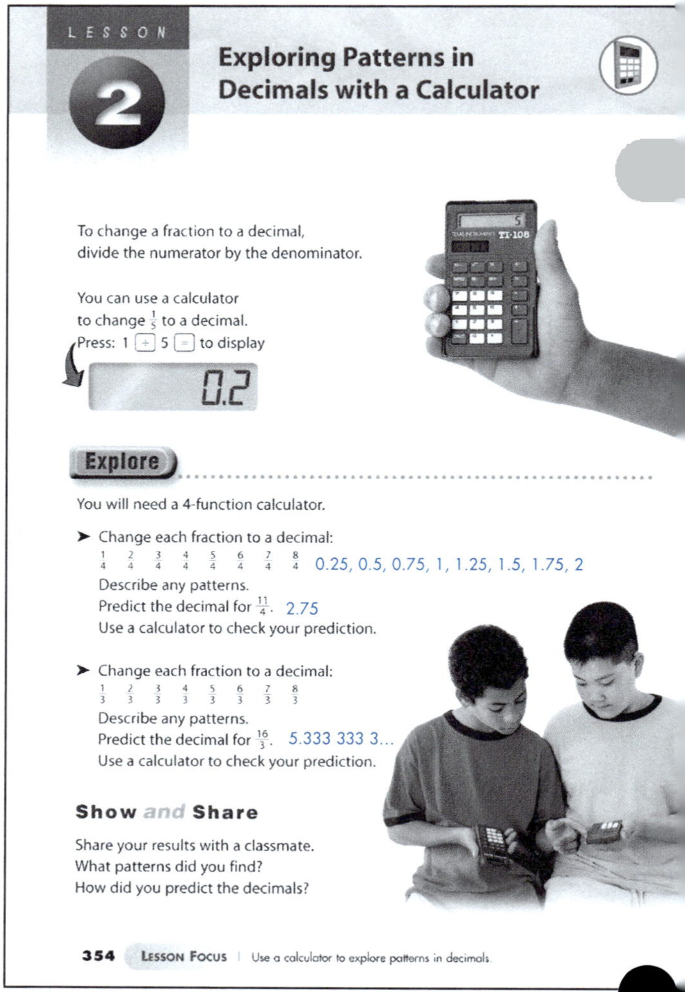
LESSON 2

Exploring Patterns in Decimals with a Calculator

To change a fraction to a decimal, divide the numerator by the denominator.

You can use a calculator to change $\frac{1}{5}$ to a decimal.
Press: 1 ÷ 5 = to display 0.2

Explore

You will need a 4-function calculator.

➤ Change each fraction to a decimal:
$\frac{1}{4}$ $\frac{2}{4}$ $\frac{3}{4}$ $\frac{4}{4}$ $\frac{5}{4}$ $\frac{6}{4}$ $\frac{7}{4}$ $\frac{8}{4}$ 0.25, 0.5, 0.75, 1, 1.25, 1.5, 1.75, 2
Describe any patterns.
Predict the decimal for $\frac{11}{4}$. 2.75
Use a calculator to check your prediction.

➤ Change each fraction to a decimal:
$\frac{1}{3}$ $\frac{2}{3}$ $\frac{3}{3}$ $\frac{4}{3}$ $\frac{5}{3}$ $\frac{6}{3}$ $\frac{7}{3}$ $\frac{8}{3}$
Describe any patterns.
Predict the decimal for $\frac{16}{3}$. 5.333 333 3…
Use a calculator to check your prediction.

Show and Share

Share your results with a classmate.
What patterns did you find?
How did you predict the decimals?

354 LESSON FOCUS | Use a calculator to explore patterns in decimals.

BEFORE Get Started

Review with an overhead calculator how to convert a fraction to a decimal. Have volunteers come up to the front of the class, and, using the overhead calculator, explain how they would find the decimal equivalents of $\frac{1}{2}$, $\frac{1}{3}$, $\frac{1}{4}$, and $\frac{1}{5}$.

($1 \div 2 = 0.5$, $1 \div 3 = 0.333\,333\,3\ldots$, $1 \div 4 = 0.25$, $1 \div 5 = 0.2$)

Present *Explore*. Remind students to record each equivalent decimal. To help predict values for other decimal equivalents, tell students it is helpful to list the fractions in one column and their corresponding decimal equivalents in a second column.

DURING Explore

Ongoing Assessment: Observe and Listen

Ask questions, such as:

- What patterns do you see in the decimals in the first part of *Explore*? (*The decimals start at 0.25, then increase by 0.25 each time.*)
- What do you notice about the decimal equivalents of the fractions with even denominators? (*The fourths show hundredths if the numerator is odd, and tenths if the numerator is even.*)
- How did you predict the decimal for $\frac{11}{4}$? (*I know that the pattern in the decimals increases by 0.25 each time. I counted on from $\frac{8}{4}$, or 2, then kept adding 0.25 until I got to $\frac{11}{4}$, to get 2.75.*)
- How can you check your prediction on your calculator? (*I pressed ON/C to clear the memory. Then I pressed $11 \div 4 =$. This gave me 2.75.*)
- What patterns do you see in the second part of *Explore*? (*The decimals start at 0.333 333 3…, then increase by 0.333 333 3… each time. Every third decimal is a whole number; the whole numbers start at 1, then increase by 1 each time.*)

Connect

➤ Look at these fractions and their equivalent decimals.

$\frac{1}{2} = 0.5$
$\frac{2}{2} = 1$
$\frac{3}{2} = 1.5$
$\frac{4}{2} = 2$
$\frac{5}{2} = 2.5$
$\frac{6}{2} = 3$
$\frac{7}{2} = 3.5$
$\frac{8}{2} = 4$
$\frac{9}{2} = 4.5$

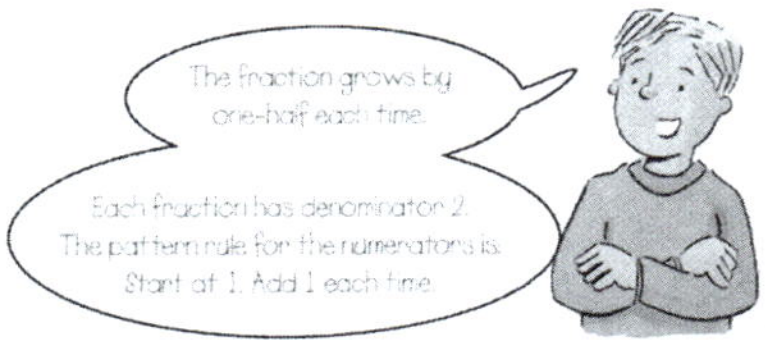

There are patterns in the decimals.
The pattern in the ones digits is:
0, 1, 1, 2, 2, 3, 3, 4, 4, ...

The pattern rule for the decimals is:
Start at 0.5. Add 0.5 each time.

➤ These fractions have been changed to decimals.
The numbers in each decimal repeat forever.
If the calculator screen was longer, we would see more repeating digits in each decimal.

$\frac{1}{11} = 0.090\ 909...$
$\frac{2}{11} = 0.181\ 818\ 1...$
$\frac{3}{11} = 0.272\ 727\ 2...$
$\frac{4}{11} = 0.363\ 636\ 3...$
$\frac{5}{11} = 0.454\ 545\ 4...$
$\frac{6}{11} = 0.545\ 454\ 5...$

355

REACHING ALL LEARNERS

Early Finishers

Students can investigate patterns in fractions with prime number denominators, such as 7, 13, 17, 19, 21, 23. A computer calculator will show them a greater number of decimal places, so it will be easier for students to identify the repeating core of the pattern.

Common Misconceptions

➤ Some students cannot recognize a pattern in the decimals.
How to Help: Help students identify what changes and what remains the same in the pattern.

➤ Some students cannot extend the pattern without a calculator.
How to Help: Have students record the pattern in a table and predict what comes next. Then, have them check their prediction with a calculator.

ESL Strategies

Provide a visual summary sheet with labelled examples to reinforce the key concepts of the lesson: fraction, decimal, equivalent, core, pattern.

- What do you notice about the decimal equivalents of the fractions with odd denominators?
  (The thirds contain repeating decimals.)
- How did you predict the decimal for $\frac{16}{3}$?
  (I know $\frac{15}{3} = 5$, so I used the pattern in the decimals. I added 0.333 333 3… to 5, to get 5.333 333 3….)
- What happens to the decimal equivalent when the numerator of the fraction becomes greater than the denominator?
  (There's no zero in the ones place anymore.)

AFTER Connect

Invite various students to tell how they predicted their results. There are many ways to make predictions, such as using previous results and counting on or finding patterns in the decimals. Encourage students to find as many different patterns as they can.

Discuss *Connect*. Review the decimal equivalents and explain how recognizing patterns in fractions and decimals can help you predict answers. Repeating patterns exist in decimals and allow us to extend the pattern and predict what comes next.

Ask:

- For the decimal equivalents of fractions with denominator 2, what is the pattern in the tenths digit? *(5, 0, 5, 0, 5, 0, ...)*
- For the decimal equivalents of fractions with denominator 11, what is the pattern in the tenths digit? The hundredths digit?
  (The pattern rule for the tenths digit is: Start at 0. Add 1 each time. The pattern rule for the hundredths digit is: Start at 9. Subtract 1 each time.)
- Does this pattern rule continue?
  (Yes; every decimal either starts at 0 and increases by 1 each time, or starts at 9 and decreases by 1 each time.)

Sample Answers

1. a) The pattern starts at 0.2, and goes up by 0.2 each time.
   b) $\frac{8}{5} = 1.6$, $\frac{9}{5} = 1.8$, $\frac{10}{5} = 2$, $\frac{11}{5} = 2.2$, $\frac{12}{5} = 2.4$
2. b) Each fraction has numerator 1. The pattern rule for the denominators is: Start at 2. Add 1 each time. The decimal equivalents of fractions with denominators that are multiples of 3 are repeating decimals. The fraction with denominator 7 is also a repeating decimal.
3. b) First table: Start at 0.25. Add 0.25 each time.
   Second table: Start at 0.125. Add 0.125 each time.
   c) The pattern in the tenths column of the first chart is the same as the pattern in the hundredths column of the second chart. The pattern in the hundredths column of the first chart is the same as the pattern in the last column of the second chart.
4. The pattern does not continue forever. 9.1 + 1.9 = 11; we no longer have a sum that has the same ones digit and tenths digit.
5. 0.111 111 1..., 0.222 222 2..., 0.333 333 3...
   a) The decimals are repeating decimals. The pattern is: Start at 0.111 111 1.... Add 0.111 111 1... each time. The repeating digit in the core is the same as the numerator of the fraction.
   b) 0.444 444 4..., 0.555 555 5..., 0.666 666 6..., 0.777 777 7..., 0.888 888 8...
   I followed the pattern from part a; the repeating digit in the core is the same as the numerator of each fraction.
   c) 1; any number divided by itself is always 1, a whole number.

When a fraction with denominator 11 is changed to a decimal:
- There is a repeating pattern in the decimal.
- There are 2 digits in the core.
- The core is the numerator multiplied by 9.

For example, $\frac{7}{11} = 0.636\ 363\ 6...$
The numerator is 7.
$7 \times 9 = 63$

The core of a repeating pattern is the smallest part that repeats.

Practice

1. Change each fraction to a decimal.
   $\frac{1}{5}$ $\frac{2}{5}$ $\frac{3}{5}$ $\frac{4}{5}$ $\frac{5}{5}$ $\frac{6}{5}$ $\frac{7}{5}$ 0.2, 0.4, 0.6, 0.8, 1, 1.2, 1.4
   a) Describe any patterns.
   b) Write five other fractions with denominator 5.
   Change these fractions to decimals.
2. a) Copy and complete the table for fractions with denominators to 10.

Fraction	Decimal
$\frac{1}{2}$	0.5
$\frac{1}{3}$	0.333 333 3...
$\frac{1}{4}$	0.25

$\frac{1}{5} = 0.2$
$\frac{1}{6} = 0.166\ 666\ 6...$
$\frac{1}{7} = 0.142\ 857\ 1...$
$\frac{1}{8} = 0.125$
$\frac{1}{9} = 0.111\ 111\ 1...$
$\frac{1}{10} = 0.1$

   b) Describe any patterns in the table.
3. a) Copy and complete each table for fractions with numerators to 10.

Fraction	Decimal
$\frac{1}{4}$	0.25
$\frac{2}{4}$	0.5
$\frac{3}{4}$	0.75

Fraction	Decimal
$\frac{1}{8}$	0.125
$\frac{2}{8}$	0.25
$\frac{3}{8}$	0.375

$\frac{4}{4} = 1$
$\frac{5}{4} = 1.25$
$\frac{6}{9} = 1.5$
$\frac{7}{4} = 1.75$
$\frac{8}{4} = 2$
$\frac{9}{4} = 2.25$
$\frac{10}{4} = 2.5$

$\frac{4}{8} = 0.5$
$\frac{5}{8} = 0.625$
$\frac{6}{8} = 0.75$
$\frac{7}{8} = 0.875$
$\frac{8}{8} = 1$
$\frac{9}{8} = 1.125$
$\frac{10}{8} = 1.25$

   b) Describe the patterns in each table.
   c) How are the patterns in the tables the same? How are they different?

356

- What do you think will happen when the numerator is greater than the denominator?
  (I think the ones digit will change from a 0 to a 1. The decimals will stay the same.)
- How do you know?
  (I checked with my calculator, and found that $\frac{12}{11} = 1.090\ 909...$, $\frac{13}{11} = 1.181\ 818\ 1...$, and so on. The ones digit is now a 1, and the decimals are the same as before.)

Assessment Focus: Question 5

Students should correctly convert fractions to decimals. Students use this information to predict the decimal for each fraction, justifying their prediction. Students should understand that a fraction with the same number in the numerator and denominator produces a whole number equivalent.

Practice

Have calculators available.

4. Add.

2.1 + 1.2 3.3 | 5.1 + 1.5 = 6.6 | 8.1 + 1.8 = 9.9

3.1 + 1.3 4.4 | 6.1 + 1.6 = 7.7

4.1 + 1.4 5.5 | 7.1 + 1.7 = 8.8

Continue the pattern. Find each sum.

Does the pattern continue forever? Explain. No

5. Change each fraction to a decimal.

$\frac{1}{9}$ $\frac{2}{9}$ $\frac{3}{9}$

a) Describe any patterns.

b) Predict the decimal for each fraction:

$\frac{4}{9}$ $\frac{5}{9}$ $\frac{6}{9}$ $\frac{7}{9}$ $\frac{8}{9}$

How did you make your predictions?

c) What is the decimal for $\frac{9}{9}$? Explain.

6. a) Copy and complete each table for factors with numerators to 10.

= 1.666 666 6…

= 2

= 2.333 333 3…

= 2.666 666 6…

= 3

= 3.333 333 3…

Fraction	Decimal
$\frac{1}{3}$	0.333 333 3…
$\frac{2}{3}$	0.666 666 6…
$\frac{3}{3}$	1
$\frac{4}{3}$	1.333 333 3…

Fraction	Decimal
$\frac{1}{6}$	0.166 666 6…
$\frac{2}{6}$	0.333 333 3
$\frac{3}{6}$	0.5
$\frac{4}{6}$	0.666 666 6…

$\frac{5}{6}$ = 0.833 333 3…

$\frac{6}{6}$ = 1

$\frac{7}{6}$ = 1.166 666 6…

$\frac{8}{6}$ = 1.333 333 3…

$\frac{9}{6}$ = 1.5

$\frac{10}{6}$ = 1.666 666 6…

b) How are the patterns in the tables the same? How are they different?

c) Use the fractions and decimals from question 5. How do the patterns for ninths compare with the patterns for thirds? For sixths?

7. Describe a rule for changing fractions with tenths to decimals.

Numbers Every Day

Number Strategies

Will each product be greater than or less than 812 × 19? How do you know?

850 × 10 Less than

800 × 20 Greater than

850 × 15 Less than

810 × 20 Greater than

Reflect

Which decimal patterns do you find most interesting? Why?

ASSESSMENT FOCUS | Question 5

357

6. b) The repeating digits of the decimals in the first chart follow a pattern of 3, 6, 0, and the repeating digits of the decimals in the second chart follow a pattern of 6, 3, 0. The same numbers 3, 6, 0 are repeating. The tenths digits of the decimals in the first chart follow the same pattern, but the tenths digits of the decimals in the second chart have this pattern: 1, 3, 5, 6, 8. 0, which is different from the pattern in any other digits in the decimals.

c) The decimal equivalent of $\frac{1}{3}$ is the same as that of $\frac{2}{6}$, which is the same as that of $\frac{3}{9}$ (0.333 333 3…). The decimal equivalent of $\frac{2}{3}$ is the same as that of $\frac{4}{6}$, which is the same as that of $\frac{6}{9}$ (0.666 666 6…). The decimal equivalent of $\frac{3}{3}$ is the same as that of $\frac{6}{6}$, which is the same as that of $\frac{9}{9}$ (1).

7. To change fractions with tenths to decimals, divide the numerator by 10 and shift the digits one place to the right.

REFLECT: I find the decimal patterns in fractions with 11 as the denominator most interesting. The core is the numerator multiplied by 9. This makes it easy for me to predict the pattern.

Numbers Every Day

Students may estimate by rounding where appropriate. 812 × 19 is about 810 × 20, or 16 200. For the second product, students may compare factors: 800 is 10 less than 810. For the third product, students may break 15 apart and use the result of the first product. Encourage students to check their answers using a calculator and to discuss their answers.

ASSESSMENT FOR LEARNING

What to Look For

Understanding concepts

✔ Students can identify and extend decimal patterns.

Applying procedures

✔ Students convert fractions to decimals.

Communicating

✔ Students use appropriate terminology when comparing decimal patterns.

What to Do

Extra Support: Have students check their conversions using a computer. Sometimes the calculator rounds the decimal, making it difficult to see the pattern.
Students can use Step-by-Step 2 (Master 10.12) to complete question 5.

Extra Practice: Students can extend question 3 to include sixteenths.
Students can complete Extra Practice 1 (Master 10.18).

Extension: Have students use a set of digit cards from 1 to 10 to play a game where the students turn over two cards to make a fraction. The students keep the cards if they correctly give the decimal equivalent.

Recording and Reporting

Master 10.2 Ongoing Observations: Patterns in Number and Geometry

Graphing Patterns

LESSON ORGANIZER 80–100 min

Curriculum Focus: Use models, tables, and graphs to represent patterns. (5m91, 5m94, 5m98, 5m105)

Teacher Materials
- overhead Colour Tiles (optional)
- overhead grid transparency (PM 23)

Student Materials
- Colour Tiles
- 1-cm grid paper (PM 23)
- Perimeter of a Square (Master 10.6)
- pencil crayons
- ruler

Optional
- 2-column charts (PM 17)
- Step-by-Step 3 (Master 10.12)
- Extra Practice 2 (Master 10.19)

Vocabulary: unit length, perimeter, horizontal axis, vertical axis, line graph

Assessment: Master 10.2 Ongoing Observations: Patterns in Number and Geometry

Key Math Learnings
1. Models, tables, and graphs can be used to represent patterns.
2. Models, tables, and graphs can be used to extend and predict patterns.
3. A graph provides a picture of a table of values.

LESSON 3

Graphing Patterns

Explore

You will need congruent squares and grid paper.
Each congruent square has sides 1 unit long.

➤ Use congruent squares to build a larger square.
Find the perimeter of the large square.
Record the side length and the perimeter in a table.

➤ Build 5 different squares.
Record the side length and the perimeter of each square.

➤ Look at the table.
What happens to the perimeter of a square as the side length increases? How do you know?

➤ Your teacher will give you a copy of this grid.
Draw a line graph to display the data in your table.

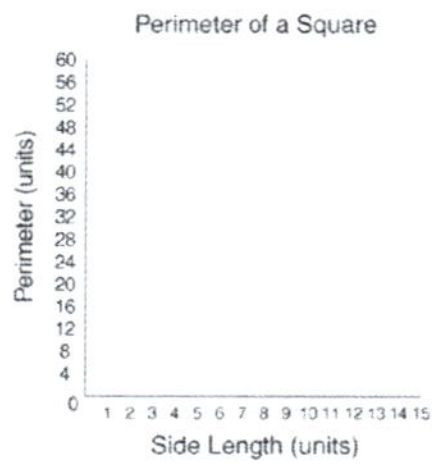

358 LESSON FOCUS | Use models, tables, and graphs to represent patterns.

BEFORE Get Started

Draw a 2-cm by 2-cm square on an overhead grid transparency. Ask:
- How can you find the perimeter of this square? (*Count the units along the outside of the figure.*)
- What is another way of finding the perimeter of the square? (*Multiply the side length by 4.*)

On the overhead grid, draw the vertical and horizontal axes for a line graph. Ask:
- What is the line that goes straight up and down called? (*The vertical axis*)
- What is the line that goes straight across called? (*The horizontal axis*)

Write a scale on the horizontal and vertical axes. Ask:
- What is the scale on my horizontal axis? (*1 square represents 2 units.*)
- What is the scale on my vertical axis? (*1 square represents 4 units.*)
- What else do I need on my graph? (*A title and labels for the vertical and horizontal axes*)

Mark a point on the graph. Ask:
- How can you identify where the point is on the graph? (*It is 4 units along the horizontal axis and 8 units upward in the direction of the vertical axis.*)

Mark another point, higher up and to the right on the graph, and join the two points. Ask:
- What happens when line segments go up to the right? (*The graph is increasing.*)

Students may use grid paper or Colour Tiles for *Explore*. Explain the concept of "1 unit long," referring to the side length of a congruent square. You may want to model the first two frames of the pattern on an overhead grid transparency.

Show *and* **Share**

Share your work with another pair of students.
Describe any patterns in your table.

Connect

The table shows the dimensions of some rectangles with perimeter 52 cm.

Length (cm)	24	20	16	12
Width (cm)	2	6	10	14

Draw a line graph to display these data.

➤ Draw 2 axes.
Label the horizontal axis "Length" and the vertical axis "Width."
Give the graph a title.
➤ Use the same scale on both axes.
The scale is 1 square represents 2 cm.
➤ Mark a point at *Length* 24 cm and *Width* 2 cm.
➤ Mark points for the rest of the data in the same way.
Use a ruler to connect the points.

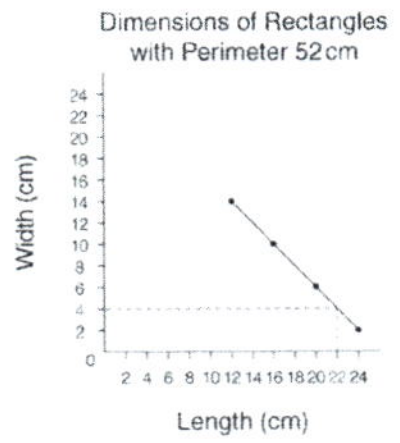

From the graph, the length of a rectangle with perimeter 52 cm and width 4 cm is 22 cm.

Numbers Every Day

Mental Math

Estimate each product. What strategies did you use?

41 × 19 About 800
52 × 30 About 1500
28 × 87 About 2700
14 × 22 About 200

359

REACHING ALL LEARNERS

Alternative Explore

Materials: square dot paper (PM 25)
Have students draw squares on dot paper, as in *Explore*. Ask them to find the area and the side length of each square, record the data in a table, and create a line graph.

Early Finishers

Students can investigate patterns in side lengths and perimeters of equilateral triangles by making a table and a graph.

Common Misconceptions

➤ Some students build rectangles that are not larger squares.
How to Help: Help students define the pattern correctly by modelling the first three frames.
➤ Some students cannot make the connection between the table representation and the graphic representation.
How to Help: Have students find each point on the graph, and read aloud the corresponding numbers from the horizontal axis and the vertical axis. Have the students find the row in the table that contains these numbers.

Numbers Every Day

Students may round one or both factors to the nearest 10.

Sample Answers

1. a) Pattern rule: multiply hours worked by 6 to get the amount earned.

Present *Explore*. Remind students to record the side length and the perimeter of each square in a table.

DURING Explore

Ongoing Assessment: Observe and Listen

Ask questions, such as:

- As you increase the side length of the square, what happens to the perimeter? (*The perimeter increases.*)
  How do you know? (*I counted the units along the outside of the square. In my table, I also see that the perimeter increases as the side length increases.*)
- What does the line graph tell you about the pattern? (*As the side length increases, the perimeter also increases.*)
  How do you know? (*The line segments on the line graph go up to the right.*)
- How are the line graph and table of values related? (*Each row in the table represents one point on the line graph. The number in the first column refers to the distance along the horizontal axis. The number in the second column refers to the distance along the vertical axis.*)

AFTER Connect

Have students share their work and their findings. Ask:

- What patterns do you see in the perimeter of the square compared to the side length of the square? (*The perimeter is 4 times the side length.*)
  How do you know? (*I multiply the number in the column labelled Side Length by 4, and get the number in the column labelled Perimeter.*)
- How does this pattern relate to the formula for the perimeter of a square? (*The formula for the perimeter of a square is 4 times side length. This is the same pattern.*)

b)

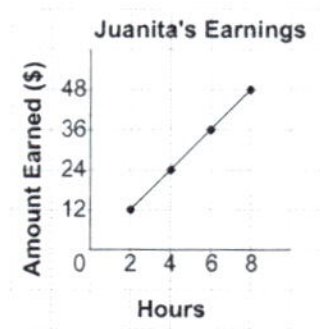

c) On the graph, 3 h is midway between 2 h and 4 h, so the corresponding earning is midway between $12 and $24. Juanita earned $18. In the table, I would follow the pattern rule and multiply 3 by 6 to get 18.

2. b) The numbers in the Perimeter column follow the pattern: Start at 6; add 4 each time.

c)

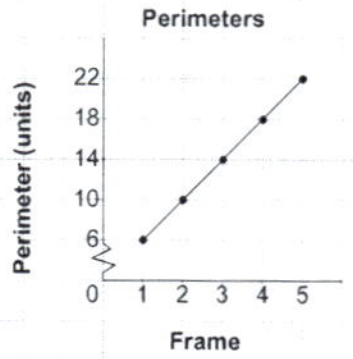

3. b)

Frame	Area (square units)
1	3
2	6
3	9
4	12
5	15

d)

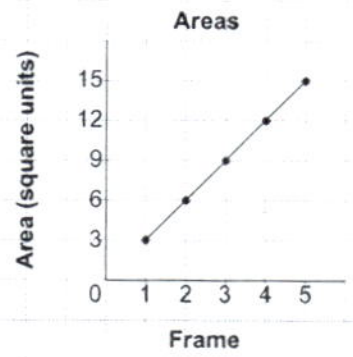

4. a) Input: Start at 2. Add 2 each time.
Output: Start at 7. Add 2 each time.

b)

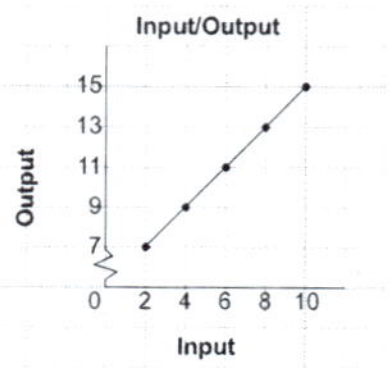

c) 7 is halfway between 6 and 8. The corresponding output is halfway between 11 and 13. The output number is 12.

d) 14 is halfway between 13 and 15. The corresponding input is halfway between 8 and 10. The input number is 9.

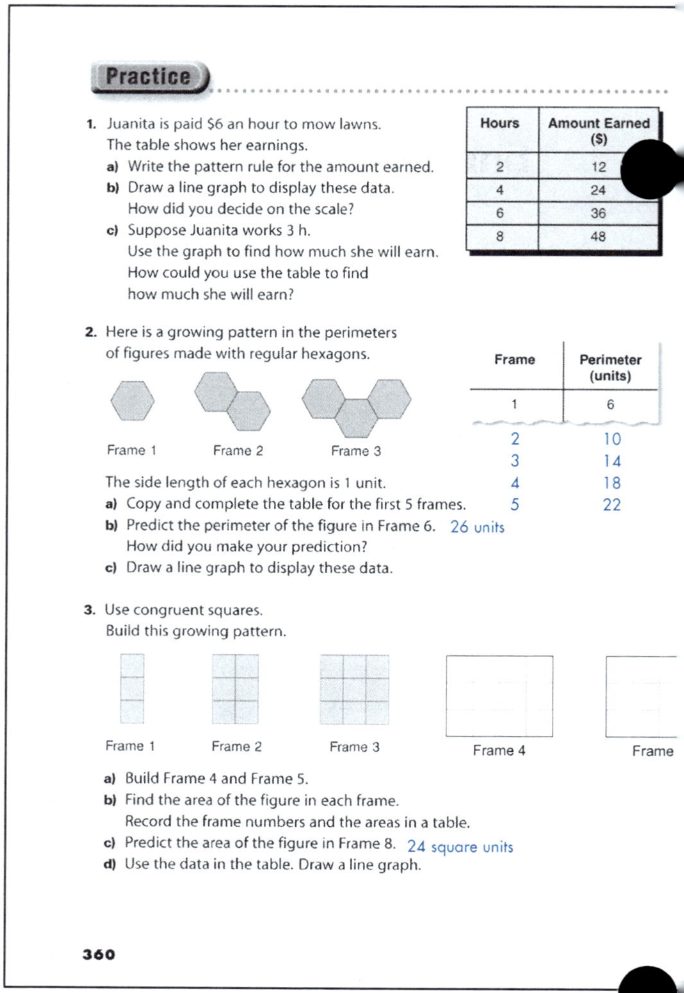

Practice

1. Juanita is paid $6 an hour to mow lawns. The table shows her earnings.
   a) Write the pattern rule for the amount earned.
   b) Draw a line graph to display these data. How did you decide on the scale?
   c) Suppose Juanita works 3 h. Use the graph to find how much she will earn. How could you use the table to find how much she will earn?

Hours	Amount Earned ($)
2	12
4	24
6	36
8	48

2. Here is a growing pattern in the perimeters of figures made with regular hexagons.

Frame 1 Frame 2 Frame 3

Frame	Perimeter (units)
1	6
2	10
3	14
4	18
5	22

The side length of each hexagon is 1 unit.
   a) Copy and complete the table for the first 5 frames.
   b) Predict the perimeter of the figure in Frame 6. 26 units
   How did you make your prediction?
   c) Draw a line graph to display these data.

3. Use congruent squares. Build this growing pattern.

Frame 1 Frame 2 Frame 3 Frame 4 Frame

   a) Build Frame 4 and Frame 5.
   b) Find the area of the figure in each frame. Record the frame numbers and the areas in a table.
   c) Predict the area of the figure in Frame 8. 24 square units
   d) Use the data in the table. Draw a line graph.

360

Discuss the table in *Connect*. Ask:

- What is the pattern in the row labelled Length? (*Start at 24. Subtract 4 each time.*)
- What is the pattern in the row labelled Width? (*Start at 2. Add 4 each time.*)

Direct students to follow the steps in the Student Book. Ensure they label and title their line graphs. Model the graph on an overhead grid transparency. Make the connection between the table data and the graphic representation of the line graph. Ask:

- What is the width of a rectangle with perimeter 52 cm and length 14 cm? (*12 cm*)
- What is the length of a rectangle with perimeter 52 cm and width 8 cm? (*18 cm*)
- What is happening on the line graph? (*The length is decreasing.*)
  How do you know? (*The line segments are going down to the right.*)

Practice

Students will need grid paper for all questions.

Assessment Focus: Question 6

Students should correctly choose 5 input numbers that are multiples of one number. Students use this information and choose an operation to create an Input/Output machine with the correct output numbers. They should explain that a line graph is a representation of the Input/Output machine. Students correctly draw a line graph based on their Input/Output table.

4. Copy and complete the table for this Input/Output machine.

Input →  → Output

Input	Output
2	7
4	9
6	11
8	13
10	15

a) Write the pattern rules for the input numbers and the output numbers.
b) Use the data in the table. Draw a line graph.
c) How could you use the graph to find the output, when the input is 7?
d) How could you use the graph to find the input, when the output is 14?

5. Use the Input/Output machine and your table from question 4.
a) Suppose the input numbers doubled. Predict the new output numbers. How do you think the graph will change?
b) Double the input numbers. Find the new output numbers.
c) Graph the new input/output numbers. How does this graph compare to your graph from question 4?

6. Draw an Input/Output machine. Choose a number and an operation.
a) Choose 5 input numbers that are multiples of any number. Find the output numbers. Make an Input/Output table for the results.
b) Draw a line graph of the data in the table. What can you find out from your graph?

Reflect

Do you prefer to display a pattern in a table or a graph? Explain your choice.

Assessment Focus | Question 6

361

5. a) The output numbers will be greater, but they will not double. The graph will still look the same, but the output numbers on the vertical axis will be different.

b)

Input	Output
4	9
8	13
12	17
16	21
20	25

c) 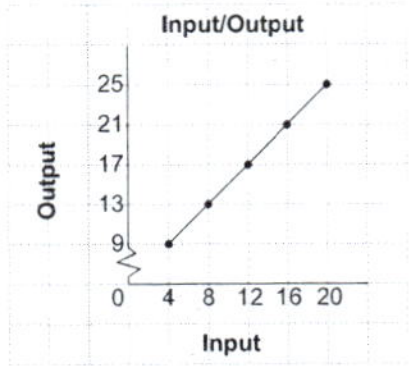

The graph does not change. Only the input and output numbers have changed.

6. Input ⟶ x 2 ⟶ Output

a)

Input	Output
2	4
4	8
6	12
8	16
10	20

b) 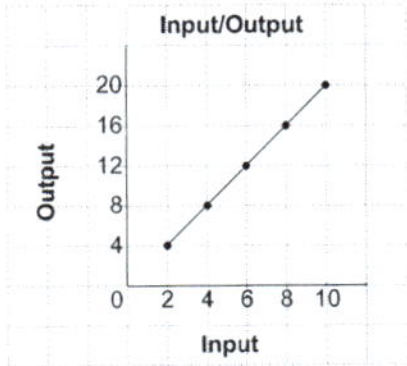

As the input numbers increase, so do the output numbers. The line graph is a representation of the Input/Output machine.

REFLECT: I prefer to display a pattern in a table if the numbers increase rapidly, because it is difficult to graph large numbers.

ASSESSMENT FOR LEARNING

What to Look For	What to Do
Understanding concepts ✔ Students understand that a table of values can be represented by a graph. ✔ Students understand that a graph can be used to predict patterns. ***Applying procedures*** ✔ Students create a table of values. ✔ Students graph a table of values.	***Extra Support:*** Have pairs of students work through the questions. Students can use Step-by-Step 3 (Master 10.13) to complete question 6. ***Extra Practice:*** Students can complete Extra Practice 2 (Master 10.19). ***Extension:*** Students can do the Additional Activity, *Graph It* (Master 10.8).

Recording and Reporting

Master 10.2 Ongoing Observations: Patterns in Number and Geometry

Another Number Pattern

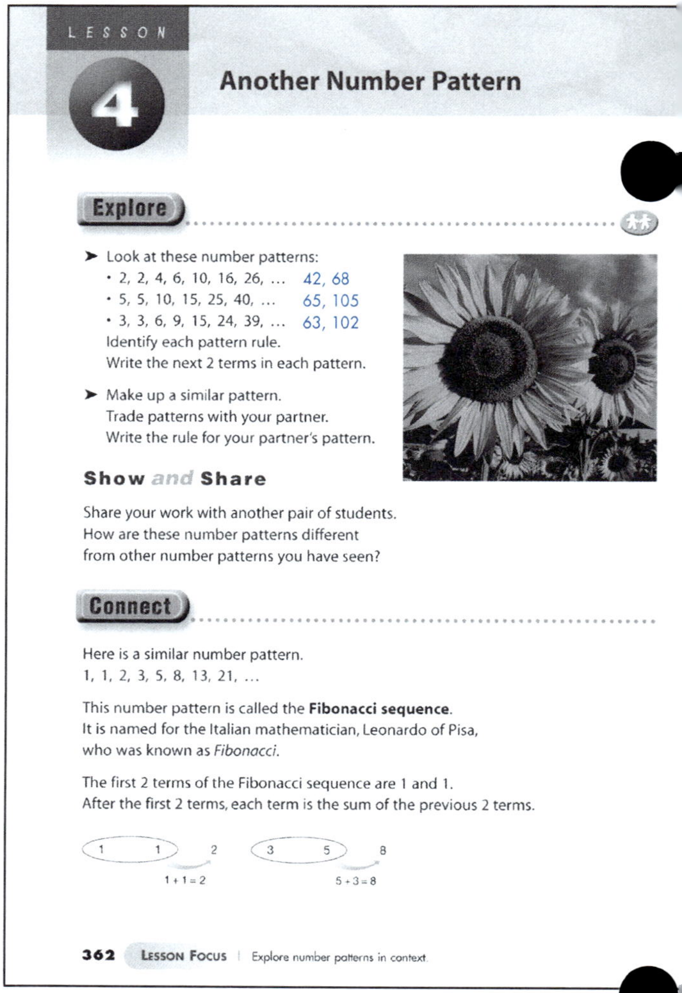
LESSON 4

Another Number Pattern

Explore

➤ Look at these number patterns:
- 2, 2, 4, 6, 10, 16, 26, ... 42, 68
- 5, 5, 10, 15, 25, 40, ... 65, 105
- 3, 3, 6, 9, 15, 24, 39, ... 63, 102

Identify each pattern rule.
Write the next 2 terms in each pattern.

➤ Make up a similar pattern.
Trade patterns with your partner.
Write the rule for your partner's pattern.

Show and Share

Share your work with another pair of students.
How are these number patterns different from other number patterns you have seen?

Connect

Here is a similar number pattern.
1, 1, 2, 3, 5, 8, 13, 21, ...

This number pattern is called the **Fibonacci sequence**.
It is named for the Italian mathematician, Leonardo of Pisa, who was known as *Fibonacci*.

The first 2 terms of the Fibonacci sequence are 1 and 1.
After the first 2 terms, each term is the sum of the previous 2 terms.

362 LESSON FOCUS | Explore number patterns in context.

LESSON ORGANIZER 40–50 min

Curriculum Focus: Explore number patterns in context. (5m92, 5m99, 5m104)

Student Materials
- dominoes
- calculators

Optional
- Step-by-Step 4 (Master 10.14)
- Extra Practice 2 (Master 10.19)

Vocabulary: Fibonacci sequence, Fibonacci number, consecutive

Assessment: Master 10.2 Ongoing Observations: Patterns in Number and Geometry

Key Math Learnings

1. Number patterns and geometric patterns exist throughout nature.
2. The Fibonacci sequence is a special number pattern, and can be found in nature.
3. Many patterns can be found in the Fibonacci sequence.

Making Connections

Nature: Write the first 6 terms of the Fibonacci sequence on the board. Have students count out the number of petals on each flower.

BEFORE Get Started

Review some of the patterns students have already seen in previous grades. Write these number patterns on the board:

2, 4, 6, 8, 10, ...   1, 3, 5, 7, 9, ...

Ask:
- What patterns do you see?
  (*First pattern: Start at 2. Add 2 each time. Second pattern: Start at 1. Add 2 each time.*)
- How are the two sets of numbers the same? How are they different?
  (*They both increase the same way, by adding 2 each time. They are different because they start at a different number, and the patterns contain different numbers.*)

Write this number pattern on the board:

2, 5, 3, 6, 4, 7, 5, ...

Ask:
- What pattern do you see in these numbers?
  (*Start at 2. Add 3 to get the next number, then subtract 2 to get the number after that. Keep adding 3, then subtracting 2.*)
- How else could you describe the pattern?
  (*For the 1st, 3rd, 5th, 7th term, and so on: Start at 2. Add 1 each time. For the 2nd, 4th, 6th term, and so on: Start at 5. Add 1 each time.*)
- How would you describe the difference between the first two number patterns, and the third one?
  (*In the first two number patterns, we add the same number each time. In the third number pattern, we add, then subtract.*)

Point out that a series of numbers can follow many different kinds of patterns, and the pattern can be described in different ways. Present *Explore*. Write the three number patterns on the board.

Any term in the Fibonacci sequence is called a **Fibonacci number**.
Fibonacci numbers are frequently found in nature.

Practice

1. a) Find the 13th Fibonacci number. 233
   b) What is the sum of the first 13 Fibonacci numbers? 609

2. a) Write the first 16 Fibonacci numbers.
   b) Choose 3 consecutive Fibonacci numbers.
   Find the product of the least and greatest numbers.
   Multiply the middle number by itself.
   What do you notice about the products?
   c) Repeat part b for 3 different consecutive Fibonacci numbers. What do you notice?

3. a) Find each product:
   2×2 4 5×5 25
   b) Find the difference of the products in part a. 21
   What is special about 2, 5, and your answer to part a?

4. Repeat question 3 using the numbers 3 and 8. 9, 64; 55
   What do you notice?
   Do you think this is always true? Explain.

5. There are 2 spiral patterns on pine cones.
   The number of spirals to the left and the number of spirals to the right are consecutive Fibonacci numbers.
   Suppose 1 spiral pattern has 21 spirals.
   How many spirals could be in the other spiral pattern? 13 or 34
   How do you know?

363

REACHING ALL LEARNERS

Alternative Explore

Materials: counters or Cuisenaire Rods

Students can model and develop the Fibonacci sequence using counters or Cuisenaire Rods, and display the results in a table. Students could also model the first pattern in *Explore* with counters.

Early Finishers

Students can start with 1, 1, 1, ... to create a pattern where, after the first three terms, each term is the sum of the *three* previous numbers. (*1, 1, 1, 3, 5, 9, 17, ...*)

ESL Strategies

Have students conduct a three-step interview based on this statement: Describe the Fibonacci sequence. The first two students conduct the interview while the third student takes notes. The students switch roles until each student has had a turn taking notes.

Sample Answers

2. a) 1, 1, 2, 3, 5, 8, 13, 21, 34, 55, 89, 144, 233, 377, 610, 987

b) I chose 3, 5, and 8; $3 \times 8 = 24$; $5 \times 5 = 25$. The product of the middle number times itself is one greater than the product of the outside numbers.

c) I chose 1, 2, and 3; $1 \times 3 = 3$; $2 \times 2 = 4$. The middle product is one greater than the outside product.

3. b) 2, 5, and 21 are all Fibonacci numbers.

DURING Explore

Ongoing Assessment: Observe and Listen

Ask questions, such as:

- How does the first pattern grow?
  (*The next number is found by adding the two numbers before it.*)
- How are the 3 patterns the same?
  (*They follow the same pattern rule: the first 2 terms are the same, and each term after is the sum of the previous 2 terms.*)
- How are the patterns different?
  (*They all start with a different number.*)

AFTER Connect

Invite students to share their work with the rest of the class. Ask:

- How are the number patterns in this lesson different from the ones we saw at the beginning of the unit?
  (*In the previous patterns, we weren't adding any of the terms to get the next term.*)

Review *Connect*. Introduce the term **Fibonacci sequence.** Explain that Leonardo Fibonacci discovered this number sequence around 1200. Many mathematicians are still discovering new patterns in this sequence. Highlight Math Link, and count the number of petals on each flower to demonstrate that the number is a Fibonacci number.

Practice

Students will need dominoes for question 6.

Assessment Focus: Question 6

Students see that the emerging pattern in the results is the Fibonacci sequence. Students who realize this in part a can use the Fibonacci sequence to make their prediction for part b. Other students will use the dominoes to build the rectangles and check.

4. 3, 8, and 55 are all Fibonacci numbers. This is always true. Check it for one more pair of Fibonacci numbers.
5. These numbers are to the left and to the right of 21. The number of spirals are consecutive Fibonacci numbers.
6. a) 1 domino: 1 rectangle; 2 dominoes: 1 rectangle; 3 dominoes: 2 rectangles; 4 dominoes: 3 rectangles
   b) 8 rectangles. I could check my prediction by building the rectangles. Since the number of rectangles are the Fibonacci numbers, I could also look up the 6th number in the sequence to see that it is 8.
   c) My results are the Fibonacci sequence.

REFLECT: Start at 1. Repeat the number 1. Add the first two numbers together to make the third number: 1 + 1 = 2. Add the second and third number to make the fourth number: 1 + 2 = 3. Add the third and fourth number to make the fifth number, and so on: 2 + 3 = 5.

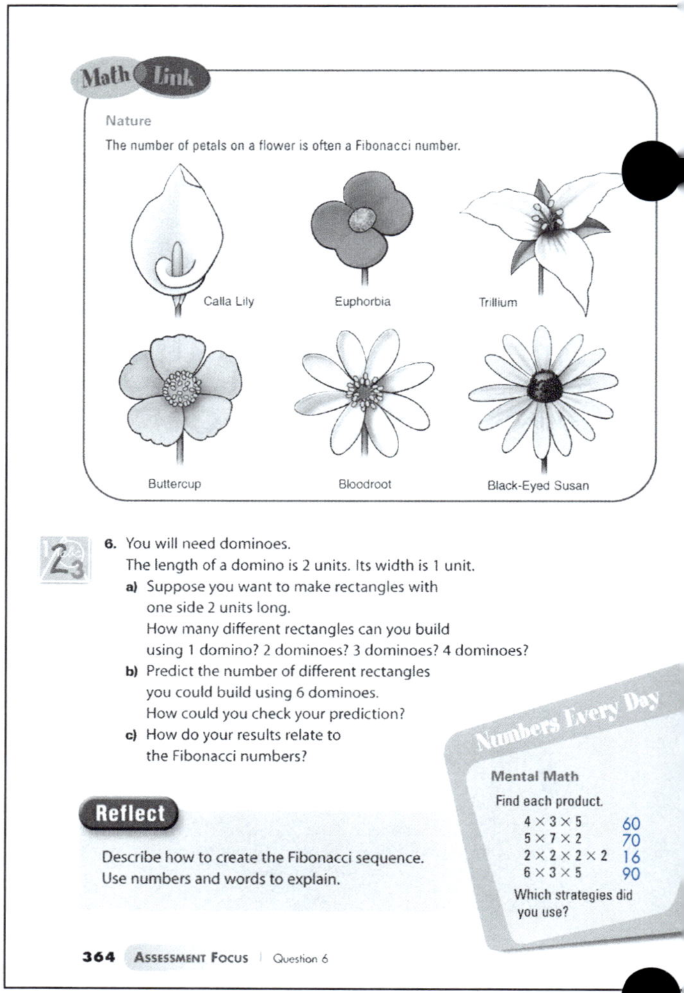

Math Link

Nature

The number of petals on a flower is often a Fibonacci number.

6. You will need dominoes.
   The length of a domino is 2 units. Its width is 1 unit.
   a) Suppose you want to make rectangles with one side 2 units long.
      How many different rectangles can you build using 1 domino? 2 dominoes? 3 dominoes? 4 dominoes?
   b) Predict the number of different rectangles you could build using 6 dominoes.
      How could you check your prediction?
   c) How do your results relate to the Fibonacci numbers?

Reflect

Describe how to create the Fibonacci sequence. Use numbers and words to explain.

Numbers Every Day

Mental Math

Find each product.

4 × 3 × 5 60
5 × 7 × 2 70
2 × 2 × 2 × 2 16
6 × 3 × 5 90

Which strategies did you use?

364 ASSESSMENT FOCUS | Question 6

Numbers Every Day

For 1, 3, and 4, reorder to find compatible numbers that are easy to multiply with.

4 × 3 × 5 = (4 × 5) × 3
5 × 7 × 2 = (5 × 2) × 7
6 × 3 × 5 = (6 × 5) × 3

ASSESSMENT FOR LEARNING

What to Look For

Understanding concepts

✔ Students understand that all Fibonacci-like patterns follow the same rule, but can have different start numbers.

✔ Students recognize Fibonacci patterns in nature.

Applying procedures

✔ Students can identify the Fibonacci pattern.

✔ Students can extend the Fibonacci pattern.

What to Do

Extra Support: Help students recognize the pattern by having them choose pairs of consecutive terms in the Fibonacci sequence and find their sum. Students should compare the sum to the sum of other pairs. In this way, they will see that the pairs of numbers and their sum are all part of the Fibonacci sequence.
Students can use Step-by-Step 4 (Master 10.14) to complete question 6.

Extra Practice: Students can complete Extra Practice 2 (Master 10.19).

Extension: Students can research Fibonacci and the Fibonacci sequence on the Internet.
Students can do the Additional Activity, *Win with Less* (Master 10.9).

Recording and Reporting

Master 10.2 Ongoing Observations: Patterns in Number and Geometry

Choreographer

Choreographer

…en you watch a music video or theatre production that has …cing, you are watching the art of a choreographer. …choreographer arranges patterns of dance steps in a performance. The dance makes the music come alive.

The choreographer must consider many things:

- the music
- the abilities of the performers
- the space available for the performance
- both group patterns and solo patterns
- the lighting
- the camera angle

Choreography is not limited to dancing, music videos, or movies. *Step and Stomp*, *Feet on Fire*, and *Funky Knees* are not new dances. They are patterns of movement designed by aerobic instructors to exercise the body. Fitness can be more functional and more fun when the pattern is right!

Over the years, choreographers have developed different systems for recording dance steps and other movement patterns. How do you think these dance steps could be recorded?

365

Choreographers are designers of dance and movement. They create and arrange the dance steps in musical productions. Their work is visible in many different forms, from the dance routines performed by boy bands and their backing groups to the graceful movements of the principal dancer in a classical ballet.

Choreographers usually specialize in a form of dance or movement, such as:

- classical ballet
- contemporary dance
- musical theatre productions
- ice dance shows
- coordinating the movements of models in fashion shows.

Choreographers can also specialize in feature films, commercials, music videos, and TV shows. The opening and closing events for the Olympics are designed by a choreographer.

The role of a choreographer is to plan and rehearse the way dancers will perform. They may invent new routines. They could choose new music or interpret existing works. They have to plan each movement of the dancers. They may have to use a form of dance notation to record the movements they design.

Choreographers work with producers, artistic directors, musicians, and costume designers, and discuss the requirements of the performance. They often assist in choosing specific dancers for certain roles.

Choreographers start by developing ideas for creating dances, keeping notes and sketches to record influences and trying out ideas informally with colleagues. Choreographers frequently absorb artistic influences from other art forms, such as theatre, the visual arts, and architecture.

Strategies Toolkit

LESSON ORGANIZER 40–50 min

Curriculum Focus: Interpret a problem and select an appropriate strategy. (5m95, 5m99)

Student Materials *Optional*
- counters

Assessment: PM 1 Inquiry Process Check List, PM 3 Self-Assessment: Problem Solving

Key Math Learnings

1. Interpret a problem involving patterns.
2. Solve a problem by drawing a diagram.

Sample Answers

1. a) The pattern is the Fibonacci sequence, starting with the number 2.

2.

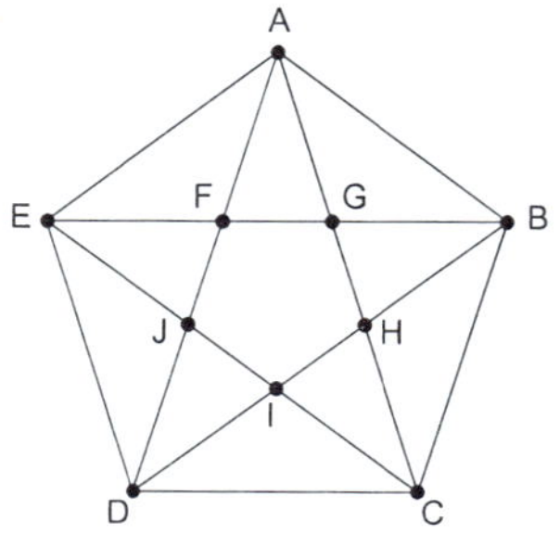

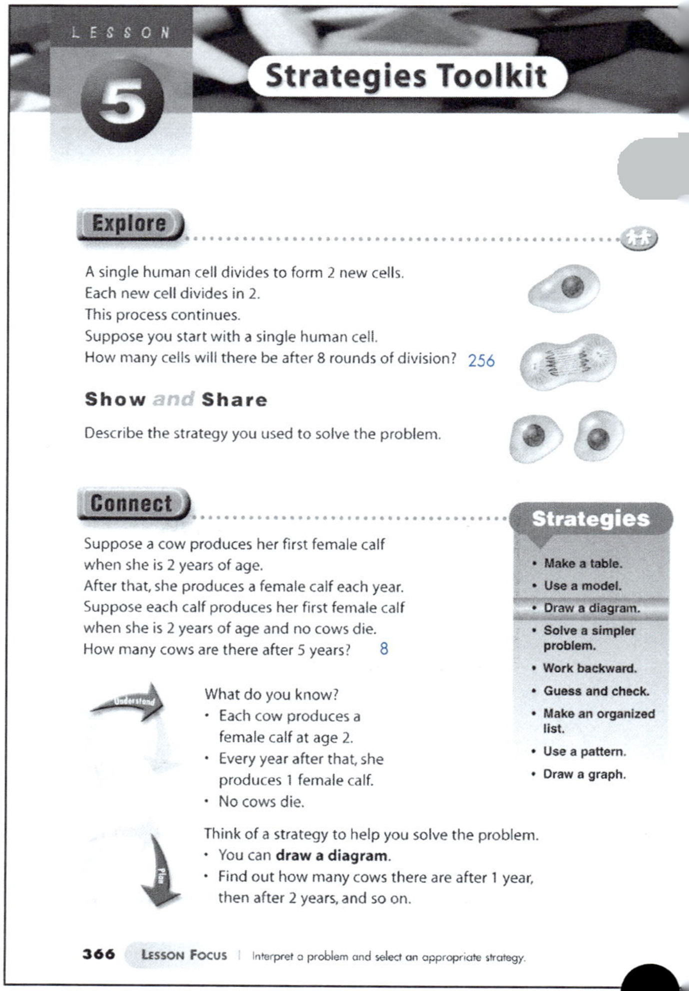

LESSON 5

Strategies Toolkit

Explore

A single human cell divides to form 2 new cells.
Each new cell divides in 2.
This process continues.
Suppose you start with a single human cell.
How many cells will there be after 8 rounds of division? 256

Show and Share

Describe the strategy you used to solve the problem.

Connect

Suppose a cow produces her first female calf when she is 2 years of age.
After that, she produces a female calf each year.
Suppose each calf produces her first female calf when she is 2 years of age and no cows die.
How many cows are there after 5 years? 8

Understand

What do you know?
- Each cow produces a female calf at age 2.
- Every year after that, she produces 1 female calf.
- No cows die.

Plan

Think of a strategy to help you solve the problem.
- You can **draw a diagram**.
- Find out how many cows there are after 1 year, then after 2 years, and so on.

Strategies
- Make a table.
- Use a model.
- Draw a diagram.
- Solve a simpler problem.
- Work backward.
- Guess and check.
- Make an organized list.
- Use a pattern.
- Draw a graph.

366 LESSON FOCUS | Interpret a problem and select an appropriate strategy.

BEFORE Get Started

Present *Explore.* Review the key steps in problem solving: understand the problem, plan how to solve the problem, solve it, then look back to check the solution.

DURING Explore

Ongoing Assessment: Observe and Listen

Ask questions, such as:
- Which strategy will you use to solve the problem? (*I will draw a diagram.*)
- Explain what is meant by the phrase, "… after 8 rounds of division." (*A round is like a frame in a growing pattern, so after 8 rounds would be the same as after 8 frames of the pattern.*)

Have students share their solutions with the class. They should explain any strategies used.

AFTER Connect

Present *Connect.* Students should recognize that the pattern follows a Fibonacci sequence. They copy and continue the diagram to check their prediction.

Ask:
- How many cows are there after 5 years? (*8*)
- What pattern do you see in the number of cows? (*The Fibonacci sequence: 1, 1, 2, 3, 5, 8, …*)

Practice

Encourage students to refer to the Strategies list to assist in selecting an appropriate strategy.

Copy and continue the diagram.

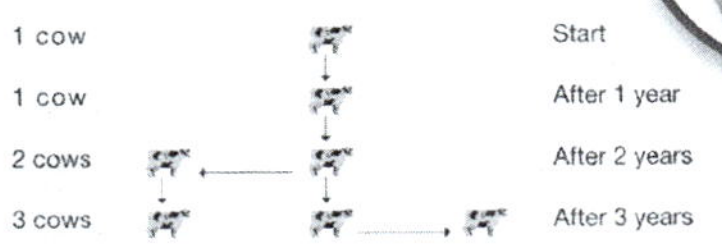

After 1 year, there is 1 cow.
After 2 years, there are 2 cows.
After 3 years, there are 3 cows.
How many cows are there after 5 years?

Check your work.
What pattern do you see in the numbers of cows?

Practice

Choose one of the **Strategies**

1. A mouse crawls through this maze. The mouse always moves forward.
   a) How many different paths could the mouse take from A to B? 2
   From A to C? From A to D? 2, 4
   What pattern do you see?
   b) Predict the number of different paths the mouse could take from A to H. 42

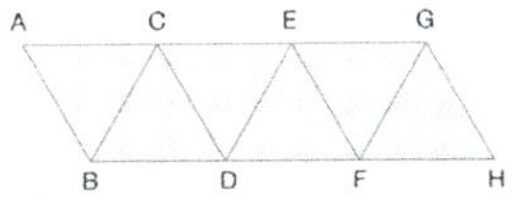

2. Here is a regular pentagon. Copy the pentagon. Draw all its diagonals.
   How many different triangles are there?
   How many of each type are there?

Reflect

How does drawing a diagram help to solve a problem?
Use words, pictures, and numbers to explain.

367

REACHING ALL LEARNERS

Common Misconceptions

➤Students have difficulty using the strategy draw a diagram.
How to Help: Students can use counters to model the pattern first, then draw a diagram of the model.

2. continued
   A total of 35 isosceles triangles can be found.
   Draw additional lines so that each vertex is connected with every other vertex. Label each vertex and each point of intersection with a letter. Then make an organized list of the triangles.
   Singles (10): ABG, GBH, BHC, HCI, CID, IDJ, DJE, JEF, EFA, FAG
   Doubles (10): AHB, GBC, BIC, DHC, CJD, DIE, EDF, AEJ, EGA, AFB
   Triples on the outside (5): DCE, EAD, AEB, ACB, BDC
   Tall in the middle (5): DAC, EBD, AEC, ADB, BEC
   Internal corners (5): DBF, EBI, AHD, CGE, ACJ

REFLECT: When I solve a problem with predictable changes I can use a diagram to solve the problem. A diagram lets me see the pattern clearly. For example, in question 2, when I drew the pentagon and all its diagonals, and then labelled all possible vertices, I could count the number of triangles inside easily.

ASSESSMENT FOR LEARNING

What to Look For	What to Do
Problem solving ✔ Students can select an appropriate strategy for solving a problem. ✔ Students can justify their solutions. ***Communicating*** ✔ Students can describe their strategy clearly, using appropriate language.	***Extra Support:*** For question 1, have students use triangular grid paper to model the diagram. For question 2, have them draw the diagonals of a square first and to label all possible vertices of triangles to find a strategy. Then ask them to draw the diagonals and label all possible vertices of triangles of a regular pentagon to solve the problem. ***Extra Practice:*** Have students repeat question 2 using a regular hexagon. ***Extension:*** Challenge students to create their own maze problem that is similar to question 1.

Recording and Reporting
PM 1 Inquiry Process Check List
PM 3 Self-Assessment: Problem Solving

Tiling Patterns

LESSON ORGANIZER

40–50 min

Curriculum Focus: Model and extend tiling patterns. (5m106)

Teacher Materials
- overhead Pattern Blocks

Student Materials
- Pattern Blocks (PM 28)
- triangular dot paper (PM 26)
- 1-cm grid paper (PM 23)
- square dot paper (PM 25)

Optional
- Step-by-Step 6 (Master 10.15)
- Extra Practice 3 (Master 10.20)

Vocabulary: tiling

Assessment: Master 10.2 Ongoing Observations: Patterns in Number and Geometry

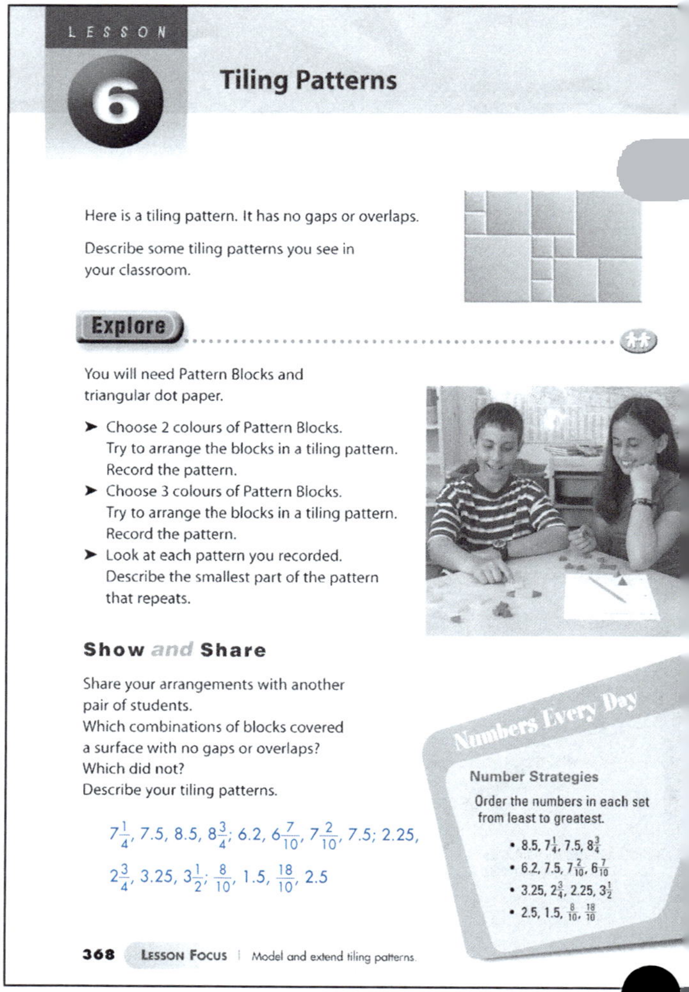
LESSON 6

Tiling Patterns

Here is a tiling pattern. It has no gaps or overlaps.

Describe some tiling patterns you see in your classroom.

Explore

You will need Pattern Blocks and triangular dot paper.

➤ Choose 2 colours of Pattern Blocks. Try to arrange the blocks in a tiling pattern. Record the pattern.

➤ Choose 3 colours of Pattern Blocks. Try to arrange the blocks in a tiling pattern. Record the pattern.

➤ Look at each pattern you recorded. Describe the smallest part of the pattern that repeats.

Show and Share

Share your arrangements with another pair of students.
Which combinations of blocks covered a surface with no gaps or overlaps?
Which did not?
Describe your tiling patterns.

$7\frac{1}{4}$, 7.5, 8.5, $8\frac{3}{4}$; 6.2, $6\frac{7}{10}$, $7\frac{2}{10}$, 7.5; 2.25, $2\frac{3}{4}$, 3.25, $3\frac{1}{2}$; $\frac{8}{10}$, 1.5, $\frac{18}{10}$, 2.5

Numbers Every Day

Number Strategies

Order the numbers in each set from least to greatest.

- 8.5, $7\frac{1}{4}$, 7.5, $8\frac{3}{4}$
- 6.2, 7.5, $7\frac{2}{10}$, $6\frac{7}{10}$
- 3.25, $2\frac{3}{4}$, 2.25, $3\frac{1}{2}$
- 2.5, 1.5, $\frac{8}{10}$, $\frac{18}{10}$

368 LESSON FOCUS | Model and extend tiling patterns.

Key Math Learnings

1. A tiling pattern is a geometric pattern that extends in different directions in a predictable way.
2. A tiling pattern has no gaps or overlaps.

Numbers Every Day

Students should recognize that they need to convert the fractions to decimal equivalents, or vice versa, and then order them from least to greatest.

BEFORE Get Started

Have a variety of examples of tiling patterns such as quilts, wallpaper, flags, tiles, and rugs available for students to look at. Ask:

- What are some of the tiling patterns you see in the classroom?
  (*There is a tiling pattern in the floor. It is made up of small rectangles that make up a square. The square repeats. The rug has a pattern of triangles and squares.*)

Present *Explore*. Explain to students that there cannot be any gaps or overlaps in a tiling pattern; it has to cover an entire region. Allow time for students to experiment with Pattern Blocks. Explain that they will make a tiling pattern on triangular dot paper that covers about one-half of a page.

DURING Explore

Ongoing Assessment: Observe and Listen

Ask questions, such as:

- Name a combination of 2 or 3 Pattern Blocks that cover the surface with no gaps or overlaps. (*Square and triangle*)
- Name a combination of 2 or 3 Pattern Blocks that cannot make a tiling pattern. (*Tan rhombus and hexagon*)

AFTER Connect

Have volunteers use overhead Pattern Blocks on an overhead projector to model their patterns. Invite the class to describe the pattern.

Review the example in *Connect*. Ask:

- How do the pentagons form a rectangle?
  (*The red pentagon and the orange pentagon fit together to form a rectangle.*)

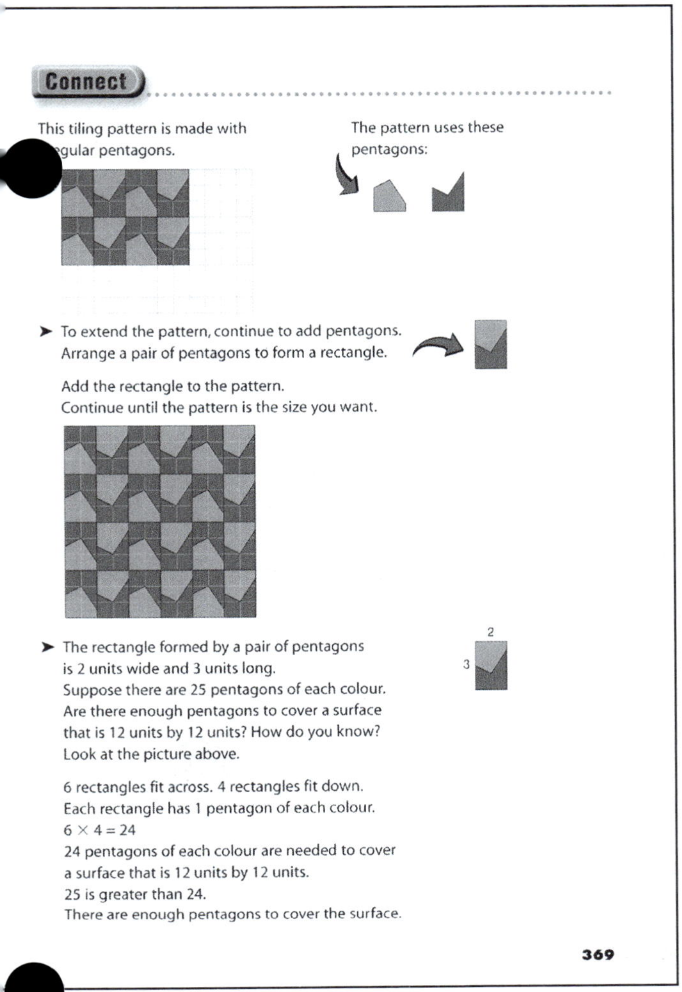
Connect

This tiling pattern is made with ...gular pentagons.

The pattern uses these pentagons:

➤ To extend the pattern, continue to add pentagons. Arrange a pair of pentagons to form a rectangle.

Add the rectangle to the pattern.
Continue until the pattern is the size you want.

➤ The rectangle formed by a pair of pentagons is 2 units wide and 3 units long.
Suppose there are 25 pentagons of each colour.
Are there enough pentagons to cover a surface that is 12 units by 12 units? How do you know?
Look at the picture above.

6 rectangles fit across. 4 rectangles fit down.
Each rectangle has 1 pentagon of each colour.
$6 \times 4 = 24$
24 pentagons of each colour are needed to cover a surface that is 12 units by 12 units.
25 is greater than 24.
There are enough pentagons to cover the surface.

369

REACHING ALL LEARNERS

Early Finishers

Have students use 4 types of Pattern Blocks to create tiling patterns on their desks. Challenge students to complete other students' patterns.

ESL Strategies

Model the idea of tiling by using specific visual materials for the student to copy. For example, have a picture of a wallpaper pattern that the student could copy using Pattern Blocks.

Sample Answers

1. a) T-shaped and U-shaped polygons
   b) 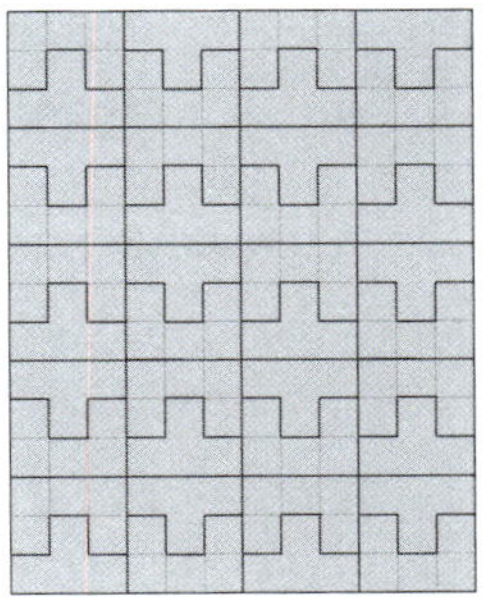
   c) 48 of each. I know this because the T-shape and U-shape make a 3 by 3 square, and 48 squares fit on a surface that is 18 units by 24 units.
2. a) Irregular pentagons; a shape formed by joining 4 pentagons repeats. To extend the pattern, I would keep drawing repeating shapes along each row, and keep adding new rows.
   b) Squares and parallelograms; the purple square with 4 parallelograms repeats. To extend the pattern, I would keep adding a purple square with 4 parallelograms.

- How do you extend the pattern? (*Continue repeating the rectangle formed from a pair of pentagons until the grid is covered.*)
- Will the pattern leave any gaps or overlaps? Explain. (*No, a tiling pattern with rectangles does not leave any gaps or overlaps.*)
- Could you extend the pattern using only one irregular pentagon? Explain. (*No, if you only use one pentagon in the tiling pattern, there will be gaps.*)

Highlight that the rectangle in the Student Book is 2 units wide and 3 units long. Ask:

- How many rows of rectangles are there in the grid? (*4*) How many columns? (*6*)
- What is the area of the grid? (*$6 \times 4 = 24$*)
- What does the number 24 mean? (*24 rectangles cover the surface.*)
- How many pentagons of each colour are in one row? (*6*) In one column? (*4*)
- How many pentagons of each colour cover the grid? (*$6 \times 4 = 24$*)

Encourage students to use terminology such as grid, area, tile, overlap, repeat, and expand when describing a tiling pattern.

Students could use the information in *Connect* to extend a pattern and predict the number of figures needed to tile a surface area.

Practice

Students will need grid paper for question 1, and square dot paper for question 3.

Assessment Focus: Question 3

Students should make sure the pattern covers the grid with no gaps or overlaps. Some students may model the pattern first using Pattern Blocks, and then record the pattern on square dot paper. Others will create and record the pattern on square dot paper.

3.

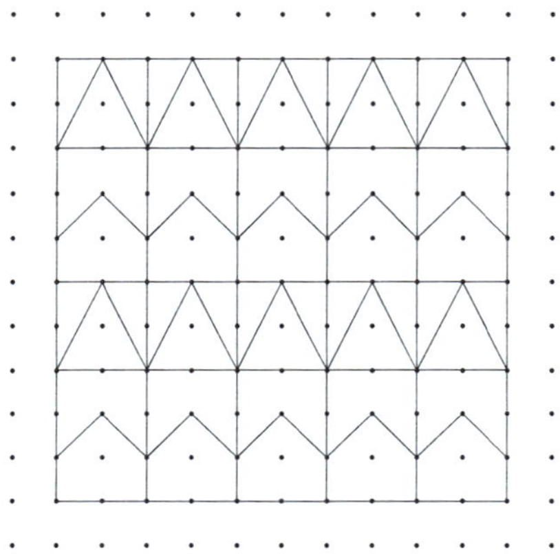

The pattern is made up of right triangles, isosceles triangles, and 2 kinds of irregular pentagons. The part of the pattern that repeats is a rectangle formed by an isosceles triangle with 2 right triangles on either side, plus 2 irregular pentagons.

REFLECT: I could use two figures that fit together to form a square or a rectangle. For example, an isosceles triangle and an irregular pentagon.

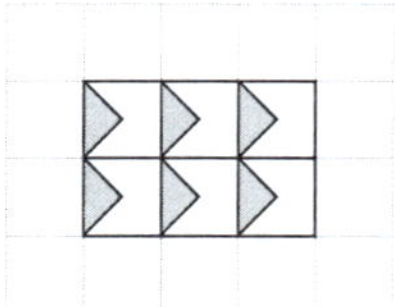

I know that squares form a tiling pattern with no gaps or overlaps. I would repeat the square to extend my tiling pattern.

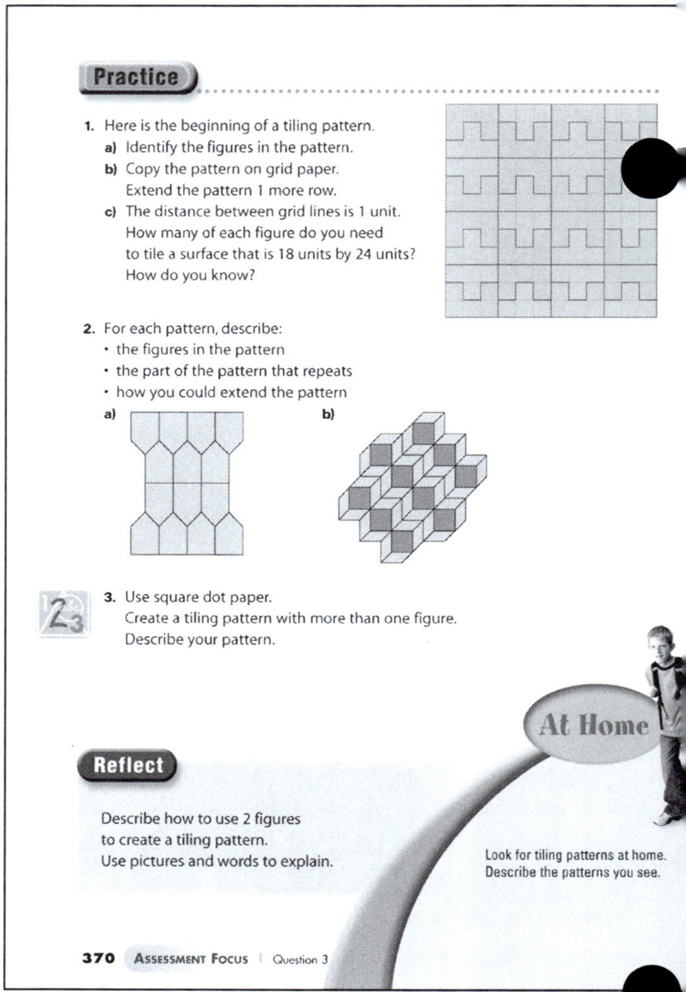

Practice

1. Here is the beginning of a tiling pattern.
   a) Identify the figures in the pattern.
   b) Copy the pattern on grid paper. Extend the pattern 1 more row.
   c) The distance between grid lines is 1 unit. How many of each figure do you need to tile a surface that is 18 units by 24 units? How do you know?

2. For each pattern, describe:
   - the figures in the pattern
   - the part of the pattern that repeats
   - how you could extend the pattern

   a) b)

3. Use square dot paper. Create a tiling pattern with more than one figure. Describe your pattern.

Reflect

Describe how to use 2 figures to create a tiling pattern. Use pictures and words to explain.

At Home

Look for tiling patterns at home. Describe the patterns you see.

370 ASSESSMENT FOCUS | Question 3

ASSESSMENT FOR LEARNING

What to Look For	What to Do
Understanding concepts ✔ Students can create more than one tiling pattern using the same combination of figures.	***Extra Support:*** Draw a pattern on square or triangular dot paper. Have students use two different colours to illustrate the pattern. Students can use Step-by-Step 6 (Master 10.15) to complete question 3.
Applying procedures ✔ Students can identify and extend tiling patterns.	***Extra Practice:*** Have students design and colour a tiling pattern on triangular dot paper. Students can complete Extra Practice 3 (Master 10.20).
	Extension: Students can do the Additional Activity, *Painted Patterns* (Master 10.10).

Recording and Reporting

Master 10.2 Ongoing Observations: Patterns in Number and Geometry

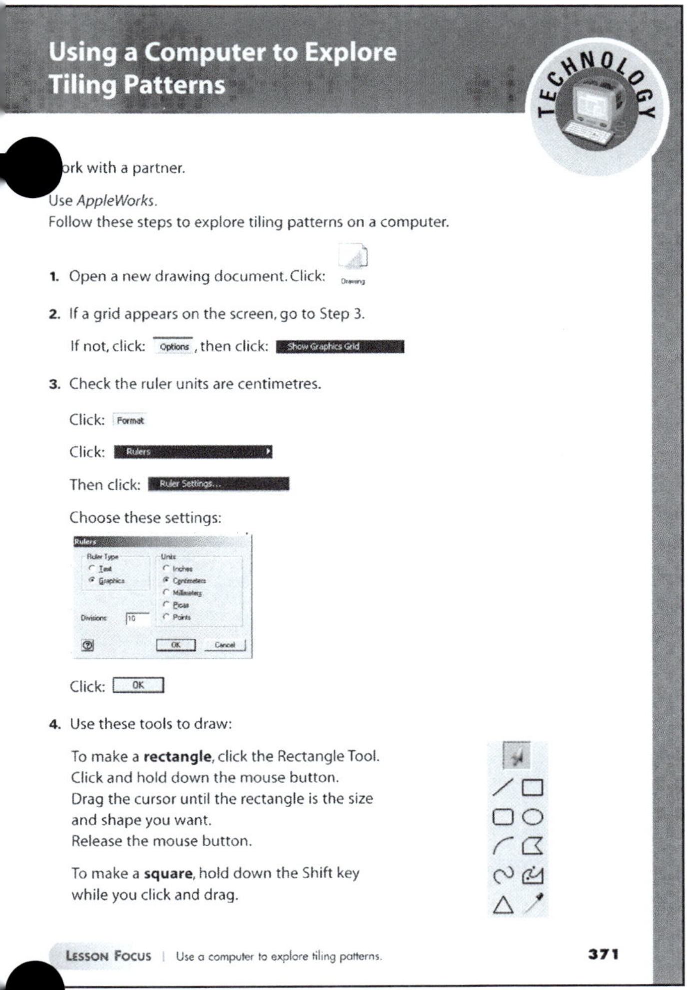

Using a Computer to Explore Tiling Patterns

Technology

...rk with a partner.

Use *AppleWorks*.
Follow these steps to explore tiling patterns on a computer.

1. Open a new drawing document. Click: Drawing
2. If a grid appears on the screen, go to Step 3.
   If not, click: Options, then click: Show Graphics Grid
3. Check the ruler units are centimetres.
   Click: Format
   Click: Rulers
   Then click: Ruler Settings...
   Choose these settings:
   Click: OK
4. Use these tools to draw:
   To make a **rectangle**, click the Rectangle Tool. Click and hold down the mouse button. Drag the cursor until the rectangle is the size and shape you want. Release the mouse button.
   To make a **square**, hold down the Shift key while you click and drag.

Lesson Focus | Use a computer to explore tiling patterns.

371

Using a Computer to Explore Tiling Patterns

LESSON ORGANIZER 40–50 min

Curriculum Focus: Use a computer to explore tiling patterns. (5m100)
Student Materials
- computers with *AppleWorks* or *The Geometer's Sketchpad*

Key Math Learning

Computers can be used to create patterns.

BEFORE

Explain to students that they will use a computer to explore tiling patterns.
Ask:
- What is a tiling pattern?
  (*It is a pattern that has no gaps or overlaps.*)

Students with stronger computer skills can be paired with students who are not as familiar with computers.

DURING

Ongoing Assessment: Observe and Listen

Watch to ensure that students read and follow the instructions carefully.

Instructions for creating a growing pattern using *The Geometer's Sketchpad:*

1. Open a new sketch in *The Geometer's Sketchpad*. Click **File.** Then click **New Sketch.**

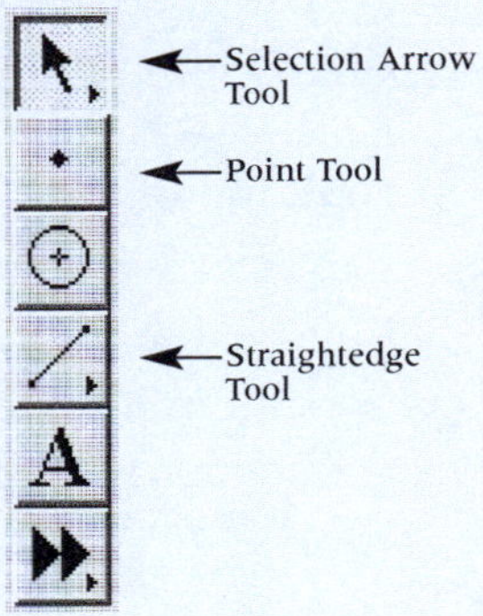

2. Select the **Point Tool.** Click to draw a point. Do this 4 times.
3. Select the **Selection Arrow Tool.** Click to select all four points.
4. Click **Construct.** Then click **Quadrilateral Interior.** This connects the points with line segments to form a quadrilateral.

REACHING ALL LEARNERS

Early Finishers

Have students create a tiling pattern with a core of four or more different figures. Ask them to write about how they extended the pattern. Did they use translation, rotation, reflection, or a combination of the three?

ESL Strategies

If possible, pair students with the same native language.

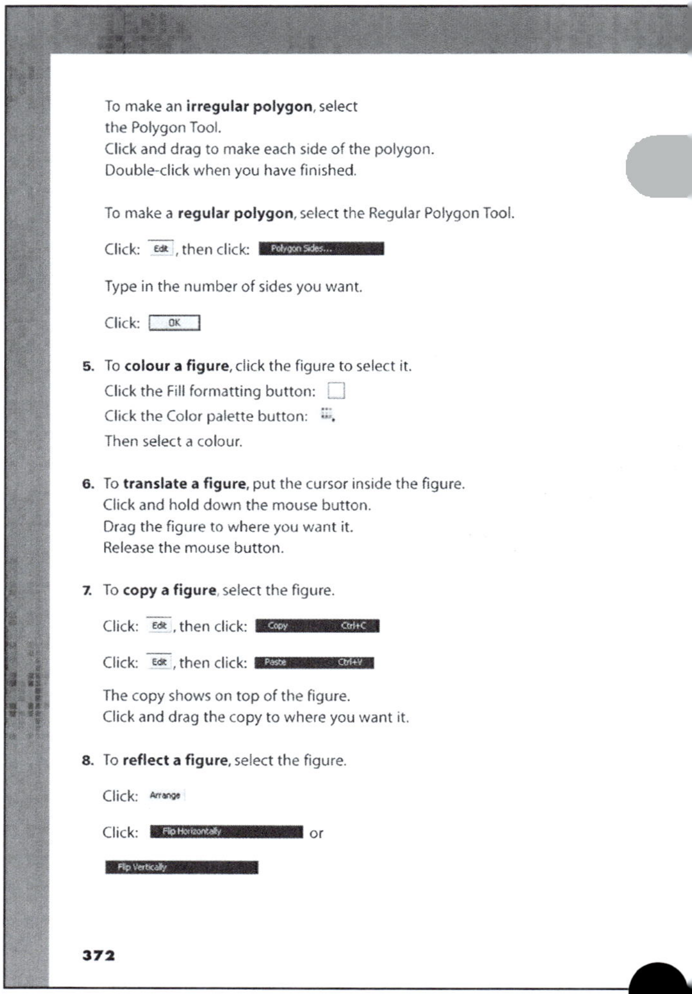

To make an **irregular polygon**, select the Polygon Tool.
Click and drag to make each side of the polygon.
Double-click when you have finished.

To make a **regular polygon**, select the Regular Polygon Tool.

Click: Edit, then click: Polygon Sides...

Type in the number of sides you want.

Click: OK

5. To **colour a figure**, click the figure to select it.
Click the Fill formatting button:
Click the Color palette button:
Then select a colour.

6. To **translate a figure**, put the cursor inside the figure.
Click and hold down the mouse button.
Drag the figure to where you want it.
Release the mouse button.

7. To **copy a figure**, select the figure.
Click: Edit, then click: Copy Ctrl+C
Click: Edit, then click: Paste Ctrl+V
The copy shows on top of the figure.
Click and drag the copy to where you want it.

8. To **reflect a figure**, select the figure.
Click: Arrange
Click: Flip Horizontally or
Flip Vertically

372

5. Click outside the quadrilateral to deselect all the points.
To change the size of the quadrilateral:
Click on a point on the figure.
Hold down the mouse button.
Drag the point until it is where you want it.
The attached line segments will stretch.
Release the mouse button.
Continue to select and move points until your quadrilateral is the shape you want.
6. To **draw a polygon**, select the **Point Tool.**
Click to draw a point.
This will be one vertex of your polygon.
Continue to draw points until you have as many vertices as you wish.
7. Select the **Selection Arrow Tool.**
Click to select the points in order.
Click **Construct.**
Then click **Polygon Interior.**
This forms a polygon with the points as vertices.
8. To **change the size of a polygon,** repeat Step 5.
9. To **colour a figure,** click to select the figure with the **Selection Arrow Tool.**
Click **Display.** Then click **Color.**
Select red, or any other colour that you wish.
10. To **copy a figure,** select the **Selection Arrow Tool.**
Click on the figure to select it.
Click **Edit.** Then click **Copy.**
Click **Edit.** then click **Paste.**
11. To **translate a figure,** follow Step 10 to copy the figure.
Click the copy.
Hold down the mouse button.
Drag the copy to where you want it.
12. To **reflect a figure,** select the **Straightedge Tool.** Click and drag the mouse to create a line. This will be your mirror line.
Select the **Selection Arrow Tool.**

9. To **rotate a figure**, select the figure.

Click: Arrange

Click: Free Rotate Shft+Ctrl+R

Put the cursor on one of the black squares on the edge of the figure.
Click, hold down the mouse button, and drag the figure until it is in the position you want.

To **rotate a figure 90°**, select the figure.

Click: Arrange

Click: Rotate 90 Degrees

10. Use Steps 4 to 9 to create a tiling pattern.

11. Save your pattern.

Click: File, then click: Save As... Shft+Ctrl+S

Name your file. Click: Save

12. Print your pattern.

Click: File, then click: Print... Ctrl+P

Click: OK

Reflect

Why would a designer use a computer to create tiling patterns? Explain.

373

REFLECT: A designer would use a computer to create tiling patterns because it is faster to extend the tiling pattern with a computer. The designer can correct or make changes to the pattern quickly, and print out many copies of the pattern.

Click on the line you just created to select it.
Click **Transform.** Then click **Mark Mirror.**
With the **Selection Arrow Tool,** click on the figure you want to reflect.
Click **Transform.** Then click **Reflect.**

13. To **rotate a figure,** select the **Selection Arrow Tool.**
Click on a point on the figure around which you want to rotate the figure.
Click **Transform.** Then click **Mark Centre.**
Click on the figure to select it.
Click **Transform.** Then click **Rotate.**
Change the number of degrees from 90, to 40, to 120, or to 180.

14. Use Steps 2 to 13 to create a tiling pattern.

15. To **save your pattern:**
Click **File.**
Then click **Save As.**
Give your file a name.
Click **Save.**

16. To **print your pattern:**
Click **File.**
Then click **Print.**
Click **OK.**

AFTER

Invite volunteers to share their tiling patterns with the class, and discuss how they created them. Elicit from students that using the copy and paste function makes it easy to extend a tiling pattern.

LESSON ORGANIZER 40–50 min

Student Materials
- Pattern Blocks (PM 28)
- calculators

Assessment: Masters 10.1 Unit Rubric: Patterns in Number and Geometry, 10.4 Unit Summary: Patterns in Number and Geometry

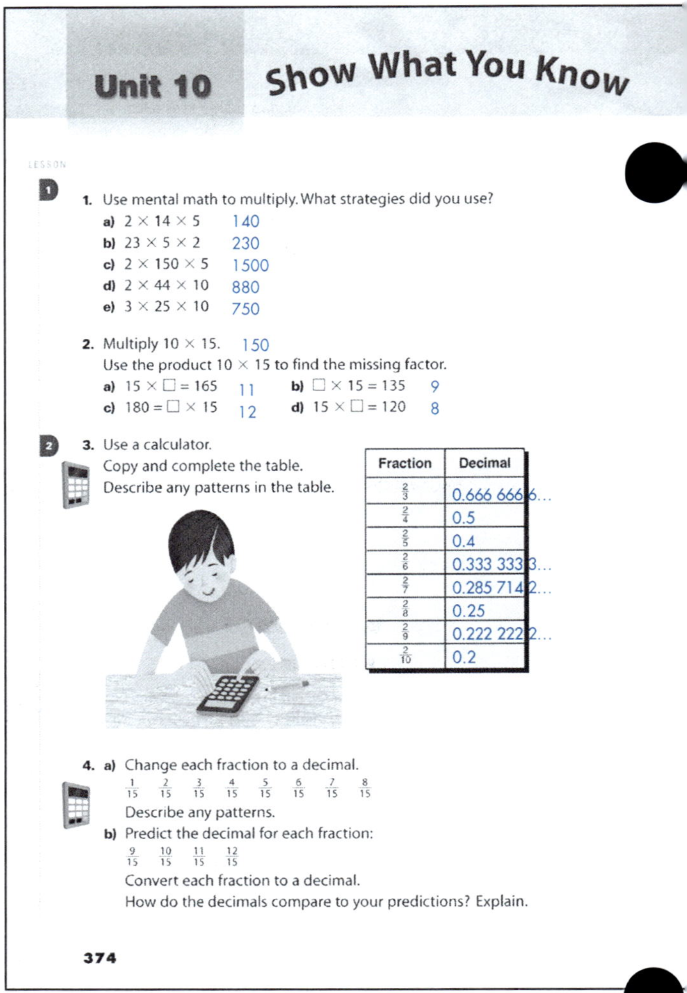

Unit 10 Show What You Know

LESSON

1

1. Use mental math to multiply. What strategies did you use?
   a) 2 × 14 × 5 140
   b) 23 × 5 × 2 230
   c) 2 × 150 × 5 1500
   d) 2 × 44 × 10 880
   e) 3 × 25 × 10 750

2. Multiply 10 × 15. 150
   Use the product 10 × 15 to find the missing factor.
   a) 15 × □ = 165 11
   b) □ × 15 = 135 9
   c) 180 = □ × 15 12
   d) 15 × □ = 120 8

2

3. Use a calculator.
   Copy and complete the table.
   Describe any patterns in the table.

Fraction	Decimal
$\frac{2}{3}$	0.666 666 6…
$\frac{2}{4}$	0.5
$\frac{2}{5}$	0.4
$\frac{2}{6}$	0.333 333 3…
$\frac{2}{7}$	0.285 714 2…
$\frac{2}{8}$	0.25
$\frac{2}{9}$	0.222 222 2…
$\frac{2}{10}$	0.2

4. a) Change each fraction to a decimal.
   $\frac{1}{15}$ $\frac{2}{15}$ $\frac{3}{15}$ $\frac{4}{15}$ $\frac{5}{15}$ $\frac{6}{15}$ $\frac{7}{15}$ $\frac{8}{15}$
   Describe any patterns.
   b) Predict the decimal for each fraction:
   $\frac{9}{15}$ $\frac{10}{15}$ $\frac{11}{15}$ $\frac{12}{15}$
   Convert each fraction to a decimal.
   How do the decimals compare to your predictions? Explain.

374

Sample Answers

1. I rearranged the factors to make multiplication easier.
   a) First, I multiplied 2 × 5 to get 10. Then I multiplied 10 × 14 to get 140.
   b) First, I multiplied 2 × 5 to get 10. Then I multiplied 23 × 10 to get 230.
   c) First, I multiplied 2 × 5 to get 10. Then I multiplied 150 × 10 to get 1500.
   d) First, I multiplied 2 × 44 to get 88. Then I multiplied 88 × 10 to get 880.
   e) First, I multiplied 3 × 25 to get 75. Then I multiplied 75 × 10 to get 750.
3. In the Fraction column, the numerator stays the same: 2. The denominator starts at 3, and increases by 1 each time. In the Decimal column, the decimal for a fraction with denominator 3, or a denominator that is a multiple of 3, is a repeating decimal. The decimal for a fraction with denominator 7 is also a repeating decimal.
4. a) 0.066 666 6…, 0.133 333 3…, 0.2, 0.266 666 6…, 0.333 333 3…, 0.4, 0.466 666 6…, 0.533 333 3…
   The pattern rule is: Start at 0.066 666 6…. Add 0.066 666 6… each time.
   b) 0.6, 0.666 666 6…, 0.733 333 3…, 0.8
   I used the pattern rule in part a, so my predictions were right.
5. a)

Time (min)	Number of Swings
1	60
2	120
3	180
4	240
5	300

   b) Start at 60. Add 60 each time.
   c)

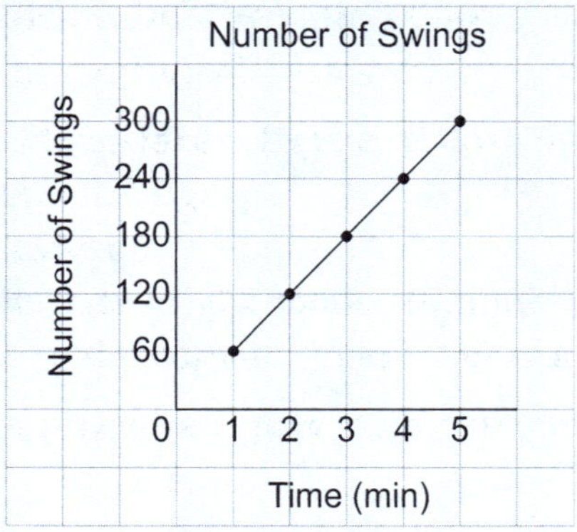

The pendulum on a grandfather clock swings back and forth 60 times each minute.
The table shows the number of swings.

Time (min)	Number of Swings
1	60
2	120

a) Copy and complete the table for the first 5 min.
b) Write the pattern rule for the number of swings.
c) Use the data in the table. Draw a line graph.

4 6. Pineapple scales show 3 sets of spirals.

One set goes up to the left. A second set goes up to the right. A third set goes up steeply to the left.

The numbers of spirals are consecutive Fibonacci numbers.
The spiral pattern that goes up steeply to the left has the greatest number of spirals, 13.
How many spirals are in the other 2 spiral patterns? How do you know? 5, 8

6 7. Devon has these Pattern Blocks:
- orange squares
- yellow hexagons
- blue rhombuses

Can he use all 3 types of blocks to create a tiling pattern?
Use words and pictures to explain.

UNIT 10 Learning Goals

- ☑ use patterns to solve multiplication problems
- ☑ use a calculator to explore patterns in decimals
- ☑ model patterns in tables and on graphs
- ☑ explore tiling patterns
- ☑ use a computer to create a tiling pattern

375

6. I know because the 3 numbers are consecutive Fibonacci numbers, ending in 13. The numbers are 5, 8, and 13.
7. No, he cannot combine all three to make a tiling pattern because there will be gaps.
For example:

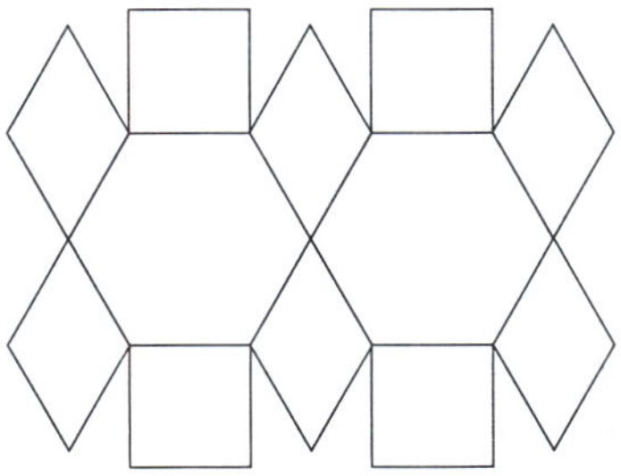

ASSESSMENT FOR LEARNING

What to Look For

Understanding of concepts

✔ **Questions 3 and 4:** Student can identify and extend decimal patterns.

✔ **Question 6:** Student recognizes Fibonacci patterns in nature.

Application of mathematical procedures

✔ **Questions 1 and 2:** Student uses mental math to multiply.

✔ **Questions 3 and 4:** Student can use a calculator to convert fractions to decimals.

✔ **Question 5:** Student can create and graph a table of values.

Problem solving

✔ **Question 7:** Student can solve problems by applying a patterning strategy.

Recording and Reporting

Master 10.1 Unit Rubric: Patterns in Number and Geometry
Master 10.4 Unit Summary: Patterns in Number and Geometry

Squares Everywhere!

LESSON ORGANIZER 40–50 min

Student Grouping: Individual
Student Materials
- 1-cm grid paper (PM 23)
- coloured pencils
- 2-column charts (PM 17)

Assessment: Masters 10.3 Performance Assessment Rubric: Squares Everywhere!, 10.4 Unit Summary: Patterns in Number and Geometry

Unit Problem

Squares Everywhere!

You will need 1-cm grid paper.

Part 1

On grid paper, draw a square with each side length:
1 cm, 2 cm, 3 cm, up to 8 cm

Find the area of each square.
Record the side lengths and areas in a table.

How is the area of a square related to its side length?
Predict the area of a square with side length 12 cm.

Draw a graph of the data in your table.
Do not connect the points.

376

Sample Response

Part 1

Student work should include:
- An accurate sketch of the squares on grid paper
- A table of values as shown:
- A statement that the side length multiplied by itself gives the area.
- A prediction of 144 cm for a side length of 12 cm
- A graph that plots area versus side length, without connected points. The horizontal axis is labelled Side Length (cm), and the vertical axis is labelled Area (cm^2).

Side Length (cm)	Area (cm^2)
1	1
2	4
3	9
4	16
5	25
6	36
7	49
8	64

Remind students of the Learning Goals in the *Unit Launch*. Students will use these skills and concepts as they complete the *Unit Problem*.

Review the patterns in the games in the *Unit Launch*. Remind students that patterns can be described and extended in many ways.

Students work individually on the *Unit Problem*. Have 1-cm grid paper, coloured pencils, and 2-column charts available. Invite volunteers to read aloud the instructions to the three parts of the *Unit Problem*. Ensure students understand what they are expected to do, and answer any questions they might have. In Part 1, they should draw a graph of the data they plotted in a table, and properly label the axes and the graph. Remind students that they must show their work.

Have a volunteer read aloud the Check List. Remind students that they should use the Check List to assess their work before handing it in.

You may also wish to provide students with copies of Master 10.3 Performance Assessment Rubric: Squares Everywhere!, so they will know how their work will be assessed.

Check List

Your work should show:

- ☑ the squares you are asked for clearly drawn and labelled on grid paper
- ☑ tables with the lengths of the sides and the area of each square
- ☑ clear explanations of your findings and predictions
- ☑ different ways of representing a pattern you create with squares

Part 2

On grid paper, draw a square with side length 16 cm.
Mark a point at the middle of each side.
Connect the points to make a smaller square.
Continue until you have a square with side length 2 cm.

How many squares did you draw?

Look at the squares with sides on grid lines.
Label each square with a different letter.

Record the side lengths and the areas of the squares in a table.
What do you notice? Explain.

Part 3

Create your own pattern with squares.
Colour your pattern to show a design.

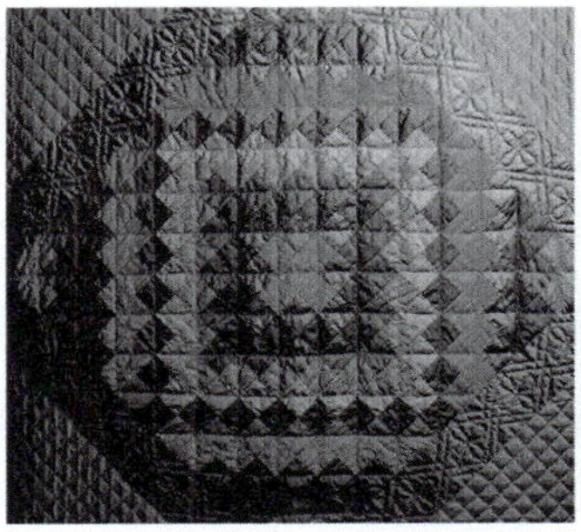

Reflect on the Unit

Write about the different ways you can represent patterns.
Use words, pictures, tables, and numbers to explain.

377

Part 2

Student work should include:

- An accurate sketch of 4 squares drawn
- A table of values as shown:
- Recognition that Part 1 and Part 2 show the same pattern. To get the area, multiply the side length by itself. In Part 1, we increased the side length, while in Part 2, we decreased the side length.

Length (cm)	Area (cm^2)
16	256
8	64
4	16
2	4

Part 3

Student work should include:

- A colourful square pattern that extends far enough so that the pattern is clearly visible

Reflect on the Unit:

Patterns follow rules. Once I know a pattern rule, I can use it to extend and predict the pattern. I can represent a pattern by a table or a graph. When I look at a table or a graph, I can see the patterns in the numbers and come up with the rule. For example, the pattern rule: Multiply the number by itself, can be written in this table or shown on this graph.

Input	Output
1	1
2	4
3	9
4	16

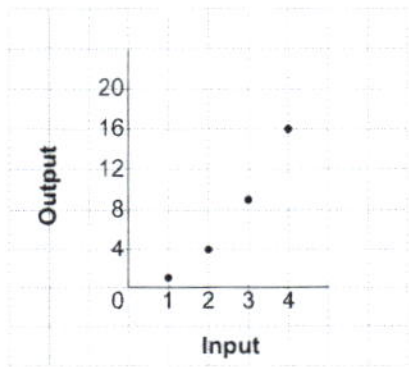

ASSESSMENT FOR LEARNING

What to Look For	What to Do
Understanding concepts ✔ Students apply and explain patterning rules appropriately. ***Applying procedures*** ✔ Students follow patterning rules accurately to extend and create geometric and/or numeric patterns. ***Problem solving*** ✔ Students choose appropriate patterning strategies to solve problems and create an area pattern.	***Extra Support:*** Break the task into manageable parts. Some students may have difficulty recognizing the pattern. Have them model the pattern with congruent squares first, and then have them record the pattern on grid paper. You may want to record the table of values for Part 1 and for Part 2 on the board. As a class, have students complete the initial entries, and then extend the pattern on their own. Students who have difficulty creating a square pattern in Part 3 may benefit from seeing models of geometric patterns. Magazines, wallpaper, and the Internet are excellent sources of these types of patterns.

Recording and Reporting

Master 10.3 Performance Assessment Rubric: Squares Everywhere!
Master 10.4 Unit Summary: Patterns in Number and Geometry

Evaluating Student Learning: Preparing to Report: Unit 10 Patterns in Number and Geometry

This unit provides an opportunity to report on the **Patterning and Algebra** strand.
Master 10.4: Unit Summary: Patterns in Number and Geometry provides a comprehensive format for recording and summarizing evidence collected.

Here is an example of a completed summary chart for this Unit:

Strand: *Patterning and Algebra*	**Problem solving**	**Understanding of concepts**	**Application of mathematical procedures**	**Communication**	***Overall***
Ongoing Observations	3	2	2	3	**2/3**
Strategies Toolkit (Lesson 5)			3		**3**
Work samples or portfolios; conferences	3	3	2	3	**3**
Show What You Know	3	3	3	3	**3**
Unit Test	3	2	2	3	**2/3**
Unit Problem Squares Everywhere!	3	3	3	2	**3**
Achievement Level for reporting					**3**

Recording	**How to Report**
Ongoing Observations	Use *Master 10.2 Ongoing Observations: Patterns in Number and Geometry* to determine the most consistent level achieved in each category. Enter it in the chart. Choose to summarize by achievement category, or simply to enter an overall level. Observations from late in the unit should be most heavily weighted.
Strategies Toolkit (problem solving)	Use *PM 1: Inquiry Process Check List* with the Strategies Toolkit (Lesson 5). Transfer results to the summary form. Teachers may choose to enter a level in the Problem solving column and/or Communication.
Portfolios or collections of work samples; conferences or interviews	Use *Master 10.1 Unit Rubric: Patterns in Number and Geometry* to guide evaluation of collections of work and information gathered in conferences. Teachers may choose to focus particular attention on the *Assessment Focus* questions. Work from late in the unit should be most heavily weighted.
Show What You Know	Teachers may choose to assign some or all of these questions. *Master 10.1 Unit Rubric: Patterns in Number and Geometry* may be helpful in determining levels of achievement. #3, 4, and 6 provide evidence of Understanding of concepts; #1–5 provide evidence of Application of mathematical procedures; #7 provides evidence of Problem solving; all questions provide evidence of Communication.
Unit Test	*Master 10.1 Unit Rubric: Patterns in Number and Geometry* may be helpful in determining levels of achievement. Part A provides evidence of Application of mathematical procedures; Part B provides evidence of Understanding of concepts; Part C provides evidence of Problem solving; all parts provide evidence of Communication.
Unit performance task	Use *Master 10.3 Performance Assessment Rubric: Squares Everywhere!* The *Unit Problem* offers a snapshot of students' achievement. In particular, it shows their ability to synthesize and apply what they have learned.
Student Self-Assessment	Note students' perceptions of their own progress. This may take the form of an oral or written comment, or a self-rating.
Comments	Analyse the pattern of achievement to identify strengths and needs. In some cases, specific actions may be planned to support the learner.

Learning Skills	**Ongoing Records**
PM 4: Learning Skills Check List Use to record and report throughout a reporting period, rather than for each unit and/or strand.	*PM 10: Summary Class Records: Strands* *PM 11: Summary Class Records: Achievement Categories* *PM 12: Summary Record: Individual* Use to record and report evaluations of student achievement over several clusters, a reporting period, or a school year. These can also be used in place of the Unit Summary.

Name ____________________ Date ______________

Master 10.1

Unit Rubric: Patterns in Number and Geometry

	Level 1	Level 2	Level 3	Level 4
Problem solving • chooses and carries out a range of patterning strategies to solve and create problems in number and geometry (e.g., using calculators and computers, making models, creating charts and tables)	with assistance, chooses and carries out a limited range of appropriate patterning strategies, rarely resulting in an accurate solution	with limited assistance, chooses and carries out appropriate patterning strategies, frequently resulting in an accurate solution	chooses and carries out appropriate patterning strategies to solve problems, usually resulting in an accurate solution	chooses and carries out appropriate patterning strategies to solve problems accurately; may offer an innovative approach
Understanding of concepts • shows understanding by appropriately demonstrating and explaining: – patterns in multiplication – explorations of patterns in decimals – patterns in tables and on graphs – tiling patterns	may be unable to demonstrate or explain: – patterns in multiplication – explorations of patterns in decimals – patterns in tables and on graphs – tiling patterns	partially able to demonstrate and explain: – patterns in multiplication – explorations of patterns in decimals – patterns in tables and on graphs – tiling patterns	demonstrates and explains: – patterns in multiplication – explorations of patterns in decimals – patterns in tables and on graphs – tiling patterns	in various contexts, demonstrates and explains: – patterns in multiplication – explorations of patterns in decimals – patterns in tables and on graphs – tiling patterns
Application of mathematical procedures • accurately: – identifies multiplication and decimal patterns using a calculator – uses mental math to multiply – changes fractions to decimals – identifies a pattern rule and predicts the next element – identifies and extends tiling patterns	limited accuracy; major errors in: – identifying multiplication and decimal patterns – using mental math to multiply – changing fractions to decimals – identifying a pattern rule and predicting the next element – identifying and extending tiling patterns	somewhat accurate; makes several minor errors in: – identifying multiplication and decimal patterns – using mental math to multiply – changing fractions to decimals – identifying a pattern rule and predicting the next element – identifying and extending tiling patterns	generally accurate; makes few minor errors in: – identifying multiplication and decimal patterns – using mental math to multiply – changing fractions to decimals – identifying a pattern rule and predicting the next element – identifying and extending tiling patterns	accurate; makes very few or no errors in: – identifying multiplication and decimal patterns – using mental math to multiply – changing fractions to decimals – identifying a pattern rule and predicting the next element – identifying and extending tiling patterns
Communication • describes patterns and explains reasoning clearly and precisely	needs assistance to describe patterns and explain reasoning; often unclear and imprecise	describes patterns and explains reasoning with some clarity and precision	describes patterns and explains reasoning clearly and precisely	describes patterns and explains reasoning clearly, precisely, and confidently
• presents work clearly	presents work with little clarity	presents work with some clarity	presents most work clearly and precisely	presents work clearly and precisely

Name ____________________ Date ________________

Master 10.2

Ongoing Observations: Patterns in Number and Geometry

The behaviours described under each heading are examples; they are not intended to be an exhaustive list of all that might be observed. More detailed descriptions are provided in each lesson under *Assessment for Learning.*

STUDENT ACHIEVEMENT: Patterns in Number and Geometry				
Student	**Problem solving** ▪ Uses appropriate strategies to solve and create problems involving patterns	**Understanding of concepts** ▪ Demonstrates and explains: – multiplication and decimal patterns – patterns in tables and on graphs – tiling patterns	**Application of mathematical procedures** ▪ Identifies and extends patterns ▪ Uses mental math to multiply	**Communication** ▪ Describes patterns and explains reasoning clearly ▪ Presents work clearly

Level 1 – very limited; Level 2 – somewhat or limited; Level 3 – satisfactory; Level 4 – thorough

Name ____________________ Date ______________

Master 10.3

Performance Assessment Rubric: Squares Everywhere!

	Level 1	Level 2	Level 3	Level 4
Problem solving • chooses and carries out appropriate patterning strategies to solve problems and create a tiling pattern	chooses and carries out a limited range of appropriate patterning strategies, with incomplete or seriously flawed results	chooses and carries out some appropriate patterning strategies, with partially successful results	chooses and carries out appropriate patterning strategies, with generally successful results	chooses and carries out innovative, appropriate, and effective patterning strategies, with consistently successful results
Understanding of concepts • shows understanding of patterns by explaining patterns and predictions involving side lengths and area of squares	shows very limited understanding by giving inappropriate explanations	shows limited understanding giving appropriate but incomplete explanations	shows understanding by giving appropriate explanations	shows thorough understanding by giving appropriate and complete explanations
Application of mathematical procedures • accurately: – records information in tables – constructs a graph using data in a table – identifies patterns – uses patterns to predict area from given side length	completes table and constructs graph with major errors or omissions limited accuracy; major errors or omissions in identifying patterns and making predictions	completes table and constructs graph with several minor errors or omissions somewhat accurate; several minor errors in identifying patterns and making predictions	completes table and constructs graph with few minor errors or omissions generally accurate; few errors or omissions in identifying patterns and making predictions	completes table and constructs graph with no minor errors or omissions accurate; very few or no errors in identifying patterns and making predictions
Communication • describes patterns and explains reasoning clearly and precisely • presents work clearly, including labels	needs assistance to describe patterns and explain reasoning; often unclear and imprecise presents work with little clarity	describes patterns and explains reasoning with some clarity and precision presents work with some clarity	describes patterns and explains reasoning clearly and precisely presents work clearly and precisely	describes patterns and explains reasoning clearly, precisely, and confidently presents work clearly and precisely

Name ____________________ Date ______________

Master 10.4

Unit Summary: Patterns in Number and Geometry

Review assessment records to determine the most consistent achievement levels for the assessments conducted. Some cells may be blank. *Overall* achievement levels may be recorded in each row, rather than identifying levels for each achievement category.

	Most Consistent Level of Achievement*				
Strand: *Patterning and Algebra*	**Problem solving**	**Understanding of concepts**	**Application of mathematical procedures**	**Communication**	***Overall***
Ongoing Observations					
Strategies Toolkit (Lesson 5)					
Work samples or portfolios; conferences					
Show What You Know					
Unit Test					
Unit Problem Squares Everywhere!					
Achievement Level for reporting					

*Use Ontario Achievement Levels 1, 2, 3, 4.

Self-Assessment:

Comments: (Strengths, Needs, Next Steps)

Name ____________________ Date ________________

Master 10.5

To Parents and Adults at Home …

Your child's class is starting a mathematics unit on patterns in number and geometry. Patterns help us make sense of the world we live in and allow us to pose and solve problems. Patterns occur regularly in mathematics and can be represented by numbers and in the discipline of geometry. They exist in tiled floors, quilts, game boards, logos, and the flags of the world. As children learn to identify, extend, and create patterns, they develop powerful connections between number relations and geometric properties.

In this unit, your child will:

- Use patterns to solve multiplication problems.
- Use a calculator to explore patterns in decimals.
- Model patterns in tables and on graphs.
- Analyse and create tiling patterns.
- Use a computer to create a tiling pattern.

Patterns occur in many forms. Ask your child to describe some of the patterns learned in class. Often adults use geometric patterns to solve problems. Masons, artists, and graphic designers all routinely use patterns in their line of work. Discuss with your child that many different careers use patterns in geometry. Making some connections with your child fosters a deeper understanding of the mathematics that is taught in school. Talk about how you use patterns in your daily life. The possibilities are endless!

Here are some suggestions for activities you can do at home:

- Search the Internet to discover the Fibonacci sequence.
- Look for number and geometry patterns in tiles, quilts, game boards, etc. in your home.

Name ____________________ Date ______________

Master 10.6

Perimeter of a Square

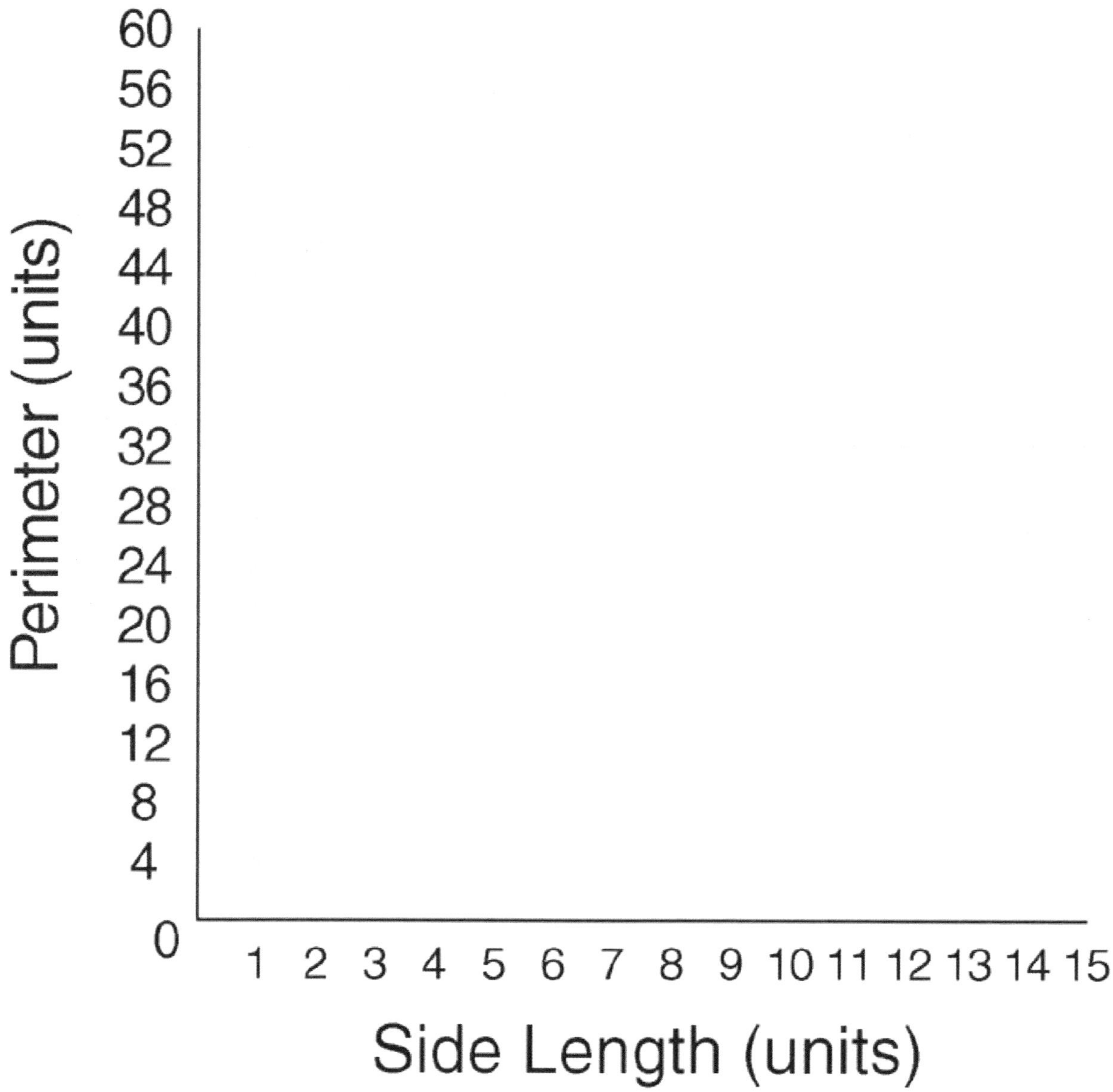

Name ____________________ Date ______________

Master 10.7

Additional Activity 1: Cover Up

Work with a partner.
You will need a hundred chart and counters of 2 colours.
The game is played on a hundred chart.

- Player 1 chooses any even number and puts a counter on that number.
- Player 2 chooses any number that is either a multiple or a factor of Player 1's number, and places a different-coloured counter on that number.
- Players continue to take turns choosing numbers. A player can choose any uncovered number as long as it is a multiple or a factor of the previous chosen number.
- The game continues until one player cannot cover a number. When this happens, the other player is the winner.

Take it Further:
Extend the game board, using a 200 chart.

Name ____________________ Date _______________

Master 10.8

Additional Activity 2: Graph It

Work with a partner.
You will need Colour Tiles and 1-cm grid paper.

- The shapes below are made with Colour Tiles.
  Look for patterns in the area of each shape.

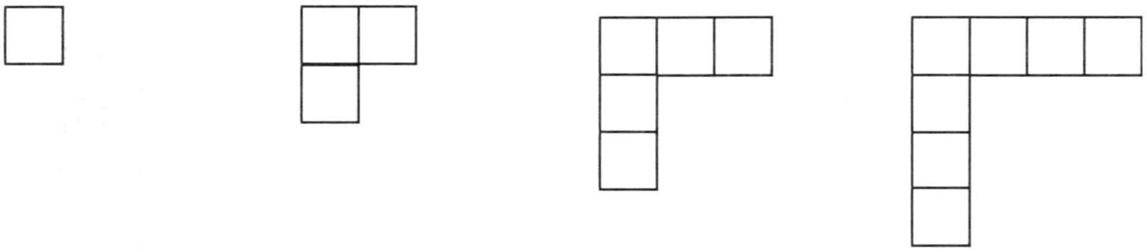

Frame 1 Frame 2 Frame 3 Frame 4

- Determine the area of the Frame 5 and of the Frame 6.
- Create a table to organize your findings.
- Draw a graph to display your data.
- Explain how you could determine the area of the shape in any frame using either a table of values or a graph.

Take it Further:
Create your own growing area pattern.
Complete a matching table.
Have a classmate graph your pattern on 1-cm grid paper.

Name ____________________ Date ______________

Master 10.9

Additional Activity 3: Win with Less

Work with a partner.
You will need Pattern Blocks, a paper bag, and pencil and paper.

- Place an assortment of Pattern Blocks in a paper bag.
- Without looking, each player chooses 3 Pattern Blocks and places them together to form a new figure.
- The object of the game is to make a figure with the least perimeter.
- Count the number of sides on each of the new figures.
  The player with the least perimeter gets a point.
- The first person to score 10 points wins the game.

Take it Further:
Repeat the activity with each player choosing 4, 5, or 6 Pattern Blocks from the bag.

Name ____________________ Date ________________

Master 10.10

Additional Activity 4: Painted Patterns

Work with a partner.
You will need different coloured Snap Cubes, a pencil, and a sheet of paper.
Use Snap Cubes to model a growing cube pattern.

- Begin with a 2 by 2 by 2 cube structure.
  Imagine that the cube has been dipped in paint.
  Try to figure out how many Snap Cubes would have 3 painted faces, 2 painted faces, 1 painted face, or no painted face.
- Use a table. Record the frame number, the number of cubes with only 3 painted faces, the number of cubes with only 2 painted faces, the number of cubes with only 1 face painted, and the number of cubes with no face painted.
- Continue to build cube structures.
- You may want to use one colour to represent the Snap Cubes with 1 face painted, another colour to represent the Snap Cubes with 2 faces painted, and a third colour to represent Snap Cubes with 3 faces painted.
- Continue to record your data in the table.
- Look for patterns in the table.
- Describe any patterns that you see.

Take it Further:
Try the activity for rectangular prisms.

Name ____________________ Date _______________

Master 10.11

Step-by-Step 1

Lesson 1, Question 8

You will need 0.5-cm grid paper.

Step 1 On grid paper, outline a 33 by 30 array.

Step 2 Draw a horizontal or a vertical line to break the array into 2 parts.

Step 3 How did you decide where to draw the line?

____

Step 4 Write a multiplication sentence for each of the 2 smaller arrays.

____

Are these products easy to find? Explain.

____

If not, draw a different line in *Step 2*, and break the array into 2 different parts. Repeat *Steps 3* and *4*.

____

____

Step 5 Find the product for each of the 2 smaller arrays you created.

____

Step 6 Find the sum of the products in *Step 5*: ____________________

What is the area of the gym floor?

____

Name ____________________ Date ________________

Master 10.12

Step-by-Step 2

Lesson 2, Question 5

Step 1 Complete the table.

Fraction	Decimal
$\frac{1}{9}$	
$\frac{2}{9}$	
$\frac{3}{9}$	

Step 2 Look at the Fraction column. What patterns do you see?

____

Step 3 Look at the Decimal column. What patterns do you see?

____

Step 4 Use the pattern you found in *Step 3*.
Do not use a calculator.
Predict the decimal equivalent of each fraction.
Complete the table.

Fraction	Decimal Prediction
$\frac{4}{9}$	
$\frac{5}{9}$	
$\frac{6}{9}$	
$\frac{7}{9}$	
$\frac{8}{9}$	

Step 5 How did you make your predictions?

____

____

Step 6 What is the decimal for $\frac{9}{9}$? Explain.

____

____

Name ____________________ Date ________________

Master 10.13

Step-by-Step 3

Lesson 3, Question 6

Step 1 Place an operation (×, ÷, +, –) and a number in the box.

Input ⟶ ☐ ⟶ Output

Step 2 Complete the table.
Use the operation and the number from *Step 1* to find the Output.

Input	Output
1	
3	
5	
7	
9	

Step 3 Graph the Input/Output numbers.
Create your own intervals for the Output axis.

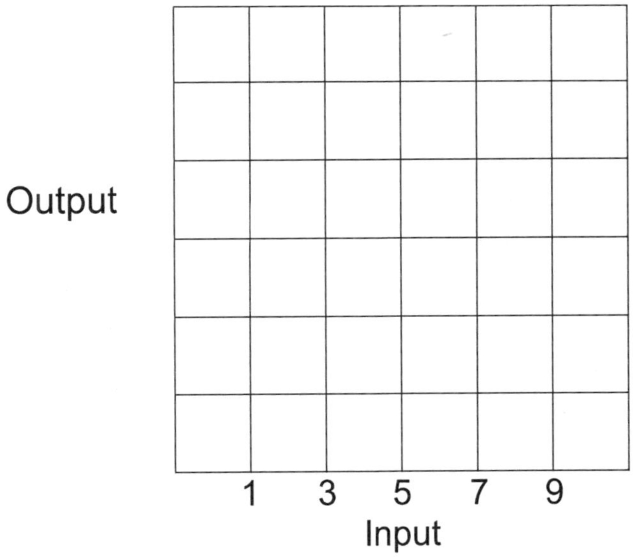

Step 4 Look at your graph. Describe it.

____

____

Name ____________________ Date ________________

Master 10.14

Step-by-Step 4

Lesson 4, Question 6

Step 1 The length of a domino is 2 units. Its width is 1 unit.
With dominoes, make a rectangle with 1 side 2 units long.

How many different rectangles can you make with 1 domino? ____________

How many different rectangles can you make with 2 dominoes? __________

How many different rectangles can you make with 3 dominoes? __________

How many different rectangles can you make with 4 dominoes? __________

Step 2 Predict the number of different rectangles you could make with 6 dominoes. __________

Step 3 How can you check that your prediction is right?

____

____

Step 4 What are the first 6 Fibonacci numbers?

____

Step 5 How do the numbers of rectangles you found relate to the Fibonacci numbers?

____

Name ____________________ Date ______________

Master 10.15

Step-by-Step 6

Lesson 6, Question 3

Step 1 Draw 2 different figures on square dot paper.

Step 2 Can these figures be put together without any gaps or overlaps? _____
If they can, then go to the next step.
If not, change one or more of the figures.

Step 3 Use your figures to make a tiling pattern.

Step 4 Describe your pattern.

____

____

____

____

Name ____________________ Date ______________

Master 10.16a

Unit Test: Unit 10 Patterns in Number and Geometry

Part A

1. Multiply. Use mental math.

a) $2 \times 13 \times 5 =$ ______ **b)** $27 \times 5 \times 2 =$ ______ **c)** $2 \times 186 \times 5 =$ ______

d) $2 \times 43 \times 10 =$ ______ **e)** $3 \times 13 \times 10 =$ ______ **f)** $4 \times 50 \times 2 =$ ______

2. Multiply.
$13 \times 30 =$ ______

Use this multiplication fact to find the missing factors.

a) $\square \times 30 = 360$ **b)** $\square \times 30 = 420$

c) $330 = \square \times 30$ **d)** $450 = \square \times 30$

3. a) Change each fraction to a decimal.

Fraction	Decimal
$\frac{1}{13}$	
$\frac{2}{13}$	
$\frac{3}{13}$	
$\frac{4}{13}$	
$\frac{5}{13}$	
$\frac{6}{13}$	

b) Describe any patterns.

____

____

Name ____________________ Date ______________

Master 10.16b

Unit Test continued

Part B

4. Evan is paid $8 per hour to mow lawns.
The table shows his earnings.

Hours	Amount Earned ($)
1	8
3	24
5	40
7	56

a) Write a pattern rule for the amount earned.

____

b) Draw a line graph to display the data.

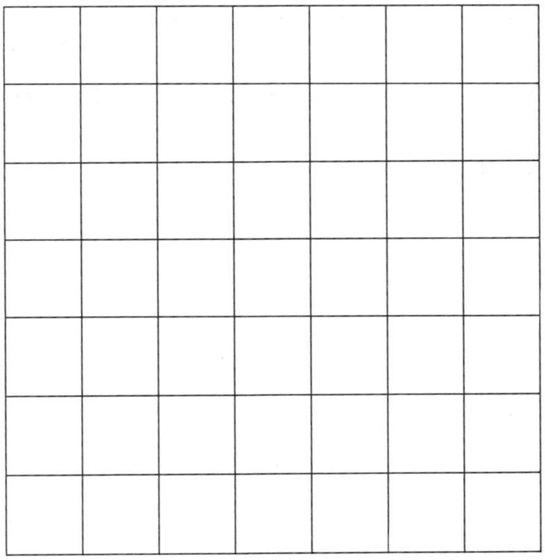

c) Suppose Evan works 6 h.
Use the graph to find how much he will earn.

____

Name ______________________ Date ________________

Master 10.16c

Unit Test continued

5. Suppose you followed the Fibonacci pattern, but started at 7.
7, 7, 14, …
Show the first 10 numbers in this pattern.

____

Part C

6. **a)** Create a tiling pattern using more than two different figures.

b) Describe your pattern.

____

____

Name ____________________ Date ______________

Master 10.17

Sample Answers

Unit Test – Master 10.16

Part A

1. a) 130 b) 270 c) 1860
   d) 860 e) 390 f) 400

2. 390
   a) 12 b) 14
   c) 11 d) 15

3. a)

Fraction	Decimal
$\frac{1}{13}$	0.076 923 …
$\frac{2}{13}$	0.153 846 1…
$\frac{3}{13}$	0.230 769 2…
$\frac{4}{13}$	0.307 692 3…
$\frac{5}{13}$	0.384 615 3…
$\frac{6}{13}$	0.461 538 4…

b) 6 decimals are repeating decimals. The repeating decimals for fractions with numerators 1, 3, and 4 have 076923 in their core, but in a different order. The repeating decimals for fractions with numerators 2, 5, and 6 have 153846 in their core, but in a different order.

Part B

4. a) Multiply the number of hours worked by $8.

b)

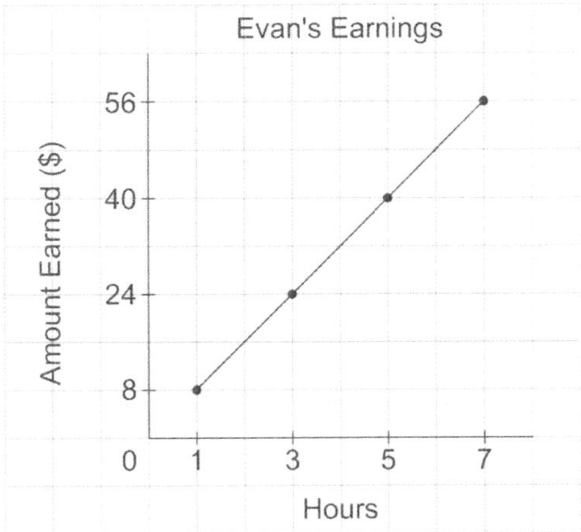

c) $48

5. 7, 7, 14, 21, 35, 56, 91, 147, 238, 385

Part C

6. a)
Sample answer:

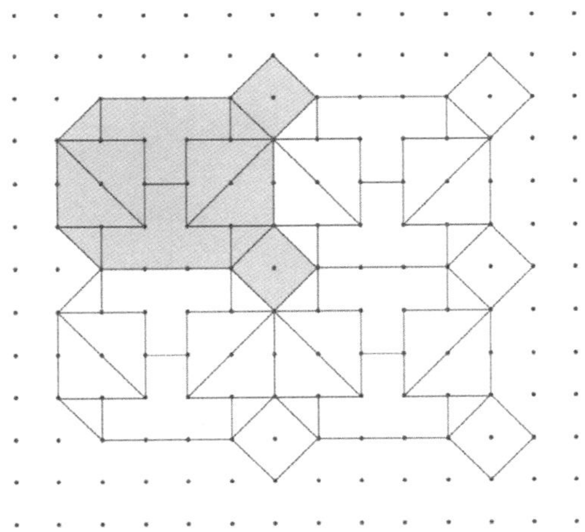

b) My tiling pattern uses 2 T-shaped figures, 2 kinds of isosceles right triangles (4 of each), and 2 squares.

Extra Practice Masters 10.18–10.21

Go to the CD-ROM to access editable versions of these Extra Practice Masters.

Name ______________ Date ______________

Master 10.18 **Extra Practice 1**

Lesson 1: Patterns in Multiplication

1. Multiply. Use mental math.
   a) 2 × 17 × 5 b) 31 × 5 × 2 c) 2 × 147 × 5
   d) 2 × 43 × 50 e) 3 × 18 × 10 f) 4 × 50 × 5
2. Multiply 10 × 35. Use this multiplication fact to find the missing factors.
   a) □ × 35 = 385 b) □ × 35 = 315
   c) 420 = □ × 35 d) 280 = □ × 35

Lesson 2: Exploring Patterns in Decimals with a Calculator

1. a) Change each fraction to a decimal.
   $\frac{1}{12}, \frac{2}{12}, \frac{3}{12}, \frac{4}{12}, \frac{5}{12}, \frac{6}{12}, \frac{7}{12}$
   b) Describe any patterns.
   c) Write five other fractions with denominator 12. Change these fractions to decimals.
2. a) Copy and complete each table for numerators to 10.

Fraction	Decimal
$\frac{1}{5}$	
$\frac{2}{5}$	
$\frac{3}{5}$	

Fraction	Decimal
$\frac{1}{10}$	
$\frac{2}{10}$	
$\frac{3}{10}$	

   b) Describe the pattern in each table.
   c) How are the patterns in the tables the same? How are they different?

Name ______________ Date ______________

Master 10.19 **Extra Practice 2**

Lesson 3: Graphing Patterns

1. Wayne is paid $7 an hour to mow lawns. The table shows his earnings.

Hours	Amount Earned ($)
2	14
4	28
6	42
8	56

   a) Write a pattern rule for the amount earned.
   b) Draw a line graph to display the data.
   c) Suppose Wayne works 7 h. Use the graph to find how much he will earn.

Lesson 4: Another Number Pattern

1. a) Find the 15th Fibonacci number.
   b) What is the sum of the first 15 Fibonacci numbers?
2. Suppose you followed the Fibonacci pattern, but started at 6: 6, 6, 12, ... Show the first 10 numbers in this pattern.

Name ______________ Date ______________

Master 10.20 **Extra Practice 3**

Lesson 6: Tiling Patterns

1. For the pattern below, describe
   - the figures used in the pattern
   - the part of the pattern that repeats
   - how you could extend the pattern

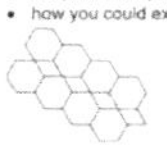

2. a) On this grid, create a tiling pattern using 2 or more different figures.

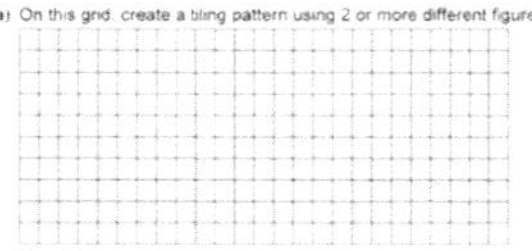

   b) Describe your pattern.

Name ______________ Date ______________

Master 10.21 **Sample Answers**

Extra Practice 1 – Master 10.18
Lesson 1
1. a) 170 b) 310 c) 1470
   d) 4300 e) 540 f) 1000
2. a) 11 b) 9
   c) 12 d) 8

Lesson 2
1. a) 0.083 333 3, 0.166 666 6, 0.25, 0.333 333 3, 0.416 666 6, 0.5, 0.583 333 3
   b) Start at 0.083 333 3 and keep adding 0.083 333 3 to get the next decimal.
   c) $\frac{8}{12}, \frac{9}{12}, \frac{10}{12}, \frac{11}{12}, \frac{12}{12}$
   0.666 666 6, 0.75, 0.833 333 3, 0.916 666 6, 1
2. a)

Fraction	Decimal
$\frac{1}{5}$	0.2
$\frac{2}{5}$	0.4
$\frac{3}{5}$	0.6
$\frac{4}{5}$	0.8
$\frac{5}{5}$	1
$\frac{6}{5}$	1.2
$\frac{7}{5}$	1.4
$\frac{8}{5}$	1.6
$\frac{9}{5}$	1.8
$\frac{10}{5}$	2

Fraction	Decimal
$\frac{1}{10}$	0.1
$\frac{2}{10}$	0.2
$\frac{3}{10}$	0.3
$\frac{4}{10}$	0.4
$\frac{5}{10}$	0.5
$\frac{6}{10}$	0.6
$\frac{7}{10}$	0.7
$\frac{8}{10}$	0.8
$\frac{9}{10}$	0.9
$\frac{10}{10}$	1

   b) In the first table, each fraction has 5 in the denominator. The pattern rule for the numerator is: Start at 1. Add 1 each time. The decimals start at 0.2 and increase by 0.2 each time. In the second table, each fraction has 10 in the denominator. The pattern rule for the numerator is: Start at 1. Add 1 each time. The decimals start at 0.1 and increase by 0.1 each time.
   c) The pattern rule for the numerator of each fraction is the same: Start at 1. Add 1 each time. The fractions are different because they have different denominators. The denominator in the second table is 2 times the denominator in the first table. The decimals in the first table start at 0.2 and increase by 0.2 each time. The decimals in the second table start at 0.1 and increase by 0.1 each time. The decimals in both tables are terminating decimals.

Extra Practice 2 – Master 10.19
Lesson 3
1. a) Multiply the number of hours worked by $7.
   b)

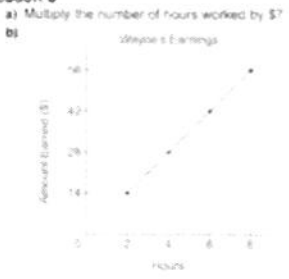

   c) $49

Lesson 4
1. a) 610
   b) 1596
2. 6, 6, 12, 18, 30, 48, 78, 126, 204, 330

Extra Practice 3 – Master 10.20
Lesson 6
1. The figures used are hexagons and rhombuses. The part of the pattern that repeats has 2 hexagons and a rhombus. I would add 2 hexagons and a rhombus on either end to extend my pattern.
2. a) A tiling pattern using 2 or more figures should be drawn on the grid. There should be no gaps or overlaps.
   b) A description of the tiling pattern, such as: The core of my pattern is a rhombus and two trapezoids. I can extend the pattern by adding another rhombus and 2 trapezoids, and so on, until my tiling pattern covers the grid.

Addison Wesley
Mathematics Makes Sense

Program Authors

Peggy Morrow
Ralph Connelly
Bryn Keyes
Jason Johnston
Steve Thomas
Jeananne Thomas
Angela D'Alessandro
Maggie Martin Connell
Don Jones
Michael Davis
Sharon Jeroski
Trevor Brown
Nora Alexander
Cynthia Pratt Nicolson

Printed and bound in Canada

8 9 MP 18 17

PEARSON
Education Canada

ADDISON WESLEY

Ontario

Math Makes Sense

5

Ontario

Teacher Guide

Unit 11: Probability

PEARSON
Addison Wesley

UNIT 11

Probability

"In the society for which we are educating children, the availability of information is exploding—computers are able to store, sort, and analyze massive amounts of data. Virtually all businesses, manufacturing firms, services, and professions require decision-making capabilities under uncertain conditions."

NCTM Addenda Series/Grades 5–8, Dealing with Data and Chance

FOCUS STRAND
Data Management and Probability

SUPPORTING STRAND
Number Sense and Numeration

Mathematics Background

What Are the Big Ideas?

- The likelihood an outcome will occur can be described as impossible, unlikely, likely, or certain.
- A fraction can describe the probability of an event occurring. The numerator is the number of outcomes favourable to the event; the denominator is the total number of possible outcomes.
- A tree diagram is an efficient way to find all possible combinations of outcomes of an event that consists of two or more simple events.
- The results of probability experiments often differ from the theoretical predictions. As we repeat an experiment, actual results tend to come closer to predicted probabilities.

How Will the Concepts Develop?

Students use probability vocabulary (impossible, unlikely, likely, certain) to describe the likelihood of different outcomes in a variety of situations.

Students find the number of possible outcomes of an event and describe the probability of a particular outcome as a fraction of all possible outcomes. They use tree diagrams and tables to record and count all possible outcomes of an event.

Students predict the probability that an outcome will occur. They use random draws and number cubes to conduct probability experiments and compare actual results to predicted results.

Why Are These Concepts Important?

Throughout their lives, students will make decisions in situations involving uncertainty. The abilities to understand, calculate, and predict probabilities are valuable life skills that refine and extend basic intuitions about chance events. The work students do in this unit will help prepare them for later studies of probability theory, data analysis, and statistics.

Curriculum Overview

Overall Expectations
- Demonstrate an understanding of probability concepts and use mathematical symbols. (5m111)
- Pose and solve simple problems involving the concept of probability. (5m112)

Specific Expectations
- Connect real-life statements with probability concepts. (5m121)
- Predict probability in simple experiments and use fractions to describe probability. (5m122)
- Use tree diagrams to record the results of simple probability experiments. (5m123)
- Use a knowledge of probability to pose and solve simple problems. (5m124)

Launch
At the Pet Store!

Lesson 1:
The Likelihood of Events

Lesson 2:
Calculating Probability

Lesson 3:
Probability and Fractions

Lesson 4:
Tree Diagrams

Lesson 5:
Strategies Toolkit

Lesson 6:
Probability in Games

Show What You Know

Unit Problem
At the Pet Store!

Curriculum across the Grades

Grade 4	Grade 5	Grade 6
Students compare experimental results with predicted results. They conduct simple probability experiments and use the results to make decisions.	Students connect real-life statements with probability concepts. They predict probability in simple experiments and use fractions to describe probability.	Students connect possible events and the probability of a particular event. They examine experimental probability results in the light of theoretical results.
Students use tree diagrams to organize data according to several criteria. They use their knowledge of probability to pose and solve simple problems.	Students use tree diagrams to record the results of simple probability experiments. They use their knowledge of probability to pose and solve simple problems.	Students use tree diagrams to count possible outcomes, and show an understanding of probability in making relevant decisions.

Materials for This Unit

Gather a collection of pennies.

Additional Activities

Match My Meaning!

For Extra Support (Appropriate for use after Lesson 1)
Materials: *Match My Meaning!* (Master 11.7), construction paper, scissors, glue

The work students do: Students work in pairs. They cut apart probability word and definition cards and use them to play a "Concentration" game. Players who turn over matching word and definition cards keep those cards and take another turn. The winner of each round is the player with the most cards. After 5 rounds, the player who has won the most rounds is the "grand winner."

Take It Further: Students write statements about situations that could be described using the probability words on their cards.

Social/Linguistic
Partner Activity

Animal Draw

For Extension (Appropriate for use after Lesson 2)
Materials: *Animal Draw* (Master 11.8), scissors, bag

The work students do: Students work with a partner. They cut apart a list of 12 animal names (4 cats, 4 insects, 2 birds, and 2 fish) and place the names in a bag. In the experiment, students will draw a card from the bag, record the result, and replace the card. Students predict the number of animal names from each category they expect to draw from the bag in 30 tries. They conduct the experiment and compare their actual results to their predictions.

Take It Further: Students find as many different equivalent fractions as they can to express the probability of drawing an insect.

Kinesthetic
Partner Activity

Fold Your Tents!

For Extra Practice (Appropriate for use after Lesson 3)
Materials: *Fold Your Tents!* (Master 11.9), small squares of paper, a tray

The work students do: Students work in pairs. They fold 20 small squares of paper (2 cm by 2 cm works well) in half to form "tents." They place the tents on a tray and toss them so that all the tents land on the floor. Students record the number of tents that land fold up, on one side, and on one end.

Take It Further: Students predict the fraction of tents that will land fold up after the 10th and 20th tosses.

Kinesthetic/Social
Partner Activity

Robot Roundup

For Extra Practice (Appropriate for use after Lesson 4)
Materials: *Robot Roundup* (Master 11.10), pencil crayons

The work students do: Students work alone. They imagine being in charge of a robot factory. Students use a tree diagram to figure out all the robots that could possibly be made from a given list of components: yellow or blue arms, green or purple wheels, and red, black, or grey bodies. They then draw and colour the robots. Students pick a component without looking, and calculate the probability of creating a grey robot with blue arms and purple wheels.

Take It Further: Students add another component (for example, a control panel in gold or silver) and figure out how many different robots can now be produced.

Visual/Spatial
Individual

Planning for Unit 11

Planning for Instruction

Suggested Unit time: About 2 weeks

Lesson	Time	Materials	Program Support
Launch: At the Pet Store!, page 2	10–15 min		
Lesson 1: The Likelihood of Events, page 4 Use the language of probability to describe events.	40–50 min	class lists paper bags scissors coloured pencils	Master 11.6: Blank Spinners Master 11.11: Step-by-Step 1 Master 11.18: Extra Practice 1
Lesson 2: Calculating Probability, page 7 Predict, then find the probability of outcomes.	40–50 min	number cubes blank spinners 2-column charts 1-cm grid paper	PM 17: 2-Column Chart PM 23: 1-cm Grid Paper Master 11.6: Blank Spinners Master 11.12: Step-by-Step 2 Master 11.18: Extra Practice 1
Lesson 3: Probability and Fractions, page 10 Interpret probabilities expressed as fractions.	40–50 min	1-cm grid paper coloured pencils coloured cubes paper bags Pattern Blocks	PM 23: 1-cm Grid Paper PM 28: Pattern Blocks Master 11.13: Step-by-Step 3 Master 11.19: Extra Practice 2
Lesson 4: Tree Diagrams, page 13 Use a tree diagram to count outcomes.	40–50 min	coins number cubes 2-colour counters	Master 11.14: Step-by-Step 4 Master 11.19: Extra Practice 2
Lesson 5: Strategies Toolkit, page 16 Interpret a problem and select an appropriate strategy.	40–50 min		
Lesson 6: Probability in Games, page 18 Explore probability in games.	40–50 min	number cubes coins	Master 11.15: Step-by-Step 6 Master 11.20: Extra Practice 3
Show What You Know, page 22 Assessment	40–50 min		
Unit Problem: At the Pet Store!, page 24 Assessment	40–50 min	Snap Cubes paper bags Bristol board coloured markers	

Planning for Assessment

Purpose	Tools and Process	Recording and Reporting
Diagnostic	*Unit Launch* Question; conference; scaffold problems throughout the unit	PM 8: Conference Prompts
Formative	*Explore* – Ongoing Assessment: Observe and Listen Prompt student's self-assessment *Practice* – Assessment Focus Questions Review student work; provide feedback; scaffold as needed; select key pieces	Master 11.2 Ongoing Observations: Probability PM 1: Inquiry Process Check List PM 6: Observation Record 1 PM 7: Observation Record 2 PM 8: Conference Prompts PM 2: Self-Assessment PM 3: Self-Assessment: Problem Solving PM 9: Work Sample Records
Summative	*Show What You Know* *Unit Problem* – Performance Assessment Unit Test Review assessment records; add unit results to ongoing records	Master 11.1 Unit Rubric: Probability Master 11.3 Performance Assessment Rubric: At the Pet Store! Master 11.4 Unit Summary: Probability PM 10: Summary Class Records: Strands PM 11: Summary Class Records: Achievement Categories PM 12: Summary Record: Individual
Learning Skills/ Mathematical Disposition	Observe and record throughout unit	PM 4: Learning Skills Check List PM 5: Mathematical Dispositions and Learning Skills

Program Masters (PM) are in the *Grade 5 Planning and Program Masters* module.
Extra Practice Masters are on the CD-ROM.

At the Pet Store!

LESSON ORGANIZER

10–15 min

Curriculum Focus: Activate prior learning about probability.
Vocabulary: likely, unlikely, certain, impossible

ASSUMED PRIOR KNOWLEDGE

- ✓ Students can use appropriate language to describe probabilities.
- ✓ Students can decide whether an event is likely, unlikely, certain, or impossible.

ACTIVATE PRIOR LEARNING

Engage students in a discussion about pets and purchasing them.

Ask:

- Has anyone visited a pet store?
- What kinds of pets might you expect to see in a pet store? (*dogs, cats, birds, fish, rabbits, hamsters, mice*)

Invite students to examine the picture of the pet store in the Student Book. Encourage them to talk about the animals they see there.

Discuss the first question in the Student Book. Encourage children to assume that the secret fish has been chosen randomly.
(*It is more likely that the secret fish is silver because there are more silver fish than pink fish.*)

Discuss the second question in the Student Book. (*It is likely that the fish is blue because there are more blue fish than any other colour fish. Choosing a red fish is less likely because out of the nine fish, only three are red. It is very unlikely that Tyler will pick the yellow fish because there's only one yellow fish. It is impossible to pick a green fish because there are no green fish in the tank.*)

Discuss the third question in the Student Book. Accept different responses and ask the students to explain their thinking.
(*Sample answers: There are 365 days in a year, so the chances are low that today is the customer's birthday. I think Tyler is the next customer and it's his birthday, so it is very likely that the next customer will win the free gift.*)

Invite a volunteer to read aloud each *Learning Goal* and check that students understand the meaning of each goal. If students are not familiar with tree diagrams, explain that these are a way of displaying and counting the possible combinations of something happening.

LITERATURE CONNECTIONS FOR THE UNIT

The Number Devil: A Mathematical Adventure by Hans Magnus Enzenberger. New York: Henry Holt and Company, 1997.
ISBN 0805062998
In his dreams, 12-year-old Robert meets the "number devil" who teaches him what math is all about. Chapter eight of this challenging and thought-provoking book deals with finding possible arrangements (permutations) of a row of children.

REACHING ALL LEARNERS

Some students may benefit from using the virtual manipulatives on the e-Tools CD-ROM. The e-Tools appropriate for this unit include Probability.

DIAGNOSTIC ASSESSMENT

What to Look For	What to Do
✔ Students can use appropriate language to describe probabilities. ✔ Students can decide whether an event is likely, unlikely, certain, or impossible.	***Extra Support:*** Students who are unable to use appropriate vocabulary to describe probabilities may benefit from a review of the terms "likely," "unlikely," "impossible," and "certain." *Work on this skill during Lesson 1.* Students who have difficulty predicting the probability of an outcome may benefit from a more direct approach. For example, have students roll a number cube, and list the possible outcomes. Then, discuss the likelihood of each outcome. *Work on this skill throughout the unit.*

The Likelihood of Events

LESSON ORGANIZER (40–50 min)

Curriculum Focus: Use the language of probability to describe events. (5m121, 5m124)

Teacher Materials
Optional
- weather forecast from a newspaper
- coloured tiles
- paper bag

Student Materials
- copies of class list
- paper bags
- scissors
- coloured pencils

Optional
- coloured tiles
- Step-by-Step 1 (Master 11.11)
- Extra Practice 1 (Master 11.18)
- Blank Spinners (Master 11.6)

Vocabulary: outcome, impossible, certain, likely, unlikely, likelihood

Assessment: Master 11.2 Ongoing Observations: Probability

Key Math Learnings

1. An outcome is *unlikely* when it occurs in only a small number of the total possible outcomes, and *likely* when it occurs in most of the total possible outcomes.
2. An outcome is *certain* when it is the only possible outcome and *impossible* when it is not included in the possible outcomes.

LESSON 1

The Likelihood of Events

How will you know what to wear when you leave the house tomorrow?

You cannot be **certain** of the weather. In each season, some weather conditions are more **likely** than others.

Explore

You will need a class list.

- Cut out each name.
  Place the names in a paper bag.
  Take turns drawing a name from the bag without looking.
  Replace the name before the next student draws.
- How likely is each **outcome**?
  Use these words to describe each outcome:
  impossible, unlikely, likely, certain
  - Someone in your class is chosen. certain
  - The student chosen is in grade 5. likely or certain
  - Your name is chosen. unlikely
  - The student chosen is not in your class. impossible
  - The name of the student chosen begins with a consonant. likely
- Conduct the experiment 20 times.
- Record your results.
  Compare the results to your predictions.

380 LESSON FOCUS | Use the language of probability to describe events.

BEFORE Get Started

Ask:

- What can help you decide what to wear tomorrow?
  (*A weather forecast*)
- Can we be certain about tomorrow's weather?
  (*No. A weather forecast tells us what will probably happen.*)
- What type of weather would be unlikely tomorrow?
  (*Snow, because it seldom snows in May*)
- Can you think of other situations when the outcome is uncertain?
  (*The outcome of a raffle, because the winning ticket is drawn without looking*)

Present *Explore.* Students should list the various outcomes and tally their results. Check that students are able to identify the names that begin with a consonant.

DURING Explore

Ongoing Assessment: Observe and Listen

As students work, make sure they replace the names in the paper bag after each draw. Ask questions, such as:

- Is it likely your name will be chosen? Why?
  (*No. I am only 1 of 25 students in the class.*)
- Does it make a difference if you wish really hard to pull your own name?
  (*No, a name is pulled by chance when the draw is made without looking.*)
- What are the chances the student chosen is not in our class? Explain. (*Zero, because we only included names from our own class list*)

Ensure students understand that the likelihood of an event depends on how frequently it is represented in the set of possible outcomes. Check that students understand that random events are not controlled by personal thoughts and feelings.

Show and Share

Compare your results with those of another
...oup of students. Are they the same?
... did you decide how likely each outcome was?
... you use a different word to describe the likelihood
of any of the outcomes? Explain.

Likelihood means how likely something is to happen.

Connect

Suzanne puts 5 red tiles, 1 yellow tile, and 1 blue tile into a paper bag.
Without looking, Marius draws a tile from the bag.
What is the likelihood of each outcome?

- Marius draws a red tile.
- Marius draws a coloured tile.
- Marius draws a yellow tile.
- Marius draws a green tile.

There are 7 tiles in the bag.
Marius could pick any 1 of the 7 tiles.
There are 7 possible outcomes.

5 of the 7 tiles are red.
It is likely that Marius draws a red tile.

All the tiles are coloured.
It is certain that Marius draws a coloured tile.

Only 1 of the 7 tiles is yellow.
It is **unlikely** that Marius draws a yellow tile.

There are no green tiles in the bag.
It is **impossible** for Marius to draw a green tile.

Practice

1. Describe a situation that is:
   a) likely
   b) unlikely
   c) certain
   d) impossible

Numbers Every Day

Number Strategies

Estimate each sum.
Which strategies did you use?

1254 + 3861 5000
3868 + 4444 8000
6514 + 2022 9000
2901 + 3101 6000

381

REACHING ALL LEARNERS

Alternative Explore

Materials: paper bag containing a collection of different coloured square tiles

Have students perform the experiment of *Explore* but describe the likelihood of drawing each colour.

Early Finishers

Have students test the spinners they designed for question 5. They should tally the results of 20 spins and compare them to the expected probabilities.

Common Misconceptions

➤ Some students may feel they have a "lucky" number or colour that is more likely to be chosen.

How to Help: Encourage students to discuss the concept of chance. Remind them that events are not controlled by thoughts or feelings.

ESL Strategies

Illustrate a poster with tiles in a bag similar to the situation in *Connect.* Next to a single tile of each colour, print the appropriate probability statement: *This outcome is likely. This outcome is unlikely,* and so on.

Numbers Every Day

Students may round to either the closest 1000, or the nearest 100 to estimate. Students may also choose to use front-end addition.

AFTER Connect

Invite volunteers to share their descriptions and the results of the experiments. Introduce *probable* and *improbable* as synonyms for *likely* and *unlikely*.

Ask questions, such as:

- Did the results of your 20 draws match your descriptions of the likelihood of each outcome? (*Yes. The impossible outcome was never pulled. The certain outcome happened every time.*)
- How often did you pull a name that started with a consonant? (*16 times out of 20. It was a likely outcome, because more than half of the students have a name that starts with a consonant.*)

Discuss and model the situation in *Connect.* Ask:

- Is it possible that Marius will draw a blue tile? (*Yes. It is possible, but unlikely, because only 1 of 7 tiles is blue.*)
- Which outcomes are equally likely? (*Drawing a blue tile or a yellow tile*)

Ask a student volunteer to draw and replace a tile 20 times while another student records the results on the board. Compare the results with student predictions. Ensure students understand that probability predictions are estimates that are not expected to match actual results exactly.

Practice

Have blank spinners and coloured pencils available for question 5.

Assessment Focus: Question 5

Students should understand that if an outcome is more likely than another, the sector for that outcome is bigger than the others. If the outcomes are equally likely, then the 2 sectors are the same size. If an outcome is certain, then the sector for that outcome covers the entire spinner. A colour can be separated into non-adjacent sectors provided the total area for the colour meets the criteria.

Sample Answers

1. a) Someone in our class has a birthday today.
   b) I will fly to Brazil tomorrow.
   c) Spring will follow winter.
   d) A dog will turn into a tree.
2. a) Unlikely
   b) Likely
   c) Likely or unlikely, depending on the season
   d) Unlikely
   e) Likely or unlikely, depending on class routines
4. Rebecca is more likely to win, because there are more odd-numbered sections than even-numbered sections on the spinner.
5. Students should design spinners that meet these criteria:
   a) Yellow has the largest sector, followed by red, then blue.
   b) Yellow has the largest sector. Green and blue have equal-sized sectors that are smaller than yellow.
   c) The spinner is completely yellow.

REFLECT: An impossible event will never happen. An unlikely event could happen, but it probably won't. For example, it is impossible that a guinea pig will become the next Prime Minister. It is unlikely that my teacher will become the next Prime Minister.

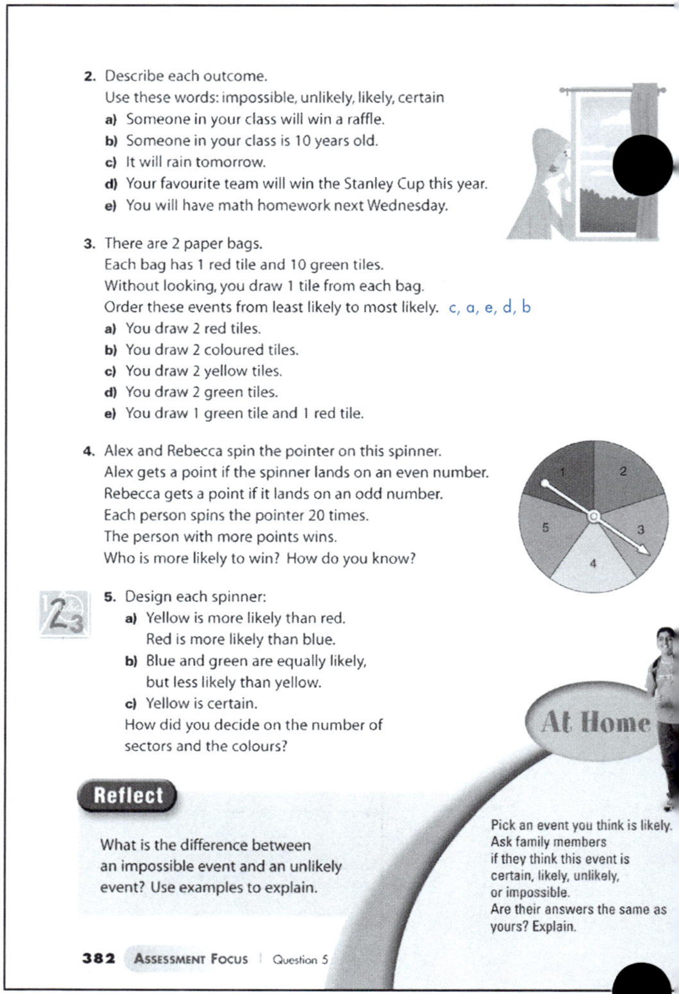

2. Describe each outcome.
Use these words: impossible, unlikely, likely, certain
a) Someone in your class will win a raffle.
b) Someone in your class is 10 years old.
c) It will rain tomorrow.
d) Your favourite team will win the Stanley Cup this year.
e) You will have math homework next Wednesday.

3. There are 2 paper bags.
Each bag has 1 red tile and 10 green tiles.
Without looking, you draw 1 tile from each bag.
Order these events from least likely to most likely. c, a, e, d, b
a) You draw 2 red tiles.
b) You draw 2 coloured tiles.
c) You draw 2 yellow tiles.
d) You draw 2 green tiles.
e) You draw 1 green tile and 1 red tile.

4. Alex and Rebecca spin the pointer on this spinner.
Alex gets a point if the spinner lands on an even number.
Rebecca gets a point if it lands on an odd number.
Each person spins the pointer 20 times.
The person with more points wins.
Who is more likely to win? How do you know?

5. Design each spinner:
a) Yellow is more likely than red.
Red is more likely than blue.
b) Blue and green are equally likely,
but less likely than yellow.
c) Yellow is certain.
How did you decide on the number of sectors and the colours?

Reflect

What is the difference between an impossible event and an unlikely event? Use examples to explain.

At Home

Pick an event you think is likely.
Ask family members if they think this event is certain, likely, unlikely, or impossible.
Are their answers the same as yours? Explain.

382 ASSESSMENT FOCUS | Question 5

ASSESSMENT FOR LEARNING

What to Look For	What to Do
Understanding concepts ✔ Students understand that the likelihood of an outcome depends on its representation in the set of all possible outcomes. ***Communicating*** ✔ Students can describe events as likely, unlikely, impossible, and certain.	***Extra Support:*** Students may benefit from the Additional Activity, *Match My Meaning!* (Master 11.7). Students can use Step-by-Step 1 (Master 11.11) to complete question 5. ***Extra Practice:*** Have students use probability vocabulary to describe events in the school day. (*We are likely to play outdoors at lunch time today. We are unlikely to have a fire drill.*) Students can complete Extra Practice 1 (Master 11.18). ***Extension:*** Have students use words such as "highly likely" and "extremely unlikely" to describe probability more precisely.

Recording and Reporting

Master 11.2 Ongoing Observations: Probability

LESSON 2

Calculating Probability

Explore — Game

Sum Fun

You will need 2 number cubes each labelled 1 to 6.

- Take turns rolling the number cubes.
- Find the sum of the 2 numbers rolled.
  If the sum is even, you score a point.
  If the sum is odd, your partner scores a point.
- Record the results in a table.
- The first player to score 20 points wins.
- Who do you think will have more points after 36 turns? Explain.

Show and Share

Compare your results with those of another pair of students. Explain any differences.
Which is more likely, an even sum or an odd sum?
How do you know?
How could you find the probability of an even sum?
An odd sum?

Numbers Every Day

Number Strategies

Find each product:

0.71 × 100	71
7.1 × 100	710
71 × 100	7100
710 × 100	71 000

What patterns do you see in the factors and the products?

LESSON FOCUS | Predict, then find the probability of outcomes. 383

LESSON 2

Calculating Probability

LESSON ORGANIZER — 40–50 min

Curriculum Focus: Predict, then find the probability of outcomes. (5m122)

Teacher Materials

Optional
- overhead transparency of two-column chart

Student Materials
- number cubes
- 1-cm grid paper (PM 23)
- 2-column charts (PM 17)
- blank spinners (Master 11.6)

Optional
- coins
- Step-by-Step 2 (Master 11.12)
- Extra Practice 1 (Master 11.18)

Vocabulary: probability, results, outcomes, predicting, fair game, equally likely

Assessment: Master 11.2 Ongoing Observations: Probability

Key Math Learnings

1. The probability of an event is the number of times outcomes favourable to the event divided by the total number of possible outcomes.
2. A table or organized list helps us find all possible outcomes.

BEFORE — Get Started

Discuss games of chance that use number cubes. Ask:

- Are some numbers easier to roll than others on a single number cube? (*No, every number is equally likely.*)
- What are the possible even sums when two number cubes are rolled? (*2, 4, 6, 8, 10, 12*)
- What are the possible odd sums when two number cubes are rolled? (*3, 5, 7, 9, 11*)
- What are the different ways you could get a sum of 4? (*Roll a 1 on the first cube and a 3 on the second cube; a 3 on the first cube and a 1 on the second cube; a 2 on both cubes.*)

Present *Explore*. Ask volunteers to read aloud the rules for the Sum Fun game. Show students how to record their tosses using tally marks on a two-column chart. Make sure they understand that players receive one point for each winning toss.

DURING — Explore

Ongoing Assessment: Observe and Listen

As students play the game, make sure they are recording their results. Ask:

- Who is winning your game? Can you explain why? (*Carla. It's just by chance.*)
- Who do you think will have more points after 36 turns? (*It's hard to say. The chances seem to be equal.*)
- Is this game fair? (*Yes, because an even sum and an odd sum are equally likely outcomes.*)

AFTER — Connect

Invite volunteers to share the results of their games. Ask students to share their strategies for figuring out all possible outcomes.

REACHING ALL LEARNERS

Early Finishers

Have students play the game described in *Practice* question 3. They should compare their actual results with predicted results.

Common Misconceptions

➤ Some students may not recognize that tossing 3 on the first number cube and 4 on the second is a different outcome than tossing 4 on the first and 3 on the second.

How to Help: Use two different coloured number cubes to distinguish the different outcomes, and list the outcomes in a table.

➤ Students think they are more likely to get an even sum than an odd sum when rolling 2 number cubes, because there are 6 possible outcomes for an even sum, and only 5 for an odd sum.

How to Help: Explain to students that they must look for the different ways of getting the outcome. Draw a table listing all the possible sums when rolling 2 number cubes, and point out that there are 18 ways to roll an even sum, and 18 ways to roll an odd sum, so the likelihood of rolling an even or odd sum is equally likely.

Numbers Every Day

In each sentence, the first factor and product are both 10 times larger than the previous one. Multiplying by 100 shifts the each digit 2 places to the left. So, the decimal point moves two places to the right.

Connect

Jamie and Alexis are playing *Predicting Products*.
They take turns rolling 2 number cubes, each labelled 1 to 6.
If the product of the 2 numbers rolled is odd, Jamie gets a point.
If the product is even, Alexis gets a point.
Who will have more points after 20 turns?

Jamie	Alexis
Odd Product	Even Pro

Organize the possible outcomes in a table.
This will help you predict the winner.

From the table:
- There are 36 possible outcomes.
- 27 outcomes are even products.
- 9 outcomes are odd products.

×	1	2	3	4	5	6
1	1	2	3	4	5	6
2	2	4	6	8	10	12
3	3	6	9	12	15	18
4	4	8	12	16	20	24
5	5	10	15	20	25	30
6	6	12	18	24	30	36

You say: "The probability of getting an even product is 27 out of 36."
"The probability of getting an odd product is 9 out of 36."

You write:

Probability $= \frac{27}{36}$

Probability $= \frac{9}{36}$

Practice

1. Two number cubes are rolled. Both cubes are labelled 1 to 6.
The numbers rolled are added.
What is the probability of each outcome?
   a) The sum is 12. $\frac{1}{36}$
   b) The sum is less than 4. $\frac{3}{36}$
   c) The sum is 7. $\frac{6}{36}$
   d) The sum is 2. $\frac{1}{36}$

384

Ask questions, such as:

- How did you know for sure that the game was fair? (*We listed all the ways to get an even sum and all the ways to get an odd sum. Both lists had 18 ways.*)
- Is there another way you could keep track of all the possible outcomes? (*Yes. We could make a table of all the different outcomes.*)

Present *Connect*. Ensure students understand that this game is based on the products of the numbers rolled. Direct students' attention to the table on page 384. Ask:

- In how many ways can you get an even product? (*You can get an even product in 27 ways.*)
- In how many ways can you get an odd product? (*You can get an odd product in 9 ways.*)
- What is the probability of getting an even product? (*The probability of getting an even product is 27 out of 36, or* $\frac{27}{36}$.)
- What is the probability of getting an odd product? (*The probability of getting an odd product is 9 out of 36, or* $\frac{9}{36}$.)

Practice

Question 1 requires grid paper. Question 4 requires blank spinners.

Assessment Focus: Question 4

Students should understand that for Vicki to be more likely to win, the spinners must provide more ways of landing on the same colour. For Alistair to be more likely to win, the spinners must provide more ways of landing on different colours. The game will be fair if the spinners provide equal chances of landing on the same colour and landing on different colours.

2. Misha rolls two number cubes labelled 1 to 6.
She finds the product of the 2 numbers rolled.
Find the probability of each outcome.
a) The product is 2. $\frac{2}{36}$
b) The product is 36. $\frac{1}{36}$
c) The product is 12. $\frac{4}{36}$
d) The product is 13. 0
e) The product is greater than 25. $\frac{3}{36}$

3. Dave and Bob play a game.
Each tosses a coin.
If the outcomes are the same, Dave scores a point.
If the outcomes are different, Bob scores a point.
The first person to score 20 points is the winner.
a) Who do you think will win? Explain.
b) Do you think this is a fair game?
Use pictures, words, and numbers to explain.

4. Vicki and Alastair have a spinner each.
They play this game:
- Each player spins his or her pointer.
- If the pointers land on the same colour, Vicki scores a point.
- If the pointers land on different colours, Alastair scores a point.

a) Design spinners so Vicki is more likely to win.
b) Design spinners so Alastair is more likely to win.
c) Design spinners so the game is fair.

5. Design a fair game that uses 2 number cubes.
Describe the rules of the game.
How do you know the game is fair?

Math Link

Your World

A meteorologist studies the weather.
She uses computers, satellites, and radar to predict if it will rain or snow.

Reflect

What does it mean when we say, "Two outcomes are equally likely."?
Use an example to explain.

ASSESSMENT FOCUS | Question 4

385

Sample Answers

3. a) It is impossible to predict who will win, because Bob and Dave have equal chances of winning.
b) This is a fair game, because there are two ways to have the same outcomes (heads, heads; tails, tails) and two ways to have different outcomes (heads, tails; tails, heads).

4. a) Both spinners are $\frac{3}{4}$ green and $\frac{1}{4}$ red.
b) Both spinners are $\frac{1}{4}$ green, $\frac{1}{4}$ red, $\frac{1}{4}$ blue, and $\frac{1}{4}$ yellow.
c) Both spinners are $\frac{1}{2}$ red and $\frac{1}{2}$ blue.

5. Roll two number cubes labelled 1 to 6. Player A gets a point if the product of the two numbers is less than 10. Player B gets a point if the product is more than 10. Both players get a point if the product is 10. The player who reaches 20 first is the winner. The game is fair, because the chance of the product being less than 10 is equal to the chance of the product being more than 10.

REFLECT: When two outcomes are equally likely, they have the same chances of happening. For example, if you flip a coin, you are equally likely to get heads or tails.

Math Link: Your World A meteorologist uses previous weather records to find patterns of behaviour in weather systems. These patterns enable her to predict the likelihood of future events such as a hurricane passing through an area.

ASSESSMENT FOR LEARNING

What to Look For

Understanding concepts

✔ Students understand that probability predictions are based on analyzing all possible outcomes.

✔ Students understand that a fair game is one where each player is equally likely to win.

Applying procedures

✔ Students can use an organized list or table to figure out all possible outcomes.

What to Do

Extra Support: Students can use Step-by-Step 2 (Master 11.12) to complete question 4.

Extra Practice: Have students list all the possible outcomes of drawing 2 coloured tiles from a bag holding one each of red, blue, green, and yellow tiles. What is the probability that the draw will include a red tile?
Students can do Extra Practice 1 (Master 11.18).

Extension: Students may benefit from the Additional Activity, *Animal Draw* (Master 11.8).

Recording and Reporting
Master 11.2 Ongoing Observations: Probability

Probability and Fractions

LESSON ORGANIZER 40–50 min

Curriculum Focus: Interpret probabilities expressed as fractions. (5m122)

Teacher Materials

Optional
- coloured cubes
- paper bag

Student Materials
- 1-cm grid paper (PM 23)
- coloured pencils
- coloured cubes
- paper bags
- Pattern Blocks (PM 28)

Optional
- Colour Tiles
- coins
- decahedron
- Blank Spinners (Master 11.6)
- Step-by-Step 3 (Master 11.13)
- Extra Practice 2 (Master 11.19)

Vocabulary: probability, fractions, sectors, congruent, decahedron

Assessment: Master 11.2 Ongoing Observations: Probability

Key Math Learnings

1. A fraction can be used to describe the probability of an event.
2. A fraction displays the ratio of desired outcomes to all possible outcomes.

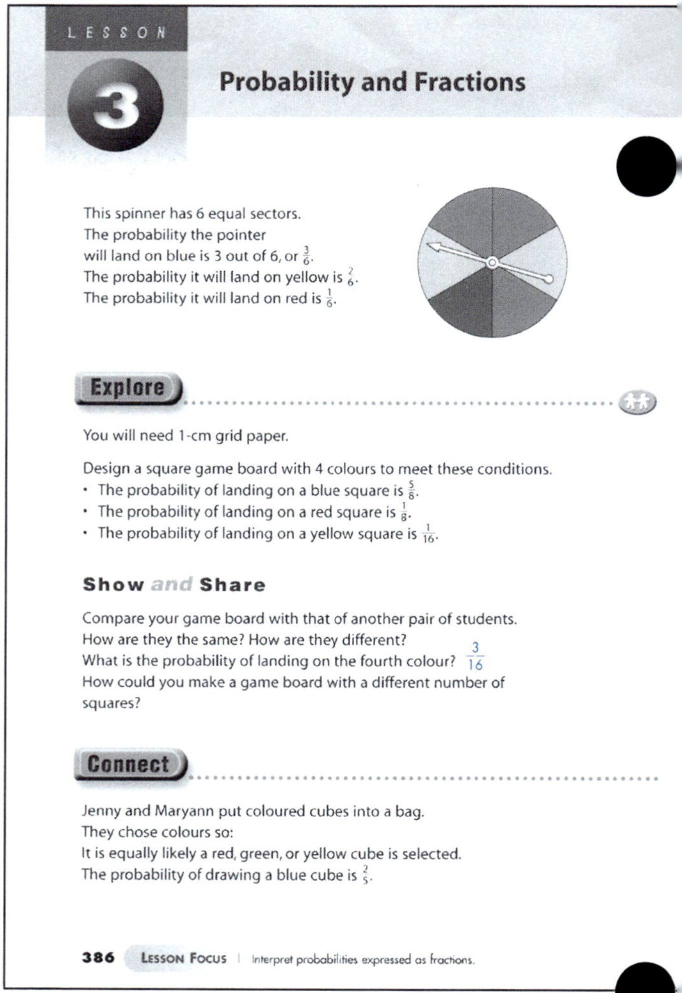

LESSON 3 Probability and Fractions

This spinner has 6 equal sectors.
The probability the pointer will land on blue is 3 out of 6, or $\frac{3}{6}$.
The probability it will land on yellow is $\frac{2}{6}$.
The probability it will land on red is $\frac{1}{6}$.

Explore

You will need 1-cm grid paper.

Design a square game board with 4 colours to meet these conditions.
- The probability of landing on a blue square is $\frac{5}{8}$.
- The probability of landing on a red square is $\frac{1}{8}$.
- The probability of landing on a yellow square is $\frac{1}{16}$.

Show and Share

Compare your game board with that of another pair of students.
How are they the same? How are they different?
What is the probability of landing on the fourth colour? $\frac{3}{16}$
How could you make a game board with a different number of squares?

Connect

Jenny and Maryann put coloured cubes into a bag.
They chose colours so:
It is equally likely a red, green, or yellow cube is selected.
The probability of drawing a blue cube is $\frac{2}{5}$.

386 LESSON FOCUS | Interpret probabilities expressed as fractions.

Math Note

A fraction can be interpreted as a ratio. For example, $\frac{2}{3}$ means in the ratio 2 to 3.

BEFORE Get Started

Invite a volunteer to read the introduction on Student Book page 386. Elicit that because there are 6 equal sectors, each sector is $\frac{1}{6}$ of the whole spinner. Ask:

- What is the probability that the spinner will land on a colour that is not yellow? *(4 out of 6, or $\frac{4}{6}$)*
- What is another way to state the probability of landing on blue? *($\frac{1}{2}$)*

Discuss the size of the game board in *Explore*. To match the given fractions, its area should be a multiple of 8. Side lengths of 8 cm or 16 cm are suitable.

DURING Explore

Ongoing Assessment: Observe and Listen

Make sure students understand the fractional probability for each colour must be matched by that colour's area on the board. Ask:

- How do you know the probability of landing on a red square is $\frac{1}{8}$? *(My board has 64 squares, and I coloured 8 of them red. $\frac{1}{8}$ of 64 is 8.)*
- How many squares will you colour yellow? *(4, because $\frac{1}{16}$ of 64 is 4.)*
- How many squares will you colour with your fourth colour? *(12)*

Watch to see that students understand the probability of landing on a colour is related to the fraction of the whole board covered by that colour.

How many cubes of each colour should Jenny and Maryann use?

The probability of drawing a blue cube o be $\frac{2}{5}$.
2 of every 5 cubes must be blue.
e total number of cubes must be a multiple of 5.
There are many ways to fill the bag.

➤ Suppose Jenny and Maryann used 5 cubes.
Two cubes must be blue.
Drawing a red, green, or yellow cube must be equally likely.
So, put 1 red, 1 green, and 1 yellow cube into the bag.

➤ Suppose Jenny and Maryann use 10 cubes.
$\frac{2}{5} = \frac{4}{10}$, so 4 of the 10 cubes must be blue.

The remaining 6 cubes must be divided equally among red, green, and yellow.
So, Jenny and Maryann placed 2 red, 2 green, and 2 yellow cubes in the bag.

Practice

1. A paper bag contains 2 green tiles, 4 yellow tiles, and 1 blue tile. Liz draws a tile without looking. What is the probability the tile is green? $\frac{2}{7}$ Yellow? Blue? $\frac{4}{7}, \frac{1}{7}$ Use fractions in your answers.

Numbers Every Day

Number Strategies

Find each sum:

12.87 + 0.15 13.02
128.7 + 0.15 128.85
1287 + 0.15 1287.15

387

REACHING ALL LEARNERS

Alternative Explore

Materials: thumb tacks, plastic cups
Provide each pair of students with 10 thumb tacks and a plastic cup. Students should shake up and spill the tacks from the cup. They should record the fraction of all tacks landing point-down. Students should repeat the experiment 10 times. Based on their experimental results, students should use a fraction to give an estimated probability for a tack landing point-down in 50 trials.

Early Finishers

Have students carry out the experiments described in *Practice* questions 1, 2, 3, and 4. They should record their results and compare them to those in the book.

Common Misconceptions

➤ Students may not understand that probabilities must be between 0 (impossible) and 1 (certain).

How to Help: Create a number line from 0 to 1. Label the end with 0 "impossible" and the end with 1 "certain." Ask students to place fractions such as $\frac{1}{2}$, $\frac{3}{4}$, and $\frac{17}{20}$ on the line. Relate the fractions to probability situations discussed in class.

Numbers Every Day

Students should estimate first to make sure their answers make sense.

AFTER Connect

Display students' game boards and ask them to compare the designs. Have them check that the boards meet the criteria for probabilities given in *Explore*.

Discuss and model the situation in *Connect*. Make sure students understand that many trials are needed for the number of predicted outcomes and the number of actual outcomes to be close. Ask:

- What does it mean to say that the probability of drawing a blue cube is $\frac{2}{5}$?
(*If I did 50 draws, I would probably pull the blue cube about 20 times.*)
- If we did 5 draws, would we pull the blue cube 2 times?
(*We might, but it is not likely. We would need more trials.*)

Practice

In question 4, you may need to remind students that the number 10 uses the digit 1.

Have Pattern Blocks available for question 5.

Assessment Focus: Question 2

Students should understand

- The total of the two fractions (for heads and tails) is one.
- The actual results are close to the probabilities based on fractions: $\frac{1}{2}$ are heads and $\frac{1}{2}$ are tails.
- Probability predictions are estimates. The greater the number of trials, the closer the actual results will be to the predicted results.

Sample Answers

2. d) Yes. These results are what we would expect because 8 and 12 are both close to 10. $\frac{1}{2}$ of 20 is 10. Heads and tails should each show up about $\frac{1}{2}$ of the time.

   e) I would expect the results to be closer to my predicted results, because the number of trials is much greater. I would expect Dave to get about 50 heads and 50 tails because heads and tails are equally likely outcomes. I know he probably wouldn't get exactly 50 of each.

3. a) I counted the tally marks.

   d) Yes, because $\frac{7}{24}$ is close to $\frac{6}{24}$, and $\frac{6}{24}$ is equivalent to $\frac{1}{4}$. One-fourth of the spinner is orange.

5. b) Students use Pattern Blocks or coloured pencils to create a game board that is $\frac{1}{4}$ blue and $\frac{3}{4}$ yellow.

REFLECT: Fractions tell about probabilities that are between impossible (0) and certain (1). The denominator tells how many outcomes are possible. The numerator tells how many of the possible outcomes we want. For example, when we roll a single number cube, there are 6 possible outcomes. There is one way to roll a 3. So, we say that the probability of rolling 3 is 1 out of 6, or $\frac{1}{6}$.

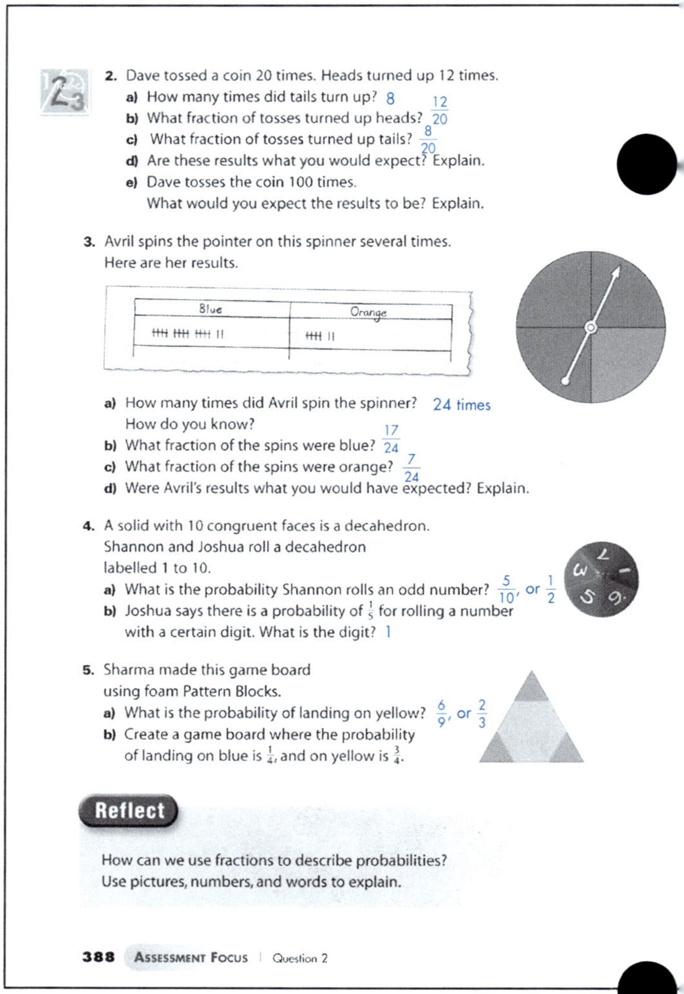
2. Dave tossed a coin 20 times. Heads turned up 12 times.
a) How many times did tails turn up? 8
b) What fraction of tosses turned up heads? $\frac{12}{20}$
c) What fraction of tosses turned up tails? $\frac{8}{20}$
d) Are these results what you would expect? Explain.
e) Dave tosses the coin 100 times.
What would you expect the results to be? Explain.

3. Avril spins the pointer on this spinner several times.
Here are her results.

Blue	Orange
𝍸𝍸𝍸 II	𝍸 II

a) How many times did Avril spin the spinner? 24 times
How do you know?
b) What fraction of the spins were blue? $\frac{17}{24}$
c) What fraction of the spins were orange? $\frac{7}{24}$
d) Were Avril's results what you would have expected? Explain.

4. A solid with 10 congruent faces is a decahedron.
Shannon and Joshua roll a decahedron
labelled 1 to 10.
a) What is the probability Shannon rolls an odd number? $\frac{5}{10}$, or $\frac{1}{2}$
b) Joshua says there is a probability of $\frac{1}{5}$ for rolling a number with a certain digit. What is the digit? 1

5. Sharma made this game board
using foam Pattern Blocks.
a) What is the probability of landing on yellow? $\frac{6}{9}$, or $\frac{2}{3}$
b) Create a game board where the probability of landing on blue is $\frac{1}{4}$, and on yellow is $\frac{3}{4}$.

Reflect

How can we use fractions to describe probabilities?
Use pictures, numbers, and words to explain.

388 ASSESSMENT FOCUS | Question 2

ASSESSMENT FOR LEARNING

What to Look For	What to Do
Understanding concepts ✔ Students understand that fractions are a way of stating probabilities. ***Communicating*** ✔ Students can describe particular outcomes as fractions of the set of all possible outcomes.	***Extra Support:*** Students may benefit from modelling question 1 with Colour Tiles, question 2 with a coin, question 3 with a spinner, question 4 with a decahedron, and question 5 with Pattern Blocks. They may need to be reminded that the denominator of a fraction tells how many pieces are in the whole object or set. Students can use Step-by-Step 3 (Master 11.13) to complete question 2. ***Extra Practice:*** Students can do the Additional Activity, *Fold Your Tents!* (Master 11.9).

Recording and Reporting
Master 11.2 Ongoing Observations: Probability

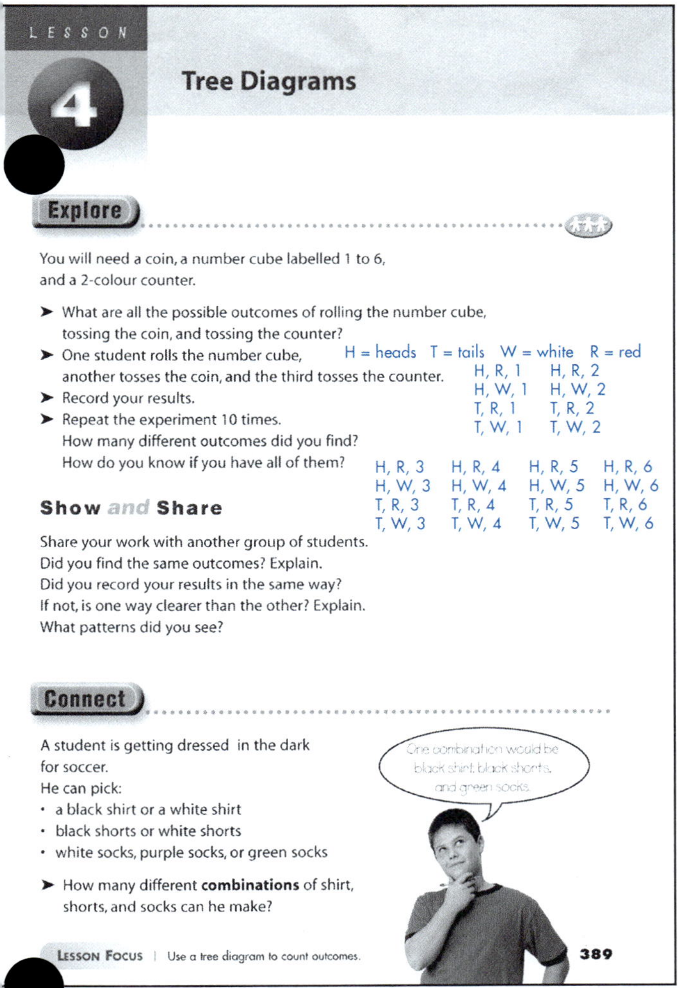

LESSON 4

Tree Diagrams

Explore

You will need a coin, a number cube labelled 1 to 6, and a 2-colour counter.

➤ What are all the possible outcomes of rolling the number cube, tossing the coin, and tossing the counter?

➤ One student rolls the number cube, another tosses the coin, and the third tosses the counter.

➤ Record your results.

➤ Repeat the experiment 10 times.
How many different outcomes did you find?
How do you know if you have all of them?

H = heads T = tails W = white R = red

H, R, 1	H, R, 2	H, R, 3	H, R, 4	H, R, 5	H, R, 6
H, W, 1	H, W, 2	H, W, 3	H, W, 4	H, W, 5	H, W, 6
T, R, 1	T, R, 2	T, R, 3	T, R, 4	T, R, 5	T, R, 6
T, W, 1	T, W, 2	T, W, 3	T, W, 4	T, W, 5	T, W, 6

Show and Share

Share your work with another group of students.
Did you find the same outcomes? Explain.
Did you record your results in the same way?
If not, is one way clearer than the other? Explain.
What patterns did you see?

Connect

A student is getting dressed in the dark for soccer.
He can pick:

- a black shirt or a white shirt
- black shorts or white shorts
- white socks, purple socks, or green socks

➤ How many different **combinations** of shirt, shorts, and socks can he make?

LESSON FOCUS | Use a tree diagram to count outcomes. 389

Tree Diagrams

LESSON ORGANIZER 40–50 min

Curriculum Focus: Use a tree diagram to count outcomes. (5m123)

Teacher Materials
Optional
- coins
- number cubes
- 2-colour counters
- coloured cubes

Student Materials
- coins
- number cubes
- 2-colour counters

Optional
- coloured cubes
- paper bags
- Step-by-Step 4 (Master 11.14)
- Extra Practice 2 (Master 11.19)

Vocabulary: tree diagram, combinations, order

Assessment: Master 11.2 Ongoing Observations: Probability

Key Math Learnings

1. A tree diagram can be used to display the possible outcomes in an event that consists of two or more simple events.
2. A tree diagram can be used to count outcomes.

BEFORE Get Started

Show students a coin, a number cube, and a 2-colour counter.

Ask:

- How many outcomes are possible when we toss this number cube? What are they? (*6; 1, 2, 3, 4, 5, and 6*)
- How many outcomes are possible when we flip this coin? What are they? (*2; heads and tails*)
- How many outcomes are possible when we toss this counter? What are they? (*2; red and white*)

Present *Explore.* Explain that the first question will be the focus for the day's activity and the topic of *Show and Share.* Ask a volunteer to read the directions for the experiment.

DURING Explore

Ongoing Assessment: Observe and Listen

As students work, ask questions, such as:

- What combinations of outcomes have you found? (*heads, 5, red; tails, 4, red; heads, 2, white*)
- How are you keeping track of what you have found? (*In a table. I list all the outcomes that have heads in one column and all the outcomes with tails in another.*)
- Have you found all the possible outcomes? (*No, other combinations could happen.*)

Watch to see students sort their results and look for ways to determine other possible outcomes. Encourage any reasonably efficient ways of organizing the outcomes.

REACHING ALL LEARNERS

Alternative Explore

Materials: paper bags

Have each group of students choose 2 starters, 6 main courses, and 2 desserts. They write each on a piece of paper and place each course of the meal in a paper bag. Each student then draws a course from one bag and the group notes the resulting meal. The group repeats the experiment 10 times.

Early Finishers

Have students make up a simple restaurant menu and create a story problem about the possible combinations of meals, drinks, and desserts. They should pose their problem to other students who are finished early.

Common Misconceptions

➤ Students launch into producing various possible outcomes without organizing their work.

How to Help: Help students begin a tree diagram by focusing on one of the variables in the situation. Talk through the process of deciding what each branch should represent.

➤ Draw a tree diagram.
First, list the shirts.
Next to each shirt, list the shorts.
Next to each pair of shorts, list the socks.
Then list all possible combinations.

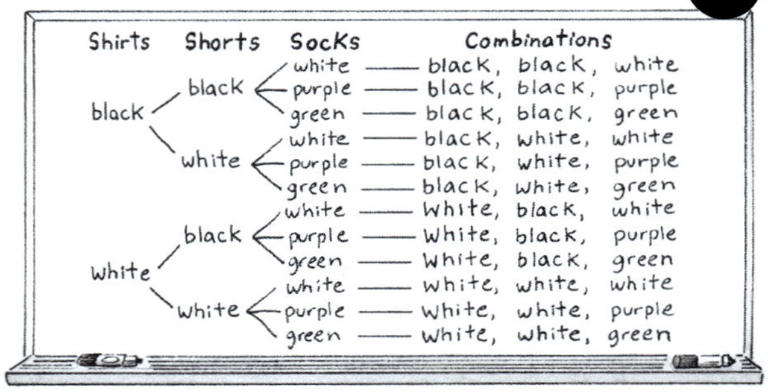

There are 12 different combinations.

➤ What is the probability the student has purple socks?
Look at the tree diagram.

Four of the 12 combinations include purple socks.
Since the socks are chosen without looking,
the probability of purple socks is $\frac{4}{12}$, or $\frac{1}{3}$.

Probability = $\frac{1}{3}$

390

Numbers Every Day

Students may choose to round both numbers to the nearest 100.

AFTER Connect

Engage students in discussing the questions in *Show and Share*. Ask students who have produced a well-organized plan to reproduce their solutions on the board.

Ask questions, such as:

- How many different combinations are possible? (*24*)
- How do you know you have found them all? (*I used a pattern: first I listed heads and red with every number from 1 to 6, then I listed heads and white, and so on.*)

If no student used a tree diagram, explain there is another efficient way to figure out possible combinations. Introduce *Connect*. Ask volunteers to use coloured cubes to model some of the possible clothing combinations. Direct students' attention to the tree diagram on Student Book, page 390. Ask:

- How does a tree diagram help us list all possible outcomes? (*It shows that we have included every choice for the combined outcome.*)
- How can you find the probability that the student has purple socks? (*I can count all the combinations that include purple socks (4), and the total number of possible outcomes (12) to make a fraction that tells the probability:* $\frac{4}{12}$.)

Practice

Assessment Focus: Question 3

Students should understand that:

- The 4 members of the relay team can be arranged in 24 different orders.
- The probability of Tansy running first can be shown as a fraction: the number of orders with Tansy in first position divided by the total number of orders.
- A coach will usually base decisions on knowledge rather than chance.

Practice

1. Suneel wants to buy a Raptors jersey and shorts.
   The jersey comes in purple, red, and black.
   The shorts come in purple and white.
   a) How many different colour combinations could Suneel choose? 6
   b) Suppose Suneel picks the colours without looking.
   What is the probability that both pieces of clothing will be purple? $\frac{1}{6}$

2. Suppose you visit the nation's capital, Ottawa, on a class trip.
   Your class wants to see Parliament Hill, the Supreme Court, and the Canadian Mint.
   In how many different orders can you see these sites? 6

3. Jawaan, Carl, Orenda, and Tansy run the 4 by 100-m relay race.
   a) Show the possible orders the 4 students could run in.
   b) The coach decides the relay order by picking names out of a hat.
   What is the probability Tansy will run first? $\frac{1}{4}$
   c) Is this really how the order would be decided? Explain.

4. Use the information in question 3.
   Jawaan is the fastest runner on the relay team.
   The coach decides he should run last.
   How many different running orders are possible now? 6

Numbers Every Day

Mental Math

Estimate each difference.
Which strategies did you use?

4048 – 53	3900
7782 – 3078	4700
1212 – 161	1000
9999 – 9901	100

Reflect

How do tree diagrams help you find all possible outcomes?
Use an example to explain.

Sample Answers

3. a)

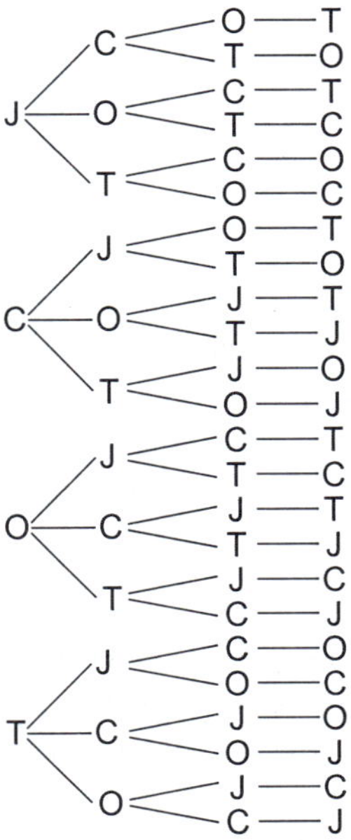

c) No. Usually, coaches put their fastest runners at the first and last positions.

REFLECT: Tree diagrams help me count all the different possibilities quickly. By looking at the diagram, I can see that I have included all the possible outcomes. For example, I could make a tree diagram to show that a clown with 3 hats, 3 wigs, and 3 suits could dress in 27 different ways.

ASSESSMENT FOR LEARNING

What to Look For	What to Do
Understanding concepts ✔ Students understand that calculating the probability of an event requires counting the total number of possible outcomes. ***Applying procedures*** ✔ Students use a tree diagram to count all possible outcomes in a situation with many different outcomes.	***Extra Support:*** Have students find and record all the possible outcomes from tossing one coin and one number cube. Students may benefit from using coloured cubes to model question 1. Students can use Step-by-Step 4 (Master 11.14) to complete question 3. ***Extra Practice:*** Students can complete the Additional Activity, *Robot Roundup* (Master 11.10). ***Extension:*** Ask students to make up combination problems related to choices in a toy store.

Recording and Reporting
Master 11.2 Ongoing Observations: Probability

Strategies Toolkit

LESSON ORGANIZER (40–50 min)

Curriculum Focus: Interpret a problem and select an appropriate strategy. (5m121, 5m123)

Teacher Materials *Optional*
- green, red, blue, and yellow sheets of paper
- photos or student drawings of basketball, volleyball, cross-country, and track-and-field athletes

Student Materials *Optional*
- cards numbered 1, 2, and 3

Vocabulary: tree diagram

Assessment: PM 1 Inquiry Process Check List, PM3 Self-Assessment Problem Solving

Key Math Learnings

1. Using a model can help you solve a problem.
2. A tree diagram is one way to find all the possible outcomes in a compound event.

LESSON 5 **Strategies Toolkit**

Explore

Ali, Brian, and Caitlin are to be photographed together.
How many different ways can they be arranged in a line? 6
What is the probability that Brian and Caitlin will be next to each other? $\frac{4}{6}$

Show and Share

Describe the strategy you used to solve this problem. I used a tree diagram.

Connect

Mayhew School has 4 championship banners to hang in a hallway.
The banners for basketball, volleyball, cross-country, and track and field are hung in line.
How many different ways can the banners be hung?
What is the probability that the banner for basketball will be next to that for volleyball?

Understand

What do you know?
- There are 4 different banners.
- The banners hang in line.

Plan

Think of a strategy to help you solve the problem.
- You can **use a model.**

Strategies
- Make a table.
- Use a model.
- Draw a diagram.
- Solve a simpler problem.
- Work backward.
- Guess and check.
- Make an organized list.
- Use a pattern.
- Draw a graph

392 LESSON FOCUS | Interpret a problem and select an appropriate strategy

BEFORE — Get Started

Invite 4 students to come to the front of the class and stand side by side. Ask:

- How else could we arrange these students? (*Move Karin from the middle to the right end of the line and put Thomas in the middle.*)

Try 2 or 3 different arrangements. Ask:

- Have we tried all the possible arrangements? (*No, there are more possibilities.*)

Present *Explore.*

DURING — Explore

Ongoing Assessment: Observe and Listen

As students work, ask questions, such as:

- How do you know you have found all the possible arrangements? (*I tried every arrangement in an organized way.*)

Encourage students to use a system as they look for the different possibilities.

AFTER — Connect

Invite students to share their solution strategies.

Introduce *Connect.* You may want to use red, green, blue, and yellow sheets of paper to model the banners. Ask:

- Can we find all the possible arrangements by shifting the banners around? (*We could, but it would take a long time and we would not be sure that we had them all.*)

Introduce the strategy **use a model**, and demonstrate using a tree diagram as a model. Ask:

- Why is drawing a tree diagram a useful strategy? (*It helps us to find possibilities quickly and to be sure we have included all of them.*)

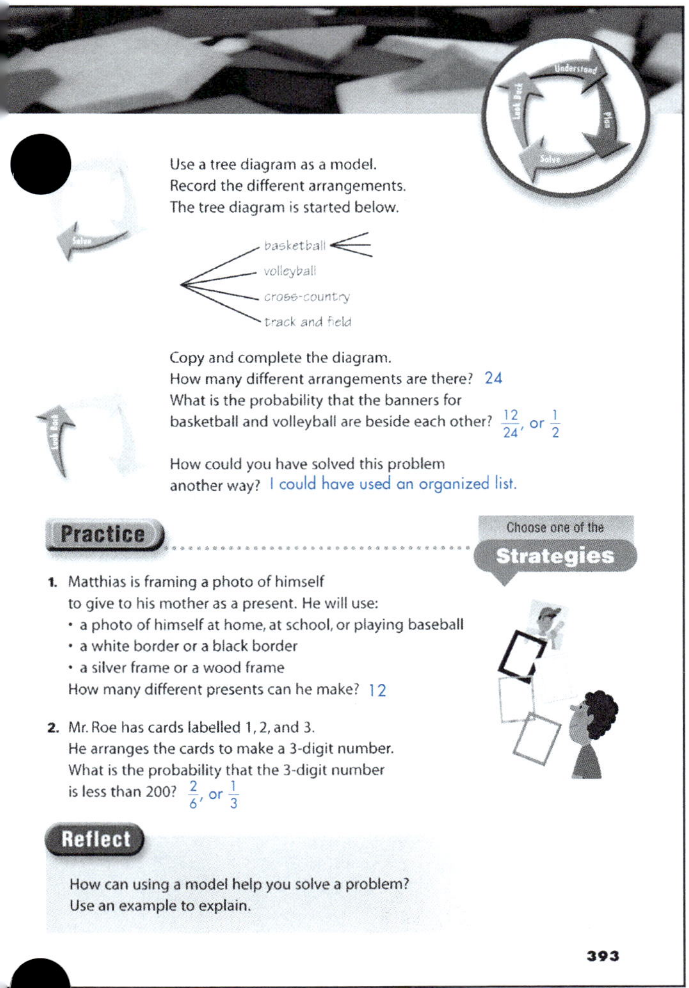
Use a tree diagram as a model.
Record the different arrangements.
The tree diagram is started below.

Copy and complete the diagram.
How many different arrangements are there? 24
What is the probability that the banners for basketball and volleyball are beside each other? $\frac{12}{24}$, or $\frac{1}{2}$

How could you have solved this problem another way? I could have used an organized list.

Practice

Choose one of the **Strategies**

1. Matthias is framing a photo of himself to give to his mother as a present. He will use:
   - a photo of himself at home, at school, or playing baseball
   - a white border or a black border
   - a silver frame or a wood frame

   How many different presents can he make? 12

2. Mr. Roe has cards labelled 1, 2, and 3. He arranges the cards to make a 3-digit number. What is the probability that the 3-digit number is less than 200? $\frac{2}{6}$, or $\frac{1}{3}$

Reflect

How can using a model help you solve a problem? Use an example to explain.

393

REACHING ALL LEARNERS

Early Finishers

Ask students to solve question 1 using two different strategies: a tree diagram and an organized list. Students should then write about which strategy seemed most appropriate and why.

Common Misconceptions

➤Students may omit some of the possibilities on a tree diagram.
How to Help: Have the students place all the different options in alphabetical categories. For example, they start with basketball, then list all the combinations for basketball first, before moving on to cross-country skiing. Once they've listed all the different combinations for cross-country skiing, they move on to track and field, and so on.

ESL Strategies

Print the name of each sport on a different coloured sheet of paper and attach a picture related to the sport. Use these "banners" to model *Connect*.

REFLECT: Using a model helps me keep my ideas organized. I can see what possibilities I have already considered and add other possibilities to them. The model lets me check that I have not left anything out or used anything more than once.

ASSESSMENT FOR LEARNING

What to Look For	What to Do
Problem solving ✔ Students can select an appropriate strategy for solving a problem. ✔ Students can justify their solutions.	***Extra Support:*** Students could use numbered cards to model the situation in question 2.
Communicating ✔ Students can describe their strategy clearly, using appropriate language.	***Extra Practice:*** Have students use a tree diagram to show all the possible outcomes of tossing a number cube and spinning a spinner that is $\frac{1}{3}$ red, $\frac{1}{3}$ blue, and $\frac{1}{3}$ yellow. ***Extension:*** Have students describe a problem-solving situation where a tree diagram would not be a suitable strategy.

Recording and Reporting
PM 1: Inquiry Process Check List
PM 3: Self-Assessment: Problem Solving

Probability in Games

LESSON ORGANIZER (40–50 min)

Curriculum Focus: Explore probability in games. (5m121)

Teacher Materials
Optional
- 2 number cubes
- deck of playing cards

Student Materials
- number cubes
- coins

Optional
- Step-by-Step 6 (Master 11.15)
- Extra Practice 3 (Master 11.20)

Vocabulary: fair, chance, prediction

Assessment: Master 11.2 Ongoing Observations: Probability

Key Math Learning

A game of chance is fair when all players have an equal probability of winning.

LESSON 6

Probability in Games

Explore — Game

What's the Difference?

You will need 2 number cubes, each labelled 1 to 6.

- Each player rolls 1 number cube.
- Find the difference of the numbers rolled.
  If the difference is less than 3, one player gets a point.
  If the difference is 3 or greater, the other player gets a point.
  The first player to score 10 points wins.
- Who do you think is more likely to win? Explain.
- Play the game 10 times.
  Record your results.
  How do your results compare to your prediction? Explain.

Show and Share

Share your results with another pair of students.
Do you think this game is fair? Explain.
If not, how could you make it fair?

Connect

Maude and Claude play a game with cards.
The standard deck of playing cards has 52 cards.
There are 4 suits: spades, diamonds, hearts, and clubs
Each suit has 13 cards.

BEFORE — Get Started

Hold up 2 number cubes. Elicit the idea that in most games a player rolls both cubes and adds the numbers to get points. Explain that students will be playing a game in which 2 players each roll one cube and use the difference rather than the sum to determine their points.

Present *Explore.* Have volunteers read aloud the rules for *What's the Difference?*

Ask:

- Who do you think is likely to win this game? (*I think both players have an equal chance. The difference can be 0, 1, 2, 3, 4, or 5, and 3 is in the middle. So, each player has $\frac{3}{6}$, or $\frac{1}{2}$ chances of winning.*)

DURING — Explore

Ongoing Assessment: Observe and Listen

As students work, make sure they are correctly figuring out their points. Ask questions, such as:

- Who has won the most rounds? Why do you think that might be?
  (*Emma has won nearly every round. I think there might be more ways to get a difference of less than 3.*)
- Is there a way you could figure out who has the best chances of winning?
  (*I could make a chart of all the differences possible with 2 number cubes, and count how many of those differences are less than 3, and how many are 3 or greater.*)

Maude picks a card and records the suit.
She replaces the card in the deck and shuffles the cards.
Claude picks a card.
If Claude's card is the same suit as Maude's,
he scores a point.
If Claude's card is a different suit,
Maude scores a point.
The player with the most points after 10 turns wins.

➤ Which player has a better chance of winning? Explain.

Suppose Maude draws a heart.
To score a point, Claude must draw a heart.
There are 13 hearts in the deck, and 39 other cards.
The probability Claude draws a heart is $\frac{13}{52}$.
The probability Claude does not draw a heart is $\frac{39}{52}$.
So, Maude has a better chance of scoring a point than Claude.

➤ How could you change the game to make it fair?

Suppose Claude gets a point if his card is the same colour as Maude's.
If the two cards are different colours, Maude gets a point.

There are 26 red cards and 26 black cards in the deck.
The probability Claude draws a red card is $\frac{26}{52}$.
The probability Claude draws a black card is $\frac{26}{52}$.
Now, Claude and Maude have equal chances of scoring a point.

Numbers Every Day

Number Strategies

Arrange the digits 2, 6, 9, and 0 so the difference is as close as possible to 5.0.

□.□ – □.□

6.9 – 2.0

395

REACHING ALL LEARNERS

Early Finishers

Have students try the fair card game described in *Connect*. Do their results show that the game is fair?

Common Misconceptions

➤ While playing with number cubes, students may reveal that they believe the next toss will be influenced by previous tosses. For example, after several low tosses, they may believe they are now "due" to get high numbers. They may justify this thinking by saying that the results need to "even out" over the long run.

How to Help: Explain that the number cubes have no memory of previous tosses. Each new toss is random. Although it is true that actual outcomes tend to come closer to theoretical probabilities over many, many trials, the likelihood of achieving a particular outcome on a single trial is unchanged by previous results.

Numbers Every Day

Students need to use their knowledge of decimal numbers and place value in a problem-solving context. Some students may use a guess-and-check strategy.

AFTER — Connect

Invite students to share the results of their games. Ask:

- Was this a fair game?
  (No. "Less than 3" came up more often than "3 or greater." There are 24 ways to get "less than 3," and only 12 ways to get "3 or greater.")
- How could you make the game fair?
  (You would have to change the rules so that each player had an equal chance of winning. The first player could get a point if the difference is 1 or 2. The second player could get a point if the difference is 0, 3, 4, or 5.)

Display a deck of playing cards. Work through *Connect*. Ensure that students understand that games of chance are fair when both players have an equal likelihood of scoring.

Ask questions such as:

- Why do you think the cards were shuffled?
  (So that each card was equally likely to be drawn)

Practice

Have number cubes available for *Practice* questions 1 and 4. Have coins available for questions 2 and 3.

Assessment Focus: Question 2

Students should understand that:

- To be fair, the game must give each player equal chances of winning.
- A toss of 3 coins has 8 different possible outcomes. Each player should have 4 ways of gaining a point.
- To design a fair game, you must list all the possible outcomes and divide them evenly between the two players.

Sample Answers

1. Carla. There are 21 ways to make a fraction less than or equal to 1, but only 15 ways to make a fraction greater than 1. My results agreed with my prediction because we rolled a fraction less than or equal to 1 more often.
2. Players take turns tossing 3 coins. Player A wins a point if there are 2 or more heads. Player B wins a point if there are 2 or more tails. This game is fair because there is a total of 8 possible outcomes: 4 ways for each player to win a point.
3. Players take turns drawing a playing card from a regular deck. Player A wins a point for drawing a face card. Player B wins a point for drawing a number card. This game is unfair because there are more number cards than face cards. To make it fair, change the rules so Player A wins a point for drawing a spade and Player B wins a point for drawing a heart. No one wins a point for drawing a club or diamond.
4. The probability I will roll a double and lose my turn is $\frac{6}{36}$, or $\frac{1}{6}$. The probability I will score points is $\frac{30}{36}$, or $\frac{5}{6}$. So, I would keep rolling to get as many points as I can. I have a higher probability of scoring a point than losing a turn.

REFLECT: The game of *Monopoly* involves strategy and probability. You use strategy to decide which properties to buy and when to add houses and hotels. You depend on chance when you roll the number cube and move around the board.

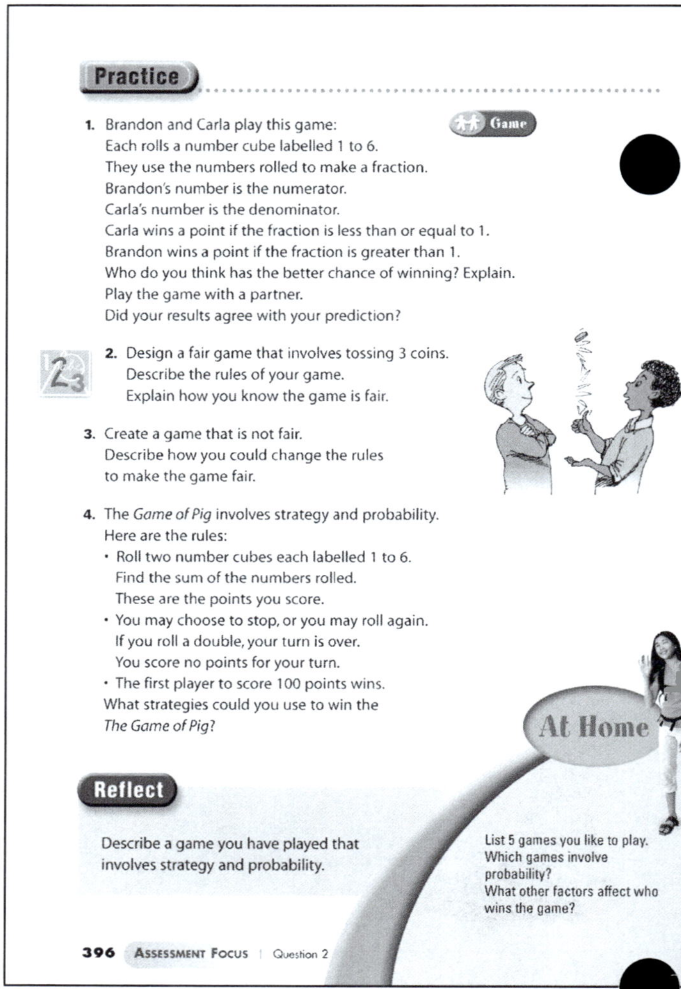

Practice

1. Brandon and Carla play this game: **Game**
Each rolls a number cube labelled 1 to 6.
They use the numbers rolled to make a fraction.
Brandon's number is the numerator.
Carla's number is the denominator.
Carla wins a point if the fraction is less than or equal to 1.
Brandon wins a point if the fraction is greater than 1.
Who do you think has the better chance of winning? Explain.
Play the game with a partner.
Did your results agree with your prediction?

2. Design a fair game that involves tossing 3 coins.
Describe the rules of your game.
Explain how you know the game is fair.

3. Create a game that is not fair.
Describe how you could change the rules to make the game fair.

4. The *Game of Pig* involves strategy and probability.
Here are the rules:
   - Roll two number cubes each labelled 1 to 6. Find the sum of the numbers rolled. These are the points you score.
   - You may choose to stop, or you may roll again. If you roll a double, your turn is over. You score no points for your turn.
   - The first player to score 100 points wins.

   What strategies could you use to win the *The Game of Pig*?

Reflect

Describe a game you have played that involves strategy and probability.

At Home

List 5 games you like to play.
Which games involve probability?
What other factors affect who wins the game?

396 ASSESSMENT FOCUS | Question 2

ASSESSMENT FOR LEARNING

What to Look For	What to Do
Understanding concepts ✔ Students understand that a fair game offers both players equal chances of winning. ***Applying Procedures*** ✔ Students can use a list or table of outcomes to identify all possible outcomes, and determine which combinations of outcomes are equally likely.	***Extra Support:*** Students may benefit from reviewing the charts of number cube outcomes in Lesson 2. Students can use Step-by-Step 6 (Master 11.15) to complete question 2. ***Extra Practice:*** Students can invent fair games using 3 or more number cubes. ***Extension:*** Have students design a fair game for 3 players using 2 number cubes.

Recording and Reporting
Master 11.2 Ongoing Observations: Probability

Professional Sports Coach

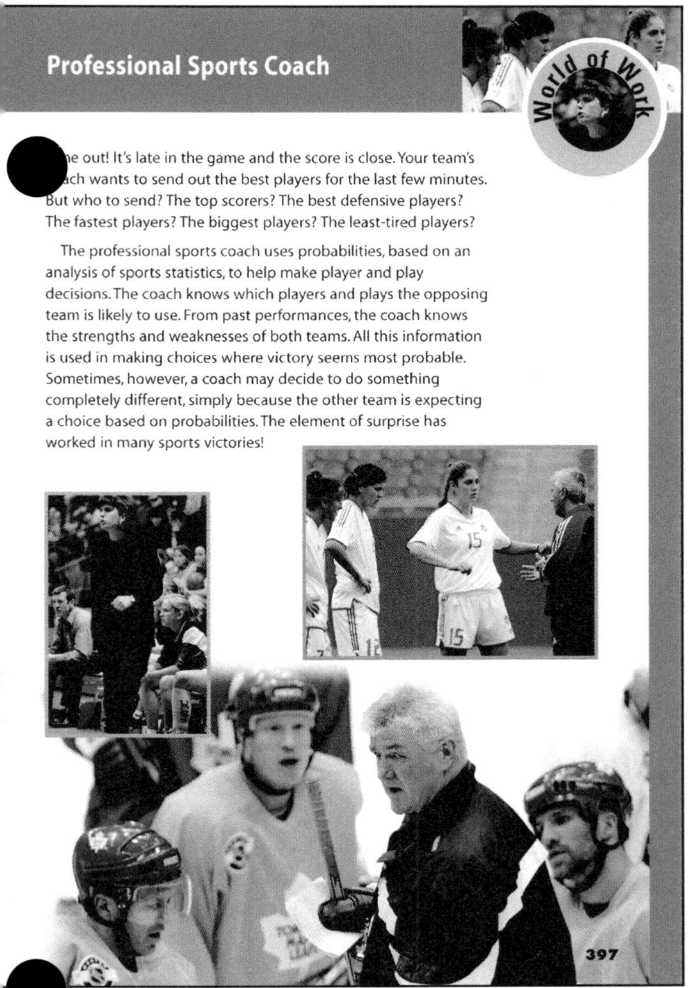
Professional Sports Coach

...e out! It's late in the game and the score is close. Your team's ...ch wants to send out the best players for the last few minutes. But who to send? The top scorers? The best defensive players? The fastest players? The biggest players? The least-tired players?

The professional sports coach uses probabilities, based on an analysis of sports statistics, to help make player and play decisions. The coach knows which players and plays the opposing team is likely to use. From past performances, the coach knows the strengths and weaknesses of both teams. All this information is used in making choices where victory seems most probable. Sometimes, however, a coach may decide to do something completely different, simply because the other team is expecting a choice based on probabilities. The element of surprise has worked in many sports victories!

397

Coaches work with teams, individuals, professional sportspeople, and amateurs. Professional sports coaches teach the rules and demonstrate the skills of a sport. They select players for teams, and seek out and encourage talented players. They organize and control practice sessions, and manage coaching staff, such as the assistant coach. Sports coaches plan fitness programs, and ensure players use appropriate training and equipment. They work out the tactics, study the skills of players' opponents, and organize courses to help improve players' skills.

Much of the early study of probability was done as a result of mathematicians' interest in games and gambling. Systematic mathematical study began in 1654 when Pierre de Fermat and Blaise Pascal corresponded about a problem. "But is it probable that probability gives assurance?", wrote Pascal. "Nothing gives certainty but truth, nothing gives rest but the sincere search for truth."

Coaches in any sport that permits substitution of players can use statistics and estimates of probability to improve their teams' chances of winning. Past records may not help—a hurdler may fall in the final of a race she is probably going to win. This happened to Perdita Felicien in an Olympic final in 2004.

Intuitive estimates of probability can be dramatically different from the actual probability. For example, in a class of 25 students, the probability of two sharing the same birthday is greater than one-half. Most people would say that two authors, unknown to each other, choosing to use exactly the same name for a character in a novel is very unlikely. Canadian authors Adele Wiseman and Marian Engel both named characters Odessa Yarker after seeing a sign on a highway for the towns of Odessa and Yarker. Another author wrote a novel published in 1898, 14 years before the sinking of the Titanic, describing the sinking of the Titan, a ship that hit an iceberg!

LESSON ORGANIZER

40–50 min

Assessment: Masters 11.1 Unit Rubric: Probability, 11.4 Unit Summary: Probability

Unit 11 Show What You Know

LESSON

1, 2, 3 — **1.** Each letter of the word MATHEMATICS is written on a card. The cards are shuffled. One card is drawn without looking.
- **a)** Which letter is most likely to be drawn? M, T, or A
- **b)** Which letter is least likely to be drawn? I, C, H, S, or E
- **c)** What is the probability of drawing each letter?

1, 2 — **2.** Order these events from most likely to least likely. State each probability as a fraction.
- **a)** The pointer on this spinner landing on red $\frac{1}{3}$
- **b)** Tossing a coin and getting heads $\frac{1}{2}$
- **c)** Rolling a number cube and getting 5 $\frac{1}{6}$
- **d)** Drawing a diamond from a standard deck of playing cards $\frac{13}{52}$

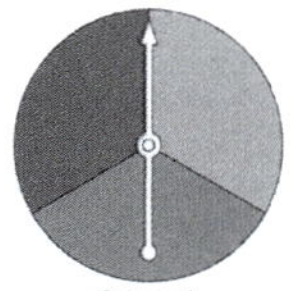

Spinner A

2 — **3.** Two number cubes are rolled. Each is labelled 1 to 6. Find the probability of each outcome.
- **a)** The product of the numbers rolled is 1. $\frac{1}{36}$
- **b)** The product is 30. $\frac{2}{36}$
- **c)** The product is less than 6. $\frac{10}{36}$
- **d)** The product is greater than 7. $\frac{22}{36}$

2, 3, 6 — **4.** Lynda has a standard deck of 52 playing cards. She shuffles the deck, then draws a card without looking.
- **a)** What is the probability Lynda draws a red card? $\frac{26}{52}$, or $\frac{1}{2}$
- **b)** What is the probability Lynda draws a 4? $\frac{4}{52}$, or $\frac{1}{13}$
- **c)** What is the probability Lynda draws the 4 of diamonds? $\frac{1}{52}$

398

Sample Answers

1. c) The probability of drawing M, T, or A is $\frac{2}{11}$.
The probability of drawing I, C, S, E, or H is $\frac{1}{11}$.

2. b, a, d, c

5. c) The results are different from what I would expect. It is unlikely Troy would roll 6 so many times. It is also unlikely he would roll the other numbers exactly 5 times each. The probability of being rolled is $\frac{1}{6}$ for each number. So, in 36 rolls, each number will probably be rolled about 6 times.

7. I know the probability of rolling a double is $\frac{6}{36}$, or $\frac{1}{6}$, because there are 6 ways to roll a double and 36 possible outcomes altogether.

Troy rolled a number cube 36 times.
A 6 was rolled 11 times.
1, 2, 3, 4, and 5 were rolled the same number of times.

a) What fraction of rolls were a 3? $\frac{5}{36}$
b) What fraction of rolls were an even number? $\frac{21}{36}$
c) Are these results different from what you would expect? Explain.

6. Haley is going to a Calgary Flames game.
She wants to buy an authentic team jersey.
The jersey comes in red, white, or black.
She also wants a cap. It comes in black or navy blue.

a) How many different combinations can Haley choose from? 6
b) Suppose Haley picks a jersey and cap without looking.
What is the probability that both pieces of clothing will be black? $\frac{1}{6}$

4 7. In the game *Monopoly*, you roll 2 number cubes, each labelled 1 to 6.
You must roll a double to get out of jail.
What is the probability you will roll a double? $\frac{1}{6}$
How do you know?

UNIT 11 Learning Goals

- ☑ use the language of probability
- ☑ conduct experiments and predict results
- ☑ use fractions to describe probability
- ☑ use tree diagrams to find probabilities
- ☑ use probability to pose and solve problems

399

ASSESSMENT FOR LEARNING

What to Look For

Understanding of concepts

✔ **Questions 2, 6, and 7:** Student can predict probability in simple experiments and use fractions to describe probability.

Application of mathematical procedures

✔ **Questions 3, 6, and 7:** Student can use a tree diagram, table, or organized list to solve a probability problem.

Communication

✔ **Questions 4, 5, and 6:** Student can connect real-life statements with probability concepts.

Problem solving:

✔ **Questions 1, 3, 4, 5, and 7:** Student can use a knowledge of probability to solve simple problems.

Recording and Reporting

Master 11.1 Unit Rubric: Probability
Master 11.4 Unit Summary: Probability

At the Pet Store!

LESSON ORGANIZER 40–50 min

Student Grouping: Groups of 2
Student Materials
- Snap Cubes
- a paper bag
- Bristol board
- coloured markers

Assessment: Masters 11.3 Performance Assessment Rubric: At the Pet Store!, 11.4 Unit Summary: Probability

Teaching notes for the Cross Strand Investigation: The Domino Effect appear in the *Grade 5 Additional Assessment Support* module.

Sample Response

Student work should include specific answers and explanations using words, numbers, and pictures where appropriate. For example:

Part 1

We think there are 20 red fish in the tank. $\frac{2}{5}$ of 50 is 20. We think there are 5 silver fish. $\frac{1}{10}$ of 50 is 5. If you subtract the silver and red fish, you have 25 fish left. The chances of picking one of the remaining orange, blue, black, white, and pink fish are equal, so there must be 5 of each of those colours in the tank.

Unit Problem At the Pet Store!

Work with a partner.
You will need:
- Snap Cubes
- a paper bag
- Bristol board

Part 1 Lucky Silver

A large tank contains 50 fish.
Suppose you pick a fish at random.
- The probability you pick a silver fish is $\frac{1}{10}$.
- The probability you pick a red fish is $\frac{2}{5}$.
- It is equally likely that you will pick one of the remaining orange, blue, black, white, or pink fish.

How many fish of each colour are in the tank?

Part 2 Red, Yellow, and Blue

➤ Choose 3 colours of Snap Cubes to represent 3 different colours of fish.
Put cubes into a bag to match these probabilities:
- The probabilities of picking a yellow fish and a blue fish are the same.
- The probability of picking a red fish is greater.

➤ Try your experiment.
Without looking, draw a cube from the bag.
Have your partner record the colour.
Return the cube to the bag.

400

Have students turn to the *Unit Launch* on pages 378 and 379 of the Student Book.

Review the Learning Goals of the unit and discuss the meanings of the Key Words. Tell students they will use these skills and concepts as they complete the *Unit Problem.*

Have Snap Cubes, paper bags, and Bristol board available.

Present the *Unit Problem.* Invite volunteers to read the guidelines and instructions for the problem aloud. Ensure students understand what they are expected to do in each of the three parts. Tell students where you would like them to record their responses to Part 1 and Part 2. Remind students that the poster for Part 3 needs to include clear explanations of their procedures.

Have one student read the Check List aloud. Ask volunteers to explain each of the criteria. Ensure students are aware of the need to explain their thinking in all their responses. Remind students that they should use the Check List to assess their work before they hand it in. You may also wish to provide students with copies of Master 11.3 Performance Assessment Rubric: At the Pet Store! to show how their work will be assessed.

Set a reasonable time for the completion of the tasks. Allow 15 min for Parts 1 and 2, and about 20 min for Part 3. Encourage students to complete the written components of Part 3 before they begin their illustrations of the fish tank.

➤ Draw a cube 10 times.
Switch roles.
Do your results match the stated probabilities? Explain.

Part 3

Suppose you are starting a fish tank.

➤ Choose 3 or 4 kinds of fish.
- Decide on the probability of picking each kind of fish.
- Decide how many fish you will have altogether.
How many fish of each kind will there be?

➤ Make a poster of your fish tank on the top half of the Bristol board.
On the bottom half, explain:
- how you chose the kind of fish
- how you decided on the probabilities
- how you found the number of fish of each kind

Check List

Your work should show
- ☑ specific answers to each of the probability questions, using fractions where appropriate
- ☑ any tables and diagrams you use to find and record your answers
- ☑ clear explanations of your procedures and results
- ☑ correct use of the language of probability

Reflect on the Unit

How can you use probability to predict outcomes?
Use pictures, words, and numbers to explain your answer.

401

Part 2

We put 4 yellow cubes, 4 blue cubes, and 12 red cubes in the bag. There should be the same number of blue and yellow because the probability of picking these colours is the same. There had to be more red cubes because the probability of picking red is greater. Altogether, we drew 20 times. Our results were:
Yellow – 3; Blue – 4; Red – 13
These results are close to the stated probabilities. We don't expect the actual results to be exactly the same as the probabilities but they are close.

Part 3

We decided to have 30 fish in our tank. We chose 3 types of fish: red, green, and yellow. We wanted the probability of picking a red fish to be $\frac{1}{2}$. This is the same as 15 out of 30, so we put 15 red fish in the tank. We wanted the probability of picking a green fish to be $\frac{1}{5}$. This is the same as 6 out of 30 so we put 6 green fish in the tank. We now had 21 fish in the tank, so we knew there needed to be 9 yellow fish to make the total add up to 30. The probability of picking a yellow fish is 9 out of 30. We could write this as $\frac{9}{30}$ or $\frac{3}{10}$.

Reflect on the Unit

When events happen by chance, I need to figure out all the possible outcomes. Then, I decide what fraction of the possible outcomes matches the outcome I am looking for. For example, if I have a bag with 10 red marbles and 5 blue marbles, there are 15 marbles altogether. The probability I will pick a red marble is $\frac{10}{15}$ and the probability I will pick a blue marble is $\frac{5}{15}$. The probability I will pick a yellow marble is zero; it's impossible to pick a yellow marble when there are none in the bag!

ASSESSMENT FOR LEARNING

What to Look For

Understanding concepts

✔ Students understand that the probability of an event depends on how often it is represented in the set of all possible outcomes.

✔ Students use fractions to describe probability.

Applying procedures

✔ Students use tables and diagrams to determine and record probability.

Communicating

✔ Students use language effectively to describe probability and explain their reasoning.

What to Do

Extra Support: Make the problem accessible. Suggest that students start Part 1 with the simpler problem of a tank containing 10 fish. Encourage the use of Snap Cubes or other manipulatives to model the problem.
Some students may have difficulty explaining their thinking in writing. Assess these students verbally. Are they able to communicate their ideas orally, using appropriate mathematical language?

Recording and Reporting

Master 11.3 Performance Assessment Rubric: At the Pet Store!
Master 11.4 Unit Summary: Probability

Cumulative Review

LESSON ORGANIZER

Student Materials
- calculators
- 1-cm grid paper (PM 23)
- square dot paper (PM 25)

Units 1–11 Cumulative Review

UNIT

1 **1.** Here is the table for an Input/Output machine.
a) The patterns continue.
Write the next 3 input and output numbers.
b) Draw the Input/Output machine for this table.

Input	Output
99	33
96	32
93	31
90	30

2 **2.** Find each result.
a) 2206 + 985 = 3191 **b)** 3436 − 3351 = 85 **c)** 3689 − 468 = 3221
d) 73 × 24 1752 **e)** 7808 ÷ 8 976 **f)** 44 × 82 3608

3. Ryan earned $162 babysitting and doing odd jobs.
He earned $5 per hour for 12 h of babysitting.
How much did he earn doing odd jobs? $102

3 **4.** Is a rhombus a regular polygon?
How do you know?

5. Name each triangle 2 ways.
How did you choose each name?

a)
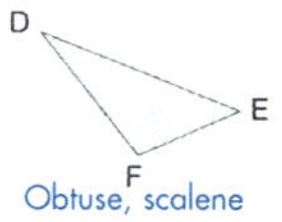

Obtuse, scalene

b)
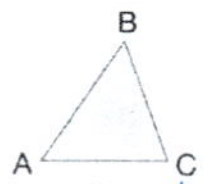

Acute, isosceles

c)
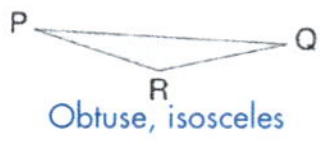

Obtuse, isosceles

4 **6.** Add, subtract, multiply, or divide.
a) 4.68 − 3.2 1.48 **b)** 48.7 ÷ 10 4.87 **c)** 153.9 ÷ 10 15.39 **d)** 12.4 − 3.03 9.37
e) 4.68 × 100 468 **f)** 5.8 + 2.02 7.82 **g)** 0.56 + 5.6 6.16 **h)** 20.31 × 10 203.1

7. A decimal with hundredths rounds to 2.
What might the decimal be? Give 3 different answers. 2.01, 2.49, 1.99

5 **8.** Find the mean and the mode of each set of data.
a) 11, 16, 15, 13, 8, 20, 8 13; 8 **b)** 44, 32, 50, 44, 50, 33, 47, 44 43; 44

404

Sample Answers

1. a) Input: 87, 84, 81
Output: 29, 28, 27
b) Input ÷ 3 = Output

4. No, because it does not have all angles equal (unless it is a square).

5. a) One angle is greater than 90° and no sides are equal.
b) All angles are less than 90° and 2 sides are equal.
c) One angle is greater than 90° and 2 sides are equal.

9.
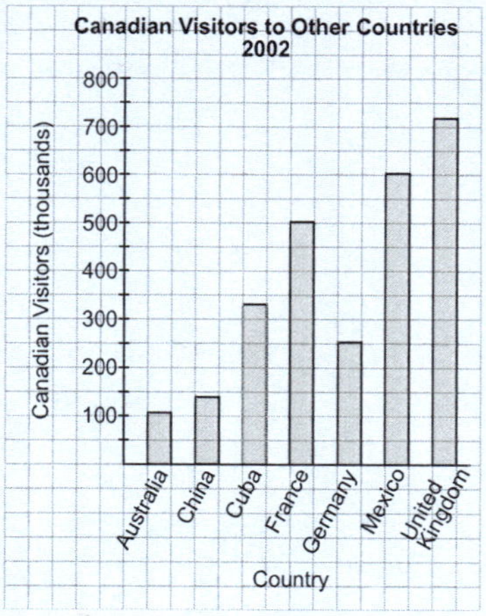

I chose a bar graph, because the differences in the data are easier to see.

12. No. Mobin should have gotten $8.71 in change. He got $8.81 in change, which is 10¢ too much.

13. a)
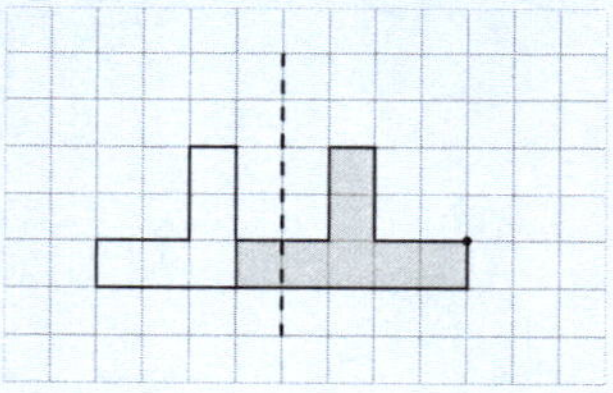

b)
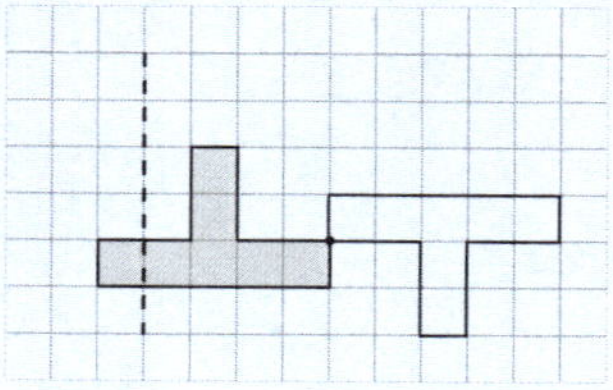

c)
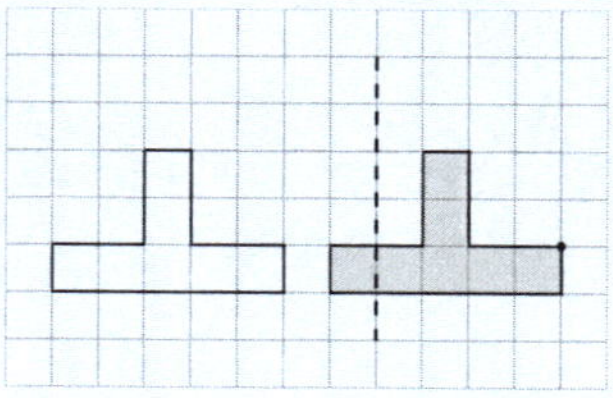

. The table shows the number of Canadians that visited various countries in 2002.
Display these data in a graph.
Which type of graph did you choose to draw? Why?

Country	Canadian Visitors (thousands)
Australia	108
China	140
Cuba	331
France	505
Germany	255
Mexico	607
United Kingdom	720

6

10. Use SI notation to write:

a) the exact time 09:43:37
b) the time to the nearest minute 09:44

11. This object was made with centimetre cubes. Find the volume of the object in cubic centimetres and in millilitres.

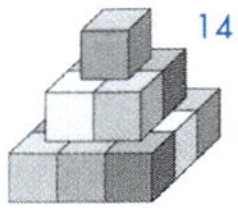

14 cm^3, 14 mL

12. Mobin bought groceries for $71.29.
He paid with two $20 bills and four $10 bills.
He got this change: a $5 bill, a toonie, a loonie, 2 quarters, 3 dimes, and a penny
Did Mobin get the correct change?
How do you know?

7

13. Copy this figure on 1-cm grid paper.
Draw the image after each transformation.
a) a reflection in the broken line
b) a $\frac{1}{2}$ turn clockwise about the dot
c) a translation of 6 squares left

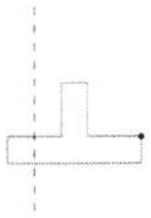

405

14. a), b)

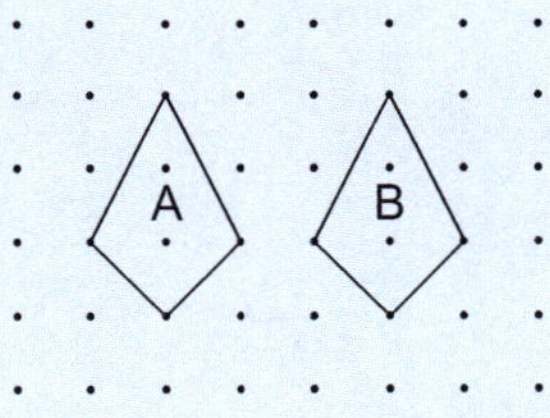

I know A and B are congruent because they have the same size and shape.

c)

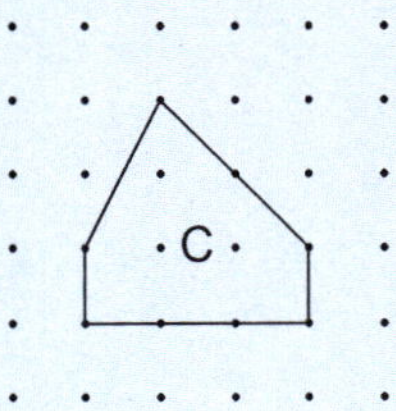

I drew C with 5 sides instead of 4, so it does not have the same size and shape as A and B.

15.

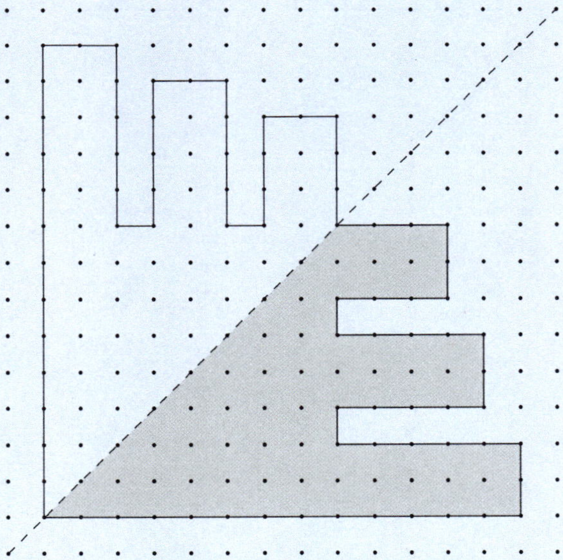

The new figure is symmetrical. The broken line is the line of symmetry.

UNIT 7

14. Use dot paper.
a) Draw a polygon on dot paper. Label it A.
b) Draw a polygon that is congruent to Polygon A.
Label it B.
How do you know Polygons A and B are congruent?
c) Draw a polygon that is not congruent to Polygons A and B.
Label it C.
How did you decide how to draw Polygon C?

15. Copy the figure and the broken line on dot paper.
Use the broken line as a mirror line.
Draw the mirror image of the figure so the two figures form a new figure.
Is the new figure symmetrical?
How do you know?

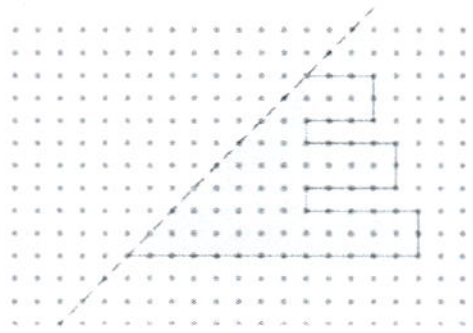

UNIT 8

16. Copy each statement.
Write a fraction to make each statement true.
a) $1\frac{4}{5} < \square$ $2\frac{4}{5}$ b) $\frac{7}{10} < \square$ $\frac{9}{10}$ c) $\square < \frac{6}{5}$ $\frac{4}{5}$ d) $\frac{13}{4} < \square$ $\frac{17}{4}$

17. Write each fraction or mixed number as a decimal. 3.75, 0.8, 0.3, 4.5, 2.1
Then write the decimals in order from least to greatest. 0.3, 0.8, 2.1, 3.75, 4.5
$\frac{15}{4}, \frac{4}{5}, \frac{3}{10}, \frac{9}{2}, \frac{21}{10}$

18. Draw a picture to represent each decimal.
Then write 2 fractions for each decimal.
a) 0.4 $\frac{4}{10}, \frac{2}{5}$ b) 0.35 $\frac{35}{100}, \frac{7}{20}$ c) 0.9 $\frac{9}{10}, \frac{90}{100}$ d) 0.25 $\frac{25}{100}, \frac{1}{4}$

19. Find each product or quotient.
a) 8.63×2 17.26 b) $29.82 \div 7$ 4.26 c) $45.4 \div 5$ 9.08 d) 3.02×9 27.18

20. An ice cream cone costs $1.97.
Hunter bought 5 ice cream cones.
How much did Hunter pay? $9.85

406

18. a) 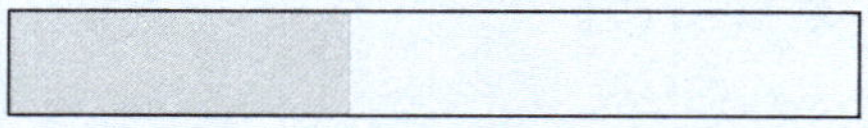 0.4

b) 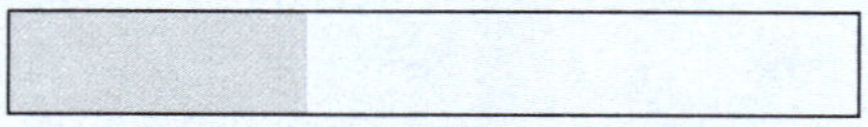 0.35

c) 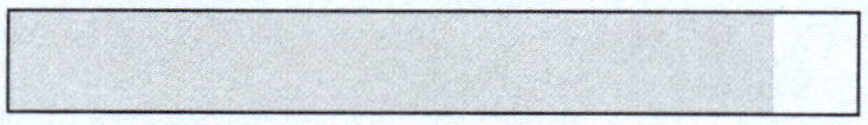 0.9

d) 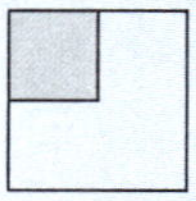 0.25

21. a) 20 cm^2; 24 cm; 2.4 dm
b) 23.43 m^2; 20.8 m; 2080 cm

22. a) 12 cm by 9 cm; 10 cm by 11 cm; 14 cm by 7 cm
b) 6 m by 6 m; 2 m by 18 m; 3 m by 12 m

24.

Fraction	Decimal	Fraction	Decimal
$\frac{1}{2}$	0.5	$\frac{1}{4}$	0.25
$\frac{2}{2}$	1	$\frac{2}{4}$	0.5
$\frac{3}{2}$	1.5	$\frac{3}{4}$	0.75
$\frac{4}{2}$	2	$\frac{4}{4}$	1
$\frac{5}{2}$	2.5	$\frac{5}{4}$	1.25
$\frac{6}{2}$	3	$\frac{6}{4}$	1.5
$\frac{7}{2}$	3.5	$\frac{7}{4}$	1.75
$\frac{8}{2}$	4	$\frac{8}{4}$	2
$\frac{9}{2}$	4.5	$\frac{9}{4}$	2.25
$\frac{10}{2}$	5	$\frac{10}{4}$	2.5

. Find the area and the perimeter of each figure.
Write each perimeter in a different unit.

a)

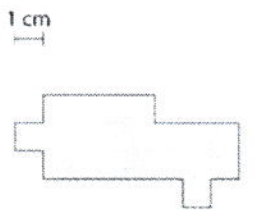

b)

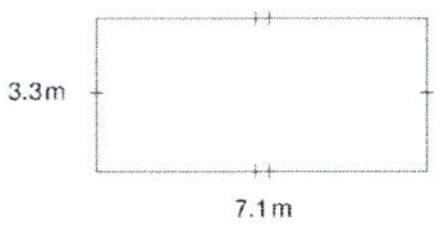

22. What might the dimensions of each rectangle be?
Give 3 different answers.

a) a rectangle with perimeter 42 cm
b) a rectangle with area 36 m^2

10 **23.** Multiply 30 × 4. 120
Use the product 30 × 4 to find each missing factor.

a) 30 × ☐ = 150 5 **b)** ☐ × 30 = 240 8
c) 900 = 30 × ☐ 30 **d)** 30 × ☐ = 330 11

24. Copy and complete each table for fractions with numerators to 10.

Fraction	Decimal	Fraction	Decimal
$\frac{1}{2}$		$\frac{1}{4}$	
$\frac{2}{2}$		$\frac{2}{4}$	
$\frac{3}{2}$		$\frac{3}{4}$	

11 **25.** Keltie rolls two number cubes.
Each number cube is labelled 3 to 8.
Find the probability of each outcome.

a) The product of the numbers rolled is 40. $\frac{2}{36}$ or $\frac{1}{18}$
b) The sum of the numbers rolled is less than 8. $\frac{3}{36}$ or $\frac{1}{12}$
c) The product of the numbers rolled is 65. 0

407

Evaluating Student Learning: Preparing to Report: Unit 11 Probability

This unit provides an opportunity to report on the **Data Management and Probability** strand. *Master 11.4: Unit Summary: Probability* provides a comprehensive format for recording and summarizing evidence collected.

Here is an example of a completed summary chart for this Unit:

Strand: *Data Management and Probability*	**Problem solving**	**Understanding of concepts**	**Application of mathematical procedures**	**Communication**	***Overall***
Ongoing Observations	2	3	2	3	**2/3**
Strategies Toolkit (Lesson 5)	3				**3**
Work samples or portfolios; conferences	2	3	3	3	**3**
Show What You Know	3	3	3	3	**3**
Unit Test	2	3	2	3	**2/3**
Unit Problem At the Pet Store!	3	3	2	3	**3**
Achievement Level for reporting					**3**

Recording	How to Report
Ongoing Observations	Use *Master 11.2 Ongoing Observations: Probability* to determine the most consistent level achieved in each category. Enter it in the chart. Choose to summarize by achievement category, or simply to enter an overall level. Observations from late in the unit should be most heavily weighted.
Strategies Toolkit (problem solving)	Use *PM 1: Inquiry Process Check List* with the Strategies Toolkit (Lesson 5). Transfer results to the summary form. Teachers may choose to enter a level in the Problem solving column and/or Communication.
Portfolios or collections of work samples; conferences, or interviews	Use *Master 11.1 Unit Rubric: Probability* to guide evaluation of collections of work and information gathered in conferences. Teachers may choose to focus particular attention on the Assessment Focus questions. Work from late in the unit should be most heavily weighted.
Show What You Know	*Master 11.1 Unit Rubric: Probability* may be helpful in determining levels of achievement. #2, 6, and 7 provide evidence of Understanding of concepts; #3, 6, and 7 provide evidence of Application of mathematical procedures; #1, 3, 4, 5, and 7 provide evidence of Problem solving; #4, 5, and 6 provide evidence of Communication.
Unit Test	*Master 11.1 Unit Rubric: Probability* may be helpful in determining levels of achievement. Part A provides evidence of Understanding of concepts; Part B provides evidence of Application of mathematical procedures; Part C provides evidence of Problem solving; all parts provide evidence of Communication.
Unit performance task	Use *Master 11.3 Performance Assessment Rubric: At the Pet Store!*. The *Unit Problem* offers a snapshot of students' achievement. In particular, it shows their ability to synthesize and apply what they have learned.
Student Self-Assessment	Note students' perceptions of their own progress. This may take the form of an oral or written comment, or a self-rating.
Comments	Analyse the pattern of achievement to identify strengths and needs. In some cases, specific actions may need to be planned to support the learner.

Learning Skills	Ongoing Records
PM 4: Learning Skills Check List Use to record and report throughout a reporting period, rather than for each unit and/or strand.	*PM 10: Summary Class Records: Strands* *PM 11: Summary Class Records: Achievement Categories* *PM 12: Summary Record: Individual* Use to record and report evaluations of student achievement over several clusters, a reporting period, or a school year. These can also be used in place of the Unit Summary.

Name ____________________ Date ______________

Master 11.1

Unit Rubric: Probability

	Level 1	Level 2	Level 3	Level 4
Problem solving • chooses and carries out appropriate strategies to pose and solve problems involving probability (e.g., tree diagrams)	with assistance, chooses and carries out a limited range of appropriate strategies to pose and solve problems; results are rarely reasonable	with limited assistance, chooses and carries out some appropriate strategies to pose and solve problems; results are frequently reasonable	chooses and carries out appropriate strategies to pose and solve problems; results are usually reasonable	chooses and carries out appropriate strategies that produce reasonable results; may be innovative
Understanding of concepts • shows understanding by appropriately explaining: – predictions of probability in simple experiments – connections between real-life statements and probability concepts	may be unable to explain: – predictions of probability in simple experiments – connections between real-life statements and probability concepts	partially able to explain: – predictions of probability in simple experiments – connections between real-life statements and probability concepts	appropriately explains: – predictions of probability in simple experiments – connections between real-life statements and probability concepts	in various contexts, consistently and appropriately explains: – predictions of probability in simple experiments – connections between real-life statements and probability concepts
Application of mathematical procedures • uses appropriate procedures to accurately: – use fractions to describe probability – use tree diagrams to find and record probabilities	limited accuracy; major errors or omissions in: – using fractions to describe probability – using tree diagrams to find and record probabilities	somewhat accurate; makes frequent minor errors/omissions in: – using fractions to describe probability – using tree diagrams to find and record probabilities	generally accurate; makes few errors/omissions in: – using fractions to describe probability – using tree diagrams to find and record probabilities	accurate; rarely makes errors/omissions in: – using fractions to describe probability – using tree diagrams to find and record probabilities
Communication • discusses procedures, results and reasoning clearly, including appropriate terminology (e.g., certain, outcome, possible, fair game, combination)	needs assistance to describe procedures, discuss results and explain reasoning; often unclear and imprecise	describes procedures, discusses results, and explains reasoning with some clarity and precision	describes procedures, discusses results, and explains reasoning clearly and precisely	describes procedures, discusses results and explains reasoning clearly, precisely, and confidently

Name ____________________ Date ________________

Master 11.2

Ongoing Observations: Probability

The behaviours described under each heading are examples; they are not intended to be an exhaustive list of all that might be observed. More detailed descriptions are provided in each lesson under *Assessment for Learning*.

STUDENT ACHIEVEMENT: Probability				
Student	**Problem solving** ▪ Uses appropriate strategies to pose and solve problems involving probability	**Understanding of concepts** ▪ Explains predictions in simple experiments ▪ Connects real-life statements and probability concepts	**Application of mathematical procedures** ▪ Uses fractions to describe probability ▪ Uses tree diagrams to find and record probabilities	**Communication** ▪ Discusses procedures, results, and reasoning clearly ▪ Uses language of probability

Level 1 – very limited; Level 2 – somewhat or limited; Level 3 – satisfactory; Level 4 – thorough

Name ____________________ Date ______________

Master 11.3

Performance Assessment Rubric: At the Pet Store!

	Level 1	Level 2	Level 3	Level 4
Problem solving • chooses and carries out appropriate strategies, including tables and diagrams, to: – solve problems involving probability – use probabilities to design the composition of a fish tank	with assistance, chooses and carries out a limited range of appropriate strategies, with little success, to: – solve problems involving probability – use probabilities to design the composition of a fish tank	chooses and carries out some appropriate strategies, with partial success, to: – solve problems involving probability – use probabilities to design the composition of a fish tank	chooses and successfully carries out appropriate strategies to: – solve problems involving probability – use probabilities to design the composition of a fish tank	chooses and successfully carries out effective strategies to: – solve problems involving probability – use probabilities to design the composition of a fish tank (introduces some complexity to the task)
Understanding of concepts • shows understanding by providing reasonable explanations of: – differences between predicted probabilities and actual results – how probabilities and number of each type of fish were determined	shows very limited understanding by giving inappropriate explanations of: – differences between predicted probabilities and actual results – how probabilities and number of fish were determined	shows limited understanding giving appropriate but incomplete explanations of: – differences between predicted probabilities and actual results – how probabilities and number of fish were determined	shows understanding by giving appropriate explanations of: – differences between predicted probabilities and actual results – how probabilities and number of fish were determined	shows thorough understanding by giving appropriate and complete explanations of: – differences between predicted probabilities and actual results – how probabilities and number of fish were determined
Application of mathematical procedures • uses appropriate procedures to accurately calculate probabilities using fractions	limited accuracy; major errors or omissions in calculating probabilities	somewhat accurate; several minor errors or omissions in calculating probabilities	generally accurate; few errors or omissions in calculating probabilities	accurate; very few or no errors or omissions in calculating probabilities
Communication • provides a clear presentation and explanation of results • uses language of probability (e.g., likely, probable, outcome)	presentation and discussion are unclear and imprecise; uses few appropriate mathematical terms	presentation and discussion are partially clear and precise; uses some appropriate mathematical terms	presentation and discussion are generally clear and precise; uses appropriate mathematical terms	presentation and discussion are clear, precise, and confident; uses the most appropriate mathematical terminology

Name ____________________ Date ______________

Master 11.4

Unit Summary: Probability

Review assessment records to determine the most consistent achievement levels for the assessments conducted. Some cells may be blank. *Overall* achievement levels may be recorded in each row, rather than identifying levels for each achievement category.

	Most Consistent Level of Achievement*				
Strand: *Data Management and Probability*	**Problem solving**	**Understanding of concepts**	**Application of mathematical procedures**	**Communication**	***Overall***
Ongoing Observations					
Strategies Toolkit (Lesson 5)					
Work samples or portfolios; conferences					
Show What You Know					
Unit Test					
Unit Problem At the Pet Store!					
Achievement Level for reporting					

*Use Ontario Achievement Levels 1, 2, 3, 4.

Self-Assessment:

Comments: (Strengths, Needs, Next Steps)

Name ____________________ Date ______________

Master 11.5

To Parents and Adults at Home …

Your child's class is starting a mathematics unit on probability. As adults, we use ideas of probability in everyday life when we estimate the likelihood of risks and predict future events. Many decisions, from carrying an umbrella to buying extra life insurance, are based on our understanding of probability.

In this unit, your child will:

- Use the language of probability.
- Conduct experiments and predict results.
- Use fractions to describe probability.
- Use tree diagrams to find probabilities.
- Use probability to pose and solve problems.

Probability concepts can be practised at home as well as at school. Here are some suggestions for activities you can do at home:

- Listen to weather forecasts with your child. Use words such as *likely*, *unlikely*, *probable*, and *possible* to talk about the next day's weather. Compare the actual weather to the forecast weather. Help your child understand that meteorologists use past weather patterns to tell us what is *probable*, rather than *certain*, in the future.

- Play board and card games with your child. Compare games that depend on chance (for example, snakes and ladders) with games that depend on skill (for example, chess). Look for games that combine chance and skill.

- Talk with your child about superstitions. For instance, you might help your child realize that wishing hard or having a "lucky number" does not influence the cards you are dealt in a game.

Name ____________________ Date ______________

Master 11.6

Blank Spinners

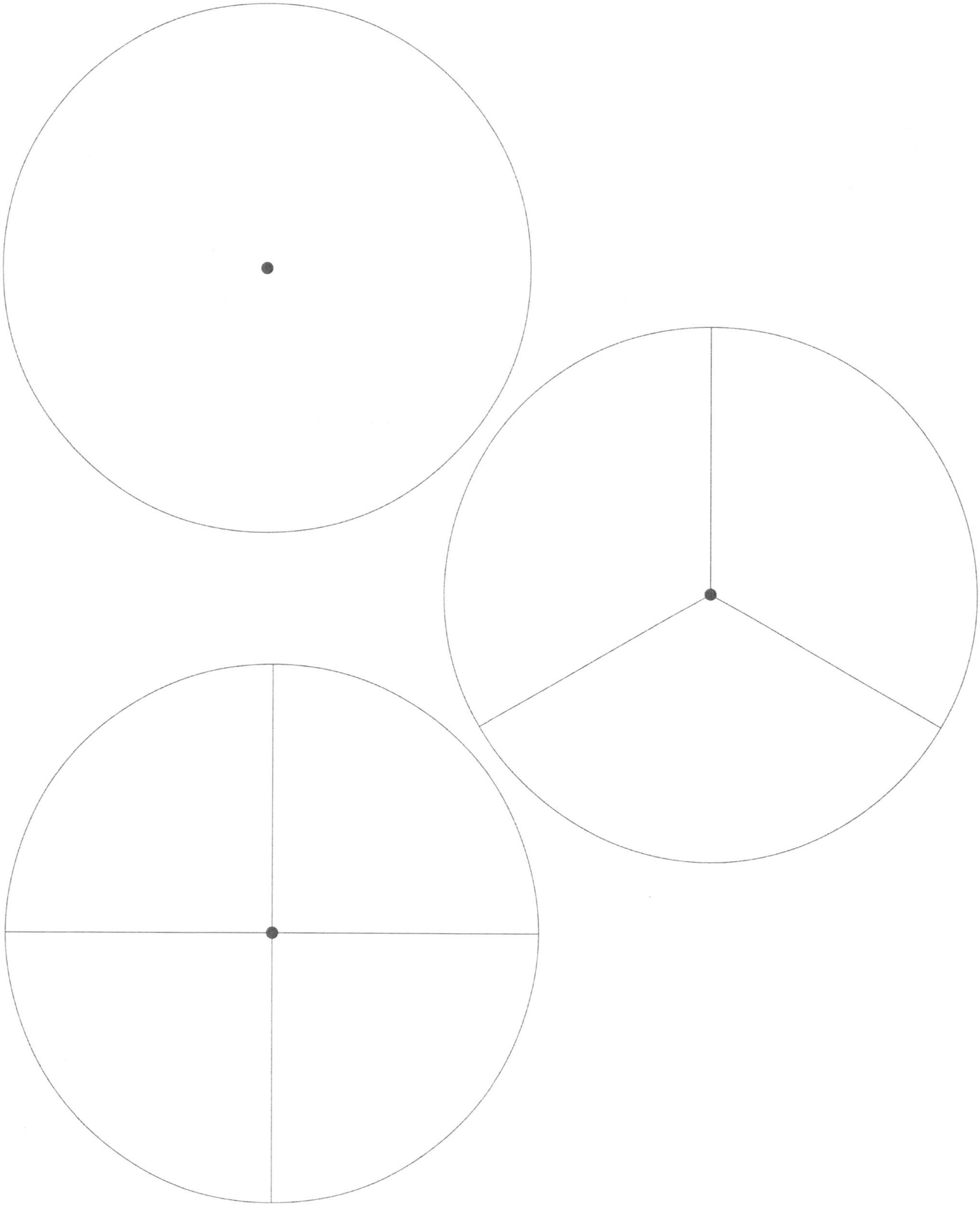

Name ____________________ Date ______________

Master 11.7

Additional Activity 1: Match My Meaning!

Work with a partner. Carefully cut apart these cards.

certain	will definitely happen
impossible	cannot happen
possible	could happen
probable	is likely to happen
improbable	is unlikely to happen

- Place all the cards face down.
- Take turns flipping over 2 cards.
- If the cards match (word and meaning), keep them and take another turn.
- The winner is the player who collects the most cards.
- Play 5 rounds. The grand winner is the player who wins the most rounds.

Take It Further:
Write about a situation that can be described using the words on the cards.

Name ____________________ Date ________________

Master 11.8

Additional Activity 2: Animal Draw

Work with a partner.

- Look at the animal names listed here. What fraction of the list are Cats? Insects? Birds? Fish?

Cougar	**Lion**	**Tiger**	**Panther**
Beetle	**Fly**	**Mosquito**	**Ladybug**
Crow	**Eagle**	**Salmon**	**Tuna**

- Cut apart the animal names and place them in a bag.
- You will pull out an animal name without looking, then replace it in the bag.
- Make a prediction. In 30 tries, about how many times do you expect to draw a cat? An insect? A fish? A bird?
- Shake up the bag. Reach in and pull out a name without looking. Record your result and replace the name. Make 30 draws in all.
- Did your actual draws match your prediction? Explain.

Take It Further:
Find as many different equivalent fractions as possible to express the probability of drawing an insect.

Name ____________________ Date ______________

Master 11.9

Additional Activity 3: Fold Your Tents!

Work with a partner.

You will need 20 matching squares of paper about 2 cm by 2 cm and a tray.

- Fold each piece of paper in half to make a small "tent."
- Stand all your tents on a tray. Each tent should have the fold facing up.
- Shake the tray so that all the tents fall off and land on the floor.
- What fraction of the tents have landed fold up?
  What fraction landed lying on one side?
  What fraction landed standing on one end?
- Repeat the experiment 4 more times.
- Record your results each time.
- Based on your results, predict what fraction of the tents will land fold up after your next toss.
- Toss the tents once more. Count the tents that landed fold up.
  Did your actual results match your prediction? Explain.

Take It Further:
Predict the fraction of the tents that will land fold up after the 10th and 20th tosses.

Name ____________________ Date ______________

Master 11.10

Additional Activity 4: Robot Roundup

Imagine you are in charge of a robot factory.

Each robot needs 2 arms, 2 wheels, and a box-shaped body.

Both arms must be the same colour. Both wheels must be the same colour.

For each component, you have the colour choices shown here:

Arms:	yellow or blue
Wheels:	green or purple
Body:	red or black or grey

- Use a tree diagram to find out how many different robots you can make.
- Draw and colour one of the robots.
- If you picked the components without looking, what are the chances you would create a grey robot with blue arms and purple wheels?

Take It Further:
Add another component (for example, a control panel in gold or silver) and work out how many different robots can now be produced.

Name ____________________ Date _______________

Master 11.11a

Step-by-Step 1

Lesson 1, Question 5

Step 1 Yellow is more likely, so there are more __________ sectors than red.

Red is more likely, so there are more ___________ sectors than blue.

Look at the first spinner on Master 11b. It has 8 sectors.

How many sectors will you colour yellow? ____ red? ____ blue? ____

Colour the spinner.

Is there a different way to colour the spinner? Explain.

____

Step 2 Blue and green are equally likely.

They cover _______ sectors.

Yellow is more likely. It covers _______ sectors.

Look at the second spinner on Master 11b. It has 5 sectors.

How many sectors will you colour blue? ___ green? ___ yellow? ___

Colour the spinner.

Is there a different way to colour the spinner? Explain.

____

Step 3 Yellow is certain.

Are there any blue sectors? _____ Are there any red sectors? _____

Look at the third spinner on Master 11b. It has 10 sectors.

Yellow covers _____ of the sectors.

Colour the spinner.

Is there a different way to colour the spinner? Explain.

____

Name ____________________ Date ________________

Master 11.11b

Spinners for Lesson 1, Question 5

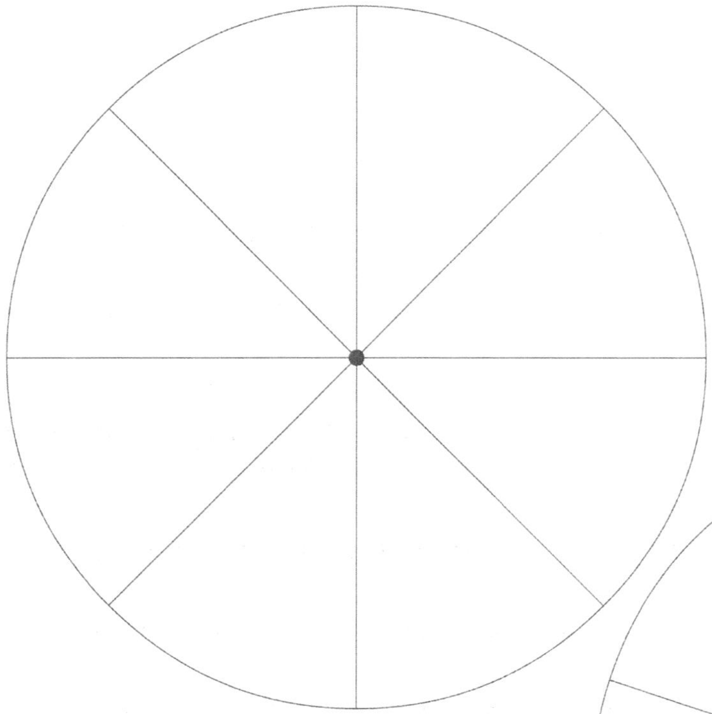

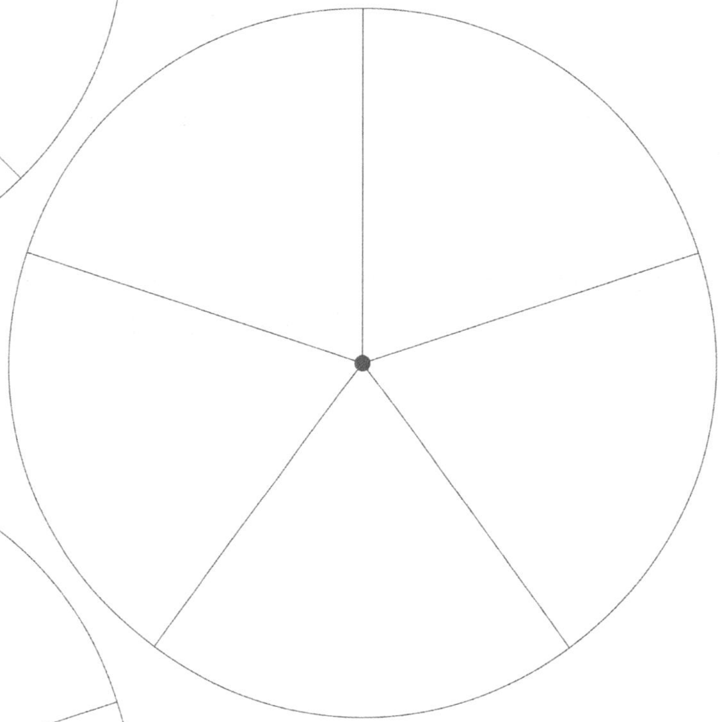

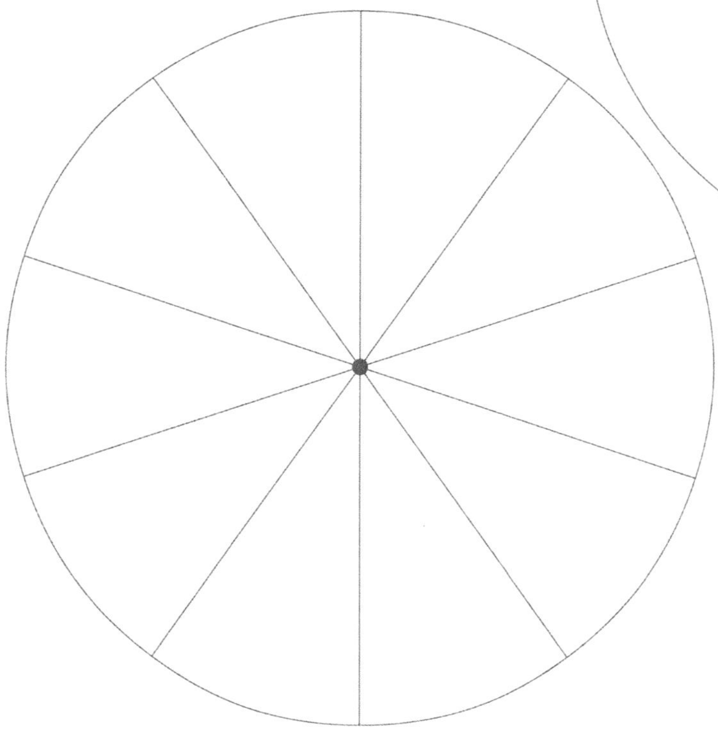

Name ____________________ Date _______________

Master 11.12

Step-by-Step 2

Lesson 2, Question 4

> Vicki scores a point if the pointers land on the same colour.
> Alastair scores a point if the pointers land on different colours.

Make the spinners identical for each case.

Step 1 Vicki will win if the spinners are mostly one colour. Choose 2 colours. Colour the spinners so that Vicki is more likely to win.

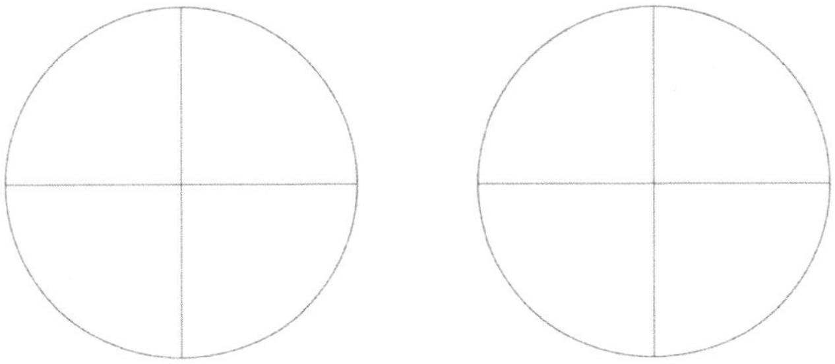

Step 2 Alastair will win if each spinner has 4 different colours. Choose 4 colours. Colour the spinners so that Alastair is more likely to win.

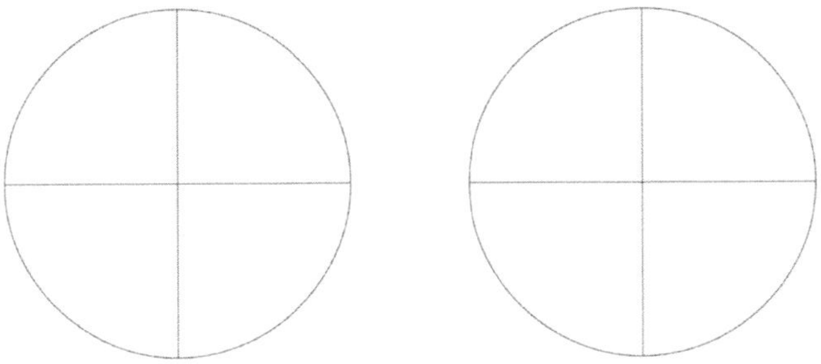

Step 3 The game is fair if the pointers are equally likely to land on the same colour or a different colour. Choose 2 colours. Colour the spinners so that Vicki and Alastair have equal chances of winning.

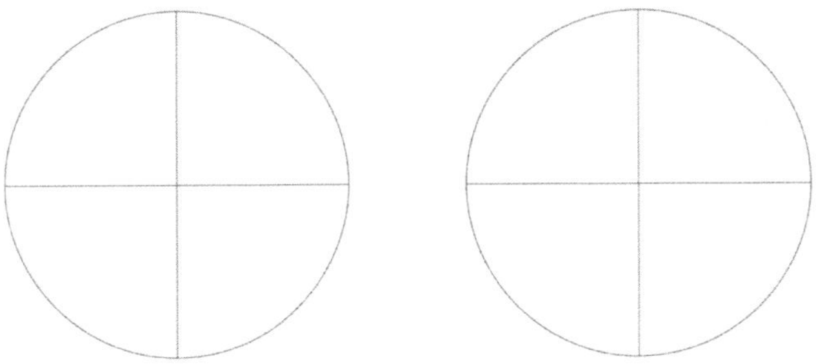

Name ____________________ Date _______________

Master 11.13

Step-by-Step 3

Lesson 3, Question 2

Step 1 What are the possible outcomes when Dave tosses a coin?

_________________ or _________________

Step 2 Dave tosses heads 12 times out of 20.

So, Dave got tails 20 – _______ = _______ times

Step 3 What fraction of the tosses were heads? $\frac{\square}{20}$

What fraction of the tosses were tails? $\frac{\square}{20}$

Step 4 How many times would you expect Dave to get heads in 20 tosses? _____

What fraction of the tosses would be heads? _____

How do Dave's results compare with what you expected?

____

____

Name ____________________ Date _______________

Master 11.14

Step-by-Step 4

Lesson 4, Question 3

Jawaan, Carl, Orenda, and Tansy run in the relay race.

Step 1 Complete this tree diagram.
Show all the possible orders for the 4 runners.

J = Jawaan C = Carl O = Orenda T = Tansy

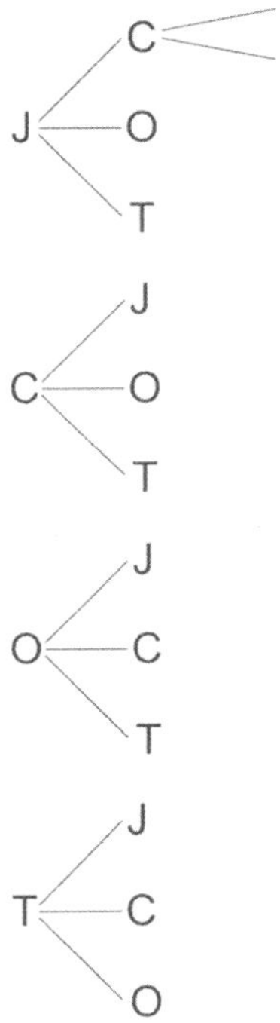

Step 2 How many possible orders did you find? ______
How many orders have Tansy running first? ______

Step 3 The runners' names are drawn from a hat.
What fraction describes Tansy's probability of running first? ______

Step 4 If you were the track coach, how would you decide on the order of your relay team? Would you pull names from a hat? Explain.

____

____

Name ________________ Date ______________

Master 11.15

Step-by-Step 6

Lesson 6, Question 2

Step 1 What are the possible outcomes of tossing 3 coins?
Complete this table.

First Coin	**Second Coin**	**Third Coin**
Heads	Heads	Heads
Heads	Heads	Tails
Heads	Tails	
Heads		
Tails	Tails	Tails
Tails		
Tails		
Tails		

Step 2 How many different outcomes are possible? ________

Step 3 If a game is fair, each player has an equal chance of winning.
How can we divide the number of possible outcomes into 2 equal parts?

____

Step 4 Look at the table in *Step 1*.

How many outcomes include at least 2 heads? ________

How many outcomes include at least 2 tails?________

Make up a fair game with 3 coins.

Player A gets a point if ______________________________.

Player B gets a point if ______________________________.

How do you know this game is fair?

____

Name ____________________ Date _______________

Master 11.16a

Unit Test: Unit 11 Probability

Part A

1. Use the words *likely*, *unlikely*, *impossible*, *possible*, or *certain* to describe each event.

   a) The sun will rise tomorrow. _______________________

   b) You will dig to the centre of the Earth. _______________________

   c) You will win a gold medal at the Olympics. _______________________

   d) You will sleep tonight. _______________________

2. Eric has red, green, yellow, and blue marbles.
   He wants to give Andrea 2 marbles.
   What possible colour combinations can he give her?

3. Colour this spinner so that green is more likely than blue and blue is more likely than red.

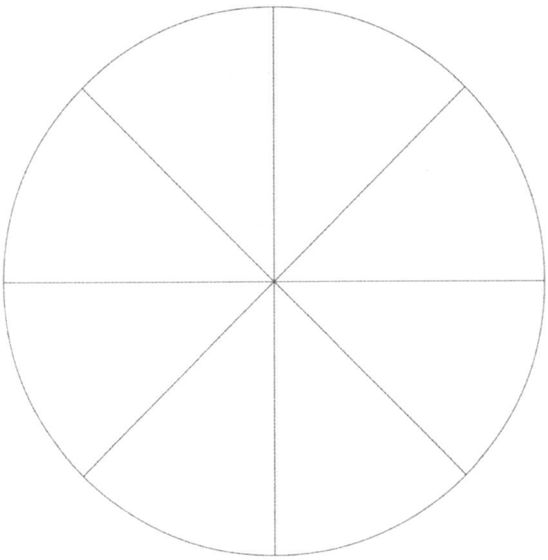

Name ____________________ Date ________________

Master 11.16b

Unit Test continued

Part B

4. Ruby will use this spinner to choose a flavour of ice cream.

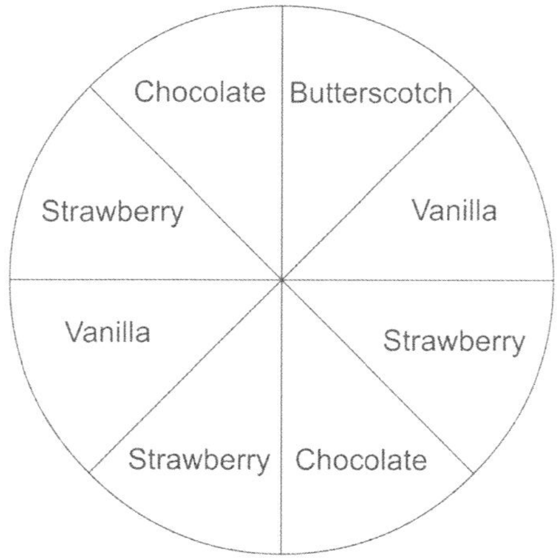

a) What is the probability that Ruby will order strawberry ice cream?

____

b) Which flavours have equal chances of being ordered?

____

c) Just for fun, Ruby spun the spinner 40 times. Here are her results:
Chocolate 8, Vanilla 10, Strawberry 17, Butterscotch 5

Are these results what you would expect? Explain.

____
____
____
____
____
____
____
____
____
____
____
____

Name ____________________ Date ________________

Master 11.16c

Unit Test continued

Part C

5. Design a fair game of chance for 2 players. Use a 2-colour counter and a number cube. Each player should have a different way of scoring a point. Explain how you know your game is fair.

____

____

____

____

____

____

____

____

Name ____________________ Date ______________

Master 11.17

Sample Answers

Unit Test – Master 11.16

Part A

1. **a)** Certain
   b) Impossible
   c) Possible or unlikely
   d) Likely

2. Red/green, red/yellow, red/blue, green/yellow, green/blue, yellow/blue

3. Students should colour the spinner so that green covers the greatest area (for example, $\frac{4}{8}$).
   The blue area is smaller than green but larger than red (for example, $\frac{3}{8}$).
   Red covers the smallest area (for example, $\frac{1}{8}$).

Part B

4. **a)** $\frac{3}{8}$
   b) Chocolate and vanilla
   c) These results are what I would expect. They are close to the predicted probabilities, even though they don't match them exactly. My predicted probabilities were: chocolate and vanilla should each be about $\frac{2}{8}$ of 40, or 10.
   Strawberry should be about $\frac{3}{8}$ of 40, or 15.
   Butterscotch should be about $\frac{1}{8}$ of 40, or 5.

Part C

5. Players take turns tossing the counter and rolling the number cube. Player A scores a point if the counter is red and the number cube shows an even number. Player B scores a point if the counter is white and the number cube shows an odd number. I know this game is fair because there is an equal number of ways for each player to score.

Extra Practice Masters 11.18–11.21

Go to the CD-ROM to access editable versions of these Extra Practice Masters.

Name ____________ Date ____________

Master 11.18 **Extra Practice 1**

Lesson 1: The Likelihood of Events

1. Describe a situation that is:
   a) likely but not certain
   b) unlikely but possible
   c) impossible
   d) certain

2. Describe each outcome.
   Use the words: *impossible, unlikely, likely, certain*
   a) Someone in your class will win the lottery.
   b) It will rain tomorrow.
   c) You will go skiing tomorrow.
   d) A dog will fly by the classroom window

Lesson 2: Calculating Probability

1. Suppose you spin the pointers on these two spinners and add the results.

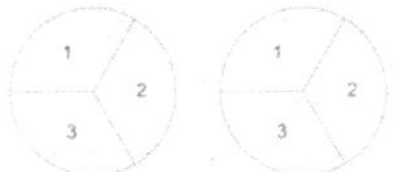

   a) What are the possible sums you can produce?
   b) What is the probability that you will produce a sum of 6?

Name ____________ Date ____________

Master 11.19 **Extra Practice 2**

Lesson 3: Probability and Fractions

1. Tara has a collection of small stuffed animals.
   She has 10 bears, 4 dogs, 4 cats, and 2 rabbits.
   Suppose Tara puts all her animals in a pillowcase and picks one without looking.
   Use a fraction to describe the probability that she will pick
   a) a bear b) a rabbit c) a dog

2. Max has a bag of 25 candies. The probability of choosing a lemon candy is $\frac{1}{5}$. The probability of choosing a mint candy is $\frac{2}{5}$. How many lemon candies are in the bag? How many mint candies are in the bag?

Lesson 4: Tree Diagrams

1. Omar's class is painting pottery.
   Students can choose to paint a bowl, a plate, or a mug.
   They can use blue, green, yellow, or purple paint.
   a) Use a tree diagram to show all the different pieces of pottery Omar could make.
   b) What fraction of the choices are mugs?
   c) What is the probability that a student will paint a yellow mug?

Name ____________ Date ____________

Master 11.20 **Extra Practice 3**

Lesson 6: Probability in Games

1. Brajit and Annie have an envelope containing 6 paper clips: 2 yellow, 2 green, and 2 blue.
   They play a game.
   Each person pulls a paper clip from the envelope without looking.
   If the clips are the same colour, Brajit wins a point.
   If the clips are different colours, Annie wins a point.
   Is this a fair game? Explain your thinking.

2. Design a fair game using coloured paper clips.

Name ____________ Date ____________

Master 11.21 **Sample Answers**

Extra Practice 1 – Master 11.19

Lesson 1

1. a) It will rain today.
   b) A rose bush will bloom in January.
   c) The moon is made of green cheese.
   d) I will go to bed tonight.

2. a) Impossible
   b) Likely
   c) Unlikely
   d) Impossible

Lesson 2

1. a) 2, 3, 4, 5, and 6
   b) $\frac{1}{9}$

Extra Practice 2 – Master 11.19

Lesson 3

1. a) $\frac{10}{20}$ or $\frac{1}{2}$
   b) $\frac{2}{20}$ or $\frac{1}{10}$
   c) $\frac{4}{20}$ or $\frac{1}{5}$

2. There are 5 lemon candies in the bag. There are 10 mint candies in the bag.

Lesson 4

1. a) B = bowl, P = plate, M = mug
   Bl = blue, G = green, Y = yellow, Pr = purple

   b) $\frac{1}{3}$ of the choices are mugs.
   c) $\frac{1}{12}$

Extra Practice 3 – Master 11.20

Lesson 6

1. This is not a fair game. There are 9 different possibilities for pulling 2 paper clips. Only 3 of these have matching colours. Annie's probability of winning is double that of Brajit.

2. Place 3 blue paper clips and 3 red paper clips in a bag. Each player draws one paper clip from the envelope. Player A gets a point if both paper clips are blue. Player B gets a point if both paper clips are red. No one scores if the clips are different colours.

Addison Wesley
Mathematics
Makes Sense

Program Authors

Peggy Morrow
Ralph Connelly
Bryn Keyes
Jason Johnston
Steve Thomas
Jeananne Thomas
Angela D'Alessandro
Maggie Martin Connell
Don Jones
Michael Davis
Sharon Jeroski
Trevor Brown
Nora Alexander
Cynthia Pratt Nicolson

Printed and bound in Canada

8 9 MP 18 17

PEARSON
Education Canada